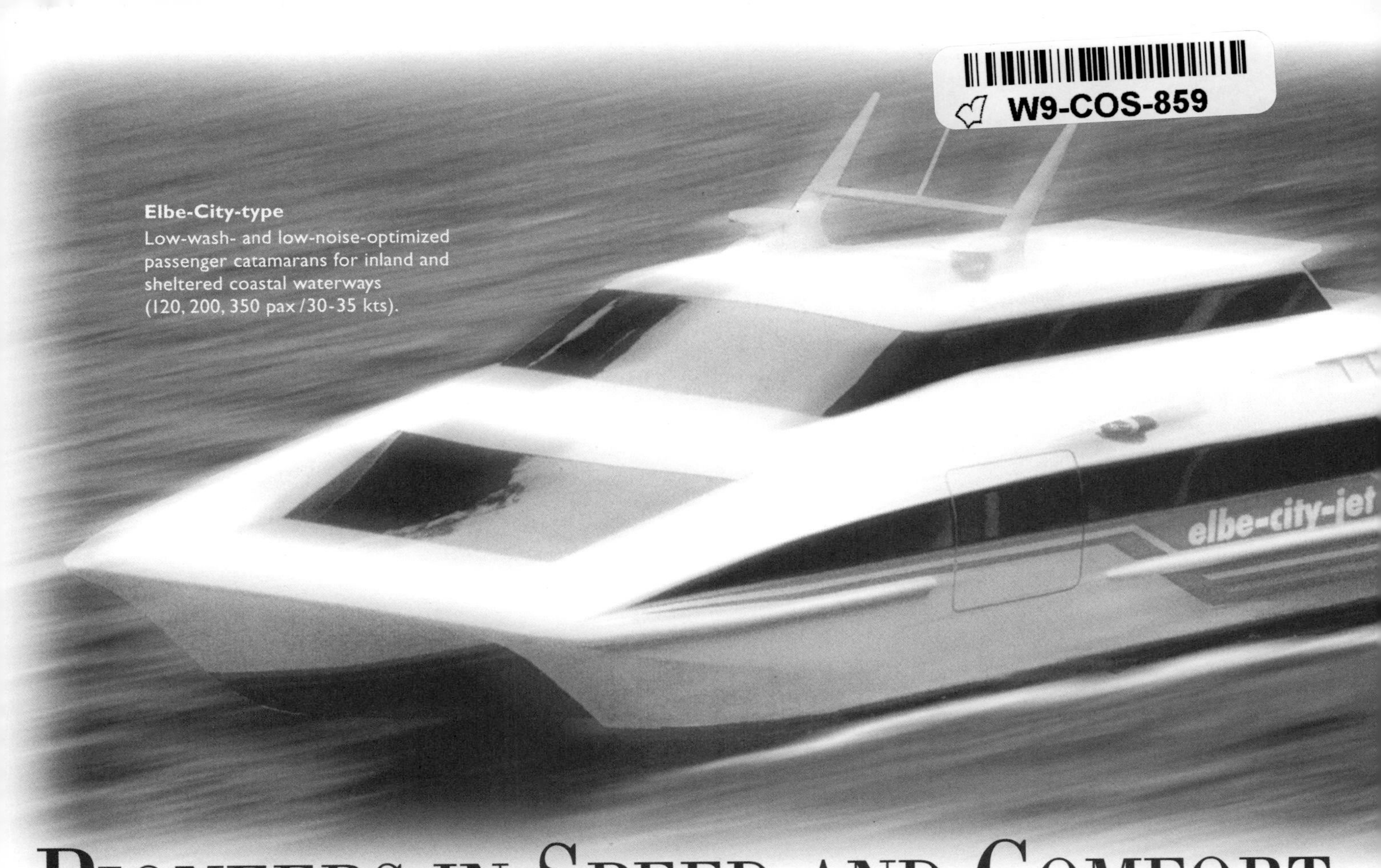

Elbe-City-type
Low-wash- and low-noise-optimized passenger catamarans for inland and sheltered coastal waterways (120, 200, 350 pax/30-35 kts).

Pioneers in Speed and Comfort

- FAST COMMERCIAL SHIPS
- SAILING YACHTS
- MOTOR YACHTS
- FAST PATROL BOATS
- MINE COUNTER-MEASURE VESSELS
- SPECIAL SHIPS

Fast Ferries

Extremely seaworthy advanced monohull day-ferry (450 pax/50 cars, 30+ kts).

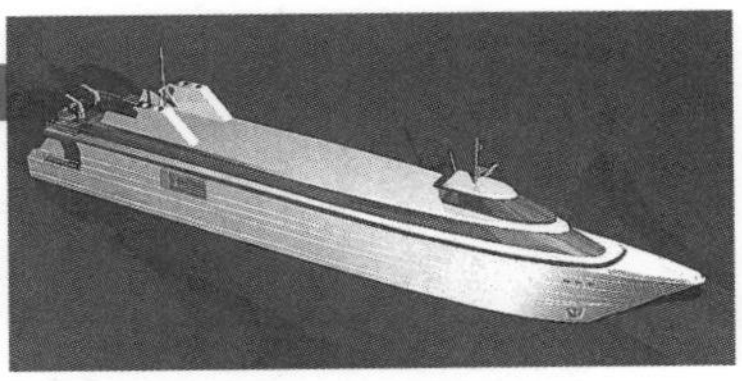

SWATH-Daycruisers with highest passenger comfort

If a shaky sea and seasick passengers are the limit of market exploitation, we have new opportunities:
SWATH-daycruisers and -dinner cruisers for 350, 800 or 1000 pax (16-25 kts), designed in cooperation with experienced partners on base of proven reference ships.

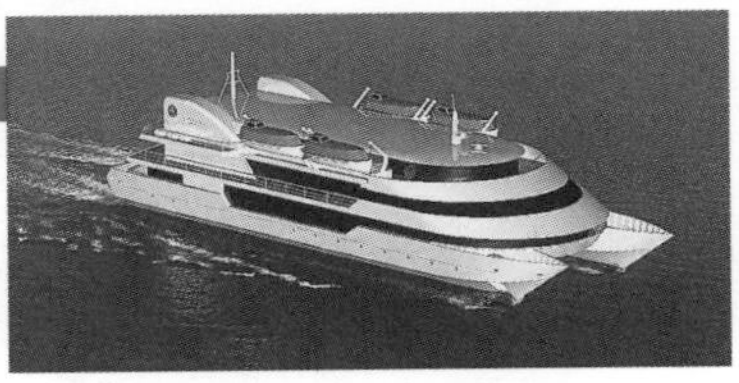

Decades of Experience

We have designed and built the first large aluminium hulls in the 60ies, the world's fastest diesel-driven yacht (46 kts!) and the largest deepVee-shaped patrol boats in the 70ies and 80ies.
For our ferry- and passenger market entry in the 90ies we have combined the results of our own research work with experiences of specialized partners.

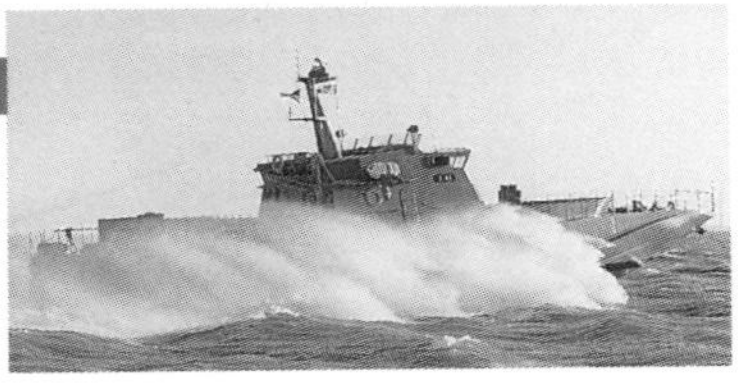

ABEKING & RASMUSSEN
SINCE 1907

Contact us for more information: Abeking & Rasmussen, P.O. Box 1160, 27805 Lemwerder, Germany, Phone 49-(0)421-67 33-0, Fax 49-(0)421-67 33 112

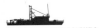

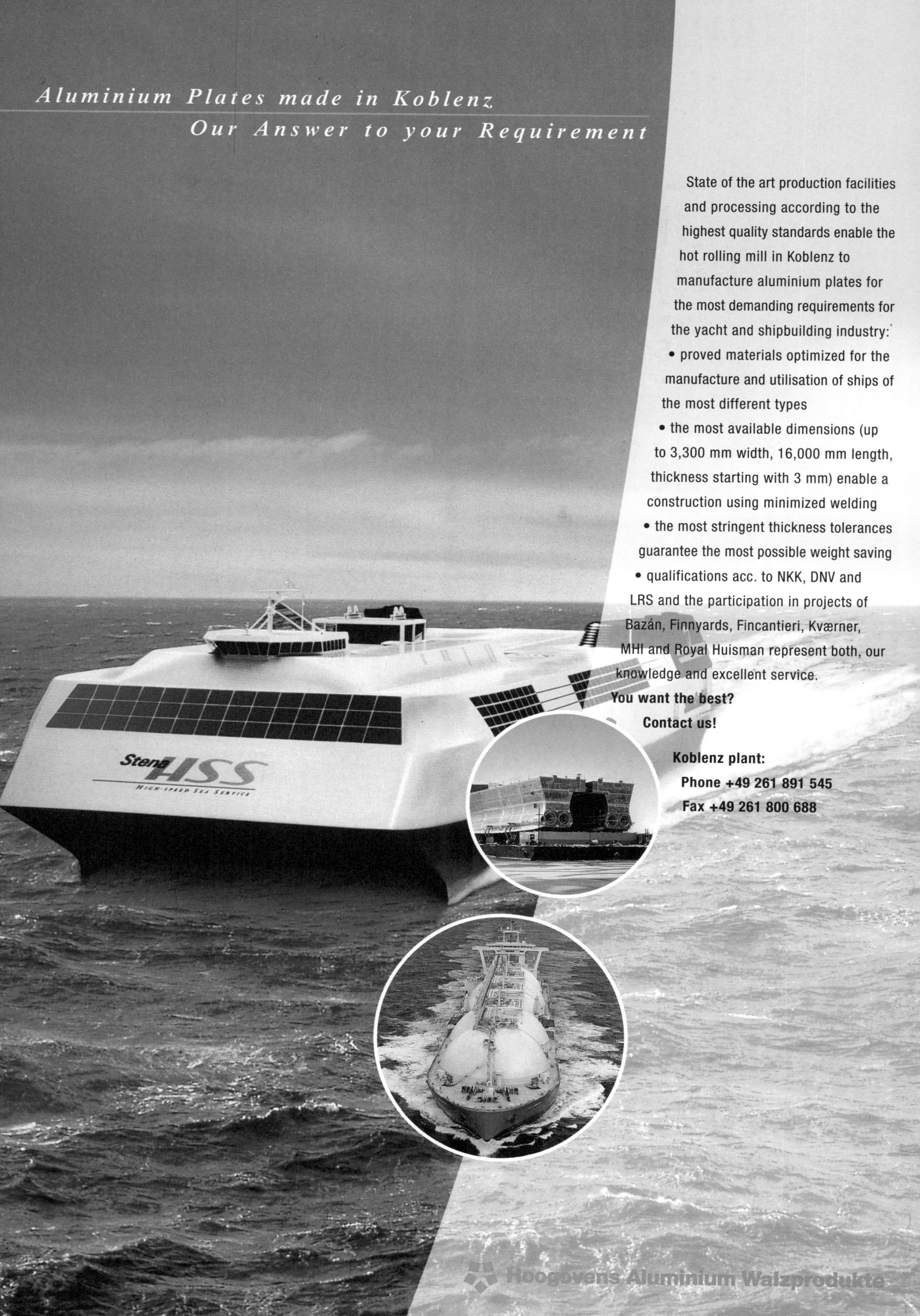

Aluminium Plates made in Koblenz
Our Answer to your Requirement
State of the art production facilities and processing according to the highest quality standards enable the hot rolling mill in Koblenz to manufacture aluminium plates for the most demanding requirements for the yacht and shipbuilding industry:
• proved materials optimized for the manufacture and utilisation of ships of the most different types
• the most available dimensions (up to 3,300 mm width, 16,000 mm length, thickness starting with 3 mm) enable a construction using minimized welding
• the most stringent thickness tolerances guarantee the most possible weight saving
• qualifications acc. to NKK, DNV and LRS and the participation in projects of Bazán, Finnyards, Fincantieri, Kværner, MHI and Royal Huisman represent both, our knowledge and excellent service.
You want the best?
Contact us!
Koblenz plant:
Phone +49 261 891 545
Fax +49 261 800 688
Stena HSS
High-Speed Sea Service
Hoogovens Aluminium Walzprodukte

Jane's

HIGH-SPEED MARINE TRANSPORTATION

Edited by Stephen J Phillips

Twenty-ninth Edition

1996-97

Join us on the Internet via WWW http://www.janes.com/janes.html

Jane's can also be accessed by FTP, GOPHER and E-MAIL on thomson.com which is the on-line portal for the products, services and resources available from Thomson Publishing. This Internet kiosk gives users immediate access to more than 34 Thomson publishers and over 20,000 information resources. Through thomson.com, Internet users can search catalogues, examine a subject-specific resource centre, purchase products, and subscribe to electronic discussion lists.

www: http://www.thomson.com GOPHER: gopher://gopher.thomson.com
FTP: ftp.thomson.com e-mail: findit@kiosk.thomson.com

Jane's products are also available on CD-ROM and other forms of electronic delivery. Please contact us for further details.

ISBN 0 7106 1370 9

In the USA and its dependencies
Jane's Information Group Inc, 1340 Braddock Place, Suite 300, Alexandria, VA 22314-1651, USA

British Library Cataloguing-in-Publication Data.
A catalogue record for this book is available from the British Library.

Printed and bound in Great Britain by Biddles Ltd, Guildford and King's Lynn.

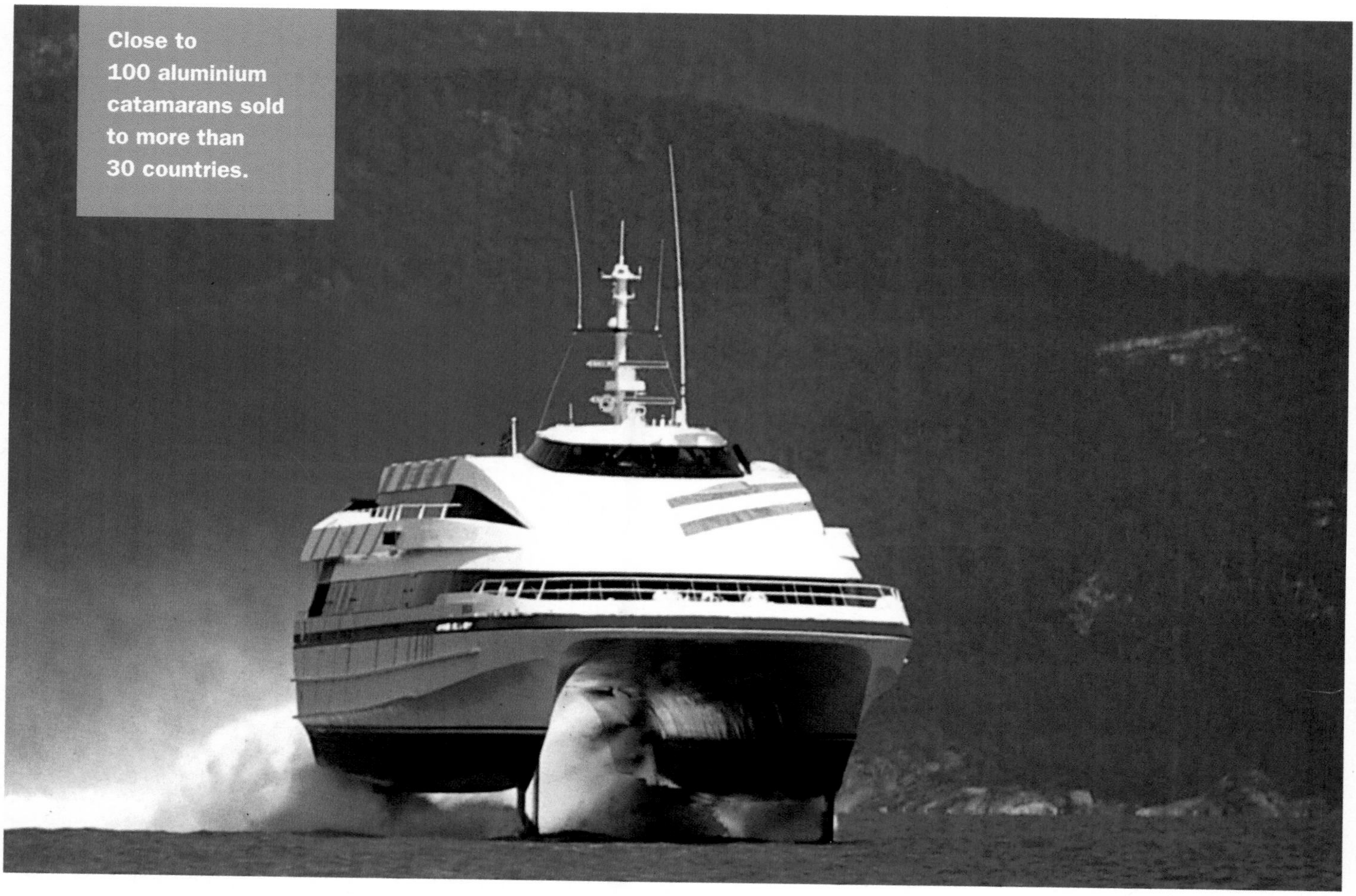

Contents

ADMINISTRATION

Publishing Director: Robert Hutchinson

Managing Editor: Keith Faulkner

Production Database Manager: Ruth Simmance

Editorial Services Manager: Sulann Staniford

Production Editor: Tarquin Acevedo

EDITORIAL OFFICES

Jane's Information Group Limited, Sentinel House,
163 Brighton Road, Coulsdon, Surrey CR5 2NH, UK

Tel: +44 181 700 3700
Telex: 916907 Janes G
Fax: +44 181 700 3900
e-mail:yearbook@janes.co.uk

SALES OFFICES

Send enquiries to International Sales Manager:
Fabiana Angelini (Europe, CIS, Africa, Middle East)
David Eaton-Jones (Scandinavia, Far East, UK)
Jane's Information Group Limited, UK address as above

Tel Enquiries: +44 181 700 3759
Fax Enquiries: +44 181 763 1006
Fax Orders: +44 181 763 1005

Send USA enquiries to:
Joe McHale, Senior Vice-President Product Sales,
Jane's Information Group Inc, 1340 Braddock Place, Suite 300,
Alexandria, VA 22314-1651

Tel: +1 703 683 3700
Telex: 6819193
Fax: +1 703 836 0029

ADVERTISEMENT SALES OFFICES

Advertisement Sales Manager: Richard West

Australia: Brendan Gullifer, Havre & Gullifer (Pty) Ltd, Level 50, 101 Collins Street, Melbourne 3000

Tel: +61 3 9650 1100
Fax: +61 3 9650 6611

Benelux: Annabel Chisholm, Jane's Information Group (see UK/Rest of World)

Brazil: L Bilyk, Brazmedia International S/C Ltda, Alameda Gabriel Monterio da Silva, 366 CEP, 01442 São Paulo

Tel: +55 11 853 4133
Telex: 32836 BMED BR
Fax: +55 11 852 6485

France: Patrice Février, Jane's Information Group – France, BP 418, 35 avenue MacMahon, F-75824 Paris Cedex

Tel: +33 1 45 72 33 11
Fax: +33 1 45 72 17 95

Germany and Austria: Annabel Chisholm, Jane's Information Group (see UK/Rest of World)

Hong Kong: Jeremy Miller, Major Media Ltd, Room 1402, 14F Capitol Centre, 5-19 Jardine's Bazaar, Causeway Bay

Tel: +852 890 3110
Fax: +852 576 3397

Israel: Oreet Ben-Yaacov, Oreet International Media, 15 Kinneret Street, IL-51201 Bene-Berak

Tel: +972 3 570 6527
Fax: +972 3 570 6526

Italy and Switzerland: Ediconsult Internazionale Srl, Piazza Fontane Marose 3, I-16123 Genoa, Italy

Tel: +39 10 583684
Telex: 281197 EDINT I
Fax: +39 10 566578

Japan: Intermart/EAC Inc, 1-7 Akasaka 9-chome, Minato-Ku, Tokyo 107

Tel: +81 3 5474 7835
Fax: +81 3 5474 7837

Korea, South: Young Seoh Chinn, JES Media International, 6th Floor Donghye Building, 47-16 Myungil-Dong, Kangdong-Gu, Seoul 134-070

Tel: +82 2 481 3411
Fax: +82 2 481 3414

Scandinavia: Annabel Chisholm, Jane's Information Group (see UK/Rest of World)

Singapore, Indonesia, Malaysia, Philippines, Taiwan and Thailand: Hoo Siew Sai, Major Media (Singapore) Pte Ltd, 6th Floor, 52 Chin Swee Road, Singapore 0316

Tel: +65 738 0122
Telex: RS 43370 AMPLS
Fax: +65 738 2108

South Africa: Annabel Chisholm, Jane's Information Group (see UK/Rest of World)

Spain: Jesus Moran Iglesias, Varex SA, Modesto Lafuente 4, E-28010 Madrid

Tel: +34 1 448 7622
Fax: +34 1 446 0198

UK/Rest of World: Annabel Chisholm, Jane's Information Group, Sentinel House, 163 Brighton Road, Coulsdon, Surrey CR5 2NH

Tel: +44 181 700 3741
Telex: 916907 Janes G
Fax: +44 181 700 3744

USA
Advertising Production Manager/USA & Canada – Maureen Nute
Jane's Information Group Inc, 1340 Braddock Place, Suite 300, Alexandria, VA 22314 USA

Tel: +1 703 683 3700
Fax: +1 703 836 0029

Eastern USA and Canada
Kimberley S Hanson
Global Media Services Inc, 299 Herndon Parkway, Suite 308, Herndon, VA 22070 USA

Tel: +1 703 318 5054
Fax: +1 703 318 9728

South Eastern USA
Kristin Schulze
Global Media Services Inc, PO Box 290706, Temple Terrace, FL 33617 USA

Tel: +1 813 987 2359
Fax: +1 813 980 0187

Western USA and Canada
Anne Marie St. John-Brooks
Global Media Services Inc, 25125 Santa Clara Street, Suite 290, Hayward, CA 94544 USA

Tel: +1 510 582 7447
Fax: +1 510 582 7448

Administration: UK: Fay Lenham
USA and Canada: Maureen Nute

How to use this book

The purpose of this book is to provide a comprehensive reference yearbook covering the design, build and operation of high-speed marine craft, worldwide - an annually updated reference book for the rapid marine transport industry.

Entries in this book cover all organisations involved in this industry and are divided into four main sections as follows:

Builders

Operators

Principal Equipment

Services

These main divisions are further divided into subsections containing entries for organisations arranged under more specific headings. For example the **Builders** section of the book is divided into six types of craft built: *Air Cushion Vehicles*, *Hydrofoils*, *Multihulls*, *Swath Craft*, *Monohulls* and *Wing-In-Ground-Effect Craft*. The **Principal Equipment** section is divided into nine types of principal components: *Engines*, *Transmissions*, *Air Propellers*, *Marine Propellers*, *Water-Jet Units*, *Ride Control Systems*, *Air Cushion Skirt Systems*, *Marine Escape Systems* and *Fast Rescue Tenders*.

Under each of these subsections, entries are arranged alphabetically into countries and thereafter into organisation names.

An *Addenda* is included at the rear of the book so that developments occurring during the main publication process are not excluded.

A comprehensive *Bibliography* is also included which lists all the relevant books, technical papers and presentations that have been made public over the last five years.

Any particular entry may be located by using one of the three indices covering *Organisations*, *Craft Type* or *Craft Name*.

To help users of this title evaluate the published data, Jane's Information Group has divided entries into three categories:-

● ***VERIFIED*** The editor has made a detailed examination of the entry's content and checked its relevancy and accuracy for publication in the new edition to the best of his ability.

● ***UPDATED*** During the verification process, significant changes to content have been made to reflect the latest position known to Jane's at the time of publication.

● ***NEW ENTRY*** Information on new equipment and/or systems appearing for the first time in the title.

In future all new pictures will be dated with the year of publication. New pictures this year are dated 1996.

We hope these measures increase the value of this title to our thousands of customers worldwide. If you have any comments or suggestions for further enhancements, the Publisher would be pleased to receive them.

This edition of *Jane's High-Speed Marine Transportation* contains a total of over 200 new photographs and drawings, as well as the normal updating of existing entries.

Alphabetical list of advertisers

Three of the most recent fast ferries delivered by WaveMaster International Pty Ltd of Australia – monohulls Ocean Flyte *and* Sea Flyte, *with catamaran* Andromeda

Jane's

HIGH-SPEED MARINE TRANSPORTATION

1996-97

Jane's Information Group Limited, Sentinel House, 163 Brighton Road, Coulsdon, Surrey CR5 2NH, UK
Jane's Information Group Inc, 1340 Braddock Place, Suite 300, Alexandria, VA 22314-1651, USA

Foreword

Introduction

You will notice that the title of this yearbook has now been changed to reflect the fast growing marine transportation market and the book's content is being reorganised and expanded to cover the industry more comprehensively. The book is intended for all branches of the business community taking part in this fast expanding sector including ferry operators, builders, technologists, equipment and material suppliers and others interested in the industry. It is designed as a comprehensive reference book for the rapid marine transport sector and is used by a growing number of business, technical, market and intelligence organisations worldwide.

Fast Marine Transport Market

Yet again we have seen a record year for ship orders, deliveries, operations and supplies of services and equipment to the fast marine transport sector worldwide.

The past year has seen the setting up of over 30 new fast ferry operations and this yearbook edition includes these and over 50 other new companies supplying to this industry. The rate of closure of companies previously covered is not quite so high but does indicate the volatility as well as the rapid expansion of the sector.

Over 70 craft were delivered this year with another 80 craft ordered. Whilst this is only marginally more than last year, the tonnage associated with these craft has increased significantly. Sales of small to medium size craft appears to be stabilising whilst the growth in orders for vessels with payload capacities of over 200 tonnes is expanding rapidly. In terms of tonnage delivered, the industry has seen a steady doubling of capacity every five years for the last two decades, which is equivalent to a 15 per cent annual growth rate.

Whilst the extent of orders for small to medium size craft has levelled off, innovation in their design is continuing to develop, improving performance and cost effectiveness. The properties of different materials are being exploited to a greater extent, propulsion systems are becoming simpler with a larger number of direct drive diesel/water-jet systems particularly for the smaller craft, new hull forms are being introduced and, in general, speed has substantially increased with some semi-displacement vessels now reaching commercially viable speeds of over 50 knots.

With this level of activity and with large fast ship technology now rapidly permeating the established shipyards, business for the service and supply sectors has changed. There is now very serious demand for higher performance and considerably lighter weight materials and equipment. Not five years ago the only way to avoid fitting standard 'steel ships' deck equipment, sometimes weighting 10 times what was required, was to design and manufacture it within your own production facility. Even now this still remains a cost effective option but many smaller firms around the world are successfully focusing on this expanding market for lightweight equipment specifically for rapid transport systems, whether by rail, road, sea or air.

Looking back six years to when the first large fast car carrying catamaran was delivered, predictions were made then that operators of conventional passenger ro-ro vessels would have little commercial choice but to embrace this new technology. The reality for fast ferry designers and builders is probably more exciting than expected with multihull vessels now operating across the Irish Sea at speeds of over 40 knots and carrying payloads of 500 tonnes and orders for large and similarly fast monohull ferries with payload capacities in excess of 700 tonnes currently being negotiated. Over 60 large fast passenger/car ferries have been delivered or ordered since the first 74 m wave piercing catamaran ro-ro craft was delivered in 1990. Prior to that time only the British Hovercraft Corporation SRN4 hovercraft of the 1960s could be described as fast passenger/car ferries. Although their payload was relatively small, they are not only still in service and still the fastest ro-ro craft in commercial operation, but in 1995 they also set a new record by crossing the English channel in 22 minutes - faster even than by car on Le Shuttle via the new Channel Tunnel!

Stena HSS 1500

The delivery of the first Stena HSS 1500 from Finnyards, the Finnish shipyard where she was built, at the beginning of this year marked another significant step in the development of higher speed craft. A payload capacity of over 500 tonnes and an operational speed of 40 knots illustrate the advances made since the delivery of the Australian-built InCat 74 m wave piercing catamaran, *Hoverspeed Great Britain*, in 1990. This craft had a payload capacity of just 150 tonnes and an operational speed of 35 knots, although she did arrive in the UK having just won the Blue Riband and Hales Trophy for the fastest crossing of the Atlantic.

The HSS 1500 at 120 m in length, 40 m in breadth and with a displacement of around 2,600 tonnes requires approximately 70,000 kW of installed power to provide for a realistic operational speed of 40 knots. With a capacity for 1,500 passengers and 365 cars, the vessel is fitted out as a modern ro-ro vessel offering a higher standard of comfort and facilities to its passengers than ever before.

From a technical view point the design of the vessel is most impressive since it combines so many novel features without the benefit of having been tested on a prototype craft. The vessel is the largest all aluminium structure in the world and has a novel, patented, semi-swath hull form combining good seakeeping and fuel efficiency. Although this form had, in concept, been developed by a number of companies, the HSS is the first craft with such a hull to be delivered.

A number of large items within the craft are made from composite materials which has provided substantial weight savings over

The first Finnish built Stena HSS 1500, the Stena Explorer, *arrived in the UK in January 1996. This vessel operates across the Irish Sea between Holyhead and Dun Laoghaire providing a considerably higher level of passenger service than the existing ro-ro ferries. The quadruple, 'father and son', gas turbine propulsion arrangement allows for efficient operation at speeds of approximately 24 knots, 32 knots and 40 knots and with a maximum payload capacity of 1,500 passengers and 365 cars, this provides for a very flexible and potentially lucrative ferry operation* **1996**

conventional fabrications. The whole depth of the vessel from keel to uppermost deck is designed to be structurally effective for primary hull loads (quite different from most other vessels which generally use their bulkhead or weather deck as the top most structural hull component). The extremely lightweight structural fire protection used within the vessel's machinery and special category spaces had not been developed when the original plans were made and so it is clear the builder's project management system was sufficiently flexible to allow for the incorporation of developments which took place during the design and build period. The same is true for the marine evacuation system, the development of which started after the main ship build contract had been placed. This inflatable escape slide system is very different from existing designs for this size of vessel, in that not only is it deployed perpendicular to the side of vessel thus ensuring that escaping passengers are kept well away from the ship's hull but that they slide out of the vessel straight into the liferafts - which are themselves the largest in the world.

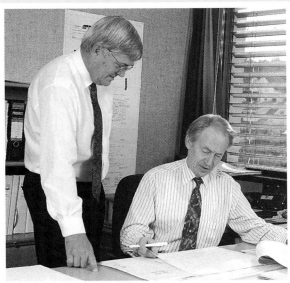

The propulsion system is made up of largely proven components although arranged in a way which provides for at least three efficient speeds of operation. Being powered by gas turbines, the fuel efficiency of the vessel is dramatically reduced if the turbines are not run at their design output. Thus to maintain efficiency, the only option is to use multiple turbines and to close them down successively to provide the level of power required, leaving the remaining turbines running at their full design power. In the HS 1500, the American GE designed and Norwegian Kværner packaged aero-derivative turbines are arranged in a 'father and son' configuration, with one LM 2500 and one LM 1600 turbine in each of the two hulls. Both turbines drive into a common gearbox which has twin input and twin output shafting allowing power from both turbines to be combined and shared between the twin identical water-jets in each hull. Thus the ship can be operated efficiently on the two smaller turbines giving a speed of approximately 24 knots, on the two larger turbines giving a speed of approximately 32 knots or on all four turbines giving a speed of over 40 knots. A speed of 43 knots was reportedly achieved on trials in a moderate sea state.

Another major innovation is the fast turnaround docking system which should allow a 30 minute unloading and loading period. This has been achieved by a completely new and integrated port facility design and a navigation and ship control system that can automatically dock and secure the ship once close enough to the berthing area.

Since the port facilities have to be put in place before the vessel can achieve the required turnaround time, the preplanning of the operational routes will be crucial to the vessels' success. The confirmed routes will be from Holyhead to Dun Loaghaire for HSS 01, from Stranraer to Belfast, also across the Irish Sea, for HSS 02 and from Harwich to Hook of Holland across the North Sea for HSS 03.

This project, probably more than any other, provides the size, complexity and courage against which future fast ship vessels will be judged for many years to come.

Technical Developments

Significant developments in materials, equipment and ship design technology, particularly over the last year, have provided a basis for yet further worthwhile innovations in the fast marine transport industry. Most developments are aimed at increasing the speed performance of these craft.

An evolution in the chemical composition of marine grade aluminium alloy material has been patented by Pechiney Rhenalu of France which provides for an alloy with a much higher post-welded strength than other suitable marine grades. This allows a lighter structure to be designed for a given strength, and hence for greater vessel operational efficiency.

The InCat Australia Pty Ltd 80 m K50 design, Sunflower, *was delivered from their Tasmanian shipyard to its South Korean owners in July 1995, and with a maximum speed of 53 knots is understood to be the fastest large catamaran passenger car ferry* **1996**

Also an evolution in the use of composite materials has made available new lightweight components such as propulsion system shafting, external shaft supports, waterjet inlets and propellers. As often occurs with such innovations, there can be significant and sometimes unforeseen beneficial knock-on effects. For example, the use of composite propulsion system shafting can allow the design of a system with far fewer support bearings and a much lighter system weight. This in turn can more than offset the apparent cost disadvantage of composites versus conventional materials. Composites have also been used extensively in superstructure components such as in the 45 m FBM Tricat craft and the bow section of the Stena HSS craft although it is unclear that there is significant technical advantage in these applications apart maybe from some cosmetic and possibly minor production benefits.

This Japanese Mitsui 30 m fast crew transport boat, Cosmos, *is understood to be the only commercial Swath vessel delivered in 1995. The sea-keeping benefits of this type of hull form are difficult to appreciate without having first hand experience - this small vessel can comfortably operate at 20 knots in sea states with over 2.5 m significant wave height. Such performance is virtually unique to Swath craft* ***1996***

Since most fast commercial craft are constructed almost entirely of aluminium, structural fire protection (fire insulation) is an important consideration in their design. The structural strength of aluminium starts to reduce at temperatures of approximately 200°C and so the internal structure of high fire risk compartments within these craft are insulated to prevent the loss of structural integrity in the event of a fire. The weight of this insulation in relation to the weight of the ship has in the past been significant. However within the last year a number of lightweight insulation systems have been designed which in some circumstances have more than halved the weight of conventional fibre insulation - a significant advance for the industry as a whole.

Also related to fire protection has been the development of a number of fire suppression systems based on water mist generation. This type of system is light in weight and can be used as a substitute for Carbon Dioxide or Halon systems for machinery rooms and as an alternative to conventional water drenching systems in special category spaces such as ro-ro ferry car decks. The water mist removes heat from the fire in its latent heat of evaporation and since the transformation from water droplets to water vapour involves an expansion ratio of over 1,500 in a typical engine room environment, it quickly and effectively excludes oxygen from the fire by creating an atmosphere that does not support combustion. Also the build up of water within the hull is minimal and so does not involve any appreciable loss of stability which has been associated with some current water drenching systems. It is understandably safer than Halon or Carbon Dioxide systems and is currently being specified by a growing number of designers of ferries, workboats and patrol craft.

One of the major differences between the application of new Code of Safety for High Speed Craft and the original concept of SOLAS regulations is that the probability for evacuation of passengers after a major fire incident is accepted as being greater. Therefore the development of rapid and safe evacuation systems has become a high priority. A number of new systems have appeared on the market, mainly based on inflatable escape slides leading directly into large liferafts but also some using vertical descent chutes, leading to inflatable liferafts via a transfer platform. Naturally they all have applications on conventional craft but the driving force behind their development is the more progressive approach to safety that is being generated by the rapid development of fast passenger ferries. One of the challenges of 1996 has been the design and testing of such systems to meet a set of stringent performance standards laid down by IMO for their final approval.

Major advances in the speed capability of certain high-speed hull forms have also been unveiled this year, notably in the form of the Australian Oceanfast ALT (Air Lubrication Technology) class of catamaran. The hull form employed on this vessel uses air lubrication techniques developed jointly between Russian technologists and the Oceanfast design team. The reduction of frictional resistance between water and the vessel's hull has long been a goal of research scientists and has resulted in numerous patents each claiming to have solved this difficult problem. However the Russian Navy have been employing similar technology on some of their smaller patrol craft for many years and this has now been developed into a commercially successful application. Oceanfast, and others, are convinced of its enormous potential, with power savings of 30 per cent or more, which could effectively make many other fast vessels redundant almost overnight!

Other resistance reduction devices, also developed jointly with Russian companies include shallow bow hydrofoils and novel stern fins known as interceptors. The foils provide lift at the bow of the vessel thus reducing the amount of hull in the water and the stern interceptors alter the pressure distribution around the aft end of the vessel, again reducing overall resistance.

Regulations and Safety

The advance of commercial high-speed craft has been so rapid that development of rational regulations to cover their commercial use has appeared to lag significantly behind. The start of this year saw the introduction of the new IMO Code of Safety for High-Speed Craft (HSC) which was incorporated within Chapter 10 of SOLAS to allow more formally for the continued development of such craft. This means that any passenger or freight craft operating on international voyages at a speed which exceeds a certain value, may use this chapter of SOLAS as their design and operational basis, if appropriate. The regulation states "the HSC Code applies to high-speed craft engaged on international voyages and includes passenger craft which do not proceed for more than four hours from a place of refuge when fully laden and cargo craft of 500 gross tonnage and above which do not go more than eight hours from a port of refuge. It requires that each passenger is provided with a seat and that no enclosed sleeping berths are provided for passengers. The Code is intended to be a complete set of comprehensive requirements for high-speed craft including equipment and conditions for operation and maintenance. A basic aim is to provide levels of safety which are equivalent to those contained in the conventional SOLAS and International Convention on Load Lines".

Consistent interpretation of the code, however, has been difficult and, in particular, the main areas of concern have been highlighted as: the requirement for a better definition of sufficiency of rescue facilities, more appropriate consideration for the use of composites within main ship structures and more appropriate formulations for collision accelerations and damage length for strength and stability safety levels. Two high-speed craft accidents have recently added weight to these latter arguments - those of *Condor 11* in Australia and the *St Malo* in the Channel Islands where bottom damage in excess of 65 per cent of the waterline length were sustained.

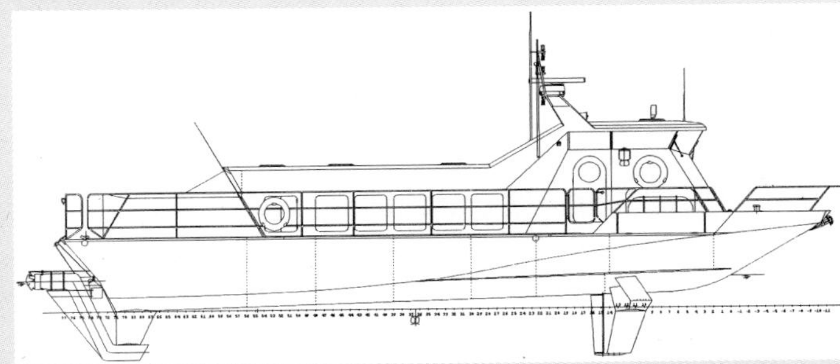

This Russian hydrofoil, the Nevka-3F, designed by Forma Ltd of St Petersburg, is one of many examples of the former Soviet Union's innovative technology being jointly commercialised by Russian companies and organisations outside the CIS ***1996***

The industry has moved quickly to provide a forum for discussion and agreement on these topics. In the UK the Rapid Marine Transport Group was formed in December 1995 to actively promote the commercial and safety issues of this growing industry, and the Royal Institution of Naval Architects has organised an international conference on the subject to be held in February 1997.

One interesting feature of the new HSC Code is that the safety culture that is called for is similar in many respects to the IMO International Safety Management (ISM) Code.

The IMO is taking this safety culture one step further within their international research and development programme. Each member nation of the IMO provides the results of relevant R&D in order to assist in the successful development of this important international organisation's activities. The UK's Marine Safety Agency (MSA) has spent the last year and the equivalent of a full year's total R&D budget on the investigation of Formal Safety Assessment (FSA) for the IMO. This is a programme of work investigating the use of Risk Assessment techniques specifically for the development of future marine regulations (rather than as applied currently to individual projects as in the Nuclear, Chemical and Offshore industries). The research uses the fast ferry industry for an application example for the assessment of the practicality of this novel risk-based approach. The results of this work should be made available within the next year.

Defence Industry

Ten years ago, few would have thought that developments in the commercial ferry business would have had any influence on military craft design and operation. Yet today the two sectors of the fast craft industry are sharing their technical and operational developments to mutual benefit.

Surprisingly the safety standards of fast ferries are putting some military standards to shame particularly in terms of damage stability. A fast ferry designed to withstand damage to only a single watertight compartment would, quite rightly, not be allowed. Yet the majority of even the most modern small patrol craft and fast coastguard cutters would sink if damaged below the waterline at the point of a single watertight bulkhead.

However, lightweight materials developed for military applications are now making good commercial sense in many ferries, where composite shafting and internal honeycomb panels are reducing weight and complexity and improving performance.

Many monohull designs and the main propulsion machinery used in current fast ferries are derived from military experience as are some navigational equipment and important operational procedures. Conversely, the development of multihull ferries has now influenced various navies to order novel types of craft - the UK MoD now have catamarans and Swath craft in operation or on order and are investing heavily in multihull (trimaran) technology for possible future frigate hulls.

There is enormous scope for the cross-fertilisation of ideas between these sectors and indeed between these and other transport industries. This challenge is being recognised by an increasing number of equipment suppliers and technologists and in particular, research and development organisations in the CIS, Europe and the USA where the drive for diversification of military technology is high.

This artist's impression of the Australian InCat Designs Pty Ltd fast catamaran cargo vessel is being marketed in two versions. A 122 m version with a payload of 1,300 tonnes and a 160 m version with a payload of 3,500 tonnes, both able to operate at over 40 knots. The new South Australian Ships Pty Ltd shipyard has been specifically arranged to build such vessels **1996**

The Way Forward

The fast marine transport market is growing and maturing. Certain classes of craft and particularly the general arrangements of monohull vessels are beginning to standardise. Larger multihull and monohull craft are being built in greater numbers although it is probable that the Stena HSS 1500 and the Fincantieri MDV 3000 Jupiter vessels are as large a ro-ro vessel as will be required for many years to come - purely from the point of view of the passenger density requirements for profitable operation and cost effective shore handling facilities.

However, innovation is not slowed so easily and it is likely that significant advances will continue to be made in materials, lightweight equipment, propulsion systems, hull design and port handling facilities.

The Italian Fincantieri MDV 3000 Jupiter design, which was understood to be on the point of being ordered by Italian State operator, Tirrenia, at the time of going to press, is larger than the Stena HSS 1500, having an overall length of 146 m and a capacity of 1,800 passengers and 460 cars whilst still apparently providing an operational speed of 40 knots with 66,000 kW of installed power. Within 1995 alone, Fincantieri received orders for eight 95 to 100 m monohull fast ferries **1996**

Then there is the fast freight vessel market - designs have been made and refined and some have been taken to the stage of large demonstrations. This is clearly the tip of a potentially huge iceberg. Certainly the Pacific Rim countries are of this opinion, where Japan has already invested billions of Yen in fast freight craft R&D, Hyundai in Korea is investing considerable resources into this area and an Australian company, AustralAsian Transport Systems (AATS), has devised a revolutionary intermodal transport network linking the main industrial centres of Australia with Asian ports via fast freight links from Darwin in the Northern Territories. It is proposed that craft with payload capacities of approximately 3,500 tonnes and service speeds of 40 knots would be required for this service.

Whilst this yearbook will contain descriptions and specifications of such developments as they occur, there are other Jane's Yearbooks which will have an increasing relevance to this market. In particular these include *Jane's Merchant Ships*, *Jane's Urban Transport Systems* and *Jane's All the World's Aircraft* to name but a few. These databases are all available on CD-ROM and EIS (Electronic Information Systems), as indeed is this yearbook.

Whatever your interest in this industry, may I wish you the very best for your business and hope that you find this yearbook of value in promoting your particular industrial strengths to assist you, and your country, to trade yet more effectively around the world.

I always welcome comment - of whatever nature - on the content of this book and would be very glad to hear from you at any time.

S J Phillips BSc CEng FRINA
Springtide
Harbour Way
Bosham
West Sussex PO18 8QH

Tel: +44 (1243) 574610

Preface

This annual reference book is aimed at providing an informed, balanced and comprehensive data source for all those organisations with an interest in high-speed marine transport worldwide.

If your company or product is not included but you feel that it should be then please do contact me: I would be delighted to include all relevant information. There is no charge for editorial entries in this book.

Whilst every effort is made to standardise and rationalise the information presented in this book, it is nonetheless not always possible to ensure that all the information is based on a common standard. For example the operational speeds quoted for each craft may be for slightly different displacement definitions. However, each year we spend a considerable time in rationalising the data and hope that in the future this will lead to still further improvements in data quality.

What constitutes high speed in the marine world has been the subject of much debate. It is clearly a relative term and for the purposes of this book, need not be defined quantitatively. However craft with speeds of less than 25 knots and with a length of less than 20 m are generally only included if they represent a development of particular interest.

It may be noted that the new International Maritime Organisation's Code of Safety for High Speed Marine Craft (Chapter 10 of SOLAS) defines high speed on the basis of a speed to displacement coefficient. In this Code a high-speed craft is a craft capable of a maximum speed equal to or exceeding $V=3.7(Displ)^{0.1667}$, where Displ is the maximum displacement in cubic metres and V is the speed in metres per second. Thus for a 100 tonne craft this speed is 15 knots, for a 1,000 tonne craft it is 23 knots and for a 10,000 craft it is 35 knots. These values of speed relative to the size of the vessel have been set low so as to make the Code available to as wide a range of craft as possible. As some stage in the re-evaluation of the Code this speed term may disappear and the Code renamed a 'Restricted Service' Code for that is what, in essence, it is.

Sea—General				Wind					Sea					
Sea State	Description	(Beaufort) Wind force	Description	Range	Wind Velocity	Wave Height			Significant Range Periods	Periods of Maximum Energy of Spectra Tmax=Tc	Average Period Tz	Average Wave Length Lw	Minimum Fetch	Minimum Duration
						Average	Significant	Average of One-Tenth Highest						
	Sea like a mirror	U	Calm	1 knot	—	—	—	—	—	—	—	—	—	—
0	Ripples with the appearance of scales are formed, but without foam crests	1	Light airs	1-3 knots	2 knots	0.04 ft	0.01 ft 0.01 ft	0.09 ft	1.2 s	0.75	0.5	10 in	5 n miles	18 min
1	Small wavelets; short but pronounced crests have a glossy appearance, but do not break	2	Light breeze	4-6 knots	5 knots	0.3 ft	0.5 ft	0.6 ft	0.4-2.8 s	1.9	1.3	6.7 ft	8 n miles	39 min
	Large wavelets; crests begin to break. Foam of glossy appearance. Perhaps scattered with horses	3	Gentle breeze	7-10 knots	8.5 knots 10 knots	0.8 ft 1.1 ft	1.3 ft 1.8 ft	1.6 ft 2.3 ft	0.8-5.0 s 1.0-6.0 s	3.2 3.2	2.3 2.7	20 ft 27 ft	9.8 n miles 10 n miles	1.7 h 2.4 h
2 3	Small waves, becoming larger; fairly frequent white horses	4	Moderate breeze	11-16 knots	12 knots 13.5 knots 14 knots 16 knots	1.6 ft 2.1 ft 2.3 ft 2.9 ft	2.6 ft 3.3 ft 3.6 ft 4.7 ft	3.3 ft 4.2 ft 4.6 ft 6.0 ft	1.0-7.0 s 1.4-7.6 s 1.5-7.8 s 2.0-8.8 s	4.5 5.1 5.3 6.0	3.2 3.6 3.8 4.3	40 ft 52 ft 59 ft 71 ft	18 n miles 24 n miles 28 n miles 40 n miles	3.8 h 4.8 h 5.2 h 6.6 h
4	Moderate waves, taking a more pronounced long form; many white horses are formed (chance of some spray)	5	Fresh breeze	17-21 knots	18 knots 19 knots 20 knots	3.7 ft 4.1 ft 4.6 ft	5.9 ft 6.6 ft 7.3 ft	7.5 ft 8.4 ft 9.3 ft	2.5-10.0 s 2.8-10.6 s 3.0-11.1 s	6.8 7.2 7.5	4.8 5.1 5.4	90 ft 99 ft 111 ft	55 n miles 65 n miles 75 n miles	8.3 h 9.2 h 10 h
5 6	Large waves begin to form; white crests are more extensive everywhere (probably some spray)	6	Strong breeze	22-27 knots	22 knots 24 knots 24.5 knots 26 knots	5.5 ft 6.6 ft 6.8 ft 7.7 ft	8.8 ft 10.5 ft 10.9 ft 12.3 ft	11.2 ft 13.3 ft 13.8 ft 15.6 ft	3.4-12.2 s 3.7-13.5 s 3.8-13.6 s 4.0-14.5 s	8.3 9.0 9.2 9.8	5.9 6.4 6.6 7.0	134 ft 160 ft 164 ft 188 ft	100 n miles 130 n miles 140 n miles 180 n miles	12 h 14 h 15 h 17 h
7	Sea heaps up, and white foam from breaking waves begins to be blown in streaks along the direction of the wind (Spindrift begins to be seen)	7	Moderate gale	28-33 knots	28 knots 30 knots 30.5 knots 32 knots	8.9 ft 10.3 ft 10.6 ft 11.6 ft	14.3 ft 16.4 ft 16.9 ft 18.6 ft	18.2 ft 20.8 ft 21.5 ft 23.6 ft	4.5-15.5 s 4.7-16.7 s 4.8-17.0 s 5.0-17.5 s	10.6 11.3 11.5 12.1	7.5 8.0 8.2 8.6	212 ft 250 ft 258 ft 285 ft	230 n miles 280 n miles 290 n miles 340 n miles	20 h 23 h 24 h 27 h
7	Moderate high waves of greater length; edges of crests break into spindrift. The foam is blown in well-marked streaks along the direction of the wind. Spray affects visibility	8	Fresh gale	34-40 knots	34 knots 36 knots 37 knots 38 knots 40 knots	13.1 ft 14.8 ft 15.6 ft 16.4 ft 18.2 ft	21.0 ft 23.6 ft 24.9 ft 26.3 ft 29.1 ft	26.7 ft 30.0 ft 31.6 ft 33.4 ft 37.0 ft	5.5-18.5 s 5.8-19.7 s 6-20.5 s 6.2-20.8 s 6.5-21.7 s	12.8 13.6 13.9 14.3 15.1	9.1 9.6 9.9 10.2 10.7	322 ft 363 ft 376 ft 392 ft 444 ft	420 n miles 500 n miles 530 n miles 600 n miles 710 n miles	30 h 34 h 37 h 38 h 42 h
8	High waves. Dense streaks of foam along the direction of the wind. Sea begins to roll. Visibility affected.	9	Strong gale	41-37 knots	42 knots 44 knots 46 knots	20.1 ft 22.0 ft 24.1 ft	32.1 ft 35.2 ft 38.5 ft	40.8 ft 44.7 ft 48.9 ft	7-23 s 7-24.2 s 7-25 s	15.8 16.6 17.3	11.3 11.8 12.3	492 ft 534 ft 590 ft	830 n miles 960 n miles 1110 n miles	47 h 52 h 57 h
9	Very high waves with long over-hanging crests. The resulting foam is in great patches and is blown in dense white streaks along the direction of the wind. On the whole, the surface of the sea takes on a white appearance. The rolling of the sea becomes heavy and shocklike. Visibility is affected	10	Whole* gale	48-55 knots	40 knots 50 knots 51.5 knots 52 knots 54 knots	26.2 ft 28.4 ft 30.2 ft 30.8 ft 33.2 ft	41.9 ft 45.5 ft 48.3 ft 49.2 ft 53.1 ft	53.2 ft 57.8 ft 61.3 ft 62.5 ft 67.4 ft	7.5-26 s 7.5-27 s 8-28.2 s 8-28.5 s 8-29.5 s	18.1 18.8 19.4 19.6 20.4	12.9 13.4 13.8 13.9 14.5	650 ft 700 ft 736 ft 750 ft 810 ft	1250 n miles 1420 n miles 1560 n miles 1610 n miles 1800 n miles	63 h 69 h 73 h 75 h 81 h
	Exceptionally high waves. Sea completely covered with long white patches of foam lying in direction of wind. Everywhere edges of wave crests are blown into froth. Visibility affected	11	Storm*	56-63 knots	56 knots 59.5 knots	35.7 ft 40.3 ft	57.1 ft 64.4 ft	72.5 ft 81.8 ft	8.5-31 s 10-32 s	21.1 22.4	15 15.9	910 ft 985 ft	2100 n miles 2500 n miles	88 h 101 h
	Air filled with foam and spray. Sea white with driving spray. Visibility very seriously affected	12	Hurricane*	64-71 knots	>64 knots	>46.6 ft	74.5 ft	94.6 ft	10-35 s	24.1	17.2	—	—	—

* For hurricane winds (and often whole gale and storm winds) required durations and reports are barely attained. Seas are therefore not fully arisen

DEFINITIONS OF SYMBOLS AND UNITS

Four of the seven base units of the SI (Système International d'Unités) which are used in this book are:

length	metre	m
mass	kilogram	kg
time	second	s
electric current	ampere	A

Decimal unit	Quantity	Formula
Pa (Pascal)	pressure or stress	N/m^2
N (Newton)	force	$kg.m/s^2$
W (Watt)	power	J/s
Hz (Hertz)	frequency	1/s (1 Hertz = 1 cycle per second in previous British practice)
V (Volt)	electric potential difference	W/A

Other units		Quantity
dB	(decibel)	sound pressure level, re 0.0002 microbar
dBA	(decibel)	sound level, A-weighted, re 0.0002 microbar

CONVERSIONS

Length

1 km = 0.6214 statute mile = 0.540 nautical mile
1 m = 3.281 ft
1 cm = 0.3937 in
1 mm = 0.0394 in

Area

1 ha (hectare = 10 000 m^2) = 2.471 acres
1 m^2 = 10.764 ft^2

Volume

1 m^3 = 35.315 ft^3
1 litre = 0.220 Imperial gallon = 0.264 US gallon

Velocity

1 km/h = 0.621 statute mile/h = 0.540 knots
1 m/s = 3.281 ft/s

Acceleration

1 m/s^2 = 3.281 ft/s^2

Mass

1 t (tonne) = 1000 kg = 0.9842 long ton = 2204.62 lb = 1.1023 short tons
1 kg (kilogram) = 2.205 lb
1 g (gram) = 0.002205 lb

Force

1 MN (meganewton) = 100.36 long ton force
1 kgf = 2.205 lbf
1 kp (kilopond) = 2.205 lbf
1 N (newton) = 0.2248 lbf (The Newton is that force which, applied to a mass of 1 kilogram, gives it an acceleration of 1 m/s^2.)

Moment of force (torque)

1 Nm = 0.7376 lbf.ft

Pressure, stress

1 atm (standard atmosphere) = 14.696 lbf/in^2
1 bar (10^5 pascal) = 14.504 lbf/in^2
1 kPa (kN/m^2) = 20.885 lbf/ft^2
1 Pa (N/m^2) = 0.020885 lbf/ft^2

Power

1 metric horsepower (ch, ps) = 0.7355 kW = 1.014 horsepower (550 ft lb/s)
1 kW = 1.341 horsepower (1 horsepower = 550 ft lb/s) = 1.360 metric horsepower

Nautical mile

The International Nautical Mile is equivalent to the average length of a minute of latitude and corresponds to a latitude of 45° and a distance of 1852 m = 6076.12 ft.

Fuel consumption

Specific fuel consumption, 1.0 g/kWh = 0.001644 lb/hph (hp = 550 ft lb/s)
1.0 litre/h = 0.220 Imperial gallon/h = 0.264 US gallon/h

tirrenia
Scatto

RODRIQUEZ
CANTIERI NAVALI SPA

New entries in this edition

Company	Section	Country
Hang Tong Shipyard	Air Cushion Vehicles	China, People's Republic
Jian Hui Shipyard	Air Cushion Vehicles	China, People's Republic
Volga Shipyard	Hydrofoils	CIS
Oceanfast, Ferries Pty Ltd	High-Speed Multihull Vessels	Australia
South Australian Ships Pty Ltd	High-Speed Multihull Vessels	Australia
Abeking and Rasmussen Shipyard	High-Speed Multihull Vessels	Germany
Lay Construction Ltd	High-Speed Multihull Vessels	UK
Derecktor Shipyards	High-Speed Multihull Vessels	USA
Marinette Marine Corp	High-Speed Multihull Vessels	USA
Sea Chrome Marine Pty Ltd	High-Speed Monohull Craft	Australia
Inma	High-Speed Monohull Craft	Italy
Damen Shipyards	High-Speed Monohull Craft	Italy
Greenbay Marine Pte Ltd	High-Speed Monohull Craft	Singapore
Tokushima Buri University	Wing-In-Ground-Effect Craft	Japan
White Dolphin Cruises	Civil Operators	Australia
Black Sea Shipping Plc	Civil Operators	Bulgaria
Shen Zhen Xun Long	Civil Operators	China, People's Republic
Wan Shan District Company	Civil Operators	China, People's Republic
Jadrolinija	Civil Operators	Croatia
Cat Link	Civil Operators	Denmark
Grenaa-Hundested	Civil Operators	Denmark
Corsica Ferries	Civil Operators	France
SNCM	Civil Operators	France
Ferry Transport	Civil Operators	French Polynesia
Schiffahrtskontor Altes Land	Civil Operators	Germany
TT-Line	Civil Operators	Germany
Catamaran Lines	Civil Operators	Greece
Giamar Lines	Civil Operators	Greece
Seajet Shipping	Civil Operators	Greece
Island Cruise Line Pacific Inc	Civil Operators	Guam
Damania Shipping	Civil Operators	India
Alilauro-Gru. So, N, Spa	Civil Operators	Italy
Alimar Spa	Civil Operators	Italy
Elba Ferries	Civil Operators	Italy
Ocean Bridge Investments	Civil Operators	Italy
Saremar	Civil Operators	Italy
Bintan Renraku Kisen	Civil Operators	Japan
Diamond Ferry Company	Civil Operators	Japan
Koshikishima Shosen Ltd	Civil Operators	Japan
Arab Bridge Investments	Civil Operators	Jordan
Dong Yang Express	Civil Operators	Korea, South
Kang won Hungup	Civil Operators	Korea, South
Sriwani Tours and Travel	Civil Operators	Malaysia
Interisland Line	Civil Operators	New Zealand
Sørlands Cruise	Civil Operators	Norway
Grand Seaways Ferries Inc	Civil Operators	Philippines
Koster Marine	Civil Operators	Sweden
Stena Line	Civil Operators	Sweden
Cross Sound Ferry Service	Civil Operators	USA
Florida Cruise	Civil Operators	USA
Hy-Line Cruise	Civil Operators	USA
New York Fast Ferry Service Inc	Civil Operators	USA
Aliscafos SA	Civil Operators	Uruguay
Virgin Hydrofoil Service	Civil Operators	Virgin Islands
Azam Marine	Civil Operators	Zanzibar
ABB Stal AB	Engines	Sweden
Liferaft Systems Australia Pty Ltd	Marine Escape Systems	Australia
Viking Lifesaving Equipment	Marine Escape Systems	Denmark
Selantic Industrier A/S	Marine Escape Systems	Norway
ML Lifeguard Equipment Ltd	Marine Escape Systems	UK
RFD Ltd	Marine Escape Systems	UK
KBM	Fast Rescue Tenders	Australia
NATAD	Fast Rescue Tenders	Australia
ASMAR	Fast Rescue Tenders	Chile
Zodiac International	Fast Rescue Tenders	France
DSB (Deutsche Schlauchboot)	Fast Rescue Tenders	Germany
Novurania SpA	Fast Rescue Tenders	Italy
Lancer Inflatables	Fast Rescue Tenders	New Zealand
Duarry	Fast Rescue Tenders	Spain
Avon Inflatables	Fast Rescue Tenders	UK
Dunlop Marine Safety Ltd	Fast Rescue Tenders	UK
Halmatic Ltd	Fast Rescue Tenders	UK
Ribtec Ltd	Fast Rescue Tenders	UK
RTK Marine	Fast Rescue Tenders	UK
Ambar Marine Inc	Fast Rescue Tenders	USA
Boston Whaler Inc	Fast Rescue Tenders	USA
Fleet Technology Ltd	Consultants and Designers	Canada
Malcolm Tennant Multihull Design	Consultants and Designers	New Zealand
Marinteknik Design (E) AB	Consultants and Designers	Sweden
Pelmatic AB	Consultants and Designers	Sweden
Hart Fenton and Co Ltd	Consultants and Designers	UK
George G Sharp Inc	Consultants and Designers	USA
Rapid Marine Transport Group	Societies Involved with High-Speed Craft	UK
InCat Designs Pty Ltd	Addenda	Australia
Afai	Addenda	China
Almaz Shipbuilding Company Ltd	Addenda	CIS
Leroux and Lotz	Addenda	France
Lürssen Werft GmbH & Co	Addenda	Germany
PT Pal Indonesia	Addenda	Indonesia
Fincantieri Cantieri Navali Italiani SpA	Addenda	Italy
Hyundai Heavy Industries Company Ltd	Addenda	Korea, South
Schelde Shipbuilding	Addenda	Netherlands
Color SeaCat KS	Addenda	Norway
Mjellem & Karlsen Verft A/S	Addenda	Norway
Westamarin A/S	Addenda	Norway
Westamarin West A/S	Addenda	Norway
Kvæner Fjellistrand (S) Pte Ltd	Addenda	Singapore
Dunlop-Beaufort	Addenda	UK

Entries deleted from this edition

Company	Section	Country
Canair Hovercrafts Inc	Air Cushion Vehicles	Canada
Tille Shipyard BV	Air Cushion Vehicles	Netherlands
FM Aerodeslizadores	Air Cushion Vehicles	Spain
Osprey Hovercraft UK Ltd	Air Cushion Vehicles	UK
Neotoric Hovercrafts Inc	Air Cushion Vehicles	USA
Akerman Industrie	Air Cushion Vehicles	France
Krasnoye Sormovo Shipyard	Hydrofoils	CIS
CMN	High-Speed Multihull Vessels	France
Tille Shipyards BV	High-Speed Multihull Vessels	Netherlands
Navysurf	High-Speed Monohull Craft	France
Hellenic Shipyards Company	High-Speed Monohull Craft	Greece
Shimon Seki Shipyard	High-Speed Monohull Craft	Japan
Berthon Boat Company Ltd	High-Speed Monohull Craft	UK
D & R Ferries	Civil Operators	Antilles
Alimar SA	Civil Operators	Argentina
P & O Heron Island Resort	Civil Operators	Australia
Badlands Hovertours	Civil Operators	Canada
Geophysical Surveys Inc	Civil Operators	China
Azov Shipping Company	Civil Operators	CIS
Caspian Shipping Company	Civil Operators	CIS
Murmansk Shipping Company	Civil Operators	CIS
City Jet	Civil Operators	Estonia
SNAT	Civil Operators	France
Vedettes de L'Odet Ferry Company	Civil Operators	France
Piraiki Naftiliaki SA	Civil Operators	Greece
Sonia Shipping	Civil Operators	Greece
Hong Kong Macao Hydrofoil Company Ltd	Civil Operators	Hong Kong
PT Bintan Barona Sakti	Civil Operators	Indonesia
PT Satmarindo	Civil Operators	Indonesia
Covemar Eolie	Civil Operators	Italy
Ministerio Della Marina Mercantile	Civil Operators	Italy
Enoh Kisen	Civil Operators	Japan
Geibi Shosen Company Ltd	Civil Operators	Japan
Hayatekaiun Company Ltd	Civil Operators	Japan
Iriomote Kaiun Company Ltd	Civil Operators	Japan

Company	Section	Country
Japan Ocean Cruise Line	Civil Operators	Japan
Kasumigaura Jet Line KK	Civil Operators	Japan
Maruto Kisen Company Ltd	Civil Operators	Japan
Mihara Kanko Kisen Co Ltd	Civil Operators	Japan
Mikatagoko Yuransen	Civil Operators	Japan
Ohmi Marine	Civil Operators	Japan
Ueda Kaiun KK	Civil Operators	Japan
Wakasawan Kanko Company Ltd	Civil Operators	Japan
Daeheung Sang-SA	Civil Operators	Korea, South
Dong Bu Express	Civil Operators	Korea, South
Jeo-Kyung Ferry Company	Civil Operators	Korea, South
Asie Crewboat SDN BHD	Civil Operators	Malaysia
Pomas SDN BHD	Civil Operators	Malaysia
Rawa Safaris	Civil Operators	Malaysia
Hovercraft Adventures	Civil Operators	New Zealand
Bergen Nordhordland Rutelag A/S	Civil Operators	Norway
Przedsiebiorstwo Usiug Turystycznych Pomerania	Civil Operators	Poland
IGSA Transport	Civil Operators	Singapore
Tan Pia Law	Civil Operators	Singapore
Yasmine Line SA	Civil Operators	Spain
Sun Island Cruises	Civil Operators	Trinidad
Zadco Productions	Civil Operators	United Arab Emirates
Dept of Transportation, USCG	Civil Operators	USA
Glacier Bay Yacht Tours Inc	Civil Operators	USA
Sea Jet Cruise Line	Civil Operators	USA
Belt SA	Civil Operators	Uruguay
Intumaca	Civil Operators	Venezuela
Maraven SA	Civil Operators	Venezuela
Nico Transmission (S) Pte Ltd	Transmissions	Singapore
OTTO Scheen Jr A/S	Consultants and Designers	Norway
Swan Hunter Singapore Pte Ltd	Consultants and Designers	Singapore
Joint Aero Marine Group	Societies involved with High-Speed Craft	UK

BUILDERS

Air Cushion Vehicles
Hydrofoils
High-Speed Multihull Vessels
SWATH Vessels (Semi-Submerged Catamarans (SSCs))
High-Speed Monohull Craft
Wing-In-Ground-Effect Craft

AIR CUSHION VEHICLES

Company Listing by Country

Australia
NQEA Australia Pty Ltd
Oceanfast Ferries Pty Ltd

Belgium
Scheepswerf SKB Polyship NV

China, People's Republic
Bei Hai Shipyard
Cactec
Dagu Shipyard
Dong Feng Shipyard
Hang Tong High-Speed Ship Development Co Ltd
Huangpu Shipyard
Hudong Shipyard
Jiang Hui Shipyard
Maric
Shanghai Aircraft Factory
Zhong Hua Shipyard

Commonwealth of Independent States
Almaz Central Marine Design Bureau
Astrakhan Shipyard
Gorkovski Philial Cnii im akad. A N Krylova
Krasnoye Sormovo Shipyard A A Zhdanov
Marijski Polytechnical Institute
Neptun CDB Corp
St Petersberg Shipyard
Sosnovskaya Shipyard
Vympel Central Design Bureau

France
DCN
DRET
ACH
CMN

Germany
Blohm+Voss AG

Italy
Fincantieri Cantieri Navali Italiani SpA
SEC

Japan
Mitsubishi Heavy Industries Ltd
Mitsui Engineering & Shipbuilding Company Ltd
Technological Research Association of Techno-Superliner

Korea, South
Korea Tacoma Marine Industries Ltd
Samsung Heavy Industries Company Ltd
Semo Company Ltd

Netherlands
Hovertrans BV
Schelde Shipbuilding

Norway
Kværner A/S Fast Ferries
Swede Ship
Ulstein International A/S

Singapore
Singapore Shipbuilding and Engineering Ltd

Spain
Chaconsa SA

Sweden
Karlskronavarvet AB

United Kingdom
ABS Hovercraft Ltd
Air Vehicles Limited
Aluminium Shipbuilders Ltd
British Hovercraft Corporation
Griffon Hovercraft Ltd
Hovermarine International Ltd
Ingles Hovercraft Associates Ltd
Slingsby Aviation Limited

United States of America
Avondale Boat Division
Textron Marine & Land Systems

AUSTRALIA

NQEA AUSTRALIA PTY LTD

62-90 Cook Street, PO Box 1105, Portsmith, Cairns, Queensland 4870, Australia

Tel: +61 (70) 527222
Telex: 48087 AA
Fax: +61 (70) 352812/352520

D G Fry, *Chairman*
E W Graham, *General Manager, Commercial*
R Bannah, *Marketing Manager*
R D Rookwood, *Senior Design Engineer*
M Richards, *Chief Naval Architect*

Craft built	Name	Seats	Launched	Operator/Owner
BHC AP1-88	*Benidorm* (ex-*Courier**)	81	December 1986	Hovertravel Ltd
BHC AP1-88	*Hover Mirage*	70	March 1987	Anfibios, Uruguay
BHC AP1-88	*Hover Freighter*	16	April 1987	Cominco Co, Canada
BHC AP1-88	*Tienpengyang I*	94	November 1989	Tien Peng Yang Hovertravel Corporation
BHC AP1-88		101		(not completed)
BHC AP1-88		101		(not completed)

*Arrived UK December 1988 from Australia, GH 2108, fitted with 100 seats and later sold to Real Maritima de Cruceros, Spain. Bought by Hovertravel Ltd in UK June 1992

In 1964 NQEA entered the shipbuilding industry with the construction of a range of vessels, including Australia's 'Attack Class' patrol boats, and the construction of several medium-sized craft, including tug boats, fishing trawlers and 22 workboats for the Australian Defence Department.

In 1977, NQEA was the successful tenderer for 14 (of a total of 15) 42 m 'Fremantle Class' patrol craft for the Australian Navy, the lead vessel being built in the UK by Brooke Marine. Taking 85 weeks to construct the craft, NQEA was delivering at a rate of one every 14 weeks.

NQEA has built a number of high-speed catamarans under licence from International Catamarans Designs Pty Ltd and AP1-88s under licence from British Hovercraft Corporation, the first order for the latter having been received in February 1986.

AP1-88 300 MODEL

In 1990 NQEA converted and delivered to Cominco, a Canadian mining company based in British Columbia, the AP1-88 previously known as *Hover Mirage II*. Cominco has renamed the craft *Hover Freighter*. The passenger cabin has been significantly reduced in size, only allowing for 16 passengers. The reduced cabin size creates a well-deck capable of lifting up to 11 tonnes in its remodelled form. The modification was formally approved by BHC, which designated the NQEA design the AP1-88 300 model.

VERIFIED

NQEA-built AP1-88 **1990**

OCEANFAST FERRIES PTY LTD

18 Clarence Beach, Henderson, Western Australia 6166, Australia

Tel: +61 (9) 410 1866
Fax: +61 (9) 410 1927

David Browning, *Manager*

Oceanfast Ferries is a member of the Oceanfast Marine Group which includes Oceanfast International, Motor Yacht International and Ferries Australia.

The company signed an agreement with Ulstein International of Norway in February 1994 to transfer the technology developed by Ulstein for the UT 928 Air Cushion Catamaran, and by early 1995 had completed the construction of two UT 928 vessels, one with Ulstein Z drives and one with KaMeWa 63SII water-jets.

Oceanfast Ferries' second UT 928 fitted with water-jets **1996**

UT 928 AIR CUSHION CATAMARAN

This design has been arranged to accept water-jet or Speed-Z propulsors, with the Speed-Z configuration offering more than a 2 knot advantage.

Specifications

Length overall	38.4 m
Beam	11.8 m
Draught, on-cushion	2.4 m
Draught, off-cushion	3.3 m
Passengers	350
Crew	9
Fuel capacity	14,000 l
Water capacity	1,500 l
Max speed	48 kts
Operational speed	45 kts

Classification: DnV +1A1 HSLC Passenger R2 EO

Propulsion: The vessel is powered by two MTU 16V 396 TE 74L diesel engines each driving an Ulstein Speed-Z drive or a KMW 63S11 water-jet, via a reduction gearbox. Lift power is derived from two MTU 12V 183 TE 72 diesels. For the water-jet craft the draft is reduced to 2.6 m hull borne and 1.0 m on cushion.

Control: The vessels are fitted with MDI ride control systems.

UPDATED

Oceanfast Ferries' first UT 928 fitted with Ulstein Speed-Z drives ***1995***

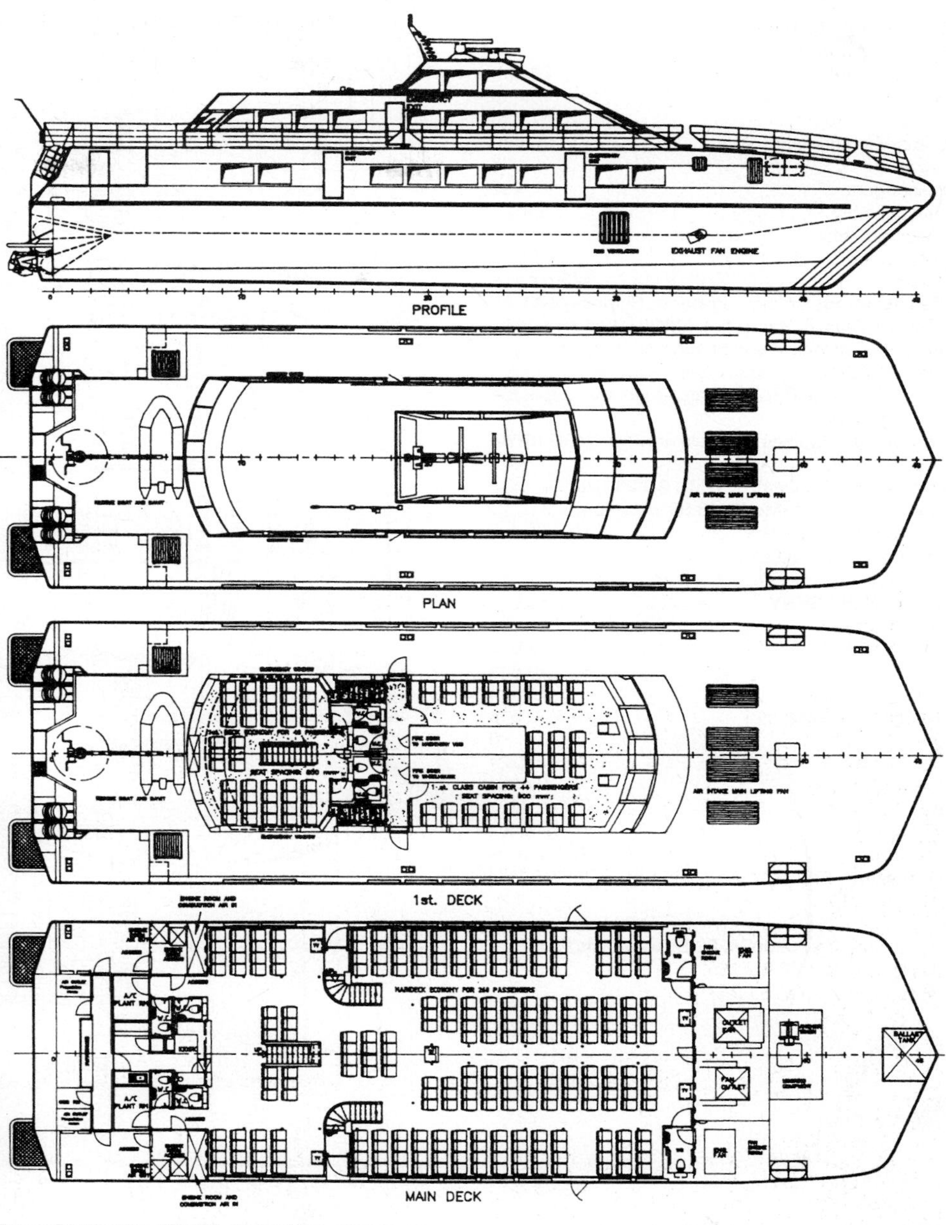

Oceanfast Ferries UT 928 air cushion catamaran ***1996***

BELGIUM

SCHEEPSWERF SKB POLYSHIP NV

H. Baelskaai 6, 8400 Ostend, Belgium

Tel: +32 (59) 324720
Fax: +32 (59) 325938

L Longueville, *Chairman and Managing Director*
J C Renault, *Sales Manager*

NV Scheepswerf 'Béliard' Polyship was taken over in 1994 by SKB which now markets the SES designs.

29.6 m/32.6 m SES FERRIES

Constructed in composite materials for the fast transport of passengers on routes of 400 to 448 n miles in sheltered waters. Adapted versions (SES and/or Catamaran) are offered for navigation on large lakes and major rivers, and mixed passenger/freight versions of craft can also be offered.

The hull is built in single skin GRP with longitudinal stiffeners and web frames. The main deck, with deckhouse, is built in a sandwich material construction. An automatic ride system is provided.

Passenger accommodation is divided into two classes although standard outfitting of both passenger saloons can also be offered. Both the passenger saloons and wheelhouse are fully air-conditioned.

SES Manto ***1994***

29.6 m SES FERRY
Specifications

Length overall	29.6 m
Beam	10.8 m
Draught, hullborne	1.7 m
Draught, on-cushion	0.9 m
Crew	6
Passengers	192
Fuel capacity	5,900 l
Water capacity	1,200 l
Max speed	40 kts
Range	448 n miles

Classification: Lloyd's register of Shipping ✠A1 Air Cushion Vehicle Group 2 + LMC UMS for machinery. These vessels are built and outfitted to the IMO-code of Safety of Dynamically Supported Vessels Res. A 373 (x) and BZI (Belgian Maritime Inspectorate) regulations.
Propulsion: Engines, propulsion: 2 × Deutz MWM TBD 604 V16.
Engines, lift: 2 × Deutz MWM TBD 234 V8.
Propulsion: 2 × KaMeWa 63 SII water-jets.
Gearboxes: 2 × ZF BW 755.
Lift fans: Air Vehicles Ltd.

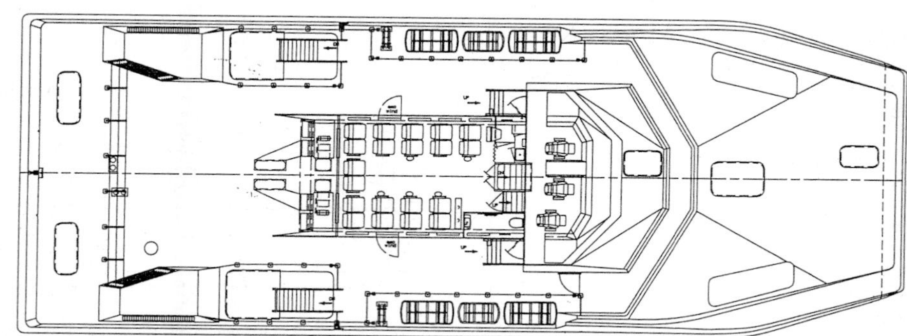

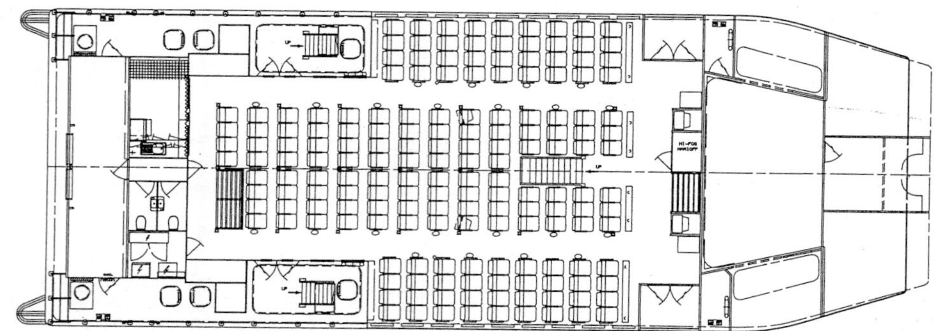

General arrangement of 29.6 m SES Manto **1994**

32.6 m SES FERRY
Specifications

Length overall	32.6 m
Beam	10.8 m
Draught, hullborne	1.85 m
Draught, on-cushion	0.9 m
Crew	6
Passengers	224
Fuel capacity	9,450 l
Water capacity	2,000 l
Max speed	40 kts
Range	400 n miles

Propulsion: Engines, propulsion: 2 × Deutz MWM TBD 604 V16.
Engines, lift: 2 × Deutz MWM TBD 234 V8.
Propulsion: 2 × KaMeWa 63 SII water-jets.
Gearboxes: 2 × ZF BU 755.
Lift fans: Air Vehicles Ltd.

VERIFIED

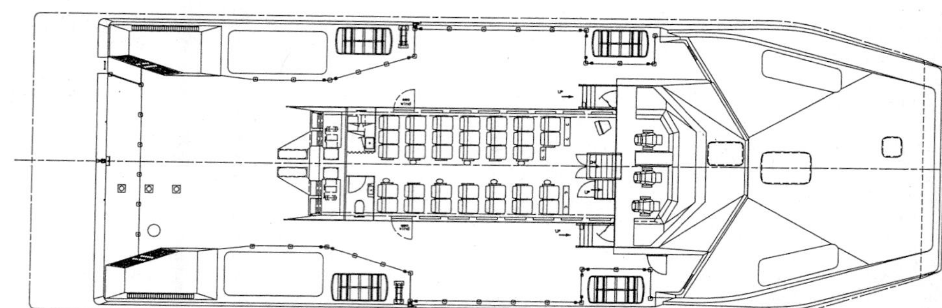

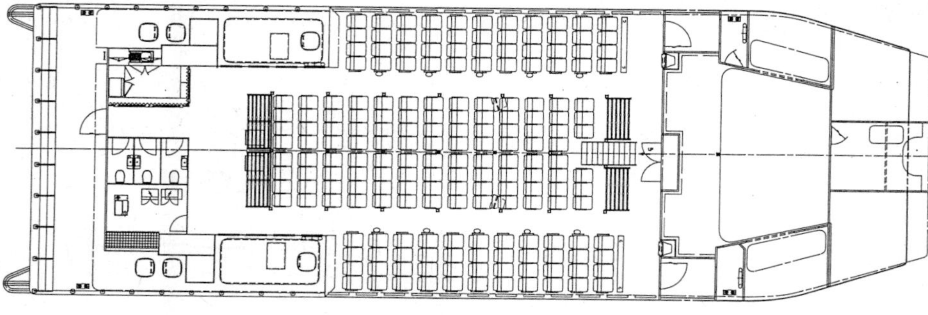

General arrangement of 32.6 m SES Alexandros **1994**

CHINA, PEOPLE'S REPUBLIC

BEI HAI SHIPYARD

Qing Dao, People's Republic of China

TYPE 7217

A Type 7217 craft was completed at Bei Hai Shipyard in December 1993 and operates as a passenger ferry at Qiao-Zhou Gulf, near Qing Dao City. A second vessel was completed in October 1995.

Specifications

Length overall	44 m
Length waterline	42.10 m
Beam	8.28 m
Height	7.0 m
Weight, max	145 t
Max speed	25 kts
Operational speed	23.5 kts
Range	250 n miles
Operational limitation	Beaufort 8, Sea State 4

Structure: The main hull is constructed of steel with an aluminium superstructure.
Propulsion: There are two sets of MWM TBD 234 V16 diesels rated at 755 kW @ 2,200 rpm each for propulsion, and a single MWM TBD 234 V16 for lift power.

MARIC Type 7217 sidewall hovercraft **1996**

UPDATED

DAGU SHIPYARD

Yangzhabei, Xigu, Tang-gu, Tianjin, People's Republic of China

Tel: +86 (22) 3901 Ext 98
Fax: +86 (22) 3128

Young Tze-Wen, *Director*

Building of various types of hovercraft (amphibious and sidewall), and design and building of medium and small size steel vessels.

TYPE 7203

Derived from Types 713 and 717 (built in the 1970s), Type 7203 is a high-speed passenger ferry for use on coastal and sheltered waters. Alternative applications include coastguard patrol and port/harbour firefighting duties.

Built at the Dagu Shipyard, Tianjin, the prototype was launched in September 1982 and underwent trials on the Hai river and in Tang-gu in late 1982.

Specifications

Length overall	22.2 m
Beam	6.9 m
Draught, hullborne	2.06 m
Draught, on-cushion	1.22 m
Weight, max	35 t
Passengers	81-100
Propulsive power	2 × 335 kW
Max speed	30 kts
Operational speed	26 kts
Range	180 n miles

Structure: The skirt is a loop and segment type in bonded natural rubber coated fabric.

Propulsion: A multifan system improves seakeeping performance. There are three centrifugal fans of different diameters fitted separately in the bow, amidships and stern. Each feeds air to the bow and stern skirts and the air cushion at different volumes and pressures. Diameters of the bow, amidships and stern fans are 800, 1,200 and 450 mm respectively. The lift system is powered by a single 12150C high-speed diesel rated at 226 kW at 1,500 rpm. The lift engine directly drives the amidships and stern fans. The bow fan is driven via a hydraulic pump and motor. Total lift power is about 188 kW. Disengaging the bow fan reduces lift power consumption to about 76 kW in calm waters. When operating in waves the bow fan is required since it affects the craft's trim. Propulsive power is supplied by two 12150CZ water-cooled, turbocharged, high-speed marine diesels, each rated at 335 kW at 1,450 rpm. Each drives a three-bladed propeller via a V-type transmission.

Type 7203 fast ferry *1987*

Control: Craft direction controlled by twin rudders and by differential use of water propellers.

Outfit: In standard configuration the passenger cabin seats 81 passengers. If required, seating capacity can be increased to 100. There are two aisles between the seats, 800 mm wide.

Jinxiang

Jinxiang, a Type 7203, is a joint project of the Marine Design and Research Institute of China and the Dagu Shipyard, Tianjin. In 1983 it successfully completed a 128 km maiden voyage along the Yangtze, from Shanghai to Vantong, in under three hours.

VERIFIED

DONG FENG SHIPYARD

Jiuxi, Hangzhou, Zhejiang, People's Republic of China

Tel: +86 (571) 791695/791694
Fax: +86 (571) 554163

Li Leng-Xing, *Director*

TYPE 7210

Two fully amphibious utility hovercraft Type 7210, designed by MARIC were completed in May 1985.

Specifications

Length overall	9.85 m
Beam	3.40 m
Weight, max	4.7 t
Payload	0.8 t
Max speed	24 kts
Range	135 n miles

Structure: Built in medium strength seawater resistant aluminium alloy of riveted construction. The skirt is of the bag and finger type in rubberised fabric, low temperature resistant down to −20°C. The total skirt height is 500 mm.

Propulsion: The craft is powered by air-cooled marine diesels. Lift is provided by a Deutz BF6L 912 diesel engine driving a centrifugal aluminium fan via a gearbox. Thrust is supplied by another diesel, a Deutz BF6L 913 driving via a transmission shaft and elastic coupling, a 1.8 m, five-blade, ducted air propeller built in GRP.

MARIC-designed Type 7210 built by Dong Feng Shipyard *1986*

TYPE 717 II and 717III

This craft is a water-jet-propelled, rigid sidewall air cushion vehicle, designed by MARIC as a high-speed inland water passenger ferry for use on shallow water and is a development of the 717 design. The Type 717 *Chungqing* and the Type 717 II *Ming Jiang* passenger ferry hovercraft were both completed in October 1984 and were delivered to Chongqing Ferry Boat Company as a high-speed passenger craft operating on the rapids of the Yangtze river. A further Type 717 III was delivered in September 1989.

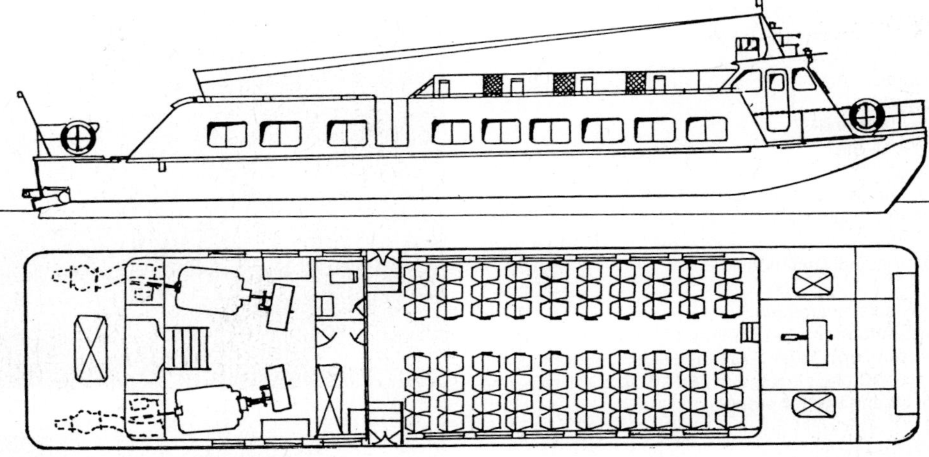

General arrangement of MARIC 717 II

Specifications

	717 II	717 III
Length overall	20.4 m	21.4 m
Beam	4.54 m	4.54 m
Weight, max	21.2 t	23 t
Passengers	54-60	70
Propulsive power	2 × 224 kW	2 × 224 kW
Max speed	24 kts	23 kts
Range	220 n miles	135 n miles

Structure: The sidewalls are built in GRP, but other parts of the hull and superstructure are built in riveted, high-strength aluminium alloy.

Propulsion: Integrated system powered by two 12 V 150C marine diesels rated at 224 kW continuous. Two engines are mounted aft and each drives a 600 mm diameter centrifugal fan, Type 4-72 for lift and, via an elastic coupling, universal joint and transmission shaft, a mixed flow water-jet pump. Another bow fan is driven via a hydraulic pump and motor by the integrated power system. The Type 717 III is powered by two Cummins high-speed diesel NTA-855-M engines 298 kW (maximum) each.

MARIC Type 717 IIIC on its delivery trip 1991

TYPE 717 IIIC *Yu Xiang*

This SES vessel was delivered to Chongqing Ferry Boat Company in September 1989.

The transverse structure is stronger than the previous Type 717 III in order to resist large stern waves.

Specifications

Length overall	21.4 m
Beam	4.54 m
Draught, hullborne	0.95 m
Draught, on-cushion	0.7 m
Weight, max	23.5 t
Crew	4
Max speed	22.7 kts
Range	220 n miles

Propulsion: 2 × Cummins NTA-855-M322 diesel engines manufactured by Sichuan Chongqing Automobile Motor Factory.

MARIC Type 7215 1996

TYPE 7215

This craft was designed by MARIC and was completed in March 1993. The craft is operated on the upper reaches of the Yangtze River in Shi Chua Province from Chongqing to Fuling and Wan Xian.

Specifications

Length overall	28.0 m
Beam overall	6.84 m
Height overall	6.4 m
Draught, hullborne	1.67 m
Draught, on-cushion	1.44 m
Crew	5
Passengers	126-135
Max speed	27 kts
Range	243 n miles

Propulsion: Engines: 2 × Cummins KTA19-M diesels, 274 kW each, 2,034 rpm (made in China under license).
Thrust device: 2 × directly driven marine propellers.
Lift engine: Cummins NT14-M diesel, 179 kW, 2,000 rpm (made in China under license).
Fans: 2 × directly driven centrifugal fans, 0.85 m diameter.

MARIC Type 7218 completed in 1994 1996

TYPE 7218

This craft is a derivative of Type 716 II and was completed in 1994. This full amphibious, all aluminium vessel is operated along the coastal line of Qin Dao City as a passenger ferry.

Specifications

Length overall	21.3 m
Beam	8.8 m
Height overall	5.8 m
Weight, max	30 t
Crew	3
Passengers	70
Operational speed	35 kts
Range	140 n miles
Operational limitation	Beaufort 6
	Sea State 3
Obstacle clearance	0.7 m

Classification: ZC (Sheltered Sea Area)

Propulsion: Three sets of Deutz air cooled BF 12L513C diesels rated at 386 kW @ 2,300 rpm, one for lift and two for propulsion.

MARIC Type 7224 1994

TYPE 7224

This craft was designed by MARIC and three were completed by December 1992, one for Zhenzhou

City as a touring boat operating on the Yellow River and two for personnel transportation at the Lieu River oilfield.

Specifications

Length overall 12.4 m
Beam 4.5 m
Passengers 15
Operational speed 24.3 kts

Structure: Hull material: medium strength aluminium alloy.
Hull construction: riveted.

Propulsion: Engines: 2 × Deutz BF6L 913C air-cooled diesel (lift and propulsion, mechanically integrated arrangement).

TYPE 7226

This fully amphibious all aluminium vessel was delivered in 1995 and operates on the coastal line of Dalian City as a passenger and tourist ferry.

Specifications

Length overall 17.85 m
Beam 7.0 m
Height overall 4.6 m
Displacement, max 16.5 t
Crew 3
Passengers 40
Operational speed 28 kts
Range 120 n miles
Operational limitation Beaufort 5, Sea State 2
Obstacle clearance 0.4 m

MARIC Type 7226 **1996**

Classification: ZC (Sheltered Sea Area)

Propulsion: Two sets of Deutz air cooled BF 12L413F diesels rated at 282 kW @ 2,500 rpm, both driving a lift fan and air ducted propeller.

UPDATED

HANG TONG HIGH-SPEED SHIP DEVELOPMENT CO LTD

Fenjiang Road, Xinhui City, Guangdong Province, People's Republic of China 529100

Tel: +86 (0750) 669 0966 / 663 2967
Fax: +86 (0750) 669 0966 / 666 6547

Hang Tong is a joint venture company that specialises in the development of high-speed craft. At present they are producing hovercraft, backed by the advanced technology of Chinese aerospace industry.

These hovercraft (the 'HT' range), are built in several shipyards around China, and are claimed to offer high reliability and good survivability at low prices.

All the craft in the range are constructed using welded corrosion resistant aluminium alloy. The propulsion systems all use a simple toothed belt transmission device for the drive propellers, the craft also have two bow thrusters to assist low-speed manoeuvres.

Typical uses for craft in the HT range include: Passenger ferry, patrol craft, amphibious assault craft, survey and exploration.

HT-901 open well-deck hovercraft **1995**

HT-903B passenger hovercraft **1996**

HT-904

This is the smallest craft in the range, capable of carrying 20 passengers, or a payload of 1.5 tonnes.

Specifications

Length overall 10.5 m
Beam 4.5 m
Weight, max 6 t
Payload 1.5 t
Passengers 20
Propulsive power 190 kW
Max speed 30 kts
Operational limitation wave height 1 m

Structure: Welded aluminium alloy

Propulsion: The main engine is a single Deutz BF12L 413C diesel, maximum output 190 kW; driving a 2.2 m diameter propeller, and the lift fan.

Control: Air rudder, bow thrusters.

HT-901

Two versions of this design have been built: a passenger ferry, of which two have been built; and an open well-deck amphibious transporter.

Specifications

Length overall 17.9 m
Beam 7.7 m
Weight, max 21 t
Payload 6 t
Passengers 50
Propulsive power 2 × 190 kW
Lift power 2 × 190 kW
Max speed 32 kts
Operational limitation wave height 2 m

Structure: Welded aluminium alloy.

Propulsion: The main engines are 4 × Deutz BF8L 413 diesels, powering both the lift fans and the two 2.3 m diameter drive propellers.

Control: Air rudders and bow thrusters.

HT-903B

One of these craft made a 1,000 mile voyage from the South China Sea to the East China Sea.

Three craft operate on a busy service across the entrance of the Yangtze river and Hangzhou Gulf.

Specifications

Length overall 24.35 m
Beam 8.8 m
Weight, max 40 t
Payload 12 t
Passengers 100
Propulsive power 2 × 360 kW
Lift power 2 × 360 kW
Max speed 40 kts
Operational limitation wave height 2.8 m

Structure: Welded aluminium alloy.

Propulsion: The engines are 4 × Deutz BF12L 413 diesels, maximum output 360 kW each; driving 2 × 2.9 m diameter air propellers, and the lift fans.

Control: Air rudders and bow thrusters.

HT-903A

Specifications

Length overall 27.95 m
Weight, max 55 t
Payload 18 t
Passengers 150
Propulsive power 5 × 360 kW
Lift power 5 × 360 kW
Max speed 40 kts

Structure: Welded aluminium alloy.

Propulsion: The engines are 5 × Deutz BF12L 413 diesels, maximium output 360 kW; driving three 2.9 m propellers and the lift fans.

Control: Air rudders and bow thrusters.

UPDATED

HUANGPU SHIPYARD

PO Box 510336, Guangzhou, People's Republic of China

Tel: +86 (20) 201345/201526
Telex: 44433 HPSPY CN
Fax: +86 (20) 201387

Gao Feng, *Director*

TYPE 7211

A contract for designing and building a new 162-passenger SES ferry was signed on 15 April 1990 in Guangzhou. Ordered by China Merchants Development Company Ltd in Hong Kong, this Type 7211 passenger ferry was designed by MARIC and delivered in November 1992 to operate between Shekou and Hong Kong, a route operated by two Hovermarine International HM218s.

Specifications

Length overall	29.95 m
Beam	7.6 m
Draught, hullborne	1.81 m
Draught, on-cushion	1.5 m
Passengers	162-171
Max speed	30 kts
Range	180 n miles

MARIC Type 7211 SES ***1993***

Classification: This Type 7211 SES ferry is designed and built to ZC rules.

Structure: The craft has a welded aluminium main structure and a riveted aluminium superstructure.

Propulsion: The craft is powered by two MWM 12V TBD 234 diesel engines, each coupled to a propeller, and one MWM 6V TBD 234 diesel driving the lift fans.

VERIFIED

HUDONG SHIPYARD

Bahaoqiao, Pudong Dadao, Shanghai, People's Republic of China

Tel: +86 (21) 840951
Telex: 33025 SHDSY CN
Fax: +86 (21) 1675

TYPE 716 II

Designed by MARIC, the amphibious hovercraft Type 716 II was completed at Hudong Shipyard in 1985. The craft underwent evaluation by the China Air Cushion Technology Development Corporation (CACTEC) and now operates in offshore areas, shallow water and marshes where it is used to transport people and equipment.

Specifications

Length overall	18.44 m
Beam	7.72 m
Weight, max	19.4 t
Payload	4 t (no passengers)
Passengers	32 (no cargo)
Propulsive power	319 kW
Max speed	39 kts
Range	120 n miles

Structure: Riveted skin and stringer structure employing high strength aluminium alloy sheet. Main hull forms a buoyancy raft based on a grid of longitudinal and transverse frames which form a number of flotation compartments.

Propulsion: One Deutz BF12L 413FC air-cooled marine diesel, 319 kW at 2,300 rpm, via a gearbox and transmission shaft drives a 2 m diameter centrifugal fan. Two identical engines, via transmission shafts, drive directly two four-blade 2.3 m diameter ducted air propellers.

Control: Directional control is by two sets of twin vertical aerodynamic rudders mounted on the rear of the propeller ducts.

VERIFIED

MARIC Type 716 II 32-passenger ACV ***1986***

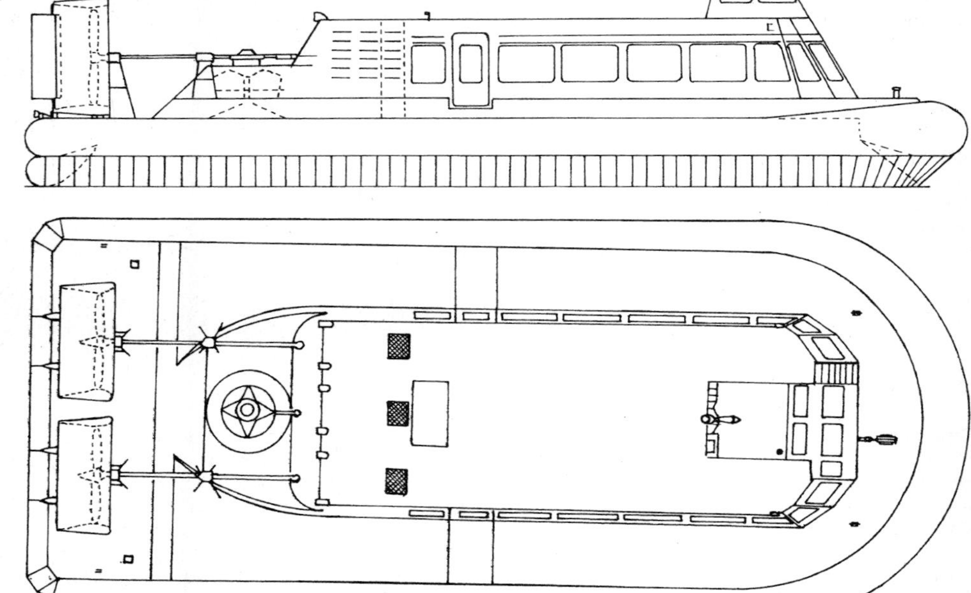

General arrangement of Type 716 III design ***1996***

JIANG HUI SHIPYARD

Shen Zhen City, People's Republic of China

TYPE 7221

This GRP sidewall hovercraft is operated in the Hong Kong - Shen Zhen river areas as a passenger vessel.

Specifications

Length overall	32.15 m
Length waterline	30.50 m
Beam	8.20 m
Height overall	6.9 m
Draught, on cushion	1.75 m
Crew	5
Passengers	225
Max speed	30 kts
Range	200 n miles

Structure: The hull and superstructure are constructed of GRP.

Propulsion: Two sets of MWM TBD 234 V16 diesels rated at 755 kW @ 2,200 rpm each driving a fixed pitch water propeller. Single MWM TBD 234 V8 diesel rated at 380 kW @ 2,100 rpm driving two fans for lift air.

NEW ENTRY

MARIC

MARINE DESIGN AND RESEARCH INSTITUTE OF CHINA

346 Sichuan Road, Central, PO Box 3053, Shanghai, People's Republic of China

Tel: +86 (21) 321 5044
Telex: 33029 MARIC CN
Fax: +86 (21) 377 9744

Sun Songhe, *Director*
Yun Liang, *Deputy Chief Naval Architect*

The Marine Design and Research Institute of China (MARIC) has been responsible for much of the ACV research, development and design programmes on both amphibious and sidewall (SES) hovercraft built in China. The table summarises the more recent developments in ACVs in China.

Since 1990 the fast marine transportation system in China has expanded rapidly with Maric co-ordinating the domestic design and build of ACV's in conjunction with the Chinese Society of Naval Architects and Marine Engineers (CSNAME).

UPDATED

Summary of craft built Builder and craft	Designer	Seats/payload	Launched
Bei Hai Shipyard			
Type 7217 (sidewall) two built	MARIC	260 seats	October 1995
Dagu Shipyard			
Type 722 (Amphibious)	MARIC	15 t payload	August 1979
Type 7203 (Sidewall) *Jinxiang*	MARIC	81 seats	September 1983
Type 7212	MARIC	33 seats	1992
Type 7224 II	MARIC	15 seats	1994
Dong Feng Shipyard			
Type 717 II (Sidewall) *Ming Jiang*	MARIC	54-60 seats	October 1984
Type 717 III (Sidewall) *Chongqing*	MARIC	70 seats	September 1984
Type 717 IIIC (Sidewall) *Yu Xiang*	MARIC	—	September 1989
Type 7210 (Amphibious) two built	MARIC	0.8 t	May 1985
Type 7218 (Amphibious)	MARIC	70 seats	October 1994
Type 7224 (Amphibious)	MARIC	15-28 seats	April 1993
Type 7224 (Amphibious)	MARIC	15-28 seats	April 1993
Type 7224 (Amphibious)	MARIC	15-28 seats	April 1993
Type 7215 (Sidewall)	MARIC	126 seats	September 1993
Type 7226 (Amphibious)	MARIC	40-50 seats	July 1995
Huang Pu Shipyard			
Type 7211 (Sidewall)	MARIC	162 seats	December 1992
Hudong Shipyard			
Type 716 II (Amphibious)	MARIC	32 seats	1985
Shanghai Aircraft Factory			
Type 7212 *Zhengzhou*	MARIC	33 seats	1989
Zhong Hua Shipyard			
Type 719 II *Hong Xiang*	MARIC	257 seats	1988
Quog Hua Shipyard			
Type 719 III	MARIC	257 seats	August 1988
Ming Jian Shipyard			
Type 717 V	MARIC	400 seats	August 1993
Jiang Hui Shipyard			
Type 7221 (sidewall)	MARIC	225 seats	October 1995

SHANGHAI AIRCRAFT FACTORY

346 Sichuan Road Central, PO Box 3053, Shanghai, People's Republic of China

Tel:+86 (21) 321 5044
Fax: +86 (21) 377 9744

TYPE 7212 *Zhengzhou*

This amphibious hovercraft, completed in June 1989, was designed to operate on inland rivers, sea beaches and shallow water areas for short-range passenger transportation or touring. *Zhengzhou* is currently operating as a tour vessel on the Yellow River, while the second craft of this type was built at Dagu Shipyard.

Specifications

Length overall	13.2 m
Beam	5.5 m
Weight, max	10.33 t
Passengers	33
Max speed	28.1 kts
Operational limitation	Beaufort 6

Structure: Built in medium strength seawater-resistant aluminium alloy, riveted construction.

MARIC Type 7212 Zhengzhou *on the Yellow River* ***1993***

Propulsion: The main engines are two Deutz BF6L 913C air-cooled diesels. These drive two fixed-pitch ducted propellers, 1.80 m diameter, driven via a flexible coupling and clutch.

The lift engine is a Deutz BF6L 913C air-cooled diesel, driving a lift fan of centrifugal type, 1.5 m diameter, via a flexible coupling and gearbox.

VERIFIED

ZHONG HUA SHIPYARD

Shanghai, People's Republic of China

Builder of MARIC 719 II SES *Hong Xiang* operating between the Shanghai Municipality and Chong Ming Island.

TYPE 719 II

This 719 II sidewall hovercraft was the second such craft to be built with a steel hull.

The vessel can carry 257 passengers and meets the requirements for ships operating in the Yangtze River Class A area.

The control of engines is by remote-control systems produced by HDW-Elektronik of Germany with manual back-up. The lift engine is directly connected to three double-intake centrifugal lift fans via a clutch system and there is no speed reduction device between them. The propulsion engines drive the propellers through a Type WVS 642 gearbox. The engine room also contains an auxiliary engine and an electric generator.

There are two double intake centrifugal fans in the fan room, arranged along the centreline of the ship.

The MARIC 719 II steel-hull SES ***1989***

Specifications

Length overall	40 m
Beam	8.28 m
Draught, hullborne	2.45 m
Draught, on-cushion	1.85 m
Displacement, max	123.5 t
Payload	22 t
Passengers	257
Max speed	27.54 kts
Operational speed	24 kts
Range	370 km
Operational limitation	Beaufort 7 wave height 1.5 m

Structure: The main structure of this vessel is welded from steel type ZCA. The superstructure is riveted from aluminium type LY12CZ.

The bow seal is a bag and finger skirt and the stern seal a two-lobe bag.

Propulsion: The vessel is powered by three MWM TBD 234 V16 high-speed diesel engines. One engine drives three centrifugal fans with double-sided air inlets for cushion lift, and each of the others drives a 1 m diameter marine propeller.

Control: There are two rudders with aerofoil section profiles fitted at the stern behind the propellers. They are interconnected and move synchronously by hydraulic actuation. A stand-by hydraulic system is provided as well as a hand pump for emergency use.

Safety equipment: To meet the lifesaving requirements, six lifebuoys, 257 lifejackets, 25 child lifejackets and seven working lifejackets for crew are provided under passenger seats and in the storerooms.

Outfit: Cabins of this ship are on two decks: the upper cabin is on the wheelhouse deck and the lower cabin is on the main deck.

The upper deck carries the wheelhouse, first class passenger cabin (48 seats), two high class cabins (with six seats each) and two storerooms. On the lower deck there is a front passenger cabin (second class, 154 seats), an aft passenger cabin (second class, 43 seats), an engine room, a crew cabin and a kitchen.

VERIFIED

COMMONWEALTH OF INDEPENDENT STATES

ALMAZ CENTRAL MARINE DESIGN BUREAU

19 Uralskaya Street, 199161 St Petersburg, Russia, CIS

Tel: +7 (812) 350 2983
Fax: +7 (812) 350 9430

Alexander V Shliakhtenko, *Chief Designer*

The ALMAZ central marine design bureau was established in 1940 and specialises in the design and construction of high-speed commercial and military craft (hydrofoils, hovercraft, SES and Swath).

BOBYOR AMPHIBIOUS CARGO CRAFT

The Bobyor is designed to transfer general cargoes of cars, tractors, construction plant or passengers over rivers or swampy ground. The first of these craft is under construction.

Specifications

Length overall	30.2 m
Beam	11.5 m
Draught	0.9 m
Payload	25 t
Propulsive power	2 × 680 kW
Lift power	680 kW
Operational speed	38 kts
Range	240 n miles

Structure: Welded aluminium hull and superstructure.

Propulsion: The main engines are two air-cooled diesels.

The lift system comprises two centrifugal fans driven by one diesel.

MISTRAL (DESIGN)

This SES craft is based on the military SES *Dergach* which was built in Russia and has operated on the Black Sea for many years. Much of the specified equipment for this craft is produced in Western Europe or the USA.

Specifications

Length overall	65 m
Beam	18 m
Draught, hullborne	3.3 m
Passengers	353
Vehicles	67 cars
Operational speed	42 kts
Range	400 n miles

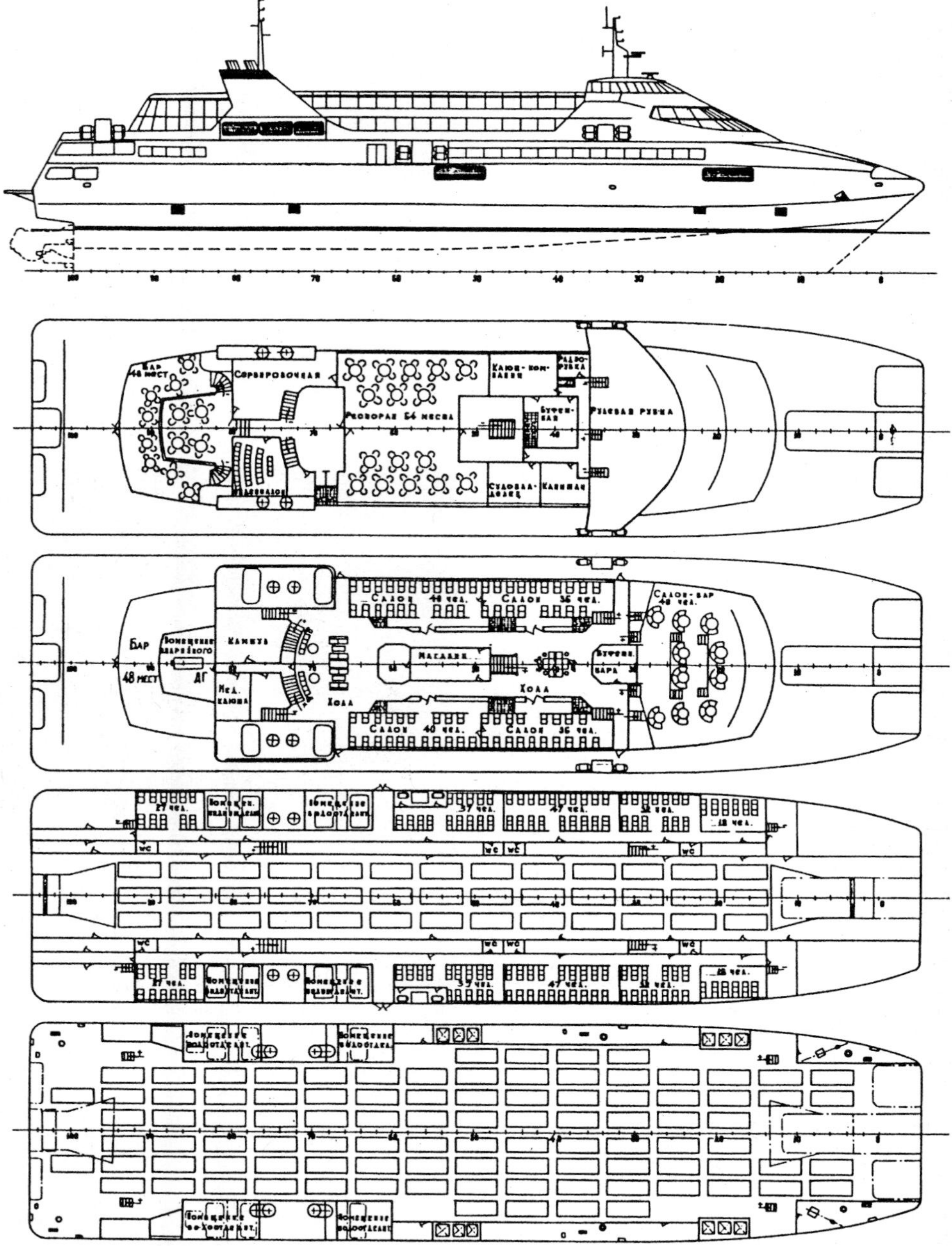

General arrangement of RSES 500 ***1996***

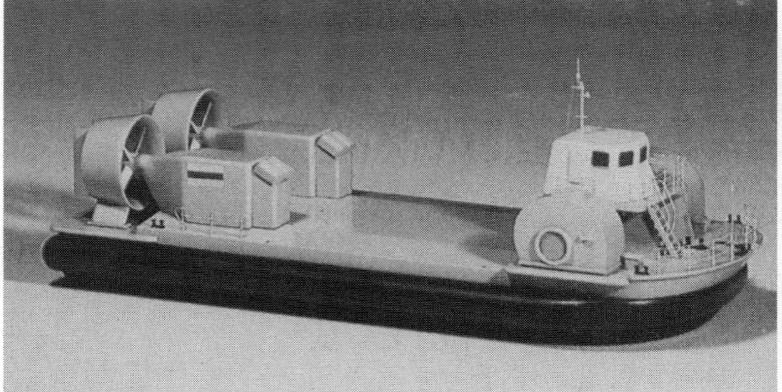

Model of Bobyor amphibious cargo craft ***1996***

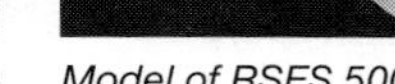

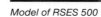

Model of RSES 500 ***1996***

Structure: Welded aluminium hull and superstructure.
Propulsion: Main engines: 2 × LM1600 gas-turbines and 2 × MTU 16V 595 TE 60 diesels.
Lift engines: 2 × MTU 12V 538 TB 82.

RSES-500 (DESIGN)

The company has also developed an extensive range of SES craft designs from 200 to 2,500 tonnes displacement. These are known as the RSES series (Russian Surface Effect Ship). Brief details of the RSES-500 have been provided which can be configured for passenger or cargo transportation:

Specifications

Length overall	93.0 m
Beam	23.5 m
Draught, hullborne	4.1 m
Draught, on-cushion	1.8 m
Passengers	450-700
Max speed	55 kts
Operational speed	50 kts
Range	600-1,000 n miles
Operational limitation	Sea State 6

Propulsion: The vessel is powered by four gas turbines with a total output power of 66,000 kW, driving water-jet propulsors. The lift power is derived from four marine diesels with a total output power of 10,000 kW.

UPDATED

ASTRAKHAN SHIPYARD

LUCH-1

A sidewall ACV for river use was completed at the Astrakhan Shipyard and underwent State trials in September 1983. Production of the ACV Luch-1 then began at the Moscow Shipyard. Designed to replace the 12 year old Zarnitsa, the Luch, Design No 14351, carries two crew and up to 66 passengers, 15 standing. Of all-welded aluminium construction, it has a maximum operating weight of 22.6 tonnes and a top speed of 24 knots. The shallow on-cushion draught of just over 0.5 m allows it to run bow-on to flat sloping river banks to embark and disembark passengers.

New design features permit operation on large rivers such as the Don, Kama, Oka and Volga, where higher waves are encountered.

Compared with the Zarnitsa, Luch has a more powerful diesel, the 382 kW 3KD12H-520, and uses a lighter form of construction. The overall dimensions of the craft permit rail transport to distant rivers and canals.

During trials before the commissioning of the first of the class, it was demonstrated that its operating and technical performance is significantly superior to that of the Zarnitsa. The craft is built to the requirements of the 'R' class of the CIS's River Craft Registry and has been produced in quantity.

Specifications

Length overall	22.81 m
Beam	3.85 m
Draught, on-cushion	0.5 m
Draught, hullborne	0.65 m
Weight, min	15.4 t
Weight, max	22.6 t
Crew	2
Passengers	66
Propulsive power	382 kW
Max speed	23.75 kts
Range	162 n miles

Structure: The buoyancy structure is built in welded marine grade aluminium alloy. The superstructure is built in D16 alloy. Superstructure and bulkheads are riveted together. Pressed panels are employed throughout the hull to improve the external appearance and reduce the volume of assembly work necessary during construction.

The skirt is a fingered-type at bow, bag-type aft. Bow segments attached to an easily replaceable module.

Propulsion: The engine is a type 81H12A diesel with a maximum power of 380 kW or a type 3KD12H-520, 382 kW. Normal operating power: 346 kW.

Luch **1993**

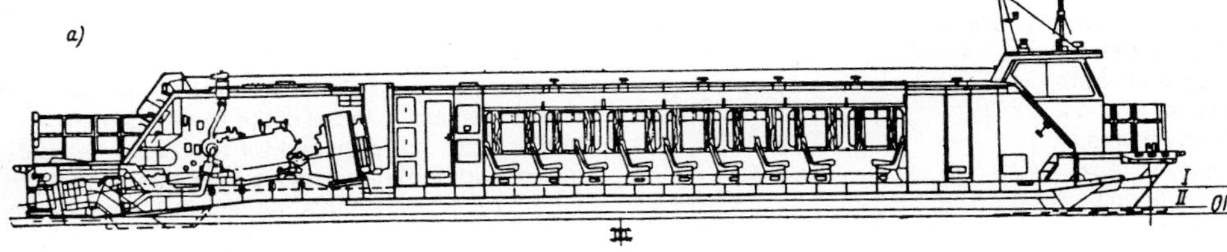

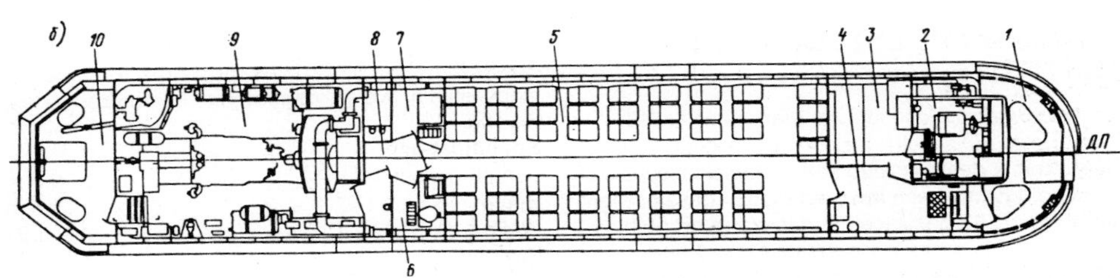

Inboard profile and plan of Luch: **a** *Longitudinal section;* **b** *Deck plan;* **I** *Waterline in displacement mode;* **II** *Waterline when cushionborne;* **1** *Fore deck;* **2** *Wheelhouse;* **3** *Duty compartment;* **4** *Vestibule;* **5** *Passenger saloon;* **6** *Toilet;* **7** *Storeroom;* **8** *Vestibule;* **9** *Engine room;* **10** *Aft deck*

The engine is mounted aft and drives, via a transmission shaft, a centrifugal fan for lift and a water-jet rotor for propulsion. The water-jet rotor and its bearing can be replaced while the craft is in displacement condition without having to lift it out of the water.

Electrical system: One 1.2 kW 24 V DC engine-operated generator and batteries. During prolonged night stops power can be supplied by a shore-based 220 V, 50 Hz electrical supply.

Control: Twin rudder vanes in the water-jet stream control craft heading. Thrust reversal achieved by water-flow deflectors.

VERIFIED

GORKOVSKI PHILIAL CNII im akad. A N Krylova

Krylov Specialised Shipbuilding Centre, Chkalovsk, Norgorod, Russia, 606429, CIS

Tel: +7 (83160) 25236
Fax: +7 (83160) 25233

Sergei Usoltsev, *Director*

SIBIR

The shipyard developed and built the cargo-carrying ACV Sibir in 1990 with ACV Typhoon as a prototype. The craft is designed for year round fast delivery of tracked or wheeled vehicles and containerised cargo on the local and main river, lakes and reservoir.

Sibir in operation **1995**

Specifications

Length overall	25.2 m
Beam	11.7 m
Weight, max	55 t
Payload	20 t
Propulsive power	1,874 kW
Max speed	43 kts
Obstacle clearance	1.25 m

Hull: The hull is built in 1561 weldable marine aluminium alloy with port and starboard superstructures. Each side structure contains an integrated axial turbine fan installation. The bow ramp provides roll-on, roll-off loading and unloading.

The skirt is a bag and finger tapered skirt 1.2 m deep at the bow and 1.4 m at the stern. Longitudinal and transverse flexible keels divide the cushion into four compartments for stability.

Propulsion: Aerodynamically integrated system, powered by twin Ivchenko AI-24 gas turbines, maximum 1,874 kW and continuous 1,310 kW each. Each turbine drives a 2.5 m axial fan mounted on the turbine shaft. This pumps the air downwards into the cushion and backwards through the duct for propulsion.

Control: Rudders fitted in the duct provide directional control. The air flow is deflected for braking by horizontal vanes, hydraulically controlled from the wheelhouse.

Outfit: All controls are in a raised port wheelhouse.

VERIFIED

KRASNOYE SORMOVO SHIPYARD A A Zhdanov

Nizhni Novgorod, Russia, CIS

M Yuriev, *Shipyard Director*
Ivan Yerlykin, *Chief Hydrofoil Designer*

ZARNITSA

Evolved from Gorkovchanin, the Zarnitsa is a 48 to 50 seat water-jet-propelled rigid sidewall ferry designed to operate on shallow rivers, some less than 0.7 m (2 ft 3 in) deep. Series production is established and large numbers have been delivered.

The prototype was put into trial service on the Vyatka river, in the Kirov region, in the Summer of 1972, and the first production models began operating on shallow, secondary rivers later in the year. During 1973-74, Zarnitsas entered service on tributaries of the Kama, Lena and Volga. More than 100 are employed on almost all the river navigation lines of the Russian Republic as well as on the rivers of Ukraine, Moldova, Belarus and Kazakhstan.

Zarnitsa **1986**

Specifications

Length overall	22.3 m
Beam	3.85 m
Weight, min	9 t
Weight, max	15 t
Operational speed	19 kts

Structure, Propulsion, Control: Arrangements almost identical to those of the Gorkovchanin.

Outfit: Seats are provided for two crew members, accommodated in the raised wheelhouse forward, and 48 to 50 passengers. Access to the passenger saloon is via a single door at the bow in the centre of the wheelhouse. The craft runs bow-on to flat sloping banks to embark and disembark passengers.

VERIFIED

MARIJSKI POLYTECHNICAL INSTITUTE

3 Lenin Square, Yoshkar-Ola, Mari, Russia, CIS

The student design group at the Marijski Institute of Technology has been involved in ACV development since 1971. It specialises in designing amphibious hovercraft for operation in the less accessible areas of the CIS and has successfully built and tested craft commissioned by the oil, gas and fisheries authorities. It has also adapted hovercraft for forestry and agricultural roles and for use in establishing communication networks.

SAV SERIES
SAVR-2 (CABP-2)

SAVR-2 made its appearance in 1982. It was designed and built to a specification prepared by the Soviet Ministry of Fisheries for a craft to serve the inaccessible water regions of North and West Siberia.

Specifications

Length overall	9.8 m
Beam	4.5 m
Weight, max	5.9 t
Payload	2 t
Passengers	2
Crew	1
Fuel capacity	800 l
Propulsive power	294 kW
Max speed	27 kts
Range	108 n miles

Structure: Believed to be a composite light alloy and glass fibre structure. Flotation compartments and basic raft structure filled with plastic foam make the hull unsinkable.

The skirts are segmented fore and aft, with bag-type skirts at the sides. An experimental model of the SAVR-2 has two flexible side skids replacing the conventional skirt. Flexible skids reduce to a minimum the air escaping from the cushion when travelling over rough ground, so reducing the power required from the lift system, as the skids follow the ground contours more accurately. When the craft is supported by the skids the pressure of the air cushion can be reduced considerably. Flexible skids provide lateral stability when the craft is stationary and when travelling over snow, ice, mud and surfaces covered in a thin layer of water.

Propulsion: Lift is provided by a single petrol engine aft of the crew cabin driving, via a split transverse shaft, two centrifugal fans. Thrust is supplied by a single 294 kW Ivchenko AI-14ChR air-cooled radial piston engine driving an AV-14 three-blade

SAVR-3 (CABP-3) **1990**

variable-pitch propeller. Fuel is carried in two 400 litre tanks, one for each engine. Fuel employed is standard automotive petrol.

Control: Craft heading is controlled by twin vertical aerodynamic rudders aft operating in the propeller slipstream. Reverse propeller pitch is employed for braking and reversing. A horizontal stabiliser is mounted between the twin rudders to adjust pitch trim. By altering its incidence angle the centre of gravity can be moved along the longitudinal axis should an uneven load distribution cause it to move.

SAVR-3

In 1981 the Ministry of Oil and Gas approved a programme for the construction of trackless modes of transport, building machines and pipe-laying equipment for muddy soils. Within this programme, spanning the period 1981 to 1985, the Institute was constructing three new transport hovercraft with the following load capacities: SAVR-3, 2 tonnes; SAVR-5, 5 tonnes and SAVR-40, 40 tonnes.

Specifications

Payload	3 t
Propulsive power	380 kW
Max speed	27 kts

At the end of 1986 a decision was taken to build a working batch of SAVR-3 craft. In the Spring of 1985 and 1986, early top-dressing of winter crops with granulated fertilisers and sowing of wheat and barley in damp soil were undertaken with the first SAVR-3.

SAVR-5

Developed by the Institute in 1983 for freight transport of year round construction of pipelines on swamps. Road tests began in the first half of 1987.

The SAVR-5 is propelled by caterpillar tracks from T54B tractors, driven by a series-produced diesel as is the fan for the air cushion system. Maximum vehicle weight is 10 tonnes.

SAVR-40

A 40 tonne load capacity air cushion vehicle for similar duties to the SAVR-5.

UPDATED

SAVR-1 (CABP-1) ***1992***

SAVR-2 (CABP-2) ***1986***

NEPTUN CDB CORP

25 Stanislavski St, Moscow, 103009 Russia, CIS

Tel: +7 (095) 229 5862
Telex: 411700
Fax: +7 (095) 292 6511

V S Sokolov, *President*
G E Andreyev, *Vice President*

The CDB (short for Central Design Bureau) Neptun Corp originally specialised in designing various types of small displacement motor boats and ships, but recently hovercraft design and production have become its main option. Having its own shipyard near Moscow the CBD is co-operating with other shipyards for serial production of hovercraft. Over 200 hovercraft of various types have been built from Neptun's designs over the last 15 years.

GEPARD (CHEETAH)

A multirole five-seater introduced in 1981, Gepard has been designed to provide convenient, reliable and inexpensive transport in more remote areas of the CIS. Specialist professions in those areas were questioned about their transport needs before finalising the design. Early in 1983 a Gepard successfully underwent trials at Andreyevskoye Lake, near the centre of the Tyumen Oblast. About sixty Gepards had entered service by the end of 1990.

The craft is designed to operate in an ambient air temperature range from −40 to +40°C.

The following service life trials have been carried out:

Moscow to Lake Seleger and back: about 1,000 km
Along small rivers to the city of Vyshnii Volochek and back: about 1,000 km
Moscow by the Volga-Baltic route to St Petersburg: about 2,000 km
Moscow to Volgograd on the lower Volga River: about 3,500 km.

Nearly 150 units have been built up to now and operate in various areas in the European and Asian parts of Russia. Its remarkable duties include anti-pollution patrol in the city of Moscow and auxiliary sevice with a hydrological expedition on the Yamal Peninsula in the Arctic. Examples of the Gepard series are also operated out of Russia by ship owners in the USA, Mexico and Canada.

Specifications

Length overall	6.63 m
Beam	3.3 m
Weight, max	1.86 t
Crew	5
Propulsive power	86 kW
Max speed	32 kts
Operational speed	24 kts
Operational limitation	−40°C to +40°C

Structure: Corrosion-resistant light alloy hull. Moulded pigmented glass fibre cabin superstructure.

Propulsion: Integrated system, powered by a ZMZ-53 lorry engine (a widely used engine), aft of the cabin. Output is transmitted to a centrifugal lift fan (0.97 m diameter with GRP blades) and a duct-mounted, multibladed 0.95 m diameter glass fibre propeller for thrust, the blade leading edges being

Cutaway of Gepard: **1** *ZMZ-53 power-plant;* **2** *Bag skirt;* **3** *Fan;* **4** *Fan air scoop;* **5** *Thrust fan;* **6** *Duct;* **7** *Main (cardan) shaft;* **8** *Fan drive (cardan) shaft;* **9** *Fan transmission belts;* **10** *Airscrew transmission belts;* **11** *Fuel tank;* **12** *Deck cabin;* **13** *Water and oil radiators;* **14** *Exhaust pipe (manifold);* **15** *Fan duct;* **16** *Vertical rudders;* **17** *Elevators;* **18** *Headlights;* **19** *Navigation and landing lights;* **20** *Drainage plate;* **21** *Ventilator heads* ***1986***

The five-seat, 42 knot Gepard powered by a single 115 hp ZMZ-53 petrol engine ***1991***

Puma twin petrol engine hovercraft designed by the Neptun Central Design Bureau, Moscow ***1991***

protected with stainless steel sheaths. Power transmission is by toothed-belt drives and a clutch is provided between the engine and propeller and fan drives.

Control: Directional control by interconnected rudder vanes hinged to the rear of the thrust fan ducts and operated by a wheel. Horizontal vane surfaces are also provided.

PUMA

Design and building of this craft was completed in less than a year. The first three variants underwent comprehensive trials in 1988. As an ambulance the Puma is equipped with an operating table and related medical apparatus including oxygen bottles, making it possible to provide urgent medical aid on board, including simple operations. The passenger variant is fitted with 16 aircraft-type seats, while the passenger/cargo variant has 10 folding seats.

Pumas are engaged in passenger transportation services in Siberia, on the Caspian Sea and in the Far East of Russia. One craft is to be delivered to Mexico. The total number of craft built since 1985 is 10.

Specifications

Length overall	12.2 m
Beam	4.5 m
Weight, min	3.6 t
Weight, max	5 t
Payload	1.45 t
Passengers	16
Propulsive power	2 × 90 kW
Max speed	35 kts
Operational speed	22 kts
Obstacle clearance	0.3 m

Propulsion: Two ZMZ-53 90 kW petrol engines driving two centrifugal fans and two reversible-pitch propellers with toothed-belt drives.

IRBIS

A twin-engine amphibious hovercraft designed to carry up to 32 passengers. Intended applications for this type include the transport of geologists and oil industry workers and their associated equipment, cargo shipment up to 2.5 tonnes and support for geophysical exploration. The craft is designed to operate in a wide range of operating conditions: in ambient temperatures from −40°C with maximum wind speeds of 29 knots, up to 30 miles from base; in significant wave heights up to 0.7 m when cushionborne, across deep or shallow water; on snow and compact ice and on broken and sludge ice. The craft has folding sidebodies for ease of transport.

From their first appearance in 1989 these craft participated in many trials and commercial services in various areas of Russia, including inland waterway routes Moscow - St. Petersburg - Astrakhan, sea routes in the Finnish bay of the Baltic sea and on the Caspian Sea as well as a scheduled passenger service on the North Dvina River and on the Amur River as a ferry across the Russian-Chinese border.

One Irbis of three in operation is based in Olcott, New York, USA, and after completing the demonstration program on Lake Ontario is passing a certification procedure to be assessed for operation in this area.

Classification: The craft is classed KM*1 SVPA Register of CIS.

Propulsion: The engines are two Deutz BF6L 913C air-cooled diesels, driving two 4-blade, variable-pitch (forward and reverse thrust) ducted propellers.

Electrical system: Two 1 kW generators.

Voltage: 24 DC.

Auxiliary systems: Trim (fuel transfer), hydraulic power provision, heating and special cold starting system (down to −40°C).

Specifications

Length overall	16.5 m
Beam	6.2 m
Draught	0.27 m
Weight, min	7.4 t, passenger version 6.5 t, freight version
Weight, max	10.7 t
Passengers	32
Fuel capacity	0.56 t
Propulsive power	2 × 141 kW
Max speed	30 kts
Operational speed	24.3 kts
Range	250 n miles
Operational limitation	Sea State 3, wind speed 8 kts
Obstacle clearance	0.4 m

VERIFIED

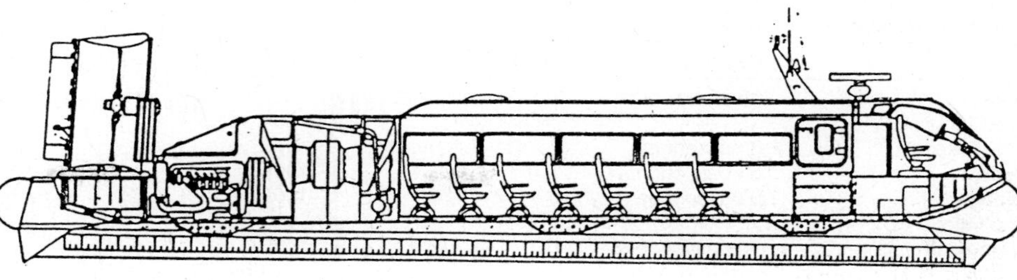

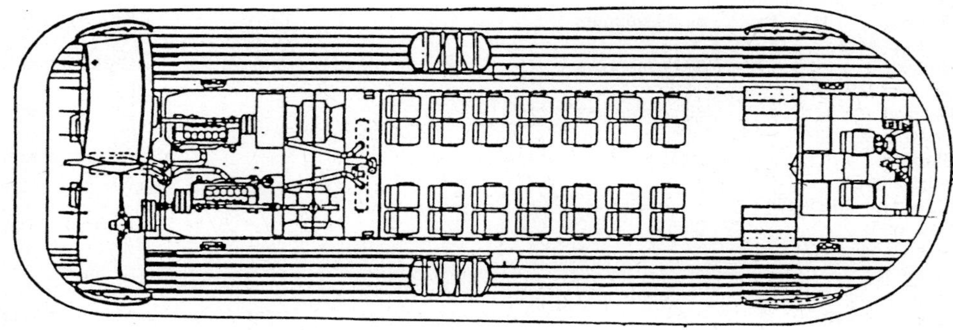

General arrangement of Irbis

Irbis

1990

St PETERSBURG SHIPYARD

St Petersburg, Russia, CIS

ORION-01

Design of the Orion, a rigid sidewall ACV with seats for 80 passengers, was approved in Moscow in Autumn 1970. The prototype, built in Leningrad, began trials in October 1973 and arrived at its port of registry, Kalinin, in late 1974, bearing the serial number 01.

The craft is used for passenger ferry services along shallow rivers, tributaries and reservoirs and can land and take on passengers bow-on from any flat sloping bank. It is faster than the Zarnitsa and its comfort and performance are less affected by choppy conditions. The cruising speed of the vessel, which is propelled by water-jets, is 28 knots. It belongs to the 'R' class of the Soviet River Register.

Series production of this vessel is being undertaken at the Sosnovskaya Shipbuilding Yard in Kirovskaya Oblast.

Specifications

Length overall	25.8 m
Beam	6.5 m
Draught, hullborne	0.84 m
Draught, on-cushion	0.5 m
Weight, max	34.7 t
Weight, min	20.7 t
Crew	3
Passengers	80
Propulsive power	2 × 452 kW
Max speed	32 kts
Operational speed	28.6 kts
Range	216 n miles
Operational limitation	wave height 1.2 m

GORKOVCHANIN Stopping and starting characteristics	
Distance run by vessel from Full Ahead to Stop	
metres	100
Time in seconds	35
Distance run by vessel from Full Ahead to Full Astern	
metres	60
Time in seconds	14
Distance necessary for attainment of Full Speed from Stop	
metres	200
Time in seconds	52

Structure: The hull is similar in overall appearance to Zarya and Zarnitsa types. All-welded structure in aluminium-magnesium alloy. Lateral framing throughout the hull with the exception of the bow and stern decks, where longitudinal frames have been fitted. The superstructure and wheelhouse are of welded and riveted duralumin construction on longitudinal framing.

Propulsion: Integrated system powered by two 3D12N-520 diesels mounted in an engine room aft. Each engine drives a Type Ts 39-13 centrifugal fan for lift via a cardan shaft, a semi-submerged single stage water-jet rotor for propulsion. Fan air is fed via ducts to the bow skirt, a transverse stability slot and to the bag and finger skirt aft. Casing of the water-jet system, which is removable, forms the stern section of the vessel. The water-jets are mounted on shock absorbers to reduce vibration.

Electrical system: Two G-73Z engine-driven generators, linked with two sets of 6STK-180M batteries, provide 28 V, 1,200 W. One battery set is employed for engine starting, the other for supplying current for the ship's systems.

VERIFIED

Summary of principal civil air cushion vehicle types built

Craft	Payload	No built	Year built	Designed by	Builders
Neva amphibious ACV	38 passengers	1			
Briz (Breeze)	6 passengers		1968		
Skate	50 passengers		1969		
Raduga amphibious ACV	5 passengers	1	1962		Krasnoye Sormovo Shipyard, Gorki
Sormovich amphibious ACV	50 passengers	1	1965		Krasnoye Sormovo Shipyard, Gorki
Gorkovchanin sidewall ACV	48 passengers	1	1969-70	CKB Vympel	Krasnoye Sormovo Shipyard, Gorki
Zarnitsa sidewall ACV (based on Gorkovchanin)	48 passengers	over 100	1972	CKB Vympel	Krasnoye Sormovo Shipyard, Gorki
Orion sidewall ACV	80 passengers		1973 1975	CKB Vympel	Leningrad Shipyard
Chayka sidewall ACV	80 passengers	1		CKB Vympel	Sosnovskaya Shipyard
Rassvet sidewall ACV	80 passengers	1		CKB Vympel	Sosnovskaya Shipyard
Plamya sidewall ACV (based on Orion hull)	firefighting craft	1		Central Design Bureau, Gorki	
Raduga-2 amphibious ACV	0.65 t	n/a		Krasnoye Sormovo Shipyard, Gorki	
SAVR-1M amphibious ACV		1	1978		
SAVR-1 (CABP-1) amphibious ACV	1.3 t	production version of the 1M	1980	Marijski A M Gorki Memorial Polytechnical Institute	
SAVR-2 (CABP-2) amphibious ACV	2 t		1982	Marijski A M Gorki Memorial Polytechnical Institute	
SAVR-3 (CABP-3) amphibious ACV	2 t		1981	Marijski A M Gorki Memorial Polytechnical Institute	
SAVR-5GD (CABP-5GD) amphibious ACV	5 t		1981 onwards	Marijski A M Gorki Memorial Polytechnical Institute	
SAVR-40 (CABP-40) amphibious ACV	50 t		1987	Marijski A M Gorki Memorial Polytechnical Institute	
MPI-18 amphibious ACV	0.6 t				
MPI-20 amphibious ACV	2 and 5 t versions				
Neptun AKVPR-001 amphibious ACV	research craft		1977	Neptun Central Design Bureau, Moscow	
Barrs-1 (Snow Leopard) amphibious ACV	0.65 t or 7 passengers	30	1981	Neptun Central Design Bureau, Moscow	
Gepard (Cheetah)	5 passengers	40+, in production	1981 onwards	Neptun Central Design Bureau, Moscow	
Taifun amphibious ACV	20 passengers or 3 t			UFA Aviation Institute, Tyumen	
Klest amphibious ACV	4 seats		1981	Vostok Central Design Bureau, Leningrad	
Luch sidewall ACV	66 passengers	reported in series	1983 onwards production	Astrakhan Shipyard	
Puma	16 passengers	2 prototypes	1985	Neptun Central Design Bureau, Moscow	
Typhoon	cargo	1	1987	Gorkovski Philial	
-	32 passengers	1 1989	1988-89	Neptun Central Design Bureau, Moscow	
Bargusin	130 passengers		1989	CKB Vympel	
Sibir	cargo	1	1990	Neptun Central Design Bureau, Moscow	
Tapir	seismic equipment	12	1990	Neptun Central Design Bureau, Moscow	Rybinsk Shipyard

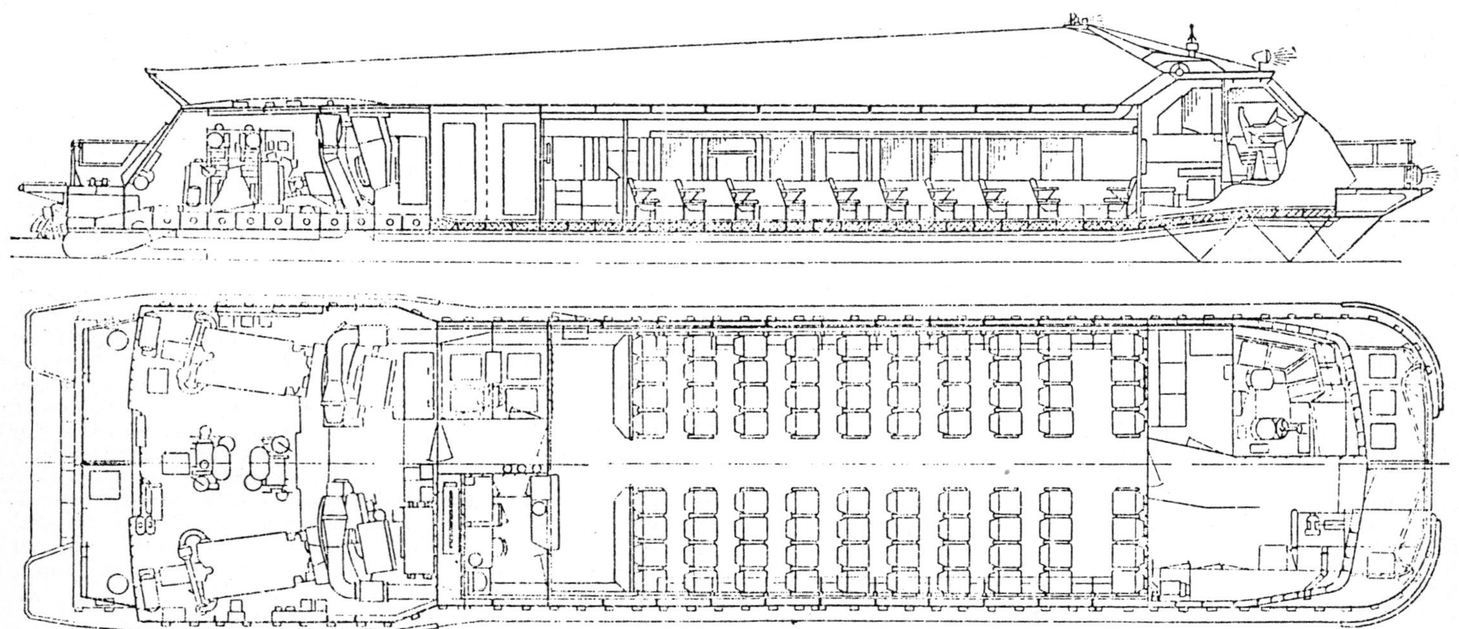

General arrangement of Orion

SOSNOVSKAYA SHIPYARD

Kirovskaya, Oblast, Russia, CIS

RASSVET (DAWN)
CHAYKA (GULL)

A water-jet-propelled sidewall passenger ferry, Rassvet is designed for local sea routes of limited water depth. It is an offshore counterpart to the Orion sidewall ACV. The Rassvet serves resort routes in the Crimea, on the Caspian and Baltic Seas as well as on large lakes and reservoirs. Like the Orion and Zarnitsa, its two predecessors, it can run bow-on to flat, sloping beaches to embark and disembark passengers. Landing on a beach is facilitated by an articulated gangway with a hydraulic drive.

Rassvet's features include shallow draught, good manoeuvrability and a relatively simple construction.

The water-jet reversing/steering system is specially protected to enable the craft to moor alongside existing berths built originally for small conventional displacement ferries.

Rassvet is designed to carry 80 passengers during daylight hours on coastal routes in conditions up to force 4. It complies with CIS Registration classification KM*II Passenger ACV Class.

Specifications

Length overall	26.7 m
Beam	7.1 m
Draught, hullborne	1.27 m
Draught, on-cushion	0.8 m
Weight, max	47.5 t
Passengers	80
Propulsive power	2 × 383 kW
Lift power	110 kW
Max speed	29 kts
Operational speed	23 kts
Range	190 n miles

Structure: The hull and superstructure are built in aluminium-magnesium alloy. The hull is of all-welded construction in AlMg-61 and the decks, superstructure, pilot-house and partitions are in AlMg-5 alloy. The hull, superstructure and pilot-house have longitudinal frames. Single piece pressed panels are employed for the lower sections of the sidewalls. Corrugated sheets are used for the hull bottom.

The skirt is a double-row segmented type at bow; two-tier bag type skirt aft. Repair or replacement of sections of the bow skirt can be undertaken with the bow run on to a flat, gently sloping beach.

Plamya ***1986***

Propulsion: Power for the water-jet system is provided by two 3D12N-520 lightweight (3.54 kg/kW) irreversible, high-speed four-cycle V-type marine diesels each with a gas-turbine supercharger and a rated power of 383 kW at 1,500 rpm. Each powers a two-stage water-jet impeller. Water inlet scoops are arranged in the sidewalls and the pump ports, each comprising two rotors and two straightening devices, are installed in the sidewalls behind the transoms. Cushion air is generated by a single 110 kW PD6S-150A diesel driving an NTs6 centrifugal fan.

Control: Craft direction is controlled by twin balanced rudders operating in the water discharged by each of the two water-jets. Reversal is achieved by applying rotatable deflectors to reverse the water-flow.

PLAMYA (FLAME) ACV RIVER FIRETENDER

The Central Design Bureau at Nizhni Novgorod has developed a river-going firetender. The craft is based on the hull of the Orion sidewall-type passenger ferry, but the passenger cabin superstructure has been replaced by an open deck forward to accommodate a tracked or wheeled firefighting vehicle and its crew. Plamya is designed for the fast delivery of an off the road firefighting vehicle and its crew to points on lakes, reservoirs and major rivers near forest fires. The craft can be beached bow-on on the river bank and the firefighting vehicle or bulldozer offloaded across the bow ramp.

Specifications

Length overall	26.1 m
Beam	6.5 m
Draught, hullborne	0.88 m
Draught, on-cushion	0.7 m
Weight, max	34.5 t
Payload	7.3 t
Crew	3
Propulsive power	2 × 452 kW
Max speed	27 kts

Classification: Plamya meets the requirements of the Register of Shipping of the CIS and is constructed to 'R' Class in the RSFSR Inland Waterways Register. It is in service on the River Kama.

Structure: All-welded structure in AlMg-61 aluminium-magnesium alloy. Frames, plates, partitions and roof of superstructure in D16 alloy.

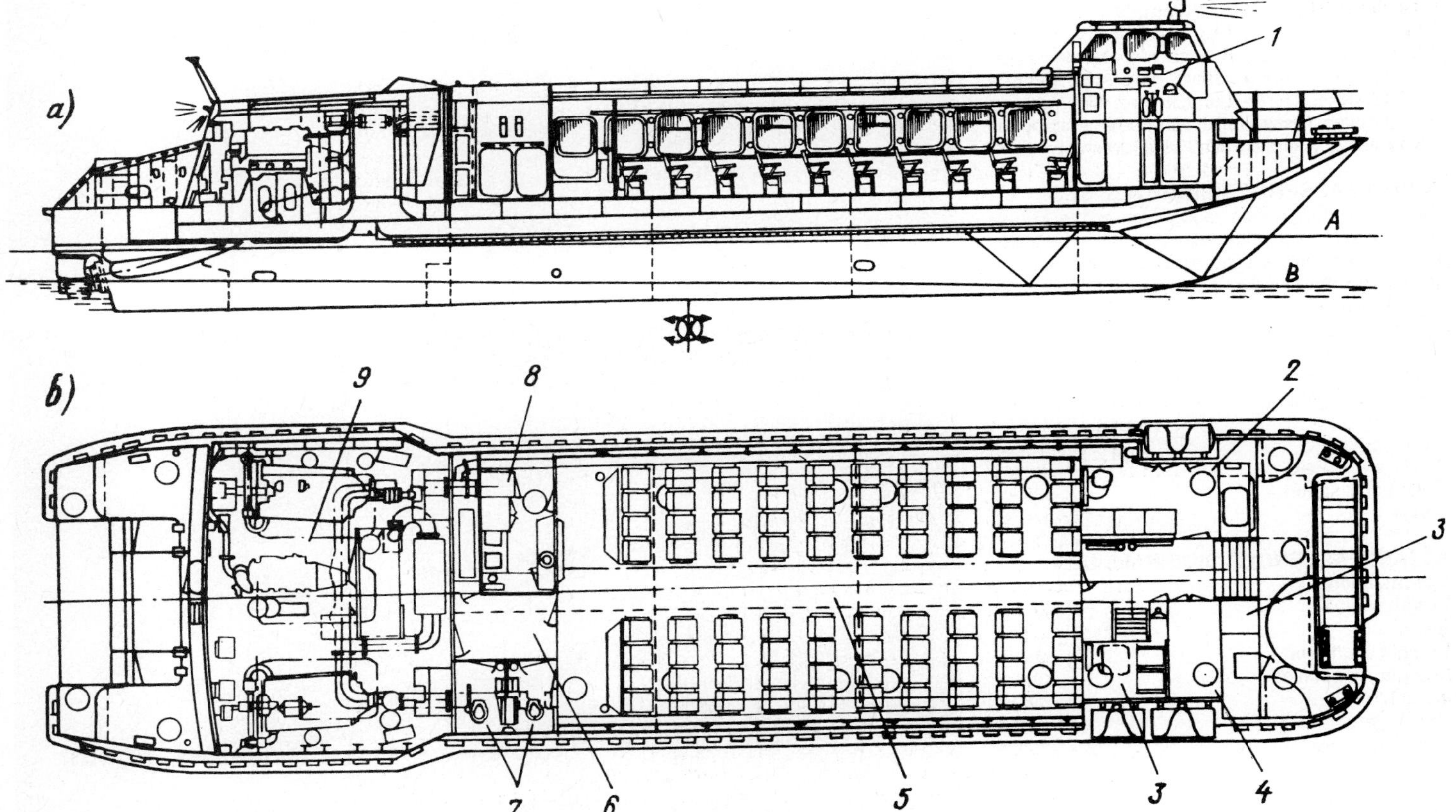

(a) *Longitudinal cross-section* **(b)** *passenger deck plan of Chayka;*
A *Water-line in displacement condition;* **B** *Water-line underway on air cushion;* **1** *Pilot-house;* **2** *Crew's off-duty cabin;* **3** *Storeroom;* **4** *Baggage compartment;* **5** *Passenger lounge;* **6** *Companionway;* **7** *Toilets;* **8** *Buffet;* **9** *Machinery space*

The bow skirt is a triple-row, fully segmented type; stern, bag and finger type.

Propulsion: Integrated system powered by two 3D12N-520 marine diesels. Each engine drives a Type Ts 39-13 centrifugal fan for lift and, via a cardan shaft, a semi-submerged single stage water-jet rotor for propulsion.

Control: Rudders aft of the water-jet inlets and two water-jet deflectors control craft direction.

RADUGA-2

Little is known about this amphibious ACV, which was first reported in the Soviet press in late Spring 1981. Designed at the Krasnoye Sormovo ship and ACV building facility at Nizhni Novgorod, Raduga-2, in common with the Gepard and Klest, is powered by an automotive engine, the Chayka. The 1962 Raduga was described in *Jane's Surface Skimmers 1985* and earlier editions.

BARGUSIN

The first production sidewall hovercraft (SES), Bargusin, was built in 1989 under the design developed by CKB "Vympel". The owner of the vessel is the Vostochno-Sibirskaya River Steamship Line.

The craft has a good seaworthiness and is intended for passenger ferry services along lakes, reservoirs and rivers. Having small draught it can land and take on passengers bow-on from any sloping bank.

The initial run of the Bargusin was organised in 1989 along the European waterways from Sosnovka to Belomorsk and then after transportation via motor-ship Kola by the North Sea Line from Tiksi to Yakutsk along the river Lena.

Bargusin's successful sea and strength trials took place at Baikal lake in Autumn 1990. Series production of this vessel started in 1991.

Bargusin **1993**

Specifications

Length overall	32.4 m
Beam	6.4 m
Draught, hullborne	1.4 m
Draught, on-cushion	0.8 m
Weight, max	70.8 t
Weight, min	54.5 t
Passengers	130
Propulsive power	2 × 590 kW
Lift power	220 kW
Operational speed	27 kts
Range	325 n miles
Operational limitation	wave height 1.2 m

Classification: M standards of the River Register of the Russian Soviet Federal Republic.

Structure: The hull and superstructure are built in AlMg-61 aluminium-magnesium alloy and are of all-welded construction. There is lateral framing throughout the hull. Casing, floors and bulkheads are of pressed panels and framing is mainly of pressed profiles.

Propulsion: Main engine: two M 401A-1 (12 CHSN 18/20) diesels, driving propellers via standard reverse-coupling.

A special centrifugal fan designed and manufactured by NPO Vint generates the air cushion. A 7D 12A (12 CHN 15/18) diesel is used for driving the fan. Pressure and air supply which are necessary for the craft's stable motion both in calm water and in waves are provided at 160 kW and 1,350 to 1,400 fan rpm. The five-blade propellers are within the draught of the sidewalls.

Electrical system: Power supply requirements are met by a 24 V generator mounted on the main engine or by the accumulator battery.

Control: Two single-plate rudders behind each propeller. The rudders can be turned by hydraulic drive together or separately.

VERIFIED

VYMPEL CENTRAL DESIGN BUREAU

3 Kostin St, 603000 Nizhni Novgorod, Russia, CIS

Tel: +7 (8312) 324149
Telex: 151158 Trap SU
Fax: +7 (8312) 342096

Viacheslav V Shatalov, *Director*
Vladimir K Zoroastrov, *Chief Designer*

This Design Bureau has been responsible for the design of the following sidewall hovercraft: Zarnitsa, Orion, Chayka, Plamya, Luch, Luch-2, Altair, Olkhon and Bargusin, these craft having been built by the Sosnovskaya, Astrakhan and Moscow shipyards.

LUCH-2 PASSENGER SIDEWALL SES

This vessel design won recognition at the Eureka 1994 exhibition for outstanding design. The water-jet propelled craft is used for passenger transportation within the Russian river system.

Specifications

Length overall	23.31 m
Beam	3.85 m
Draught, hullborne	0.67 m
Draught, on-cushion	0.6 m
Weight, min	17.63 t
Passengers	57
Propulsive power	382 kW
Operational speed	22 kts
Range	173 n miles

ALTAIR PASSENGER SIDEWALL SES

Specifications

Length overall	31.81 m
Beam	6 m
Draught, hullborne	1.4 m
Draught, on-cushion	0.8 m
Weight, min	58.6 t
Passengers	122
Propulsive power	2 × 735 kW
Lift power	220 kW
Operational speed	27 kts
Range	320 n miles

OLKHON PASSENGER SES (DESIGN)

This is a double-deck, twin-screw vessel with passenger saloons in the fore and middle portions of the

LUCH-2 at speed **1996**

Model of SES Olkhon **1996**

ship. The craft has a bow platform to embark/disembark passengers at an unequipped bank.

Specifications

Length overall	32.4 m
Beam	6.4 m
Draught, hullborne	1.46 m
Draught, on-cushion	0.8 m
Weight, min	62.5 t
Passengers	130
Propulsive power	2 × 735 kW
Lift power	220 kW
Operational speed	27 kts
Range	540 n miles

TOURIST CAR/PASSENGER SES (DESIGN)

This vessel has been designed to meet the IMO HSC Code of Safety for operation in river estuaries and coastal areas and is the largest SES design proposed by the Vympel yard.

Specification

Length overall	64.0 m
Beam	12.0 m
Draught, hullborne	2.8 m
Draught, on-cushion	1.7 m
Crew	12
Passengers	370
Vehicles	45
Range	600 n miles
Operational limitation	Beaufort 5

Classification: Russian Marine Register KM +2 A3 SES Ferry.

Structure: All aluminium hull and superstructure.

Propulsion: Two main propulsion diesels each rated at 3,925 kW and two lift fan diesels each rated at 400 kW.

UPDATED

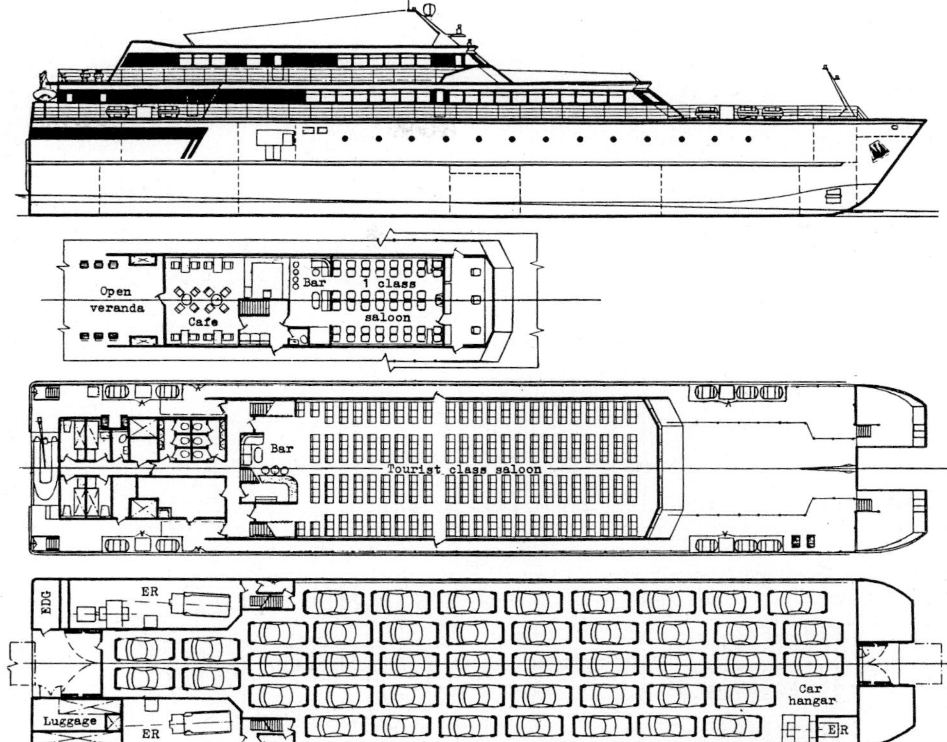

General arrangement of the Tourist SES *(Design)* ***1996***

FRANCE

DCN

DIRECTION DES CONSTRUCTIONS NAVALES

2 rue Royale, F-75008 Paris, France

Tel: +33 (1) 40 59 16 06
Telex: 202 184F
Fax: +33 (1) 45 54 06 89

DCN INTERNATIONAL

19-21 rue du Colonel Pierre Avia, F-75015 Paris, France

Tel: +33 (1) 41 08 71 71
Fax: +33 (1) 41 08 00 27

and

DRET

DIRECTION DES RECHERCHES, ETUDES ET TECHNIQUES

26 boulevard Victor, F-75015 Paris Armées, France

Tel: +33 (1) 45 52 49 24
Telex: 204 648 F

and

ACH

SOCIETE NOUVELLE DES ATELIERS ET CHANTIERS DU HAVRE

PO Box 1390, F-76066 Le Havre Cedex, France

Tel: +33 35 26 81 77
Fax: +33 35 25 09 70

and

AGNES 200 (in Brighton to Dieppe route, Summer 1992) entering Dieppe harbour (Roger Fayolle, STCAN) ***1993***

CMN

CONSTRUCTIONS MECANIQUES DE NORMANDIE

PO Box 539, F-50105 Cherbourg Cedex, France

Tel: +33 33 20 12 50
Telex: 170507F
Fax: +33 33 44 01 09

AGNES 200 (ex-NES 200)

The AGNES 200 has been developed within the framework of an inter-ministry programme, in which the following are participating: the Ministry of Defence, the Ministry of Research and the Ministry of Industry. The vessel was delivered at the end of 1990.

Involved in conducting the programme is Direction des Recherches, Etudes et Techniques (DRET).

Industrial concerns involved are DCN, in respect

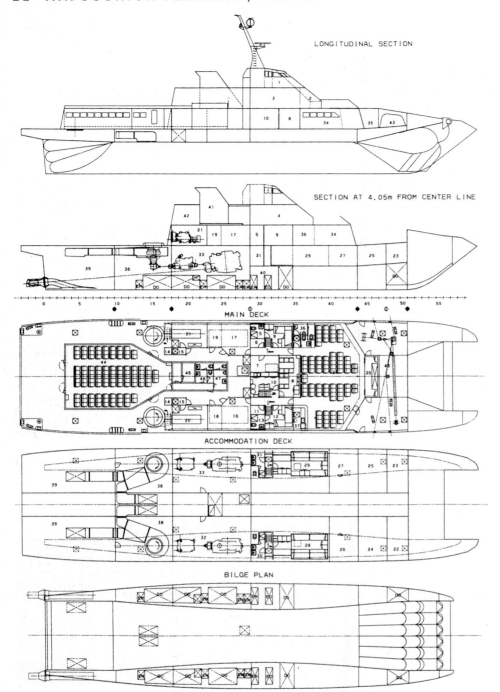

LONGITUDINAL SECTION

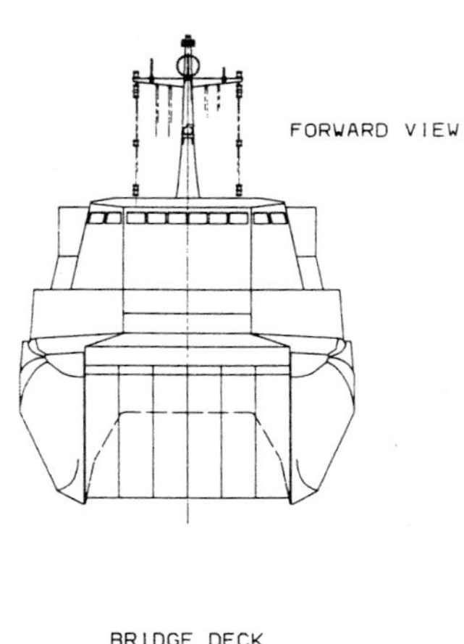

SECTION AT 4.05m FROM CENTER LINE

BRIDGE DECK

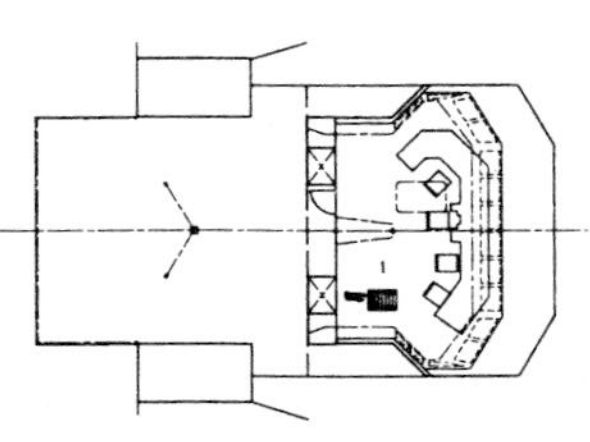

MAIN DECK

ACCOMMODATION DECK

BILGE PLAN

Agnes 200 key

1 *Wheelhouse/Radio room;* **2** *Storeroom;* **3** *Lounge;* **4** *Ventilation;* **5** *Toilet;* **6** *Fire cabinet;* **7** *Technical room;* **8** *Cafeteria;* **9** *Two berth cabin;* **10** *Pantry;* **11** *Storeroom;* **12** *Captain's cabin;* **13** *Toilet;* **14** *Fire cabinet;* **15** *Alleyway;* **16** *Storeroom;* **17** *Storeroom;* **18** *Engine casing starboard;* **19** *Engine casing port;* **20** *Generator set room starboard;* **21** *Generator set room port;* **22** *Void;* **23** *Void;* **24** *Storeroom starboard;* **25** *Storeroom port;* **26** *Void;* **27** *Void;* **28** *Six + two berth cabin;* **29** *Six + two berth cabin;* **30** *Toilet;* **31** *Toilet;* **32** *Engine room starboard;* **33** *Engine room port;* **34** *Forward saloon;* **35** *Boarding gate;* **36** *Men's toilet;* **37** *Bar;* **38** *Ventilators—Starboard and port;* **39** *Water-jets—Starboard and port;* **40** *Cofferdam;* **41** *Funnels;* **42** *Ventilation casing;* **43** *Covered deck;* **44** *Aft saloon;* **45** *Duty free kiosk;* **46** *Women's toilet;* **47** *Men's toilet*

AGNES 200 in passenger ferry configuration

of the project design, and ACH and CMN shipyards, in construction.

Agnes 200 is designed in the form of a basic air cushion platform for both civil and military versions and with an aft deck area of 208 m^2 is able to support a four tonne helicopter.

The major components (propulsion system, lift fans and so on) all use existing technology, and have therefore required only a limited degree of development. The evaluation prototype, named Agnes 200, has been built at Constructions Mécaniques de Normandie (CMN) and was launched on 2 July 1990. Maximum speed achieved during French Navy trials was 45 knots. The vessel is also fitted with a Codod propulsion system allowing the lift engines to drive the water-jets. The maximum speed in this mode is 15 knots.

During low-speed transits it is possible to lift the bow and stern seals to the wet-deck and operate as a catamaran. Supplied by Zodiac Espace, the bow seal consists of a double loop and six segments, the stern seal is a more conventional triple loop design.

After 18 months with the French Navy the vessel entered passenger service on a 68 n mile route between Dieppe and Brighton Marina, operated by Advanced Channel Express. The main modifications to prepare the vessel for its ferry role were the refitting of the existing bow saloon and the installation of a passenger saloon on the helicopter deck. Configured for 78 passengers in the bow saloon and 93 in the aft saloon, there was also a lounge on the upper deck with 12 first class seats for guests of the operator.

While on the English Channel the vessel had a crew of 12 comprising captain, mate, chief engineer, three sailors and six cabin crew.

Specifications

Length overall	51 m
Beam overall	13 m
Draught, hullborne	2.3 m
Draught, on-cushion	1 m
Displacement, max	250 t
Propulsive power	2 × 2,983 kW
Lift power	2 × 746 kW
Max speed	over 40 kts
Range	750 n miles (25 kts)

Propulsion: Main propulsion: 2 × 2,983 kW MTU 16V 538 TB 93 diesels driving 2 × KaMeWa 71 S II water-jet units.

Lift: 2 × 746 kW MTU 8V 396 TB 83 diesels each driving 1 × NEU centrifugal fan via a Renk 2-stage reduction gearbox, 180,000 m^3/h at 600 kg/m^2. Off-cushion, power transferable to the 2 × KaMeWa water-jet units.

1,200 TONNE ASW SES (DESIGN)

The Délégation Générale pour l'Armement (DGA) is engaged in a research and development programme on surface effect ships. So as to be able to fulfil perceived naval requirements for 1995, DCN is studying an SES project of approximately 1,200 tonnes for Anti-Submarine Warfare (ASW) on the high seas. These studies are being conducted by the Service Technique des Constructions et Armes Navales (STCAN) under the aegis of a technical-operational working group, within the framework of a project named EOLES (light oceanic surface effect escort craft). The task lays down a requirement for an off-cushion speed of 18 knots but with speeds in the order of 50 knots on-cushion. Apart from its ASW armaments, the craft will be equipped with self-defence systems against air attack and surface ships.

Several stages of technology have to be passed through before this craft reaches the production phase. The experimental model, codenamed MOLENES, has now finished its trials. In addition, DCN is involved in an inter-ministry programme aimed at developing the 200 tonne craft designed by STCAN. The experience from the AGNES 200 will give guidance to the operational and technological options arising from the EOLES project.

MOLENES (Modèle Libre Expérimental de Navire à Effet de Surface)

In 1980, DCN built under contract from DRET a five tonne craft, which had its trials in 1981 in the

Toulon area. MOLENES is a dynamic manned model capable of proving the NES (Navire à Effet de Surface) concept of a high length-to-beam ratio, and confirmed results obtained in the experimental tank. It has provided data on seaworthiness, performance and manoeuvrability, as well as acceleration levels and their effects on the structure, equipment and fittings.

Specifications

Length overall	12.1 m
Beam	3.43 m
Displacement, max	5.5 t

Propulsion: Propulsion is provided by two 55 hp water-jet units. The air cushion is effected by two centrifugal fans on vertical axes, giving a pressure of 1,800 Pa (37.6 lb/ft²) and a flow of 4 m³/s (141 ft³/s).

Structure: The timber side keels are joined together by a tubular pyramid structure of light aluminium alloy 7020.

VERIFIED

GERMANY

BLOHM+VOSS AG

PO Box 100720, D-20005 Hamburg, Germany

Tel: +49 (40) 3119 1803
Telex: 2 11 047 BV D
Fax: +49 (40) 3113 3300

Blohm+Voss has built the SES prototype Corsair and since 1989 extensive test programmes and trials have been carried out to gain comprehensive technical data and experience for civil as well as military operations.

Blohm+Voss is entering the market with SES designs for passenger ferries and fast patrol craft, both based upon the operational experience of the prototype Corsair.

The original *Corsair* was modified for research purposes and now operates as *Mekat* for navy trials.

SES Mekat **1994**

Mekat

Specifications

Length overall	36 m
Beam	13 m
Draught, hullborne	2.2 m
Draught, on-cushion	0.8 m
Displacement	170 t
Payload	35 t
Propulsive power	2 × 2,560 kW
Max speed	52 kts

Structure: The skirts are manufactured by Avon Rubber.

Propulsion: The main engines are two MTU 16V 396 TB 94, driving two Escher-Wyss surface-piercing CP propellers, 7-blade; through Maag MG-57 RO 2000/950 gearboxes.

The lift engines: 2 × MTU 6V 396 diesels driving 2 × centrifugal lift fans, through ZF gearboxes.

CORSAIR 300 PASSENGER FERRY (DESIGN)

Specifications

Length overall	36.8 m
Beam	12.7 m
Draught, hullborne	1.8 m
Draught, on-cushion	0.6 m
Propulsive power	2 × 2,000 kW diesel
Lift power	1 × 800 kW diesel
Fuel capacity	12,000 l
Water capacity	2,000 l
Operational speed	approx 42 kts
Range	450 n miles

Classification: GL or DnV

GL: GL +100 A4 High-Speed Air Cushion Vehicle, MC AUT.

DnV: DnV +1 A1 R45, Light Craft, SF-LC, EO.

IMO (Resolution A. 373 (X)) and national regulations.

Propulsion: 2 × KaMeWa (or equivalent) water-jets or 2 × Sulzer-Escher Wyss surface-piercing CPP.

Auxiliary systems: 2 × 70 kVA generators.

Control: Maritime Dynamics ride control system or equivalent.

CORSAIR 600 PASSENGER/CAR FERRY (DESIGN)

Through co-operation between Blohm+Voss and Cirrus A/S of Norway, Blohm+Voss has extended the development programme for a combined car and passenger SES ferry, the Corsair 600, based upon the CIRR 200 design.

Specifications

Length overall	61.4 m
Beam	16.4 m
Draught, hullborne	2.8 m
Draught, on-cushion	1.2 m
Passengers	360

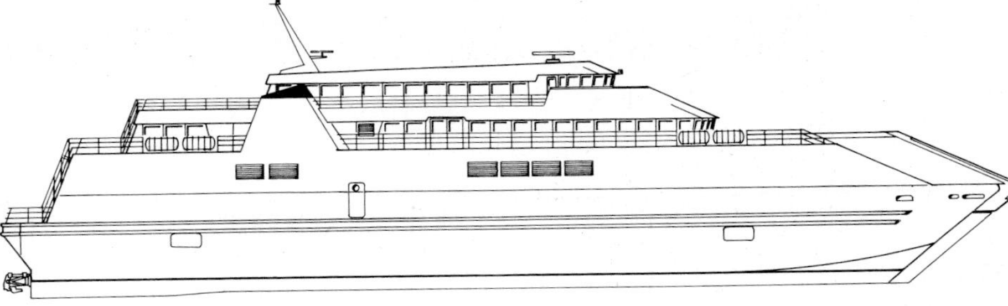

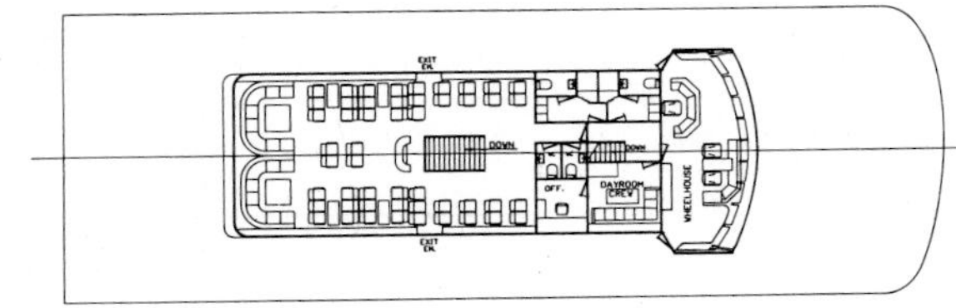

Upper Deck

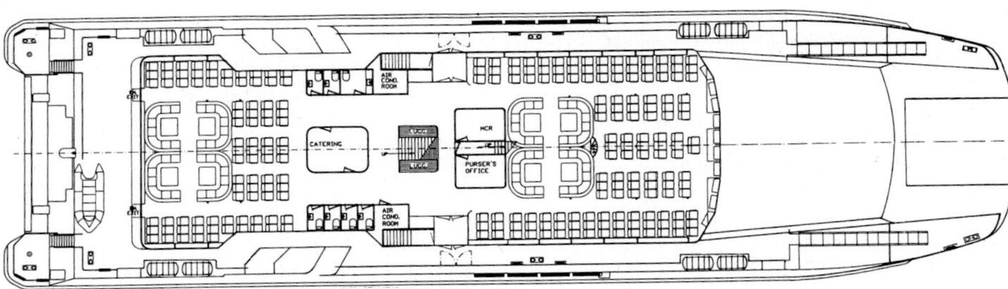

Passenger Deck

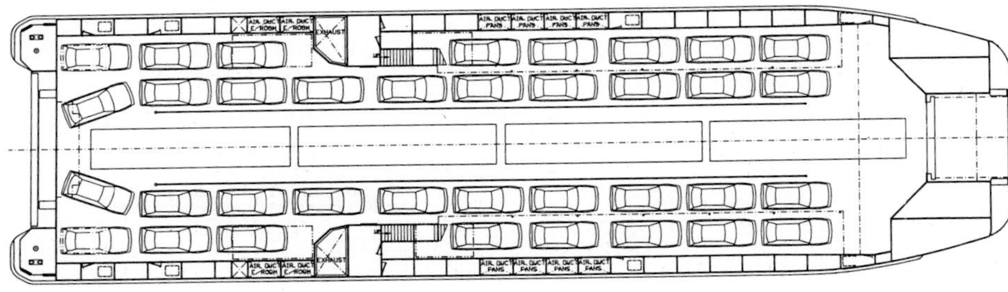

Car Deck

Passenger/car ferry Corsair 600 design **1996**

Vehicles	36 cars
	4 coaches
Fuel capacity	29,000 l
Water capacity	5,000 l
Max speed	46 kts
Range	370 n miles

Classification: GL or DnV

GL: 100 A4 High-Speed Air Cushion Vehicle, MC AUT.

DnV: 1A1 HSLC Passenger Car Ferry, R2, EO with notifications: 3 dk, 7 WTB, Surface Effect Ship.

Structure: Hull material: Aluminium and FRP sandwich.

Propulsion: The vessel will be powered by four gas-turbines running water-jets through reduction gearboxes. Lift fans and generators will be powered by separate diesel engines. Total installed power will be approximately 12,500 kW.

CORSAIR 900 PASSENGER/CAR FERRY (DESIGN)

This new design from Blohm+Voss will have a total installed power of approximately 28,000 kW.

Specifications

Length overall	90 m
Beam	23 m
Draught, hullborne	2.8 m
Draught, on-cushion	1.2 m
Passengers	770
Vehicles	140 cars
	10 coaches
Fuel capacity	95,000 l
Water capacity	8,000 l
Max speed	45 kts
Range	500 n miles

SES MULTIPURPOSE CRAFT (DESIGN)

Blohm+Voss has also developed an SES multipurpose craft applying the established MEKO technology for naval purposes in four versions: Surface warfare, Mine warfare, Anti-Submarine warfare and a Helicopter version.

UPDATED

ITALY

FINCANTIERI CANTIERI NAVALI ITALIANI SpA

Via Genova 1, I-34121 Trieste, Italy

Naval Shipbuilding Division: Via Cipro 11, I-16129 Genoa, Italy

Tel: +39 (10) 59951
Telex: 270168 FINCGE I
Fax: +39 (10) 599 5272

Mario de Negri, *Naval Shipbuilding Division General Manager*

Fincantieri Naval Division has completed the detail design stage of three SES projects: the SES 250, a 450 passenger vessel; the SES 500, a 350 to 450 passenger plus 80 car vessel; and the SES 1000, a 450 to 600 passenger plus 118 to 180 car vessel. These designs were developed by applying the

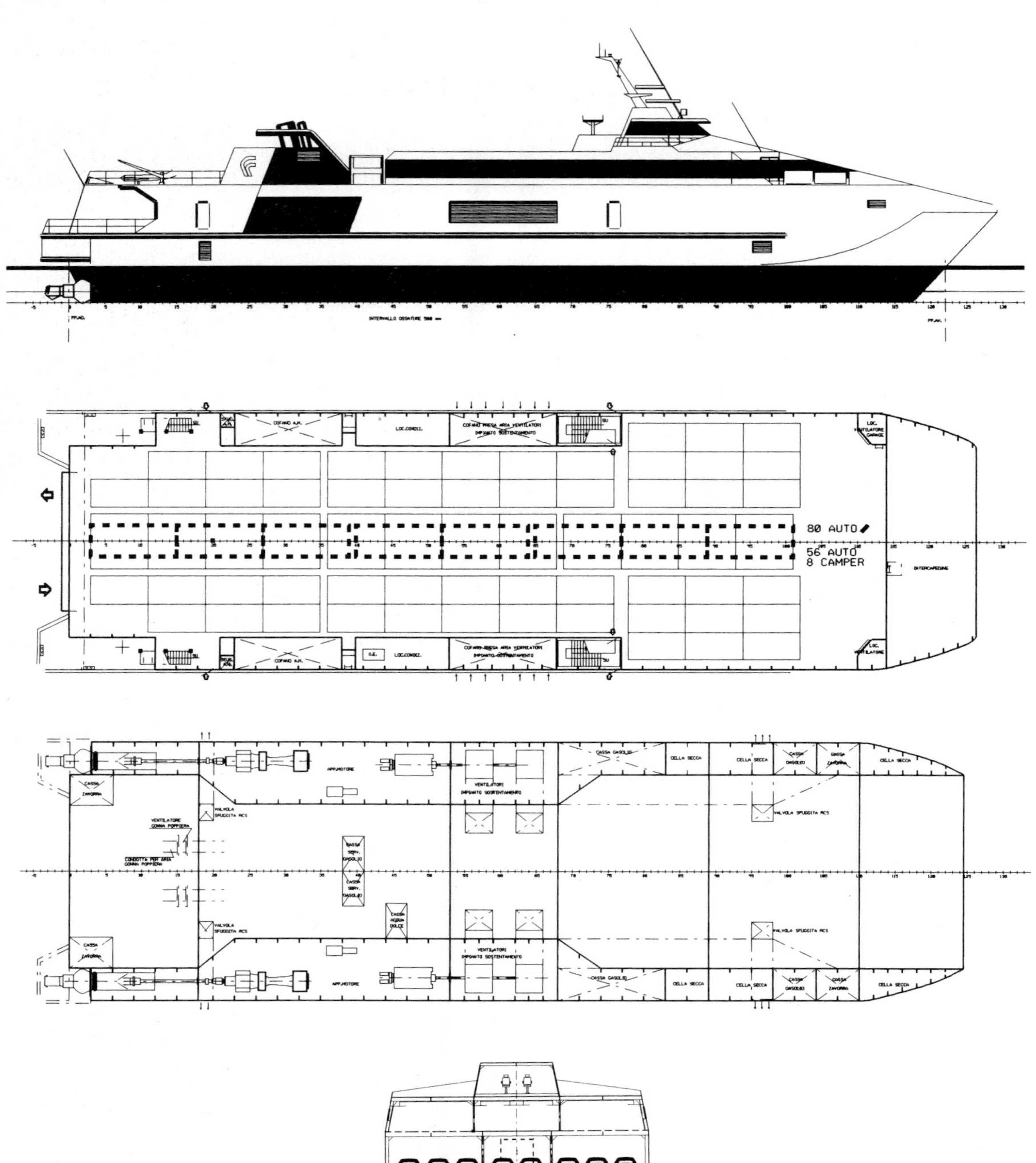

General arrangement of Fincantieri SES 500 design

technology acquired in the naval field (Sparviero class hydrofoils and fast craft) to solve problems of high speed, noise reduction and accommodation comfort. Extensive model testing has been carried out to optimise the hull shapes, lift systems (cushion seals, fans and ducts) and the propulsion system in relation to hull resistance and sea-keeping in rough waters.

The structural design and drawings were presented for approval by the classification societies RINa and DnV, as well as the firefighting insulation and evacuation plans.

Cost analyses, both capital and operating, were developed for the most important Mediterranean routes for passenger and accompanied car services, and these considerations have considerably influenced the design aspects.

SES 250 (DESIGN)

Specifications

Length overall	42 m
Beam	14.5 m
Draught, hullborne	2.5 m
Draught, on-cushion	0.8 m
Passengers	450
Max speed	44 kts
Range	350 n miles

Propulsion: 2 × MTU 16V 396 TB 84 engines.

The SES 250 has also been developed in two different naval configurations and was presented at the Italian Naval Exhibition in 1992.

SES 500 (DESIGN)

Specifications

Length overall	66 m
Beam	18.4 m
Draught, hullborne	2.5 m
Draught, on-cushion	1.1 m
Passengers	350-450
Vehicles	80 cars
Max speed	46 kts (Allison 571KF)
	42 kts (MTU 20V 1163)
Range	550 n miles

Propulsion: Choice of 2 × Allison 571KF or MTU 20V 1163 engines.

SES 1000 (DESIGN)

Specifications

Length overall	84 m
Beam	23.2 m
Draught, hullborne	3.1 m
Draught, on-cushion	1.2 m
Passengers	450-600
Vehicles	118-180 cars
Operational speed	52 kts, 118 cars
	48 kts, 180 cars
Range	550 n miles

Propulsion: 2 × GE LM 1600 gas-turbines.

VERIFIED

SEC

SOCIETA ESERCIZIO CANTIERI SpA

Via dei Pescatori 56, Viareggio, Italy

Tel: +39 (584) 3801
Telex: 500369 SEC I
Fax: +39 (584) 384559

Dr Renzo Pozzo, *Managing Director*
Dr Ing Claudio Pesce, *Sales*
Dr Ing Leonardo Auoiarri, *Technical*

Società Esercizio Cantieri SpA (SEC) is the largest private shipbuilding company in Italy. In the 1980s a new project department became fully engaged on a study for determining the best configuration for new types of ferry suitable for the transport of up to 750 passengers and up to 200 vehicles, at maximum speeds above 50 knots. The choice fell on SES because of its high development potential.

By the middle of 1991 three vessel designs had been formulated and were designated SEC 450, SEC 550 and SEC 750.

Model of SEC 750 (design) ***1993***

SEC 750

Construction of the SEC 750 began in early 1992 but was suspended later that year due to a cut in the Italian Subsidy Law. Sea-keeping model trials were performed for SEC 750 at SSPA Maritime Consulting, Sweden. The design is aimed at providing the following features:

(1) high speed at full load compared to other high-speed vessels
(2) low vertical acceleration, comparable to a car travelling at 120 km/h on a motorway
(3) low internal noise levels, comparable to a conventional passenger ferry (55 dBA)
(4) a large number of passenger facilities
(5) a high level of acoustic isolation between different areas
(6) a low external noise level of 70 dBA
(7) a hull designed to minimise wave creation
(8) a very short crash stop distance
(9) a very high manoeuvrability
(10) a computerised anti-collision system
(11) infra-red night vision
(12) a very high capacity with respect to speed
(13) a shallow water sailing capability.

Specifications

Length overall	93 m
Beam	23 m
Draught, hullborne	4.45 m
Draught, on-cushion	0.95 m
Passengers	750
Vehicles	200 cars
	or 80 and cars 10 coaches
Propulsive power	2 × 18,643 kW
Max speed	42 kts
Range	600 n miles

Classification: RINa: *100. A.1.1. (UL) NAV. S (Mediterraneo) IAQ1.
ABS: +A.1. +AMS +ACCU (E) FERRY SERVICE.
Regulations: SOLAS 74, protocol 78, amended up to 1990.
Structure: Hull material: high-tensile steel.
Superstructure material: aluminium alloy.
Skirt system: stern lobes, bow fingers.
Propulsion: The engines are two GE LM 2500 gas-turbines, driving two KaMeWa 180 SII water-jet units. The lift engines are four diesels.

VERIFIED

JAPAN

MITSUBISHI HEAVY INDUSTRIES

5-1, Marunouchi 2-chome, Chiyoda-ku, Tokyo, Japan

Tel: +81 (3) 3212 3111
Telex: 22443 J
Fax: +81 (3) 3212 9772

Mitsubishi Heavy Industries is a joint partner in the technological research association of Techno-Superliner. The company developed its own SES technology with the construction of an 18.5 m SES in 1989.

The research and development project on SES at the Technical Research and Development Institute (TRDI) of Japan Defence Agency started in 1976. Since 1981, the project has been carried out in collaboration with Mitsubishi Heavy Industries Ltd (MHI) and Mitsui Engineering and Shipbuilding Co Ltd. In August 1989, the 18.5 m SES test craft *Méguro* was built at MHI Shimonoseki Shipyard and delivered to the TRDI in order to verify the technological results in the R&D process. The technical trials completed successfully in March 1991.

Méguro 2 is a conversion of *Méguro* and was delivered to the TRDI in September 1994. The hull length was increased to 25 m and the existing prime movers, IHI IM-100, replaced by the Allison 501-KF gas turbine engines. Following this conversion the craft achieved speeds of over 60 knots in September 1994 and further tests are currently under way.

18.5 m SURFACE EFFECT SHIP

In August 1989 Mitsubishi completed the construction of an 18.5 m SES for the Japanese Defence Agency.

In mid-April 1989 a joint research and development programme was announced by the Japanese Defence Agency and Mitsubishi Heavy Industries for a 50 knot SES designed to operate safely in rough coastal waters. The interest of the Defence Agency is in applying the technology to minesweepers, torpedo boats and patrol ships and stems from work started in 1983.

Méguro 2

Specifications

Length overall	25.0 m
Beam	7.5 m
Draught, hullborne	1.3 m
Draught, on cushion	0.4 m
Displacement, max	48.0 t
Max speed	60+ kts

Propulsion: The vessel is propelled by two Allison 501-KF gas turbines each rated at 3,185 kW and each driving a water-jet via a reduction gearbox. Lift is supplied by six centrifugal fans, driven by two IM100 gas turbines each rated at 772 kW.

UPDATED

Méguro 2 during trials
1996

MITSUI ENGINEERING & SHIPBUILDING COMPANY LTD

6-4 Tsukiji 5-chome, Chuo-ku, Tokyo 104, Japan

Tel: +81 (3) 3544 3462
Telex: 22821 J, 22924 MITZOSEN J
Fax: +81 (3) 3544 3031

Hiroshi Kitashima, *Director and General Manager, Ship and Ocean Projects Division*
Yutaka Ikeda, *General Manager, Marine Department*

Mitsui's Hovercraft Department was formed in May 1964, following the signing of a licensing agreement in 1963 with Hovercraft Development Ltd and Vickers Ltd, whose ACV interests were later merged with those of British Hovercraft Corporation. The company has been developing Mitsui hovercraft independently after terminating the licensing agreement in March 1986. The Mitsui ACVAS and MV-PP10 represent such developments. The company has built 19 MV-PP5s, four MV-PP15s, two MV-PP05s, two MV-PP10s and two ACVASs. Details of the earlier hovercraft are given in the 1992-93 edition of this book.

ACVAS (ACV with Aft Skegs)

A new form of hovercraft was developed by the Mitsui company in the early 1980s with trials of the 10 m prototype *Eaglet* started in early 1986. The craft employs water-jet propulsion and is not therefore amphibious. The inlets for the two water-jet units are positioned in the underside of the two skegs which extend either side of the craft for approximately one-third of overall craft length. Over this length immersed areas of the skegs seal the air cushion; for the remainder of the cushion periphery a conventional loop and segment type skirt is employed. Unlike the sidewall hovercraft or surface effect ships the craft is almost totally supported by its air cushion at cruising speed. The craft is provided with a Mitsui motion control system exerting control over cushion air pressure variation and is fitted with fin stabilisers. The skirt/skeg combination is also found to give good ride comfort over waves through its soft response.

The Mitsui ACVAS concept is aimed principally towards applications in shallow rivers, lakes and other smooth waters and for ultra-fast ferries for operation in coastal and inland sea routes.

Eaglet

Specifications

Length overall	10.9 m
Beam	5.1 m
Propulsive power	2 × 75 kW
Lift power	16 kW
Max speed	27 kts

The Mitsui Sumidagawa *in operation with the Tokyo Metropolitan Government Bureau of Construction*
1990

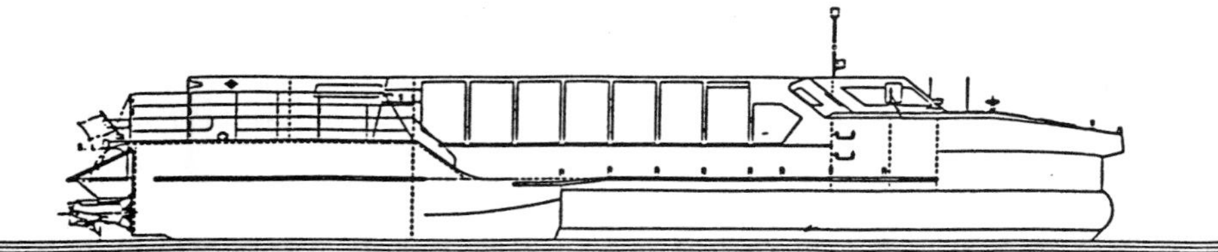

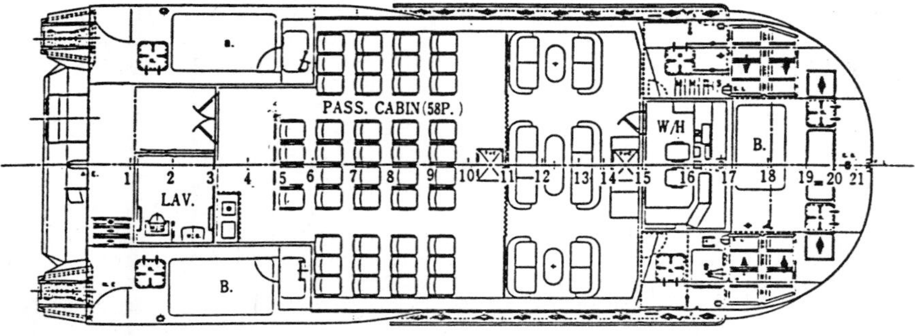

Layout of Sumidagawa

Structure: Glass reinforced plastic.
Propulsion: Main engines: 2 × Nissan HA 120 (petrol).
Lift engine: 2 × Robin petrol.
Water-jet: 2 × Hamilton 771 units.

Sumidagawa

In August 1988, Mitsui received an order from the Tokyo Metropolitan Government Bureau of Construction for a river observation craft that can be used for observation and inspection of rivers in the Metropolis. The craft is fitted out in a manner suitable for international conferences to be held on board. This ACVAS vessel, named *Sumidagawa*, was delivered in March 1989.

Specifications

Length overall	19.95 m
Beam	7.9 m
Draught, hullborne	1.5 m
Draught, on-cushion	0.5 m
Passengers	52-80
Propulsive power	2 × 346 kW
Lift power	2 × 272 kW
Max speed	30.4 kts
Operational speed	28.5 kts

Structure: The vessel structure is made of anti-corrosive aluminium alloy with the hull longitudinally stiffened. Extruded sections are used extensively. The upper structure is of plate construction consisting of welded and riveted antiflexure material.

A flexible skirt made of rubberised nylon cloth is provided around the vessel excepting the skegs at the aft. The front part of the skirt system consists of a bag and fingers and the rear part has lobe seal construction. Air is supplied to the lobe seal from the bag at the front through a duct. The forward skirt is designed to minimise water spray for ease of navigation in rivers.

Propulsion: Two high-speed diesel engines are used for propulsion. The power is transmitted to two water-jet units through reduction gears. One high-speed diesel engine drives two lift fans, DC generator and cooler compressors through clutch and flexible joint.

MV-PP10

The most recent hovercraft developed by Mitsui is the MV-PP10, which can accommodate 84 to 100 passengers and has a maximum speed of 50 knots. This hovercraft embodies the technological progress of the hovercraft developed by MES over the years and has been designed for low cost, easy maintenance and a comfortable ride.

The main hull of the craft is constructed of marine grade aluminium alloy as for other MES high-speed craft. The MV-PP10 is fitted with a flexible skirt of improved durability and is powered by air-cooled, high-speed diesel engines.

MV-PP5

Craft built	Seats	Launched	Operator
Hakuchyo No 3	75*	June 1970	Oita Hoverferry Co Ltd
Hobby No 1	75*	May 1971	Oita Hoverferry Co Ltd
Hobby No 6	75*	October 1974	Oita Hoverferry Co Ltd
Angel No 5	75*	April 1975	Oita Hoverferry Co Ltd
plus 15 others			

*Converted to Mk II configuration.

MV-PP5 Mk II

1986

MV-PP10 Dream No 2

1993

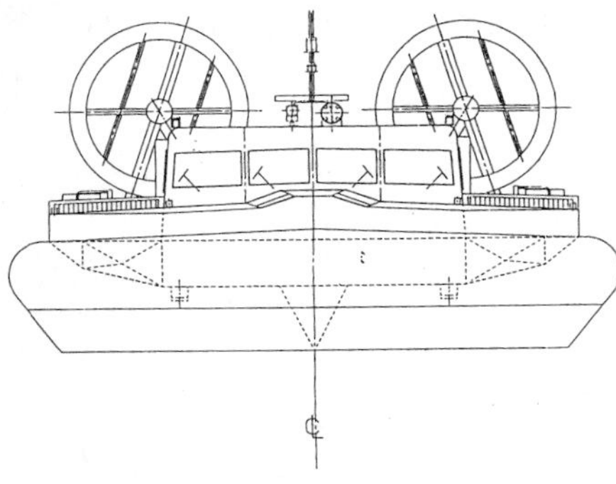

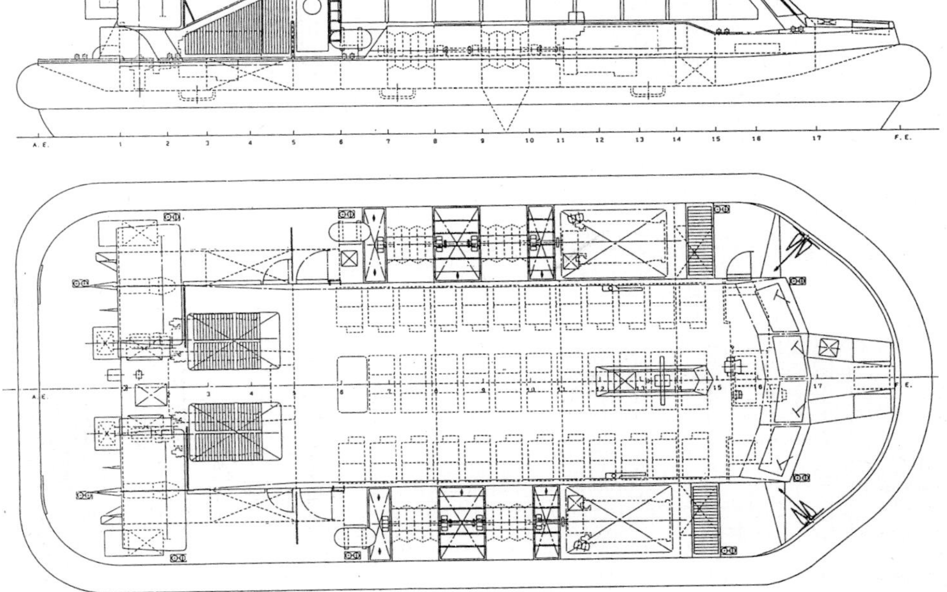

MV-PP10 general arrangement

The MV-PP10 can also be fitted out for such purposes as surveying and rescue operations.

Three MV-PP10 type craft, *Dream No 1*, *Dream No 2* and *Dream No 3* were delivered in March 1990, March 1991 and October 1995 respectively to the Oita Hoverferry Company Ltd.

Specifications

Length overall	23.1 m
Beam	11 m
Weight, max	40 t
Payload	9 t
Crew	3
Passengers	125
Propulsive power	2 × 441 kW
Max speed	50 kts
Operational speed	45 kts

Structure: The main hull of the craft is built in weldable anti-corrosive aluminium alloy, and the superstructure is of riveted construction.

The skirt is of bag and finger type and cushion depth is about 1.2 m. The lower side parts of fingers, particularly susceptible to wear, are replaceable in sections.

Propulsion: The MV-PP10 is powered by four Deutz BF12L 513CP air-cooled turbocharged diesels, each rated at 441 kW (600 hp) at 2,300 rpm maximum and 383 kW (520 hp) continuous. On each side of the craft, one engine drives two double-entry mixed flow fans for lift and two engines aft drive two ducted variable-pitch propellers.

Control: Twin aerodynamic rudders mounted on the rear of the propeller ducts and differential thrust of the propellers provide directional control. Air bleed thruster ports are installed (one at the forward end and two at the aft end of the craft). Each thruster has an opening and shutting vane.

UPDATED

TECHNOLOGICAL RESEARCH ASSOCIATION OF TECHNO-SUPERLINER

Japan Research Centre Building, 1-3-8 Mejiro, Toshima Ku, Tokyo 171, Japan

Tel: +81 (3) 3985 3841
Fax: +81 (3) 3985 3740

Tokashi Nakaso, *President*
Kazuo Sugai, *Managing Director*

The programme of research and development of a super high-speed vessel named 'Techno-Superliner' is being continued in Japan. A target of the programme is to accomplish the technological foundation for developing and building a high-speed ocean-going cargo vessel with a speed of 50 knots, a payload of 1,000 tonnes and a range of 500 n miles. In addition, seaworthiness adequate to meet schedules in rough seas is desired.

In order to accomplish the Research and Development programme, Technological Research Association of Techno-Superliner was established in 1989 by seven leading shipbuilders in Japan.

This Research and Development programme ran from 1989 to 1994, throughout which the technological foundation for Techno-Superliner was established through analysis, experiments and tests. The last year of the programme consolidated these technologies by scale model tests in actual seas. The programme was extended until the end of 1995 to complete the sea transportation tests. Debut of the actual ships is expected to be made in the latter half of the 1990s.

As members of the association, Mitsubishi Heavy Industries Ltd and Mitsui Engineering and Shipbuilding Company Ltd are jointly investigating an SES type of novel super high-speed cargo ship (called TSL-A). The concept of buoyancy/air cushion combination has three hull components: twin side hulls, an air cushion chamber and fully submerged foils. A 13 m test model (TSL-A12) was built in 1991 in order to confirm the basic performance of TSL-A in calm water. The model is controlled by the motion control systems operating on both air pressure and fins. A larger model, the TSL-A70 'Hisho', was completed and tested in 1994/1995. The design of an actual vessel for commercial use, the TSL-A127, was also carried out under the R&D programme.

TSL-A70 HISHO

The large scaled sea model named TSL-A70 Hisho was constructed separately at two major shipyards. The fore part was constructed at Mitsui Tamano Shipyard and the aft one at Mitsubishi Nagasaki. These two blocks were connected at Nagasaki and the vessel was launched in June 1994. A maximum speed of 54.4 knots was achieved at the official speed trial. The TSL-A70 Hisho completed sea transportation trials in 1995.

Specifications

Length overall	70 m
Beam	18.6 m
Draught, hullborne	3.5 m
Draught, on-cushion	1.1 m
Propulsive power	2 × 12,000 kW
Lift power	4 × 1,500 kW
Max speed	54.4 kts
Range	500 n miles

Structure: The hull material is aluminium.

The TSL-A70 Hisho **1995**

The TSL-A127 design (artist's impression) **1992**

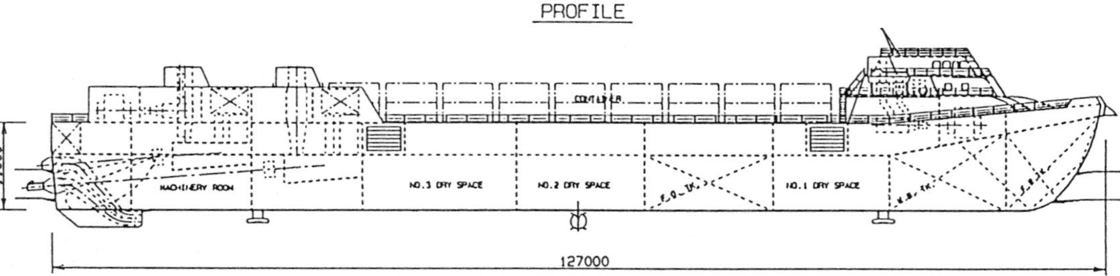

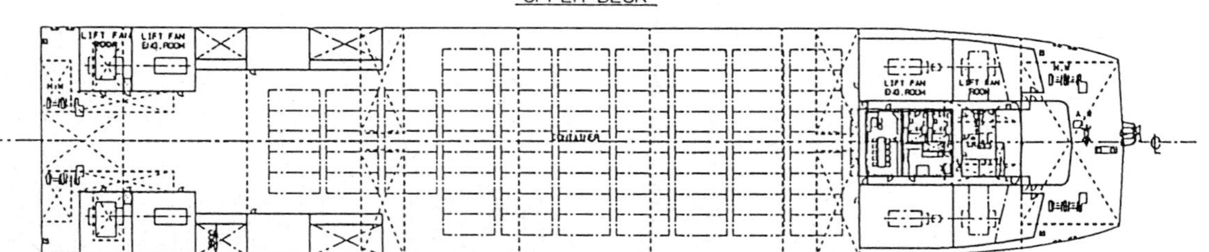

General arrangement of TSL-A127 (design) **1995**

Propulsion: There are two propulsion engines, driving a water-jet each.

The lift engines are three 1,500 kW diesels and a 1,500 kW gas-turbine, driving eight centrifugal lift fans.

The skirt system is: full finger (bow), lobe (stern).

TSL-A127 (DESIGN)

At this stage of the design the following figures are approximate.

Specifications

Length overall	127 m
Beam	27.2 m
Draught, hullborne	5 m
Draught, on-cushion	1.4 m
Payload	1,000 t
Propulsive power	4 × 18,640 kW
Lift power	4 × 3,200 kW
Max speed	50 kts
Range	500 n miles
Operational limitation	wave height 4-6 m

Structure: The hull material is aluminium.

Propulsion: The propulsion engines are four gas-turbines, each driving a water-jet.

The lift engines are four gas-turbines, each driving a centrifugal lift fan.

The skirt system is: full finger (bow), lobe (stern).

UPDATED

Manned test craft model TSL-A12 ***1993***

KOREA, SOUTH

KOREA TACOMA MARINE INDUSTRIES LTD

Hanjin Group

PO Box 339, 974-15 Yangduck-dong, Masan, South Korea

Tel: +82 (551) 551181/551188
Telex: 53662 KOTAMAN K
Fax: +82 (551) 949449/949903

Choong-Hoon Cho, *Chairman*
Yi-Taek Chim, *President*
Chul-Kyu Chun, *Vice President*
Shin-Doo Kang, *Executive Managing Director*

Seoul office: PO Box 4296, 118, 2-Ga, Namdaemun-Ro, Chung-Ku, Seoul, South Korea

Tel: +82 (2) 728 5446/8
Fax: +82 (2) 757 0884

Since its founding in 1971, Korea Tacoma Marine Industries Ltd (KTMI) has built a variety of fast patrol boats and high-speed passenger boats, and has concentrated its efforts on the development of high-speed SES and amphibious hovercraft for civil and paramilitary applications.

In 1977 KTMI began an ACV development programme, and the company designed and constructed a test surface effect ship in 1978.

KTMI named its first surface effect ship Turt II. This had a length of 8.2 m, weight of 3.8 tonnes, and capacity for seven passengers. To date KTMI has developed and constructed five 18 m SES (90 passenger), one 11 m SES (56 passenger), one 17 m SES (72 passenger), two 26 m SES (158 passenger), one 28 m SES (200 passenger, modified 26 m SES), a manned test amphibious hovercraft, a 12 m diesel-powered prototype hovercraft and a 14 m diesel-powered sea ambulance hovercraft.

The company has now developed a 40 m SES design (Turt VI) and a range of catamaran craft.

Craft built (18 m SES)	Delivered to	Route
Air Ferry	Seo-Kyung Ferry Co	Pusan to Geoje Island
Cosmos	Geo-Je Ferry Co	Masan to Geoje Island
Phinex	Geo-Je Development Co	Pusan to Geoje Island
Sun Star	Kumsan Hungup	Yeosu to Near Island

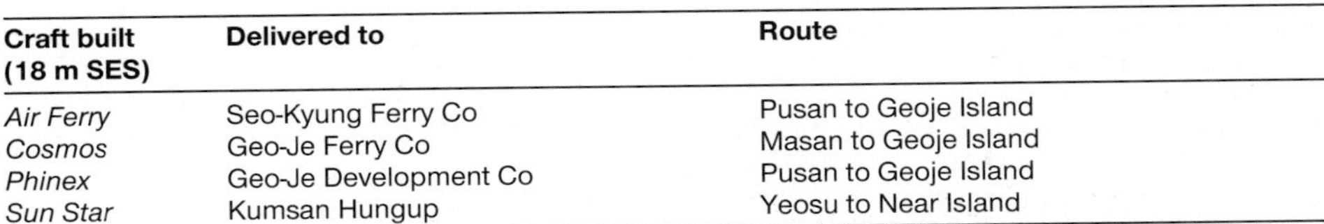

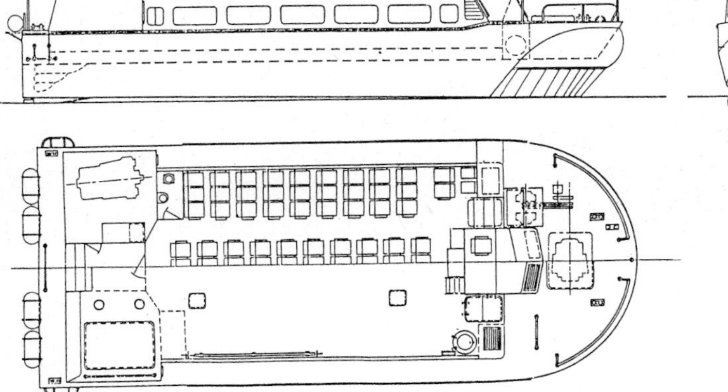

KTMI 18 m SES

KTMI 26 m SES ***1986***

TURT III
18 m SES

The 18 m design has buoyant catamaran-type sidewalls almost identical in shape to those of the smaller craft.

Specifications

Length overall	18.1 m
Beam	9 m
Draught, hullborne	1.74 m

Draught, on-cushion	1.08 m
Weight, max	36 t
Passengers	max 90
Propulsive power	2 × 485 kW, 596 kW or 970 kW
Max speed	35, 40 or 50 kts

Propulsion: Power for the lift system is provided by a single marine diesel in the 298 to 373 kW range. Power for the propulsion system is provided by twin diesels of 485, 596 or 970 kW, each driving a water propeller via a reversing gearbox and an inclined shaft.

Control: Twin water rudders aft, one on each sidehull. Differential propeller thrust for slow-speed manoeuvring.

Structure: Main structure built in welded marine aluminium alloy. Segmented skirt at the bow and stern.

26 m SES

Specifications

Length overall	25.7 m
Beam	10.2 m
Draught, hullborne	2.45 m
Draught, on-cushion	1.45 m
Displacement, max	65 t
Payload	16.5 t
Crew	10
Passengers	158
Propulsive power	2 × 755 kW
Lift power	380 kW
Max speed	35 kts
Range	250 n miles

Structure: The main structure is built in welded marine aluminium alloy and the superstructure is constructed in riveted marine aluminium alloy.

The bow skirt consists of single-bag and multisegments. The stern skirt is a multibag type, consisting of three bag sections, inflated to a pressure slightly above that of the cushion by two 0.61 m fans on the deckhouse of the engine rooms.

Propulsion: The lift system is powered by a single General Motors Detroit Diesel Allison 12V-71TI. This engine directly drives a dual 1.075 m diameter lift fan, to provide cushion air to the plenum chamber and, via toothed belts and a hydraulic system, two secondary 0.61 m diameter fans for stern skirt inflation. Propulsive power is supplied by two MTU 8V 396 TB 83 diesels, each driving a water propeller via a reversing gearbox and an inclined shaft.

Electrical system: One GM 2-71 diesel generator, rated at 30 kW 60 Hz, 220 V, is provided.

Control: Craft heading is controlled by twin balanced stainless steel rudders operated hydraulically by a steering wheel. Additional control is provided by differential use of the water propellers.

Craft built (26 m SES)	Seats	Delivered to	Route
Duridoong Sil (ex-*Young-Kwang I*)	158	Semo Co Ltd	Pusan to Geoje Island
Dudoong Sil (ex-*Young-Kwang II**)	200	Semo Co Ltd	Pusan to Geoje Island
Soon Poong (ex-*Tacoma III*)	158	Semo Co Ltd	Yeosu to Geomoon Island

*Modified to 28 m

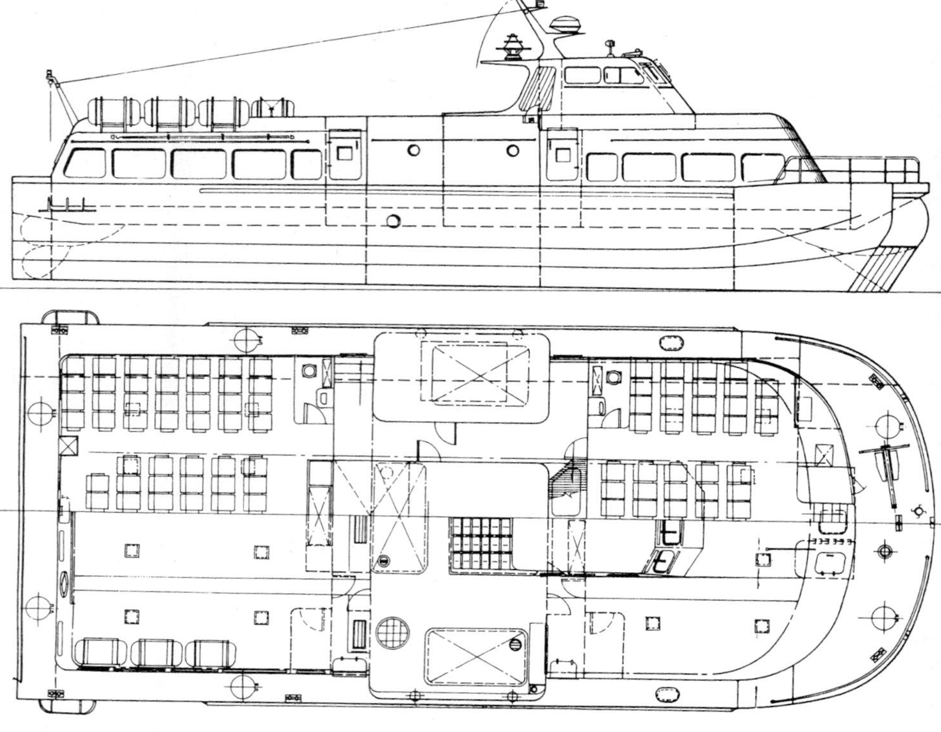

KTMI 26 m SES

KTMI 28 m SES (Modified 26 m SES) **1992**

TURT IV

In December 1984, KTMI developed an amphibious hovercraft Turt IV type, the first diesel-powered amphibious hovercraft in Asia.

Specifications

Length overall	12.65 m
Beam	7.04 m
Weight, min	8.1 t
Payload	1.5 t
Propulsive power	315 kW
Lift power	240 kW
Max speed	55 kts
Operational speed	40 kts
Range	200 n miles
Operational limitation	wave height 2 m

Structure: The main hull is built in welded aluminium alloy 5086-H116 (plate) and 6061-T6 (extrusion), and the deckhouse is riveted.

The skirt is an open loop and segment type and anti-bouncing ties are built into the loop.

Propulsion: The lift system comprises two single 1.075 m fans driven by a Deutz air-cooled diesel engine. Thrust is supplied by a Deutz air-cooled diesel engine driving a 2.75 m ducted propeller.

Control: One rudder and one elevator positioned in the ducted propeller slipstream provide directional control and trim control respectively. Additional control in low speed is provided by two puff ports which are designed specially for turning and reversing and are supplied by cushion air.

TURT IV Mk 1

As a sea ambulance version, Turt IV Mk 1 is intended for quick transportation of patients from islands to land. The distinctive features of the craft, compared with Turt IV, are the twin propulsion units for increased manoeuvrability and the reduced lift power due to the developed skirt. Turt IV Mk 1 was constructed in 1987 and was delivered in April 1988.

Specifications

Length overall	13.35 m
Beam	7.44 m
Weight, min	11 t
Payload	2 t
Propulsive power	2 × 203 kW
Lift power	203 kW
Max speed	50 kts
Operational speed	40 kts
Range	150 n miles
Operational limitation	wave height 2 m

Structure: The main hull is built in welded aluminium alloy 5086-H116 (plate) and 6061-T6 (extrusion), and the deckhouse is riveted.

The skirt is an open loop and segment type and anti-bouncing ties are built into the loop.

Propulsion: The lift system consists of two single 1.07 m diameter fans driven by a Deutz air-cooled diesel engine rated at 203 kW at 2,300 rpm. Thrust is supplied by two 205 kW Deutz air-cooled diesel engines at 2,300 rpm driving two 2.0 m diameter ducted propellers.

Craft built (TURT IV Mk 1)	Seats	Delivered to	Route
Jun-Nam 540	9	The Ministry of Health and Social Affairs	Coastal service

TURT IV Mk 2

This craft, of which three have been built, is a stretched version of the Turt IV Mk 1. Lift and propulsion systems are identical to those of the Turt IV Mk 1, but the hull has been lengthened by 1.75 m and propulsion engines are upgraded from 203 kW (Deutz) to 254 kW to improve the performance in rough seas.

Specifications

Length overall	15.3 m
Beam	7.64 m
Weight, min	15 t
Payload	1.3 t
Propulsive power	2 × 254 kW
Lift power	203 kW
Max speed	40 kts
Operational speed	35 kts
Range	150 n miles
Operational limitation	wave height 2 m

Turt IV Mk 2 **1992**

TURT V

The prototype of the Turt V was constructed at end of 1989.

Turt V is a multipurpose amphibious vehicle capable of operating in open sea and confined shallow waterways including swamps, scrubland, sandbanks and mudflats.

Specifications

Length overall	26.5 m
Beam	13.8 m
Weight, max	95 t
Payload	30 t
Propulsive power	2 × 1,864 kW
Lift power	2 × 1,211 kW
Max speed	60 kts
Operational speed	50 kts
Range	300 n miles

Structure: The main hull and the supersturcture are built in welded aluminium alloy 5086-H116 (plate) and 6061-t6 (extrusion).

The skirt is an open loop and segment type and anti-bouncing webs are built into the loop.

Propulsion: The lift system consists of six double inlet 1.07 m diameter fans driven by two gas-turbines rated at 1,211 kW each. Thrust is supplied by two 1,864 kW gas-turbines driving two 3.6 m diameter ducted controllable pitch air propellers.

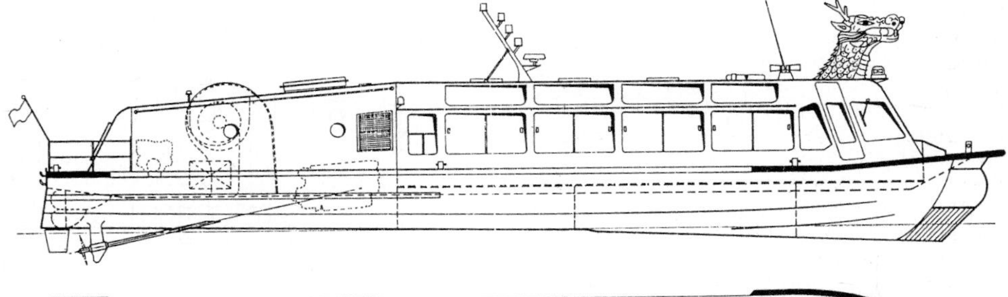

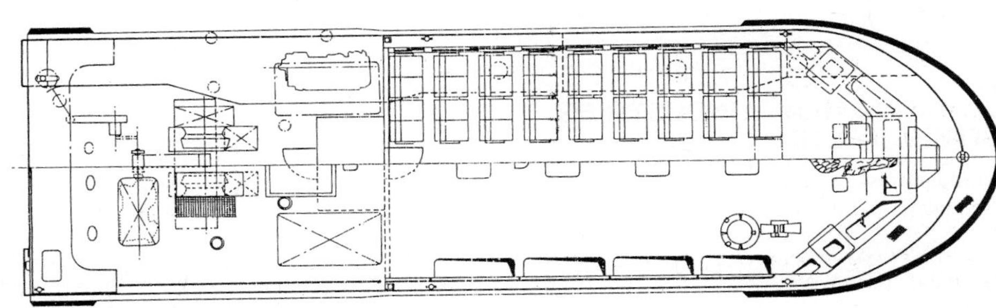

KTMI 17 m SES

17 m SES

The first 17 m craft *Que-Ryong II* is a high-speed waterbus which was delivered and entered service on So-Yang man-made lake near Seoul in September 1988. The 17 m SES is designed as a very reliable, cost-effective, high-speed waterbus with good transportation efficiency for operating on inland waters such as lakes, rivers and inland waterways. Good ride quietness and comfortable passenger space enhance this craft.

Specifications

Length overall	17.3 m
Beam	5 m
Crew	3
Passengers	72
Propulsive power	2 × 217 kW
Lift power	127 kW
Weight, max	21.5 t
Max speed	30.0 kts

Craft built (17 m SES)	Seats	Delivered to	Route
Que-Ryong II	72	Dong-Bu Co Ltd	So-Yang river to In-Je

Structure: The hull is built in welded marine grade aluminium alloy and the deckhouse is constructed in riveted marine grade aluminium alloy.

The bow and stern skirt consists of single-bag and multisegments which are attached to the bag and connected to the underside of the hull by straps.

Propulsion: Power for the lift fan is supplied by a single VOLVO PENTA TAMD 41A marine diesel engine. Propulsion engines are two VOLVO PENTA TAMD 71A marine diesels.

Control: Twin rudders, one on each side of the hull, provide directional control. Additional control is provided by the differential thrust of the propellers.

Outfit: Audio system and airline-type seating is provided for 72 passengers and 3 crew members.

Turt IV Mk 1 **1989**

KTMI 17 m SES Que-Ryong II **1989**

Artist's impression of 40 m SES **1995**

40 m SES (DESIGN)

KTMI's 40 m SES was designed as a high performance passenger craft.

Hull material is marine aluminium alloy rather than GRP for higher reliability and easier maintenance. Noise and vibration levels have been minimised and a ride control system is adopted on this craft.

Specifications

Length overall	40 m
Beam	12 m
Draught, hullborne	2.5 m
Draught, on-cushion	0.9 m
Passengers	336
Propulsive power	2 × 2,000 kW
Lift power	2 × 410 kW
Max speed	50 kts
Range	300 n miles

Control: Remote-control and monitoring system, ride control system, autopilot system.

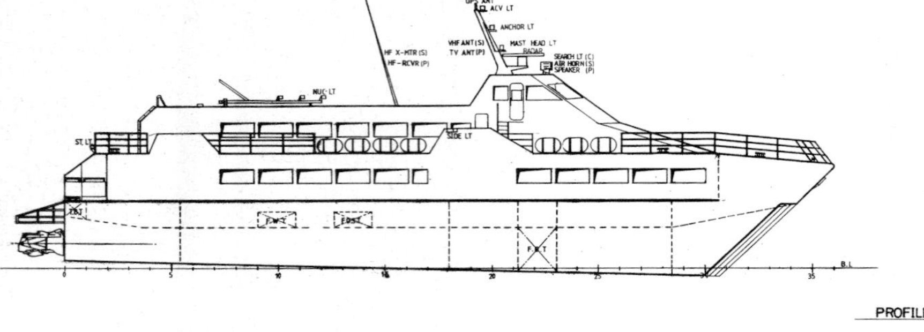

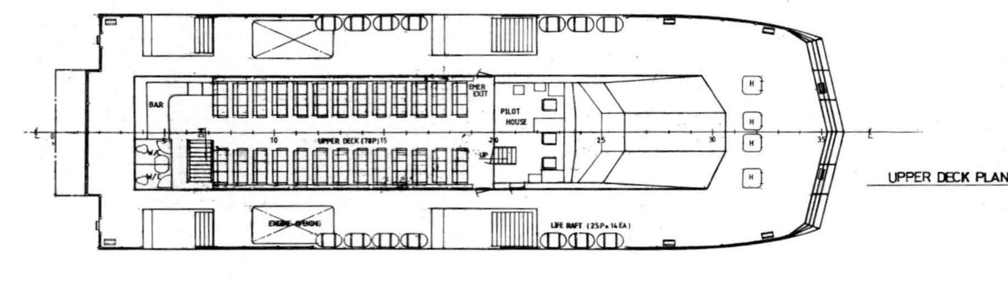

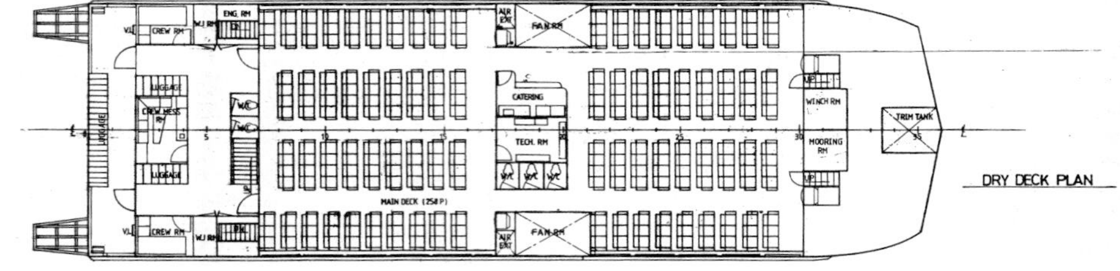

General arrangement of 40 m SES **1994**

SAMSUNG HEAVY INDUSTRIES COMPANY LTD

Headquarters: Namdaemun Building, 25 1-Ka, Bongrae-Dong, Chung-Ku, Seoul, Korea

Tel: +82 (2) 728-6570
Fax: +82 (2) 728-6789

Shipyard: 530 Jangpyung-ri, Sinhyun-up, Koje-Kun, Kyongnam, Korea

Tel: +82 (558) 303015
Fax: +82 (558) 322160

Hae Kyu Lee, *President*
Sung Ki Kim, *Marketing Director*
Young Ryeal Joo, *Principal Researcher*
Byung Lee, *Director Passenger Ship Construction*

Samsung Heavy Industries Co Ltd was established in 1974 and operates three very large production facilities in Korea.

The Koje shipyard builds various types of ships and offshore structures, large scale processing facilities and industrial machinery.

Since the shipbuilding business commenced in 1977, SHI has successfully built various types of vessels such as VLCCs, tankers, product carriers, full container vessels and bulk carriers.

In the area of high-speed craft, SHI has been performing research and development since 1991. The SES project was started in 1992 and its first passenger vessel, *Dong Yang Gold*, was delivered to the domestic owner in May 1994.

In addition to conventional catamarans and monohull vessels, SHI has also developed and designed an SES type high-speed passenger car ferry.

Dong Yang Gold

Ordered by Dong Yang Express Co Ltd, the 37 m SES vessel *Dong Yang Gold* was delivered in May 1994 and entered service on a route off the west coast of the country linking Mokpo with the islands of Heuksan-do and Hong-Do.

Specifications

Length overall	36.5 m
Beam	12 m

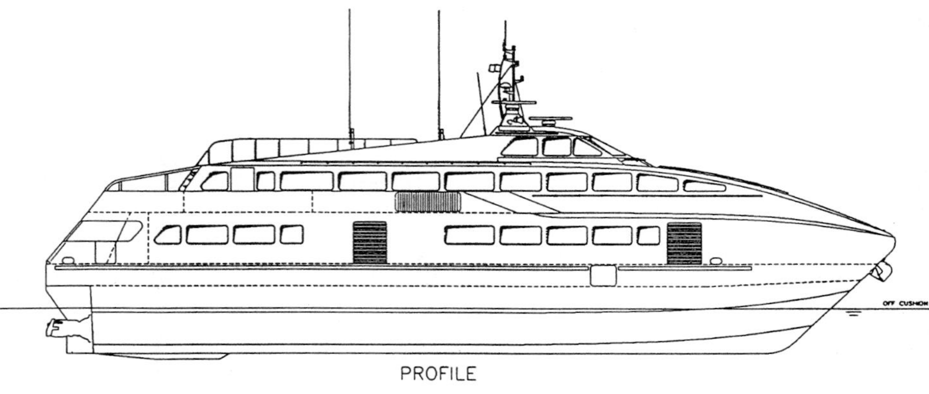

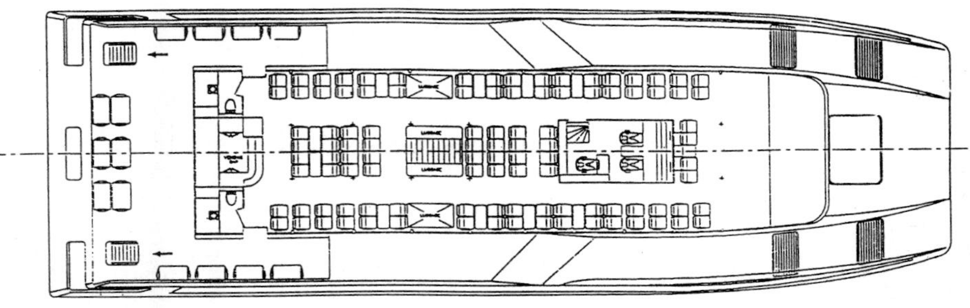

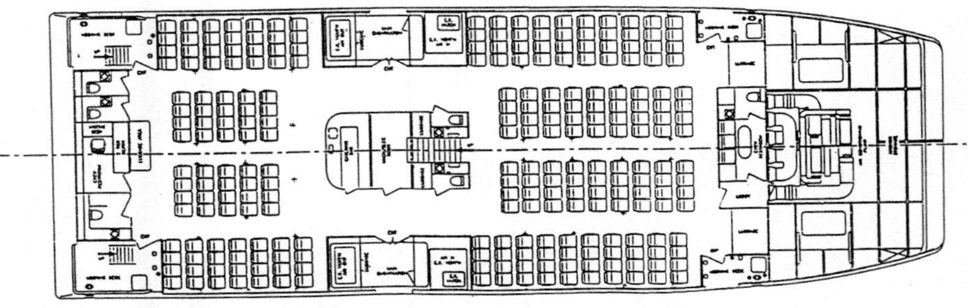

General Arrangement of Dong Yang Gold **1995**

Draught, hullborne	2 m
Draught, on-cushion	0.8 m
Crew	7
Passengers	352
Fuel capacity	7.2 t
Water capacity	0.8 t
Propulsive power	2 × 2,000 kW
Lift power	2 × 405 kW
Max speed	50 kts
Operational speed	45 kts
Range	250 n miles

Classification: Korea Register of Shipping.
Structure: FRP single skin in main hull, FRP sandwich in deck and superstructure.
Propulsion: Main engines: 2 × MTU 16V 396 TE74L diesel engines, each driving a Kamewa 63SII water-jet.
Lift engine: 2 × MTU 8V 183 TE72 diesels.
Navigation and communications: Two radars, one gyrocompass and magnetic compass, autopilot, Global Positioning System (GPS) navigator. Two VHF radio telephones, MF/HF radio telephone, satellite E. P. I. R. B.
Control: A microprocessor-controlled Ride Control System (RCS) for damping the vertical acceleration of the vessel by means of venting the overpressure in the main cushion chamber.

Dong Yang Gold **1995**

80 m SES Passenger Car Ferry (DESIGN)

SHI's 80 m SES was developed as a high-speed passenger car ferry in January 1994. A decision was made to select an SES, primarily because of the proven savings in power and cost, and its high development potential. The vessel is designed to carry a total of 500 passengers and 75 cars, and is capable of a fully loaded maximum speed at 100 per cent MCR in calm water of 50 knots.

Specifications

Length overall	79.84 m
Beam	20.18 m
Draught, hullborne	2.83 m
Draught, on-cushion	0.95 m
Crew	16
Passengers	500
Vehicles	75
Propulsive power	2 × 13,500 kW
Lift power	3 × 1,700 kW
Max speed	50 kts
Operational speed	45 kts
Range	600 n miles
Operational limitation	Sea State 3

Classification: DnV +1A1 HSLC Passenger car ferry R2.
Structure: The hull is constructed in alluminium alloy.
Propulsion: Main engines: 2 × gas-turbines, each driving a water-jet.
Lift engine: 3 × diesels, driving 3 × 2 × (1.3 m DWDIs).
Control: A microprocessor-controlled RCS for damping the vertical acceleration of the vessel by means of venting the overpressure in the main cushion chamber.

VERIFIED

SEMO COMPANY LTD

Shipbuilding Division, 1 Jangiri Donghaemyun, Kosungkun, Kyungnam, South Korea

Tel: +82 (556) 723535
Fax: +82 (556) 723570

Bok-Hoon Lee, *Vice President*

Semo is known for its ferry operating division which includes, in a fleet of 30 ferries, three hydrofoils, three amphibious hovercraft and now two SESs. Semo Company Ltd delivered in 1992 from their Kosungkun Shipyard the 36.4 m SES *Democracy* which began service in December 1992 in their fleet, operating between Inchon and Baknyung Island. Journey time for the route is approximately 3½ hours.

The Semo Company yard had delivered a further three 40 m SESs (Democracy II, III and V) by the end of 1994.

36.4 m SES *Democracy*

Specifications

Length overall	36.4 m
Beam	11.3 m
Draught, hullborne	2.15 m
Draught, on-cushion	0.7 m
Crew	10
Passengers	340
Fuel capacity	14,000 l
Water capacity	2,000 l
Propulsive power	2 × 1,680 kW
Lift power	2 × 373 kW
Max speed	50 kts
Operational speed	45 kts

Propulsion: Main engines: 2 × MWM TBD 604B V16 diesels, 1,680 kW each at 1,800 rpm.
Lift engines: 2 × DDC GM8V-92 TA diesels, 373 kW each at 2,100 rpm.

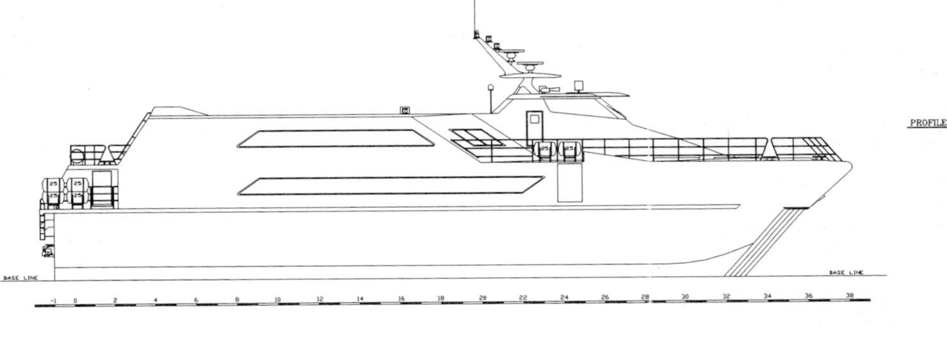

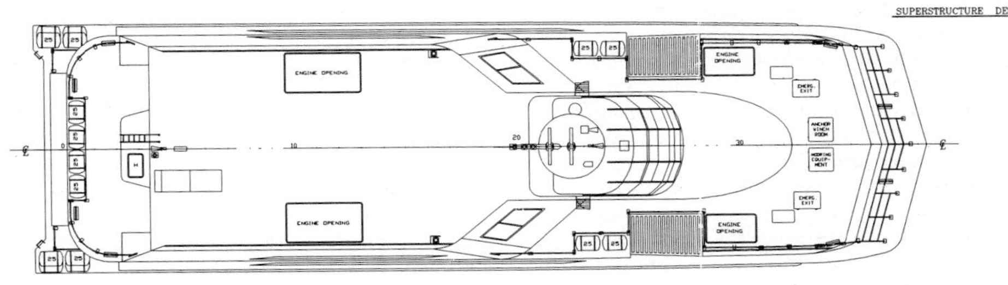

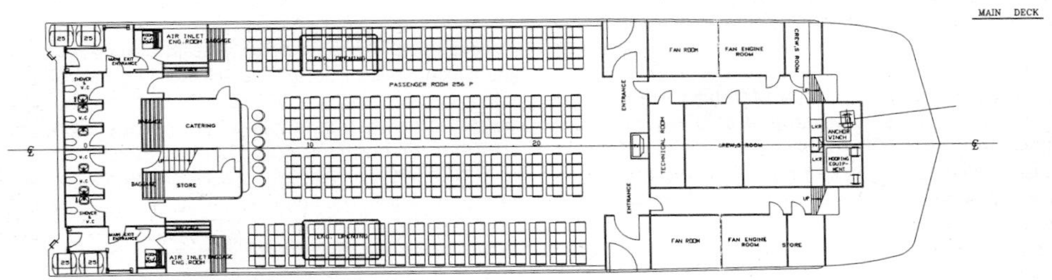

General arrangement of Democracy II **1995**

40 m SES

Democracy II, III & V

These 40 m craft are developments of the 36.4 m vessel built in 1992. *Democracy II* entered service in April 1994 followed by *Democracy III* in August and *Democracy V* in November 1994.

Specifications

Length overall	40 m
Length waterline	33.8 m
Beam	11.6 m
Draught, hullborne	1.9 m
Draught, on-cushion	0.6 m
Crew	10
Passengers	390
Propulsive power	1,970 kW
Lift power	529 kW
Max speed	50 kts
Operational speed	45 kts

Propulsion: Main engines: 2 × MTU 16V 396 TE 74L rated at 1,970 kW each at 1,920 rpm.

Lift engine: 2 × DDC 12V-92TA rated at 529 kW each at 2,100 rpm.

VERIFIED

Democracy III built by Semo Company Ltd. ***1995***

NETHERLANDS

HOVERTRANS BV

Keizersveer 9, 4273 LD Hank, Netherlands

Tel: +31 (1622) 3062/3089
Fax: +31 (1622) 3075

R J Lubbers, *General Manager*
A M Koevoets, *Design Manager*

Hovertrans BV designs and builds special products applying state-of-the-art composite and metal bonding techniques. The production programme includes a single-engined hovercraft, the Colibrie, a twin-engined hovercraft, the Polar Bear, and a small four-seat rescue craft. Feasibility studies are currently also being made for a 30- to 50-seat high-speed craft. Incorporated in the design of these craft are the standards of the CAA, IMO, Bureau Veritas and Canadian Coast Guard.

Hovertrans Colibrie ***1995***

Colibrie

The Hovertrans Colibrie amphibious hovercraft is an FRP single engine powered multiple role craft. The application of standard mechanical parts and easy access to vital parts of the craft ease and reduce maintenance and associated costs.

The most significant feature of Hovertrans hovercraft is the low noise production. The Colibrie craft produces, under cruising conditions, 75 dB(A) at 25 m.

The design of the Colibrie is based on safe life as well as on fail-safe principles. The safe life of mechanical parts extends well over the inspection and maintenance schedule period interval.

The combined hull and sideboards supply the craft with over 10 tonnes of floating capacity. The damage stability is in accordance with international rules and regulations. The propeller is protected by an FRP duct, placed well above the deck. The craft is controlled using three FRP rudders placed directly in the slipstream of the propeller. A skirt shift system is optional.

The Colibrie was tested by the Dutch Agency for Transport and Public Works in the Zeeland Delta area, fulfilling hydrographic surveying and supply tasks. This led to the frequent use of Hovertrans' own hovercraft, *Tuchone Princess*, by the agency on a lease basis. A second Colibrie hovercraft is currently employed at a holiday resort in the Indonesian Arcipel.

Colibrie is powered by a standard truck diesel engine, has a maximum speed of 37 knots and a cruising speed of 30 knots.

In 1994 a craft was successfully used in a round the clock evacuation and relief action when an abnormally high water level in the Dutch rivers caused the flooding of a large area in the south-east of Netherlands. The craft evacuated inhabitants and transported medical equipment, firefighters, policemen, and the supplies for two villages.

Specifications

Length overall	11.5 m
Beam	5.7 m
Weight, min	3.3 t
Payload	2.2 kg
Passengers	12 (Business class)
Passengers	16 (Tourist class)
Passengers	19 (High density)
Fuel capacity	600 l
Propulsive power	200 kW
Max speed	40 kts
Operational speed	30 kts
Operational limitation	wave height 1 m
Obstacle clearance	0.4 m

Classification: CAA, IMO, Bureau Veritas and Canadian Coast Guard.

Structure: The hull is of semi-monocoque sandwich construction, selectively combining glass and aramid fibres with polyester resin, using PVC foam as a core material.

Propulsion: The propulsion and lift engine is a single MAN Rollo water-cooled diesel D 0826, which produces 199 kW at 2,500 rpm. This drives a three-blade Hoffmann adjustable-pitch air propeller, 1.5 m diameter, through a toothed belt transmission.

The lift fan is an Asselberg & Nachenlue axial flow fan, or a centrifugal flow fan.

Polar Bear

Specifications

Length overall	8.0 m
Beam	4.7 m
Weight, min	2.1 t
Payload	1,000 kg
Passengers	10 max
Fuel capacity	600 l
Propulsive power	2 × 68 kW or 1 × 140 kW
Max speed	35 kts
Operational speed	27 kts
Range	270 n miles
Operational limitation	-40°C

Classification: CAA, IMO, Bureau Veritas and Canadian Coast Guard.

Propulsion: The main engine can be either an automotive diesel, or an industrial engine, driving a Hoffmann four bladed wooden fixed-pitch propeller.

The lift fan is a centrifugal Asselburg & Nanchenius type.

Electrical system: 12-24 V. 1 set of batteries, standard 2 × 120 Ah. Alternator: 2 × 55 Ah.

Outfit: Storage benches with artificial leather covered cushions and soft interior finish.

Operations equipment: If the craft is to be operated in extreme cold conditions (-40°C), it would be fitted with heated windscreens, heated fuel tanks, heated fuel valves, and special air intakes.

VERIFIED

SCHELDE SHIPBUILDING (ROYAL SCHELDE)

PO Box 16, 165 Glacisstraat, NL-4380 AA Vlissingen, Netherlands

Tel: +31 (118) 482118
Telex: 37815 KMS NL
Fax: +31 (118) 485010

Th P Winde, *Director of Shipbuilding*
E Bilterijsk, *Marketing and Sales*
A van der Knaap, *Marketing and Sales*
B Oving, *Marketing and Sales*

Royal Schelde has developed a range of high-speed vessels in the past, starting with SES craft of which they built a 26 m demonstrator vessel, Seaswift 23, which operated for a period between Southampton and the Isle of Wight in the UK. Subsequent to this vessel, Schelde Shipbuilding also developed a range of catamarans and monohulls, drawing on their experience of building naval frigates.

In view of the market developments, the company has committed itself to the marketing of large high-speed vessels such as the Seaswift 60, the Cat 70 catamaran and the 90 and 128 m monohull designs.

Royal Schelde Seaswift 23 **1996**

SEASWIFT 23

The Seaswift 23 is a prototype/demonstrator vessel, used for demonstrating and testing the design of Royal Schelde's Seaswift series and has been used for demonstration purposes for prospective clients as well as having formed the basis of the further designs. In August 1991 the vessel entered service with Cowes Express, operating a passenger ferry service between Southampton and the Isle of Wight in the UK for a period of 12 months.

Specifications

Length overall	24.25 m
Length waterline	20 m
Beam	7.7 m
Beam overall	approx 7.94 m
Draught, hullborne	1.45 m
Draught, on-cushion	0.8 m
Crew	3
Passengers	132
Fuel capacity	3.6 m^3
Water capacity	0.5 m^3
Propulsive power	2 × 520 kW
Max speed	31 kts
Operational speed	26 kts

Classification: DnV +1A1 R30 Light Craft, ECO.
Structure: Welded marine grade aluminium alloy; scantling dimensions assume a maximum amidships vertical acceleration of 1 *g*.
Propulsion: Three centrifugal lift fans, resiliently mounted, the forward two being driven directly by the lift system diesel engine and the aft one being driven hydraulically by the same engine. Propulsion is provided by two MWM TBD 234 12V diesels, 520 kW each at 2,200 rpm MCR, driving KaMeWa 40S water-jet units.
Auxiliary systems: Fire prevention, detection and extinguishing equipment, including Halon 1301 flooding systems for the engine rooms. Normal fuel, seawater cooling, hydraulic oil and bilge systems.
Outfit: 132 passenger seats on main deck. Passenger cabin and wheelhouse ventilated by two-speed ventilation system which incorporates heating elements.

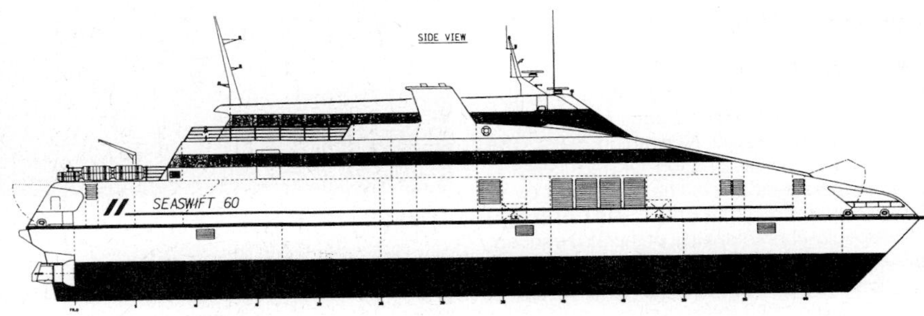

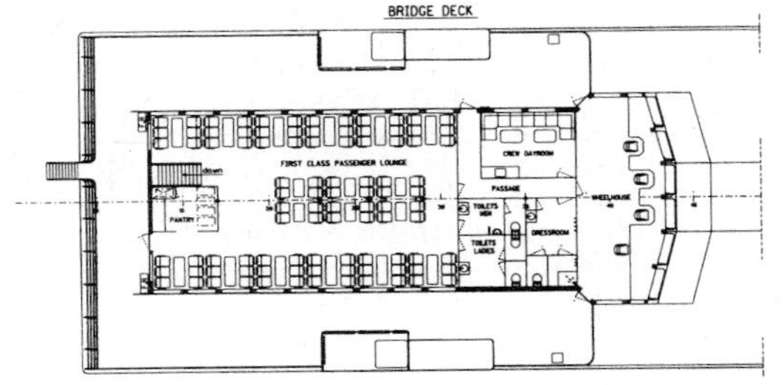

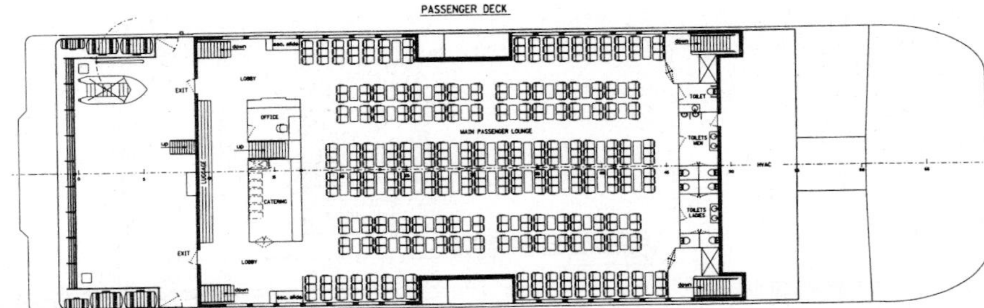

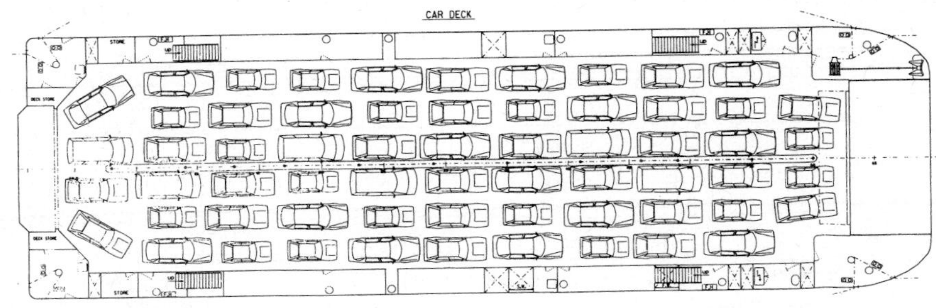

Royal Schelde Seaswift 60 (design)

SEASWIFT 60 (DESIGN)

At present the largest SES vessel in the Royal Schelde Seaswift range, this passenger/car ferry is available in both diesel and gas-turbine versions. The vessel is designed to carry 434 passengers and 62 cars.

Specifications

Length overall	59.5 m
Length waterline	53 m
Beam	17.5 m
Draught, hullborne	2.8 m
Draught, on-cushion	1.2 m
Payload	154.6 t
Crew	12
Passengers	434
Vehicles	62 cars
Fuel capacity	43,000 kg
Water capacity	4,000 l
Propulsive power	2 × 6,470 kW
Lift power	2 × 848 kW
Max speed	45 kts
Operational speed	42.5 kts
Range	550 n miles

Classification: DnV +1A1 R1 HS, EO.
Structure: Welded marine grade aluminium alloy, asymmetric V-shaped hulls with spray-rails on outer and inner sides.
Propulsion: Cushion air is provided by two lift fans, one in each hull, powered by two Deutz MWM TBD 604B V8 diesels, 848 kW each at 1,800 rpm. Propulsion is provided by two SEMT Pielstick 20 PA6 V280

MPC diesels each having a maximum continuous rating of 6,470 kW at 1,050 rpm and each driving one KaMeWa 112 SII water-jet.

Auxiliary systems: An RCS is fitted for damping the vertical acceleration of the vessel by means of venting the overpressure in the main cushion and the aft seal.

Outfit: Seating is provided for a total of 434 passengers at a seat pitch of 90 cm and arranged so that the main passenger lounge provides seating for 338 passengers and the first class passenger lounge for 96 passengers.

Doors at the forward and aft end of the car compartment avoid the necessity of vehicles turning when on board. Six straight car lanes are provided with a width of 2.35 m. The two centre lanes are designed for a maximum axle load of 1,950 kg, the four side lanes for a maximum axle load of 840 kg. The free deck height is at least 2.6 m, so that passenger cars, caravans, vans and small campers can be loaded.

UPDATED

NORWAY

KVÆRNER A/S FAST FERRIES

PO Box 303, Skøyen, N-0212 Oslo, Norway

Tel: +47 (2) 296 7400
Fax: +47 (2) 296 7410

KVÆRNER MANDAL A/S

Gismerøya, PO Box 283, N-4501 Mandal, Norway

Tel: +47 (3) 827 9200
Fax: +47 (3) 826 0388

Fredrik Behrens, *Managing Director*

SES MINE COUNTERMEASURES VESSEL

'OKSØY' Class and 'ALTA' Class

A series consisting of four minehunters and five minesweepers is now under production at Kværner Mandal A/S for the Royal Norwegian Navy. The minehunters have the designation 'Oksøy' class and the minesweepers 'Alta' class. The design of the vessels is based on the Surface Effect Ship (SES) principle. The special characteristics of the SES concept are utilised to obtain advantages both with respect to operational capability and economy. Delivered between 1993 and 1996 these craft will replace the present class of eight US-built 1950s MSC-60 coastal minesweepers/hunters. The Kværner Group will provide engineering support, quality assurance services and financial assistance.

Kværner Mandal moved into new production facilities in 1991, the yard is located at Gismerøya Island near Mandal. The production hall has been built for the particular purpose of building high-speed military and civil vessels in composite materials and to the highest quality standards.

'Oksøy' ***1996***

Based on the existing design of the MCMVs, Kværner Mandal has further developed and modified the vessel design in order to meet international demands. The first vessel, 'Oksøy', undertook sea trials in 1993 and was commissioned in August 1994. The sixth vessel is now on trials.

Specifications

Length overall	55.2 m
Beam	13.3 m
Draught, hullborne	2.15 m
Draught, on-cushion	0.87 m
Weight, max	370 t
Crew	29 (+12 extra capacity)
Water capacity	5,000 l
Propulsive power	2 × 1,400 kW
Lift power	2 × 700 kW
Operational speed	20+ kts (transit)
	5+ kts (minehunting)
	12+ kts (minesweeping)
Range	1,200 n miles

Propulsion: The propulsion engines are two MTU 12V 396 TE 84, driving two Kværner Eureka water-jets.

Engines, lift: 2 × MTU 8V 396 TE 54, 700 kW each.

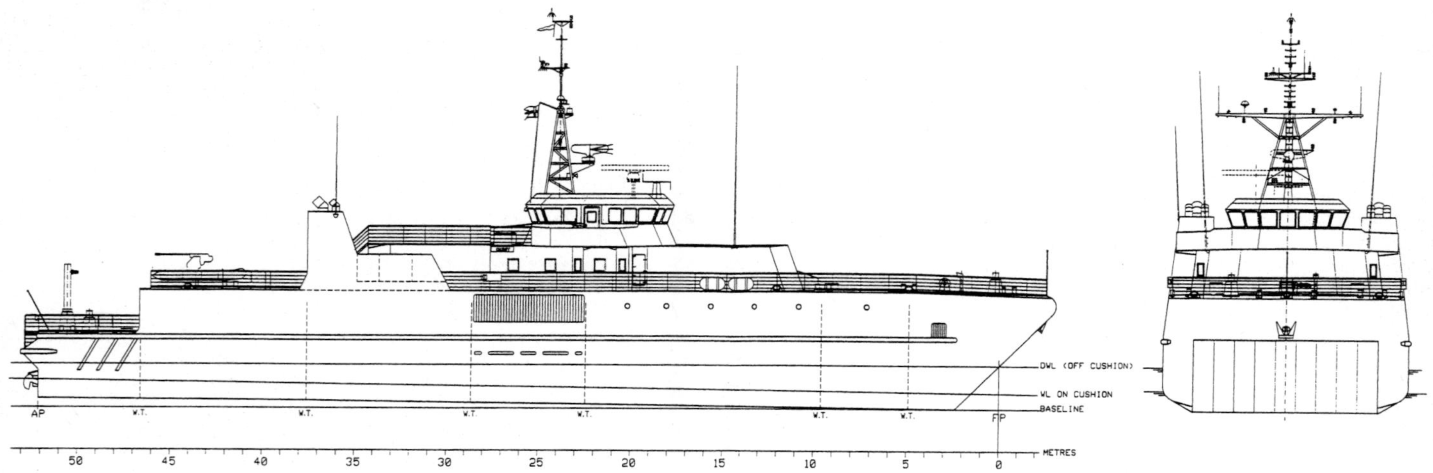

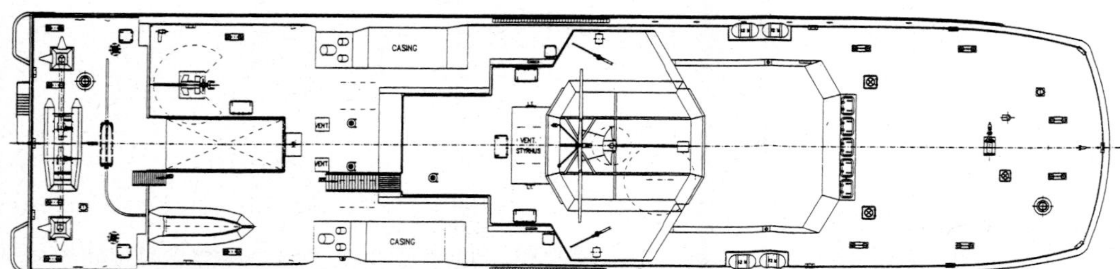

General arrangement of Kværner Mandal mine countermeasures SES

12 m MANNED SES TEST CRAFT

On the 20 January 1993, Kværner Mandal launched a one-third scale prototype of a new air cushion catamaran high-speed patrol vessel. The first of nine mine countermeasure vessels was launched two months later. The vessel is based on the air cushion catamaran principle (SES) and built of composite materials.

The favourable properties of air cushion catamarans are further enhanced in this vessel by a new single-skin hull construction of fibre-reinforced polymer, and by a novel hull geometry, developed by Kværner Mandal and their project partners.

To study materials, design and performance, Kværner Mandal has gone to the rather unusual step of building a 12 m, 40 knot manned model.

The Kværner Mandal new form of hull construction gives a reduction of 25 per cent in the hull structural weight over conventional GRP hull structures and even more when compared to aluminium hulls.

The 12 m model is part of an international research project called 'Advanced FRP Composite Hull Structures for High-Speed Craft'. The study programme includes sea-going performance, speed and acceleration in calm and rough seas, dynamic stability in high waves, reactions to wave-induced slamming loads on the hull materials and improvement in air cushion design.

The other project participants are Du Pont, Conoco, Det Norske Veritas, Veritas Research, the Marine Consulting Group, Devold AMT, Jotun Polymer, the Norwegian Defence Research Establishment, the Norwegian Industry Fund and the Royal Norwegian Research Council.

Kværner Mandal 12 m manned test craft **1993**

Kværner Mandal has patented a new production method for series building under controlled conditions. The production hall allows indoor building of large air cushion catamarans side by side.

UPDATED

SWEDE SHIP

PO Box 143, N-4501 Mandal, Norway

Tel: +47 (38) 262222
Telex: 21514 WRIN N
Fax: +47 (38) 262302

Svein Berntsen, *Technical Manager*
Gowart Askildsen, *Purchasing Manager*
John Ihme, *Production Manager*

Swede Ship's Westamarin West shipyard (Mandal, Norway) entered SES work in 1986 when the company concluded a licence agreement with Karlskronavarvet AB of Sweden for the fitting out of two GRP hull SES 3400 Jet Rider vessels designed by Karlskronavarvet under which entry details of these craft are given. Following this development Westamarin embarked on the design of a larger SES, designated SES 4000, and built in aluminium. These craft employ air cushion systems licensed from Karlskronavarvet AB. There have been two Westamarin SES 4000 vessels built.

SES 4000
Super USA & Super Mexico (ex-*Super Dane & Super Swede*)

Specifications

Length overall	40 m
Beam	12.6 m
Draught	2.21 m
Passengers	309
Fuel capacity	22,800 l
Water capacity	1,500 l
Propulsive power	2 × 2,720 kW
Lift power	4 × 270 kW
Operational speed	46 kts
Max speed	52 kts
Range	780 n miles

Classification: DnV +1A1 R45 EO, Light Craft Passenger Vessel.

Propulsion: 2 × SACM M7 UD 33 V16 main engines, each 2,720 kW at 1,600 rpm, driving 2 × Liaaen Speed-Z type CPZ 60/42-125 Mk II propeller units.
Lift: 4 × GM V6-92 TA, each 270 kW.

Navigation and communication: 2 × radars, 1 × gyrocompass/magnetic compass, log, navigator echo-sounder.

2 × VHF transceivers, radiotelephones, mobile telephone, intercom, TV, radio and PA facility.

Auxiliary systems: 2 × GM V6-71T generators, each 201 kW.

UPDATED

Westamarin SES 4000 Super Mexico *(ex-*Super Dane*)* **1990**

ULSTEIN INTERNATIONAL A/S

N-6065 Ulsteinvik, Norway

Tel: +47 (70) 014000
Fax: +47 (70) 014002

Steinar Sivertsen Kulen, *Managing Director*
Harald Nordal, *General Manager High-Speed Craft*
Arne Mortensen, *Technical Manager High-Speed Craft*

The Ulstein group designs and builds air cushion catamarans in addition to conventional catamarans and monohull vessels.

The group has delivered 18 air cushion catamarans in FRP sandwich construction. The UT 904 Air Cushion Catamaran (ACC) is the latest design from the group, two having been launched in 1992.

A licence/technology transfer agreement was signed with International Shipyards of Australia in 1993 for the production of a series of UT 928 craft.

UT 904

The UT 904 is designated an Air Cushion Catamaran by Ulstein International, a design in the category of surface effect ships and air cushion vehicles in general.

Construction of the first UT 904 started in September 1990. The vessel has accommodation for 320 passengers.

The lift fan engines power double-sided stainless steel centrifugal fans and in addition drive (hydraulically) two centrifugal booster fans which provide pressurising for the aft seal bag.

A hydraulically operated ride control system is fitted, employing louvre valves, pressure sensors and a microprocessor control unit. This system is designed to reduce vertical accelerations.

Specifications

Length overall	39 m
Beam	12 m
Draught, hullborne	2.6 m
Draught, on-cushion	1 m
Passengers	320
Fuel capacity	13,800 l
Water capacity	2,000 l
Propulsive power	2 × 2,000 kW
Lift power	3 × 380 kW
Max speed	50 kts
Operational speed	46 kts

Classification: DnV +1A1 R90 Light Craft EO.
Additional class:
SF-LC, stability and subdivision
F-LC, fire protection.
Regulations: National Flag Authorities.

Structure: The hulls are built in FRP/PVC foam sandwich or aluminium.

Ulstein UT 904 Ocean Flower *1993*

Ulstein UT 904 Santa Eleonora *1993*

Propulsion: 2 × water-jet units.

The two lift fans are double-sided, stainless steel.

Auxiliary systems: The ride control system operates hydraulically controlled louvres, microprocessor-controlled, that vent the air chamber.

VERIFIED

Air Cushion Catamarans from Ulstein/Brødrene Aa/Ulstein Eikefjord yards

Yard No	Type	Year delivered	Name	No of seats	Operation area	Delivered to	Flag
170	CIRR 105P	1984	*Fjordkongen* (ex-*Norcat*)	264	North Norway	Troms Fylkes D/S	Norway
184	CIRR 115P	1986	*Santa Lucia* (ex-*Ekwata*)	290	Mexico	Marítima Turística del Mar de Cortés	NIS
190	CIRR 120P	1988	*Wight Queen* (ex-*Virgin Butterfly* ex-*Ekwata II*)	280			UK
198	CIRR 60P	1988	*Harpoon*	85	(Test vessel)		Norway
199	CIRR 120P	1988	*Express La Paz* (ex-*San Pawl*)*	315	Mexico	Marítima Turística del Mar de Cortés	NIS
200	CIRR 120P	1989	*Santa Maria*	330	Brazil	Tidewater	NIS
201	CIRR 120P	1989	*Wight King* (ex-*Sant' Agata*)	280			NIS
202	CIRR 120P	1989	*San Pietro*	330	North Norway	Finnmark Fylkesrederi og Ruteselskap	Norway
210	CIRR 120P	1989	*San Frangisk*	330	Virtu Ferries	NIS	
211	CIRR 120P	1990	*Catamaran II* (ex-*Golden Olympics*)**	330	Greece	Piraiki Naftiliaki SA	Greece
212	CIRR 120P	1990	*La Vikinga*	330	Cuba	KS Pantheon	NIS
213	CIRR 120P	1990	*Perestroika*	368	South Korea	Semo Marine Craft	South Korea
218	CIRR 120P	1990	*Nissho*	320	Japan	Yasuda Ocean Line	Japan
219	CIRR 120P	1990	*Fjordkongen*	320	North Norway	Troms Fylkes D/S	Norway
204	CIRR 120P	1991	*Sea Flower*	349	South Korea	Dae-A Kwaesok Ferry	South Korea
226	CIRR 120P	1991	*Catamaran I*	330	Greece	Piraiki Naftiliaki SA	Greece
208	UT 904	1991	*Ocean Flower*	360	South Korea	Dae-A Kwaesok Ferry	South Korea
205	UT 904	1992	*Santa Eleonora*	342	Italy-Corfu	Misano Alta Velocita	Italy

NIS=Norwegian International Shipping Register   * constructive total loss, Feb 1993   ** constructive total loss, 1992

SINGAPORE

SINGAPORE SHIPBUILDING AND ENGINEERING LTD

7 Benoi Road, Singapore 2262
PO Box 138, Jurong Town Post Office, Singapore 9161

Tel: +65 861 2244
Telex: 21206 SINGA RS
Fax: +65 861 3028/1601

Boon Swan Foo, *Managing Director*
See Leong Teck, *Deputy General Manager*
Wong Kin Hoong, *Assistant General Manager, Commercial*
Tan Pheng Hock, *Assistant General Manager, Yard*
Teh Yew Shyan, *Senior Manager, Quality Assurance*

TIGER 40

This Air Vehicles Tiger 40 was built by Singapore Shipbuilding and Engineering Ltd for a leasing company in Singapore, SAL Leasing, which owns the craft. In 1987 this craft was leased to the Singapore Navy. Tiger 40 craft are marketed in the Far East by Singapore Shipbuilding and Engineering Ltd.

Air Vehicles Tiger 40 Hovercraft built by Singapore Shipbuilding and Engineering Ltd **1989**

SPAIN

CHACONSA SA

COMPANIA HISPANO AMERICANA DE CONSTRUCCIONES CONSERVERAS SA

Mayor 57, 30006 Puente Tocinos, Apartado 419, E-30080 Murcia, Spain

Tel: +34 (68) 230200/238512/230604
Telex: 67248 ABRO E
Fax: +34 (68) 238508

Carlos Ruiz Valero, *ACV Programme Manager*

CHACONSA launched its air cushion vehicle research programme in 1973. In 1976 it received a contract for the development of the VCA-36 from the Spanish Ministry of Defence. Design of the lift and propulsion system was aided by experiments with laboratory models. Two manned research models, the 750 kg VCA-2 and the five tonne VCA-3, were later built to evaluate and refine the system. Details of these two craft are given in the 1992-93 edition of this book.

In addition to its military programme, CHACONSA has also examined industrial and agricultural applications of air cushion technology.

CHACONSA VCA-36 during anti-submarine sea trials **1989**

VCA-36

Designed to improve the rapid lift capability of the Spanish armed forces, the VCA-36 carries a 14 tonne payload, equivalent to three Land Rovers and 70 fully armed marines or infantrymen, to a beach landing zone at a speed of 60 knots. It can also be used for lighter-over-the-shore applications. Its dimensions allow it to operate from the docking wells of a number of LSDs and from roll-on/off vessels with sufficient headroom and suitable ramps. Lifting eyes in the hull enable it to be hoisted on and off the decks of cargo ships. A removable roof above the cargo deck permits the craft to be loaded alongside supply ships.

Specifications

Length overall	25.5 m
Beam	11.04 m
Weight, max	36 t
Payload	14 t
Propulsive power	2 × 2,500 kW
Max speed	60 kts

Structure: Riveted aluminium structure based on a grid of longitudinal and transverse frames which form a number of watertight buoyancy compartments. Fuel, ballast tanks and bilge systems are contained within these compartments. Access to the cargo deck is via hydraulically operated bow and stern ramps or the removable cargo deck roof. The central cargo deck is 18.65 m long, 2.6 m wide and 2.25 m high. Two main longitudinal vertically stiffened bulkheads run the length of the hull. These separate the central vehicle/cargo deck from the sidestructures which contain the gas-turbines, lift fans, transmissions, auxiliary power systems and cabins. Marines or assault troops are accommodated in two 35-seat cabins, 7.4 m long by 2.35 m wide, one in the forward section of each sidestructure. There are four landing pads fitted to the hull base. Four lifting eyes are provided for hoisting the craft.

The skirt is 1.4 m deep, bag and finger type of CHACONSA design in nylon fabric coated with synthetic rubber.

Propulsion: Integrated system powered by two Textron Lycoming TF25 gas-turbines, each with a maximum output of 1,860 kW. Each drives two centrifugal fans and a 4 m diameter, five-bladed, variable-pitch propeller. Power is transmitted via two gearboxes with auxiliary outputs for lubrication, hydraulic pumps and generators. The combined epicyclic and bevel (splitter) gearbox (lower unit) transmits 620 kW from 14,500 rpm to 1,080 rpm for the lift fans and 1,400 kW from 14,500 rpm to 1,988 rpm for the pylon propulsion gearbox (upper unit). The pylon bevel gearbox reduces the speed from 1,988 rpm to the 1,011 rpm of the propulsion propeller.

BES (BUQUE DE EFECTO SUPERFICIE)

Early in 1987 it was announced that CHACONSA SA had teamed up with the Bazan yard (builder of fast naval craft) to develop a new surface effect ship, BES (Buque de Efecto Superficie).

BES-16

At the end of 1987 CHACONSA established a 50/50 joint programme with Empresa Nacional Bazan for the study, analysis and development of SES craft technology in order to design and build these craft in the range of 50 to 500 tonnes, full load displacement.

The first craft to be built was the BES-16 research craft, launched in 1988.

Specifications

Length overall	16.78 m
Beam	5.4 m
Draught	0.75 m
Displacement	14 t
Propulsive power	2 × 335 kW
Lift power	2 × 82 kW

Structure: The hull is welded AlMg 4, 5 alloy.

Propulsion: Two Isotta Fraschini diesel engines, driving two Castoldi 06 water-jet units.

The lift engines are two VM-HRI 492 diesel engines, six centrifugal lift fans.

VERIFIED

CHACONSA BES-16

1990

SWEDEN

KARLSKRONAVARVET AB

S-371 82 Karlskrona, Sweden

Tel: +46 (455) 19440
Telex: 8395018 KKRV S
Fax: +46 (455) 17934

Hans Hedman, *Managing Director*

Karlskronavarvet is a subsidiary of Kockums AB, Malmø. It is a dockyard for construction, maintenance and modernisation activities mainly for the Royal Swedish Navy.

Extensive design and development work has been carried out to develop a surface effect ship for naval use as well as passenger transportation.

SMYGE

1992

SES 3400 JET RIDER

***Jet Cruise 2* (ex-*Jet Prince*, ex-*Sleipner*, Yard No 427)**

***Jet Cruise 3* (ex-*Jet Princess*, ex-*Draupner*, Yard No 428)**

These two surface effect ships were built as a result of a co-operative agreement between Karlskronavarvet AB of Sweden and Westamarin A/S of Norway for the supply of two SESs for the Stavanger to Bergen 'Flaggruten' service. This contract was cancelled when the craft failed to meet the required performance, but they were subsequently bought (23 March 1988) by JKL Shipping for service between Copenhagen (Kastrup) and Helsingborg. The craft were then leased to Interscandic Line which operated them under the name Fast Ferry Siam from June 1989 till 24 August 1989 when Interscandic went into liquidation. In mid-1991 the two craft were sold to an operator in Thailand.

Karlskronavarvet obtained air cushion and skirt technology from Textron Marine Systems, USA in exchange for their fibre-reinforced plastics. Design of the Karlskronavarvet surface effect ships was supported by extensive model testing at the SSPA in Gothenburg.

Specifications

Length overall	33.4 m
Length waterline	28.2 m
Beam	10.5 m
Draught, hullborne	1.75 m
Draught, on-cushion	0.25 m
Crew	6
Passengers	244
Fuel capacity	10,000 l
Max speed	39 kts
Range	200 n miles

Classification: DnV +1A1 R15 EO.

Structure: Fibre-Reinforced Plastics (FRP) construction. Divinylcell PVC cellular plastic core, 40 to 60 mm thick, density 60 to 100 kg/m³. Facing of sandwich construction: glass-reinforced polyester resin, E grade glass, 800 g/m² woven roving and 100 or 300 g/m² chopped strand mat.

The skirt is made from rubber-coated nylon, the bow skirt has eight open segments, the rear skirt or

Karlskronavarvet SES 3400 Jet Princess *(ex-*Draupner*) sister vessel to* Jet Prince *(ex-*Sleipner*)*

1989

seal has three lobes, bolted to each other; air is fed into the upper lobe and via feed holes into the lower lobes. Skirt design and manufacture by Karlskronavarvet AB.

Propulsion: Two KaMeWa 63562/6 water-jet units driven through ZF BU 750 reduction gearboxes.

The lift fans are four 0.76 m diameter double-inlet, centrifugal type, welded aluminium (designed and made by Karlskronavarvet AB) and driven via hydraulic transmission. Two fans in bow and two in stern.

Outfit: Initially 244 passengers and six crew (upper deck overnight cabins for crew), later modified to carry 292 passengers by removing overnight crew cabins, allowing a 48-seat 'Royal class' saloon to be provided.

Auxiliary systems: Heave damping, pressure monitoring system with electronic feedback.

Generators: 2 × Stamford MSC 334A.

SMYGE

This 30 m SES test craft was delivered to the Swedish Defence Materiel Administration (FMV) in Spring 1991, the contract having been received in June 1989.

The vessel has been built principally in order to develop 'stealth' technology and to gather operational SES experience.

One of the purposes of SMYGE is to test newly developed systems such as missile foundations, anti-submarine and minehunting equipment, various sensor systems and gun and antenna systems in realistic conditions.

Smaller vessels cannot carry all the weapons systems simultaneously. In Swedish conditions with relatively few units and limited space, flexibility is a precondition for obtaining the required objectives. Missiles and torpedoes and anti-submarine equipment are designed so that they can be placed on any ship and the ships in their turn are designed to carry these various pieces of equipment. It is anticipated that it will be possible to carry out this development work very efficiently on board SMYGE.

One advantage of SMYGE's hull construction is that there is an open work shaft from the hold down to the water, a 'moon pool'. The shaft is located at the ship's centre of gravity thus reducing movement forces on the equipment located there while at sea. Examples of such equipment are hydrophones and other anti-submarine and minehunting equipment.

Specifications

Length	30.4 m
Length waterline	27 m
Beam	11.4 m
Draught, hullborne	1.9 m
Draught, on-cushion	0.7 m
Displacement	140 t
Crew	14
Propulsive power	2 × 2,040 kW
Lift power	2 × 460 kW
Max speed	>40 kts

Structure: The hull is of sandwich construction in Kevlar and fibreglass-reinforced plastic.

Propulsion: The main engines are two MTU 16V 396 TB 94 diesel motors, driving a pair of KaMeWa water-jet 63s.

Lift engines: Scania DS1 14, 460 kW.

Lift fans: 1.14 m intake diameter.

Electrical system: Mains: 440 V, 60 Hz, 3-phase.

Secondary supply: 220 V, 60 Hz, 3-phase.

Low voltage net: 24 V DC.

Generator: 72 kW.

VERIFIED

UNITED KINGDOM

ABS HOVERCRAFT LTD

1590 Parkway, Solent Business Park, Fareham, PO15 7AG, UK

Tel: +44 (1489) 578916
Fax: +44 (1489) 577812

K Blum, *Director*
A F White, *Chief Designer*
A Byrne, *Operations Manager*

ABS Hovercraft Ltd has designed the world's first third generation hovercraft, taking advantage of advanced composite technology. The M-10 has a length of 19 m and is powered by standard diesel engines. Its advantages over other hovercraft include low maintenance costs, durability and better manoeuvrability. The M-10 has comfortably exceeded 50 knots fully laden at a continuous rating and in rough weather has coped on-cushion in waves of over 4 m in gale force winds. The M-10 has also demonstrated its rugged nature by becoming the first hovercraft to circumnavigate the Baltic.

The M-10 military version has a payload of 77 personnel or 10 tonnes of stores. One vessel has been completed in the UK by Vosper Thornycroft (UK) Ltd and a workboat version subsequently sold to a European operator.

Artist's impression of ABS P-89 hovercraft ***1994***

ABS P-89

Besides military and workboat versions, ABS has developed a passenger version based on the proven M-10 design.

Specifications

Length overall	19.8 m
Beam	7.8 m
Weight	29 t
Passengers	77
Propulsive power	2 × 390 kW
Operational speed	40 kts
Obstacle clearance	1 m

Propulsion: 2 × Deutz BF12L 513C 390kW at 2300 intermittent, driving twin ducted, low-noise CP propellers.

Electrical system: Twin 24 V alternator system

ABS M-10 on trials ***1995***

ABS M-10

One vessel has been completed in the UK, built under subcontract to Vosper Thornycroft (UK) Ltd. The craft underwent trials and performance demonstration in November 1994.

Specifications

Length overall	18.84 m
Beam	8.80 m
Payload	10 t
Crew	4
Fuel capacity	4,600 l
Propulsive power	386 kW
Max speed	50 kts
Operational speed	40 kts
Range	600 n miles
Obstacle clearance	1 m

Classification: Hull survey to Lloyd's Register Certification.

Structure: Single-skin FRP hull, FRP foam sandwich deck.

Propulsion: Main engines: 2 × Deutz BF12L 513C air cooled diesels, driving twin 4-bladed controllable pitch, low-noise propellers.

Electrical system: 24 V DC via transmission driven alternators charging 2 battery banks.

UPDATED

AIR VEHICLES LTD

Unit 4, Three Gates Road, Cowes, Isle of Wight PO31 7UT, UK

Tel: +44 (1983) 293194
Telex: 86513 HVWORK G
Fax: +44 (1983) 291987

C B Eden, *Director*

Air Vehicles Limited was founded in 1968 and has concentrated on the design and development of rugged fully amphibious hovercraft using welded marine aluminium hulls, simple systems and conventional piston engines. The company offers craft from four seats with designs of up to 200 seats and customers include the British, French and Canadian Ministries of Defence, the People's Republic of China, Nigerian Police, Bahrain Ministry of the Interior and the Republic of Singapore Navy.

Air Vehicles Limited is approved by the Civil Aviation Authority and undertakes modifications to larger craft. These have included flat-deck freight conversions of the BHC SR. N5 and SR. N6 hovercraft, power-assisted rudder packs for both types, and the conversion of an SR. N6 Mk 1S for high-speed hydrographic surveying.

Air Vehicles produced a conceptual feasibility study for a four-engined diesel-powered hovercraft to meet the requirements of Hovertravel Ltd. The eventual requirement of Hovertravel led to the design of the BHC AP1-88 for which Air Vehicles undertook much of the detail design work.

Tiger 12 with high-speed, hydrographic 'fish' deployed in the water **1986**

TIGER 12

The standard production craft has 12 seats (including the driver's) and the non-structural cabin top can be removed to suit various requirements. Fully amphibious, the craft can operate over a variety of surfaces such as mud, ice, sand and shallow water.

Specifications

Length	8.0 m
Beam	3.85 m
Weight, min	1.9 t
Weight, max	2.7 t
Payload	0.9 t
Crew	1
Passengers	11
Fuel capacity	213 l
Propulsive power	134 kW
Max speed	35 kts
Operational speed	25 kts
Operational limitation	windspeed 25 kt wave height 1.25 m

Structure: Superstructure and all bulkheads are of marine grade aluminium sheet welded to form a strong rigid box structure. Side members are inflatable, giving additional buoyancy and protection for the craft when mooring. By deflating the side members the vehicle can be trailed behind any large car or small truck. A built-in jacking system provides for loading and maintenance.

The skirt is a pressurised bag type with separate segments. The inflatable sides and skirt are attached to the craft with quick-release piano hinges.

Propulsion: Motive power for the integrated lift/propulsion system is provided by a single AMC 5,900 cc petrol engine delivering 134 kW at 3,600 rpm. The engine output is transferred to a 12-blade centrifugal lift fan and a 1.37 m diameter, four-blade, ducted propeller through a toothed belt system.

Control: Multiple rudders hinged at the aft end of the propeller duct provide directional control. Elevators provide trim and, when raised fully, assist braking by reducing thrust. A water ballast system is used to adjust trim in pitch for varying load states.

TIGER 16

The Tiger 16 is a fully amphibious hovercraft capable of carrying 16 people over a variety of terrain including shallow water, sand, mud and ice. The first craft was completed at the end of 1985.

Specifications

Length	11.27 m
Beam	4.1 m
Weight, min	2.5 t
Payload	1.5 t
Fuel capacity	790 l
Propulsive power	141 kW or 270 kW
Max speed	33 kts
Operational speed	25 kts
Operational limitation	windspeed 25 kt wave height 1.25 m

Structure: The hull is a fully welded, light but robust aluminium structure and offers a variety of options in the cabin layout. Seat mounting/load tie-down rails allow easy conversion of the cabin for passenger or load-carrying duties. The cabin options give any combination from fully trimmed and enclosed to a simple open workboat.

Rigid sidebodies provide a convenient work platform when surveying and a carrying area for long loads. For transportation the side decks are easily removed.

An inflatable ring around the periphery of the craft provides for coming alongside and a 'soft edge' when working off the side decks.

An open loop and segment skirt is fitted. The skirt assembly is attached to the craft using an aluminium piano hinge. Segments are individually and easily replaced. A skirt shift system is fitted.

Propulsion: Various engine options are available according to duty and include the Deutz BF6L 913C air-cooled diesel rated at 141 kW at 2,500 rpm, and the Deutz BF8L 513 rated at 270 kW at 2,300 rpm. The engine power is transmitted via a toothed belt drive system to a 12-blade centrifugal lift fan and a 1.5 m diameter, Robert Trillo Ltd designed four-blade ducted propeller. The propeller duct is designed to give efficient air entry and the outlet is shaped to provide for larger control surfaces. The propeller is designed to give high thrust per horsepower with low noise and is fitted with full length stainless steel leading edge protection.

VERIFIED

Tiger 16 with forward cabin and open well-deck **1989**

ALUMINIUM SHIPBUILDERS LTD

Fishbourne Quay, Ashlake Copse Road, Fishbourne, Isle of Wight, PO33 4EE, UK

Tel: +44 (1983) 882200
Fax: +44 (1983) 884720

John Davies, *Managing Director*

Aluminium Shipbuilders is mainly known for its building of catamarans to the designs of International Catamaran Designs Pty Ltd, Australia. The company has however engaged in considerable hovercraft fabrication work. In particular contracts have been received from Griffon Hovercraft Ltd and Westland Aerospace. By the end of 1995 ASL had completed 30 hulls covering the current range of Griffon Hovercraft. For Westland Aerospace, ASL was involved in the total fabrication, fit out, and trials of a BHC AP1-88 hovercraft for operation by The Northern Shipping Company in the White Sea area of Russia.

UPDATED

BRITISH HOVERCRAFT CORPORATION

Division of GKN Westland Aerospace

East Cowes, Isle of Wight PO32 6RH, UK

Tel: +44 (1983) 294101
Telex: 86761 WAD G
Fax: +44 (1983) 298872

C C Gustar, *Managing Director, GKN Westland Aerospace*
J M George, *Commercial Director*

The roots of the Corporation extend back to the world's first hovercraft, the SR. N1, which was built by Saunders Roe Limited in 1959, just prior to its being taken over by Westland.

BHC was formed in 1966, uniting the hovercraft interests of Westland and Vickers and also involving NRDC.

The world's first full-scale hovercraft production line was established at East Cowes in 1964. Since then BHC has produced 10-17 tonne SR. N6 craft, 50 tonne BH.7 craft and 200-325 tonne SR. N4 craft. The 39 tonne AP1-88 is the current production craft.

One BH.7 has been in service with the Royal Navy and six with the Iranian Navy. There have been four Iranian BH.7s refurbished by BHC at Cowes.

Military and general duty variants of the SR. N6 hovercraft are in service in the Middle East and Canada. This design is also used for general-purpose roles including hydrographic and seismic survey, freighting and search and rescue duties.

The current production AP1-88 diesel-powered, general-purpose hovercraft is built in welded aluminium alloy. Employing shipbuilding techniques, it combines a 10-12 tonne payload with a performance equal to that of the SR. N6. Full cabin versions of the AP1-88 operate regular passenger services and the type has also built up extensive charter experience. A half-well-deck variant is operated by the Canadian

SR. N4 Mk 1 modified to Mk 3

Craft built	No of Seats	No of Cars	Yard No	Delivered to	Route
BHC SR. N4 Mk 1 *The Princess Margaret* (GH 2006) in service 1968, modified to Mk 3 in 1979	424	60	001	Hoverspeed Ltd	Dover to Calais
BHC SR. N4 Mk 1 *The Princess Anne* (GH 2007) in service 1969, modified to Mk 3 in 1978	424	60	004	Hoverspeed Ltd	Dover to Calais

SR. N4 Mk 3 (Super 4), The Princess Anne **1996**

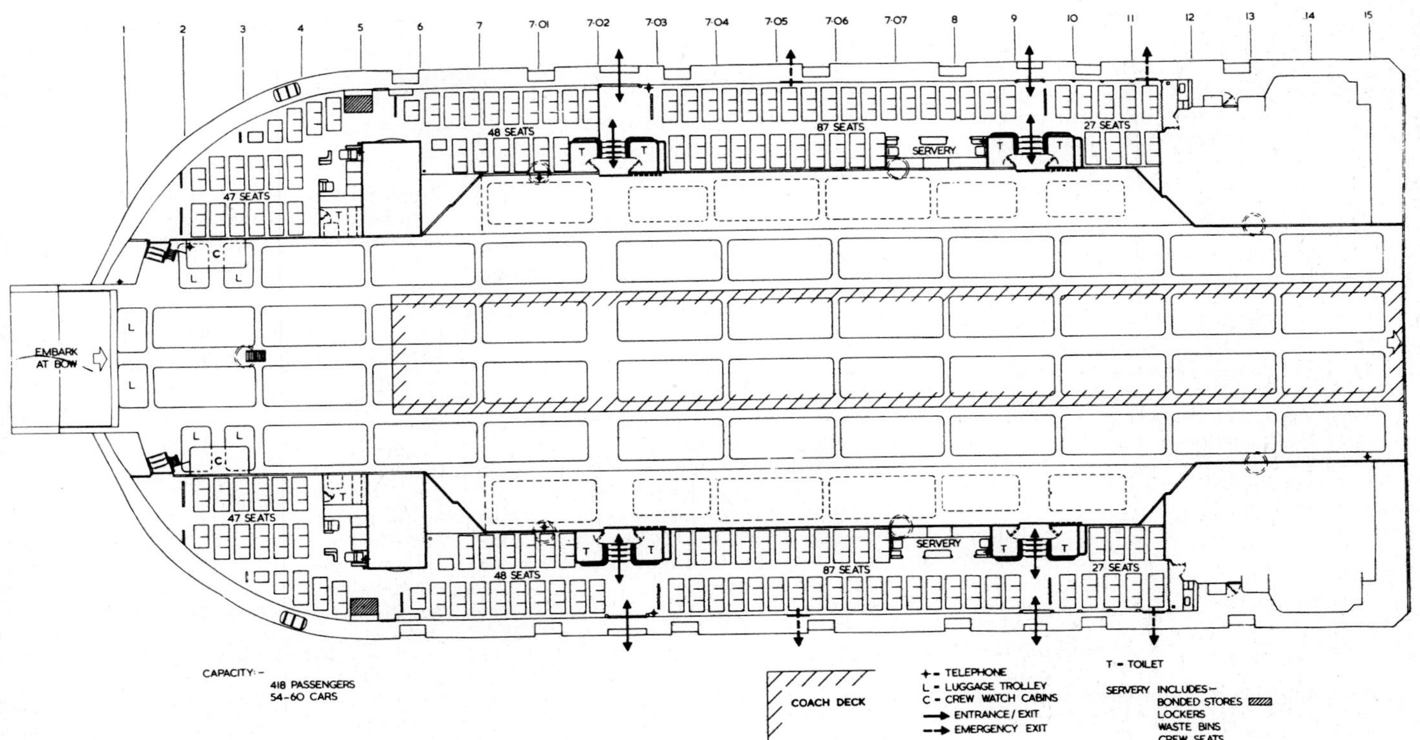

Layout of vehicle deck and passenger cabins on SR. N4 Mk 3 (Super 4)

Coast Guard and an open-top freighter built under license by NQEA Australia Pty Ltd works in the gold mining industry in north-west Canada. A new enlarged version of the AP1-88, designated the AP1-88/400 is currently under development.

SR. N4 Mk 3

This type has a payload of 418 passengers and 60 vehicles, a laden weight of 325 tonnes and a top speed in excess of 65 knots.

Specifications

Length overall	56.38 m
Beam	23.16 m
Weight, max	325 t
Payload	112 t
Passengers	424
Vehicles	60
Fuel capacity	23,500 l
Propulsive power	2 × 2,834 kW
Max speed	65 kts
Operational speed	50 kts
Operational limitation	wave height 2.5 m Beaufort 6

Propulsion: Motive power is supplied by four Rolls-Royce Marine Proteus Type 15M/529 free-turbine turboshaft engines, located in pairs at the rear of the craft on either side of the vehicle deck. Each engine is rated at 2,834 kW and is connected to one of four identical propeller/fan units, two forward and two aft. The propellers are of four-bladed, controllable-pitch type. The lift fans are of 12-bladed centrifugal type, 3.5 m in diameter. Maximum fuel tankage, 28.45 tonnes; normal fuel allowing for ballast transfer, 18.29 tonnes.

SR. N6 Mk 1

Designed primarily as a fast ferry for operation in sheltered waters, the SR. N6 Mk 1 can accommodate either 38 passengers or 3 tonnes of freight.

Fully amphibious, it can operate from bases above the high water mark, irrespective of tidal state.

Directional control is achieved by twin rudders and skirt lift, with a thrust port system to assist in low-speed manoeuvring. Two manually actuated elevators provide pitch trim at cruising speed.

SR. N6s have been in regular civil operations since 1965. Operators include the Canadian Coast Guard and Eurosense in Belgium. Military variants are in service in the Middle East.

Specifications

Length overall	14.8 m
Beam	7.7 m
Weight, max	10 t
Payload	3 t
Passengers	38
Fuel capacity	1,205 l
Propulsive power	671 kW
Max speed	52 kts
Operational speed	35 kts
Range	186 n miles

Propulsion: Power for the integrated lift/propulsion system is provided by a Rolls-Royce Marine Gnome gas-turbine with a maximum continuous rating at 15°C of 671 kW. This drives a BHC 12-blade centrifugal 2.13 m diameter lift fan and a Dowty Rotol four-blade controllable-pitch 2.74 m diameter propeller for propulsion.

Outfit: Cabin size (length × width): 6.62 × 2.34 m. Cabin headroom centreline: 1.83 m.

SR. N6 Mk 6 GENERAL-PURPOSE

The SR. N6 Mk 6 represents a significant step forward in terms of all-weather performance and increased manoeuvrability, especially in high winds and at low speeds. There is also a significant reduction in the external noise level.

These advances have been achieved by the introduction of twin propellers and a redesigned skirt.

Specifications

Length overall	18.8 m
Beam	7.92 m
Weight, max	17 t
Propulsive power	840 kW
Max speed	60 kts
Operational limitation	wave height 3.04 m Beaufort 8

Propulsion: Originally motive power was supplied by a single 840 kW Rolls-Royce Marine Gnome GN 1301 but the craft has been modified for hydrographic survey work and is now fitted with a Gnome GN 1051/1. Two 3.05 m diameter Dowty Rotol controllable-pitch propellers are fitted.

SR. N6 Mk 1 operated by Canadian Coast Guard hovercraft units **1986**

SR. N6 Mk 6 general-purpose hovercraft fitted out for survey work **1991**

SR. N6 Craft built	
SR. N6 Mks 1 to 5	42
SR. N6 Mk 6	7
SR. N6 Mk 8	8

SR. N6 Mk 8

The Mk 8 is the last military variant of the single propeller SR. N6.

In the logistic support role the Mk 8 can carry up to 55 fully equipped troops or loads reaching 6 tonnes. Access to the cabin, which measures 9.5 × 2.3 m, is via a bow door. Loads up to 500 kg which are too long for the cabin may be carried externally on the side decks.

Specifications

Length overall	17.78 m
Beam	7.97 m
Payload	6 t
Passengers	55
Fuel capacity	3,022 l
Propulsive power	805 kW
Max speed	50 kts

Propulsion: Single Rolls-Royce GN 1451 marine gas-turbine rated at 805 kW at 15°C.

Auxiliary systems: Lucas SS923 gas-turbine driving a three-phase alternator.

BH.7

BH.7 is a 55 tonne hovercraft which was designed specifically for naval and military roles.

Specifications

Length overall	23.9 m
Beam	13.8 m
Weight, max	56 t
Payload	18.3 t
Crew	3
Passengers	170 troops
Fuel capacity	13,635 l
Propulsive power	3,169 kW
Max speed	58 kts

Structure: Construction is of corrosion-resistant light alloy. Extensive use is made of components which were designed for the N4.

The fan delivers air to the cushion via a continuous peripheral bag and finger skirt made in neoprene-coated nylon fabric. The skirt provides an air cushion depth of 1.68 m. The cushion is divided into four compartments by a full length longitudinal keel and by two transverse keels located slightly forward of amidships.

Propulsion: Power for the integrated lift and propulsion system on the Mk 4 is provided by a Rolls-Royce Marine Proteus 15M/541 gas-turbine. On the Mk 5A, a 15M/549 is installed. In both types the engine drives a BHC 12-blade, centrifugal 3.5 m diameter lift fan and a four-blade, controllable-pitch pylon-mounted propeller. Propeller diameter on the Mk 4 is 5.79 m and 6.4 m on the Mk 5A.

Control: Craft direction is controlled by swivelling the propeller pylon angle by a foot pedal. Thrust ports are fitted at each quarter to assist directional control at low speed, and a hydraulically operated skirt-lift system helps to bank the craft into turns, thereby reducing drift.

Fuel is transferred between forward and aft tanks via a ring main to adjust fore and aft trim.

BH.7 Mk 4 LOGISTICS VERSION

In this role, the main hold floor area of 56 m² (600 sq ft) of the Mk 4 provides an unobstructed space suitable for loading wheeled vehicles, guns and military stores.

Two side cabins, filled with paratroop-type seats, can accommodate up to 60 troops and their equipment.

Access at the bow is through a 'clamshell' door.

Machine guns can be fitted in gun rings on the roof on either side of the cabin and provision can be made for armour plating to protect personnel, the engine and vital electrical components.

A typical military load would be 170 fully equipped troops or three field cars and trailers plus 60 troops or two armoured scout cars, or up to 20 NATO pallets.

BH.7 Mk 5A COMBAT/LOGISTICS VERSION

There were four BH.7 Mk 5As built for the Iranian Navy.

Designed for coastal defence operations, the BH.7 Mk 5A carries medium-range surface-to-surface missiles, such as Exocet, on its side decks. Secondary armament consists of two roof-mounted 20 mm guns.

The main central cabin is equipped as an operations and fire-control room. The bow door is retained providing a dual missile/logistic capability. Since it is fully amphibious, the BH.7 can be operated from relatively unprepared bases on beaches and can head directly towards its target on interception missions regardless of the tidal state and marginal terrain. Also, since none of its solid structure is immersed, it is almost invulnerable to underwater defences such as acoustic, magnetic and pressure mines or to attack by torpedoes.

A full range of electronic navigational aids permits the craft to operate by day or night.

AP1-88

Major advances in hovercraft technology enabled British Hovercraft Corporation to offer a 10 tonne payload craft with a performance equal to that of the well proven SR. N6. Built in welded aluminium alloy, AP1-88 is powered by four turbocharged diesels. This craft has low crew and maintenance requirements, footprint pressure and noise levels.

The AP1-88 craft can be employed in a wide variety of commercial, military and paramilitary roles including:

- Passenger ferrying
- Search and rescue
- Hydrographic surveying
- Ice-breaking
- Anti-smuggling
- Firefighting
- Logistic support
- Counter-insurgency
- Mine countermeasures
- Anti-submarine warfare
- Minelaying.

The AP1-88/100 in civil passenger configurations can seat up to 101 passengers. The first two AP1-88s *Tenacity* and *Resolution* began operating with Hovertravel between Ryde and Southsea in 1983. A similar craft, *Perseverance,* was built in 1985. These three craft are built to the 2.4 m shorter/80 configuration with Deutz 278 kW BF10L 413F lift engines and Deutz 367 kW BF12L 413FC propulsion engines.

BH.7 Mk 5A combat/logistics craft **1992**

Northern Shipping AP1-88 Siverko **1992**

During 1984 two of the production standard craft entered service with A/S Dämpskibsselskabet Øresund (DSØ) of Denmark on a route linking Copenhagen's Kastrup airport and Malmø. A third AP1-88 joined the route in 1988.

Two new production standard craft, fitted out to carry 95 passengers, entered service on the Hovertravel Ryde to Southsea route in 1989 and 1990.

In 1991 a further craft was completed for Northern Shipping to operate in Russia on the White Sea. This craft is fitted out for 68 passengers and incorporates sleeping accommodation for the crew, a galley forward and two marine lavatories aft.

A half-well-deck variant, designated AP1-88/200, is in service with the Canadian Coast Guard undertaking search and rescue, navaid maintenance ice-breaking and oil-spill clean-up tasks on the St Lawrence River and its tributaries.

The craft is of a half-well-deck configuration with accommodation for up to 12 crew members or technicians and up to 12 tonnes of cargo. This AP1-88 is equipped with a hydraulic crane, a capstan and winch to facilitate the conduct of a variety of specialised coastguard tasks.

Specifications

Length overall	24.4 m
Beam	11 m
Weight, min	29.48 t
Weight, max	40.82 t
Payload	11.34 t
Passengers	101
Fuel capacity	1,800 l
Propulsive power	2 × 336 kW
Lift power	2 × 336 kW
Max speed	50 kts
Operational limitation	wave height 2.4 m windspeed 30 kts

Classification: BHSR, IMO, and DnV.

Structure: The basic hull is formed by a buoyancy tank made almost entirely of very wide aluminium alloy extrusions, one extrusion being used for the I-beams forming the transverse frames and a second

Craft built (in UK)	Reg No	No of seats	Name	Launched	Delivered to
AP1-88-80	GH 2087	80	*Tenacity*	1983	Hovertravel Ltd
AP1-88-80	GH 2088	80	*Resolution*	1983	Hovertravel Ltd
AP1-88-80	GH 2100	80	*Perseverance*	1985	Hovertravel Ltd
AP1-88-100	GH 9029	81	*Idun Viking,* (ex-*Expo Spirit*)	1984	A/S DSØ
API-88-100	GH 9030	81	*Freja Viking*	1984	A/S DSØ
AP1-88-100	GH 9031	81	*Liv Viking*	1984	A/S DSØ
AP1-88-200	CH-C-CG	12	*Waban-Aki*	1987	Canadian Coast Guard
AP1-88-100	GH 2107	95	*Double-O-Seven*	1989	Hovertravel Ltd
AP1-88-100	GH 2114	95	*Freedom 90*	1990	Hovertravel Ltd
AP1-88-100	099808	71	*Siverko*	1991	Northern Shipping, CIS

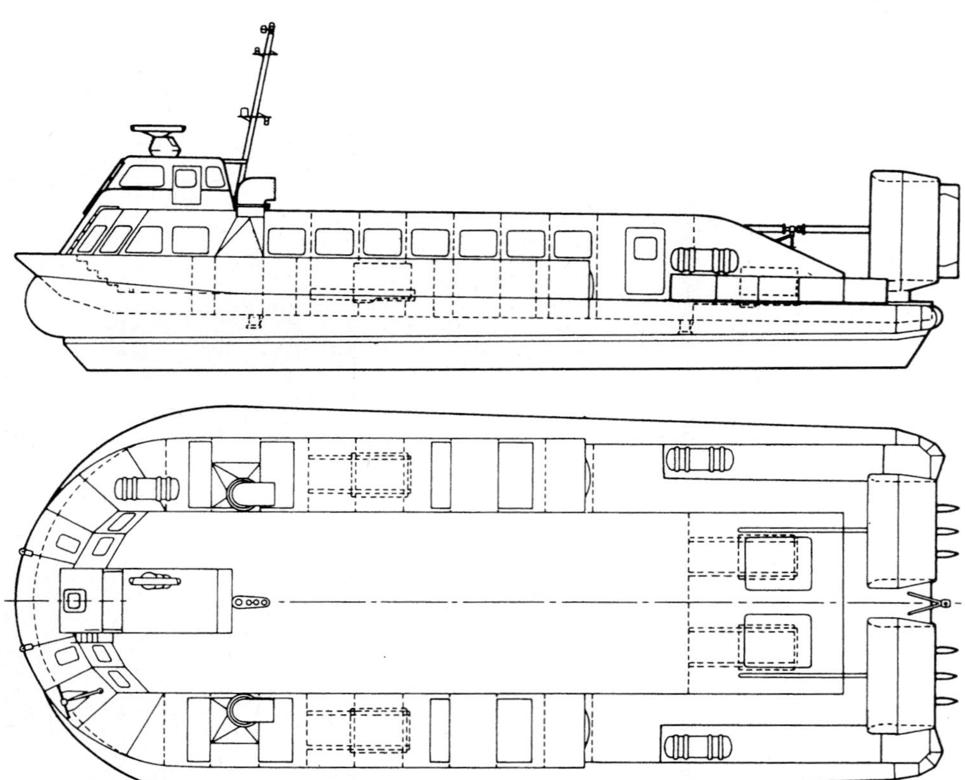

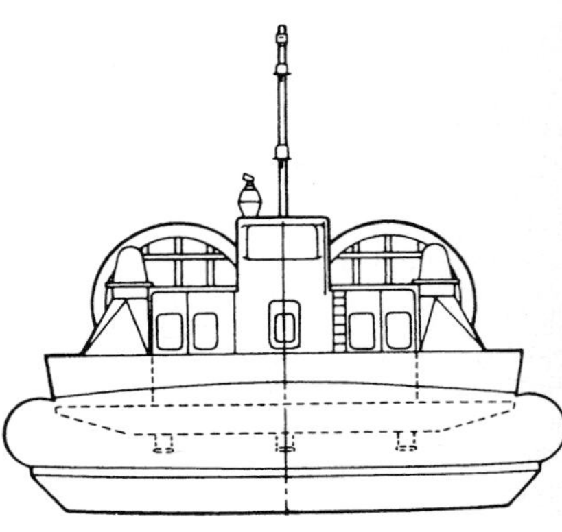

General arrangement of AP1-88/100 hovercraft

for the integrally stiffened planking used for the bottom and deck. The remainder of the rigid structure is built from smaller welded extrusions and plating, with the exception of the roof, made from riveted light gauge corrugated panels. The propeller ducts are a composite structure of light alloy and Kevlar reinforced plastic. Marine alloys are used, including N8 plate and HE30 extrusions. In general, plate thicknesses are 2 or 3 mm except for the light gauge roof plating. The structure is welded throughout to eliminate mechanical fastenings which can be sources of corrosion. Detachable panels give easy access for engine and fan removal and facilitate the inspection of ventilation ducting and tail control cable runs. Lifting, for the inspection of the craft underside and skirts, is achieved by three jacks which are fitted and operated from inside the craft. However, for general maintenance, the craft is put down on flyover blocks.

The skirt is a low pressure ratio tapered skirt based on that of the Super 4. Mean cushion depth 1.37 m.

Propulsion: The AP1-88/100 craft is powered by four Deutz BF12L 513FC 12-cylinder air-cooled diesels. Two 2.74 m diameter four-blade Hoffmann ducted propellers are each driven by one of the diesels via a toothed belt. On standard craft the propellers are of fixed-pitch type, but ground adjustable through ±5°. The belt-drive reduction ratio is 1:0.6.

Two of the engines, housed in the side box structures, power the lift and bow thruster systems. On each side of the craft one engine drives three 0.84 m diameter double-entry centrifugal fans, two of which supply air to the cushion via the skirt system and the third supplies air to the rotatable bow thruster. The well-deck version for the Canadian Coast Guard has four 0.885 m diameter fans for the lift system with two 0.84 m fans for the bow thrusters.

Navigation and communications: Remote reading gyrocompass; a Lambda T.12 spherical compass. Optional range of automatic and semi-automatic navigational aids.

The communications are provided by a Sailor RT 145 VHF international marine band radio or similar equipment.

The radar systems installed are the Racal-Decca 914C, with the antenna turning unit and transceiver on the control cabin roof. The display unit is mounted in the control cabin on the port side and is north-up stabilised by gyrocompass.

Control: Directional control is provided by two sets of triple aerodynamic rudder vanes mounted on the rear of the propeller ducts, differential propeller thrust and by swivelling bow thrusters. In the straight-aft position, the bow thrusters contribute to forward thrust. Trim is controlled by fuel ballast transfer.

Outfit: The superstructure is divided into four main components: a large central accommodation area forward of the propulsion machinery bay and two sidebodies containing the lift system machinery. A control cabin is mounted on top of the main cabin. In addition to the full cabin and half-well-deck versions, full well-deck variants are available. The commercial full cabin version seats a maximum of 101 passengers with the seats arranged in rows of seven across the cabin. The rows are divided by two gangways 600 mm wide which separate the seats into a 2-3-2 configuration. There are two doors, one port and one starboard, at the aft end of the cabin. Doorways are 1.75 × 0.9 m. An emergency door 1.06 × 0.9 m is at the forward end of the passenger cabin. Craft built to standard include a cabin heating and ventilation system adequate for operation in temperate climates; more elaborate systems are available as options. There are two sets of four luggage panniers on the side decks aft of the cabin doors. Total volume of the eight panniers is approximately 6.6 m³.

AP1-88/200
Waban-Aki

This craft entered service with the Canadian Coast Guard in 1987.

Specifications

Length overall	24.5 m
Beam	11.2 m
Weight, max	47.15 t
Payload	12.45 t
Fuel capacity	5,912 l
Propulsive power	4 × 441 kW
Max speed	50 kts

Propulsion: Four Deutz BF12L 513CP air-cooled turbocharged diesels, 441 kW each, at 2,300 rpm. Two Hoffmann 2.75 m diameter controllable-pitch propellers Type HOV-254P2DFR/D275, ducted. Four centrifugal lift fans 0.885 m diameter. Two bow thrusters, centrifugal fans 0.840 m diameter.

The following details are specifically applicable to *Waban-Aki*.

Electrical system: Main system 28 V DC; auxiliary system 240/120 V AC 60 Hz single phase. DC supply: four Bosch Type T1, 28 V, 120A-17 generation. AC supply: diesel engine auxiliary power unit, 12 kW

The Canadian Coast Guard Waban Aki *on oil clean-up duties*

output. Batteries: start/service S1 two 12 V, 143 Ah; start/service S2 two 12 V, 143 Ah; essential service two 12 V; 143 Ah.
Navigation and communications: VHF radio FM Wulfsberg RT 7200, VHF radio AM King KY 196 Silver Crown, HF King KHF 990.
Radar: Decca RM 914C, VHF (FM/AM) ADF: OAR Type ADFS-347EH, HF ADF Sitex 511 AADF Navigator.
Plotter: Loran 'C' with RS 200 Shipmate colour track plotter. Gyromagnetic compass: AIM system.
Auxiliary systems: Power assistance to rudders; control of variable-pitch propellers; auxiliary hydraulic components.

AP1-88/300

This type is an open-top freighter developed from the standard AP1-88-100 design and sharing the same external dimensions and mechanical installation. AP1-88-300 was produced under license by NQEA Australia.

One craft has been built to this design and is in service between the Snip gold mine, north-west Canada and Wrangell, Alaska.

AP1-88/400

The new craft is an enlarged version of the AP1-88, with a longer well deck and a payload capacity twice that of the current design in service with the Canadian Coast Guard. It is thus able to handle much larger buoys and other navigational aids.

Specifications

Length overall	28.5 m
Beam	12.0 m

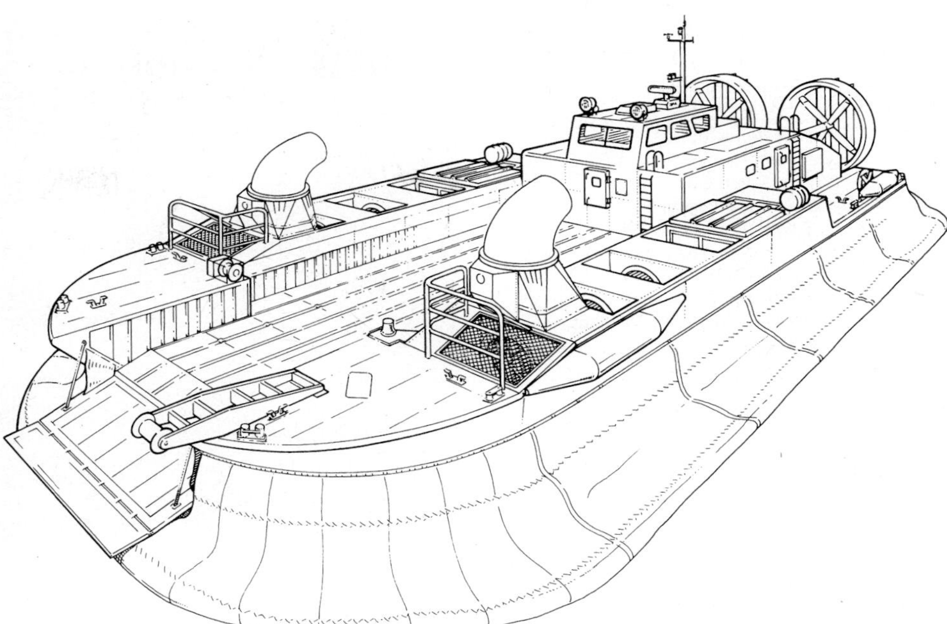

Arrangement of the AP1-88/400 ***1996***

Structure: This all aluminium vessel has a well-deck length of 13.1 m, a well-deck width of 4.6 m and a bow ramp width of 3.9 m.
Propulsion: Machinery layout is understood to be similar to that of other AP1-88 craft except that the four diesels will be watercooled.

UPDATED

GRIFFON HOVERCRAFT LTD

Head Office: Carlton House, Ringwood Road, Woodlands, Southampton, Hampshire SO40 7HT, UK

Tel: +44 (1703) 814022
Fax: +44 (1703) 813698

Dr E W H Gifford, *Chairman*
J H Gifford, *Managing Director*
G A Gifford, *Sales Director*

Founded in 1976, Griffon Hovercraft has concentrated on the design and development of small to medium sized amphibious hovercraft.

The company's first design, Griffon, used a four-blade ducted propeller for propulsion with a centrifugal fan for lift, both driven by a Jaguar automobile engine. This craft was subsequently put into production as the Skima 12, built by Pindair Ltd under licence from Griffon Hovercraft Ltd. Many of this type of craft have been in service throughout the world in a variety of roles.

The development of the turbocharged air-cooled diesel led to the company's decision, early in 1982, that a small commercial diesel-powered hovercraft would be feasible and would carry a useful payload.

Construction of the diesel-engined Griffon 1000 TD prototype began in June 1982. Performance trials began in May 1983 and exceeded expectations. The first three production craft of this type were supplied to Geophysical Surveys Inc of Dallas, USA, for use in an oilfield survey on the Yellow River, China. Due to the intensive nature of these operations, thousands of operating hours have been accumulated with minimal maintenance, proving the inherently rugged nature of the design. In 1987, a 1000 TD was supplied to the Water and Power Development Authority of Pakistan (WAPDA) for survey work. There were three Griffon 1000 TDs supplied to the Royal Thai Navy in 1990, used for search and rescue, flood control, logistics and VIP transportation. A second 1000 TD was delivered to WAPDA Pakistan in 1993.

The success of the 1000 TD has led to a range of craft being developed with 1-4 four tonne payloads, using similar machinery units and control systems. The company intends to concentrate on the requirements for a low-cost easily maintained craft for use in workboat, navy, paramilitary and ferry applications.

In 1994 a new rigid inflatable five-seat hovercraft with a Land Rover diesel engine (designated the Griffon 375TD) was produced for the fire department of Venice, Italy, and new 375TD's are destined for surveying and paramilitary organisations.

Griffon 375 TD Rigid Inflatable Hovercraft ***1995***

Of the larger craft, the Griffon 1000 TD continues to attract survey users and the new Griffon 2000 TD and 2000 TDX have replaced the 1500 TD and 1500 TDX respectively (the numerals in the name/title of these craft reflect their payload in kilogrammes). The 2500 TD and 2500 TDX have been replaced by the 37-seat 3000 TD, while the 4000 TD carries 48 to 60 passengers or a four tonne payload, and the larger engined Griffon 4000 TDX carries 60 to 72 passengers or 6 tonnes of payload. All craft in the Griffon range have commonality of design, systems and spare parts, and are designed to comply with the requirements of IMO, the UK CAA and Lloyd's Register.

375 TD

The 375 TD is the smallest craft in the Griffon range and is built on rigid inflatable boat lines. Powered by a 75 kW water-cooled diesel engine this craft carries a payload of 375 kg or five passengers. It can be fitted with a GRP hard top or a PVC soft top.

1000 TD

The smallest craft in the TD (Turbocharged Diesel) range, the 1000 TD carries a payload of 1,000 kg or 10 passengers. The craft is powered by a single diesel engine and is available with a variety of superstructures. Folding side decks enable it to be loaded onto its purpose-built trailer and towed behind a small truck. It can also be fitted into a 20 ft container, after removal of bow and stern sections.

Please see the 1992-93 edition of this book for further details of this type.

The Water And Power Development Authority (WAPDA) of Pakistan ordered a second Griffon 1000 TD hovercraft in 1992.

Equipped with a special hatch (or 'moon pool') in the base of the craft through which a water sampling 'fish' will be trawled at depths of 100 m, the craft operates on the Tarbela Dam (and on the rivers that feed it) in north-western Pakistan. The hovercraft is required to maintain a stationary position, hovering over fast water flows of over 5 knots whilst carrying out water sampling. The 1000 TD carries six engineers plus half a tonne of specialised equipment and is used as a hydrographic survey vessel in shallow waters and for high-speed transportation along the 60 n mile (110 km) length of the dam.

Craft built 1000 TD

001	Hover Systems Inc
002	Geophysical Surveys Inc, USA for Yellow River, China, 1984
003	Geophysical Surveys Inc, USA for Yellow River, China, 1984
004	Geophysical Surveys Inc, USA for Yellow River, China, 1984
008	Water And Power Development Authority, (WAPDA), Pakistan (GH 8456)
012	Royal Thai Navy, 1990
014	Royal Thai Navy, 1990
015	Royal Thai Navy, 1990
023	Water And Power Development Authority, (WAPDA), Pakistan, 1993

1000 TD for WAPDA, Pakistan **1995**

1500 TD

This variant is 1.8 m longer than the 1000 TD, but with identical machinery. Capacity is increased to 1.5 tonnes or 16 persons. Bow and stern sections are not removable but folding side decks allow transportation within a 40 ft container.

Craft built 1500 TD

001	Griffon 1500 TD, Clements, Solomon Islands (GH 9452), 1987
002	Chiriqui Hovercraft, Panama, November 1985 to 1987
003	Griffon Hovercraft charter craft (GH 2102)

These craft have been sold for tourism, survey work and pilot duties and have now been replaced by the Griffon 2000 TD.

Details of the 1500 TD are as for the 1000 TD with the following exceptions:

Specifications

Length overall	10.15 m
Weight, min	2.3 t
Payload	1.5 t
Max speed	33 kts
Operational speed	27 kts

Griffon 2000 TD for Texaco on the River Thames **1996**

2000 TD

The Griffon 2000 TD has now replaced the 1500 TD. Whereas the basic design, the engine and the systems remain the same, the 2000 TD has a larger propeller, a larger fan, and an improved design of skirt. These modifications enable the 2000 TD to carry a 33 per cent larger payload but still retain exactly the same performance as its predecessor. The cabin has also been slightly enlarged enabling the 2000 TD to carry a total of 20 to 24 persons.

Specifications

Length overall	10.6 m
Beam	4.5 m
Weight, min	2.6 t
Payload	2 t
Crew	2
Passengers	22
Propulsive power	140 kW
Max speed	31 kts
Operational speed	27 kts

Classification: IMO, the UK CAA and Lloyd's Register classification.

Propulsion: Integrated lift and propulsion system powered by a single Deutz BF6L 913C air-cooled six-cylinder, in-line, turbocharged and intercooled diesel rated at 190 hp (140 kW) at 2,500 rpm. A 0.91 m diameter centrifugal lift fan is driven from the front of the crankshaft via an HTD toothed belt. Power for the 1.8 m diameter four-blade Robert Trillo designed ducted propeller is transmitted from the back of the engine via an automotive clutch to another HTD toothed belt transmission running inside the propeller support pylon.

The engine, transmission, duct and pylon are mounted on a welded aluminium alloy subframe attached to the hull via resilient mounts.

Cooling air for the engine passes through a Knitmesh filter to remove spray and is drawn into the front of the engine by the engine cooling fan before passing over the cylinders and being drawn out from the rear of the engine bay by the propeller.

Structure: Main hull is of welded riveted and bonded marine grade aluminium.

Sidebodies made from composite materials fold upward for transport and are locked into the running position by use of struts either side. Forward and aft ballast tanks are fabricated from aluminium.

The skirts are a tapered HDL open loop type with similar segments at bow and sides. Cones are fitted at the stern. Segments are fitted to the loop with stainless steel bolts and inner ends are attached using plastic shackles. All skirt maintenance can be done without lifting the craft.

Electrical system: 24 V standard with 12 V option. 35 A alternator, two 75 A/h 12 V batteries fitted.

Control: Triple rudders in the GRP duct provide directional control. Elevators within the duct provide a degree of fore and aft trim augmented by a fuel ballast system. The craft is fitted with a skirt shift system operated by a small electrohydraulic ram which provides responsive control on roll trim, offsets cross-wind effects and banks the craft into the turn.

Outfit: Two or three persons (including the driver) can be carried in the wheelhouse and a further 18 to 22 passengers can be carried in inward-facing bench-type seats in the cabin.

2000 TDX

This craft is virtually the same as the 2000 TD but is powered by the more powerful 239 kW V8 Deutz BF8L 513 engine, which gives it a superior into-wave and into-wind performance. A 2000 TDX was ordered by the Swedish Coast Guard in 1991 and, having operated the craft for nine months, an order for a further two was signed in January 1993.

In 1994/95 the Frontier Guard of Finland took delivery of three Griffon 2000 TDX craft and two

Griffon 2000 TDX with the Belgian Army recovering a drone **1996**

Griffon 2000 TDX with Elf Petroleum, Nigeria **1996**

Four Griffon 2000 TDXs in service with the British Royal Marines **1995**

Craft built 2500 TD	Name	In service	Owner
001 Griffon Hovercraft 2500 TD	*Rain Dance*	November 1985	Hover Systems Inc, USA, (1986 Canadian registration CH-FHI)

further similar craft were delivered to Brazil as crash rescue craft at Rio de Janiero airport. In 1995 a number of Griffon TDX's were delivered to the Belgian Army, Elg Petroleum in Nigeria and to Nicaragua as a mobile medical clinic.

The British Ministry of Defence ordered four Griffon 2000 TDX(M) hovercraft. Designed to carry a crew of two, driver and commander, plus 16 fully equipped Marine Commandos, each craft is equipped with a 7.62 mm GPMG (General-Purpose Machine Gun), HF and VHF radios, radar, GPS and a variety of specialised equipment. Capable of speeds of over 35 knots, these craft are for 539 Assault Squadron (an integral part of three Commando Brigade) and are used worldwide for high-speed coastal insertion/amphibious assault, logistics support and other Commando-type applications. Each craft carries a payload of two tonnes which can be quickly converted from the all-troop to the all-cargo configuration, or to a variable combination of both.

Details for the 2000 TDX are very similar to the 2000 TD except for the propulsion and the following:

Specifications

Max speed	40 kts
Operational speed	35 kts

2500 TD

This craft has now been superseded by the Griffon 3000 TD. One craft of this type was built by Griffon Hovercraft Ltd and the other was built by a licensee in the USA. Both are in operation in North America.

3000 TD

The Griffon 3000 TD design supersedes the original 2500 TD and the 2500 TDX. Seating up to 37 passengers, the 3000 TD uses two Deutz BF8L 513 engines and incorporates the very latest in skirt design and technology. The hover height is also increased over its predecessors and with its larger propellers and fans it now has a significantly improved rough weather capability.

Specifications

Length overall	15 m
Beam	7 m
Weight, min	8.2 t
Payload	3,000 kg
Passengers	30-36
Propulsive power	2 × 239 kW
Max speed	40 kts
Operational speed	35 kts

Classification: IMO, the UK CAA and Lloyd's Register.

Structure: The main hull is of welded marine grade aluminium alloy providing a very cost-effective light and durable structure. It consists of a number of fore and aft spars linked by the cabin floors and the craft bottom. This provides an immensely stiff structure.

Sidebodies, made of composite materials, fold upwards reducing width for road and sea transportation.

The skirt is of a tapered HDL open loop type.

Propulsion: The 3000 TD uses two identical machinery units from the 2000 TDX, fitted next to each other.

Electrical system: The system is 24 V. Main and emergency supplies are provided. Each engine has a 35 A alternator.

Control: Similar controls to the single engine craft are fitted except no elevators are used.

Three rudders mounted in each duct are operated by a steering yoke via stainless steel cables to provide directional control. Fore and aft trim is achieved by an electrically operated skirt shift system. Twin engine throttles are mounted near to the driver's left hand whilst clutch pedals (operated by the driver's feet) are provided for the propellers. By using only one propeller at low speed, together with the rudder and skirt shift, the craft can turn in its own length. Control systems are powerful enough to allow the craft to be operated and controlled on only one engine, although at a much reduced speed.

Outfit: The superstructure can be designed to suit the customer's specification. The standard passenger cabin is constructed in light alloy with GRP mouldings at the front and back. Great emphasis has been placed on giving the passengers clear uninterrupted views through the large windows, and narrow pillars are featured. A portion of the roof can be transparent if required and air-conditioning and heating systems can be installed. Aircraft-type seating is arranged in up to six rows of six seats, three either side of a central aisle. Luggage racks, toilets and a galley may also be provided to suit customers' specific requirements.

4000 TD

The 4000 TD is a stretched version of the 3000 TD (and the proven 2500 TD). It can carry up to 60 passengers at a cruising speed of 35 knots. There are

Griffon 3000 TD (Paul Rapson) **1992**

two of these craft in India operating a 45 n mile route across the bay of Cambay, between Surat and Bhavnagar.

Specifications

Length overall	17.85 m
Beam	7.3 m
Weight, max	15.85 t
Payload	4.05 t
Passengers	60
Propulsive power	2 × 298 kW
Max speed	38 kts
Operational speed	35 kts

Classification: IMO, the UK CAA and Lloyd's Register.

Structure: Exactly the same cross-section and construction method as the 3000 TD but 2.85 m longer.

A tapered HDL open loop type skirt is fitted.

Propulsion: The same twin engine system as the 3000 TD but Deutz engines BF10L 513 V10 (298 kW each) are fitted.

Transmission details are similar to the smaller craft.

Electrical system: As the 3000 TD.

Control: As for the 3000 TD.

Outfit: The accommodation is normally arranged in up to nine rows of six seats, similar to those of the Griffon 3000 TD. Customers can specify their freight/passenger requirements and versions of this craft, like the 3000 TD, can include roll-on/off facilities, with a bow ramp.

4000 TDX

The 4000 TDX is a stretched version of the 4000 TD carrying 60 to 72 passengers or 6 tonnes of payload. It has two of the larger BF12L 513C, 386 kW engines installed and is two metres longer than the 4000 TD.

12000 TD (DESIGN)

A proposed 120- to 150-seat (12 tonne payload) craft designated the 12000 TD has been designed in outline and is currently under negotiation with potential clients.

UPDATED

Craft built 4000 TD	Name	Seats	Delivered	Owner
4000 TD	*Shri Bajarangdasbapa*	51	1992	New India Business House Ltd
4000 TD (GH 9462)	*Shri Saibaba*	51	1992	New India Business House Ltd

Griffon 4000 TD
1994

HOVERMARINE INTERNATIONAL LTD

Spitfire Quay, Hazel Road, Woolston, Southampton, Hampshire SO2 7GB, UK

Tel: +44 (1703) 443122
Fax: +44 (1703) 444429

P J Hill, *Managing Director*
E G Tattersall, *Technical Consultant*

Since its formation in 1966, Hovermarine has sold 106 Surface Effect Ships (SESs) to 33 countries and is one of the most experienced designers and builders of these craft. Hovermarine has its yard at Woolston, Southampton with an undercover area of more than 2,300 m^2.

Production designs are the 200, 400 and 500 series craft. The 200 series comprises the HM 218 (18 m, 84- to 103-seat) passenger ferries, 29 of which have been delivered to The Hong Kong and Yaumati Ferry Company; the HM 218 multirole harbour craft, four of which have been delivered to the Port of Rotterdam Authority; the HM 218 crewboat for the oil industry, five of which have been delivered to Shell Eastern Petroleum; the HM 221 (21 m) fireboat (two of which were delivered to the city of Tacoma and two to New York); the HM 221 (21 m) 112- to 135-seat ferry and the HM 221 (21 m) crewboat. Other variants of the 200 series craft are offered for hydrographic survey, coastguard and patrol duties. The HM 500 series includes the Series 2 (27 m, 256-seat) and the Series 3 (27 m, 300-seat) passenger ferry design. The new HM 424 design is larger than the HM 200 series but smaller than the HM 500 series. Incorporating all the well proven systems (the results of 25 years' experience in design, manufacture and operation of SES) the HM 424 can be specified with DDC or Deutz MWM engines, giving cruising speeds of 40 and 50 knots respectively, with full payloads. Other designs are available for the following roles: naval fast strike and patrol craft, crewboat, hydrographic survey and coastguard patrol. All craft are type-approved in the UK by the Civil Aviation Authority, with Passenger and Safety Certificates issued by the Department of Transport. The craft have also been certified by Lloyd's Register of Shipping, Bureau Veritas and USCG.

HM 216 FERRY

About five of this early 16 m HM2 type are still with operators. Full details of these craft are given in the 1978 edition of *Jane's Surface Skimmers.*

Craft built HM 216 (16 m SES) (list not complete)

Type	Name	No of seats	Yard No	Original delivery date	Delivered to	Country of operation
HM 216	(ex-*HYF 101*)	60	326	1974	Associated Marine Sdn Bhd	Malaysia
HM 216	*Sea Express 101*	-	-	1976		Philippines (laid up)
HM 216	*Sea Express 102*	-	-	1976		Philippines (laid up)
HM 216	*Sea Express 103*	-	-	1976		Philippines (laid up)
HM 216	*Gavea*	65	321	1976	TRANSTUR	Brazil*
HM 216	*Gragoata*	65	322	1976	TRANSTUR	Brazil*
HM 216	*Suratiba*	65	323	1976	TRANSTUR	Brazil*
HM 216	*HYF 103*	74	328	1974	The Hong Kong Yaumati Ferry Company	Hong Kong
HM 216	*HYF 104*	60	329	1975	The Hong Kong Yaumati Ferry Company	Hong Kong (laid up)
HM 216	*American Skimmer*	62	-	1974 (USA built)		USA (laid up)

* none operating

HM 218 FERRY

The HM 218 ferry provides a 40 per cent improvement in payload over the earlier HM 216 ferry for only a 15 per cent increase in operating costs. It can carry 84 to 103 passengers at cruising speeds up to 35 knots. An extended bow skirt permits passenger operations in up to 1.5 m (5 ft) waves.

The first HM 218 ferry went into service in 1976. A major operator of the type is The Hong Kong and Yaumati Ferry Company, which has 22 in commuter service within Hong Kong and on a 100 n mile international route to Guangzhou (Canton) in China. Other HM 218 ferries operate in Brazil, Indonesia, Iraq, Japan, Malaysia, Singapore, Venezuela and Malta.

Structure: Built in GRP mouldings the outer shell of the hull, including the bottom between the sidewalls and under the bow, is moulded in one piece, gunwale to gunwale. Frames and bulkheads are manufactured from sandwich panels of expanded PVC foam covered with GRP. All frames and bulkheads are laminated into the hull.

The extended bow skirt consists of a single loop extending from the bow chine to a line just below the base of the main hull. An inner loop overlaps the fan volute outlet and causes the bow skirt to inflate.

The rear seal consists of a membrane and loop which is suspended front and rear by transverse continuous sheets of material. It is inflated, to a pressure slightly above that of the cushion, by the rear fan in the starboard propulsion engine room.

Specifications

Length overall	18.29 m
Beam	6.1 m
Draught, hullborne	1.72 m
Draught, on-cushion	1.07 m
Weight, max	27.9 t
Payload	7,154 kg
Crew	2

Craft built HM 218 (18 m SES)

Type	Name	No of seats	Yard No	Original delivery date	Delivered to	Country of operation
HM 218	*HYF 105*	100	435	1976	Hong Kong Yaumati Ferry Co	Hong Kong
HM 218	*HYF 106*	100	443	1976	Hong Kong Yaumati Ferry Co	Hong Kong
HM 218	*HYF 107*	100	445	1976	Hong Kong Yaumati Ferry Co	Hong Kong
HM 218	*HYF 111*	100	457	1979	Hong Kong Yaumati Ferry Co	Hong Kong
HM 218	*HYF 112*	100	458	1979	Hong Kong Yaumati Ferry Co	Hong Kong
HM 218	*HYF 113*	100	459	1980	Hong Kong Yaumati Ferry Co	Hong Kong
HM 218	*HYF 114*	74	462	1980	Hong Kong Yaumati Ferry Co	Hong Kong
HM 218	*HYF 115*	100	463	1980	Hong Kong Yaumati Ferry Co	Hong Kong
HM 218	*HYF 116*	84	464	1980	Hong Kong Yaumati Ferry Co	Hong Kong
HM 218	*HYF 117*	100	469	1980	Hong Kong Yaumati Ferry Co	Hong Kong
HM 218	*HYF 118*	74	470	1980	Hong Kong Yaumati Ferry Co	Hong Kong
HM 218	*HYF 119*	74	473	1980	Hong Kong Yaumati Ferry Co	Hong Kong
HM 218	*HYF 120*	100	474	1980	Hong Kong Yaumati Ferry Co	Hong Kong
HM 218	*HYF 121*	74	475	1980	Hong Kong Yaumati Ferry Co	Hong Kong
HM 218	*HYF 122*	100	476	1980	Hong Kong Yaumati Ferry Co	Hong Kong
HM 218	*HYF 123*	74	477	1980	Hong Kong Yaumati Ferry Co	Hong Kong
HM 218	*HYF 124*	74	478	1980	Hong Kong Yaumati Ferry Co	Hong Kong
HM 218	*HYF 125*	100	479	1980	Hong Kong Yaumati Ferry Co	Hong Kong
HM 218	*HYF 126*	100	480	1980	Hong Kong Yaumati Ferry Co	Hong Kong
HM 218	*HYF 127*	100	481	1980	Hong Kong Yaumati Ferry Co	Hong Kong
HM 218	(ex-*HYF 129*)	-	-	1983	Changjiang Shipping	China, PR
HM 218	(ex-*HYF 130*)	74	484	1980	Changjiang Shipping	China, PR
HM 218	(ex-*RTS 101*)	100	466	1986	Discovery Bay Transportation Services	Hong Kong
HM 218	(ex-*RTS 102*)	100	468	1987	Discovery Bay Transportation Services	Hong Kong
HM 218	(ex-*RTS 103*)	100	471	1986	Discovery Bay Transportation Services	Hong Kong
HM 218	(ex-*HYF 108*)	100	446	1976	Discovery Bay Transportation Services	Hong Kong
HM 218	(ex-*HYF 109*)	100	447	1979	Discovery Bay Transportation Services	Hong Kong
HM 218	(ex-*HYF 110*)	100	448	1979	Discovery Bay Transportation Services	Hong Kong
HM 218	(ex-*HYF 129*)	-	-	1983	Changjiang Shipping	China, PR
HM 218	(ex-*HYF 130*)	74	484	1982	Changjiang Shipping	China, PR
HM 218	*Kijang Mas*	-	-	1984	Kedah & Perlis Ferry Service Sdn Bhd	Malaysia
HM 218	*Rey del Titikaka*	-	-		Hovermarine Titikaka Transport (not in service)	Bolivia
HM 218	*Reina del Titikaka*	-	-		Hovermarine Titikaka Transport (not in use)	Bolivia
HM 218	-	-	-		Shenzou Transport Company	China, PR
HM 218	*Semandera Satu*	78	-	1986	PT Hover Maritim Semandera	Indonesia
HM 218	*Semandera Desu*	78	-	1986	PT Hover Maritim Semandera	Indonesia
HM 218	*Havendienst 7*	n/a	-	1979	Port of Rotterdam	Netherlands (laid up)
HM 218	*Havendienst 10*	n/a	452	1979	Port of Rotterdam	Netherlands (laid up)
HM 218	*Havendienst 9*	n/a	451	1980	Port of Rotterdam	Netherlands (laid up)
HM 218	*Havendienst 8*	n/a	-	1980	Port of Rotterdam	Netherlands
HM 218	*Innovator I*	-	-	1977	Ministry of Transport	Nigeria (laid up)
HM 218	*Innovator II*	-	440	1977	Ministry of Transport	Nigeria (laid up)
HM 218	*Innovator III*	-	439	1977	Ministry of Transport	Nigeria (laid up)
HM 218	*Auto Batam 1*	78	472	1982	Yang Passenger Ferry Service	Singapore
HM 218	*Auto Batam 2*	-	-	-	Yang Passenger Ferry Service	Singapore
HM 218	*Zumbador*	70	454	1979	Maraven SA	Venezuela
HM 218	*Zumaya*	70	455	1980	Maraven SA	Venezuela
HM 218	*Barroso*	70	471	1980	Maraven SA	Venezuela
HM 218	*Auhah*	82	-	Feb 1983	Kuwait Public Transport	Kuwait
HM 218	*Umn Al Maradam*	82	-	1983	Kuwait Public Transport	Kuwait
HM 218	*J/Kubbar*	82	-	1984	Kuwait Public Transport	Kuwait
HM 218	*Yin Bin 1*	-	-	1986	China Merchants	China, PR
HM 218	*Pomas No 1*	95	-	1986	Pomas Sdn Bhd	Malaysia
HM 218	*Calypso*	84	-	May 1988	Gozo Line	Malta
HM 218	*Klassis*	82	-	1989	Naviga Line	Turkey
HM 218	*Hover Express*	84	485		Hoverlines	Norway
HM 218	*Bukom Deras*	90	-	1983	Shell Eastern Petroleum	Singapore
HM 218	*Bukom Pantas*	90	-	1983	Shell Eastern Petroleum	Singapore
HM 218	*Bukom Lekas*	90	-	1983	Shell Eastern Petroleum	Singapore
HM 218	*Bukom Maju*	90	-	1983	Shell Eastern Petroleum	Singapore
HM 218	*Bukom Jaya*	90	-	1983	Shell Eastern Petroleum	Singapore

HM 218 Klassis *operating on the Sea of Marmara in Turkey* **1990**

Passengers	84-103
Fuel capacity	1,455 l
Propulsive power	2 × 347 kW
Lift power	154 kW
Operational speed	34 kts
Range	200 n miles
Operational limitation	wave height 1.5 m

Propulsion: Two DDEC 8V-92TI V, eight-cylinder marine diesels, each developing 347 kW at 2,300 rpm, provide propulsive power. A single Caterpillar 3208 90° V, eight-cylinder marine diesel rated at 154 kW at 2,800 rpm, drives the 0.6 m diameter centrifugal lift fans.

The lift engine drives two pairs of forward fans through toothed belts and one aft fan through a hydraulic system.

The two propulsion engines each drive a 0.45 m diameter aluminium-bronze three-blade propeller through a reversing gearbox and 1:1 ratio vee box.

Control: Craft direction is by twin balanced stainless steel rudders operated hydraulically by a steering-wheel. Additional control is by differential use of the water propellers.

HM 218 CREWBOAT

Since 1979 three HM 218 crewboats have been operating in Venezuela with Maraven, transporting crew to and from oil rigs on Lake Maracaibo. Five more have been delivered to Shell Eastern Petroleum in Singapore. The crewboat is based on the HM 218 passenger ferry but has a substantially reinforced hull.

A bow-loading technique has been developed; rollers are fitted to the bow allowing the craft to approach installations and transfer crew over the bow. This is safer than the conventional stern transfer system as the captain can view the whole operation.

Specifications

Length overall	18.29 m
Beam	6.1 m
Draught, hullborne	1.72 m
Draught, on-cushion	1.07 m
Passengers	99
Propulsive power	2 × 347 kW
Lift power	154 kW
Max speed	34 kts
Range	200 n miles
Operational limitation	wave height 1.5 m

Classification: Construction is to Lloyd's Register survey requirements.

Structure: Shell mouldings, submouldings, frames, bulkheads and major attachments in GRP, using polyester resins and PVC foam.

Propulsion: Two DDC 8V-92TI marine diesels driving fixed-pitch propellers through Capitol reversing gearboxes and BPM V-drive gearboxes. Lift is by one Caterpillar 3280 V8 marine diesel driving two pairs of forward fans through toothed belts and one aft fan through a hydraulic system.

HM 218 MULTIROLE HARBOURCRAFT

A total of four HM 218 multirole harbour craft were delivered to the Port of Rotterdam Authority in 1979-80. The design retains the standard HM 218 passenger ferry hull fitted with two superstructure modules to house port-monitoring and emergency service equipment.

Details are given in the 1988 edition, page 84.

HM 221 FIREBOAT

In November 1991 Hovermarine International Ltd announced a major technology transfer deal with Textron Marine Systems Inc. This agreement between the two companies followed the 1990 order by the City of New York for two HM 221 fire and rescue vessels, (a US$6.5 million package) and allows Textron to build the HM 221 fireboat within the USA.

Details of these vessels are given under the Textron Marine Systems entry. Delivery of the fireboats was made in 1992. The hulls will be built by Hovermarine International Ltd, UK, together with various kits of parts.

There were two HM 221 firefighting craft ordered by the city of Tacoma, Washington, USA in 1978. The first of these was delivered in May 1982 and the second late in 1982. They are fitted with a comprehensive range of firefighting, rescue, navigation and communications equipment.

Specifications

Length overall	20.9 m
Beam	6.1 m
Draught, hullborne	1.55 m
Draught, on-cushion	1.1 m
Crew	2
Fuel capacity	2,950 l
Water capacity	90 l
Max speed	33 kts

Range: 120 n miles.

Propulsion: Two DDC 8V-92TI marine diesels drive fixed-pitch propellers via direct-drive reversing gearboxes and V-drive gearboxes. Lift power is from one DDC 6V-92TI marine diesel which is also used as a pump engine. A second pump engine is provided by a DDC 8V-92TI marine diesel. Propulsion, lift and pumping machinery is controlled from the wheelhouse. All engines are started electrically.

Operations equipment: Two remotely controlled

HM 221 FIREBOAT

Craft built	In service	Delivered to
HM 221 *Defiance* (Fireboat No 5)	December 1982	City of Tacoma Fire Department
HM 221 *Commencement* (Fireboat No 15)	February 1983	City of Tacoma Fire Department
HM 221	mid-1992	City of New York
HM 221 *John P Devaney*	mid-1992	City of New York

HM 221 CREWBOAT

Craft built	In service	Delivered to
HM 221 *Grayspear*	1982-1985	-

Details are given in the 1988 edition, page 85

HM 221 PASSENGER FERRY

Craft built	Seats	Built	Delivered to
HM 221	112	1985	Donau Dampfschiffahrts-Gesellschaft (DDSG)
HM 221	112	1994	Not Released

HM 221 passenger ferry delivered in 1995 **1996**

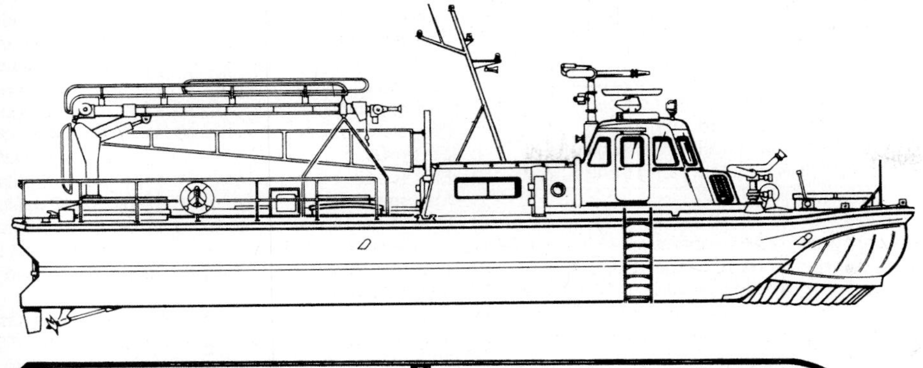

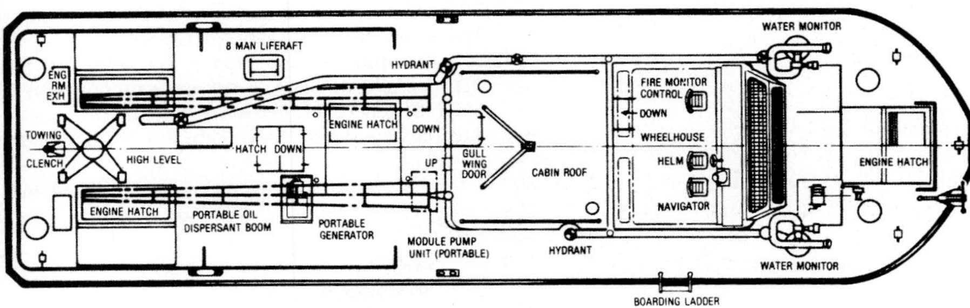

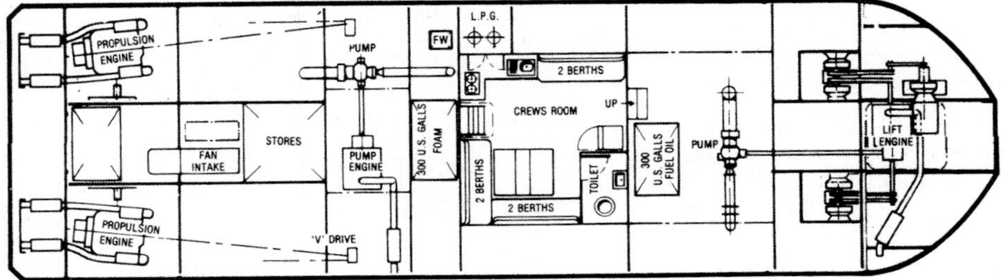

HM 221 firefighting craft

bow-mounted monitors each of 9,400 l/min water-flow rate; one wheelhouse-mounted monitor of 20,800 l/min water-flow rate; two under-wharf monitors of 9,400 l/min water-flow rate and one remotely controlled 5,600 l/min foam/water monitor fitted to the telescopic end of a high-level (10.5 m) ladder which doubles as a crane. The monitors are remotely controlled for rotation and elevation from a console in the wheelhouse. The ladder is controlled from its base. All fire monitors, except the wheelhouse monitor, can be controlled from a straight stream to 90° fog.

HM 221 PASSENGER FERRY

Based on the HM 221 (21 m) hull, this variant seats 112 to 135 passengers depending on route requirements and has a continuous speed in excess of 34 knots in calm conditions and a range of 140 n miles.

Specifications

Length overall	21.19 m
Beam	5.91 m
Draught, hullborne	1.76 m
Draught, on-cushion	1.21 m
Payload	8.4 t
Crew	3
Passengers	112-135
Fuel capacity	1,610 l
Propulsive power	2 × 380 kW
Lift power	201 kW
Operational speed	35 kts
Range	200 n miles

Classification: Lloyd's Register + Class ACV, Group 2, +LMC.

Structure: Single shell GRP mouldings, with sub-mouldings, frames, bulkheads and other attachments bonded together.

Propulsion: Power for the lift system is provided by a single Caterpillar 3280T V8 marine diesel with a continuous rating of 201 kW at 2,800 rpm. Propulsive power is supplied by two DDC 8V-92TI marine diesels, each rated at 380 kW at 2,100 rpm continuous.

Electrical system: Electrical voltage: 24 V DC nominal negative earth.

Generation/charging equipment: Two propulsion engine-driven AC/DC alternators rated at 27.5 V, 100 A. One lift engine-driven AC/DC alternator rated at 27.5 V, 100 A.

Two 24 V lead acid batteries, each with sufficient capacity to provide six starts for each engine.

Control: Power-assisted manual/hydraulic system operating twin rudders with a hard over angle of ±30° when set with a zero rudder divergence. A hydraulic pump is mechanically operated from the lift engines.

HM 424 (DESIGN)

Hovermarines HM 424 Cushion-Jet will transport 165-200 passengers in extreme comfort on an all year round basis on short sea routes. The craft will cruise at full load at 44 knots with machinery at 85 per cent Maximum Continuous Rating (MCR) and will have a continuous speed capability of 48 knots at maximum engine rating. Other engines can be fitted to customer choice to give cruising speeds in the range 40-57 knots.

Specifications

Length overall	26 m
Beam	10 m
Draught, hullborne	1.6 m
Draught, on-cushion	0.8 m
Payload	16.3 t
Passengers	199
Max speed	48 kts
Operational speed	44 kts
Range	300 n miles

Classification: IMO Code of safety for Dynamically Supported Craft; Lloyd's Register - Class ✠A1 Air Cushion Vehicles, Group 2, with +LMC; United Kingdom Civil Aviation Authority (CAA).

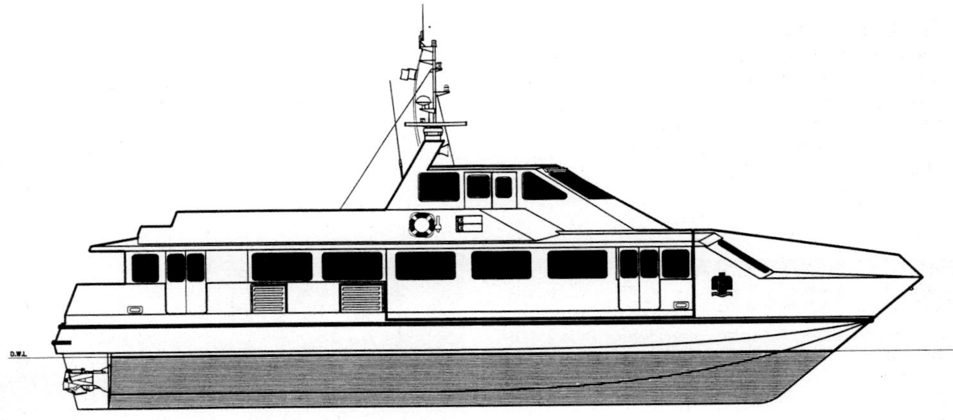

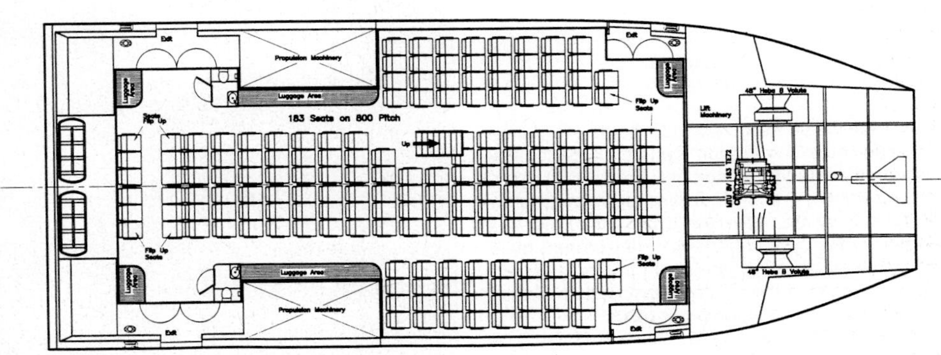

General arrangement of the HM 424 Cushion-Jet design

1995

HM 527

The first HM 527 was launched in January 1982. It has been designed to operate on coastal and inland waters. A computerised roll stabilisation system is fitted as standard. The first of four craft, ordered by Sealink Ferries Ltd, was delivered before the end of 1983.

Other designs based on the HM 527 hull include a hydrographic survey vessel and all passenger crew-boats and mixed payload supply boats for the offshore oil industry.

Specifications

Length overall	27.2 m
Beam	10.2 m
Draught, hullborne	2.55 m
Draught, on-cushion	1.7 m
Weight, max	87 t
Payload	21 t
Passengers	200
Fuel capacity	4,940 l
Propulsive power	2 × 1,050 kW
Lift power	550 kW
Operational speed	36 kts
Range	200 n miles
Operational limitation	wave height 3 m

HM 527

Craft built HM 527	No of seats	In service	Delivered to
HM 527 *Tejo*	200	1983	Sealink Ferries Ltd, Hong Kong
HM 527 *Douro*	200	1984	Sealink Ferries Ltd, Hong Kong
HM 527 *Sado*	200	1984	Sealink Ferries Ltd, Hong Kong
HM 527 *Mondego*	200	1984	Sealink Ferries Ltd, Hong Kong

Structure: Single shell GRP moulding with sub-moulding, frames, bulkheads and cabin sole panels bonded together. Materials used include expanded PVC foam, glass fibre, polyester resins, wood and aluminium alloy.

The bow skirt is made up of two tailored neoprene/nylon loops suspended in 180° arcs sidewall to sidewall and joined at their lower edges to form an irregularly shaped inflatable compartment. When inflated, the loops support 20 single fabric segments, attached at the loop joint line, and absorb wave impact shock to a degree. Four additional corner segments are attached on each side by ropes and shackles.

Propulsion: The marine diesels are in two amidships engine rooms, both accommodating one propulsion engine and one auxiliary power unit. The lift engine is an MTU 6V 396 TB 83 rated at 550 kW at 2,300 rpm which drives lift fans via a gearbox, to provide cushion air and drives, via a hydraulic pump and hydraulic motors, two secondary fans for skirt inflation. The propulsion engines are MTU 12V 396 TB 83 diesels rated at 1,050 kW at 1,800 rpm. Each incorporates a ZF BW 455 reverse-reduction gearbox and drives a single three-bladed propeller via transmission shafting inclined at 13°. The outward rotating propellers operate at up to 900 rpm.

The main plenum chamber receives air from the two lift fans via ducts located amidships port and starboard. Bow and stern skirts receive air from port and starboard fans, driven hydraulically by lift engine gearbox pumps, via ducts forming part of the superstructure.

Electrical system: The two Perkins 4.236M marine diesels rated at 27.2 kW, 50 Hz, 220 V drive the AC alternators and compressors for the air-conditioning system.

Control: Vessel heading is controlled by power-operated twin water rudders. Additional control is provided by differential use of the propellers. An automatic roll stabilisation system operates through inclined independant rudders.

HM 780 CAR FERRY (DESIGN)

The HM 780 is designed to carry a payload of 650 passengers in one large saloon and a vehicle mix of typically 74 cars, 6 coaches and 8 light vans. The construction of hull, deck and superstructure can be in marine grade aluminium or composite materials, subject to customer requirements.

The craft is designed to operate at 48 knots in Sea State 5, on typical cross-channel routes these conditions are only exceeded for about 10 per cent of the year. Onboard motion levels in Sea State 5 will be low with vertical acceleration levels less than 0.15 *g* rms.

Specifications

Length overall	80 m
Beam	25 m
Draught, hullborne	4.2 m
Draught, on-cushion	2 m
Weight	975 t
Payload	243.25 t
Passengers	650
Vehicles	74 cars 8 vans 6 coaches
Fuel capacity	48,000 l
Propulsive power	2 × 12,000 kW or 4 × 5,400 kW
Lift power	2 × 3,000 kW
Max speed	64 kts (Gas-turbines)
Max speed	58.5 kts (Diesels)
Operational speed	48 kts
Operational limitation	Sea State 5

Classification Lloyd's Register ✠A1, Air Cushion Vehicle, Group 1 ✠LMC.

Propulsion: The main engines are 2 × LM 1600 gas-turbines, 12,000 kW each or 4 × MTU 20V 1163 TB 73 diesels, 5,400 kW each.

Thrust devices: 2 × KaMeWa 125 S2.

The lift power is provided by 2 × MTU 12V 1163 TB 73, 3,000 kW each; and the aft skirt power by 1 × MTU 8V 396 TE 74, 840 kW.

Auxiliary systems: Powered by 2 × 300 kW diesels.

UPDATED

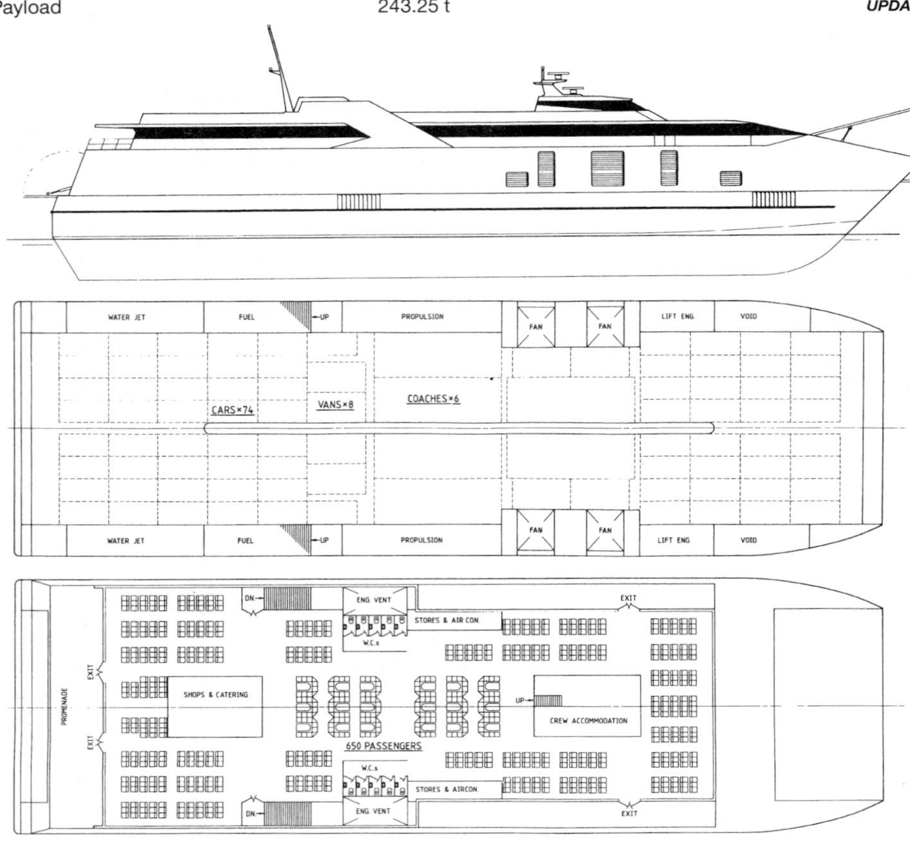

General arrangement of the HM 780 (design)

INGLES HOVERCRAFT ASSOCIATES LTD

101A High Street, Gosport, Hampshire PO12 1DS, UK

Tel: +44 (1705) 510593
Fax: +44 (1705) 502302

N A H Pool, *Director*
J W Wilson, *Director*
T J R Longley, *Design Consultant*
N J Smith, *Design Consultant*

Ingles Hovercraft Associates Ltd holds the patent rights relating to the 'Elevon' system of control. Under a manufacturing agreement, production of the River Rover Mk 4 and Mk 5 hovercraft is currently carried out by the HoverAid Trust. HoverAid is a registered charity, established to design and build appropriate technology hovercraft primarily for use in developing countries. Sales are made to missions and aid agencies on a non-profit basis.

The River Rover series has been developed over the last two decades to create a vehicle capable of reliably coping with the most arduous of river and

River Rover Mk 4 craft operating in Papua New Guinea ***1995***

River Rover Mk 5, powered by a Land Rover Gemini 3 diesel engine ***1996***

delta conditions. The patented Elevon control system was first proven on a British joint services expedition to conquer the rapids of the Nepalese Kali Gandaki in 1978. Similar expeditions to the Amazonian headwaters in Peru, and to the snowbound source of the Yangtze, on the Tibetan plateau, have shown the River Rover to be unparalleled in terms of manoeuvrability.

The first River Rover Mk 4 was completed in April 1992. Several craft are at present in service with medical aid programmes. The River Rover Mk 5 was completed in 1995.

RIVER ROVER Mk 4

The River Rover Mk 4 is a natural development of the River Rover series and is available with either a Volkswagen or Land Rover turbocharged and intercooled engine, providing greater economy, reliability, and global parts availability with either installation.

Specifications

Length overall	6.83 m
Beam	2.77 m
Weight, min	0.95 t
Weight, max	1.55 t
Crew	1
Passengers	8
Fuel capacity	180 l
Propulsive power	97 kW
Max speed	32 kts
Operational speed	24 kts
Range	190 n miles

Structure: To fulfil its intended operational parameters, the River Rover Mk 4 has been designed for simple maintenance and repair. The hull consists of a bolted aluminium spaceframe with repeated glass fibre box structures attached; the removable side decks are built from two sets of identical deck panels. The outer set can be lowered for containerisation or road transportation.

Propulsion: The operator has the choice of either a Volkswagen or Land Rover 2.4 litre turbocharged engine, developing 97 kW at 4,000 rpm. Two thrust fans and an axial flow pressure fan for lift, are driven directly from the engine via a clutch and a torsionally resilient coupling.

All fuel is filtered twice and passed through a sedimentation and water separation system to ensure engine safety when available fuel composition is less than ideal.

Electrical system: Voltage is nominally 12 V DC. Two maintenance-free, sealed for life batteries are supplied as standard.

Control: The unique twin cascade Elevon system allows precise positional control. Pitch and roll are actively adjusted by vertical thrust vectoring, this effect is enhanced by the wide separation of the thrust fans. When combined with the conventional rudders a high degree of lateral control is achieved, allowing, for example, operation in crosswinds without side-slip. High-speed power turns can be performed without tail breakaway, an undesirable characteristic of many conventional hovercraft; this allows River Rover to negotiate intricate river systems well above hump speed.

Safety equipment: The River Rover Mk 4 contains sufficient closed cell protective foam to ensure against sinking, even when ruptured.

UPDATED

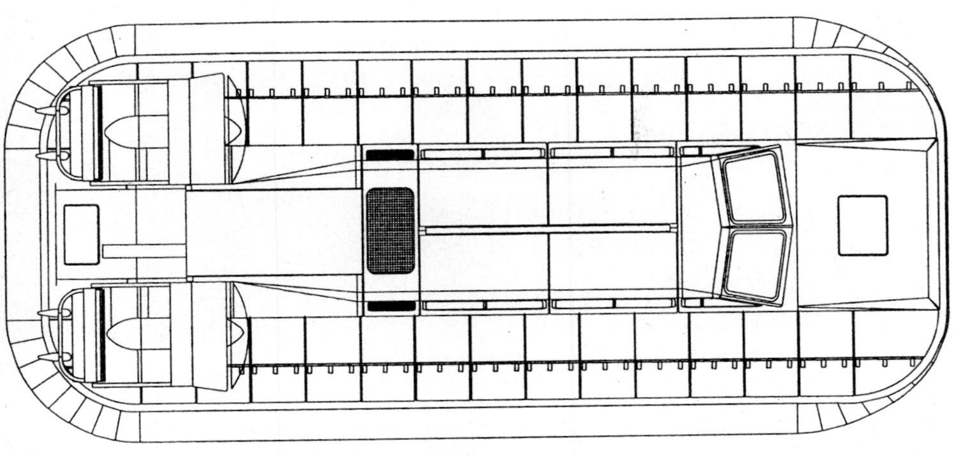

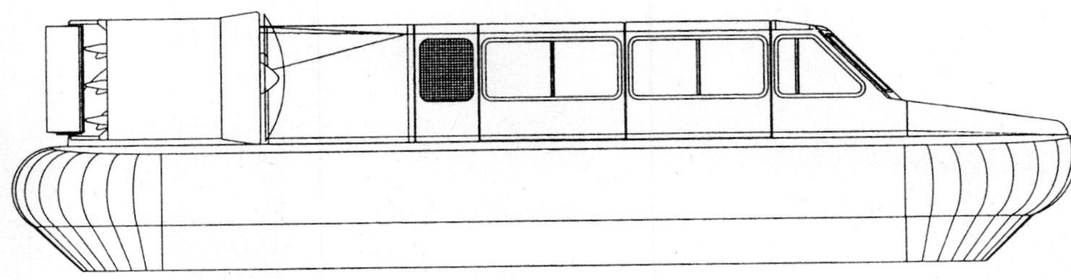

River Rover Mk 4

SLINGSBY AMPHIBIOUS HOVERCRAFT LTD

Kirkbymoorside, Yorkshire YO6 6EZ, UK

Tel: +44 (1751) 432474
Telex: 57597 SLINAV G
Fax: +44 (1751) 431173

Michael D Jones, *Group Chief Executive*
Russell D Haworth, *Managing Director*
Simon A Cooper, *Contracts Director*
Stephen B Boulton, *Marine Sales Manager*

Since its formation in the 1930s as Slingsby Sailplanes, building gliders, the Slingsby Group of Companies has grown in size and greatly expanded its capabilities. The development into composite materials design and manufacturing, has led into building aircraft, airships, submersibles and hovercraft.

In 1984 the hovercraft development commenced and this has resulted in the SAH 2200 amphibious hovercraft, of which more than 25 are in service around the world, both in military and commercial applications.

SAH 2200

The SAH 2200 is a single diesel-engined hovercraft manufactured in a composite of glass and Kevlar fibre, epoxy resin and PVC foam. This combination produces an exceptionally strong, lightweight structure with excellent fatigue life and resistance to corrosion from saltwater. These characteristics give the hovercraft a very good payload and performance for the engine horsepower used, making it easy and inexpensive to maintain. With a maximum payload of 2,200 kg the craft is certificated to carry up to 22 passengers and can hold sufficient fuel for more than 12 hours of operations.

Current operations include coastal patrol work in areas ranging from Scandinavia, where winter use is over ice and snow, to the Arabian Gulf, as a safety patrol craft on firing ranges, around coastal airports and as a training craft for crews on large military hovercraft.

Commercial and passenger-carrying operations have been established in the UK and other parts of Europe, South-east Asia, the Caribbean and the Indian subcontinent. In these operations the craft has been used for transporting people and equipment, carrying out survey work and acting as a safety craft around shallow water drilling operations.

Operational areas have included large tidal ranges with associated sand and mud flats, inland waters with large areas of shallow, weed infested water, mangrove swamp coastal waters and major river complexes with conditions ranging from low water level sand banks to flood conditions with strong currents and a lot of debris in the water.

The hovercraft can be airlifted, trailed or shipped within a 40 ft flat rack. Packed dimensions with duct removed:
Length: 12 m
Height: 2 m
Beam: 2.4 m
Weight: 3 t

Specifications

Length overall	10.6 m
Beam	4.2 m
Payload	2.2 t
Passengers	22
Fuel capacity	510 l
Propulsion power	142 kW
Max speed	40 kts
Range	500 n miles
Obstacle clearance	0.5 m

Structure: Heavy-duty composite plastics structure strengthened with Kevlar in high load areas. Heavy-duty landing skids are provided. Four marine bollards on the deck form lifting rig attachments and guides for the integral jacking system. Side decks are rigid and enable large, bulky items to be carried outside the main load space. The side decks fold to allow transport of the craft by road vehicles or shipping within a 40 ft flat rack container.

The skirt is of a loop and segment type.

Propulsion: Integrated propulsion and lift system. The standard SAH 2200 is powered by a single Deutz BF6L 913C turbocharged air-cooled diesel, rated at 142 kW at 2,500 rpm, driving a centrifugal lift fan and a Hoffmann variable-pitch ducted propeller. Alternatively, a Deutz BF8L 513 turbocharged air-cooled diesel, rated at 223 kW at 2,300 rpm, or a Cummins 6CTA3M-1 turbocharged water-cooled diesel rated at 223 kW at 2,500 rpm have been used to suit customer requirements. A deeper open loop skirt with increased lift height is also used with the higher powered engines as required.

Electrical system: 24 V electrical supply is standard. Provision is made for optional extras such as radar, air-conditioning, heating and searchlights.

Control: Rudders mounted in the propeller slipstream provide directional control; similarly mounted elevators provide fore and aft trim. Fuel ballast and roll control systems are incorporated to counteract adverse loading and to improve craft performance in high wind and sea states. A controllable pitch propeller allows variable thrust both in forward and reverse giving enhanced control particularly over land and in difficult downwind sea conditions.

Outfit: Seats forward for commander and passenger/navigator are in a self-contained wheelhouse. The load space is flexible in layout and two quick-release composite canopies allow conversion to three versions:

Passenger Version: Bench seating running fore and aft providing a total of 22 passenger seats. Access is port and starboard through gull wing doors mounted in canopies.

Supply Boat Version: Covered accommodation for eight passengers with open load space with a capacity for up to 1,400 kg of cargo.

Logistic Support Version: With canopies and seats removed, integral cargo lashing rails are provided to enable a disposable load of up to 2,200 kg to be carried.

In addition to the above, purpose-designed pods to fit the load space are manufactured to carry specialist equipment.

VERIFIED

SAH 2200 operating with the Finnish Coast Guard **1995**

SAH 2200 operating between Bombay and Vashi (New Bombay) **1995**

SAH 2200 operating with the UK Ministry of Defence **1995**

UNITED STATES OF AMERICA

AVONDALE BOAT DIVISION

Avondale Industries Inc

400 River Road, Westwego, Louisiana 70094, USA

Tel: +1 (504) 436 3322
Fax: +1 (504) 436 3363

BHC AP1-88

In 1990 Avondale was appointed the United States licensee for AP1-88 amphibious hovercraft.

AIR RIDE 109

In late 1988 Avondale Boat Division announced the building under licence from Air Ride Craft Inc of Air Ride Craft 109 (400-passenger) surface effect ships for Tri-State Marine Transport Inc to operate between John F Kennedy Airport and lower Manhattan. The Air Ride Craft concept developed by Don Burg represents a unique form of surface effect ship, in that a flexible seal or skirt is only used at the bow to contain the air cushion. The Avondale craft are built in marine grade aluminium alloy and form part of the diversified range of ship and boat building, conversion, repair, foundry and propeller work undertaken by the company.

Two Air Ride 109 SESs have been delivered by Avondale Boat Division.

Specifications

Length	33.23 m
Beam	10.37 m
Draught, on-cushion	0.91 m
Displacement	140 t (½ load)
Passengers	360-400
Fuel capacity	9,463 l
Water capacity	1,514 l
Propulsive power	2 × 1,603 kW
Lift power	336 kW
Operational speed	44 kts

Classification: USCG + ABS.

Air Ride 109 400-passenger ferry ***1990***

Structure: Hull: aluminium
Propulsion: The main engines are two Deutz MWM TBD 604B V16, driving KaMeWa water-jet units.The lift engine is a Deutz MWM TBD 234 V12.
Auxiliary systems: Ride control system: standard

UPDATED

TEXTRON MARINE & LAND SYSTEMS

Division of Textron Inc

6600 Plaza Drive, New Orleans, Louisiana 70127-2584, USA

Tel: +1 (504) 245 6600
Fax: +1 (504) 245 6634

John J Kelly, *President*
James W Kratzer, *Executive Vice President*
H J Smedley, *Vice President, Engineering*
Thomas A Corcoran, *Executive Director, Human Resources*
Irwin F Edenzon, *Vice President, Business Development and Marketing (Marine)*
Frank P Higgins, *Vice President, Customer Support*
Robert G Moore, *Director of Technology*
Donald W Horen, *Executive Director, Product Assurance*
Windsor E Ward, *Executive Director, Combat Vehicle Marketing*
John P Schneider, *Vice President, Manufacturing*

Textron Marine & Land Systems (TM&LS), a division of Textron Inc, began in 1969 as the New Orleans operations of Bell Aerospace Textron, which had been pursuing air cushion vehicle development programmes since 1958. It was renamed Textron Marine Systems in 1986 and acquired its manufacturing facility in 1988. In April 1994, TMS operations were joined with those of Cadillac Gage Textron under the name of Textron Marine & Land Systems. Cadillac Gage products include combat vehicles; weapon stations; and control, stabilisation and suspension systems for military vehicles.

The Textron Marine Systems Shipyard Operations, formerly Bell Halter Inc, was acquired in 1988 when TMS purchased it from Halter Marine Inc. Prior to that, the shipyard was operated as a joint venture of Bell Aerospace Textron and Halter Marine.

The TM&LS facility is located on a 10.1 ha (25 acre) site in eastern New Orleans, Louisiana, and has direct access to the Intra-coastal Waterway, the Mississippi River and the Gulf of Mexico. Vessels built at the facilty are in service with the US Army, the US Army Corps of Engineers, the US Navy, the US Coast Guard and the commercial sector, and have accumulated many thousands of hours of service.

TM&LS also maintains a 1,115 m² advanced suspension lab (for military and commercial vehicles) in eastern New Orleans and a 5,202 m² storage facility in Slidell, Louisiana (32 km from the manufacturing facility).

The company has rights to manufacture and sell in the USA, machines employing the hovercraft principle, through a licensing arrangement with the British Hovercraft Corporation and Hovercraft Development Ltd. TM&LS produces Air Cushion Vehicle (ACV) products using aluminium and/or composite materials.

Craft built by TM&LS range in size from the 7.32 m Utility Air Cushion Vehicle (UACV 1200), to the 26.8 m Landing Craft, Air Cushion (LCAC) currently in production for the US Navy, to the 48.7 m SES-200 which has undergone modification for the US Navy.

TM&LS had delivered a total of 66 LCACs to the US Navy by October 1995.

Of the 17 LCAC's deployed to the Persian Gulf during the Gulf War, all were operational 100 per cent of the time.

LCACs provided relief to the outer islands of Bangladesh during the devastating cyclone of 1991. A total of 34 sorties was carried out in 14 days delivering 900 tonnes of desperately needed relief cargo.

Beginning in 1992, LCACs also played a vital role during Operation Restore Hope in Somalia.

Earlier work on air cushion vehicles, that has led to current TM&LS developments, is summarised in the 1991 and earlier editions of this book.

LCAC-39 undergoing trials near New Orleans, Louisiana ***1993***

LCAC
LANDING CRAFT, AIR CUSHION

Craft built	Delivered to US Navy
LCAC-1	December 1984
LCAC-2	February 1986
LCAC-3	June 1986
LCAC-4	August 1986
LCAC-5	November 1986
LCAC-6	December 1986
LCAC-7	March 1987
LCAC-8	June 1987
LCAC-9	June 1987
LCAC-10	September 1987
LCAC-11	December 1987
LCAC-12	December 1987
LCAC-13	September 1988
LCAC-14	November 1988
LCAC-24	March 1990
LCAC-25	June 1990
LCAC-26	June 1990
LCAC-27	August 1990
LCAC-28	October 1990
LCAC-29	December 1990
LCAC-30	December 1990
LCAC-31	February 1991
LCAC-32	May 1991
LCAC-33	June 1991
LCAC-37	July 1991
LCAC-38	September 1991
LCAC-39	September 1991
LCAC-40	November 1991
LCAC-41	November 1991
LCAC-42	December 1991
LCAC-43	February 1992
LCAC-44	February 1992
LCAC-45	March 1992
LCAC-46	May 1992
LCAC-47	June 1992
LCAC-48	July 1992
LCAC-52	September 1992
LCAC-53	October 1992
LCAC-54	October 1992
LCAC-55	December 1992
LCAC-56	January 1993
LCAC-57	February 1993
LCAC-58	March 1993
LCAC-59	April 1993
LCAC-60	June 1993
LCAC-61	July 1993
LCAC-62	August 1993
LCAC-63	September 1993
LCAC-64	October 1993
LCAC-65	November 1993
LCAC-66	December 1993
LCAC-67	February 1994
LCAC-68	March 1994
LCAC-69	April 1994
LCAC-70	May 1994
LCAC-71	June 1994
LCAC-72	July 1994
LCAC-73	September 1994
LCAC-74	October 1994
LCAC-75	December 1994
LCAC-76	February 1995
LCAC-77	March 1995
LCAC-78	May 1995
LCAC-79	July 1995
LCAC-80	August 1995
LCAC-81	October 1995

Principal craft built

SESs		
SES-100B	Surface effect ship test craft (see *Jane's Surface Skimmers 1984* and earlier editions)	on trials February 1972
Model 210A (110 Mk I)	Demonstration SES, became USCG *Dorado* (WSES-1)	launched 1978 June 1981
Model 730A	Became Model 730A, US Navy SES-200, with 15.24 m extension	re-powered and water jets fitted 1990
Model 720A	*Rodolf*-hydrographic survey boat for US Army Corps of Engineers	delivered 1980
Model 212A (110 Mk II)	Crewboats: *Speed Command* *Swift Command*	 delivered February 1981 delivered July 1981
Model 522A (110 Mk II)	'Seabird' class: *Sea Hawk* (WSES-2) US Coast Guard *Shearwater* (WSES-3) Key West, Florida *Petrel* (WSES-4)	 October 1982 June 1983
Model 212B	Model 212A *Speed Command* and *Swift Command* converted to become Model 212B crewboats: *Margaret Jill* (chartered by Tidewater Inc) *Speed Tide* (chartered by Tidewater Inc)	 1984 1985
HM 221	Fire and rescue vessel. Two craft	delivered July and October 1992
AMPHIBIOUS AIR CUSHION VEHICLES		
AALC JEFF(B)	Amphibious Assault Landing Craft	completed March 1977
LACV-30	Lighter, Air Cushion Vehicle. 24 completed by 1986 for US Army Troop Support Command	first ones delivered 1981
LCAC	Landing Craft, Air Cushion	66 delivered by October 1995
UACV	Utility Air Cushion Vehicle Demonstrator	1988
UACV 1200	Delivered to Shell Offshore Inc, *Hover 1*	June 1989
Model C-7 Hovercraft	High-speed ACV passenger/ cargo ferry, executive transporter configuration delivered to Freeport Indonesia	1994
Model FR-7	Fire/rescue vessel delivered to Singapore CAAS	1994

Bowramp of LCAC **1987**

LCAC
LANDING CRAFT, AIR CUSHION

On 5 June 1981 TM&LS signed a US$40 million contract with the US Navy for the detail design and long-lead materials for an amphibious assault landing craft, designated by the Navy as the LCAC (Landing Craft, Air Cushion). The LCAC is the production version of the JEFF(B) craft. The contract contained two options for the later construction of six craft. In February 1982 the US Navy exercised the first option for the production of three lead craft and in October 1982 ordered a further three craft.

In March 1984 TM&LS was awarded a contract to build six LCACs. By December 1986 a further contract had been awarded, to build two more LCACs bringing the total to 14 craft. On 1 July 1987, the US Navy awarded a $187 million contract to TM&LS to construct another 10 LCACs. This marked the start of full production for the LCAC programme.

On 15 December 1988 a second full production contract for 12 LCACs was awarded to TM&LS, along with central procurement activities for long-lead time materials. This was valued at $228 million. An option to this contract was exercised on 22 December 1989, for an additional nine LCACs. On 24 April 1991, another full production contract, valued at $139 million, for 12 LCACs was awarded to TM&LS with additional central procurement activities for long-lead time materials. A $181 million option to this contract, for 12 LCACs, was exercised 22 May 1992.

Since March 1992, TM&LS has won all seven contracts in support of the LCAC midlife overhaul and refurbishment program aimed at upgrading the US Navy LCAC fleet and maintaining it in operational readiness. LCACs -1, -2, -3, -4, -6 and -14 have been overhauled at TM&LS West Coast Operations, and LCAC-8, -10 and -11 have been overhauled on the east coast.

In January 1993, TM&LS was awarded a $117 million contract for the production of seven LCACs. This award made TMS the sole LCAC producer for the US Government's FY92 acquisition.

In April 1994, the Japan Defence Agency awarded TM&LS a contract to build and deliver a large air cushion vehicle based on the US Navy LCAC. Valued at $50 million, the contract includes delivery of engineering documentation, training manuals, reserve subsystems, spare parts, and support and test equipment. The ACV is scheduled for delivery in 1997.

The LCAC is a high-speed, ship-to-shore and over-the-beach amphibious landing craft, capable of carrying a 60 tonne payload. It can transport equipment, personnel and weapons systems (including the main battle tank) from ships located at increased stand-off distances, through the surf zone, and across the beach to hard landing points beyond the waterline. The craft is supported on a pressurised cushion of air and travels at much higher speeds than are presently possible with current conventional landing craft. Over-the-horizon assaults are made possible by the high transit speeds of the LCAC.

The LCAC is capable of travelling over land, water, marshes and mud flats. Compared to conventional landing craft, the percentage of the world's shorelines suitable for landing is increased from 17 to 80 per cent. The LCACs will operate from well-deck equipped amphibious ships. In the future, LCAC's may be deployed from shore based facilities by navies having missions within the operating range of the craft.

LCAC's multimission capability has led to the designation of Multipurpose Craft, Air Cushion (MCAC). Personnel transport modules can be fitted to the deck of the LCAC to carry up to 180 personnel or to convert the LCAC to a medical evacuation or mobile field hospital role. A mine countermeasures modular sweep deck, installable in 12 hours or less includes a winch and crane for sweep gear. Other potential roles for the MCAC include patrol, civil emergency, lighterage, and coastal anti-submarine warfare.

Specifications

Length overall	26.82 m
Beam	14.33 m
Draught, hullborne	0.91 m
Weight, max	153.5 t
Payload	54.3 t
Propulsive power	4 × 3,955 kW
Max speed	50 kts

Propulsion: Four TF40B gas-turbines are installed, driving two Dowty Rotol 3.582 m diameter 4-blade variable, reversible-pitch propellers; and four double-entry centrifugal type lift fans of 1.6 m diameter.

Personnel transport module rigged MCAC in the well deck of an LSD **1996**

MODEL 210A (110 Mk I) DEMONSTRATION SES

Launched in late 1978, the Model 110 demonstration boat has undergone extensive successful testing by both commercial operators and the US Coast Guard. The basic hull and machinery layout permits modification of the deckhouse and arrangement of the deck space for a number of alternative applications, from crewboat and 275-seat passenger ferry to fast patrol boat.

In September 1980 the US Navy purchased the Demonstration SES (110 Mk I) to be used in a joint US Navy/US Coast Guard programme. The US Coast Guard, designating the boat the USCG *Dorado* (WSES-1), conducted an operational evaluation of the craft for the first six months of the programme. The craft was modified to conform to US Coast Guard requirements for an operational evaluation vessel. On completion of its USCG evaluation a 15.24 m hull extension was added to the boat for the US Navy to assess the performance of a higher length-to-beam vessel. The craft has been designated the SES-200 by the US Navy (see later subentry for Model 730A and SES-200 conversion).

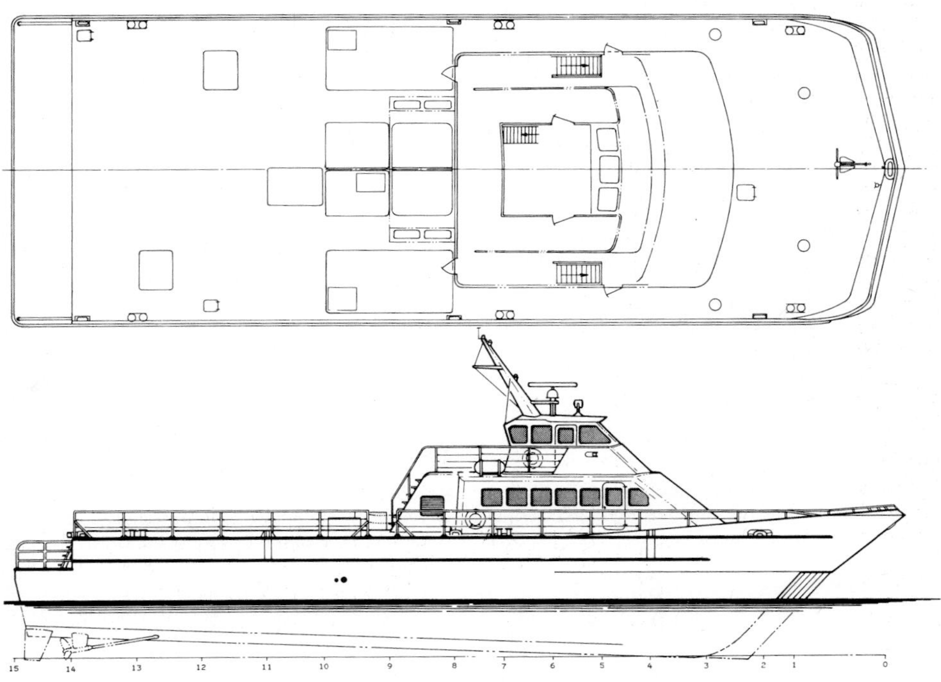

Original outboard profile and plan of Model 110 Mk I demonstration SES

MODEL 522A US COAST GUARD SES

In June 1981 the US Coast Guard awarded a contract for the purchase of three Model 522A (110 Mk II) high-speed cutters, the first two of which were delivered in October 1982.

The craft, known as the 'Seabird' class, were designated *Sea Hawk* (WSES-2), *Shearwater* (WSES-3) and *Petrel* (WSES-4). *Petrel* was delivered in June 1983. These vessels, now decommissioned, were based at Key West, Florida, at a Coast Guard facility, where they were highly successful at intercepting drug runners operating in the Gulf of Mexico and the Caribbean Sea.

Specifications

Length overall	33.52 m
Beam	11.88 m
Draught, hullborne	2.51 m
Draught, on-cushion	1.67 m
Displacement, max	152 t
Crew	12
Fuel capacity	34,050 l
Propulsive power	2 × 1,800 kW
Lift power	260 kW
Max speed	30 kts
Range	1,550 n miles

Sea Hawk *and* Shearwater, *the first two Model 522A cutters to be delivered to the US Coast Guard* **1988**

Structure: Primary structure is built in welded marine aluminium alloy 5086. The structure is of catamaran configuration and consists of two side hulls separated by decks and transverse bulkheads. The side hull shell plating varies between ¼ and ½ in depending on local pressures and is stiffened by T-section longitudinals. The spacing of the longitudinals is 457 mm on the bottom plating and 381 mm on the side plating. Side hull shape is maintained by bulkheads spaced generally at 2.44 m which support the hull longitudinals. Bulkheads have ¼ in webs with T-section and flat bar stiffening and flat bar caps sized appropriately for each bulkhead.

Six of the bulkheads in each side hull and across the centre section between the hulls are watertight. There are two in the accommodation area and one forward of the deckhouse. The latter also forms a collision bulkhead. The bulkheads provide the transverse bending and torsional continuity to the hull structure.

The cabin superstructure consists of T-section frames fabricated from flat bars and spaced as the frames on the hull. T-stiffened plate is welded to the framing.

The bow seal consists of eight equally spaced fingers, each of which is attached to the underside of the centre hull. The stern seal, which has a constant cross-section, consists of two inflated horizontal lobes of coated-fabric material.

Propulsion: Motive power for the propulsion system is furnished by two DDA 16V-149TIB marine diesels. Each drives a 1.06 m diameter, 1.17 m pitch, three-bladed, fixed-pitch NiBrAl propeller Gawn-Burrill Series type.

Cushion lift is provided by two Detroit Diesel Allison 8V-92N marine diesels each driving a double-inlet centrifugal fan.

Control: Craft direction is controlled by twin rudders, one aft on each side hull. Differential propeller thrust is employed for slow-speed manoeuvring. The steering system is electrohydraulic and can be operated from any of the control stations in the pilot-house and the wing bridges.

Outfit: Deckhouse superstructure contains pilot-house at 01 level with communications and navigation equipment. Auxiliary control stations are provided plus additional controls on each wing bridge. Main deckhouse contains the ship's office, armoury, captain's stateroom, quarters for three officers and three crew. Second deck accommodation includes galley and additional quarters for 12 crew.

Textron Marine 48.78 m SES-200 before propulsion and hull structure change programme **1988**

MODEL 212B (110 Mk II)

The Model 212B is a conversion of the Model 212A. The two craft converted are the *Margaret Jill* (ex-*Speed Command*) and *Speed Tide* (ex-*Swift Command*).

Specifications

Length overall	33.25 m
Beam	11.89 m
Draught, hullborne	2.52 m
Draught, on-cushion	1.68 m
Crew	6
Passengers	119
Fuel capacity	20,212 l
Water capacity	3,181 l
Propulsive power	2 × 1,230 kW
Lift power	2 × 260 kW
Operational speed	31 kts

Structure: 5086 aluminium.

Propulsion: Main engines: two Detroit Diesel Allison 16V-149TIB engines, diesel, turbocharged, inter-cooled, heat exchanger cooled, air start.

Lift engines: two GM 8V-92 engines, diesel, heat exchanger cooled, air start.

Gears: two ZF BW 455 reduction gears. Input shafts - identical rotation, output shafts - opposite rotation (2:1 ratio).

Lift fans: two TMS 42 in welded aluminium centrifugal fans.

Propeller shafts: 4 in diameter 17-4 PH stainless steel.

Bearings: 4 in BJ Byplex rubber bearings.

Propellers: 3-blade stainless.

Rudders: stainless steel built-up blades with 5 in diameter stainless rudder stocks.

Bearings: 5 in BJ Byplex rubber bearings.

Outfit: Passenger accommodation: 119 × 4 in thick cushioned bench seats on two deck levels. Two passenger heads provided.

Crew accommodation: six in two single and two two-person cabins with hanging lockers. Two crew toilets with showers provided. Mess area for six adjoins galley.

Auxiliary systems: Two GM 3-71 65 kVA heat exchanger cooled generators, one air start, one hydraulic start.

Model 212B, Margaret Jill **1988**

MODEL 730A (USN SES-200) HIGH LENGTH-TO-BEAM RATIO TEST CRAFT

The original 33.53 m SES demonstration boat is now owned by the US Navy. The boat was modified by adding a 15.24 m hull extension. The hull was cut amidships; the lift fans and engines remaining in the bow and the main engines remaining in the stern. Bow and stern sections were then moved apart and a 15.24 m plug section inserted between them. All major systems remained the same as they were in the original vessel, including the GM 16V-149TI engines.

In this configuration, the vessel had a 60 per cent greater disposable load than the demonstration boat, while its maximum speed was only reduced by 3 to 4 knots. At intermediate speeds, the power requirements were lower than for the shorter vessel, despite the greater displacement.

In 1986, the SES-200 successfully completed an eight-month series of joint technical and operational trials. The trials, which were conducted in Canada, France, Germany, Norway, Spain, Sweden and the UK, provided each host nation opportunities for direct evaluation of the high length-to-beam SES in their own waters.

Specifications

Length overall	48.7 m
Beam	11.88 m
Draught, hullborne	2.83 m
Draught, on-cushion	1.67 m
Displacement, max	207 t
Fuel capacity	80,128 l
Propulsive power	1,230 kW
Lift power	325 kW
Max speed	28 kts
Operational speed	22 kts
Range	3,850 n miles

Propulsion: The main engines are two DDC 16V-149TI, each driving 1.016 m diameter fixed-pitch propellers. The lift engines are four DDC 8V-92TI, each driving 1.067 m diameter Bell centrifugal fans.

Electrical system: DDC diesel generator, 85 kW plus 55 kW backup driven off one lift engine.

Reference: *The United Kingdom Trials of the SES-200* by B J W Pingree, B J Russell and J B Wilcox. Paper given at the Fourth International Hovercraft Conference, 6-7 May 1987.

SES-200 CONVERSION

On 11 April 1990, Textron Marine & Land Systems announced the award of a $1,744,858 contract by the US Army Corps of Engineers for the conversion, modification and upgrading of the propulsion system and hull structure of the 48.78 m SES-200.

The conventional propellers and existing 16V 149 TI diesel engines and gearboxes have been replaced by two MTU 16V 396 TB 94 diesel engines, using two ZF BW 755 gearboxes driving KaMeWa 71 S62/6-SII water-jet systems. Following the conversion, which increases the propulsion power from 2,386 to 4,265 kW, the SES-200 achieved speeds in excess of 40 knots in calm water, had greater manoeuvrability, produced lower in-water noise emission and was able to operate in shallower waters.

SES 200 after propulsion upgrading in 1990 1991

To conduct the conversion/re-powering work, the SES-200 was lifted from the water at the Textron Marine & Land Systems shipyard, transported 160 m overland and brought into position in a high-bay construction building.

After successfully completing acceptance trials in the Gulf of Mexico, the SES-200 returned to its home port at the David Taylor Research Center (DTRC), located at the Naval Air Station, Patuxent River, Maryland on the Chesapeake Bay. The DTRC, the Navy's laboratory for advanced naval vehicle development, deploys the craft in evaluation programmes.

HM 221 FIRE AND RESCUE VESSEL

In 1992, TM&LS delivered two SES fire and rescue vessels to the City of New York. The Hovermarine International HM 221 hulls are equipped for firefighting by TM&LS. Highly automated to allow operation by a crew of two, the vessels will provide the capability for firefighting, search and rescue, harbour patrol and pollution monitoring.

The Fire Department of the City of New York accepted delivery of the *John P Devaney*, the first of two SES fire and rescue vessels, on 17 July 1992. TM&LS delivered the second, the *Alfred E Ronaldson*, on 24 November 1992. The contract was valued at $6.5 million.

Specifications

Length overall	21.23 m
Beam	5.88 m
Draught, hullborne	1.75 m
Weight, max	36.45 t
Crew	2
Fuel capacity	2,460 l
Water capacity	76 l
Propulsive power	2 × 373 kW
Lift power	287 kW
Max speed	30 kts
Operational speed	20 kts
Range	60 n miles

Structure: Shell mouldings, submouldings, frames, bulkheads and major attachments in glass-reinforced plastic. Fendering is fitted to the gunwale.

Propulsion: The main engines are two Detroit Diesel Corporation 8V 92TA diesels driving 48.26 cm, three-blade propellers through direct-drive reversing gearboxes (ZF IRM 310 PL) and V-drive gearboxes (BPM VD/180; overdrive ratio 1.06:1).

Lift power is provided by a Detroit Diesel Corporation 6V 92TA which is also used as a pump engine. A second pump engine is provided by a Detroit Diesel Corporation 8V 92TA diesel.

Controls: Hydraulic pump: Hobourn Eaton HE 3501 8014-34 driven from lift engine.

Steering unit: Danfoss OSPB 100, OSP 8100, NR 150 0027.

Hydraulic actuator: Adam Hydraulics 4.45 cm (1¾ in) bore × 30.5 cm (12 in) stroke.

Outfit: Utility-standard crew accommodation includes a two-tiered bunk, cooking facilities, a sink and a toilet compartment.

Operations equipment: Three fire pumps (port, starboard, forward) with capacity for 6,938 l/min (1,833 US gal/min) at 1,427 KPa (207 lb.ft/in^2). The port and starboard pumps are driven by the fire pump engine and the forward pump by the lift engine. The firefighting equipment is remotely controlled for rotation and elevation from the wheelhouse: one 20,818 l/min (5,500 US gal/min) master monitor mounted on the wheelhouse; two 9,629 l/min (2,500 US gal/min) monitors mounted on the foredeck; and two 9,629 l/min (2,500 US gal/min) monitors mounted on either side of the bow beneath the foredeck. All fire monitors, except the wheelhouse monitor, can be controlled from a straight stream to a 90° fog. There is a deck hydrant with connections for four 7.62 cm (3 in) and one 11.43 cm (4 ½ in) fire hoses.

MODEL C-7

The C-7 Hovercraft is designed for minimum-cost operation with high payloads and extreme environmental conditions. The 17.8 m craft combines a lightweight composite superstructure with a welded aluminium hull and is available in a number of configurations.

The concept chosen for the entire superstructure, propeller ducts and rudders is a Resin Transfer Moulding (RTM) process employing primarily an E-glass composition. The process uses resin injection under vacuum with a room temperature cure to consistently achieve a glass content of over 60 per cent. This compares to a conventional wet lay-up process that typically produces a 40 per cent glass content. Parts can be fabricated with virtually zero void content and an exceptional surface finish ready for paint.

The C-7 superstructure is composed of 12 basic sections, plus hatches, doors and bulkheads. The curved bow section, which is 139 by 247 in, is considered the largest production part ever fabricated using this process: it weighs 450 lb without the windows installed. To obtain maximum stiffness at

C-7 executive transporter 1995

MCAC firing on M-58 line charge on the beach 1996

MCAC rigged with an AQS-14 minehunting sonar kit 1996

minimum weight, carbon fibre composite is used in several transverse frames and in the centre ring section of the propeller shroud.

The basic C-7 hovercraft features a 40 plus knot capacity, low noise levels, low operating costs, and environmentally safe operations. It is available in four configurations: fire and rescue craft (FR-7), passenger ferry, executive transport and patrol craft (P-12).

In 1994, TM&LS delivered an executive C-7 transporter for use by Freeport Indonesia. The *Kasuari*, as it was named, features modern, quiet, first class accommodation, windows forward and on both sides, bar, kitchen, and an interior design tailored to the customer.

An FR-7 configured for firefighting and rescue was delivered to the Civil Aviation Authority of Singapore at Changi International airport. The FR-7 has a bow ramp, a fire monitor that delivers preselected concentrate strength foam at more than 1,500 litres per minute at least 30 feet from the craft, and accommodates 50 passengers/50 Stokes stretchers.

The P-12 patrol craft design, a stretched derivative of the C-7, features 45 knot speed and 6 tonne payload; crew berthing and galley; bow ramp for roll-on/off capability; carrying capacity for a light vehicle (HMMWV) and a 500 n mile range.

Specifications

Length overall	16 m
Beam	9.46 m
Weight, max	29.5 t
Payload	5.4 t
Crew	2
Passengers	46
Fuel capacity	3,785 l
Water capacity	152 l
Propulsive power	2 × 386 kW
Lift power	235 kW
Max speed	40 kts
Range	500 n miles

Classification: USCG Sub-chapter T Small Passenger Vessels (under 100 gross tons) and IMO Code of Safety for Dynamically Supported Craft.

Structure: Hull material; welded 5456 aluminium.
Superstructure material: advanced marine composite.
Air cushion sealing: Bag and semi-closed finger, high stability skirt system with planing stern fingers. Bag material is neoprene-coated, open-weave, nylon fabric. Finger material is rubber-coated, open-weave, nylon fabric.

Propulsion: Two Dowty 2.44 m diameter, 4-bladed, ducted, controllable-pitch propellers driven by two Deutz BF12L 513C air-cooled diesel engines.

C-7 fire/rescue craft (FR-7) **1995**

C-7 Patrol craft (P-12), artist's impression **1995**

The lift system consists of two 0.92 m diameter double-width double-inlet centrifugal fans powered by one Deutz BF8L 51C air-cooled diesel engine.

Electrical system: 24 V DC. Four 24 V DC battery installations. 208 V AC, 100 A, 60 Hz, 3-phase shore power feed.

Auxiliary systems: One 25 kW air-cooled diesel generation set 120/208 V AC, 60 Hz, 3-phase.
Two 100 A 28 V DC alternators driven from the main engines.

UPDATED

HYDROFOILS

Company Listing by Country

Commonwealth of Independent States
Feodosia Shipbuilding Association (Morye)
Volga Shipyard
Gomel Yard
Ś Ordzhonikidze Ship Building and Repair Yard

Indonesia
PT Pal Indonesia (Persero)

Italy
Fincantieri-Cantieri Navali Italiani SpA
Rodriquez Cantieri Navali SpA

Japan
Hitachi Zosen Corporation
Kawasaki Heavy Industries Ltd
Sumitomo Heavy Industries Ltd
Technological Research Association of Techno-Superliner

United States of America
Boeing
Westfoil International

COMMONWEALTH OF INDEPENDENT STATES

FEODOSIA SHIPBUILDING ASSOCIATION (MORYE)

Feodosia 334871, Crimea, Ukraine, CIS

Tel: +7 (6562) 69905
Telex: 187125 PTB SU KAFA
Fax: +7 (6562) 32373

L Astakhov, *General Director*
Victor Oleinik, *Chief Engineer*
Gregory Klebanov, *Head of Foreign Economic Relations Department*

CYCLONE (*Liisa*)

Cyclone was built at the shipbuilding yard at Feodosia. The design is approved by certificate No 19931, 20 June 1985 and by the inventor's certificate dating from 1969 to 1984. Acceptance and precommissioning trials took place in 1986 and experimental operation of the vessel was first undertaken in 1987. This vessel is designed to Hydrofoil Passenger Class KM*2A2 of the Register of Shipping of the former Soviet Union. Cyclone is a gas-turbine powered hydrofoil designed for coastal routes and operations up to 100 miles from a port of refuge. It may operate foilborne in waves up to 3.5 m in height.

Liisa has been operating on the route Tallinn to Helsinki.

Specifications

Length overall	44.2 m
Beam	7.3 m
Foil width	12.6 m
Draught, hullborne	4.3 m
Draught, foilborne	2.4 m
Displacement, max	137.1 t
Displacement, min	100.8 t
Payload	37 t
Crew	9
Passengers	250
Operational speed	7 kts hullborne
Operational speed	42 kts
Range	300 n miles

Propulsion: 1 × M37 gas-turbine.
1 × 735 kW diesel (for slow running).

The gas-turbine powered 250-seat Cyclone at sea

1993

Cyclone

1991

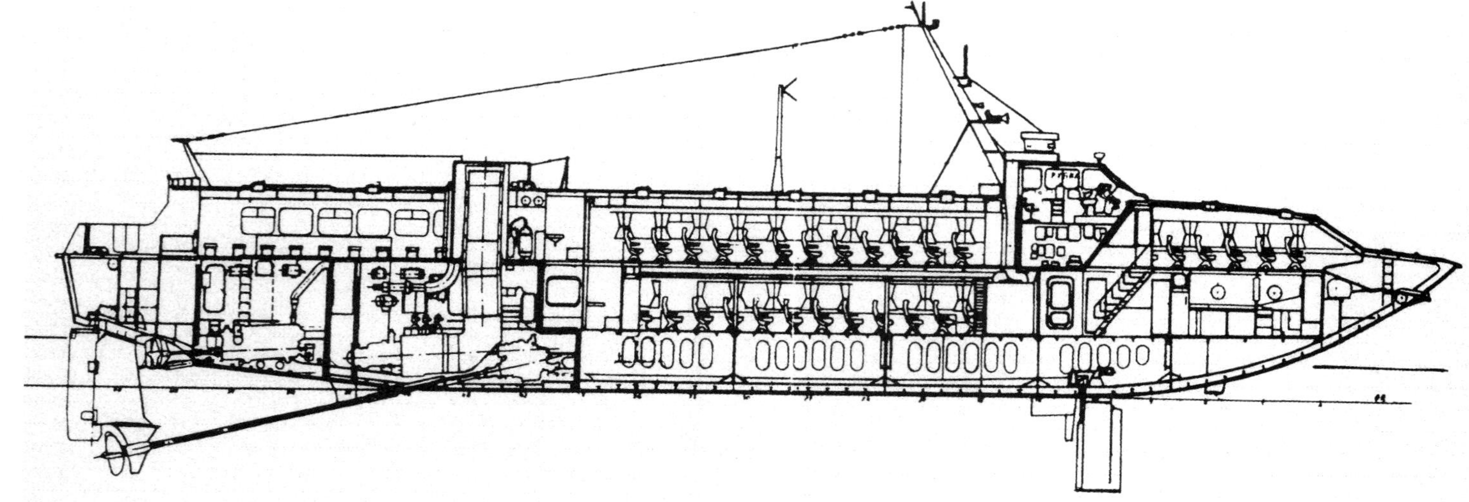

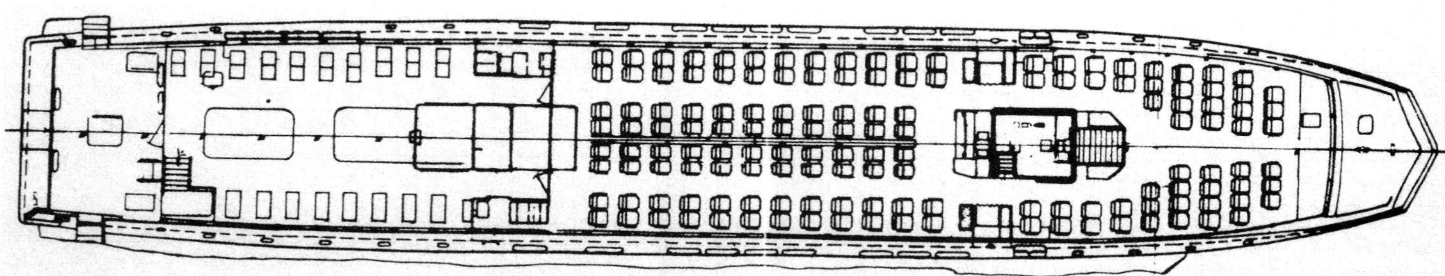

Layout of Cyclone

CYCLONE-M

Cyclone-M is an improved version of Cyclone and is powered by two gas-turbine engines. The vessel is designed to operate on sea routes of up to 100 miles from the port of refuge in countries with moderately cold climates; a tropical version of Cyclone is available. The production of Cyclone-M started in 1993-94.

Specifications

Length overall	44.2 m
Beam	12.5 m
Draught, hullborne	4.3 m
Draught, foilborne	2.4 m
Displacement, max	146 t
Displacement, min	108 t
Passengers	210
Propulsive power	2 × 2,960 kW
Operational speed	42 kts
Range	300 n miles
Operational limitation	wave height 3 m Beaufort 6

Structure: Hull material: aluminium.
Propulsion: Engines: 2 gas-turbines.
Thrust devices: propellers.

OLYMPIA

Olympia is a sea-going hydrofoil designed to operate on sea routes under tropical and temperate climatic conditions up to 50 miles from a port of refuge in open seas and up to 100 miles in inland seas and large lakes.

In a Sea State of 0 to 2 and in wind conditions up to Force 3 the speed of *Olympia* is 36 to 37 knots when foilborne and 10 to 12 knots when hullborne.

The first Olympia, *Laura*, was introduced on the Helsinki to Tallinn route in 1993 with the second craft delivered in September 1994.

Specifications

Length overall	43.3 m
Beam	14 m
Draught, hullborne	4.6 m
Draught, foilborne	2 m
Displacement, max	135 t
Displacement, min	103 t
Crew	6
Passengers	250
Fuel capacity	6,000 kg
Water capacity	2,000 kg
Propulsive power	2 × 1,905
Operational speed	37 kts
Range	300 n miles
Operational limitation	wave height 3.5 m Beaufort 7

Structure: Hull material: aluminium.
Propulsion: Engines: 2 × MTU 16V 396 TE 74L diesels, each rated at 2,000 kW at 2,000 rpm driving fixed pitch propellers via a ZFBW 755S reverse reduction gearbox.

Voskhod-2M **1993**

VOSKHOD-2

Designers of the Voskhod, which has been gradually replacing craft of the Raketa series, drew on engineering experience gained with the Raketa and also the more sophisticated Meteor and Kometa. Visually the Voskhod is more akin to a scaled-down Kometa with its engine room aft, replacing the rear passenger saloon.

Voskhod 14 was launched in June 1980 and delivered to the Amur Line for summer services along the Amur river.

The vessel is designed for high-speed passenger ferry services during daylight hours on rivers, reservoirs, lakes and sheltered waters. It meets the requirements of Soviet River Register Class O with the following wave restrictions (3 per cent safety margin): foilborne, 1.3 m; hullborne, 2 m.

Specifications

Length overall	27.6 m
Beam	6.2 m
Draught, hullborne	2 m
Draught, foilborne	1.1 m
Displacement, min	20 t
Displacement, max	28 t
Payload	5.9 t
Crew	4
Passengers	71
Fuel capacity	1,647 l

Water capacity	138 l
Propulsive power	810 kW
Max speed	37.8 kts
Operational speed	32.4 kts
Range	270 n miles
Operational limitation	wave height 1.3 m

Structure: Similar in shape to the Kometa and earlier models of the Sormovo hydrofoil series, with a wedge-shaped bow, raked stem and spoon-shaped stern. A single step is provided to facilitate take-off. In fabricating the basic structure, which is largely in AlMg-61 aluminium-magnesium alloy, extensive use has been made of arc and spot welding. The hull is framed on longitudinal and transverse formers. Below deck is divided into eight watertight compartments by transverse bulkheads. It will remain afloat with any one compartment or the machinery space flooded.

The craft has a fixed foil system, comprising one bow foil with a pitch stability sub-foil immediately behind, one aft foil, plus an amidships foil to facilitate take off. Bow and amidship foils appear to be of shallow V configuration and each has four vertical struts. The fully submerged stern foil has two side struts and is supported in the centre by the end bracket of the propeller shaft. The surface and lower parts of the foil struts and stabiliser are in Cr18Ni9Ti stainless steel, while the upper parts of the struts and stabiliser and also the amidships foil are in AlMg-61 plate alloy.

Propulsion: Power is supplied by a single M-401A four-stroke water-cooled, supercharged 12-cylinder V-type diesel, delivering 810 kW at 1,600 rpm maximum and 736 kW at 1,550 rpm cruising. The engine, which has a variable-speed governor and a reversing clutch, is sited aft with its shaft inclined at 9°. Output is transferred via a flexible coupling to a single six-bladed variable-pitch propeller via an R-21 V-drive gearbox. Guaranteed service life of the engine before the first overhaul is 3,000 hours. Specific oil consumption is not more than 8 g/kWh.

Electrical systems: Power supply is 24 to 27 V DC. A 3 kW generator is attached to the engine and supplies 27.5 V while the craft is operating. Four 12 V storage batteries, each of 180 Ah capacity and connected in series-parallel to form a single bank, supply power during short stops. An auxiliary circuit can be connected to shore systems for 220 V, single-phase, 50 Hz AC supply.

Control: Single semi-balanced rudder in AlMg plate provides directional control. Operation of the engine, rudder, reverse gear and fuel supply is effected hydraulically from the wheelhouse.

VOSKHOD-2M

This version is a sea-going hydrofoil for daylight operation within 25 miles of a port of refuge. The dimensions are the same as Voskhod-2.

Production of the sea-going Voskhod-2M started in 1993.

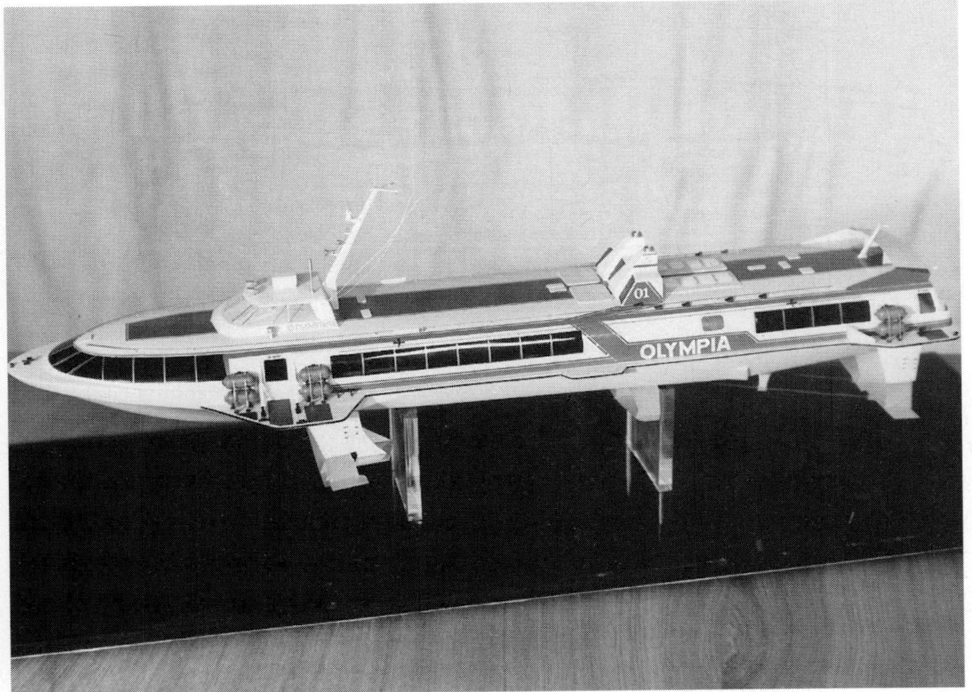

Olympia **1993**

Voskhod-2

1988

Specifications	
Length overall	27.6 m
Beam	4.4 m
Foil width	6.4 m
Draught	2 m
Displacement, min	24.6 t
Displacement, max	32.5 t
Passengers	65
Operational speed	30 kts
Range	200 n miles
Operational limitation	wave height 1.25 m Beaufort 4

Propulsion: Engines: 1 × M419A diesel.
Thrust device: fixed-pitch 6-blade bronze propeller.

VERIFIED

GOMEL YARD

Belarus, CIS

BYELORUS

This craft was developed from the Raketa, via the Chaika, for fast passenger services on shallow winding rivers less than 1 m deep and too shallow for conventional vessels.

It was put into series production at the river shipyard at Gomel, Belarus in 1965. Byelorus was expected to be succeeded in service by the 53-seat Polesye.

Specifications

Length overall	18.55 m
Beam	4.64 m
Draught hullborne	0.9 m
Draught foilborne	0.3 m
Displacement, min	9.6 t
Displacement, max	14.5 t
Passengers	40
Propulsive power	708 kW
Operational speed	34 kts

Structure: Hull and superstructure are built in aluminium-magnesium alloy. The hull is of all-welded construction and the superstructure is riveted and welded.

The shallow draught submerged foil system consists of one bow foil and one rear foil.

Propulsion: Power is supplied by an M-50 F-3 or M-400 diesel rated at 708 kW maximum and with a normal service output of 447 kW. The wheelhouse is fitted with an electrohydraulic remote-control system for the engine and fuel supply.

Outfit: Aircraft type seats for 40 passengers. The prototype seated only 30.

Byelorus on Karakum Canal, Turkmenia

1986

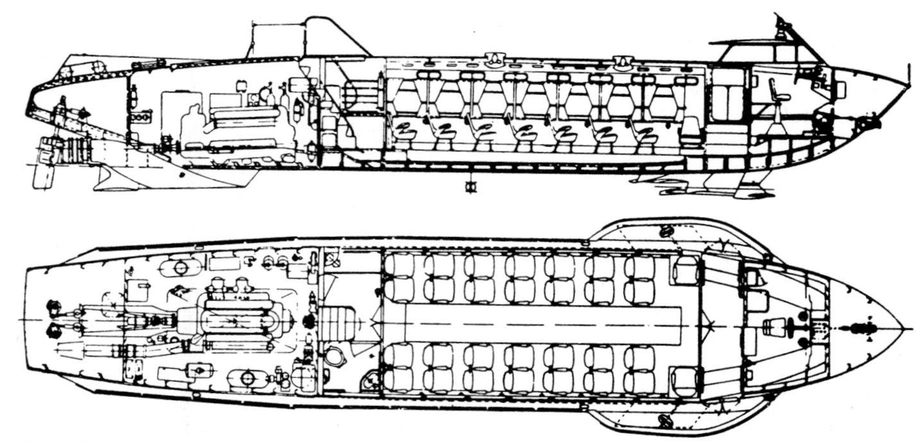

Profile and deck plan of Byelorus

POLESYE

This shallow-draught hydrofoil craft (27 built by early 1989) is intended for the high-speed transportation of passengers and tourists during daylight hours in the upper reaches of major rivers, river tributaries and freshwater reservoirs in regions with temperate climate. Two Polesyes entered service in 1992 with MAHART on the Budapest to Vienna route. The craft is classified *R on the RSFSR Register of River Shipping and is suitable for use in conditions with a wave height of 0.5 m when running on the hydrofoils, and with a wave height of up to 1.2 m in the displacement mode.

The craft has capacity for a maximum of 53 passengers. The passengers are accommodated in a single lounge area in the mid-section of the vessel. In calm waters with wind conditions up to Beaufort 3, the vessel is capable of a speed of 35.1 knots. The vessel is capable of running on the hydrofoils on river channels with a radius of turn up to 100 to 150 m.

The time to accelerate from the stationary condition to becoming fully foilborne does not exceed 1.5 minutes. The distance from service speed to stop, with the propeller in reverse, is five to six boat lengths.

The hull is divided into five compartments by means of watertight bulkheads. The foils and side fenders are removable to facilitate overland transport.

The vessel is powered by a 12-cylinder 'V' diesel engine with a maximum capacity of 810 kW at 1,600 rpm. The engine is installed at an angle of 12.5° to the horizontal and transmits power to the propeller via a direct-coupled reversing gear unit.

Specifications

Length overall	21.25 m
Beam	3.6 m
Foil width	5 m
Draught, hullborne	0.95 m
Draught, foilborne	0.4 m
Displacement, min	13.7 t
Displacement, max	20 t
Passengers	53
Propulsive power	810 kW
Operational speed	35 kts
Range	216 n miles
Operational limitation	wave height 0.5 m

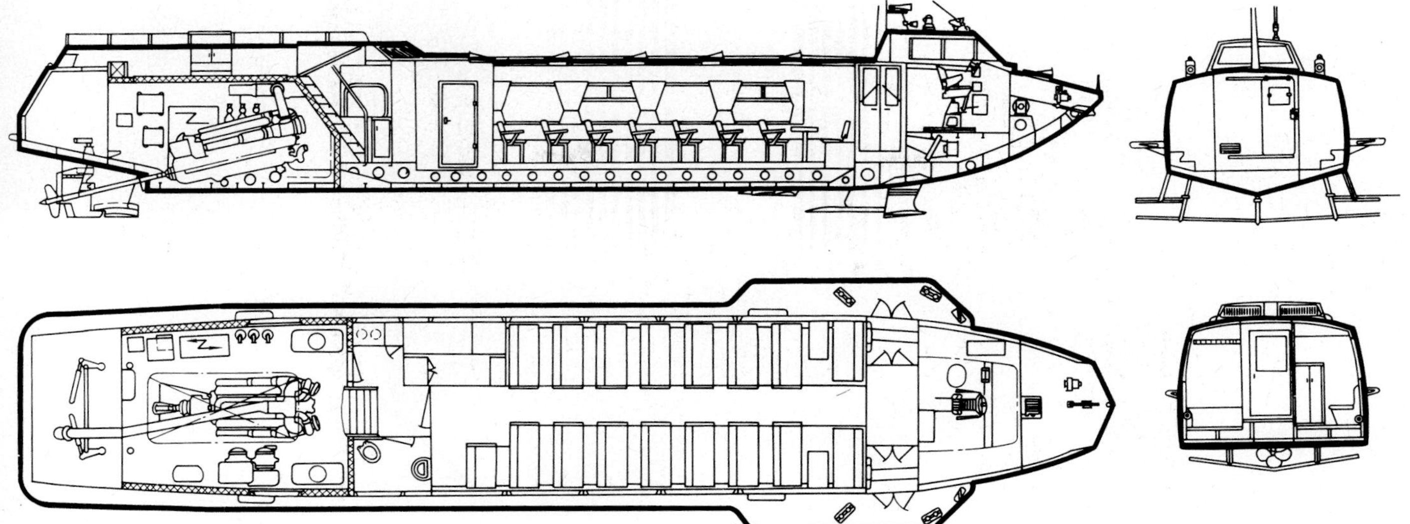

General arrangement of Polesye

Polesye 1988

MALAKHIT

A river ambulance hydrofoil designed for emergency medical calls for people living in remote regions and for passengers and crews of river-craft.

Malakhit is designed to take five patients. The project is based on the SPK Polesye series hydrofoil.

Specifications

Length	22 m
Beam	3.6 m
Draught, hullborne	0.9 m
Draught, foilborne	0.4 m
Crew	2
Operational speed	35 kts
Range	216 n miles

VERIFIED

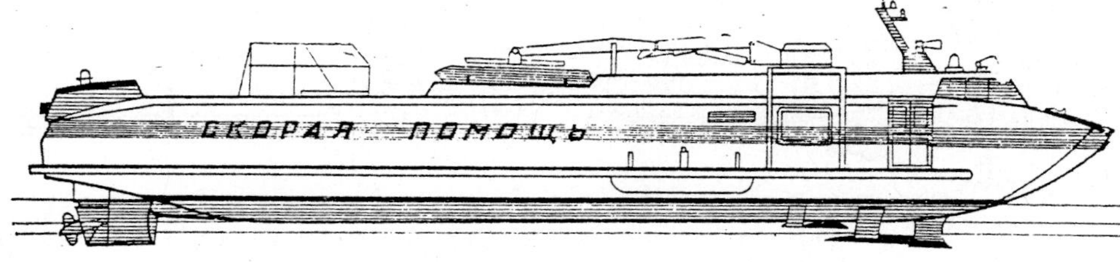

Malakhit river ambulance

Ś ORDZHONIKIDZE SHIP BUILDING AND REPAIR YARD

Head Office and Yard: Poti, Georgia, CIS

Z N Archaidze, *Yard Director*
I Ye Malechanov, *Chief Designer*
Yu Golubkin, *Deputy Chief Designer*
B Pavlyuk, *Chief Engineer*
G A Terentyeb, *Manager, Sea Trials*

KOLKHIDA

Designed to replace the 20 year old Kometa fast passenger ferry, Kolkhida is available in two versions: the Albatros, which operates on domestic services within the CIS, and the Kolkhida, intended for export.

Kolkhida is faster than Kometa, seats more passengers, uses less fuel and can operate foilborne in higher sea states. Among the various design innovations are a new foil system with automatic lift control, the use of new materials in the hull structure and a more rational cabin layout, permitting a substantial increase in seating capacity. The engine room is aft, as on the Voskhod, to reduce the noise level. Overall dimensions are almost identical to those of Kometa-M.

Trials of the Kolkhida prototype took place in the Baltic between March and June 1981 and the vessel has been in production since with sales being achieved in Greece, Italy and Yugoslavia.

Kolkhida is designed to operate under tropical and moderate climates up to 50 miles from a port of refuge in open seas and up to 100 miles from a port of refuge in inland seas and large lakes, with a permissible distance between two ports of refuge of not more than 200 miles.

Foilborne, the craft can operate in waves up to 2 m and winds up to Beaufort 5; hullborne it can operate in waves up to 3 m and winds up to Beaufort 6.

Kolkhida forward starboard foils and struts 1987

Specifications

Length overall	34.5 m
Beam	5.8 m
Foil width	10.3 m
Draught, hullborne	3.5 m
Draught, foilborne	1.9 m

Kolkhida aft foil arrangement

1988

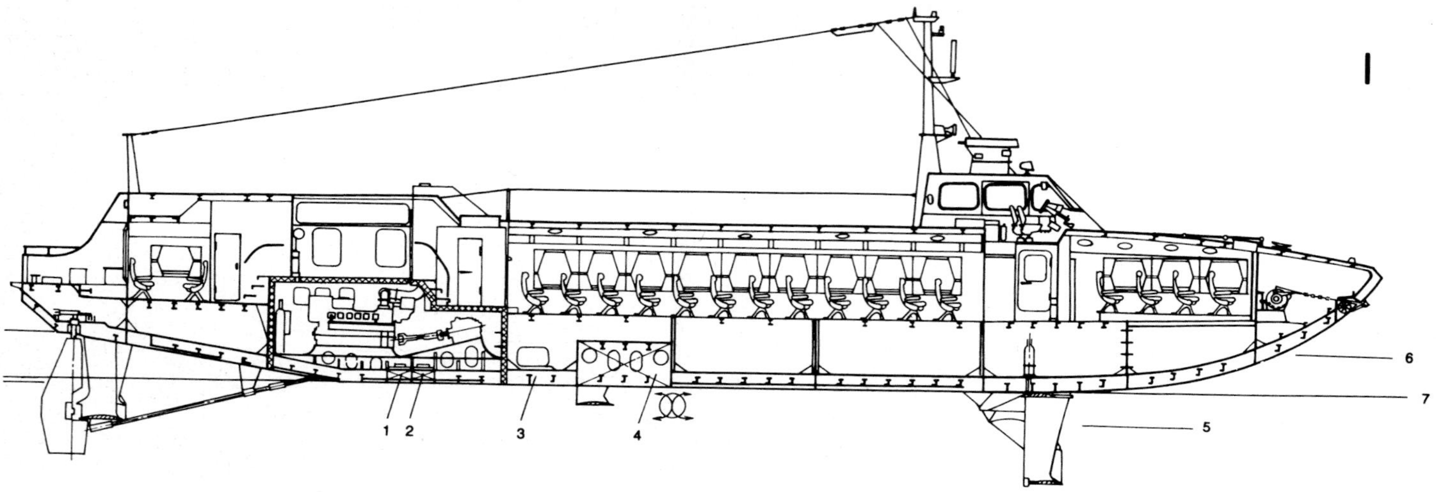

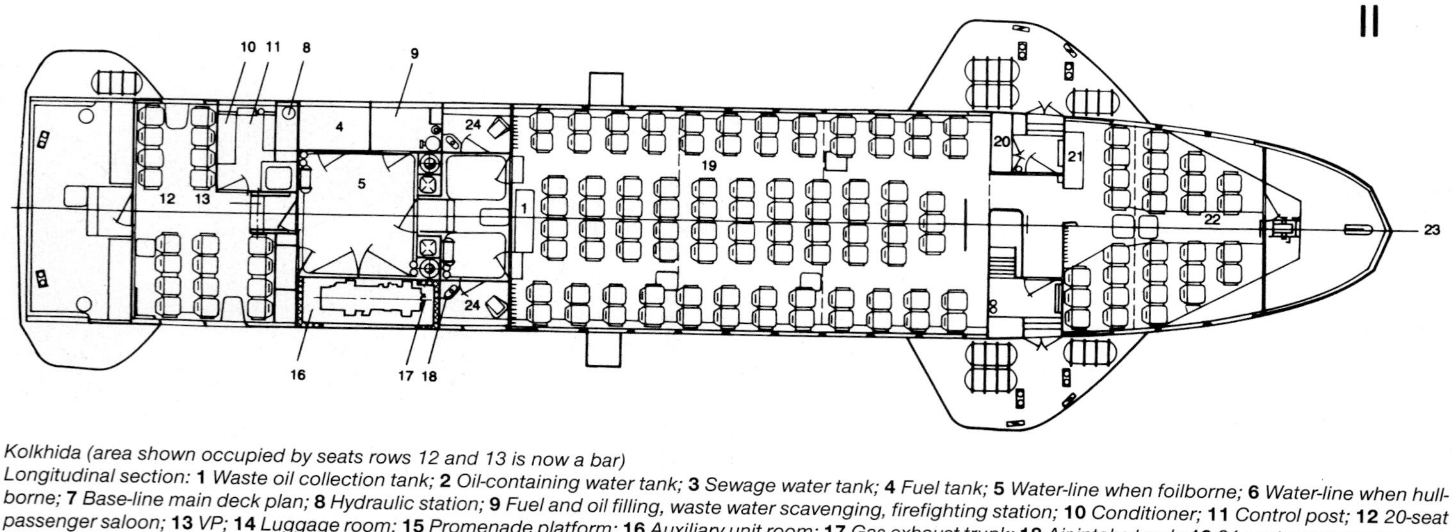

Kolkhida (area shown occupied by seats rows 12 and 13 is now a bar)
Longitudinal section: **1** *Waste oil collection tank;* **2** *Oil-containing water tank;* **3** *Sewage water tank;* **4** *Fuel tank;* **5** *Water-line when foilborne;* **6** *Water-line when hull-borne;* **7** *Base-line main deck plan;* **8** *Hydraulic station;* **9** *Fuel and oil filling, waste water scavenging, firefighting station;* **10** *Conditioner;* **11** *Control post;* **12** *20-seat passenger saloon;* **13** *VP;* **14** *Luggage room;* **15** *Promenade platform;* **16** *Auxiliary unit room;* **17** *Gas exhaust trunk;* **18** *Air intake trunk;* **19** *91-seat passenger saloon;* **20** *Aggregate room;* **21** *Conditioner;* **22** *29-seat passenger saloon;* **23** *Central line;* **24** *Toilet*

Kolkhida **1991**

Displacement, min	56 t
Displacement, max	72 t
Crew	6
Passengers	155
Propulsive power	2 × 1,050 kW
Operational speed	34 kts
Range	150 n miles
Operational limitation	wave height 2 m
	Beaufort 5

Classification: The craft meets the requirements of the Register of Shipping of the CIS and is constructed to Hydrofoil Class KM* 2AS Passenger Class SPK under the Register's technical supervision. It complies fully with the IMO Code of Safety for Dynamically Supported Craft.

Structure: Double-chine, V-bottom type, with raked stern and streamlined superstructure. The hull and superstructure are built in aluminium-magnesium alloys. Framing is based on T and T-angle webframes. Frame spacing is 600 mm. Longitudinal framing of the sides, decks and hull bottom is based on stiffening ribs, keelson, stringers and deck girders. Below the main deck the hull is subdivided by watertight bulkheads into nine compartments. The craft will remain afloat with any two adjacent compartments flooded.

The foil system, which is similar to that of Kometa, comprises a trapeze-type bow foil, an aft and amidships foil, close to the longitudinal centre of gravity to assist take-off. The foils are connected to the hull by struts and brackets. Bow and stern foil surfaces and the lower ends of the bow and stern foil struts are in steel alloy. The amidships foil, struts, upper sections of the bow and stern foil struts are in aluminium-magnesium alloy. A cast, balanced rudder in 40 mm thick aluminium-magnesium alloy is fitted. Total blade area is 2.75 m^2.

Propulsion: Power is supplied by two MTU 12V 396 TC 82 water-cooled, supercharged 12-cylinder V-type four-stroke marine diesels, each with a normal service output of 960 kW, 1,745 rpm and 1,050 kW, 1,800 rpm maximum. Guaranteed service life of each engine before first major overhaul is 9,000 hours; maximum service life is 12 years. Output is transferred to twin 740 mm diameter contrarotating fixed-pitch propellers through reversible gearboxes which are remotely controlled from the wheelhouse. The propeller shafts are inclined at 14° and supported by rubber and metal bearings.

Electrical system: Engine-driven generators supply power while the craft is operating. The 4.5 kW generator included in the auxiliary unit supplies power when the craft is at rest. Acid storage batteries connected in series supply power during short stops.

Control: A sonic/electronic autopilot controls lift by operating trailing edge flaps on the centre section of the bow foil and on the inner sections of the aft foil. The foil flaps are adjusted hydraulically to dampen heave, pitch, roll and yaw motions in heavy seas and provide co-ordinated turns.

Rudder movement is controlled hydraulically by any one of three systems: push-button, manual or via the autopilot.

VERIFIED

Kolkhida **1987**

Craft built to 1988

Type	Name	Built	Delivered to
Kolkhida		1983	Black Sea Shipping Co, Odessa, CIS
Kolkhida	*2*	1984	Black Sea Shipping Co, Odessa, CIS
Kolkhida	*3*	1984	Black Sea Shipping Co, Odessa, CIS
Kolkhida	*4*	1984	Black Sea Shipping Co, Odessa, CIS
Kolkhida	*5*	1984	Black Sea Shipping Co, Odessa, CIS
Kolkhida	*6*	1985	Black Sea Shipping Co, Odessa, CIS
Kolkhida	*Magnolija*	1986	Kvarner Express, Yugoslavia
Kolkhida	*Kamelija*	1986	Kvarner Express, Yugoslavia
Kolkhida	*Mirta*	1986	Kvarner Express, Yugoslavia
Kolkhida	*Mimosa*	1986	Kvarner Express, Yugoslavia
Kolkhida	*Aliatlante*	1986	Alilauro SpA, Italy
Kolkhida	*Alieolo*	1986	Alilauro SpA, Italy
Kolkhida	*Flying Dolphin XVII*	1986	Ceres Flying Hydroways Ltd, Piraeus, Greece
Kolkhida	*Flying Dolphin XVIII*	1986	Ceres Flying Hydroways Ltd, Piraeus, Greece
Kolkhida	*Flying Dolphin XIX*	1986	Ceres Flying Hydroways Ltd, Piraeus, Greece
Kolkhida	*Aligea*	1986	Alilauro SpA, Italy
Kolkhida	*Alikenia*	1986	Alilauro SpA, Italy
Kolkhida	*Tiburon*	1988	Compania Naviera Mallorquina, Spain
Kolkhida	*Aliflorida*	1988	Alilauro SpA, Italy

VOLGA SHIPYARD

51 Svoboda Street, 565, Nizhny Novgorod, 603600, Russia, CIS

Vitaly G Alekseyev, *Marketing Manager*
Leonid G Filippov, *Marketing Manager*

Tel: +7 (8132) 253217
Fax: +7 (8312) 251372

Volga Shipyard is one of the oldest established shipyards in the CIS. In addition to building displacement craft of many kinds for the CIS River Fleet, the yard constructs the world's widest range of passenger hydrofoils, many of which are equipped with the Alexeyev shallow draught submerged foil system. The late Dr Alexeyev started work at the end of 1945 on the design of his foil system which had to be suitable for operation on smooth, but open and shallow rivers and canals. He succeeded in making use of the immersion depth effect, or surface effect, for stabilising the foil immersion in calm waters by the use of small lift coefficients.

The system comprises two main horizontal lifting surfaces, one forward and one aft, with little or no dihedral, each carrying approximately half the weight of the vessel. A submerged foil loses lift gradually as it approaches the surface from a submergence of about one chord. This effect prevents the submerged foils from rising completely to the surface. Means therefore had to be provided to assist take off and prevent the vessel from sinking back to the displacement condition. The answer lay in the provision of planing sub-foils of small aspect ratio in the vicinity of the forward struts arranged so that when they are touching the water surface the main foils are submerged approximately to a depth of one chord.

The approach embodies characteristics of the Grunberg principle of inherent angle of attack variation, comprising a 'wing' and a stabiliser system. When the Alexeyev foils drop below the shallow draught zone, the craft converts momentarily to the Grunberg mode of operation, duplicating its configuration. The otherwise inactive sub-foils, coming into contact with the water surface, become the Grunberg stabilisers and cause the foils to climb up into the shallow draught zone where they resume normal operation in the Alexeyev mode.

The foils have good riding characteristics on inland and sheltered waters.

The system was first tested on a small launch powered by a 77 bhp converted car engine. Three more small craft were built to prove the idea, then work began on the yard's first multiseat passenger craft, the Raketa, the first of which was launched in June 1957 and completed more than 25 years of service.

The yard also co-operates with the Leningrad Water Transport Institute in the development of seagoing craft with fully submerged V-type and trapeze-type surface-piercing foils, similar in configuration to those of the Schertel-Sachsenberg system. Craft employing V or trapeze foils are generally described as being of the Strela-type, Strela being the first operational Soviet design to use trapeze foils. Seating 82 to 94 passengers, the vessel is powered by two M-50 diesels and in appearance is a cross between the PT 20 and the PT 50, though smaller than the latter.

Passenger hydrofoils in production at yards on the Baltic and Black Seas are the Zenit (designed to replace Meteor hydrofoils) and the Albatros and Kolkhida, which are Kometa replacements, with seats for 120 passengers. Smaller hydrofoils are also under development including the 50-seat Polesye at the river-craft shipyard at Gomel and Lastochka, which has been designed to supersede Voskhod.

Substantial numbers of hydrofoils have been exported, especially Kometas, Meteors, Raketas, Voskhods, Volgas and recently Kolkhidas which have been sold to Greek and Italian operators. Countries in which they are being or have been operated include Austria, Bulgaria, Cyprus, Czechoslovakia, Finland, France, East and West Germany, Greece, Iran, Italy, Morocco, the Philippines, Poland, Romania, Spain, the UK, the USA and Yugoslavia.

Principal civil hydrofoil craft built in the former Soviet Union

Type	Yard	No of seats	First launched
Raketa (produced in quantity and exported)		58	1957
Meteor (produced in quantity and exported)	Gorki	116	1960
Kometa (produced in quantity and exported)	Poti & Feodosia	100	
Sputnik	Gorki	300	1961
Mir		92	1961
Strela (two built)		94	1962
Vikhr (sea-going version of Sputnik)		268	1962
Burevestnik (one built)		130-150	1964
Chaika	Gomel		1965
Byelorus			1965
Kometa-ME		116-120	1968
Typhoon (one built)	Leningrad	98-105	1969
Voskhod (produced in quantity and exported)	Gorki	71	1969
Delphin (Strela derivative)			pre-1968
Nevka (in production 1969-70)	Leningrad		1969
Volga		6	1972
Voskhod-2			1974
Kolkhida (exported to Greece, Italy and Yugoslavia) & Albatros (replacement for Kometas)	Poti	120	1980
Polesye	Gomel	53	1985
Lastochka (replacement for Voskhod)		64	1986
Cyclone	Feodosia	250	1986

Principal military hydrofoil craft built in the former Soviet Union

Type	Number built	Weight	In service
P8-Class (wooden hull)		-	retired
Pchela	2	75 t	1968 or earlier
Turya	30	250 t	1973 or earlier
Matka	16	260 t	1977 or earlier
Sarancha (NATO codename)	1	320 t	1977 or earlier
Babochka	1	400 t	1978 or earlier
Muravey	1+	230 t	1983

RAKETA

The prototype Raketa was launched in 1957 and was the first multiseat passenger hydrofoil to employ the Alexeyev shallow draught submerged foil system. Several hundred are now in service on all the major rivers of the CIS.

In August 1982 it was announced that the prototype was still in service and has carried more than two million passengers. The distance travelled by the craft during the period was stated to be equal to '52 voyages around the equator'.

A substantial number of Raketas has been exported. Examples are in service in Austria, Bulgaria, the Czech Republic, Germany, Hungary, Poland, Romania, Slovakia and the former Yugoslavia.

Production of the Raketa has now stopped and yards previously involved in their construction are building Voskhod and other designs.

The description that follows applies to the Raketa T, the standard export variant, powered by an M-401A diesel and with a cruising speed of about 58 km/h (32 knots).

The vessel is designed for high-speed passenger ferry services during daylight hours on rivers, reservoirs and sheltered waters in tropical climates. It meets the requirements of the Soviet River Register Class O with operation restricted to 0.8 m waves when foilborne and up to 1.5 m when hullborne.

The passenger saloon is provided with natural and induced ventilation and seats 58. The crew comprises a captain, engineer, deckhand and barman.

Specifications

Length overall	26.96 m
Beam	5 m
Draught, hullborne	1.8 m
Draught, foilborne	1.1 m
Displacement, min	27.09 t
Displacement, max	20.31 t
Crew	4
Passengers	58
Fuel capacity	1,647 l
Propulsive power	671 kW
Operational speed	31.32 kts
Operational limitation	wave height 0.8 m

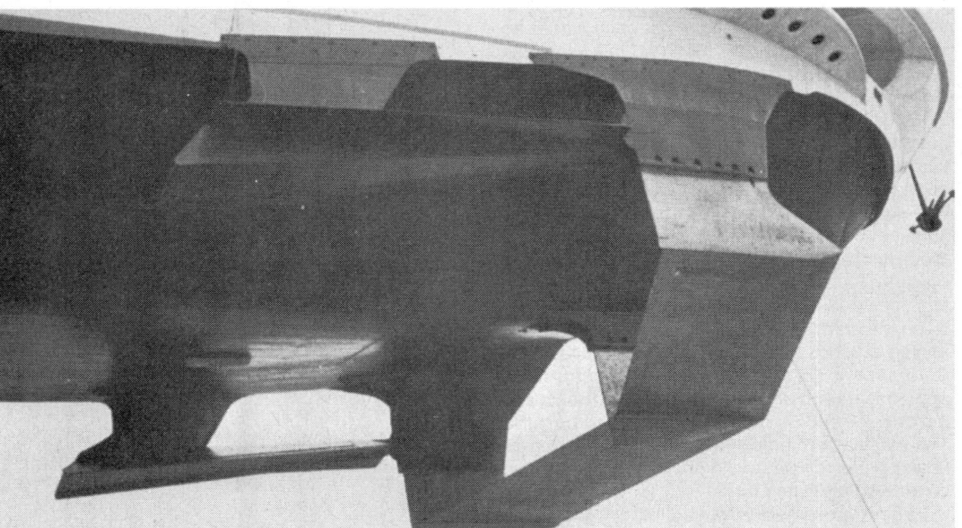

Bow foil and planing stabiliser foils of Raketa **1986**

Raketa M ***1986***

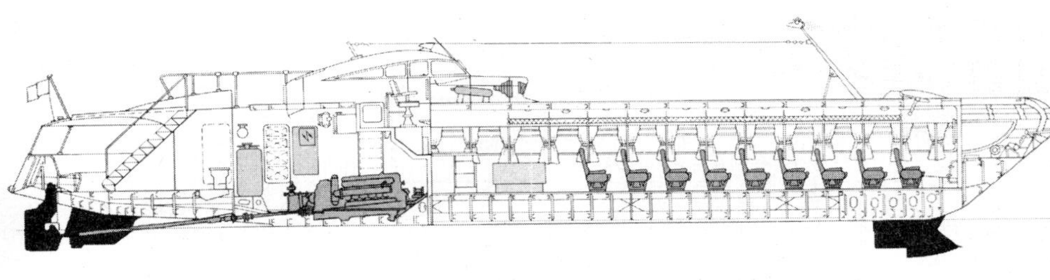

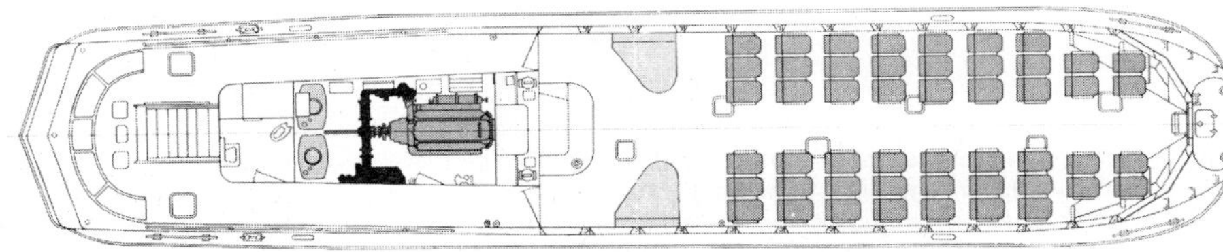

Inboard profile and plan view of standard 50-seat Raketa

Structure: The hull is framed on longitudinal and transverse formers and all the main elements - plating, deck, partitions, bulkheads, platforms and wheelhouse - are in riveted duralumin. The stem is fabricated in interwelded steel strips. Below the freeboard deck the hull is divided into six watertight compartments employing web framing.

The foil system comprises one bow foil, one aft foil and two dart-like planing sub-foils, the tips of which are attached to the trailing edges of the outer bow foil struts. Foils, sub-foils and struts are in welded stainless steel. The bow foil, which incorporates sweepback, and the straight aft foil, are both supported by three vertical struts.

The base of the centre strut aft provides the end bearing for the propeller which is beneath the foil.

Propulsion: Power is supplied by a single M-401A water-cooled, supercharged 12-cylinder V-type diesel, with a normal service output of 671 kW. The engine drives, via a reverse gear and inclined stainless steel propeller shaft, a three-bladed cast bronze propeller. The fuel system comprises two fuel tanks with a total capacity of 1,647 litres, a fuel priming unit and a hand fuel booster pump. A compressed air system, comprising a propeller shaft-driven air compressor and two 40 litre compressed air bottles, is provided for main engine starting, emergency stopping, operating the foghorn and scavenging the water intake.

METEOR

Dr Alexeyev's Meteor made its maiden voyage from Gorki to Moscow in 1960, bringing high performance and unprecedented comfort to river boat fleets, and setting the pattern for a family of later designs.

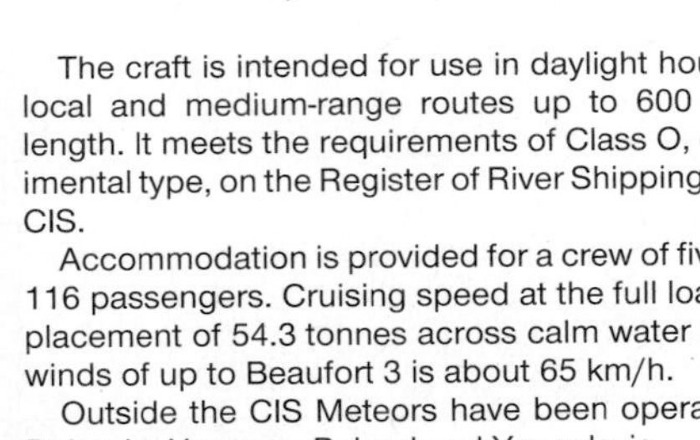

The craft is intended for use in daylight hours on local and medium-range routes up to 600 km in length. It meets the requirements of Class O, experimental type, on the Register of River Shipping in the CIS.

Accommodation is provided for a crew of five and 116 passengers. Cruising speed at the full load displacement of 54.3 tonnes across calm water and in winds of up to Beaufort 3 is about 65 km/h.

Outside the CIS Meteors have been operated in Bulgaria, Hungary, Poland and Yugoslavia.

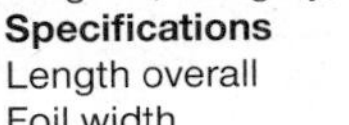

Specifications

Length overall	34.6 m
Foil width	9.5 m
Draught, hullborne	2.35 m
Draught, foilborne	1.2 m
Displacement, min	36.4 t
Displacement, max	53.4 t
Crew	5
Passengers	116
Fuel capacity	3,000 l
Propulsive power	2 × 820 kW
Operational speed	35.1 kts
Range	324 n miles
Operational limitation	Beaufort 3

Structure: With the exception of the small exposed areas fore and aft, the Meteor's hull and superstructure are built as an integral unit. The hull is framed on longitudinal and transverse formers and both hull and superstructure are of riveted duralumin construction with welded steel members. Below the main deck the hull is subdivided longitudinally into eight compartments by seven bulkheads. Access to the compartments is via hatches in the main deck. The craft will remain afloat in the event of any two adjacent compartments forward of amidships flooding or any one compartment aft of midship. Frame spacing in the hull is about 500 mm while that in the superstructure is 1,000 mm.

The foil arrangement comprises a bow foil and a stern foil, with the struts of the bow system carrying two additional planing sub-foils. The foils are attached to the struts, which are of split type, by flanges and bolts. The foils are in stainless steel and the sub-foils in aluminium-magnesium alloy. The foil incidence can be adjusted when necessary by the insertion of wedges between the flanges and the foils when the vessel is in dock.

Propulsion: Power is supplied by two M-401A 12-cylinder, four-stroke, supercharged, water-cooled diesels with reversing clutches. Each engine has a normal service output of 745 kW at 1,700 rpm and a maximum output of 820 kW at 1,800 rpm. Specific

Meteor operating in St Petersburg (J K Pemberton)

1986

Meteor ***1988***

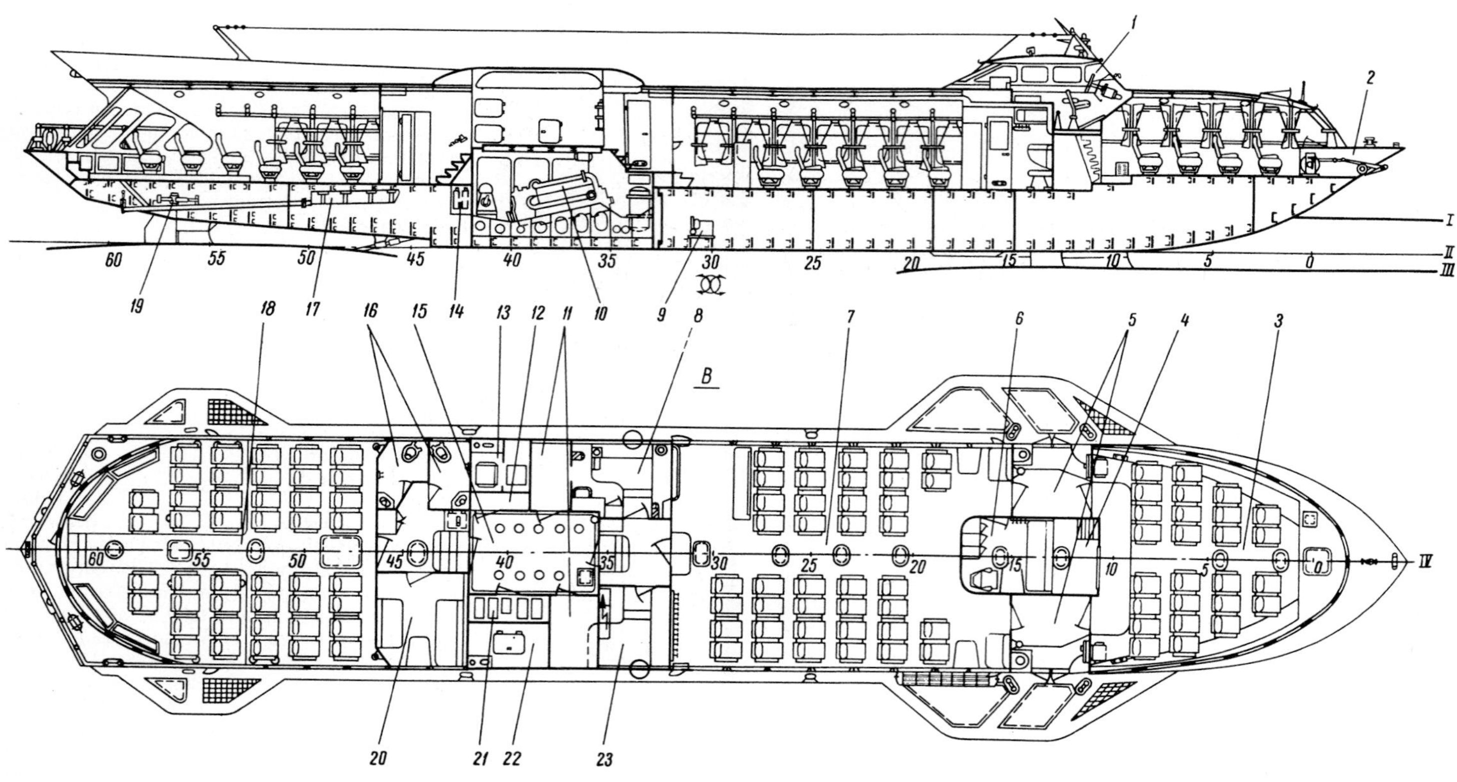

Meteor:
A *Inboard profile;* **B** *Main deck plan;* **I** *Water-line hullborne;* **II** *Hull base line;* **III** *Water-line foilborne;* **IV** *Longitudinal centreline;* **1** *Wheelhouse;* **2** *Anchor compartment;* **3** *Forward passenger saloon, 26 seats;* **4** *Luggage rack;* **5** *Embarkation companionway;* **6** *Crew duty room;* **7** *Midship passenger saloon, 42 seats;* **8** *Bar;* **9** *Refrigeration unit;* **10** *Engine room;* **11** *Pantry;* **12** *Boatswain's store;* **13** *Calorifier;* **14** *Firefighting equipment;* **15** *Promenade deck;* **16** *WCs;* **17** *Tank;* **18** *Aft passenger saloon, 44 seats;* **19** *Tiller gear;* **20** *Four-seat passenger cabin;* **21** *Storage batteries;* **22** *Hydraulic units;* **23** *Main switchboard*

consumption at rated output g/bhp/h is not more than 193, and oil, not more than six. Guaranteed overhaul life is 1,000 hours. Each engine drives its own inclined propeller shaft through a reverse clutch. The propeller shafts are in steel and the propellers, which are five-bladed, are in brass. The drives are contrarotating.

Control: Control of the engines, reverse gear and fuel supply is effected remotely from the wheelhouse with the aid of a hydraulic system comprising transmitter cylinders in the wheelhouse, and actuators on the engine. The engines can also be controlled from the engine room.

Craft heading is controlled by two hydraulically controlled balanced rudders, the blades of which are in solid aluminium-magnesium alloy.

At low speed the craft can turn in its own length by pinwheeling - employing both engines with equal power in opposite directions - one ahead, the other astern.

Minimum diameter of the turning circle is approximately 250 m with the engines running at low speed (700 to 750 rpm) and with the rudder put through an angle of 35°. Turning circle diameter when operating foilborne with the rudder at an angle of 10° is approximately 750 m.

The vessel takes off for foilborne flight in 120 to 140 seconds, that is, within a distance of 25 to 28 lengths of its hull.

Landing run, with engines reversed, ranges from 1.5 to 2 hull lengths, while the braking distance without reversing the engines is within 3 to 4 lengths of the hull.

KOMETA

Derived from the earlier Meteor, the Kometa was the first sea-going hydrofoil to be built in the Soviet Union. The prototype, seating 100 passengers, made its maiden voyage on the Black Sea in 1961, after which it was employed on various passenger routes on an experimental basis. Operating experience accumulated on these services led to the introduction of various modifications before the craft was put into series production.

Kometa operators outside the CIS have included Kompas Line, Yugoslavia; Alilauro SpA, Naples, Italy; and Transportes Touristiques Intercontinentaux, Morocco. Other vessels of this type have been supplied to Bulgaria, Cuba, the former German Democratic Republic, Greece, Iran, Poland, Romania and Turkey. More than 60 have been exported.

Export orders have been mainly for the Kometa-ME, designed for service in countries with a moderate climate, which was introduced in 1968. Two distinguishing features of this model are the employment of new diesel engines with increased operating hours between overhauls, and a completely revised surface-piercing foil system, with a trapeze bow foil instead of the former Alexeyev shallow draught submerged type.

A fully tropicalised and air conditioned version is now in production and designated Kometa-MT.

The present standard production Kometa-ME seats 116 to 120. Due to the additional weight of the Kometa-MT's air conditioning system and other refinements, the seating capacity is reduced in the interest of passenger comfort to 102.

Official designation of the Kometa in the CIS is Hydrofoil Type 342. The craft meets the requirements of the Rules of the Register of Shipping of the CIS and is constructed to Hydrofoil Class KM*211 Passenger Class under the Register's technical supervision.

The standard craft has proved to be exceptionally robust and has a good, all-round performance. On one charter, a Kometa-ME covered 2,867 n miles by

A Kometa of Kompas Line, Yugoslavia, arriving at Venice, June 1986

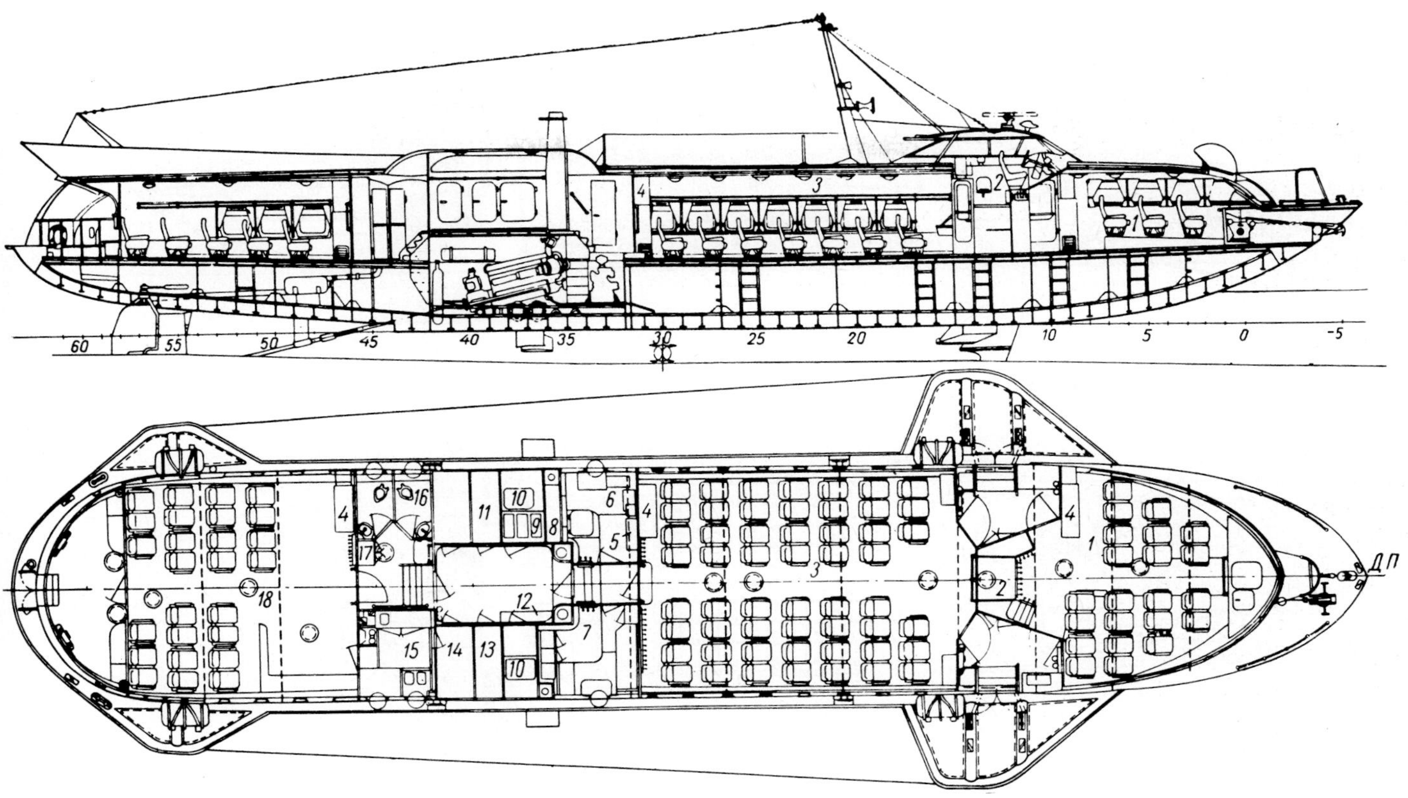

Internal arrangement of Kometa-MT, designed for tropical operation: **1** *22-seat forward passenger saloon;* **2** *Wheelhouse;* **3** *54-seat main passenger saloon;* **4** *Luggage rack;* **5** *Engine room door;* **6** *Control position;* **7** *Duty cabin;* **8** *Liquid fire extinguisher bay;* **9** *Battery room;* **10** *Engine room;* **11** *Boiler room;* **12** *Installation point for portable radio;* **13** *Store;* **14** *Provision store;* **15** *Bar;* **16** *Toilet wash basin units;* **17** *Boatswain's store;* **18** *26-seat aft passenger saloon*

sea and river in 127 hours. It can operate foilborne in waves up to 1.7 m and travel hullborne in waves up to 3.6 m.

One of the features of the more recent models is the relocation of the engine room aft to reduce the noise in the passenger saloons and the employment of a V-drive instead of the existing inclined shaft. The revised deck configuration allows more seats to be fitted. These modifications are also incorporated in the Kometa derivative, the Kolkhida, which is fitted with two 1,120 kW engines.

Kometa-ME ***1986***

KOMETA-ME

Specifications

Length overall	35.1 m
Foil width	11 m
Draught, hullborne	3.6 m
Draught, foilborne	1.7 m
Displacement, min	44.5 t
Displacement, max	60 t
Crew	6
Passengers	102
Propulsive power	2 × 820 kW
Max speed	36 kts
Operational speed	31 kts
Range	200 n miles
Operational limitation	Sea State 4 Beaufort 5

Structure: The hull is similar in shape to that of the earlier Meteor, with a wedge-shaped bow, raked stem and a spoon-shaped stern. The hull and superstructure are built in AlMg-61 and AlMg-6 alloys. Hull and superstructure are of all-welded construction using contact and argon arc welding. The hull is framed on longitudinal and transverse formers, the spacing throughout the length of the hull is 500 mm and in the superstructure 1,000 mm.

Employment of a surface-piercing trapeze-type bow foil provides the Kometa-ME with improved seakeeping capability in waves. The foil system comprises a bow foil, aft foil and two auxiliaries, one (termed 'stabiliser') located above the bow foil for pitch stability, the other sited amidships near the longitudinal centre of gravity to assist take-off. The foils are connected to the hull by struts and brackets; middle and side struts of the bow foil are of the split type, the lower and upper components of each strut are connected by flanges and bolts. The upper sections are connected to the hull by the same means.

The bow and stern foils are of hollow welded stainless steel construction. The midship and pitch stability foils and the upper components of the foil struts are in aluminium-magnesium alloy.

Propulsion: Power is supplied by two M-401A water-cooled, supercharged 12-cylinder V-type diesels, each with a normal service output of 745 kW at 1,550 rpm and a maximum output of 820 kW at 1,600 rpm. Guaranteed service life of each engine before first overhaul is 2,500 hours. Each engine drives via a reverse gear its own inclined shaft and the twin propellers are contrarotating. The shafts are of steel and are parallel to the craft.

The propellers are of three-bladed design and made of brass.

Development of the Kometa is continuing. Current research is aimed at the introduction of a stability augmentation system employing either control flaps on the bow foil or air stabilisation on the stern foil and struts; the reduction of labour involved in construction; the introduction of design improvements through the use of GRP and sandwich construction; noise reduction in the saloons and the extension of the cruising range.

KOMETA-MT

Specifications

Length overall	35.1 m
Foil width	11 m
Draught, hullborne	3.6 m

Lastochka ***1990***

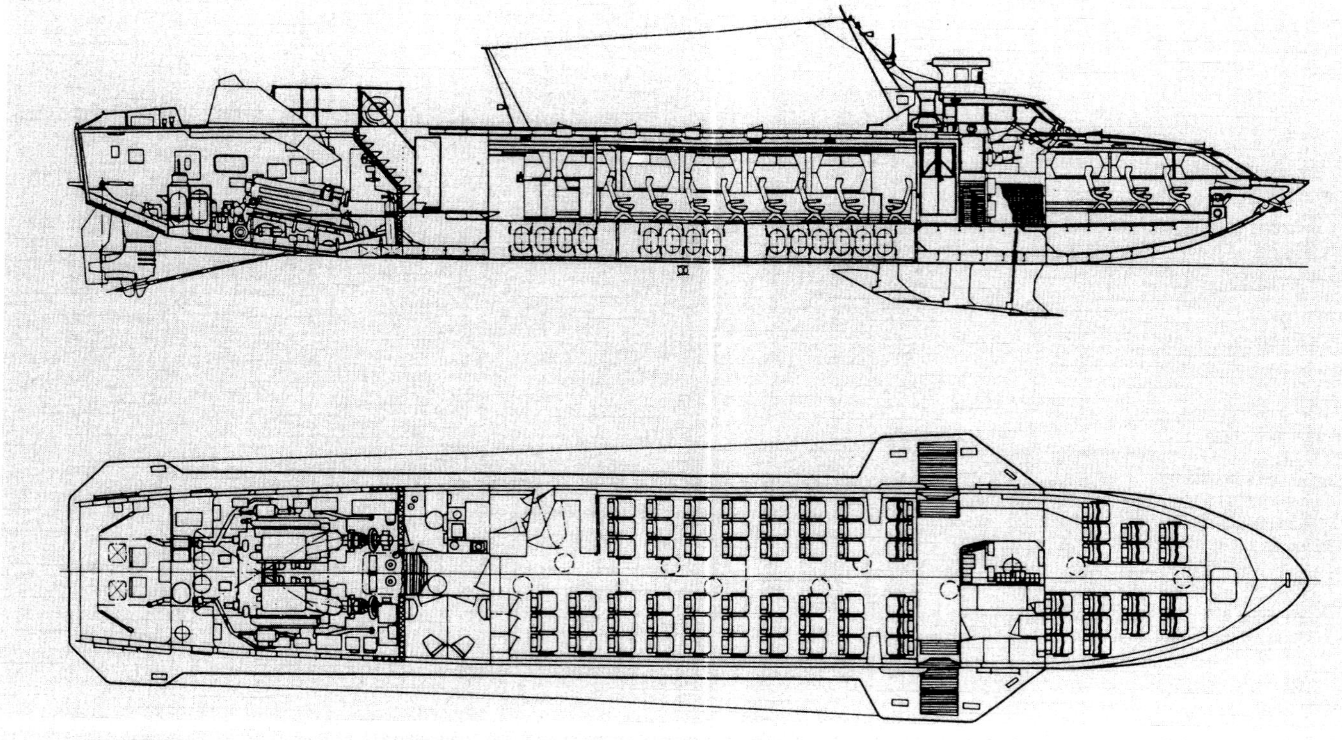

Layout of Lastochka

Draught, foilborne	1.7 m
Displacement, min	45 t
Displacement, max	58.9 t
Crew	6
Passengers	102
Propulsive power	2 × 820 kW
Max speed	33 kts
Operational speed	31 kts
Range	130 n miles

LASTOCHKA

Successor to the 71-seat Voskhod, the first Lastochka was launched in 1986. The vessel is designed specifically for use over major rivers and reservoirs whose wave heights are unlikely to exceed 1.5 m in height. Loading conditions are optimised by means of a flap control on the bow foil arrangement.

Specifications

Length overall	29 m
Beam	4.4 m
Foil width	7.2 m
Draught, foilborne	2.5 m
Displacement, min	28 t
Displacement, max	37.3 t
Propulsive power	2 × 994 kW
Max speed	48 kts
Range	270 n miles

UPDATED

INDONESIA

PT PAL INDONESIA (PERSERO)

Head office: Arthaloka Building, 5th Floor, JL Jend Sudirman No 2, Jakarta 10220, Indonesia

Tel: +62 (21) 570 3257/8, 570 5302/3
Telex: 65295 PAL JKT 1A
Fax: +62 (21) 570 4275

Works: Ujung Surabaya, PO Box 134, Indonesia

Tel: +62 (31) 291403, 333438/9
Telex: 31223 PAL SB
Fax: +62 (31) 22516

With origins as a repair and maintenance facility for the navy in 1892, PT PAL now employs 6,000 people, occupies an area of 150 hectares and has capacity for designing and building vessels from 60 to 30,000 tonnes.

Apart from the first Jetfoil 929-115 (*Bima Samudera I*) to be fitted out, no information has been received on any further Jetfoil fitting out or conversion by PT PAL but the company has two non-commercial versions of the Jetfoil for Indonesian Government use.

VERIFIED

ITALY

FINCANTIERI-CANTIERI NAVALI ITALIANI SpA

Via Genova 1, I-34121 Trieste, Italy

Naval Shipbuilding Division: Via Cipro 11, I-16129 Genoa, Italy

Tel: +39 (40) 59951
Telex: 270168FINCGE I
Fax: +39 (40) 599 5272

Mario de Negri, *Naval Shipbuilding Division General Manager*
Franco Baracchini, *Naval Vessel Director*

The original Cantieri Navali Riuniti SpA took over the interests of Alinavi which was formed in 1964 to develop, manufacture and market advanced military marine systems.

Under the terms of a licensing agreement, Fincantieri had access to Boeing technology in the field of military fully submerged, foil hydrofoil craft.

In October 1970, the company was awarded a contract by the Italian Navy for the design and construction of the P420 Sparviero hydrofoil missile craft. This is an improved version of the Boeing PGH-2 Tucumcari. The vessel, given the design name Sparviero, was delivered to the Italian Navy in July 1974. An order for a further six of this type was placed by the Italian Navy in February 1976.

In 1991 Sumitomo Heavy Industries received an order for the building of two of a planned class of six Sparviero hydrofoils for the Japanese Defence Agency, successfully launched in July 1992. A third hydrofoil was launched in June 1994.

SPARVIERO

The Sparviero missile-launching hydrofoil gunboat displaces 60.5 tonnes and is designed for both offensive and defensive missions. Its combination of speed, fire-power and all-weather capability is unique in a ship of this class.

The vessel has fully submerged foils arranged in canard configuration and an automatic control system. A gas-turbine powered water-jet system provides foilborne propulsion and a diesel-driven propeller outdrive provides hullborne propulsion. A typical crew comprises two officers and eight enlisted men.

Sparviero's advanced automatic control system considerably reduces the vertical and transverse acceleration normally experienced in rough seas. In Sea State 4 the maximum vertical acceleration likely to be found is in the order of 0.25 *g* (rms), while the maximum roll angle is not likely to be greater than ±2°.

In the lower Sea States Sparviero class hydrofoils have a maximum continuous speed of 44 knots, decreasing to 40 knots in Sea State 4.

Craft built	Commissioned
P420 *Sparviero* (now withdrawn)	1974
P421 *Nibbio*	1981
P422 *Falcone*	1982
P423 *Astore*	1982
P424 *Grifone*	1982
P425 *Gheppio*	1983
P426 *Condor*	1983

The foils are in a fully submerged canard configuration, with approximately one-third of the dynamic lift provided by the bow foil and two-thirds by the two aft foils.

Anhedral is incorporated in the aft foils to enhance the directional stability of the craft at shallow foil depths. In addition, the anhedral assures positive roll control by eliminating tip broaching during rough water manoeuvres.

Specifications

Length overall	22.95 m
Beam	7 m
Foil width	10.8 m
Displacement, max	60.5 t
Crew	10
Propulsive power	3,356 kW
Max speed	50 kts
Operational speed	44 kts
Range	1,000 n miles hullborne

Structure: The hull and superstructure are built in corrosion-resistant aluminium, the hull being welded and the superstructure riveted and welded.

Propulsion: Power for a water-jet is supplied by one 3,356 kW Rolls-Royce Proteus 15M/553 gas turbine.

Turning radius of Sparviero hydrofoils at 40 knots is under 125 m ***1986***

Engine output is transferred to a single double-volute, double-suction, two impeller centrifugal pump. Water is taken in through inlets on the nose of each aft foil at the foil/strut intersection and passes up through the hollow interiors of the struts to the hull, where it is ducted to the pump. From the pump, the water is discharged through twin, fixed-area nozzles located beneath the hull under the pump.

An Isotta Fraschini ID 38 6VN marine diesel drives via a toothed belt a steerable propeller outdrive unit, which is mounted on the centreline of the transom. The unit is retractable and rotates through 360°. Propeller is fixed-pitch. Continuous speed, hullborne, is 8 knots.

UPDATED

RODRIQUEZ CANTIERI NAVALI SpA

Via S Raineri 22, I-98122 Messina, Italy

Tel: +39 (90) 7765
Telex: 980030 RODRIK I
Fax: +39 (90) 675294

Basbasso Gattuso, *President*
Giovanni Morace, *Managing Director*
Alcide Sculati, *Technical Manager*
Diego Mazzeo, *Sales and Marketing*

Rodriquez Cantieri Navali SpA was the first company to produce hydrofoils in series, and is the biggest hydrofoil builder outside the CIS. On the initiative of the company's former president, Carlo Rodriquez, the Aliscafi Shipping Company was established in Sicily to operate the world's first scheduled sea-going hydrofoil service in August 1956 between Sicily and the Italian mainland.

The service was operated by the first Rodriquez-built Supramar PT 20, *Freccia del Sole.* Cutting down the port-to-port time from Messina to Reggio di Calabria to one-quarter of that of conventional ferry boats, and completing 22 daily crossings, the craft soon proved its commercial viability. With a seating capacity of 72 passengers the PT 20 carried between 800 and 900 passengers a day and conveyed a record number of some 31,000 passengers in a single month.

Eight main types of hydrofoil have now been produced: the Supramar PT 20 and PT 50, the RHS 70, RHS 110, RHS 140, RHS 150, RHS 160 and RHS 200. Many of the early craft built are still operating. Please see earlier editions of *Jane's High-Speed Marine Craft* for details of PT 20 and PT 50 hydrofoils; the 1990 edition, pages 174 and 175 list the PT 20s built by the Rodriquez yard.

Forward foil arrangement of Rodriquez Supramar PT 50 Freccia del Mediterraneo ***1988***

RHS 70 Shearwater 3, *sister vessel to three other RHS 70s delivered to Red Funnel Ferries* ***1986***

RHS 70

This is a 32 tonne coastal passenger ferry with seats for 71 passengers. Power is supplied by a single 1,066 kW MTU diesel and the cruising speed is 32.4 knots.

Specifications

Length overall	22 m
Foil width	7.4 m
Draught, hullborne	2.7 m
Draught, foilborne	1.15 m
Displacement, max	31.5 t
Payload	6 t
Passengers	71
Propulsive power	1,066 kW
Max speed	36.5 kts
Operational speed	32.4 kts

Structure: V-bottom hull of riveted light metal alloy construction. Watertight compartments are below the passenger decks and in other parts of the hull.

The foils are surface-piercing type in partly hollow welded steel.

Propulsion: A single MTU 12V 331 TC 82 diesel, developing 1,066 kW at 2,340 rpm, drives a three-bladed bronze-aluminium propeller through a Zahnradfabrik W 800 H 20 gearbox.

Control: During operation the angle of the bow foil can be adjusted within narrow limits from the steering position by means of a hydraulic ram operating on a foil support across the hull.

Craft built (Supramar PT 50) 1959 to 1970

Type	Name	Yard No	No of seats	Operated in	Date built	Owner/Operator
Supramar PT 50	*Freccia di Messina**	059	125	Italy	1959	-
Supramar PT 50	*Freccia di Sorrento*	062	125	Italy	1959	Ministero dei Mercantile Marine
Supramar PT 50	*Freccia d'Oro*	063	130	Italy	1959	Destroyed in storm 1992
Supramar PT 50	*Freccia Atlantica*	064	125	Italy	1960	Aliscafi SNAV SpA
Supramar PT 50	*Freccia del Sud*	065	50+ 7 t cargo	Italy	1960	Aliscafi SNAV SpA
Supramar PT 50	*Pisanello*	066	130	Italy	1961	SIREMAR
Supramar PT 50	*Queenfoil* (ex-*Sleipner*)	076	125	-	1961	Transtour SA
Supramar PT 50	*Freccia di Lipari*	077	125	Italy	1961	Aliscafi SNAV SpA
Supramar PT 50	*Flecha de Buenos Aires*	078	125	Argentina	1962	Alimar SA
Supramar PT 50	*Flecha de Colonia* (ex-*Flecha de Montevideo*)	079	125	Argentina	1962	Alimar SA
Supramar PT 50	*Flecha del Litoral**	080	125	Argentina	1963	-
Supramar PT 50	*Freccia del Mediterraneo*	081	125	Italy	1963	Aliscafi SNAV SpA
Supramar PT 50	*Freccia di Sicilia*	088	125	Italy	1964	Aliscafi SNAV SpA
Supramar PT 50	*Nibbio*	089	125	Italy	1964	Adriatica di Navigazione SpA
Supramar PT 50	*Flying Albatross*	090	125	Hong Kong	1964	Hongkong Macao Hydrofoil Co Ltd
Supramar PT 50	*Flying Skimmer*	091	125	Hong Kong	1965	Hongkong Macao Hydrofoil Co Ltd
Supramar PT 50	*Svalan**	092	125	-	1965	ex-Tarnan Line, Limassol, Cyprus
Supramar PT 50	*Flying Condor*	093	125	Hong Kong	1966	Hongkong Macao Hydrofoil Co Ltd
Supramar PT 50	*Freccia delle Isole*	111	125	Italy	1966	Destroyed in storm 1992
Supramar PT 50	*Tarnan*	118	120	-	1966	ex-Tarnan Line, Limassol, Cyprus
Supramar PT 50	*Freccia Adriatica*	119	125	Italy	1969	Aliscafi SNAV SpA
Supramar PT 50	*Fairlight* (scrapped 1988)	120	140	Australia	1966	-
Supramar PT 50	*Flying Flamingo* (scrapped)	121	125	-	1967	ex-Hongkong Macao Hydrofoil Co Ltd
Supramar PT 50	*Star Capricorn* (ex-*Springeren*)	122	117	Italy	1967	COVEMAR Eolie
Supramar PT 50	*Stilprins* (ex-*Teisten*)	123	128		1970	
Supramar PT 50	*Long Reef* (laid up)	124	140	Australia	1969	NSW State Transit Authority
Supramar PT 50	*Sun Arrow*	125	125	Italy	1968	Aliscafi SNAV SpA
Supramar PT 50	*Dee Why* (scrapped 1988)	132	140	Australia	1970	-

*destroyed by fire 1986

Craft built (RHS 70) 1972 to 1982

Type	Name	Yard No	No of seats	Operated in	Date built	Owner/Operator
RHS 70	*Shearwater 3*	150	67	UK	1972	Red Funnel Ferries
RHS 70	*Shearwater 4*	156	67	UK	1973	Red Funnel Ferries
RHS 70	*Freccia delle Betulle*	185	71	Italy	1974	Navigazione Lago di Como
RHS 70	*Freccia delle Camelie*	186	71	Italy	1974	Navigazione Lago Maggiore
RHS 70	*Freccia del Benaco*	187	71	Italy	1974	Navigazione Sul Lago di Garda
RHS 70	*Freccia delle Magnolie*	188	71	Italy	1975	Navigazione Lago Maggiore
RHS 70	*Freccia delle Gardenie*	189	71	Italy	1976	Navigazione Lago di Como
RHS 70	*Freccia dei Gerani*	196	71	Italy	1977	Navigazione Sul Lago di Garda
RHS 70	*Shearwater 5*	197	67	UK	1980	Red Funnel Ferries
RHS 70	*Shearwater 6*	221	67	UK	1982	Red Funnel Ferries

Craft built (RHS 110) 1971 to 1973

Type	Name	Yard No	No of seats	Operated in	Date built	Owner/Operator
RHS 110	*Cacilhas*	147	110	Hong Kong	1971	-
RHS 110	*Flecha de Angra* (ex-*Flying Phoenix*)	148	140	Brazil	1970	Laid up
RHS 110	*Barca*	157	122	Hong Kong	1972	-
RHS 110	*Praia*	158	111	Hong Kong	1973	-
RHS 110	*Cerco*	159	111	Hong Kong	1973	-

RHS 110

A 54 tonne hydrofoil ferry, the RHS 110 was originally designed to carry a maximum of 110 passengers at a cruising speed of 37 knots.

Specifications

Length overall	25.6 m
Beam	5.95 m
Foil width	9.2 m
Draught, hullborne	3.3 m
Draught, foilborne	1.25 m
Displacement, max	54 t
Passengers	110
Fuel capacity	3,600 l
Propulsive power	2 × 1,006 kW
Max speed	40 kts
Operational speed	37 kts
Range	262 n miles

Structure: V-bottom of high-tensile riveted light metal alloy construction, using Peraluman plate and Anti-corrodal profiles. The upper deck plates are 3.5 mm thick Peraluman. Removable deck sections permit the lifting out and replacement of the main engines. The superstructure, which has a removable roof, is in 2 mm thick Peraluman plates, with L and C profile sections. Watertight compartments are below the passenger decks and other parts of the hull.

The foils are a surface-piercing type, in partly hollow welded steel.

Propulsion: Power is supplied by two 12-cylinder supercharged MTU MB 12V 493 Ty 71 diesels, each with a maximum output of 1,006 kW at 1,500 rpm. Engine output is transferred to two three-bladed bronze-aluminium propellers through Zahnradfabrik W 800 H20 gearboxes. Each propeller shaft is 90 mm in diameter and supported at three points by seawater-lubricated rubber bearings. Steel fuel tanks with a total capacity of 3,600 l are aft of the engine room.

Control: Hydraulically operated flaps, attached to the trailing edges of the bow and rear foils, are adjusted automatically by a Hamilton Standard stability augmentation system for the damping of heave, pitch and roll motions. The rear foil is rigidly attached to the transom, its incidence angle being determined during tests.

Auxiliary systems: Steering, variation of the foil flaps and the anchor windlass operation are all accomplished hydraulically from the wheelhouse. Plant comprises two Bosch pumps installed on the main engines which convey oil from a 60 l tank under pressure to the control cylinders of the rudder, foil flaps and anchor windlass.

RHS 140

This 65 tonne hydrofoil passenger ferry seats up to 150 passengers and has a cruising speed of 32.5 knots.

Specifications

Length overall	28.7 m
Foil width	10.72 m
Draught, hullborne	3.5 m
Draught, foilborne	1.5 m
Displacement, max	65 t
Payload	12.5 t
Passengers	150
Propulsive power	2 × 1,007 kW
Max speed	36 kts
Operational speed	32.5 kts
Range	297 n miles

Structure: Riveted light metal alloy design framed on longitudinal and transverse formers.

The foils are surface-piercing V-foils of hollow welded steel construction.

Propulsion: Power is provided by two MTU 12V 493 Ty 71 12-cylinder supercharged engines, each developing 1,007 kW at 1,500 rpm. Engine output is transmitted to two, three-bladed 700 mm diameter bronze propellers through Zahnradfabrik gearboxes.

Control: Lift of the bow foil can be modified by hydraulically operated trailing-edge flaps.

Craft built (RHS 140) 1971 to 1977

Type	Name	Yard No	No of seats	Operated in	Date built	Owner/Operator
RHS 140	*Colonia del Sacramento* (ex-*Condor*)	133	140	Uruguay	1971	Belt SA
RHS 140	*Flying Dragon*	134	140	Hong Kong	1971	Hongkong Macao Hydrofoil Co Ltd
RHS 140	*Flying Egret*	152	125	Hong Kong	1972	Hongkong Macao Hydrofoil Co Ltd
RHS 140	*Santa Maria del Buenos Aires* (ex-*Tyrving*)	153	116	Uruguay	1972	Belt SA
RHS 140	*Farallón* (ex-*Loberen*)	154	111	Uruguay	1972	Belt SA
RHS 140	*Curl-Curl*	155	140	Australia	1972	NSW Transit Authority
RHS 140	*Rapido de Ibiza* (ex-*Viggen*)	161	120	Spain	1973	Flebasa Lines
RHS 140	*Flying Sandpiper* (ex-*Flying Goldfinch*)	180	125	Hong Kong	1972	Hongkong Macao Hydrofoil Co Ltd
RHS 140	*Flying Swift*	180	125	Hong Kong	1973	Hongkong Macao Hydrofoil Co Ltd
RHS 140	*Flying Ibis*	182	125	Hong Kong	1975	Hongkong Macao Hydrofoil Co Ltd
RHS 140	*Condor 4*	184	136	UK	1974	Condor Ltd
RHS 140	*Duccio* (ex-*Fabricia*)	193	140	Italy	1977	TOREMAR SpA
RHS 140	*Albireo*	194	150	Italy	1977	CAREMAR SpA

Craft built (RHS 150) 1980

Type	Name	Yard No	No of seats	Operated in	Date built	Owner/Operator
RHS 150	*Xel-Ha* (laid up)	203	151	Mexico	1980	Secretaria de Turismo, Mexico

RHS 150

Combining features of both the RHS 140 and the RHS 160, the RHS 150 hydrofoil passenger ferry is powered by two 1,066 kW MTU supercharged four-stroke diesels which give the craft a cruising speed of 32.5 knots and a cruising range of 130 n miles.

Specifications

Length overall	28.7 m
Foil width	11 m
Draught, hullborne	3.1 m
Draught, foilborne	1.4 m
Displacement, max	65.5 t
Passengers	150
Propulsive power	2 × 1,066 kW
Operational speed	32.5 kts
Range	130 n miles

Structure: Riveted light metal alloy design framed on longitudinal and transverse formers.

Surface-piercing W-foils of hollow welded steel construction.

Propulsion: Motive power is furnished by two supercharged MTU MB 12V 331 TC 82 four-stroke diesels each developing 1,066 kW at 2,140 rpm continuous. Engine output is transmitted to two bronze propellers via two Zahnradfabrik BW 255L gearboxes.

Control: Lift of the bow foil can be modified by hydraulically operated trailing edge flaps.

RHS 150 SL

This variant has been designed for inland navigation, particularly on the Great Lakes in Northern Italy. Due to the less severe conditions on such waters it has been possible to redesign the hull structure to allow for larger windows in the lower saloons and the superstructure, greatly increasing visibility for sightseeing. In addition, because the safety rules are less demanding than for open-water routes, there is a saving in weight in the design allowing an increase in passenger numbers, so that 200 may be carried, with lightweight seats fitted.

RHS 150F

This variant has a wider deck and the superstructure volume has been increased to give a more aesthetic shape as well as greater volume for passengers, giving greater comfort. Improvements have also been incorporated in this variant increasing performance and reducing maintenance costs.

RHS 150FL Voloire *delivered 1989 for service on Lake Como, Italy*

1993

RHS 150F Salina operated by Aliscafi SNAV SpA

1995

Craft built (RHS 150SL and FL) 1979 to 1989

Type	Name	Yard No	No of seats	Operated in	Date built	Owner/Operator
RHS 150SL	*Freccia del Giardini*	204	190	Italy	1980	Navigazione Lago Maggiore
RHS 150SL	*Freccia delle Valli*	199	190	Italy	1979	Navigazione Lago di Como
RHS 150SL	*Freccia dei Gerani*	196	190	Italy	1980	Navigazione Lago Maggiore
RHS 150SL	*Freccia delle Riviere*	206	190	Italy	1981	Navigazione Lago di Garda
RHS 150SL	*Galileo Galilei*	208	190	Italy	1982	Navigazione Lago di Garda
RHS 150SL	*Enrico Fermi*	220	190	Italy	1984	Navigazione Lago Maggiore
RHS 150SL	*Guglielmo Marconi*	207	190	Italy	1983	Navigazione Lago di Como
RHS 150FL	*Goethe*	232	200	Italy	1988	Navigazione Lago di Garda
RHS 150FL	*Voloire*	237	200	Italy	1989	Navigazione Lago di Como
RHS 150FL	*Byron*	238	200	Italy	1990	Navigazione Lago Maggiore

Craft built (RHS 150F) 1984

Type	Name	Yard No	No of seats	Operated in	Date built	Owner/Operator
RHS 150F	*Dynasty*	210	161	Italy	1984	Aliscafi SNAV SpA
RHS 150F	*Salina*	233	161	Italy	1990	Aliscafi SNAV SpA
RHS 150F	*Panarea*	234	161	Italy	1990	Aliscafi SNAV SpA

Craft built (RHS 160) 1974 to 1986

Type	Name	Yard No	No of seats	Operated in	Date built	Owner/Operator
RHS 160	*Princess Zoe* (ex-*Alijumbo Ustica*, ex-*Lilau*)	181	160	Italy	1974	Aliscafi SNAV SpA
RHS 160	*Diomedea*	190	160	Italy	1975	Adriatica di Navigazione SpA
RHS 160	*Condor 5*	191	180	UK	1976	Condor Ltd
RHS 160	*Algol*	195	180	Italy	1978	CAREMAR
RHS 160	*May W Craig* (ex-*Alijumbo*)	198	180	Italy	1979	Aliscafi SNAV SpA
RHS 160	*Alioth*	200	180	Italy	1979	CAREMAR
RHS 160	*Botticelli*	201	180	Italy	1980	SIREMAR
RHS 160	*Donatello*	202	180	Italy	1980	SIREMAR
RHS 160	*Nicte-Ha*	205	160	Mexico	1982	Secretaria de Turismo, Mexico

RHS 160

A 95 tonne passenger ferry with seats for up to 180 passengers and a cruising speed of 32 knots.

In March and May 1986 two RHS 160s were used for oil spill clean-up trials.

Specifications

Length overall	30.95 m
Beam	6.2 m
Foil width	12.6 m
Draught, hullborne	3.7 m
Draught, foilborne	1.35 m
Displacement, max	95 t
Payload	13.5 t
Passengers	180-200
Propulsive power	2 × 1,400 kW
Max speed	36 kts
Operational speed	32 kts
Range	260 n miles

Structure: Riveted light metal alloy longitudinal structure, welded in parts using inert gas. The hull shape of the RHS 160 is similar to the RHS 140 series. In the manufacture of the hull, plates of aluminium and magnesium alloy of 4.4 per cent are used while angle bars are of a high-resistant aluminium, magnesium and silicon alloy.

The surface-piercing W-foils are of hollow welded steel construction.

Propulsion: Power is provided by two supercharged MTU MB 12V 652 TB 71 four-stroke diesel engines each with a maximum output of 1,454 kW at 1,460 rpm under normal operating conditions. Engine starting is accomplished by compressed air starters. Engine output is transmitted to two, three-bladed bronze propellers through two Zahnradfabrik 900 HS 15 gearboxes.

Control: Craft in this series feature a bow rudder for improved manoeuvrability in congested waters. The bow rudder works simultaneously with the aft rudders. Hydraulically operated flaps, attached to the trailing edges of the bow and rear foils, are adjusted automatically by a Hamilton Standard electronic stability augmentation system, for the damping of heave, pitch and roll motions in heavy seas.

RHS 160F

A further addition to the Rodriquez range is the RHS 160F, a 91.5 tonne passenger ferry with seats for up to 238 passengers and a cruising speed of 34.5 knots.

Specifications

Length overall	31.2 m
Length waterline	26.25 m
Beam	6.7 m

RHS 160F Citti Ships

1995

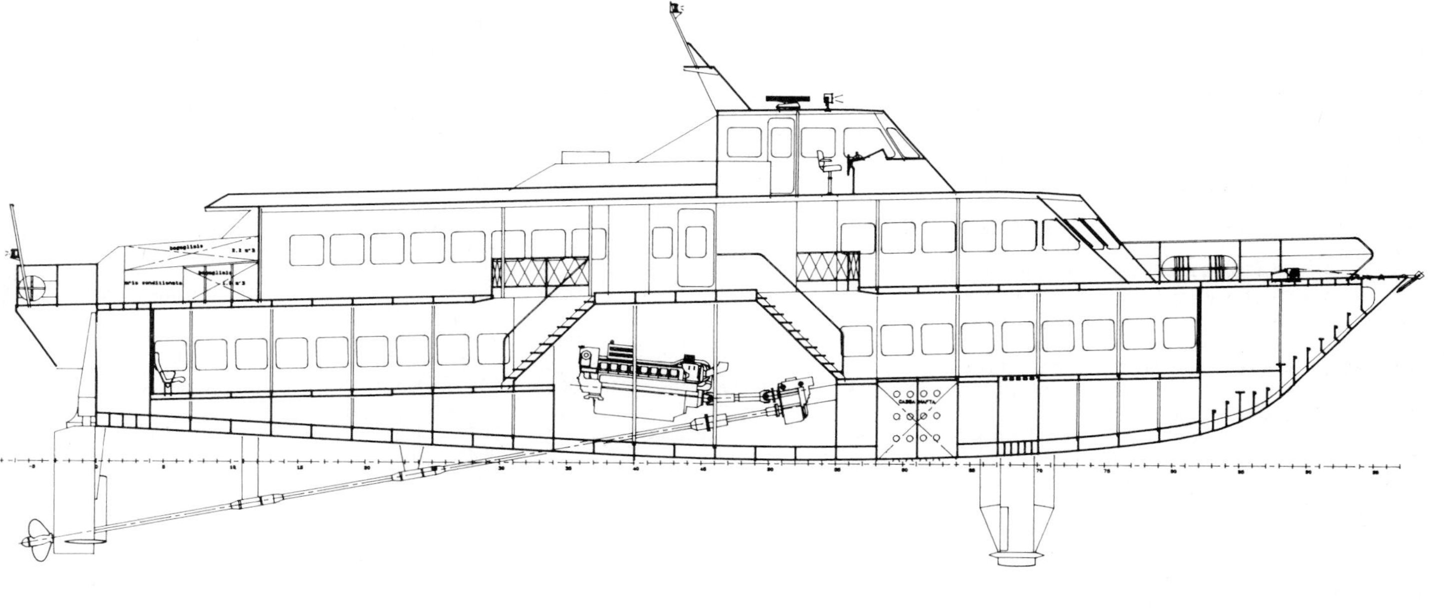

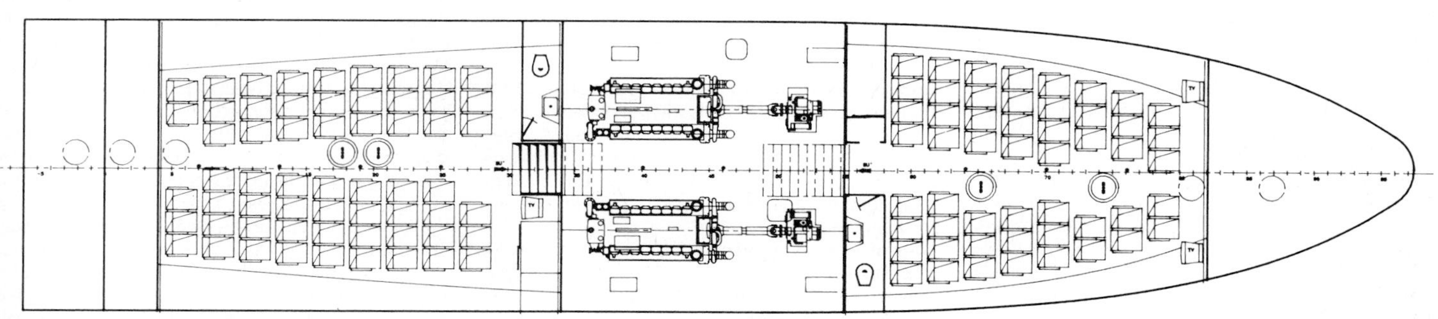

RHS 160F inboard profile and lower deck arrangement

1995

RHS 160F Alijumbo Stromboli **1995**

Foil width	12.6 m
Draught, hullborne	3.76 m
Draught, foilborne	1.7 m
Displacement, max	91.5 t
Payload	17.8 t
Passengers	210-238
Propulsive power	2 × 1,400 kW
Max speed	38 kts
Operational speed	34.5 kts
Range	100 n miles

Structure: Riveted light metal alloy longitudinal structure, welded in parts using inert gas. The hull shape of the RHS 160F is similar to the RHS 140 series. In the manufacture of the hull, plates of aluminium and magnesium alloy of 4.4 per cent are used while angle bars are of a high-resistant aluminium, magnesium and silicon alloy.

Surface-piercing W-foils of hollow welded steel construction.

Propulsion: Power is provided by two supercharged MTU 16V 396 TB 83 four-stroke diesel engines each with a maximum output of 1,400 kW at 2,000 rpm under normal operating conditions. Engine starting is accomplished by compressed air starters. Engine output is transmitted to two, three-bladed bronze propellers through two Zahnradfabrik BW 7505 gearboxes, or, alternatively, through two Reintjes WVS 1032U gearboxes as fitted to the RHS 160F craft supplied to the NSW State Transit Authority, Australia.

Control: Craft in this series feature a bow rudder for improved manoeuvrability in congested waters. The bow rudder works simultaneously with the aft rudders. Hydraulically operated flaps, attached to the trailing edges of the bow and rear foils, are adjusted automatically by a Hamilton Standard electronic stability augmentation system, for the damping of heave, pitch and roll motions in heavy seas.

Craft built/being built (RHS 160F) 1984 to 1992

Type	Name	Yard No	No of seats	Operated in	Date built	Owner/Operator
RHS 160F	*Manly*	211	238	Australia	1984	NSW State Transit Authority
RHS 160F	*Sydney*	216	238	Australia	1985	NSW State Transit Authority
RHS 160F	*Condor 7*	217	200	UK	1985	Condor Ltd
RHS 160F	*Pez Volador* (ex-*Alijumbo Eolie*)	218	220	Spain	1986	Compañia Naviera Mallorquina
RHS 160F	*Alnilam*	227	210	Italy	1986	CAREMAR
RHS 160F	*Fabricia*	228	210	Italy	1987	TOREMAR
RHS 160F	*Aldebaran*	229	210	Italy	1987	CAREMAR
RHS 160F	*Masaccio*	230	210	Italy	1988	SIREMAR
RHS 160F	*Mantegna*	231	210	Italy	1989	SIREMAR
RHS 160F	*Citti Ships*	236	210	Italy	1990	Alisafi SNAV SpA
RHS 160F	*Giorgione*	239	210	Italy	1989	SIREMAR
RHS 160F	*Monte Gargano*	240	210	Italy	1989	Adriatica SpA di Navigazione
RHS 160F	*Barracuda*	002/ 160	204	Spain	1989	Trasmediterranea SA
RHS 160F	*Marrajo*	003/ 160	204	Spain	1989	Trasmediterranea SA
RHS 160F	*Tintorera*	004/ 160	204	Spain	1990	Trasmediterranea SA
RHS 160F	*Alijumbo Zibibbo*	243	204	Italy	1991	Aliscafi SNAV SpA
RHS 160F	*Moretto I*	244	204	Italy	1991	Aliscafi SNAV SpA
RHS 160F	*Alijumbo Eolie*	245	204	Italy	1991	Aliscafi SNAV SpA
RHS 160F	-	246	-	-	1992	-
RHS 160F	*Alijumbo Messina*	248	204	Italy	1992	Aliscafi SNAV SpA
RHS 160F	*Alijumbo Stromboli*					

RHS 200

Powered by two supercharged MTU MB 16V 652 TB 71 four-stroke diesel engines, the 254-seat RHS 200 has a cruising speed of 35 knots.

Specifications

Length overall	35.8 m
Foil width	14.5 m
Draught, hullborne	4.55 m
Draught, foilborne	2.05 m
Displacement, max	130 t
Passengers	254
Propulsive power	2 × 1,938 kW
Max speed	37 kts
Operational speed	35 kts
Range	200 n miles

Structure: V-bottom hull of high-tensile riveted light metal alloy construction, employing Peraluman plates and Anti-corrodal frames. The rake of the stem is in galvanised steel.

Surface-piercing W-foils of hollow welded steel construction.

Propulsion: Motive power is supplied by two supercharged MTU MB 16V 652 TB 71 four-stroke diesel engines, each with a maximum output of 1,938 kW at 1,460 rpm under normal operating conditions. Engine output is transferred to two super cavitating, controllable-pitch propellers.

Electrical system: Two generating sets: one 220 V, three-phase AC, for all consumer services, the second for charging 24 V battery sets and operating fire-fighting and hydraulic pumps. Power distribution panel in wheelhouse for navigation light circuits, cabin lighting, radar, RDF, gyrocompass and emergency circuits.

Control: Craft in this series feature a bow rudder for improved manoeuvrability in congested waters. This control operates simultaneously with the aft rudders. An advantage of the W configuration bow foil is its relatively shallow draught requirement in relation to the vessel's overall size. Hydraulically operated flaps are fitted to the trailing edge of the bow foil to balance out longitudinal load shifting, assist take-off and adjust the flying height. The craft can also be equipped with the Hamilton Standard electronic stability augmentation system, which employs sensors and servo-mechanisms to position flaps automatically on the bow and stern foils for the damping of heave, pitch and roll motions in heavy seas.

Outfit: Seats for up to 400 passengers, according to the route served. In typical configuration there are three main passenger saloons and a bar. The standard seating arrangement allows for 116 in the main deck saloon, 58 in the aft lower saloon and 66 in the bow passenger saloon. Seating is normally four abreast in two lines with a central aisle. The bar, at the forward end of the wheelhouse belvedere superstructure, either has an eight-seat sofa or 19 seats.

The wheelhouse, which is raised to provide a 360° view, is reached from the main deck belvedere saloon by a short companionway. Controls and instrumentation are attached to a panel on the

Belvedere cabin of RHS 200 **1987**

Rexroth hydrostatic power transmission with tandem propellers as applied to an early Rodriquez Supramar PT 20, Aligrado *for trial purposes* **1989**

forward bulkhead which extends the width of the wheelhouse. In the centre is the steering control and gyrocompass, on the starboard side are controls for the two engines, gearboxes and controllable-pitch propellers, and on the port side is the radar. Seats are provided for the captain, chief engineer and first mate. In the wheelhouse are a radiotelephone and a chart table.

Safety equipment: Fixed CO_2 firefighting self-contained automatic systems for power-plant and fuel tank spaces, plus portable extinguishers for cabins and holds.

Craft built (RHS 200) 1981 to 1984

Type	Name	Yard No	No of seats	Operated in	Date built	Owner/Operator
RHS 200	*Superjumbo Capri* (ex-*Superjumbo*)	92	254	Italy	1981	Aliscafi SNAV SpA
RHS 200	*San Cristobal* (ex-*Stretto di Messina*)	209	254	Italy	1984	Aliscafi SNAV SpA

MEC 1
MAXIMUM EFFICIENCY CRAFT
Mec Ustica

Replacing the MEC 2 design previously reported, construction of MEC 1 started in July 1990. MEC 1 follows the same design principles and advances and is a new hydrofoil design developed in a joint effort with CETENA (the Italian Ship Research Institute) and incorporating Rexroth hydrostatic power transmission now continued by Hydromarine SA of Switzerland as the Power Shaft Concept. The design embodies a new Rodriquez surface-piercing foil system and hull form (fully automatic welding construction), with the rear foil unit carrying the maximum possible weight. It has been shown to be

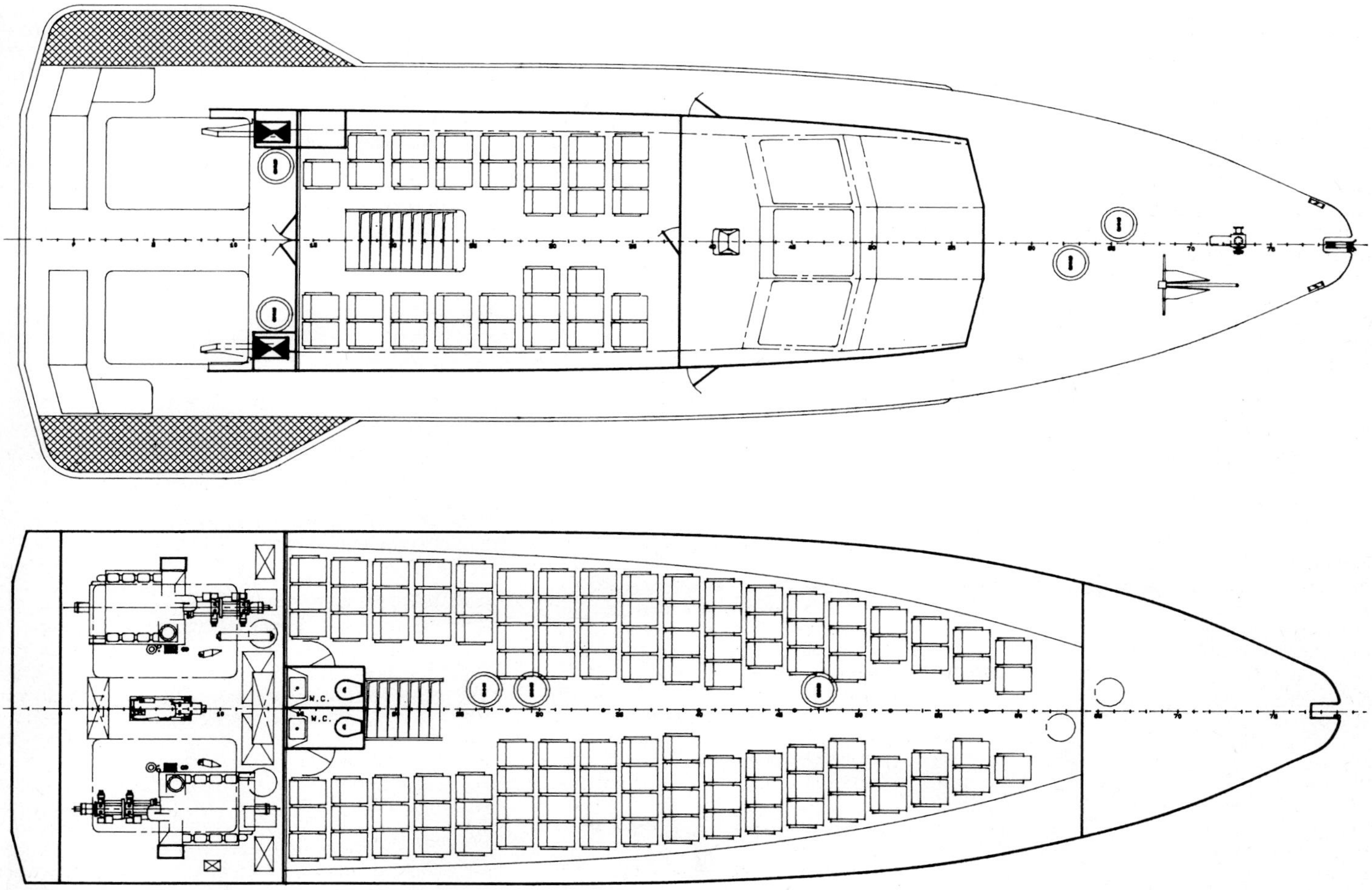

MEC 1

Rodriquez MEC 1 Mec Ustica **1993**

Craft built (MEC) 1991

Type	Name	Yard No	No of seats	Operated in	Date	Owner/Operator
MEC 1	*Mec Ustica*	242	146	-	1991	Aliscafi SNAV SpA
MEC 3						Yard No 260
MEC 4						Yard No 251, 1992

desirable to have a very stiff (in response to waves) front foil with low damping and a very soft rear foil with high damping. It is then convenient to carry the maximum possible weight on the rear foil, the Canard lift distribution allowing a finer hull bow form to be used.

The hull form has been derived from the well known 65 Series.

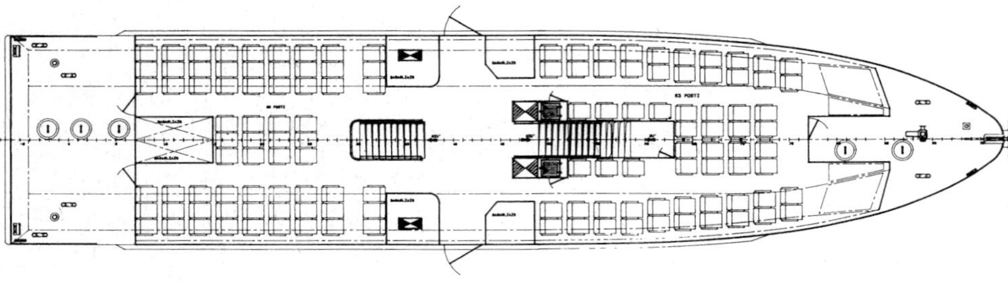

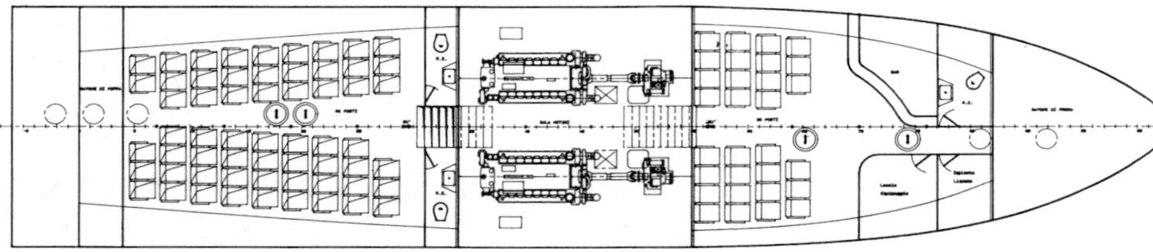

Foilmaster deck layouts

In comparison with comparable hydrofoils, a passenger capacity increase of about 25 per cent is anticipated, a speed increase of 9 per cent, while displacement increases by less than 5 per cent. For equal passenger capacity, the installed power would be reduced by some 18 per cent with a consequent reduction in fuel consumption. Due to the aft location of the power-plant a passenger cabin noise reduction of 3 to 5 dBA is expected.

Specifications

Length overall	25 m
Length waterline	20.8 m
Beam	6.7 m
Foil width	8.4 m
Draught, hullborne	2.8 m
Draught, foilborne	1.2 m
Displacement, max	55 t
Passengers	146
Operational speed	38 kts
Range	200 n miles

Propulsion: Engines: 2 × Deutz MWM TBD 604B V8, driving hydrostatic power transmission.

Please see the Rexroth entry in the *Transmission* section of this book for discussion of the basic concept and for details of the system as applied to an early Rodriquez Supramar PT 20 hydrofoil craft, *Aligrado.*

FOILMASTER

The Foilmaster is an advanced variant of the RHS 160 surface-piercing hydrofoil. Improvements include resilient mounting of engines and gearboxes, exhaust gas silencers, the use of carbon fibre components in foil construction and more powerful engines. Tandem configuration foils are fitted with trailing edge flaps. There are two sets of rudders provided, two flap rudders on the aft foil and a single flap rudder fitted to the fore foil. An air conditioning system is installed in all passenger saloons as well as in the wheelhouse.

The first of a number of Foilmasters was delivered to SIREMAR in late 1994.

Specifications

Length overall	31.4 m
Length waterline	26.4 m
Beam	6.7 m
Foil width	13.3 m
Draught, hullborne	3.76 m
Draught, foilborne	1.6 m
Displacement, max	107 t
Crew	7
Passengers	219
Fuel capacity	2.5 t
Water capacity	0.6 t
Propulsive power	2 × 1,550 kW
Operational speed	38 kts
Range	150 n miles

Propulsion: Engines: 2 × MTU 16V 396 TE 74.

VERIFIED

Foilmaster Tiziano **1995**

JAPAN

HITACHI ZOSEN CORPORATION

Head Office: 3-28 Nishikujo 5-chome, Konhana-ku, Osaka, 554 Japan

Tel: +81 (6) 466 7546
Telex: 63376 J
Fax: +81 (6) 466 7578

Works: 4-1 Mizue-cho, Kawasaki-ku, Kawasaki, Kanagawa Pref, Japan

Tel: +81 (44) 288 1111
Telex: 3842524 J
Fax: +81 (44) 276 0022

T Arii, *General Manager*

Hitachi Zosen, the Supramar licensee in Japan, has been building Supramar PT 20, PT 32 and PT 50 hydrofoils since 1961. By 1970 some 32 hydrofoils had been built with another 10 by 1981. The majority of these have been built for fast passenger ferry services across the Japanese Inland Sea, cutting across deep bays which road vehicles might take two to three hours to drive round, and out to offshore islands. Other PT 20s and 50s have been exported to Hong Kong, Australia and South Korea for ferry services.

Specifications of the PT 32 (*Jane's Surface Skimmers 1967-68*), PT 20 and PT 50 will be found under Supramar (Switzerland) (*Jane's Surface Skimmers 1985*). The Hitachi Zosen craft are almost identical.

In 1974 the company completed the first PT 50 Mk II to be built at its Kawasaki yard. The vessel, *Hikari No 2,* is powered by two licence-built MTU MB 820Db diesels, carries 123 passengers plus a crew of seven and cruises at 33 knots. It was delivered to Setonaikai Kisen KK of Hiroshima in March 1975. Hitachi Zosen has constructed 25 PT 50s and 17 PT 20s.

In conjunction with Supramar, Hitachi Zosen has developed a new roll stabilisation system for the PT 50. The first to be equipped with this new system was completed in January 1983.

PT 20 Ryusei *operated by Ishizaki Kisen KK* **1987**

PTS 50 Mk II Housho **1986**

ROLL-STABILISED SUPRAMAR PTS 50 Mk II

Housho, a PTS 50 Mk II, was delivered to Hankyu Kisen KK on 19 January 1983 and is operating on the Kobe-Naruto route. The system, developed by Hitachi Zosen in conjunction with Supramar, reduces the PTS 50's rolling motion by between one-half and one-third.

The underside of the bow foil is fitted with two flapped fins to improve riding comfort. Operated by automatic sensors, the fins augment stability and provide side forces to dampen rolling and transverse motions.

Specifications

Length overall	27.55 m
Beam	5.84 m
Foil width	10.8 m
Draught, hullborne	3.5 m
Draught, foilborne	1.4 m
Displacement, max	62 t
Passengers	123
Propulsive power	2 × 1,029 kW
Max speed	38 kts

UPDATED

Hitachi hydrofoils believed to be currently in operation

Type	Name	Seats	Launched	Delivered to
Hitachi Supramar PT 20	*Hayate No 1*		April 1962	Showa Kaiun Co Ltd
Hitachi Supramar PT 20	*Kansei*		July 1962	Ishizaki Kisen KK
Hitachi Supramar PT 20	*Hibiki*		November 1966	Setonaikai Kisen KK
Hitachi Supramar PT 20	*Hibiki No 3*	66	March 1968	Setonaikai Kisen KK
Hitachi Supramar PT 20	*Shibuki No 2*		June 1969	Boyo Kisen Co Ltd
Hitachi Supramar PT 20	*Myojo*		June 1970	Ishizaki Kisen KK
Hitachi Supramar PT 20	*Kinsei*		July 1972	Ishizaki Kisen KK
Hitachi Supramar PT 20	*Ryusei*		March 1981	Ishizaki Kisen KK
Hitachi Supramar PT 50	*Ohtori*	113	January 1968	-
Hitachi Supramar PT 50	*Kosei*		February 1969	Ishizaki Kisen KK
Hitachi Supramar PT 50	*Ohtori No 2*	113	February 1970	Setonaikai Kisen KK
Hitachi Supramar PT 50	*Zuihoh*		December 1971	Hankyu Kisen KK
Hitachi Supramar PT 50	*Hoh'oh*		February 1972	Hankyu Kisen KK
Hitachi Supramar PT 50	*Condor*	121	June 1972	Setonaikai Kisen KK
Hitachi Supramar PT 50	*Ohtori No 3*		October 1972	Setonaikai Kisen KK
Hitachi Supramar PT 50	*Ohtori No 5*		May 1973	Setonaikai Kisen KK
Hitachi Supramar PT 50	*Shibuki No 3*		October 1973	Boyo Kisen Co Ltd
Hitachi Supramar PT 50	*Saisei*		March 1974	Ishizaki Kisen KK
Hitachi Supramar PT 50	*Condor No 2*	121	April 1974	Setonaikai Kisen KK
Hitachi Supramar PT 50	*Condor No 3*	100	August 1974	Setonaikai Kisen KK
Hitachi Supramar PT 50 Mk II	*Hikari No 2*	123	March 1975	Setonaikai Kisen KK
Hitachi Supramar PT 50 Mk II	*Shunsei* (ex-*Kariyush I*)		June 1975	Ishizaki Kisen KK
Hitachi Supramar PTS 50 Mk II	*Housho*	123	January 1983	Hankyu Kisen KK

KAWASAKI HEAVY INDUSTRIES LTD

Ship Group Tokyo Head Office: World Trade Center Building, 4-1 Hamamatsu-cho 2-chome, Minato-ku, Tokyo 105, Japan

Tel: +81 (3) 3435 2186
Telex: 242 4371 KAWAJU J
Fax: +81 (3) 3436 3038 G3/G2

Kobe Works: 1-1 Higashi Kawasaki-cho 3-chome, Chuo-ku, Kobe 650-91, Japan

Tel: +81 (78) 682 5120
Telex: 5623 931 KHIKOB J
Fax: +81 (78) 682 5512

Ryúnosuke Kawazumi, *Managing Director and Senior General Manager of Ship Group*

JETFOIL 929-117

In January 1987, Kawasaki Heavy Industries Ltd acquired a licence for the design, manufacture, marketing, maintenance and repair of Jetfoil 929-117 hydrofoil craft. By June 1994 14 Kawasaki Jetfoils had been built. The majority of these craft have been built for fast passenger ferry services between mainland Japan and offshore islands. Two Jetfoils have been exported to Spain.

Specifications

Length overall	27.4 m
Beam	9.1 m
Draught, hullborne	4.9 m
Max speed	45 kts

Propulsion: Two Allison 501-KF gas-turbines, each rated at 2,795 kW at 13,120 rpm. Each is connected to a Kawasaki Powerjet 20 axial flow water-jet propulsor through a gearbox drive train.

For details of the Jetfoil 929 series please see entry under Boeing Aerospace.

VERIFIED

Craft built (Kawasaki Jetfoil 929-117 type)

Yard No	Name	Seats	Delivery	Delivered to
KJ01	*Tsubasa*	266	March 1989	Sado Kisen Kaisha
KJ02	*Toppy*	264	June 1989	Kagoshima Shosen Co Ltd
KJ03	*Pearl Wing* (*ex-Nagasaki*)	230	September 1989	Kaijyo Access Co
KJ04	*Pegasus*	265	March 1990	Kyúshu Shósen Co Ltd
KJ05	*Sapphire Wing* (*ex-Beetle*)	230	April 1990	Kaijyo Access Co
KJ06	*Princesa Dacil*	286	July 1990	Compania Trasmediterranea, SA
KJ07	*Unicorn*	233	October 1990	Higashi-Nihon Ferry Co Ltd
KJ08	*Beetle II*	232	February 1991	Kyushu Railway Co
KJ09	*Venus*	263	March 1991	Kyūshū Yusen Co Ltd
KJ10	*Suisei*	262	April 1991	Sado Kisen Kaisha
KJ11	*Princesa Teguise*	286	June 1991	Compania Trasmediterranea, SA
KJ12	*Toppy 2*	244	April 1992	Kagoshima Shosen Co Ltd
KJ14	*Crystal Wing*	230	June 1994	Kaijyo Access Co
KJ15	*Emerald Wing*	230	June 1994	Kaijyo Access Co

Kawasaki Crystal Wing
1995

SUMITOMO HEAVY INDUSTRIES LTD

5-9-11 Kitashinagawa, Shinagawa-Ku, Tokyo 141, Japan

Tel: +81 (3) 5488 8181
Fax: +81 (3) 5488 8178

Kenya Koseki, *General Manager*

PG Class

Sumitomo Industries are licensee of Sparviero Class hydrofoils, granted by Fincantieri (Italy).

Three PGs were constructed and delivered for the Japanese Defence Agency.

Specifications

Length overall	21.8 m
Beam	7 m
Draught	1.4 m
Displacement	50 t
Crew	11
Max speed	46 kts

Propulsion: 2 × GE/IHI LM 500 gas-turbines, driving a water-jet pump; and an Isuzu diesel 180PS for hull-borne operations.

PG Class craft built

Name	Yard No	Delivered
PG01	821	22 May 1993
PG02	822	22 May 1993
PG03	823	13 May 1995

UPDATED

TECHNOLOGICAL RESEARCH ASSOCIATION OF TECHNO-SUPERLINER

Japan Shipbuilding Research Centre Building, 1-3-8 Mejiro, Toshima Ku, Tokyo 171, Japan

Tel: +81 (3) 3985 3841
Fax: +81 (3) 3985 3740

Tokashi Nakaso, *President*
Kazuo Sugai, *Managing Director*

The Techno-Superliner Project in Japan involves seven leading shipbuilders, among them Kawasaki Heavy Industries Ltd, NKK Corporation, Ishikawajima-Harima Heavy Industries Company Ltd, Sumitomo Heavy Industries Ltd and Hitachi Zosen Corporation which are jointly investigating the concept of a novel super high-speed ship with all the load being borne by a fully submerged hull and fully submerged foils, so called TSL-F.

Prototype TSL-F trials craft Hayate
1995

The TSL-F superliner has been designed to achieve the following performance targets:
Ship speed: 50 kts
Payload: approx 1,000 t
Endurance range: >500 n miles
Seaworthiness: regular service at Sea State 6

For this purpose, the speed liner must have a hull form which can reduce the influence of the wave as far as possible and minimise motion and speed reduction in rough seas, giving at least a 98 per cent yearly operation rate on the expected route.

To avoid the influence of the sea surface, the main hull containing the cargo, machinery and navigation systems is supported at a height well above the waves; a lower hull for buoyancy and the foils for dynamic lift are deeply submerged, and the struts to connect the main hull, the lower hull and foils are placed vertically as shown in the accompanying profile of the TSL-F concept. The planned TSL-F concept has been shown to have a high level of seaworthiness, with almost no speed reduction in high sea states through the extensive research and Development programme.

TSL-F (DESIGN)
Specifications

Length overall	85 m
Beam	37 m
Draught, hullborne	12 m
Draught, foilborne	8.1 m
Payload	1,000 t
Max speed	50 kts
Range	500 n miles
Operational limitation	wave height 6 m

Propulsion: Engines: gas-turbines and water-jet propulsors.

TSL-F PROTOTYPE CRAFT *Hayate*

A large scale model of a hydrofoil-type hybrid ship (TSL-F) named *Hayate* was completed in Kobe Works of Kawasaki Heavy Industries Ltd (KHI) at the beginning of July 1994.

Artist's impression of TSL-F design ***1995***

Hayate, which is a ⅙ scale model of an R&D objective TSL-F ship, is composed of an upper hull, a fully submerged lower hull which bears buoyancy, fully submerged foils which generate dynamic lift, and struts which connect the upper hull and the lower hull or the foils. The main propulsion system of *Hayate* consists of a water-jet propulsor, a reduction gear and a gas-turbine.

Various at-sea tests of *Hayate* were conducted until March 1995 to acquire data unobtainable through laboratory tests and to evaluate and verify the overall performance of TSL-F as well as numerous elemental research findings.

Specifications

Length overall	17.1 m
Beam	6.2 m
Draught, hullborne	3.1 m
Draught, foilborne	1.6 m
Propulsive power	2,835 kW
Max speed	41 kts

Propulsion: 1 × gas-turbine, driving water-jet propulsor.

UPDATED

UNITED STATES OF AMERICA

BOEING

Although this company is no longer engaged in the marketing of commercial or military hydrofoil vessels, details of the Boeing Jetfoil are included here since these craft represented a most significant step in high-speed marine craft technology.

The Boeing Company has licensed Kawasaki Heavy Industries Ltd for the design, manufacture, marketing, maintenance and repair of Boeing Jetfoil 929-117 hydrofoil craft. Boeing's entry into the hydrofoil field was announced in June 1960, when the company was awarded a US$2 million contract for the construction of the US Navy's 120 ton PCH-1 *High Point*, a canard design which was the outcome of experiments with a similar arrangement in the US Navy test craft, *Sea Legs*.

The history of Boeing hydrofoil development work is given in the 1990 and earlier editions of this book. As a result of Boeing's extensive hydrofoil programmes two principal vessel types evolved, the 235 ton NATO/PHM patrol boat (six built, 1977 to 1982) and the Jetfoil type of which, by January 1990, 39 had been built or ordered, including the Kawasaki vessels, almost entirely for ferry operations. Kawasaki has built 11 Jetfoil 929-117 craft.

Details of the NATO/PHM patrol boats are given in the 1992-93 edition of this book.

JETFOIL 929-100

This is a 110 ton water-jet propelled commercial hydrofoil for services in relatively rough waters. It employs a fully submerged, automatically controlled canard foil arrangement and is powered by two 2,767 kW Allison 501-K20A gas-turbines. Normal foilborne cruising speed is 42 knots.

Typical interior arrangements include a commuter configuration with up to 350 seats and a tourist layout for 190 to 250 plus baggage.

Keel-laying of the first Jetfoil took place at the company's Renton, Washington, plant in January 1973 and the craft was launched in March 1974.

Craft built (Jetfoil 929-100)

Name	Launched	Current Operator
Flores (ex-*Kalakoua*, 1978 Boeing No 001)	29 Mar 1974	Far East Hydrofoil Co Ltd, Hong Kong
Madeira (002)	Oct 1974	Far East Hydrofoil Co Ltd, Hong Kong
Corvo (ex-*Kamehameha*) (003)	Feb 1975	Far East Hydrofoil Co Ltd, Hong Kong
Santa Maria (005)	Apr 1975	Far East Hydrofoil Co Ltd, Hong Kong
Pico (ex-*Kuhio*) (004)	Jun 1975	Far East Hydrofoil Co Ltd, Hong Kong
Sâo Jorge (ex-*Jet Caribe I*) (006)	Dec 1975	Far East Hydrofoil Co Ltd, Hong Kong
Acores (ex-*Jet Caribe II*, 1980, ex-*Oriente*, 1978) (008)	Nov 1976	Far East Hydrofoil Co Ltd, Hong Kong
Urzela (ex-*Flying Princess*) (007)	May 1976	Far East Hydrofoil Co Ltd, Hong Kong
Ponta Delgada (ex-*Flying Princess II*) (010)	May 1977	Far East Hydrofoil Co Ltd, Hong Kong
Guia (ex-*Okesa*)	Dec 1976	Far East Hydrofoil Co Ltd, Hong Kong

Boeing Jetfoil 929-115 Cu na Mara *renamed* Ginga *and in service with Sado Kisen Kaisha* ***1987***

The 1976-launched Acores *Jetfoil 929-100 in service on the Hong Kong to Macao route* **1987**

After testing on Puget Sound and in the Pacific, the craft was delivered to Pacific Sea Transportation Ltd for inter-island services in Hawaii. High-speed foilborne tests began in Puget Sound in mid-July and it was reported that the vessel attained a speed of 48 knots during its runs.

During a rigorous testing programme to prove the boat's design and construction, Boeing No 001 operated for 470 hours, including 237 hours foilborne. The latter phase of testing was conducted in the rough waters of the straits of Juan de Fuca and the Pacific Ocean, where it encountered wave swells as high as 9.1 m, winds gusting up to 60 knots and wave chop averaging 1.8 m high.

The first operational Jetfoil service was successfully initiated in April 1975 by Far East Hydrofoil Company Ltd, Hong Kong, with Jetfoil 002, *Madeira.* Before this, the Jetfoil received its ABS classification, was certificated by the Hong Kong Marine Department and passed US Coast Guard certification trials. A US Coast Guard certificate was not completed as the craft would not be operating in US waters.

The first US service began in Hawaii in June 1975 and the tenth Jetfoil was launched in May 1977.

Specifications

Length overall	27.4 m
Beam	9.5 m
Draught, hullborne	5 m
Displacement	110 t
Passengers	190-350
Fuel capacity	15,140 l
Propulsive power	2 × 2,767 kW
Max speed	50 kts
Operational speed	42 kts
Operational limitation	wave height 3.65 m

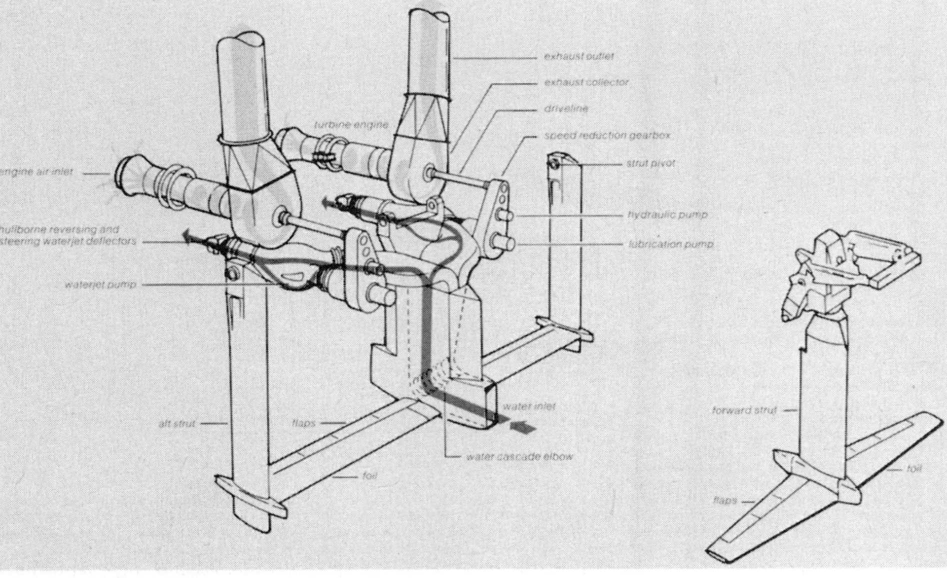

Principal elements of the Jetfoil propulsion and foil system **1992**

Structure: Hull and deckhouse in marine aluminium. Aircraft assembly techniques are used, including high-speed mechanised welding processes.

All structural components of the foil/strut system are in 15.5PH corrosion-resistant all-welded steel construction.

Propulsion: Power for the water-jet propulsion system is supplied by two Allison 501-K20A free-power gas-turbines, each rated at 2,767 kW at 27°C at sea level. Each is connected to a Rocketdyne Powerjet 20 axial flow pump through a gearbox drive train. The system propels the craft in both foilborne and hullborne modes. When foilborne, water enters through the inlet at the forward lower end of the aft centre foil strut. At the top of the duct, the water is split into two paths and enters into each of the two axial flow pumps. It is then discharged at high pressure through nozzles in the hull bottom. The water path is the same during hullborne operations with the foils extended. When the foils are retracted, the water enters through a flush inlet located in the keel. Reversing and steering for hullborne operation only are accomplished by reverse-flow buckets located immediately aft of the water exit nozzles. A bow thruster is provided for positive steering control at low forward speeds.

A 15,140 litre integral fuel tank supplies the propulsion turbine and diesel engines. Coalescent-type water separating fuel filters and remote-controlled motor-operated fuel shut-off valves provide fire protection.

Electrical system: A 60 Hz, 440 V AC electrical system, supplied by two diesel-driven generators each rated at 62.5 kVA. Either is capable of supplying all vital electrical power. 90 kVA capacity shore connection facilities are provided and equipment can accept 50 Hz power. Transformer rectifier units for battery charging provide 28 V DC from the AC system.

Control: The foil system is a fully submerged canard arrangement with a single inverted T strut/foil forward and a three-strut, full-span foil aft. The forward foil assembly is rotated hydraulically through 7° in either direction for steering. All foils have trailing

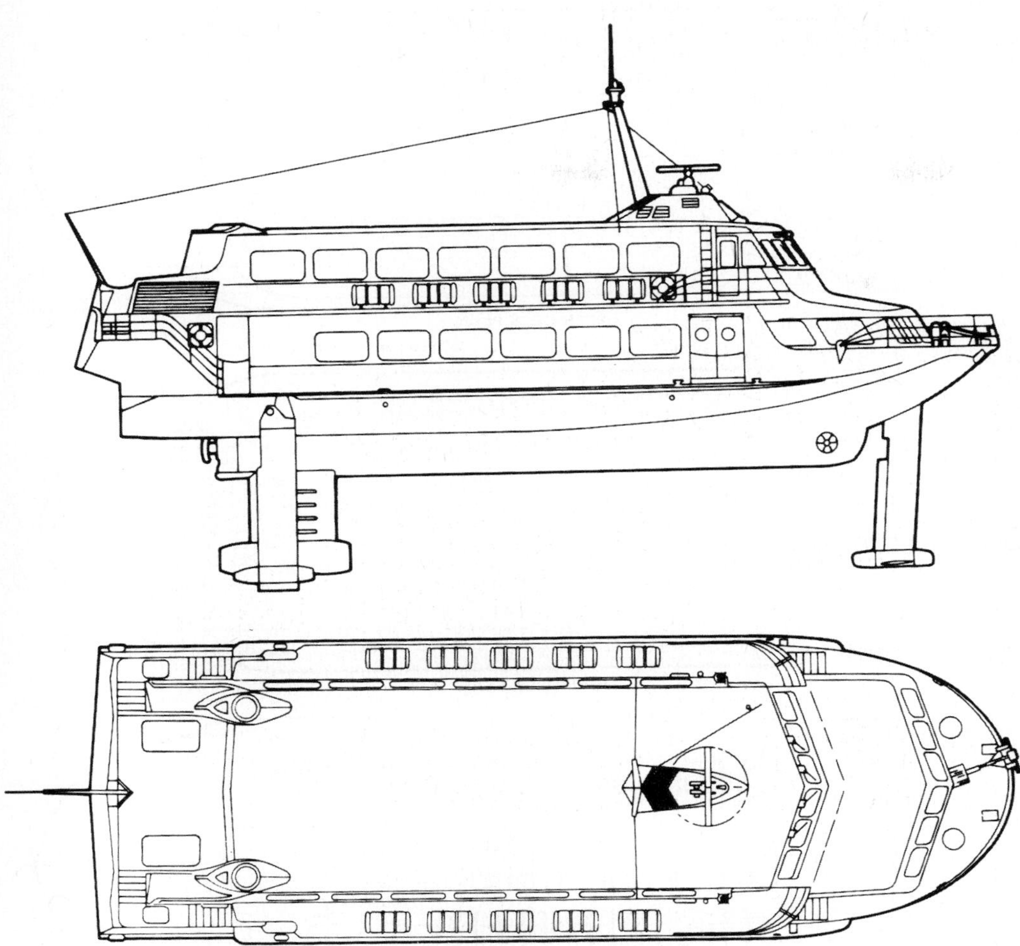

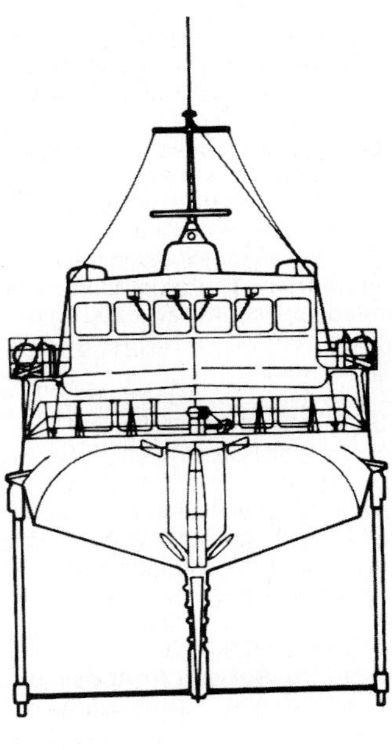

General arrangement of the Kawasaki Jetfoil Model 929-115 passenger ferry ***1986***

JETFOIL 929-115

Craft built (Jetfoil 929-115 type and conversions)

Name	Launched	Owner
Mikado (011)	Jun 1978	Sado Kisen Kaisha, Japan
Ginga (ex-*Cu na Mara*)	Nov 1979	Sado Kisen Kaisha, Japan
Terceira (ex-*Normandy Princess*)	Jan 1979	Far East Hydrofoil Co Ltd, Hong Kong
Funchal (ex-*Jetferry One*)	May 1979	Far East Hydrofoil Co Ltd, Hong Kong
Horta (ex-*Jetferry Two*) (016)	Mar 1980	Far East Hydrofoil Co Ltd, Hong Kong
Calcilhas (ex-*Princesa Guayarmina*)	Nov 1980	Far East Hydrofoil Co Ltd, Hong Kong
Taipa (ex-*Princesa Guacimara*)	Jul 1981	Far East Hydrofoil Co Ltd, Hong Kong
Bima Samudera I (Boeing No 022)	Oct 1981	PT PAL, Indonesia
Princesse Clementine	Feb 1981	Regie des Transports Maritimes, Belgium
Prinses Stephanie	Apr 1981	Regie des Transports Maritimes, Belgium
Jet 7 (ex-*Spirit of Friendship*, ex-*Aries*, ex-*Montevideo Jet*)	Aug 1980	Kato Kisen Co Ltd/Kansai Kisen Co Ltd
Jet 8 (ex-*Spirit of Discovery*)	Apr 1985	Kato Kisen Co Ltd/Kansai Kisen Co Ltd
- (modified to 929-119)	Aug 1984	Indonesian Government (Navy)
- (modified to 929-119)	Nov 1984	Indonesian Government
Lilau (ex-*Speedy Princess* 929-320) *(shipped 1986 to Hong Kong* to be modified to type 929-320)	Jul 1979	Far East Hydrofoil Co Ltd, Hong Kong (*Speedy Princess* (ex-British Royal Navy, *HMS Speedy*) was purchased in September 1986 by FEH (departed UK, 16 Oct 1986) and converted to a commercial passenger vessel)
- (modified to 929-120)	Jan 1986	Indonesian Government
- (modified to 929-120)	June 1986	Indonesian Government

edge flaps for controlling pitch, roll and yaw and for take-off and landing. Foils and struts retract hydraulically above the waterline, the bow foil forward, and the rear foil aft.

The craft is controlled by a three-axis automatic system while foilborne and during take-off and landing. The system senses the motion and position of the craft by gyros, accelerometers and height sensors, signals from which are combined in the control computer with manual commands from the helm. The resulting computer outputs provide control surface deflections through electrohydraulic servo actuators. Lift control is by full-span trailing edge flaps on each foil. Forward and aft flaps operate differentially to provide pitch variation and height control. Aft flaps operate differentially to provide roll control for changes of direction.

The vessel banks inwardly into all turns to ensure maximum passenger comfort. The ACS introduces the correct amount of bank and steering to co-ordinate the turn in full. Turn rates of up to 6°/s are attained within one second of providing a heading change command at the helm.

There are three basic controls required for foilborne operation: the throttle is employed to set the speed, the height command lever to set the required foil depth, and the helm to set the required heading. If a constant course is required, a 'heading hold' circuit accomplishes this automatically.

For take-off, the foil depth is set, the two throttles advanced and the hull clears the water in about 60 seconds. Acceleration continues until the craft automatically stabilises at the command depth and the speed dictated by the throttle setting. The throttle setting is reduced for landing, the craft settling as the speed drops. The speed normally diminishes from 45 knots (cruising speed) to 15 knots in approximately 30 seconds. In emergencies more rapid landings can be made by the use of the height command lever to provide hull contact within two seconds.

Quality of the ride in the craft is comparable with that of a Boeing 727 airliner. The vertical acceleration at the centre of gravity is very low and depends on sea state, for example, at 2 m significant wave height the vertical acceleration is only 0.05 *g* rms. Lateral acceleration is substantially less than vertical. Angles of pitch and roll are less than 1° rms. A structural fuse is provided which limits deceleration to less than 0.4 *g* longitudinally and 0.8 *g* vertically. In the event of the craft striking a major item of floating debris at full speed, the structural fuse, when actuated, allows the foil and strut to rotate backwards, preventing the system from sustaining significant damage.

Crew comprises a captain and first officer plus cabin attendants.

The last of the Jetfoil 929-100 series was the 010 *Flying Princess II.* The first of the improved 929-115 series, Jetfoil 011 *Mikado*, was launched at Renton, Washington in June 1978, and is operated by Sado Kisen in the Sea of Japan.

The improved model Jetfoil has a lighter structure allowing an increased payload and greater reliability, and is easier to maintain. Some of the modifications are listed below.

Specifications

Length overall	27.4 m
Beam	9.5 m
Draught, hullborne	5.2 m
Displacement, max	117 t
Max speed	43 kts

Structure: The bow structure design has been simplified to provide equivalent strength with increased payload and bulkhead two has been revised for decreased stress levels. Based on a seven minute evacuation time in case of fire the following fire protection provisions have been made:

(1) Fibreglass is used for thermal insulation where required throughout the passenger accommodation areas

(2) Aluminium ceiling panels and air conditioner sleeves are employed throughout, together with aluminium doors and frames

(3) One ½ in thick Marinite is employed in machinery spaces, with US Coast Guard-type felt added wherever required for insulation to comply with 30 minute fire test

(4) External stiffeners on the foil struts have been eliminated and the bow foil has been changed from constant section to tapered planform for improved performance. Stress levels have been reduced for extended life.

Propulsion: The propulsion system has been uprated to operate at 2,200 maximum intermittent pump rpm with an increase of 3 tons in maximum gross weight.

JETFOIL 929-117

Since 1985 Boeing has not manufactured any model of the Jetfoil. The 929-117 model, an updated version, has been licensed for production outside the USA, with Kawasaki Heavy Industries Ltd, Kobe, Japan and PT PAL Indonesia. See Kawasaki entry for further details.

JETFOIL 929-320

***Lilau* (*ex-Speedy Princess, ex-HMS Speedy*)**

The Jetfoil 929-320 was delivered to the Royal Navy in June 1980 for use in fisheries patrol in the North Sea. Named *HMS Speedy,* the craft was a modified Model 929-115 commercial Jetfoil and was built on the commercial Jetfoil production line. The craft was decommissioned by the Royal Navy in April 1982 and eventually sold to the Far East Hydrofoil Company Ltd (FEH) in Autumn 1986. The craft has been converted to passenger configuration and operates on their Hong Kong to Macao route.

VERIFIED

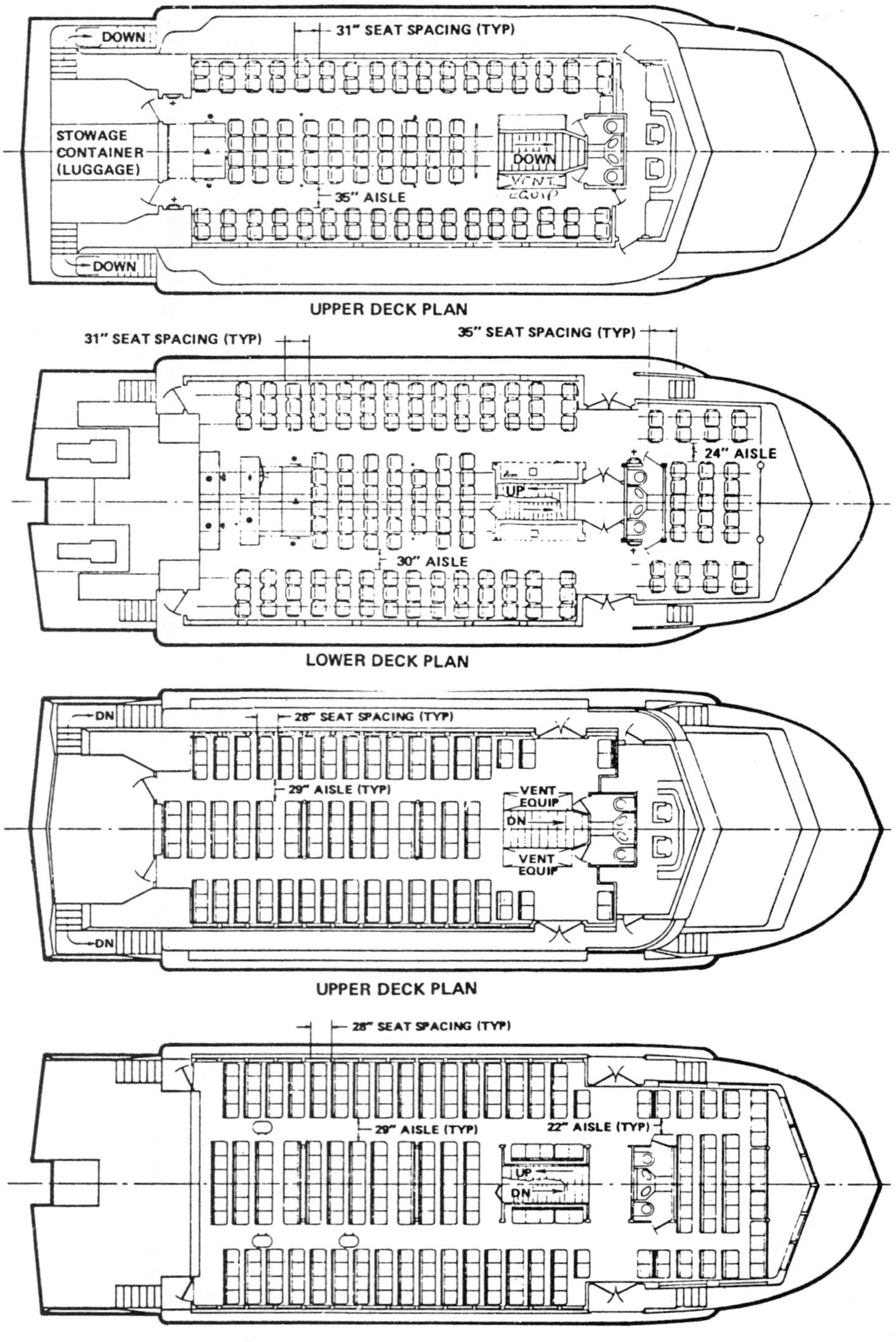

UPPER DECK PLAN

LOWER DECK PLAN

UPPER DECK PLAN

LOWER DECK PLAN

Jetfoil 929-100 interior arrangements

WESTFOIL INTERNATIONAL

PO Box 1757, Westport, Washington 98595, USA

Tel: +1 (206) 268 0117
Fax: +1 (206) 268 0119

Randy Rust, *Representative*

WESTFOIL 25 m

Design started on the Westfoil 25 m fully submerged hydrofoil in Autumn 1986 and construction started during Summer 1987. The hull lines come from Westport Shipyard's latest mould, for a boat designed to meet the rigours of year round commercial service. The submerged foil and automatic control system are based on 25 years of hydrofoil experience by the designers using the latest proven technology to provide a ride which should be better than existing hydrofoils. The ducted air propellers provide thrust at low tip speed while the ducts have acoustical treatment to further reduce noise. Some parts of the design have now been patented.

Trials of the Westfoil 25 m hydrofoil started in Summer 1991.

Westfoil 25 m hydrofoil **1992**

Specifications

Length overall	24.39 m
Beam	7.16 m
Draught, hullborne	4.88 m
Displacement	71.11 t
Passengers	149
Fuel capacity	5,677 l
Water capacity	378 l
Propulsive power	4 × 805 kW
Max speed	42 kts

Structure: The foils are Nitronic 50 stainless steel and composite structure.

Propulsion: Four DDC 12V-92 TA diesels with 145 type injectors, each 805 kW max, at 2,300 rpm. Engine rpm is limited to 2,100, driving two ducted air propellers by Pacific Propeller Inc with low tip speed variable-pitch propellers.

Control: The foils are arranged in a canard arrangement. The front and aft foil and strut systems can be retracted independently.

An Automatic Control System (ACS) includes the flaps located at the trailing edges of both the fore and aft foils, the front strut rudder, the foil flap actuation system and the automatic stabilisation and control system. The foil flaps provide control of the craft in pitch, roll and yaw to provide a smooth ride in all seas up to design sea conditions and for take-off and landing. The foil flap actuators use input from the automatic stabilisation and control system to select the angle of the foil flaps so that the wave motions are counteracted. Flaps are moved in response to helm control to turn the boat in a banked attitude. The automatic stabilisation and control system employs a computer, motion sensors, a height sensor and gyroscopes to generate the commands sent to the actuators so that the foil flaps move to maintain the desired stable attitude and foil depth.

Foilborne steering is accomplished by actuating the aft flaps differentially (in response to helm commands) to roll the boat into a turn with appropriate front strut rudder setting to maintain a co-ordinated turn. The flaps and front strut rudder settings will be maintained by the ACS in response to helm commands and motion and height sensor feedback.

Hullborne steering utilises an Arneson drive system. A bow thruster is installed.

VERIFIED

HIGH-SPEED MULTIHULL VESSELS

Company Listing by Country

Australia
Alufast International Pty Ltd
Astra Bay Enterprises
Atlay Catamarans Australia Pty Ltd (Cougar Catamarans)
Austal Ships Pty Ltd
Ferries Australia
Incat Australia Pty Ltd
Lloyd's Ships Holdings Pty Ltd
NQEA Australia Pty Ltd
Oceanfast Ferries Pty Ltd
Oceanfast International Pty Ltd
Sabre Catamarans Pty Ltd
SBF Engineering
Wavemaster International Pty Ltd

Chile
Asenav MR

China, People's Republic
Hang Tong High Speed Ship Development Co Ltd

Commonwealth of Independent States
Almaz Shipyard Central Marine Design Bureau
Sudoexport

Denmark
Danyard A/S

Finland
Finnyards Ltd

France
CMN
Constructions Aluminium Navales Sarl

Germany
HDW
Ultimar GmbH & Co KG

Hong Kong
A Fai Engineers and Shiprepairers Ltd

Italy
Moschini
Rodriquez Cantieri Navali SpA

Japan
Hitachi Zosen Corporation
IHI
Kawasaki Heavy Industries Ltd Ship Group
Mitsubishi Heavy Industries Ltd
Mitsui Engineering & Shipbuilding Company Ltd
NKK Corporation
Yamaha Motor Company Ltd

Korea, South
Daewoo Shipbuilding and Heavy Machinery Ltd
Hyundai Heavy Industries Company Ltd
Korea Tacoma Marine Industries Limited

Netherlands
Royal Schelde BV
Tille Shipyards
Van Der Giessen-de Noord

Norway
BÅtservice Holding A/S
CPS Production A/S
CPS Drive A/S
Holen Mek Verksted A/S
Hydrocat Techno A/S
Kværner a.s. Fast Ferries
Kværner Fjellstrand A/S
Lindstøls Skips- & BÅtbyggeri A/S
Rosendal Verft A/S
Westamarin A/S
Westamarin West A/S

Singapore
Aluminium Craft (88) Pte Ltd
Kværner Fjellstrand (S) Pte Ltd
Marinteknik Shipbuilders (S) Pte Ltd
Singapore Shipbuilding and Engineering Ltd

South Africa
Teknicraft Design

Sweden
Oskarshamns Varv AB

Thailand
Italthai Marine Ltd

United Kingdom
Aluminium Shipbuilders Ltd
FBM Marine Group

United States of America
Allen Marine, Inc
Derecktor Shipyards
Gladding-Hearn Shipbuilding
Nichols Brothers Boat Builders Inc
Peterson Builders Inc
USA Catamarans Inc

AUSTRALIA

ALUFAST INTERNATIONAL PTY LTD

Lot 5, Clarence Beach Road, Coogee, Western Australia, 6166

Tel: +61 (9) 437 3033
Fax: +61 (9) 437 3110

John Mason, *Managing Director*
Simon Thornton, *Production Technical Director*

Alufast International is a builder of aluminium high-speed ferries. The company specialises in the construction of total vessels or complete hulls with final assembly and componentry fabrication carried out in overseas shipyards. It also provides a refurbishment refit service for ferries throughout the world with the work carried out in its shipyards in Australia or on site location.

They currently have two vessels under construction:

Nansha 38
Nansha 68

These two vessels are 42 m aluminium ferries which will achieve full load speeds of over 43 knots and lightship speeds of approximately 48 knots. They were designed to provide a high quality and fast transportation link between Hong Kong and China.

Specifications

Length overall	42.0 m
Length waterline	36.0 m
Beam	12.0 m
Draught	1.5 m
Crew	12
Passengers	380
Fuel capacity	12,000 l
Water capacity	1,250 l
Max speed	48 kts
Operational speed	43.5 kts

Classification: China Classification Society (CCS), in accordance with IMO res A373X, 1978.
Structure: Marine grade aluminium (MIG welded).
Propulsion: The main engines are 4 × MTU 16V 396 TE 74L diesels; driving 4 × KaMeWa 63 S62.6 water-jets; via 4 × Reintjes VLJ 930 gearboxes.

UPDATED

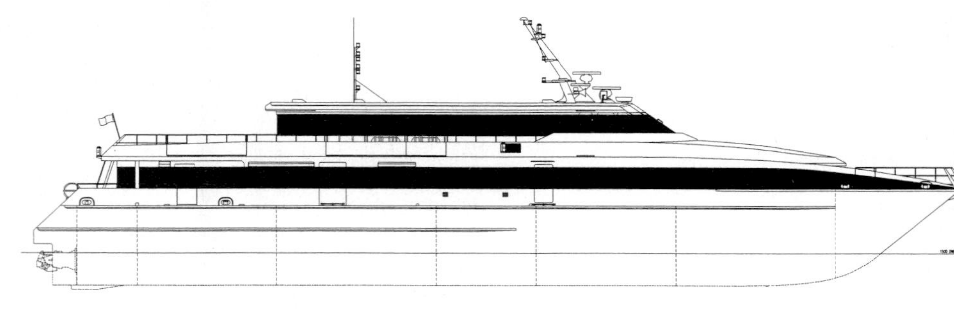

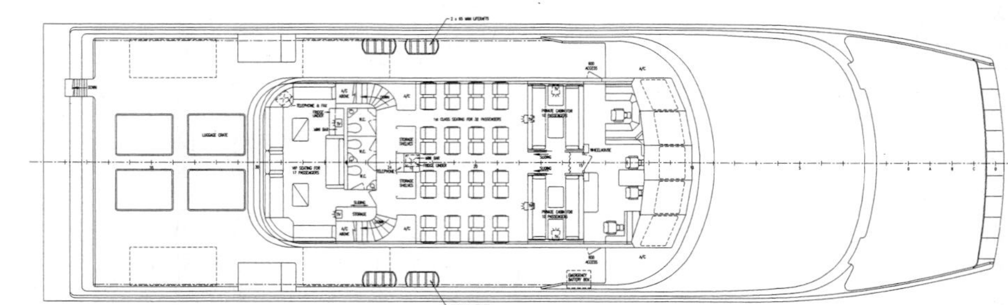

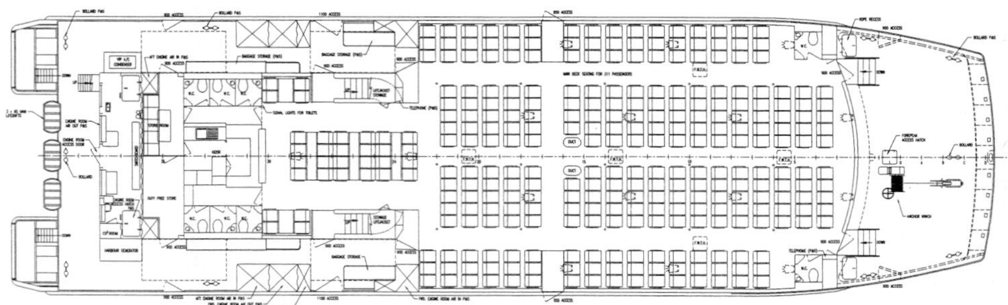

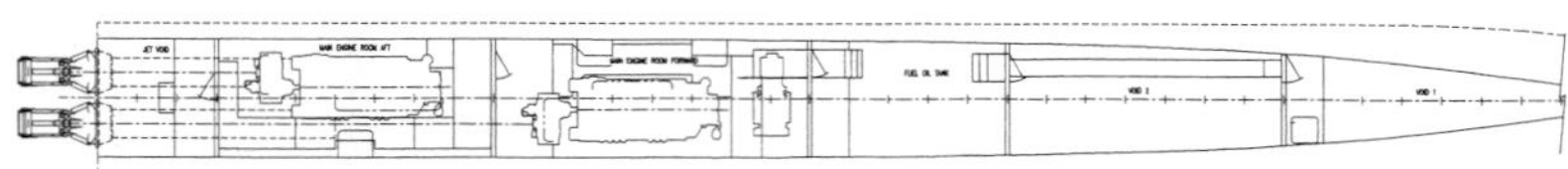

General arrangement of Nansha 38 and 68 ***1995***

ASTRA BAY ENTERPRISES

4 Sultan Way, Rous Head, North Fremantle, Western Australia

Tel: +61 (430) 6336
Fax: +61 (430) 6338

Ian Mcintosh, *Managing Director*
Simon Clifford, *Manager*
Arthur Broere, *Project Manager*

Astra Bay Enterprises was formed by Condor marine as a seperate company to build the designs of Advanced Multihull Designs (AMD), under a licensing agreement.

The first AMD 350 was launched from the Yard in August 1995 for an undisclosed Australian owner. following completion of the vessel, a series of sea trials were undertaken to collect seakeeping data for comparison with the tank test results received from MARIN and the Australian Maritime College.

AMD 350 WPC

Specifications

Length overall	42.5 m
Beam	12.2 m
Draught	1.4 m
Passengers	350
Propulsive power	2 × 1,960 kW
Max speed	36 kts
Operational speed	32 kts

Classification: DnV +1A1 HSLC R2 EO.

AMD 350 on trials ***1996***

Propulsion: The main engines are 2 × MTU V16 396, each driving a KaMeWa 71SII water-jet.

UPDATED

ATLAY CATAMARANS AUSTRALIA PTY LTD (COUGAR CATAMARANS)

39-41 Activity Crescent, Ernest Junction, Southport 4214, Australia

Tel: +61 (75) 392244/392482
Telex: 43470 AA
Fax: +61 (75) 971075

Harry Roberts, *Managing Director*
Elizabeth Hay, *Export Manager*

Cougar Catamarans has been in continuous operation for some 24 years and has designs available for boats between 7.5 and 39 m in length. Speeds are typically in the range of 20 to 35 knots.

Whitsunday Freedom

A 14.6 m, 27 knot catamaran ferry delivered in 1988 to the Whitsunday Water Taxis company. Six Cougar Catamaran boats have been delivered to this operator.

Specifications

Length overall	14.6 m
Crew	3
Passengers	60
Propulsive power	2 × 304 kW
Max speed	27 kts
Operational speed	22-23 kts

Propulsion: Engines: 2 × MAN 2866 LE diesels.

Encore

A 16.15 m catamaran servicing South Strabroke Island on the Gold Coast, Queensland.

Specifications

Length	16.15 m
Beam	5.18 m
Crew	57+ (inshore)
	23 (offshore)

San Bei **1995**

Propulsion: Engines: 2 × 266 kW Volvo diesels.
Auxiliary power: 8.5 kVA.

San Bei

A 27.2 m catamaran ferry delivered in 1994 to Shanghai, China.

Specifications

Length overall	27.2 m
Passengers	220
Crew	5
Max speed	31 kts
Operational speed	27 kts

Propulsion: Engines: 2 × 820 kW Detroit Diesel 16V 9TA.
Auxilliary systems: 2 × 50 kVA Perkins generators.

Yun Tong **1995**

Yun Tong

A 32 m catamaran ferry delivered in 1994 to Shanghai, China.

Specifications

Length overall	32 m
Beam	8.38 m
Passengers	266
Crew	5
Propulsive power	2 × 1,342 kW
Max speed	32 kts
Operational speed	28 kts

Propulsion: Engines: 2 × 1,342 kW Detroit Diesel 16V 149TI.
Auxilliary systems: 2 × 67 kVA Perkins generators.

Ying Bin 5

A 25 m catamaran ferry delivered in 1993 to Hong Kong.

Specifications

Length overall	25 m
Beam	8.38 m
Passengers	200
Crew	5
Max speed	28 kts
Operational speed	25 kts

Propulsion: Engines: 2 × 820 kW Detroit Diesel 16V 92TA.
Auxilliary systems: 2 × 37 kVA Isuzu generators.

VERIFIED

AUSTAL SHIPS PTY LTD

100 Clarence Beach Road, Henderson, Perth, Western Australia, Australia 6166

Tel: +61 (9) 410 1111
Fax: +61 (9) 410 2564

John Rothwell, *Managing Director*
Christopher Norman, *Director, Marketing*
Garry Heys, *Director and General Manager*
Kevin Stanley, *Director and General Manager*

Austal Ships was established in 1988 and is recognised as a world leader in the design and manufacture of high-speed aluminium passenger catamarans.

Since 1990, Austal has delivered 25 high-speed catamarans in the 40 m size range to owners in the Peoples's Republic of China alone, including five of which are gas turbine powered.

In May 1995, Austal delivered their first vessel to Japan, a stylish 43 m passenger catamaran, which is the first Australian built ferry for regular commuter service in Japan.

34 m CATAMARAN
Bali Hai

Delivered in March 1990 to run day cruises from Bali to the islands of Nusa Penida and Lembongan. *Bali Hai* is constructed in aluminium and designed to carry 300 passengers at 20 knots.

Specifications

Length overall	33.6 m
Length waterline	30.7 m
Beam	10.8 m
Draught	1.95 m
Crew	8
Passengers	300
Fuel capacity	16,000 l
Water capacity	4,000 l
Propulsive power	2 × 735 kW
Operational speed	20 kts

Classification: DnV.
Structure: Hull, superstructure and deck construction material: marine grade aluminium alloy.
Propulsion: Engines: 2 × MAN D284 2LYE diesels developing 735 kW each at 2,300 rpm.

Bali Hai II *1995*

Tong Zhou *1994*

Xin Duan Zhou *1993*

Equator Triangle *1994*

Vessel	Engines	Hull No	Length	Seats	Delivery date	Operating country
Bali Hai	2 × MAN D2842 LYE 735 kW each	3	33.6 m	300	March 1990	Indonesia
Tong Zhou	2 × MTU 16V 396 TB 83 1,470 kW each	8	38.0 m	430	November 1990	China
Shun Shui	2 × MWM TBD 604B V16 1,680 kW each	18	40.1 m	354	January 1991	China
Equator Triangle	2 × Caterpillar 3516 TA 1,430 kW each	14	40.1 m	216	July 1991	Singapore
Ex-*Shun De*	2 × MWM TBD 604B V16 1,680 kW each	28	40.1 m	354	February 1992	China
Xin Duan Zhou	2 × MTU 16V396 TE 74L 1,825 kW each	38	40.1 m	338	February 1992	China
Zhuhai	2 × MWM TBD 604B V16 1,680 kW each	288	40.1 m	338	May 1992	China
Nan Gui	2 × MTU 16V 396 TE 74L 1,825 kW each	48	40.1 m	338	August 1992	China
Kai Ping	2 × MWM 16V 396 TE 74L 1,920 kW each	68	39.9 m	318	September 1992	China
Cui Heng Hu		78	39.9 m	354	November 1992	China
Lian Shan Hu		88	39.9 m	354	November 1992	China
Nan Xing		98	39.9 m	338	March 1993	China
Hai Chang		99	39.9 m	338	March 1993	China
*Hui Yang**		100	39.9 m	368	July 1993	China
*Tai Shan**		101	39.9 m	354	July 1993	China
Gang Zhou		102	39.9 m	318	September 1993	China
Gao Ming		103	39.9 m	338	September 1993	China
Gui Feng		109	39.9 m	318	December 1993	China
San Bu		110	39.9 m	338	December 1993	China
*Bali Hai II**	2 × MTU 12V 396 TE 74L 1,470 kW each	15	35.7 m	337	April 1994	Singapore
Shun Jing	2 × Textron Lycoming TF40	105	39.9 m	354	March 1994	China
Lian Gang Hu	2 × Textron Lycoming TF40	106	39.9 m	354	March 1994	China
Yi Xian Hu	2 × Textron Lycoming TF40sszhong	108	39.9 m	354	March 1994	China
*Free Flying**	2 × MTU 12V 396 TE 74L 1,960 kW each	168	40.1 m	450	April 1994	China
Xin He Shan	2 × MTU 12V 396 TE 74L 1,940 kW each	111	40.1 m	300	August 1994	China
Zhong Shan	2 × Textron Lycoming TF40	115	40.1 m	354	December 1994	China
Speeder	4 × MTU 16V 396 TE 74L 1,960 kW	39	43.0 m	331	May 1995	Japan
Shun De	2 × Allied Signal TF40	116	40.1 m	332	September 1995	China
Hai Yang	2 × MTU 16V 396 TE74L	118	40.1 m	338	September 1995	China

*Fitted with Austal 'Ocean Leveller' ride control system.

36 m CATAMARAN
Bali Hai II

Bali Hai II is the second catamaran to be built for Tropic Charterers Pte Ltd to run day cruises from Bali to the islands of Nusa Penida and Lembongan. This vessel was delivered in April 1994.

Specifications

Length overall	35.7 m
Beam	10.5 m
Draught	1.2 m
Crew	8
Passengers	322
Fuel capacity	12,000 l
Water capacity	6,000 l
Propulsive power	2 × 1,470 kW
Operational speed	29 kts

Structure: Hull, superstructure and deck construction material: aluminium alloy.

Propulsion: Main engines: 2 × MTU 12V 396 TE 74L diesels rated at 1,470 kW each at 1,940 rpm, driving 2 × MJP J650R DD water-jets.

38 m CATAMARAN
Tong Zhou

In June 1989, Austal Ships secured a contract for the construction of a 38 m, 430 passenger catamaran ferry for the Nantong High-Speed Passenger Ship Company in China. Valued at A$5.5 million, the delivery was in November 1990. The vessel is fitted with two MJP water-jet units.

Specifications

Length overall	38 m
Length waterline	32.4 m
Beam	11.8 m
Draught	1.3 m
Displacement, max	145 t
Fuel capacity	2 × 7,500 l tanks
Water capacity	1,200 l
Crew	12
Passengers	430
Max speed	30 kts

Structure: Hull, superstructure and deck construction material: marine grade aluminium alloy.

Propulsion: Main engines: 2 × MTU 16V 396 TB83 marine diesels developing 1,470 kW each at 1,940 rpm. 2 × MJP J650R water-jet units.

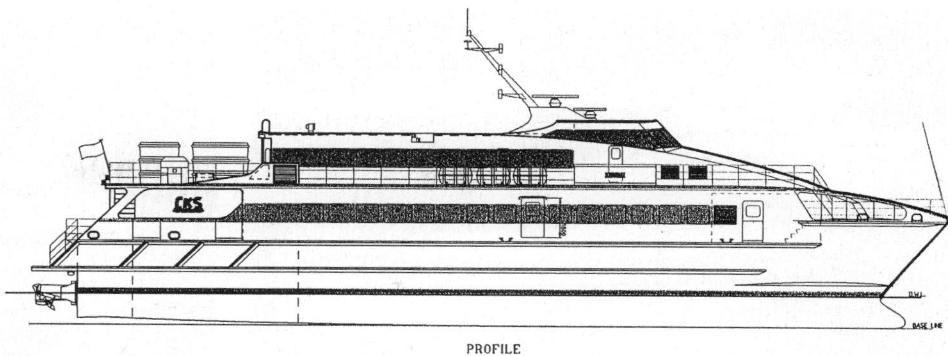

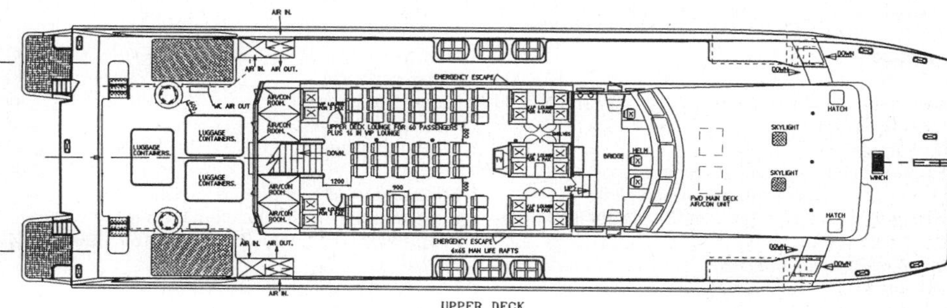

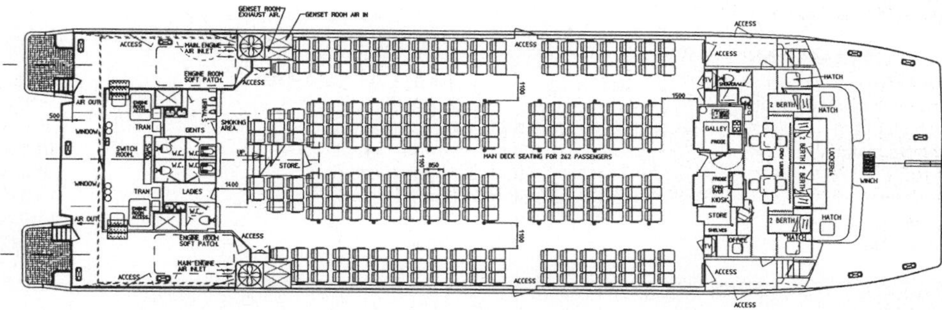

Austal 40 m catamaran Hai Yang *general arrangement* **1996**

40 m CATAMARAN
Shun Shui

Specifications

Length overall	40.1 m
Beam	13.3 m
Displacement, max	162 t
Crew	8
Passengers	354
Fuel capacity	10,000 l
Water capacity	1,500 l
Propulsive power	2 × 1,680 kW
Max speed	31.4 kts

Structure: Hull, superstructure and deck construction material: marine grade aluminium alloy.

Propulsion: Main engines: 2 × MWM TBD 604B V16 diesels 1,680 kW each at 1,800 rpm, driving 2 × KaMeWa 71S water-jets.

40 m CATAMARAN
Equator Triangle

Specifications

Length overall	40.1 m
Beam	13.3 m
Draught	2.4 m
Displacement, max	176 t
Crew	34
Passengers	216
Fuel capacity	4 × 5,000 l
Water capacity	2 × 5,000 l
Propulsive power	2 × 1,430 kW
Max speed	25.5 kts

Structure: Hull, superstructure and deck construction material: marine grade aluminium alloy.

Propulsion: Main engines: 2 × Caterpillar 3516 TA diesels, 1,430 kW each at 1,800 rpm, driving fixed-pitch propellers.

40 m CATAMARAN
Xin Duan Zhou

Specifications

Length overall	40.1 m
Length waterline	35.4 m
Beam	11.5 m
Draught	1.4 m
Crew	12
Passengers	338
Fuel	10,000 l
Water capacity	1,500 l
Propulsive power	2 × 1,825 kW
Max speed	32 kts

Structure: Hull material: aluminium alloy.
Superstructure material: aluminium alloy.

Propulsion: Engines: 2 × MTU 16V 396 TE 74L diesels, 1,825 kW each.
Transmissions: 2 × Reintjes VLJ930 gearboxes.
Thrust devices: 2 × KaMeWa 71S water-jets.

Auxiliary systems: Engines: 2 × MTU 6V 183 AA51 diesels, 98 kW each.

40 m CATAMARAN
Ex-*Shun De*

Specifications

Length overall	40.1 m
Length waterline	35.4 m
Beam	12.9 m
Draught	1.4 m
Crew	12

43 m catamaran Speeder **1996**

Gas-turbine propelled *Shun Jing, Lian Gang Hu* and *Yi Xian Hu* **1995**

Kai Ping **1994**

Passengers	354
Fuel capacity	10,000 l
Water capacity	1,500 l
Propulsive power	2 × 1,680 kW
Max speed	31.5 kts

Structure: Hull material: aluminium alloy.
Superstructure material: aluminium alloy.
Propulsion: Engines: 2 × MWM TBD 604B V16 diesels, 1,680 kW each.
Transmissions: 2 × ZF BU755 2.235:1 reduction gearboxes.
Thrust devices: 2 × KaMeWa 71S water-jets.
Auxiliary systems: Engines: 2 × MTU 6V 183 AA51 diesels, 98 kW each.

40 m CATAMARAN
Nan Gui
Specifications

Length overall	40.1 m
Length waterline	35.4 m
Beam	11.5 m
Draught	1.4 m
Crew	12 (8 berths)
Passengers	338
Fuel capacity	9,000 l
Water capacity	1,500 l
Propulsive power	2 × 1,825 kW
Max speed	34 kts
Operational speed	32 kts
Range	300 n miles

Structure: Hull material: aluminium alloy.
Superstructure material: aluminium alloy.
Propulsion: Engines: 2 × MTU 16V 396 TE 74L diesels.
Transmissions: 2 × ZF BU755 gearboxes.
Thrust devices: 2 × KaMeWa 71SII water-jets.
Auxiliary systems: Engines: 2 × MTU 6V 183 AA51 diesels, 98 kW each
Electrical systems: 380 V/220 V 50 Hz AC, 24 V DC

40 m CATAMARAN
Zhuhai
Specifications

Length overall	40.1 m
Length waterline	35.4 m
Beam	11.5 m
Draught	1.46 m
Crew	12
Passengers	338
Fuel capacity	9,000 l
Water capacity	1,500 l
Propulsive power	2 × 1,680 kW
Operational speed	32
Range	265 n miles

Structure: Hull material: aluminium alloy.
Superstructure material: aluminium alloy.
Propulsion: Engines: 2 × MWM TBD 604B V16 diesels.
Transmissions: 2 × ZF BU755 gearboxes.
Thrust devices: 2 × KaMeWa 71S II water-jets.
Auxiliary systems: Engines: 2 × MTU 6V 183 AA51 diesels, 98 kW each.

Gas-turbine propelled Shun De **1996**

Hai Yang **1996**

40 m CATAMARAN
Kai Ping **Class**
Eleven of these craft have been delivered to various owners in China.
Specifications

Length overall	39.9 m
Length waterline	35 m
Beam	10 m
Draught	1.4 m
Crew	12
Passengers	318-368
Fuel capacity	10,000 l
Water capacity	1,500 l
Propulsive power	2 × 1,580 kW
Operational speed	32 kts

Structure: Hull material: aluminium alloy.
Superstructure material: aluminium alloy.
Propulsion: Engines: 2 × MTU 16V 396 TE 74 diesels, 1,580 kW each.
Transmissions: 2 × Reintjes VLJ930 gearboxes.
Thrust devices: 2 × KaMeWa 71S water-jets.
Auxiliary systems: Engines: 2 × MTU 6V 183 AA51 diesels, 98 kW each.
Electrical system: 380 V/220 V 50 Hz AC, 24 V DC.

40 m GAS-TURBINE CATAMARAN CLASS
Five of these vessels have been constructed, *Shun Jing, Lian Gang Hu, Yi Xian Hu, Zhong Shan* and *Sun De*, all for Chinese owners.
Specifications

Length overall	40.0 m
Length waterline	35.0 m
Beam	11.5 m
Draught	1.4 m
Crew	12
Passengers	354
Fuel capacity	10,000 l
Water capacity	1,500 l
Propulsive power	2 × 2,570 kW
Max speed	39.5 kts

Propulsion: These vessels are powered by two Textron Lycoming TF40 gas-turbines rated at 2,570 kW at 15,400 rpm. Each turbine drives through a MAAG MPG-80 gearbox to a KaMeWa 71S water-jet. (For *Zhong Shan* and *Shun De* the gearbox is a Cincinnati Gear MA-107 model).
Auxiliary systems: Two MTU 6V 183 AA51 diesel generators rated at 98 kW at 1,500 rpm.

43 m CATAMARAN
Speeder
Speeder was delivered to Diamond Ferry, a subsidiary of Mitsui, in May 1995. It was Austal's first sale to Japan and represents the first Australian-built ferry constructed for regular commuter service in Japan. It operates in the inland sea of Japan between the

cities of Oita and Matsayama, completing the journey in 2 hours.

Specifications

Length overall	43.0 m
Length waterline	37.7 m
Beam	11.2 m
Draught	1.3 m
Crew	6
Passengers	331
Fuel capacity	14,000 l
Water capacity	1,500 l
Propulsive power	7,840 kW
Max speed	42.5 kts

Propulsion: The vessel is powered by four MTU 16V 396 TE 74L diesels each driving through a ZF BU755-D reduction gearbox to a KaMeWa 63S11 water-jet.

Hai Yang

This is the 25th fast catamaran delivered to the China region by Austal Ships and was handed over to Zhuhai Jinzhou Port Shipping Company in August 1995.

Specifications

Length overall	40.1 m
Length waterline	35.0 m
Beam	11.5 m
Draught	1.4 m
Crew	12
Passengers	338
Fuel capacity	10,000 l
Water capacity	1,500 l
Operational speed	33.5 kts

Propulsion: The vessel is powered by two MTU 16V 396 TE74L diesels each driving a KMW 71S water-jet via a ZF BU755 reduction gearbox.

UPDATED

FERRIES AUSTRALIA

100 Clarence Beach Road, Henderson, Perth, Western Australia, Australia 6166

Tel: +61 (9) 410 1111
Fax: +61 (9) 410 2564

John Rothwell, *Chairman*
Chris Norman, *Managing Director*
John Farrel, *Director*
Don Johnston *Director*

Ferries Australia is the joint venture between two of Australia's most successful shipbuilders, Austal Ships and Oceanfast International. The venture was formed in early 1994 to cater specifically to the larger end of the fast ferry industry. Design and production to date has specialised in fast car and passenger carrying catamaran vessels in the 80 m size range.

Currently under construction are two Auto Express 82 m vehicle and passenger catamarans, one of which is for German-based operator, TT-Line GmbH & Co of Hamburg and due for delivery in May 1996.

The Auto Express design series utilises Austal's semi swath round bilge hull shape and bulbous bows, and incorporates the company's fully computerised stabilising system, 'Ocean Leveller' to ensure optimal passenger comfort.

For larger capacity, a new design has been introduced in 1996 - the 95 m Auto Express 95 with a substantial carrying capacity of 1,000 passengers and 241 cars.

AUTO EXPRESS 79

The Auto Express 79, which represents the first in a new generation of vehicle and passenger carrying ferries was successfully launched in April 1995. The 79 m design has now been superseded by a standard 82 m design, Auto Express 82.

The design of this vessel is based on the Austal semi-Swath round bilge hull and incorporates the use of the company's 'Ocean Leveller' stabilisation system. With the main structure built entirely of aluminium, the outfit of the vessel incorporates many advanced material components such as ceramic fibre fire protection insulation and carbon fibre propulsion shafting.

Specifications

Length overall	78.68 m
Length waterline	68.50 m
Beam	23 m
Draught	2.4 m
Crew	24
Passengers	600
Vehicles	163 cars or 38 cars + 10 coaches
Fuel capacity	60,000 l
Water capacity	4,000 l
Operational speed	34.2 kts
Range	360 n miles

Propulsion: The main propulsion consists of quadruple Ruston 16 RK270 diesel engines each driving a KMW water-jet via Reintjes VLJ 4430 reduction gearboxes.

Electrical system: Electrical power is provided by four Caterpillar 3406T/SR4 rated at 200 kW each.

AUTO EXPRESS 82

Presently two of these vessels are under construction, the first of which is for TT-Line of Germany and is due for delivery in May 1996. In the 82 m design,

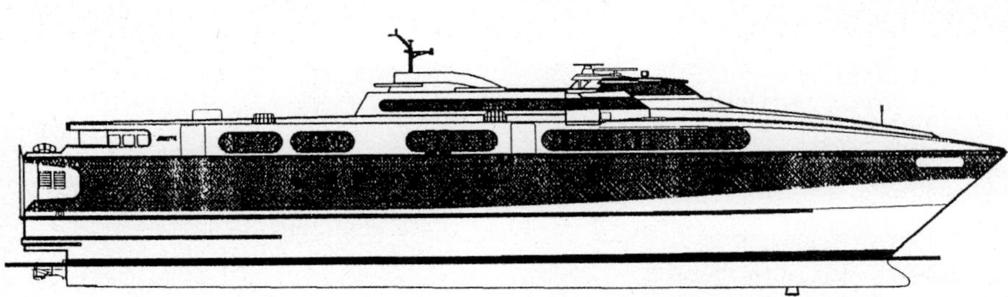

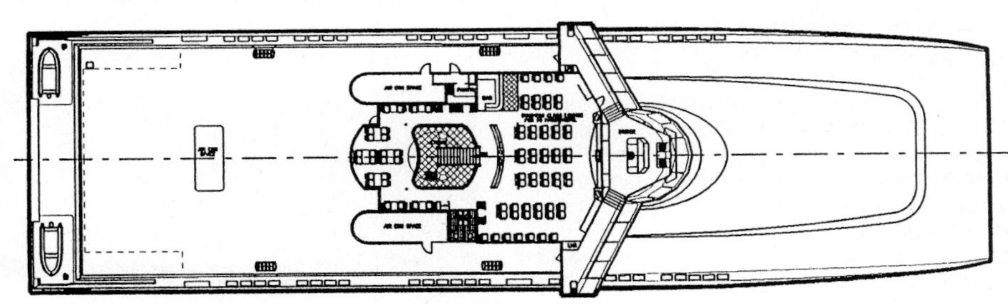

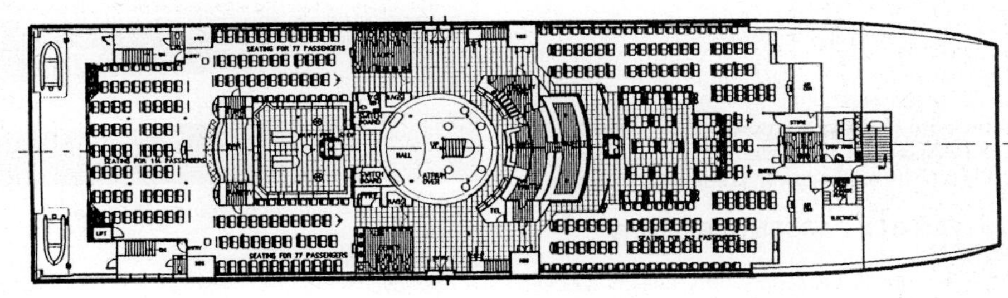

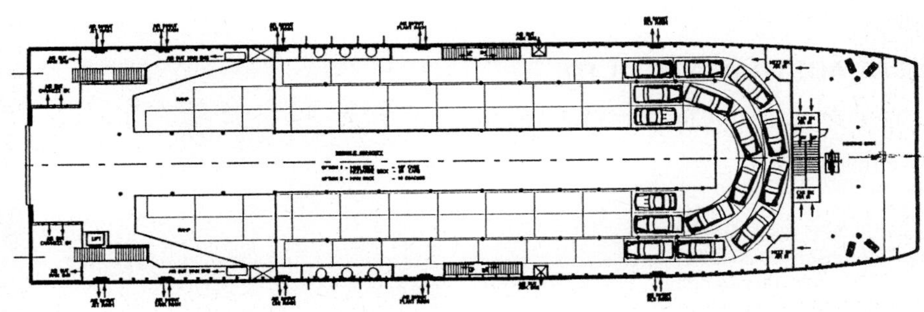

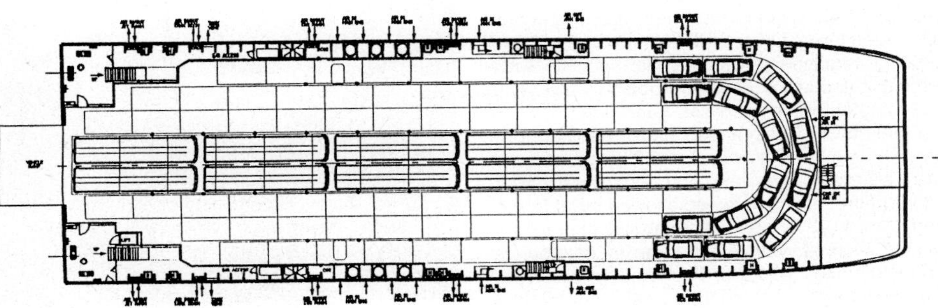

Auto Express 82, general arrangement ***1996***

Auto Express 79 on trials **1996**

the bow door has been eliminated in favour of a drive around layout for cars. The TT-Line vessel will operate between the German Ports of Rostock/Warnemund and Trelleborg in Sweden. TT-Line hold an option on the second vessel.

Specifications

Length overall	82.3 m
Length waterline	69.0 m
Beam	23.0 m
Draught	2.5 m
Crew	24
Passengers	600
Vehicles	175
Fuel capacity	60,000 l
Water capacity	4,000 l
Operational speed	36 kts

Propulsion: The vessel is powered by four MTU 20V 1163 TB73 diesels each rated at 6,000 kW and each driving a KMW water-jet via a reduction gearbox.

Model of the 82 m catamaran for TT-Line **1996**

95 m VEHICLE PASSENGER FERRY (DESIGN)

This large vehicle/passenger ferry design is based on the smaller 82 m vesels currently under construction. The design has a substantial carrying capacity with a similar maximum speed.

Specifications

Length overall	95.0 m
Length waterline	80.8 m
Beam	27 m
Draught	2.5 m
Passengers	1,000
Vehicles	241 cars or 198 cars + 12 buses

UPDATED

INCAT AUSTRALIA PTY LTD

18 Bender Drive, Moonah, Tasmania 7009, Australia

Tel: +61 (02) 730677
Fax: +61 (02) 730932

Robert Clifford, *Chairman and Managing Director*
Leith Thompson, *Financial Director*
Trevor Hardstaff, *Yard Director*
Lance Balcome, *Company Secretary*

The building of InCat designs has been proceeding for over 18 years. As well as craft being built at the Hobart facilities, builders have been licensed in Australia, Hong Kong, UK and USA. There were 17 conventional high-speed catamarans and 17 wave piercing catamarans built at Hobart in the years 1977 to 1996 for ferry services worldwide.

In 1983 InCat Designs conceived a design for a wave piercing catamaran and an 8.7 m test craft was built. This craft, *Little Devil*, first underwent trials in 1984 and the results obtained allowed InCat to proceed with a 28 m wave piercing catamaran, the *Spirit of Victoria*, which has been in commercial operation since mid-1985. This craft was followed by *Tassie Devil 2001* launched in December 1986, a 31 m wave piercing catamaran of similar

K50 Sunflower *on trials* **1996**

construction to its predecessor but with enclosed side supports and improved appearance. It operated in the rough waters off Perth during the America's Cup races. Continuing catamaran development has been concentrated by International Catamaran Designs Pty Ltd on the passenger/vehicle market and nine 74 m passenger/vehicle ferries have now been delivered by InCat Australia Pty Ltd. The first of these, *Hoverspeed Great Britain,* became a holder of the Hales Trophy for the Blue Riband of the Atlantic, achieved in June 1990 during its delivery from Hobart, Tasmania to Portsmouth, UK. Since May 1994 three larger 78 m versions have been delivered.

A new design, the K Class has also been developed based on the conventional catamaran philosophy. During the first six months of 1995 two passenger/car carrying catamarans in this class, the *Sunflower* and *Juan Patricio*, both over 70 m in length and with speeds in excess of 50 knots, were delivered. Incat, from its Hobart shipyard is scheduled to have delivered three 81 m WPC's by mid-1996 and an 84 m WPC before the end of 1996.

Due to the high demand for their large catamarans, Incat is currently investigating the establishment of a number of international shipyards for a worldwide production schedule. Incat Australia continues to retain its position as the most innovative and prolific builder of large fast catamarans in the world.

K50 CLASS CATAMARAN *Sunflower*

In August 1994 Incat Australia received an order from the Dae A Gosok Ferry Company of South Korea for a 79.25 m conventional catamaran. The *Sunflower* was designed and built for operation on a 117 nautical mile route between Pohang on the Korean mainland and Ullung Island in the Japan Sea. The vessel transports tourists to a resort on this extinct volcanic island. Construction of the vessel commenced in late November 1994 and the vessel was delivered in late July 1995. The vessel has a capacity of 750 passengers and 32+ cars and has a maximum speed of 53 knots. At the time of sea trials *Sunflower* was the fastest large ferry in the world.

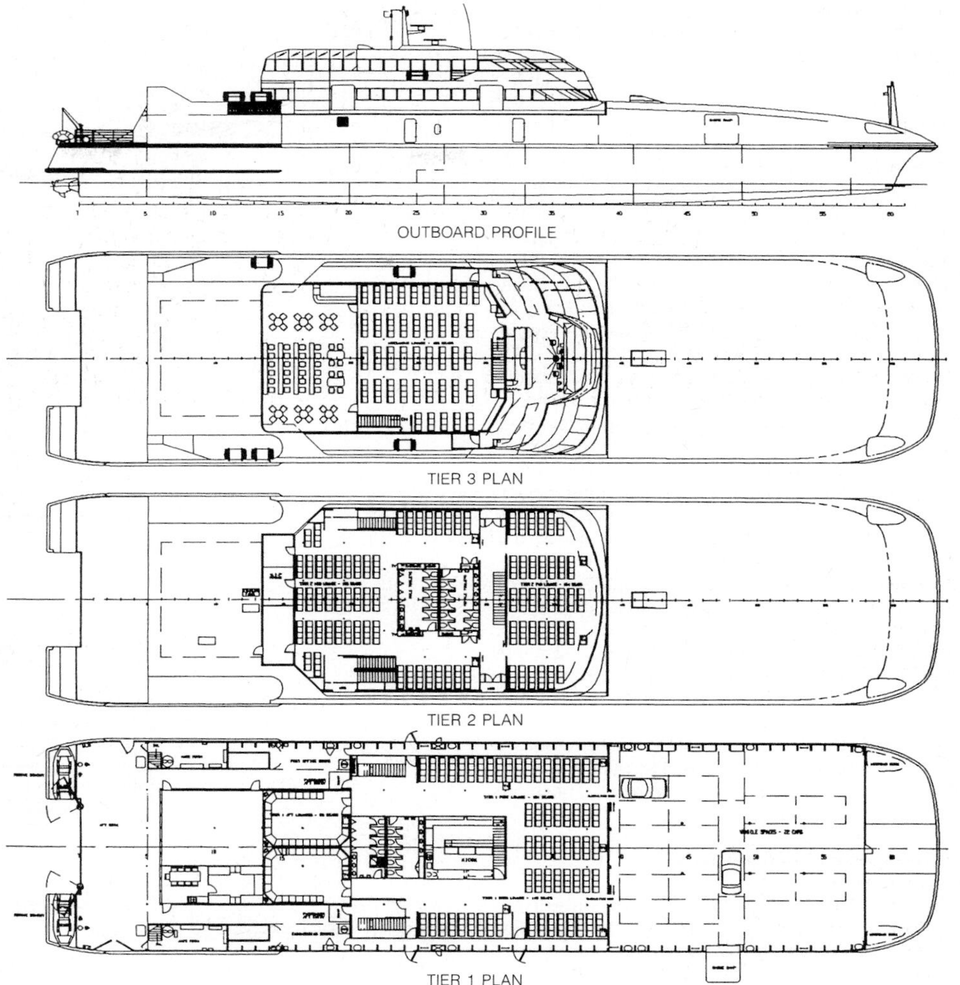

K50 general arrangement **1996**

InCat 74 m Condor 10 *at the InCat shipyard in Hobart.* **1995**

Specifications

Length overall	79.25 m
Length water-line	72.3 m
Beam	19.5 m
Hull beam	5.0 m
Draught	2.16 m
Deadweight	174.0 t
Passengers	750
Vehicles	32+ cars
Fuel consumption	200 g/kW h
Propulsive power	4 × 5,420 kW
Max speed	53 kts
Operational speed	50 kts

Classification: The vessel is built to the requirements of DnV HSLC Car Ferry 'A' and the requirements of the Korean Registry.

Structure: The vessel is constructed from marine grade aluminium alloys. Each waterborne hull is subdivided into eight watertight compartments. These are connected by an arched bridging structure above the loaded waterline. An aluminium superstructure supported on vibration damping mounts provides seating for up to 750 passengers and crew. A full width wheelhouse is provided with central and wing positions for docking.

Propulsion: The vessel is powered by a 2 × 2 Caterpillar 3616 conventional high-speed diesel engines (Ruston 16 RK270 are optional). Each engine directly drives a transom-mounted water-jet (KaMeWa 80 Waterjets are standard) providing an arrangement for thrust vectoring and jet reverse and steering.

Ride Control: A Maritime Dynamics ride control system is fitted to the vessel, consisting of an active trim tab mounted at the transom of each hull. These provide trim and motion dampening.

K55 CLASS CATAMARAN

Juan Patricio

The *Juan Patricio* was the first K Class conventional catamaran built. It was designed for operation across the Rio del la Plata between Uruguay and Argentina. The vessel has a capacity of 436 passengers and 60+ cars or a mix of cars with light trucks on the aft open deck.

Specifications

Length overall	70.36 m
Length water-line	63.9 m
Beam	19.46 m
Hull beam	5.0 m
Draught	2.15 m
Deadweight	125.0 t
Passengers	436
Vehicles	60+ cars
Fuel consumption	200 g/kW hour
Propulsive power	4 × 5,420 kW
Max speed	50 kts
Classification	DnV (Car Ferry B)

Classification: The vessel is built to the requirements of DnV HSLC +1A1 R4 Car Ferry 'B' EO.

Structure: The vessel is constructed from marine grade aluminium alloys. Each waterborne hull is subdivided into seven watertight compartments. These are connected by an arched bridging structure above the loaded waterline. An aluminium superstructure supported on vibration damping mounts provides seating for up to 436 passengers and crew. A full width wheelhouse is provided with central and wing positions for docking.

Propulsion: The vessel is powered by 2 × 2 Caterpillar 3616 medium speed diesel engines (Ruston 16 RK270 are optional). Each engine directly drives a transom mounted water-jet (KaMeWa 80 water-jets are standard) providing an arrangement for thrust vectoring and jet reverse and steering.

Ride Control: A Maritime Dynamics ride control system is fitted to the vessel, consisting of an active trim tab mounted at the transom of each hull. These provide trim and motion dampening.

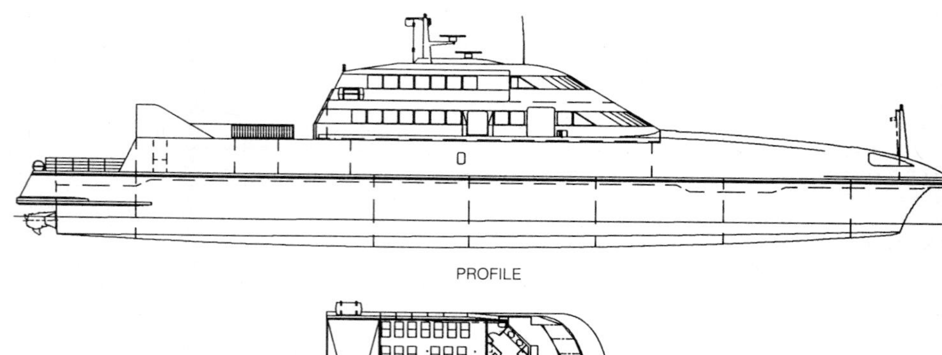

PROFILE

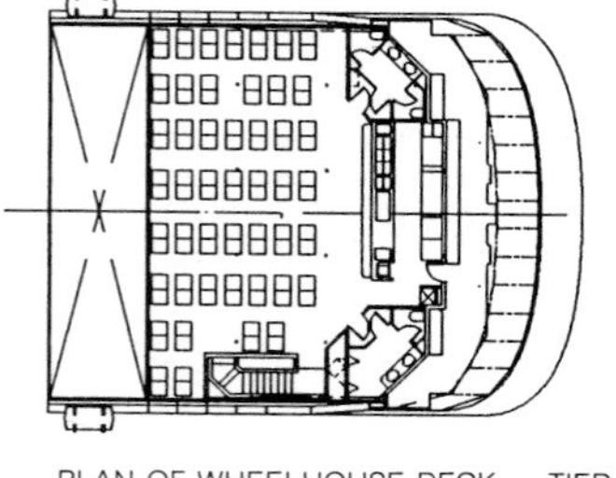

PLAN OF WHEELHOUSE DECK — TIER 3

VIEW ON BOW

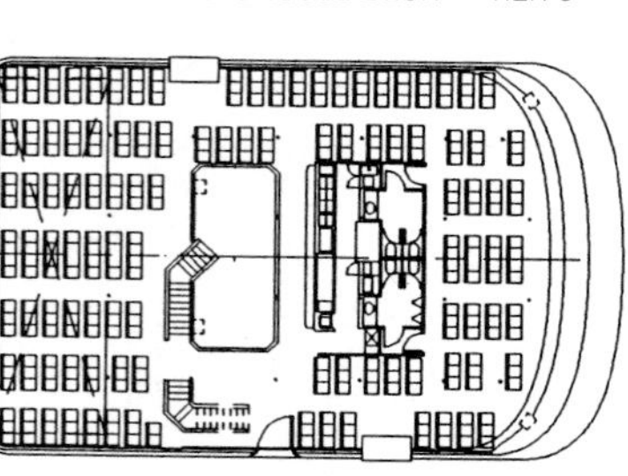

PLAN OF PASSENGER DECK — TIER 2

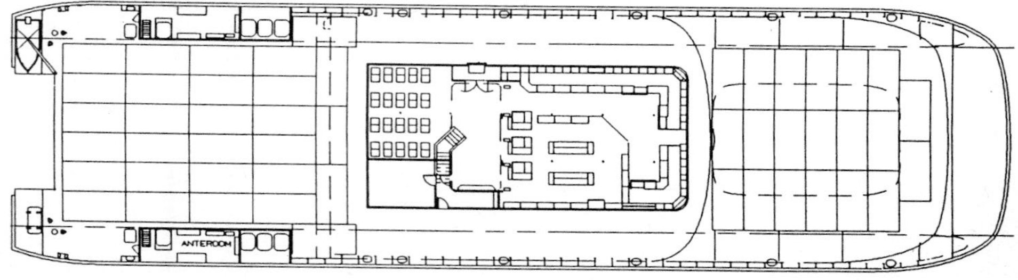

PLAN OF MAIN DECK — TIER 1

K55 general arrangement **1996**

K40 CLASS CATAMARAN (DESIGN)

This design, not yet built, is a 58 m conventional catamaran which has a capacity of 350 passengers and 45 cars. The K40 concept has been developed to provide or improve service on shorter routes, (most probably 10 to 30 nautical miles) where there is a volume of light vehicle and passenger traffic. During the design stage particular attention was given to fast turn around. In conjunction with a suitable berth, disembarkation and embarkation of both vehicles and passengers can take as little as five minutes.

Specifications

Length overall	58 m
Length water-line	52 m
Beam	14.5 m
Draught	2.0 m
Deadweight	117 t
Passengers	350
Vehicles	45 cars
Fuel consumption	200 g/kW h
Propulsive power	2 × 4,320 kW
Max speed	40 kts
Operational speed	36 kts

Classification: The vessel will be built according to DnV HSLC +1A1 R5 Car Ferry 'B' EO. The vessel is built to comply with the IMO High Speed Craft Code.

Propulsion: The propulsion machinery will consist of two turbocharged marine diesel engines (one in each hull) each directly driving a water-jet through a

78 m WPC Condor 11 **1996**

flexible coupling. Each waterjet shall be fitted with a thrust vectoring arrangement for steering and reversing. The main engines are Ruston 16 RK270 or Caterpillar 3616, operating at 4,320 kW @ 782 rpm as standard.

84 m WAVE PIERCING CATAMARAN

The 84 m vessel is a further development of the successful 74, 78 and current 81 m Incat car ferries. The first 84 m vessel will be completed in late 1996. A considerable number of design changes have been incorporated into this vessel including the fitting of ride control systems (an active trim tab is fitted as standard and a forward foil system is optional).

Specifications

Length overall	84.06 m
Length water-line	71.50 m
Beam	26.15 m
Hull beam	4.48 m
Draught	3.0 m
Deadweight	330 t (approximately)
Passengers	800
Vehicles	200 cars
Fuel consumption	200 grams/kW hour
Propulsive power	4 × 6,875 kW
Max speed	43 kts
Operational speed	38 kts

Classification: The vessels are built to the requirements of DnV HSLC +1A1 R1 Car Ferry 'A'.

Structure: The vessel is constructed from marine grade aluminium alloys. Each waterborne hull is subdivided into seven watertight compartments. These are connected by an arched bridging structure with a central forward hull above the smooth water loaded waterline. An aluminium superstructure supported on vibration damping mounts provides seating for up to 800 passengers and crew. A full width wheelhouse is provided with central and wing positions for docking.

Propulsion: The vessel is powered by 2 × 2 conventional medium speed diesel engines developing 6,875 kW each. Ruston 20V RK270 engines are standard. Each engine drives a transom mounted water-jet (Lips IR45D is standard) through a Reintjes VLJ 6831 reduction gearbox with internal clutch. The jet control system provides, apart from steering and reversing, the option of thrust vectoring. MTU 20V 1163TB73L developing 6,500 kW is an option. A Reintjes VLJ 4431 gearbox is fitted to this engine and various jets can be fitted to this option.

Ride Control: A Maritime Dynamics ride control system is fitted to the vessel, consisting of an active trim tab mounted at the transom of each hull. These provide trim and motion dampening. This vessel is also fitted with structural foundations and hydraulic services for the fitting of forward active ride control foils.

Craft built and ordered	Yard No	Completed	Max speed	Seats	Engines	Delivered to
18 m *Derwent Explorer* (ex-*Jeremiah Ryan*)	001	September 1977	26 kts	145	2 × Cummins V8	
18 m *Tropic Princess*, (ex-*James Kelly I*)	002	June 1979	28 kts	100	-	Ecrolight
20 m *Fitzroy Flyer* (ex-*Fitzroy*)	004	June 1981	28 kts	-	-	Great Adventures
20 m *Tangalooma*	005	December 1981	28 kts	200	-	Tangalooma Island Resort
15 m *Amaroo*	006	December 1981	12 kts	120	-	
20 m *Islander*, (ex-*Green Islander*)	007	June 1982	28 kts	220	-	
20 m *Low Isles Reef Express* (ex-*Quicksilver*)	008	August 1982	28 kts	100	-	Outer Barrier Reef Cruises
29 m *Spirit of Roylen*	009	December 1982	27 kts	250	-	McLeans Roylen Cruises Pty Ltd (ex-Barrier Reef Holdings)
20 m *Magnetic Northerner* (ex-*Keppel Cat 2*, ex-*Trojan*)	010	1983		200	-	Hydrofoil Seaflight Services Pty Ltd
20 m *Keppel Cat I* (ex-*Tassie Devil)*	011	September 1984		195	-	Hydrofoil Seaflight *Services Pty Ltd*
27.4 m WPC Spirit of Paradise, (ex-*Spirit of Victoria*)	016	June 1985	28 kts	-	2 × DDC GM 12V 92 TA	(Indonesia)
30 m *Our Lady Patricia*	020	March 1986	31 kts	452	2 × MTU 16V 396 TC 83	Wightlink Ferries Ltd
30 m *Our Lady Pamela*	021	July 1986	31 kts	452	2 × MTU 16V 396 TC 83	Wightlink Ferries Ltd
31 m WPC 2001 (ex-*Tassie Devil 2001*)	017	December 1986	30 kts	196	2 × MWM TBD 234 V16	InCat Charters
22.8 m (*Starship Genesis*), (ex-*Genesis*)	018	July 1987	36 kts	200	2 × DDC GM 16V 92 TA	In NSW
31 m WPC *2000*	019	1988		231	-	Hamilton Island Cruises
37.2 m WPC *Seaflight*	022	1988	30 kts	-	2 × DDC GM 16V 149 TIB	Seaflight Ltd, New Zealand
74 m WPC *SeaCat Great Britain* (ex-*Hoverspeed Great Britain*, ex-*Christopher Columbus*)	025	1990	35 kts	600 + 90 vehicles	4 × Ruston 16 RK 270	Sea Containers, Hoverspeed Ltd
74 m WPC *SeaCat Isle of Man* (ex-*SeaCat Boulogne*, ex-*Hoverspeed France*)	026	1990	35 kts	483 + 80 vehicles	4 × Ruston 16 RK 270	Sea Containers, Hoverspeed Ltd
74 m WPC *Patricia Olivia*	024	mid-1992	37 kts	450 + 84 vehicles	4 × Caterpillar 3616	Los Cipreses SA Buquebus
74 m WPC *Lynx* ex-*Condor 10*	030	January 1993	37 kts	584 + 84 vehicles	4 × Ruston 16 RK 270	Condor Ltd
74 m WPC *Stena Sea Lynx*	031	June 1993	37 kts	450 + 84 vehicles	4 × Ruston 16 RK 270	Buquebus under charter to Stena Sealink Line
74 m WPC *Atlantic 11* (ex-*SeaCat Calais*, ex-*SeaCat Tasmania*)	023	1990	35 kts	350 + 84 vehicles	4 × Ruston 16 RK 270	Sea Containers, Hoverspeed Ltd
74 m WPC *Seacatamaran Denmark* (ex-*Hoverspeed Boulogne*, ex-*Hoverspeed Belgium*)	027	1991	35 kts	420 + 85 vehicles	4 × Ruston 16 RK 270	Sea Containers, Hoverspeed Ltd
74 m WPC *SeaCat Scotland*	028	mid-1991	35 kts	450 + 80 vehicles	4 × Ruston 16 RK 270	Sea Containers, Hoverspeed Ltd
74 m WPC *Juan L*	032	October 1993	37 kts	600 + 110 vehicles	4 × Caterpillar 3616	Los Cipreses SA Buquebus
78 m WPC *Stena Sea Lynx II*	033	February 1994	37 kts	640 + 150 vehicles	4 × Ruston 16 RK 270	Stena Sealink Line
78 m WPC *Condor II*	034	October 1994	37 kts	600 + 150 vehicles	4 × Ruston 16 RK 270	Condor Int
78 m WPC *Catlink I*	035	May 1995	37 kts	640 + 150 vehicles	4 × Caterpillar 3616	Holyman, Sydney
70 m CAT *K55 Juan Patricio*	036	November 1995	55 kts	450 + 63 vehicles	4 × Caterpillar 3616	Los Cipreses SA Buquebus
78 m CAT *K50 Sunflower*	037	August 1995	51 kts	720 + 32 vehicles	4 × Caterpillar 3616	Dae A Gosok, Korea
81 m WPC *Condor 12*	038	-	43 kts	700/180 vehicles	4 × Ruston 20 RK 270	Condor Ltd
81 m WPC *Stena Sea Lynx III*	040	-	43 kts	700/18 vehicles	4 × Ruston 20 RK 270	Del Bene SA
81 m WPC	041	-	43 kts	700/18 vehicles	4 × Ruston 20 RK 270	Del Bene SA
84 m WPC	042	-	43 kts	800/200 vehicles	4 × Ruston 20 RK 270	Condor Ltd

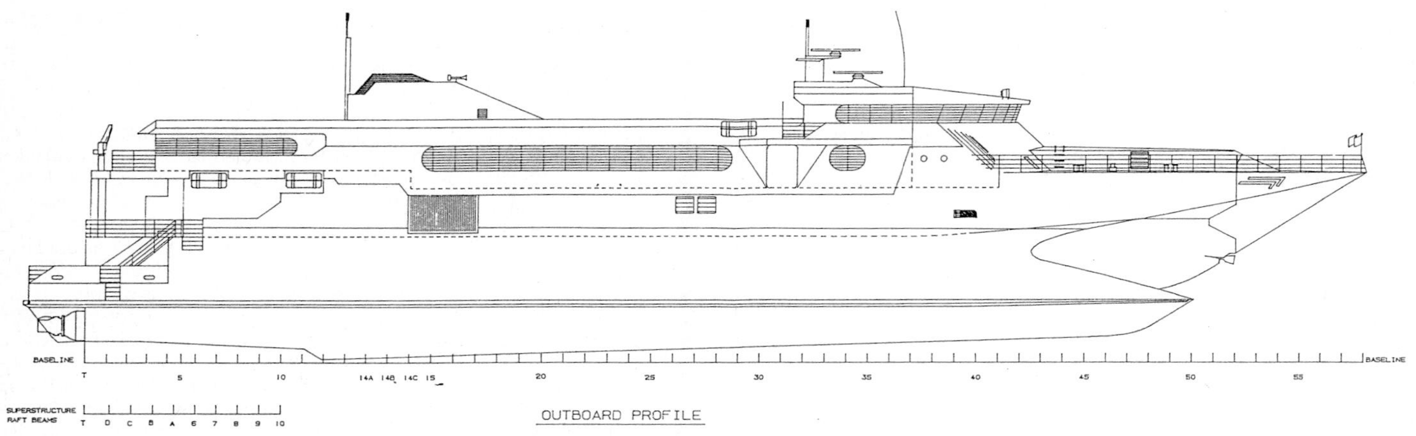

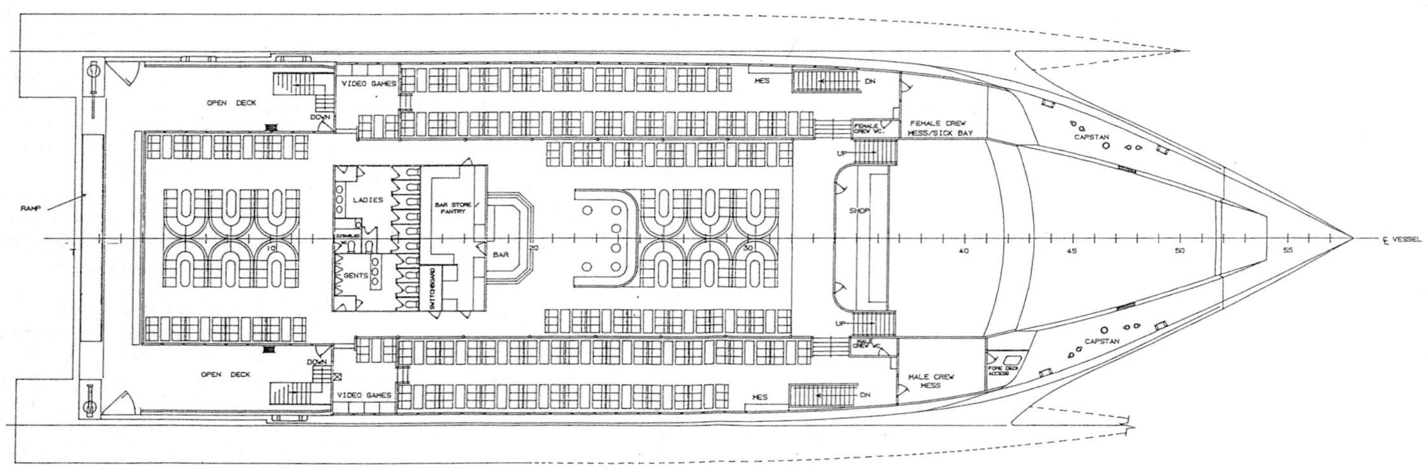

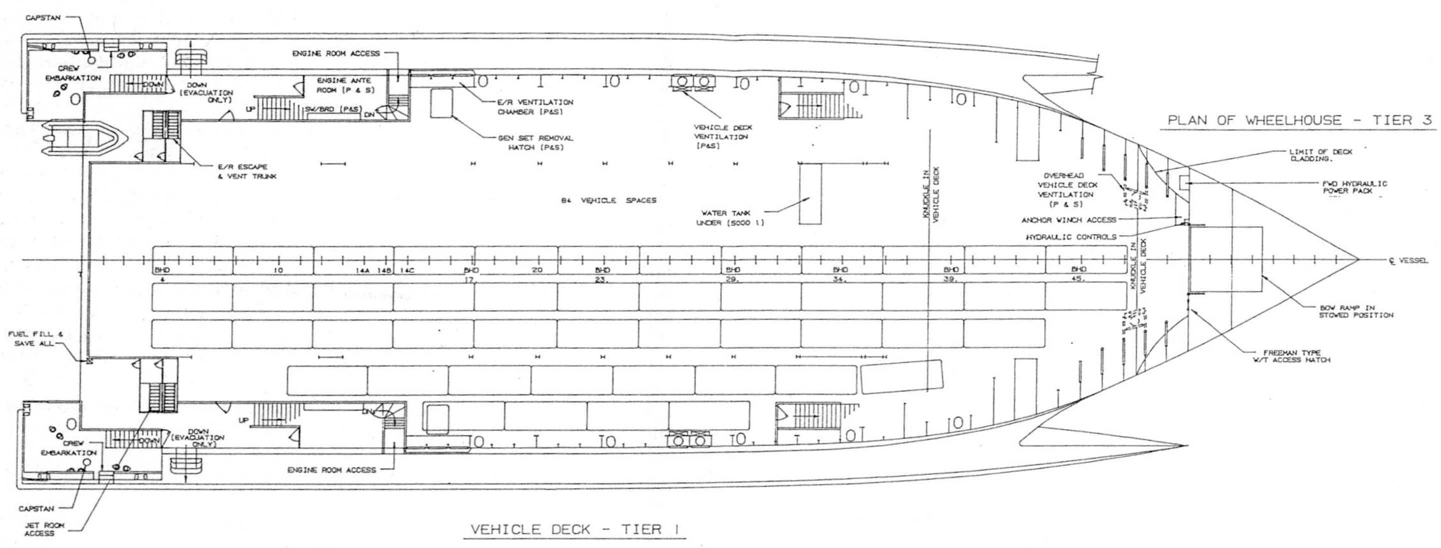

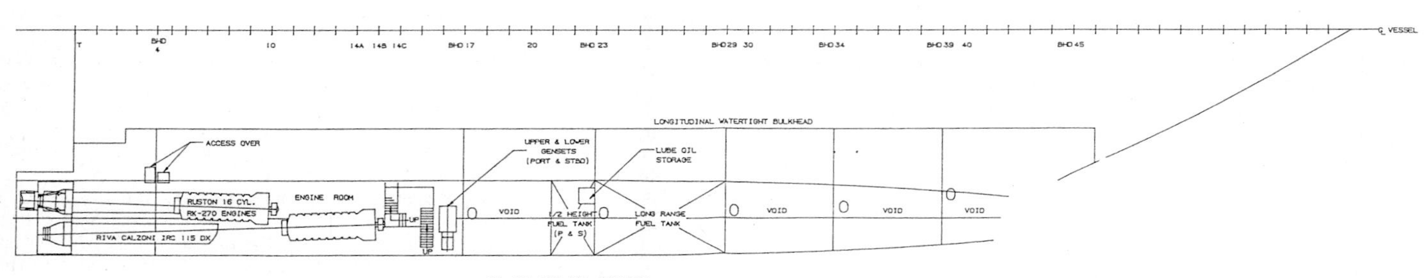

General arrangement of InCat 74 m as delivered to Sea Containers

81 m WAVE PIERCING CATAMARAN

The 81 m vessel is a further development of the successful 74 m and 78 m Incat car ferries. A considerable number of design changes have been incorporated into the current vessels including the fitting of ride control systems (an active trim tab is fitted as standard and a forward foil system is optional). Three of these vessles are currently under construction at Incat's Hobart Shipyard.

Specifications

Length overall	81.15 m
Length water-line	66.30 m
Beam	26.0 m
Hull beam	4.33 m
Draught (fully loaded)	3.0 m
Deadweight	310 t (approximately)
Passengers	700
Vehicles	181 cars
Fuel consumption	200 g/kW h
Propulsive power	4 × 5,500 kW
Max speed	43 kts
Operational speed	37 kts

Classification: The vessels are built to the requirements of DnV HSLC +1A1 R1 Car Ferry 'A'.

Structure: The vessel is constructed from marine grade aluminium alloys. Each waterborne hull is subdivided into seven watertight compartments. These are connected by an arched bridging structure with a central forward hull above the smooth water loaded waterline. An aluminium superstructure supported on vibration damping mounts provides seating for up to 700 passengers and crew. A full width wheelhouse is provided with central and wing positions for docking.

Propulsion: The vessel is powered by 2 × 2 conventional high-speed diesel engines developing 5,500 kW each. Ruston 16V RK270 or Caterpillar 3616 engines are standard. Each engine drives a transom mounted waterjet (Lips IR135D is standard) through a Reintjes VLJ 4431 reduction gearbox with internal clutch. The jet control system provides, apart from steering and reversing, the option of thrust vectoring.

Ride Control: A Maritime Dynamics ride control system is fitted to the vessel, consisting of an active trim tab mounted at the transom of each hull. These provide trim and motion dampening. This vessel is also fitted with structural foundations and hydraulic services for the fitting of forward active ride control foils.

78 m WAVE PIERCING CATAMARAN

The 78 m design evolved directly from developments to the 74 m design.

Specifications

Length overall	77.76 m
Length water-line	64.05 m
Beam	26.0 m
Hull beam	4.33 m
Draught	3.1 m
Deadweight	250 t
Passengers	600
Vehicles	150 cars
Fuel consumption @ 35 kts	3,400 l/h
Propulsive power	4 × 4,320 kW
Max speed	41 kts
Operational speed	35 kts

Classification: The vessels are built to the requirements of DnV HSLC +1A1 R1 Car Ferry 'A'.

Structure: The vessel is constructed from marine grade aluminium alloys. Each waterborne hull is subdivided into seven watertight compartments. These are connected by an arched bridging structure with a central forward hull above the smooth water loaded waterline. An aluminium superstructure supported on vibration damping mounts provides seating for up to 600 passengers and crew. A full width wheelhouse is provided with central and wing positions for docking.

Propulsion: The vessel is powered by 2 × 2 conventional high-speed diesel engines (Ruston 16 RK270 or Caterpillar 3616 engines are standard. Each engine drives a transom mounted waterjet (Lips IR11DX are standard) providing an arrangement for thrust vectoring and jet reverse and steering.

Ride Control: A Maritime Dynamics ride control system is fitted to the vessel, consisting of an active trim tab mounted at the transom of each hull. These provide trim and motion dampening.

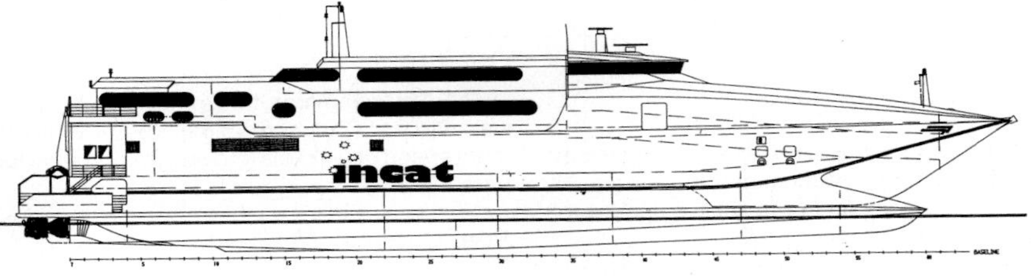

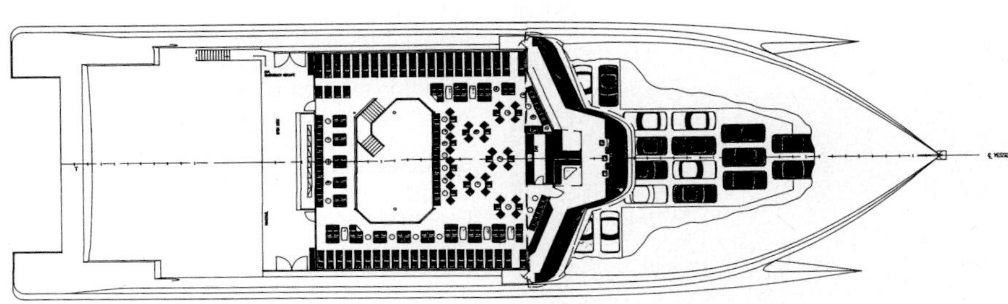

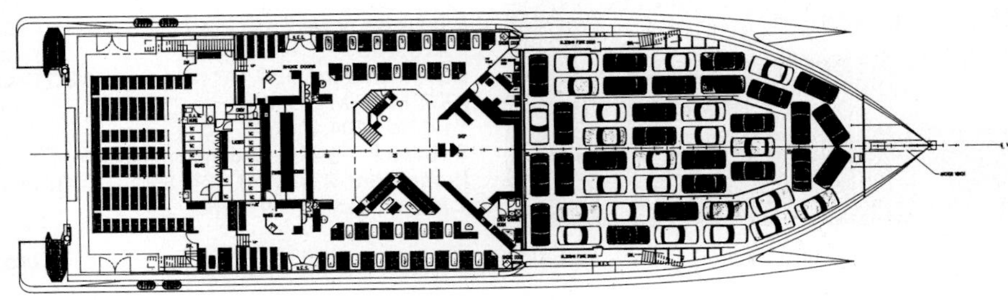

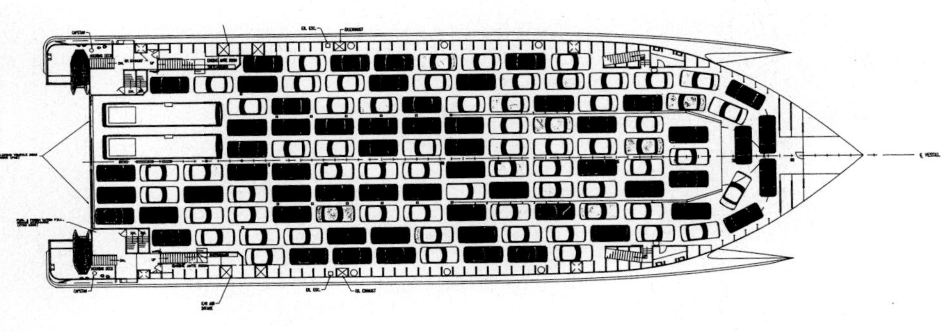

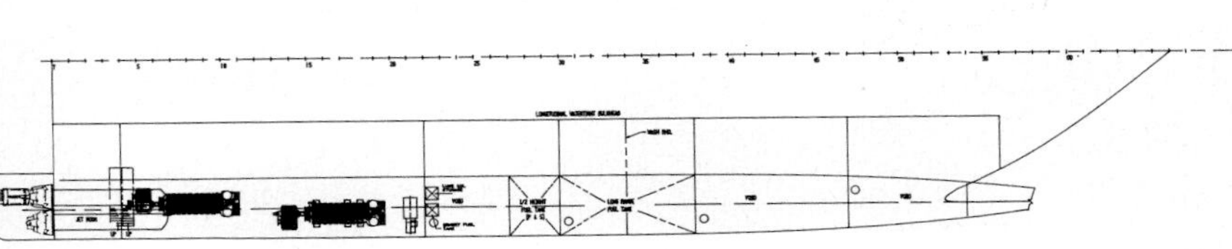

84 m WPC, general arrangement **1996**

74 m WAVE PIERCING CATAMARAN

In January 1991, five of these vessels were ordered, four for Hoverspeed Ltd, a subsidiary of Sea Containers Ltd. and one for Tasmanian Ferry Services for the Bass Strait crossing. The first two were ordered by Sea Containers on 18 September 1988 and the next two on 26 January 1990. The vessels had an approximate price of A$20 million each. Of exceptional interest is the decision to employ relatively heavy, medium-speed diesel engines in an advanced lightweight aluminium vessel structure. The aim was to exploit the low fuel consumption and long time between overhaul of these engines as well as avoiding the use of gearboxes. The nominal dry weight, with flywheel, of the 16 RK 270 Ruston engine to be used is 25.82 tonnes.

By January 1995 a further nine 74 m wave piercing catamarans had been delivered. A considerable number of design changes have been made in the recent vessels including the fitting of ride control systems (an active trim tab is fitted as standard and a forward foil system is optional) and in the sixth craft the use of Caterpillar 3616 medium-speed diesels instead of the Ruston 16RK 270 diesels. Power rose from 3,650 kW in the first vessel to 4,050 kW in the last. In addition, large superstructure and accomodation changes were made in the vessels built for Buquebus, Argentina, Condor Ltd and Stena, U.K. This has allowed passenger numbers to increase to 600 and vehicle numbers to over 100.

Specifications

Length overall	73.65 m
Beam	26.0 m
Hull beam	4.4 m
Draught (fully loaded)	3.0 m
Displacement, max	650 t
Deadweight	171 t
Passengers	383
Vehicles	80 cars
Fuel capacity	20,000 l
Water capacity	3,000 l
Fuel consumption	200 g/kW h
Propulsive power	4 × 4,050 kW
Operational speed	35 kts

Classification: The vessels are built to the requirements of DnV +1A1 LCC + MV R280 passenger ship, EO, Car Ferry 'A'.

Structure: All welded construction, most plating thickness 6mm to 20mm and up to 50mm in the transom/water-jet areas. Superstructure (65 t) is built as as separate unit and fitted to the hulls with resilient mountings.

Propulsion: Four Ruston 16 RK 270 or Caterpillar 3611 medium speed diesels, each 4,050 kW at

720 rpm. These directly drive four Riva Calzoni (now Lips Jet) IRC 115 DX water-jet units, with only one on each side being equipped with steering and reversing systems.

Controls: The manoeuvring of the ship is controlled by a Lips Ancos 2000/joystick system called LIPS-STICK. The control system is split up in individual controls for each water-jet (two steerable and two boosters) through which rpm, angle of thrust and reversing of thrust are controlled. The LIPS-STICK system combines all individual controls in one single lever.

The 78m InCat/AMD K55 on sea trials prior to delivery
1996

LLOYD'S SHIPS HOLDINGS PTY LTD

41 Oxford Street, Bulimba, Queensland 4171, Australia

Tel: +61 (7) 3399 6866
Telex: +61 (7) 3395 5000

John Hardie, *General Manager*

Lloyd's Ships design and construct a range of luxury motor yachts and large catamaran ferry vessels. All Lloyd's ships are constructed to 'Class' and are of the highest standard.

The company has as its parent company, Daikyo Australia Pty Ltd, with 70 people directly employed and a turnover in excess of A$10 million per annum.

Lloyd's Ships Reef Queen ***1994***

The first catamaran to be built by Lloyd's Ships was *Equator Dream*, a 35.6 m vessel with a maximum speed of 24 knots and accommodation for 260 passengers.

Reef Queen
Reef Prince

These fast catamaran ferries to complement the existing Great Adventures fleet were launched in March 1993 and June 1995 respectively and are being used to transport passengers around the islands in the North Queensland region. The vessels were designed by Lock Crowther/Lloyd's Ships.

Specifications

Length overall	37.39 m
Length waterline	34 m
Beam	12.25 m
Displacement	130 t
Crew	25
Passengers	406
Fuel capacity	10,000 l
Fresh water	6,000 l
Propulsive power	2 × 1,720 kW
Max speed	33 kts

Classification: DnV +1A1 light ship R3 EO Class 1C (DOT Marine Ports Qld)
Yard No V104,106

Structure: All-welded aluminium alloy.

Propulsion: 2 × MTU 16V 396 TE 74L engines, 1,720 kW each @ 1,940 rpm.

UPDATED

NQEA AUSTRALIA PTY LTD

60-92 Cook Street, PO Box 1105, Cairns, Queensland 4870, Australia

Tel: +61 (70) 527222
Telex: 48087 AA
Fax: +61 (70) 352812/352520

D G Fry, *Chairman*
E W Graham, *General Manager*
R Bannah, *Marketing Manager*
R D Rookwood, *Senior Design Engineer*
M Richards, *Chief Naval Architect*

NQEA started services in 1948 from the residence of its founder with a staff of three, the principal activity being the operation of general engineering agencies, leading to general engineering manufacture. In 1964 it entered the shipbuilding industry with the construction of dumb barges. This was followed by work on many types of vessel, including Australian Navy patrol boats until in 1975 the first construction

Quicksilver VIII ***1996***

Craft built	Yard No	Delivered	Class 1D	Engines	Delivered to
23 m *Green Island Express*	106	June 1982	230	2 × DDC 12V 92TA	Great Adventures
23 m *South Molle Reef* (ex-*Telford Reef*)	107	October 1982	204	2 × DDC 12V 92TA	Fantasea Cruises
23 m *Magnetic Express*	108	March 1983	240	2 × DDC 12V 92TA	Great Adventures
29.2 m *South Molle Capricorn* (ex-*Telford Capricorn*)	111	November 1983	326	2 × DDC 16V 92TA	Fantasea Cruises
23 m *Cougar*	113	1984	200	2 × DDC 12V 92TA	Great Adventures
23 m *Reef Link*	109	1984	200	2 × MTU 8V 396 TC 82	Magnetic Link Townsville
24 m *Quickcat I*	115	August 1984	145-200	2 × DDC 16V 92TA	-
24 m *Quickcat II*	123	1985	195	2 × DDC 16V 92TA	Fantasea Cruises
30 m *Reef Cat*	126	May 1986	345	2 × DDC 16V 92TA	Great Adventures
30 m *Quicksilver III*	127	October 1986	308	2 × MWM TBD 604 V12	Philippines
24 m *Auto Battam III* (ex-*Supercat II*)	138	October 1988	205	2 × MWM TBD 234 V12	Singapore
30 m *Reef Link II*	147	February 1987	403	2 × MWM TBD 604B V12	Fullers NZ
24 m *Taupo Cat*	148	March 1987	205	2 × MWM TBD 234 V16	Fullers NZ
30 m *Quicksilver IV*	130	May 1987	300	2 × MWM TBD 604 V12	Philippines
30 m *Supercat III*	125	August 1987	390	2 × MWM TBD 604 V12	IGSA Shipping
24 m *Roylen Sunbird*	151	August 1987	245	2 × MWM TBD 234 V16	Roylen Cruises Pty Ltd
30 m *Reef King*	152	December 1988	390	2 × MWM TBD 604B V12	Great Adventures
25.3 m *Wauri*	129	1988		2 × MWM TBD 234 V12	Queensland Fisheries
26.9 m *Adaire*	156	August 1988	150	2 × MWM TBD 234 V16	Kuwait Public Transport Co
26.9 m *Na'Aye*	157	September 1988	150	2 × MWM TBD 234 V16	Kuwait Public Transport Co
38.6 m WPC *Quicksilver V*	158	November 1988	252 + 66 externally	2 × DDC 16V 149 TIB	Quicksilver Connections
38.6 m WPC *Quicksilver VI*	159	February 1989	350	2 × DDC 16V 149 TIB	Quicksilver Connections
38.6 m WPC *Quicksilver VII*	161	September 1989	350	2 × DDC 16V 149 TIB	Quicksilver Connections
39.6 m WPC *Prince of Venice*	160	6 June 1989	303	2 × DDC 16V 149 TIB	Kompas Touristik
34.8 m *Blue Fin*	163	March 1990	250	2 × MWM TBD 604B V16	NSW State Transit Authority
39 m WPC *Seacom I*	170	July 1990	300	2 × DDC 16V 149 TIB	SeaCom Corporation
34.8 m *Sir David Martin*	172	December 1990	250	2 × MWM TBD 604B V16	NSW State Transit Authority
34.8 m *Sea Eagle*	173	March 1991	250	2 × MWM TBD 604B V16	NSW State Transit Authority
34 m *Dawn Fraser*	180	February 1992	200	2 × DDC 8V 92TA	NSW State Transit Authority
34 m *Betty Cuthbert*	181	February 1992	200	2 × DDC 8V 92TA	NSW State Transit Authority
34 m *Shane Gould*	184	January 1993	200	2 × DDC 8V 92TA	NSW State Transit Authority
34 m *Marlene Mathews*	185	January 1993	200	2 × DDC 8V 92TA	NSW State Transit Authority
34 m *Evonne Goolagong*	186	September 1993	200	2 × DDC 8V 92TA	NSW State Transit Authority
34 m *Marjorie Jackson*	187	September 1993	200	2 × DDC 8V 92TA	NSW State Transit Authority
45 m *Quicksilver VIII*	192	April 1995	456	4 × DDC 16V 149 TIB	Quicksilver Connections

Blue Fin **1991**

of vessels was undertaken. In 1977 NQEA was the successful tenderer for 14 'Freemantle' 42 m class patrol craft for the Australian Navy, the first having been built by Brooke Marine in England.

Throughout the 1980s, NQEA built large numbers of high-speed ferry craft for the international market-place as well as some special purpose vessels. Search and rescue vessels, luxury motor yachts, dredge and barge units (capable of being linked using an NQEA designed Autodock system), hover-craft and patrol boats have all been produced at the Cairns Australia NQEA facilities. However, the majority of vessels produced in recent years have been high-speed passenger ferries of the International Catamaran designs.

After delivery of the 34.8 m catamarans (Yard Nos 163, 172 and 173) to the New South Wales State Transit Authority as hydrofoil replacements, NQEA was awarded a contract to build six low-wash catamaran passenger ferries for the same operator, which were delivered in 1993.

In April 1995 the shipyard delivered a 45 m wave piercing catamaran to Quicksilver Connections.

Quicksilver V **1996**

28 m CATAMARAN

InCat design with an all-welded aluminium hull and a resiliently mounted superstructure to minimise noise and vibration.

Specifications

Length overall	29.2 m
Length waterline	25 m
Beam	11.2 m
Draught	1.76 m
Fuel capacity	2 × 5,000 l tanks
Propulsive power	2 × 1,200 shp
Max speed	29 kts
Operational speed	26 kts

Classification: Queensland Marine Board, Class 1C, November 1983.

Propulsion: Two 1,200 shp GM 16V-92 TA high-speed diesels with ZF reverse/reduction gearbox 2.4:1; driving a 5 blade aluminium-bronze propeller.

Electrical systems: 415 V AC from shore power, or 80 kVA GM diesel alternator set 24 V DC.

38.6 m WPC
Quicksilver V

The first of these vessels *Quicksilver V* was completed by NQEA in November 1988 for Quicksilver Connections with a further two identical craft delivered in February and September 1989 for the same operator and a fourth vessel delivered to Yugoslavia, also in June 1989.

A 39 m variation of the Quicksilver style was constructed for Kompas Touristik International, underwent an 11,000 mile delivery voyage from the builder's yards to Piran in Yugoslavia, and immediately went into operation, plying between the Istrian ports and Venice. This vessel is fitted with KaMeWa water-jet units driven by DDC 16V 149 TA diesel engines.

Specifications

Length overall	38.6 m
Length waterline	31.4 m
Beam	15.6 m
Hull beam	2.6 m
Draught	1.6 m
Passengers	340
Fuel capacity	2 × 2,000 l tanks
Water capacity	3,000 l
Propulsive power	2 × 1,230 kW
Max speed	30 kts
Operational speed	27 kts

Structure: All-welded aluminium generally using alloys 5083 H321 and 6061 T6. Some light plates are 5086 H32.

Classification: DnV +1A1 R45 Queensland Department of Harbours and Marine, Class 1G.

Propulsion: Two GM diesel engines model 16V-149 TIB, each coupled to ZF gearbox model BU 460. Each engine is rated at 1,230 kW at 1,800 rpm, and drives two KaMeWa water-jets model 63S 62/6.

Electrical system: Main services are supplied by either of two diesel engine (Cummins 6BT5) driven 100 kVA Stamford alternator sets. These supply 415 V three-phase and 415 V, single phase 50 Hz power. Engine starting, auxiliary and emergency services are supplied from 24 V DC battery banks.

Outfit: 350 passengers. Interior seats are individual armchairs with woollen upholstery. Exterior seats are moulded polypropylene shells. A food service area is fitted at the aft end of the lower cabin and a drinks bar in the middle of the lower cabin. Passenger spaces are air conditioned.

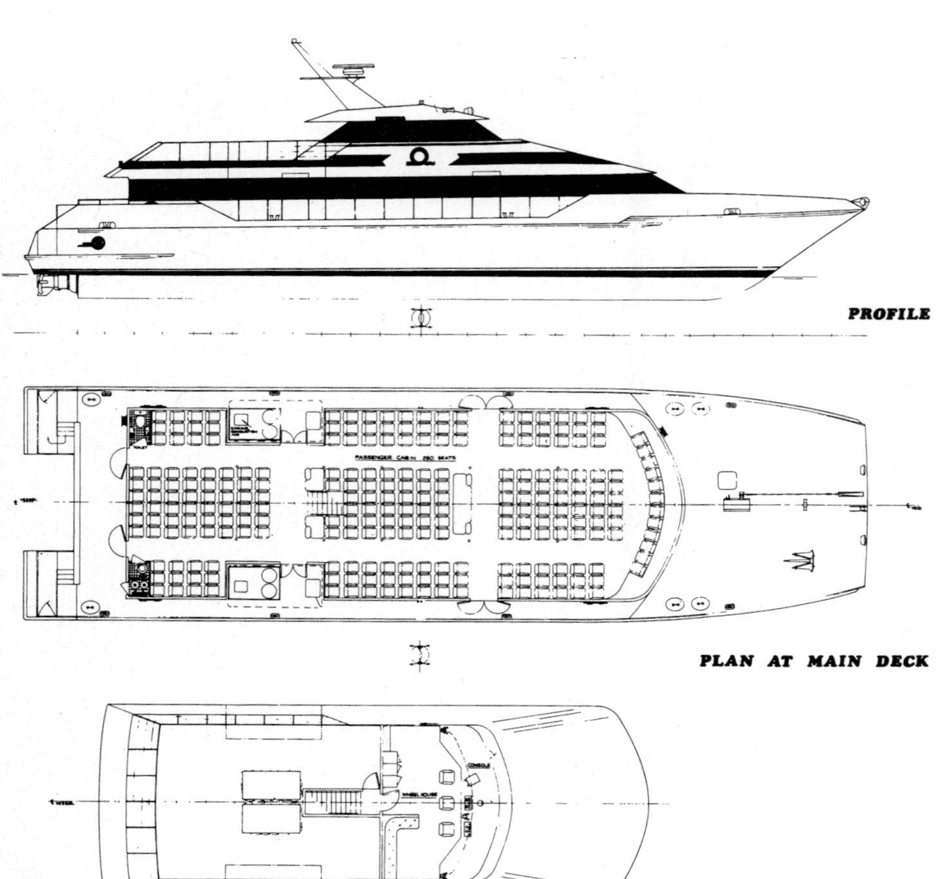

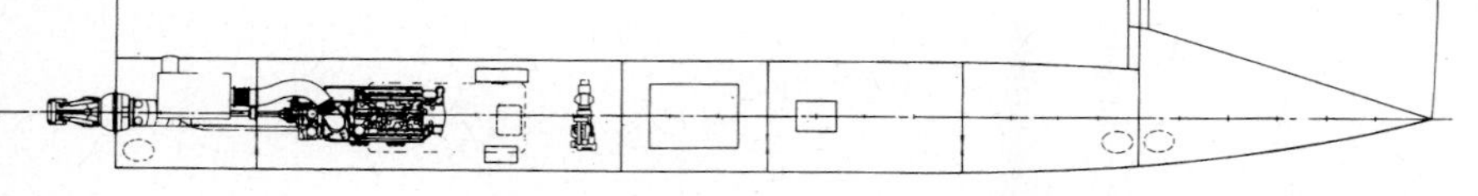

General arrangement of Blue Fin

40.17 m WPC
Seacom I

SeaCom Corporation of Japan (formerly known as the Nisshin Steamship Company) took delivery of this vessel in Cairns in July 1990. The ferry sailed to Japan under its own power and is operating as a ferry south of Tokyo Bay between Izu and Bohsoh Peninsula.

Specifications

Length overall	40.17 m
Length waterline	31.4 m
Beam	15.6 m
Hull beam	2.5 m
Draught	1.6 m
Crew	5
Passengers	302
Fuel capacity	2 × 4,500 l
Water capacity	3,500 l
Propulsive power	2 × 1,435 kW
Operational speed	29 kts

NQEA low-wash catamarans **1993**

Max speed	32 kts

Classification: Nippon Kaiki Kyokai NS (restricted coastal service/aluminium catamaran/passenger ship).

Propulsion: Two GM Detroit diesel engines model 16V-149 TIB, each coupled to ZF BU460 gearboxes. The engines are each rated at 1,435 kW at 2,000 rpm. Propulsion is delivered through two KaMeWa 63 water-jets.

Electrical system: Provided by two Hino WO6/DTI engines driving Stamford 100 kVA UCM274D marine alternators.

45 m WPC
Quicksilver VIII

This is the largest fast ferry delivered by NQEA to date and represents the flagship of the owners, Quicksilver Connections. As with Quicksilver V, the vessel operates out of Port Douglas on Queensland's north-east coast, to the Agincourt Reef on the outer section of the Great Barrier Reef.

Specifications

Length overall	45.5 m
Length waterline	39.6 m
Beam	16.2 m
Hull beam	3.0 m
Draught	1.90 m
Crew	8
Passengers	450
Fuel capacity	12,000 l
Water capacity	6,000 l
Max speed	42.4 kts
Operational speed	35.6 kts
Range	220 n miles

Classification: DnV +1A1 R2 HSLC Passenger Ferry EO

Propulsion: The vessel is powered by four DDC 16V 149TI diesels each rated at 1,343 kW @ 1,900 rpm and each driving a KMW 56 SII water-jet via a reduction gearbox.

CHEETAH PATROL BOAT

NQEA has designed a patrol boat variant of the 23 m commercial catamaran design. These boats will be identified as the 'Cheetah' class. One has been constructed for the Queensland Fisheries department and will be used for surveillance work in northern Australian waters. Normally operated by a six-man crew, the craft has facilities to carry an additional 12-man landing party and has extended range cruising capabilities.

Specifications

Length overall	25.3 m
Beam	8.7 m
Hull beam	2.5 m
Draught	2 m
Crew	6
Propulsive power	2 × 605 kW
Operational speed	25 kts
Range	1,000 miles at 20 kts

Propulsion: 2 × Deutz MWM TBD 234 V12 engines, 605 kW each at 2,200 rpm; driving 2 × ZF BW195 gearboxes, ratio 2.46:1; to 2 × 5-blade, 1 m diameter, aluminium-bronze propellers.

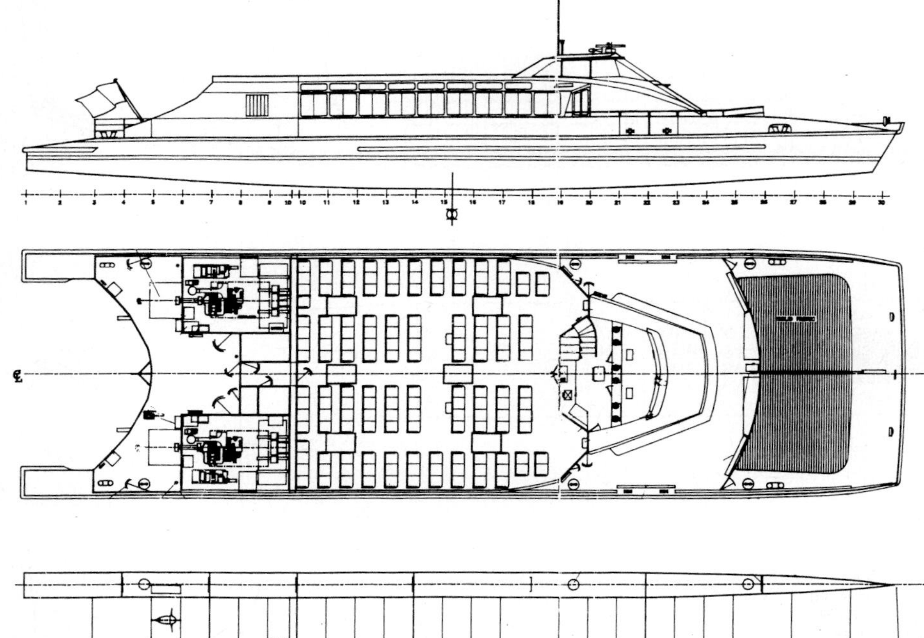

General arrangement of 150-seat low-wash ferry for NSW State Transit Authority

34.8 m CATAMARAN
Blue Fin

One of three InCat catamarans ordered by the State Transit Authority of New South Wales.

Survey: Maritime Services Board of NSW class 1D.

Specifications

Length overall	34.8 m
Length waterline	28.4 m
Beam	9.75 m
Hull beam	2.80 m
Draught	1.0 m
Passengers	250
Fuel capacity	8,830 l
Water capacity	500 l
Propulsive power	2 × 1,675 kW
Operational speed	35 kts
Max speed	41 kts

Classification: Lloyd's Register of Shipping ✠ 100 A1 Catamaran Passenger Vessel + LMC.

Propulsion: Engines: 2 × MWM TBD 604B V16, 1,675 kW each, driving 2 × KaMeWa 63 S11 water-jets.

LOW-WASH CATAMARAN

The NSW State Transit Authority, in June 1991, placed an order with NQEA to build two 36.8 m low-wash catamaran ferries to link the city of Parramatta with Sydney's Circular Quay. In 1992 the same client placed an order for a further four vessels with NQEA after the successful operation of the first Rivercats. All six were completed by September 1993.

Designed by Grahame Parker construction is light aluminium with foam FRP coring in the deck/cabin structure.

The propulsion system for these vessels is unusual. The designers chose Schottel Rudderpropellers, an uprated system based on the Schottel SRP 132/131 type. The modifications of this unit enable power input to be raised to about 367 kW. The position of these thrust and steering devices is also unusual in that they are positioned beneath the bridging structure of the catamaran towards its aft end with the propellers facing forward.

Specifications

Length overall	36.8 m
Length waterline	35 m
Beam	10.5 m
Draught	1.35 m
Displacement, min	45 t
Passengers	200
Fuel capacity	5,500 l
Water capacity	600 l
Propulsive power	2 × 373 kW
Operational speed	22.5 kts
Max speed	23.7 kts
Range	660 n miles

Propulsion: 2 × DDC 8V 92TA engines, 373 kW each at 2,100 rpm; driving 2 × Schottel steerable propeller units SRP 132/131.

SEAJET PV 250-SS-T

The Seajet PV 250 SS.T is a joint venture between NQEA Australia and Danyard of Frederikshavn, Denmark. Two of these vessels are currently under construction at the Danyard Shipyard and are scheduled for delivery in mid-1996.

The semi-Swath hull form was developed with the Swedish Marine Research Institution, SSPA. The resultant hull form experiences relatively low vertical accelerations compared to a conventional catamaran for a given sea state without the use of a ride control system.

The four loading lanes at the bow and twin side exit lanes aft would allow for very fast turnaround times.

Specifications

Length overall	76.1 m
Beam	23.4 m
Draught	3.4 m
Passengers	450
Vehicles	120 cars
Propulsive power	2 × 12400 kW
Operational speed	40 kts
Range	240 n miles

Classification: DnV +1A1 HSLC R2 Passenger Car Ferry A EO ICS NAUT.

Propulsion: Engines: 2 × GE LM1600 gas-turbines each rated at 12,400 kW and 2 × MTU 1163 diesel engines each rated at 6,000 kW. This CODOG arrangement drives four KaMeWa water-jets.

SEAJET PV 330-SS-D (DESIGN)

A slightly larger version than the two Seajets currently under construction, the PV 330 SS.D has a total deadweight capacity of 330 tonnes and an operational speed of 42 knots with gas turbine propulsion and 38 knots with diesel propulsion.

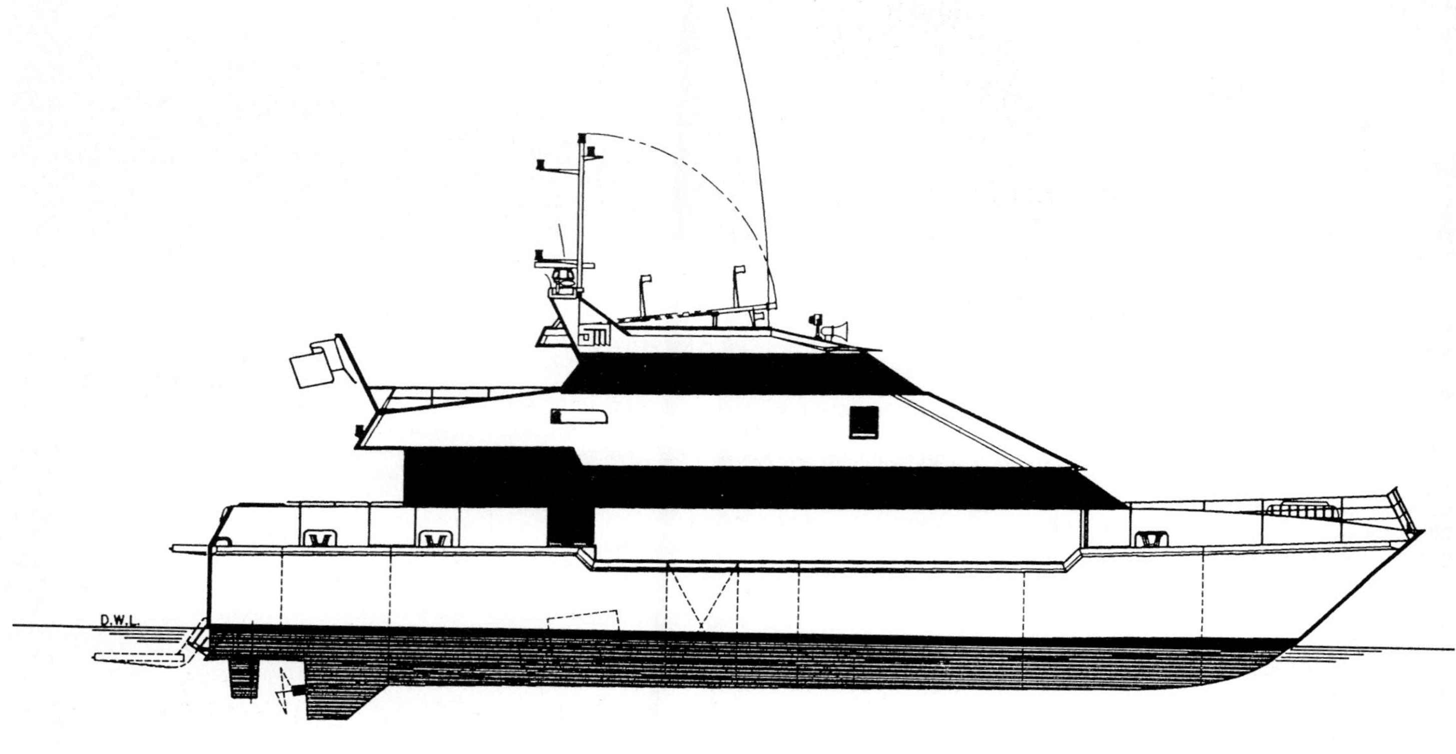

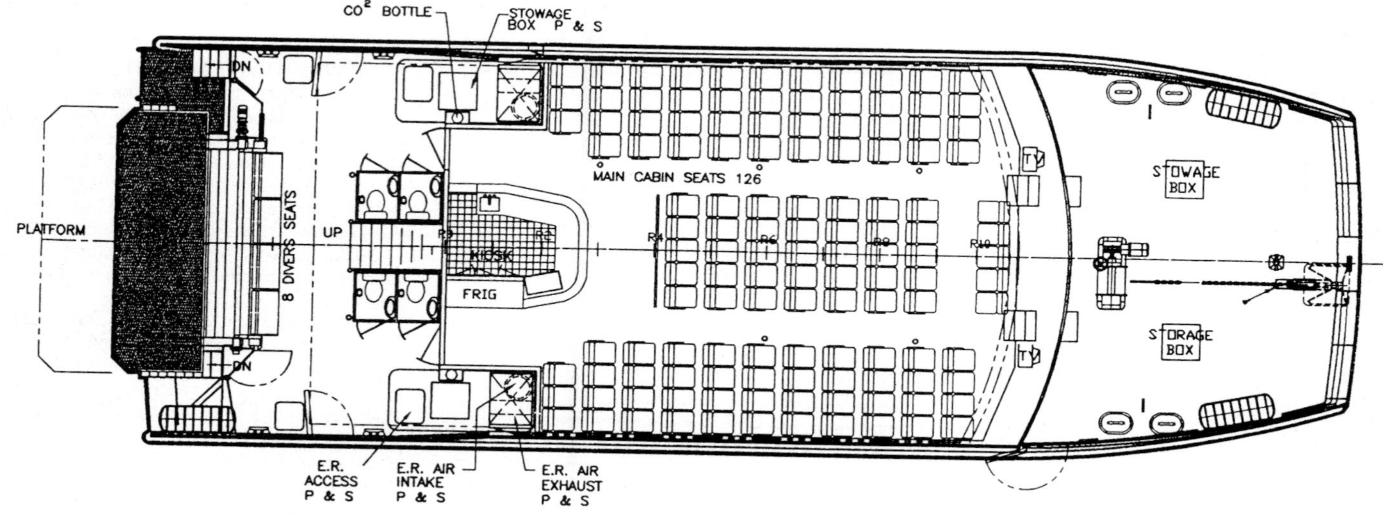

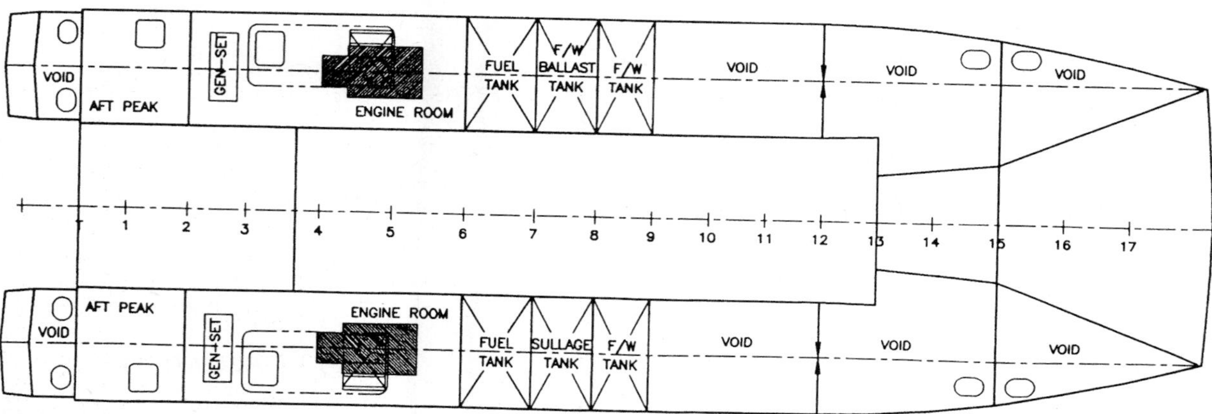

General arrangement of Payar

The NQEA Danyard Seajet PV 250-SS-T (design)
1993

Specifications

Length overall	81.0 m
Length waterline	75.0 m
Beam	23.4 m
Passengers	600
Vehicles	216 cars
Fuel capacity	50,000 l
Water capacity	7,000 l
Operational speed	42 kts

Payar

This is a 25 m catamaran built for Sriwani Tours and Travel Snd Bhd, for transporting tourists from Langkawi, Malaysia, to a small island called Pulau Payar.

Specifications

Length overall	26.5 m
Length waterline	23 m
Beam	8.70 m
Draught	2.00 m
Passengers	210
Fuel capacity	4,800 l
Water capacity	2,500 l
Propulsive power	2 × 736 kW
Max speed	27.2 kts

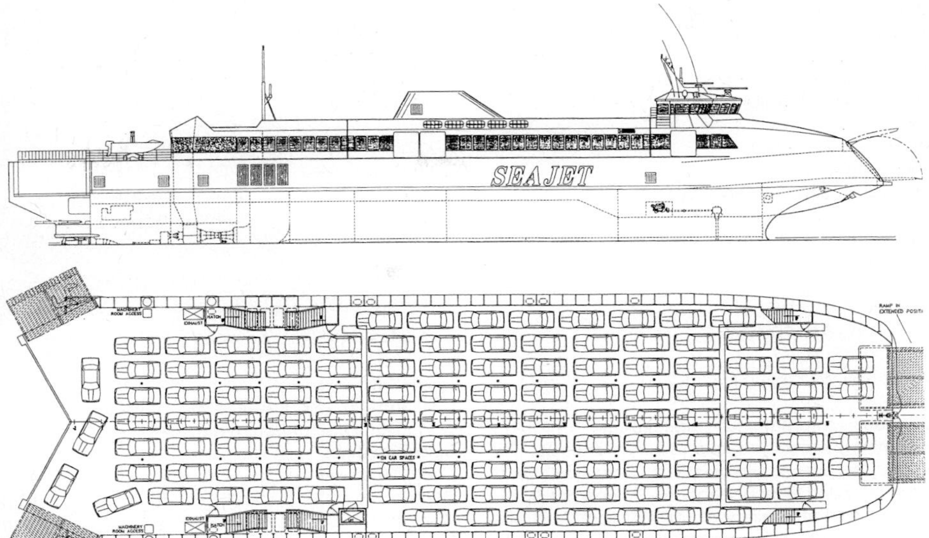

The NQEA Danyard Seajet PV 250-SS-T (design)

Classification: DnV +1A1 HSLC R4 Passenger EO.
Propulsion: The main engines are 2 × MAN D2842 LE402 diesels; driving 2 × Veem 5-bladed series 'B' 1,000 mm × 1,015 mm; via ZF BW 255 Rev Red gearboxes.

UPDATED

OCEANFAST FERRIES PTY LTD

18 Clarence Beach, Henderson, Western Australia 6166, Australia

Tel: +61 (9) 410 1866
Fax: +61 (9) 410 1927

David Browning, *Manager*

Oceanfast Ferries is a member of the Oceanfast Marine Group which includes Oceanfast International, Motor Yacht International and Ferries Australia.

The company has been developing the concept of air lubrication of high-speed craft with Russian technologists over the past few years, this research culminating in the design and construction of their first Oceanfast 942 ALT 50 catamaran.

TYPE 942 ALT 50 CATAMARAN

This 42 m all aluminium catamaran is the first of the Air Lubricated Technology (ALT) vessels to be constructed. This technology provides a 20 per cent to 30 per cent improvement in vessel speed for the same power and is potentially the most significant technological development for many years. The vessel is currently under construction and is scheduled for delivery in March 1996.

Specifications

Length overall	42.0 m
Beam	12.0 m
Draught	2.2 m
Crew	14
Passengers	450
Fuel capacity	14,000 l
Water capacity	1,500 l
Max speed	54 kts
Operational speed	50 kts
Range	185 n miles

Classification: DnV +1A1 HSLC Passenger R1 EO.
Propulsion: The vessel is powered by four MTU 16V 396 TE 74L diesel engines each driving an MJP 650 water-jet via a reduction gearbox.

NEW ENTRY

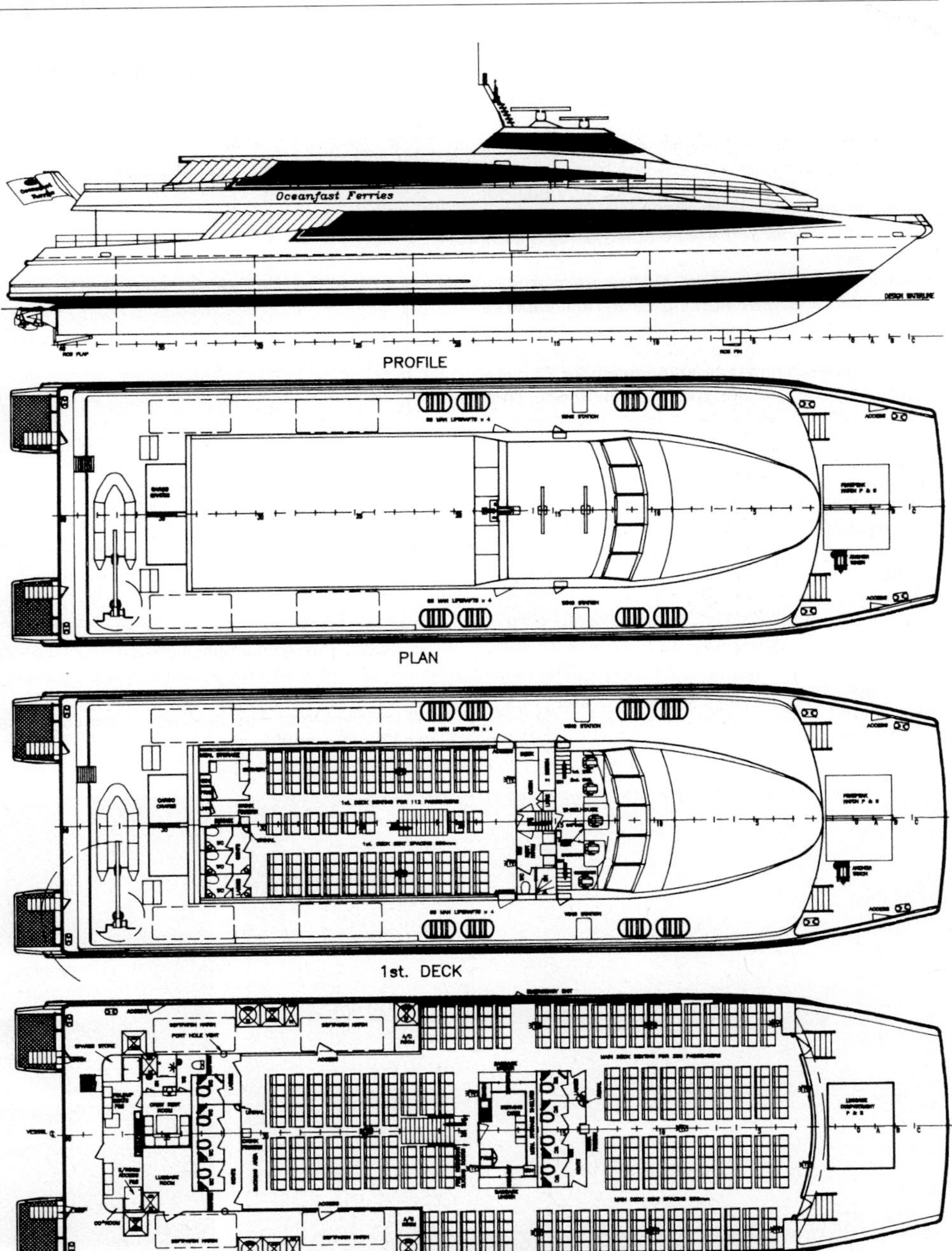

Oceanfast Ferries Type 942 ALT 50 Catamaran with air lubricated hulls
1996

OCEANFAST INTERNATIONAL PTY LTD

26 St George's Terrace, Perth, PO Box X2256, Western Australia, Australia

Tel: +61 (9) 325 8599
Telex: 94598 IAL AA
Fax: +61 (9) 325 6484/221 1813

Boat Factory: 15 Egmont Road, Hendersen, Western Australia 6166, Australia

Tel: +61 (9) 410 1900
Fax: +61 (9) 410 2095

John Farrell, *Managing Director*

Oceanfast International specialises in high-performance motor yachts and luxury cruisers. The company's naval architect is Phil Curran and yacht design is by Jon Bannenberg Ltd. The company is a wholly owned subsidiary of the Western Australia-based International Assets Ltd group, with over 250 people directly employed and a turnover in excess of A$30 million per annum.

Oceanfast Moecca: *the world's first catamaran megayacht* **1993**

Moecca

Delivered in December 1992, this vessel is the world's first catamaran megayacht.

Specifications

Length overall	45 m
Beam	13 m
Draught	2 m
Displacement, min	250 t
Fuel capacity	82,000 l
Water capacity	10,000 l
Max speed	25 kts
Operational speed	20 kts

Propulsion: The main engines are 2 × MTU 12V 396 TB 94 diesels, driving 2 × KaMeWa 80 water-jets.

Auxiliary systems: Engines: 2 × MTU 10V 183 AA51 diesels, 172 kW each.

Outfit: Owner's suite and 6 guest cabins; Captain's cabin and 6 crew cabins.

UPDATED

SABRE CATAMARANS PTY LTD

156 Barrington Road, Spearwood, Western Australia 6163, Australia

Tel: +61 (9) 418 3000
Fax: +61 (9) 434 1457

Bill Harry, *Principal*

Builder of a number of aluminium fast catamaran fishing and passenger vessels. The most recent is *Aremiti II*, a 29 m 30 knot catamaran ferry built for Aremiti Pacific Cruises. The two earlier catamarans *Aremiti* and *Saladin Sabre* were operated by Stirling Marine Services during the construction of the Saladin oilfield off the coast of Western Australia. *Saladin Sabre* is now working as a Tahiti-Moorea ferry. Two smaller high-speed catamarans have also been built, the *OT Manu* and *Paia*. These 16.7 m catamarans each have accommodation for 73 passengers and a maximum speed of 25 knots. They operate in Bora Bora lagoon in French Polynesia.

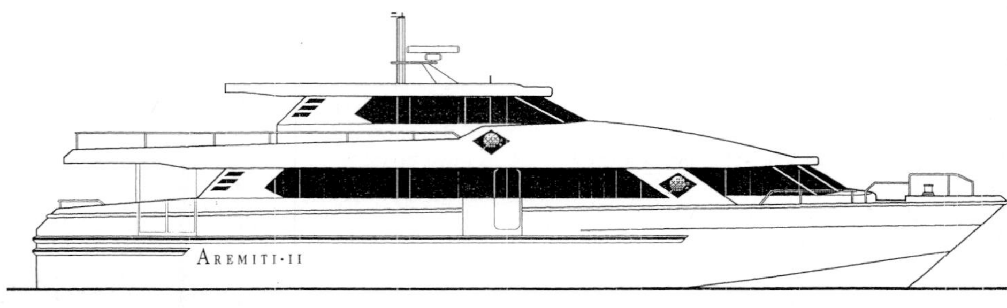

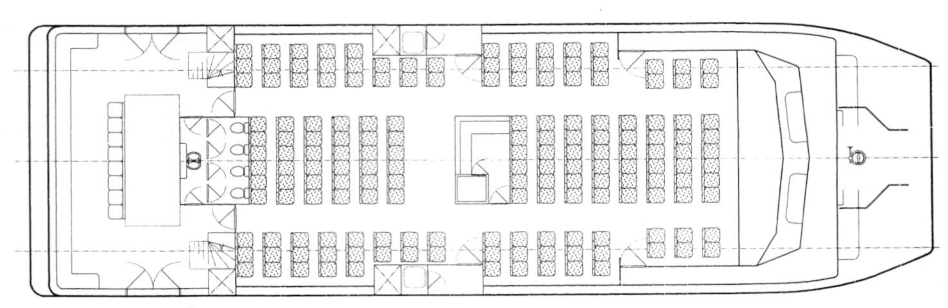

Aremiti II

SABRE 55
Aremiti
Saladin Sabre

Specifications

Length overall	16.76 m
Length waterline	14.95 m
Beam	7.2 m
Draught	0.72 m
Passengers	100
Fuel capacity	2 × 1,000 l tanks
Water capacity	500 l
Max speed	34.6 kts
Operational speed	28 kts

Propulsion: The main engines are 2 × DDC 8V 92T diesels, driving 2 × Levi 800 series surface-piercing drive units.

Auxiliary systems: The auxiliary generator is an Isuzu 17 kVA model.

Saladin Sprint

Built for the same purpose as *Saladin Sabre*.

Specifications

Length overall	13.19 m
Length waterline	11.6 m

The Sabre 55 Aremiti **1994**

Aremiti II. *The fourth high-speed commuter ferry delivered to Tahiti by Sabre Catamarans* **1994**

OT Manu *and* Paia *1994*

Foveaux Express *1994*

Beam	5.4 m
Draught	0.6 m
Passengers	40
Fuel capacity	1,800 l
Water capacity	500 l
Propulsive power	2 × 266 kW
Max speed	28 kts
Operational speed	24 kts
Range	350 n miles

Propulsion: The main engines are 2 × Volvo Penta 266 kW, TAMD 71A turbocharged, after-cooled diesels, driving Levi 400 series surface-piercing drive units.

Aremiti II

Owned by Aremiti Pacific Cruises, this vessel operates from Papeete, Tahiti. Delivered June 1992.

Specifications

Length overall	29.95 m
Length waterline	26.95 m
Beam	9.3 m
Draught	1.5 m
Passengers	288
Fuel capacity	2,000 l
Propulsive power	2 × 1,360 kW
Max speed	32 kts

Propulsion: 2 × Detroit Diesel 12V 149TIB diesels rated at 1,360 kW each.

OT Manu and Paia

Owned by Bora Bora Navettes, these vessels were delivered in 1991.

Specifications

Length overall	16.7 m
Length waterline	13.25 m
Beam	6.51 m
Draught	0.9 m
Passengers	73
Fuel capacity	3,000 l
Operational speed	25 kts

Foveaux Express

Owned by Stewart Island Marine Services and delivered in 1991.

Specifications

Length overall	19.9 m
Length waterline	17.6 m
Beam	7.2 m
Draught	1.5 m
Passengers	67
Fuel capacity	8,000 l
Operational speed	30 kts

VERIFIED

SBF ENGINEERING

Waters Edge, Lot 33 Cockburn Road, South Coogee, Western Australia 6166, Australia

Tel: +61 (9) 410 2244
Telex: +61 (9) 410 1807

Don Dunbar, *Managing Director*
Alan McCombie, *Director, Finance*
Don Johnston, *General Manager*
Capt Kim Cleggett, *Director, Technical Sales*

High-speed catamaran craft built	Seats	Delivered to	Route
33 m *Victory III*	448	Tourist Services Pty Ltd	Great Keppel Island
33.37 m *Tropic Sunbird*	500+	Sunseeker Cruises, Queensland, Australia	Cairns-Townsville-Dunk Island
33.37 m *Quickcat*	500+	Waiheke Shipping, Auckland, New Zealand	Auckland-Waiheke
31.7 m *Lada Satu*	250	Lada Langkawi, Malaysia	Lada Langkawi
31.7 m *Lada Dua*	250	Lada Langkawi, Malaysia	Lada Langkawi
31.7 m *Lada Tiga*	250	Lada Langkawi, Malaysia	Lada Langkawi
31.7 m *Lada Empat*	250	Lada Langkawi, Malaysia	Lada Langkawi
19.9 m *Seabreeze*	116	Mackenzies Marine, Esperance Western Australia	— —
22 m *Lada Lima*	106	Lada Langkawi, Malaysia	Lada Langkawi
28 m Unknown	130	Development Consultants Ltd	Calcutta - Haldia

Victory III

Passenger ferry.

Designer: Lock Crowther, Sydney.

Owner: Great Keppel Island Tourist Services Pty Ltd, Rockhampton, Queensland, Australia.

Legislation authority: Queensland Marine and Harbours Department.

Specifications

Length overall	33 m
Beam	10 m
Draught	1.4 m
Passengers	448
Propulsive power	2 × 807 kW
Max speed	28 kts
Operational speed	24 kts

Structure: The catamaran hull and superstructure are constructed in all-welded marine grade aluminium alloy. Each bow has a streamlined bulb on the forefoot which increases waterline length and performance. Draught of hulls forward is slightly over 1 m and the craft is designed to be beached by the bow to allow passengers to embark and disembark using an SBF-designed telescopic ramp lowered from the foredeck.

Propulsion: Two MWM 16-cylinder marine diesels, each producing 807 kW (1,082 bhp); driving two right-handed 970 mm × 1,760 mm propellers.

Electrical systems: Electrical generator: 1 × MWM 3-cylinder generator producing 33 kVA.

Navigation and communications: JRC JMA 3425 colour radar; NWU 51 colour plotter; JAX2 Weatherfox; JLE 3850 satellite navigator; JFX 80 colour sounder.

Seabreeze *in service* *1995*

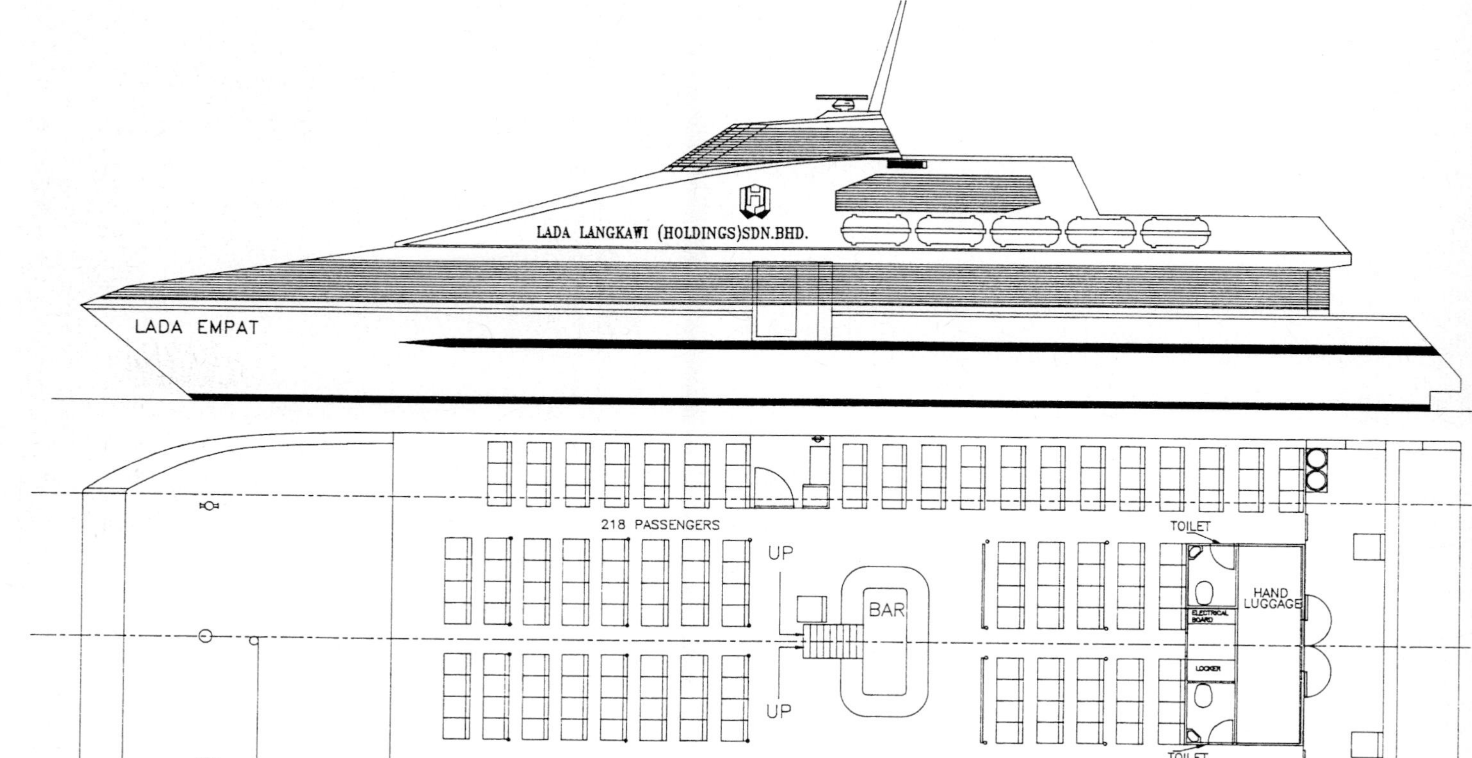

General arrangement of Lada Empat **1995**

Codan 8121 SSB radio; Icom IC M80 VHF radio.
Safety equipment: Lifesaving: 450 coastal lifejackets; 450 flotation rafts.
Firefighting: Halon gas fire extinguishers.

Tropic Sunbird

Passenger ferry, but first employed as a top press and spectator boat at the 1987 Americas Cup.
Designer: Lock Crowther, Sydney.
Owner: Sunseeker Cruises, Cairns, Queensland.
Legislation authority: Department of Marine and Harbours, Western Australia.
Specifications

Length overall	33.37 m
Length waterline	30.01 m
Beam	13 m
Draught	1.36 m
Passengers	600
Max speed	32 kts
Operational speed	27 kts

Structure: The catamaran hull and superstructure are constructed in all-welded marine grade aluminium alloy. The hulls incorporate bulbous bows which reduce pitching through their extra buoyancy.
Propulsion: The main engines are 2 × Deutz-MWM TBD 604B V12, driving through 2 × ZF BW 455 gearboxes.
Navigation and communications: Koden MDC 4105 colour radar; Koen CVS 88 colour echo-sounder; Robertson AP-40 autopilot; Codan P121 12 V radio.

Quickcat

Passenger ferry.
Designer: Lock Crowther, Turramurra, NSW, Australia.
Owner: Waiheke Shipping Company Ltd, Auckland, New Zealand.
Legislation authority: New Zealand Ministry of Transport.
Specifications
As for *Tropic Sunbird* except that the passenger cabin behind the wheelhouse for *Quickcat* extends to the full width of the craft over its whole length.
Navigation and communications: Koden 410 colour radar; Raytheon echo-sounder; Wagner SE autopilot; Codan 8121 24 V radio.

Lada Empat **1995**

SBF 31.7 m catamaran Lada Satu **1994**

31.7 m CATAMARANS
Lada Satu
Lada Dua
Lada Tiga
Lada Empat

By the end of 1994 SBF Engineering had delivered all four 250-passenger catamarans under construction following contracts signed in 1992 and 1993 with Lada Langkawi in Malaysia
Specifications

Length overall	31.7 m
Length waterline	27 m
Beam	9.6 m
Draught	1 m
Passengers	250
Fuel capacity	5,000 l (12,000 l for *Lada Empat*)
Water capacity	1,000 l
Propulsive power	2 × 1,435 kW
Operational speed	35 kts

Propulsion: The main engines are 2 × MTU 12V 396 TE 74L, 1,435 kW each at 2,000 rpm; driving 2 × KaMeWa 56 water-jets, via 2 × ZF BUK455-1 gearboxes

Seabreeze
This vessel was delivered to Western Australian operator Mackenzies Marine in mid-1994.
Specifications

Length overall	19.9 m
Length waterline	18 m
Beam	7 m
Draught	1.4 m
Passengers	116
Fuel capacity	3,000 l
Water capacity	1,000 l
Propulsive power	2 × 550 kW
Max speed	25 kts

Structure: Marine grade aluminium.
Propulsion: The main engines are 2 × MTU 12V 183 TE62 diesels, each producing 550 kW at 2,000 rpm; driving 2 × 5 blade Stone Marine propellers; via 2 × Twin Disc MG 5141 gearboxes.

Lada Lima
This vessel was delivered to Lada Langawi Holdings in Malaysia in late 1994.
Specifications

Length overall	19.9 m
Length waterline	17.95 m
Beam	6.6 m
Draught	0.8 m
Passengers	106
Fuel capacity	7,000 l
Water capacity	1,000 l
Propulsive power	2 × 610 kW
Max speed	28 kts

Classification: Bureau Veritas.
Structure: Marine grade aluminium.
Propulsion: The main engines are 2 × MTU 12V 183 TE 72 diesels, each producing 610 kW at 2,100 rpm; driving 2 × Castoldi 07 series water-jets.

Lada Lima *on trials* ***1995***

28 m CATAMARAN
Built for Development Consultants of India, this ferry will operate on the Hooghly river between Calcutta and Haldia. The vessel is scheduled for delivery in March 1996.
Specifications

Length overall	28.0 m
Length waterline	26.0 m
Beam	9.4 m
Draught	0.83 m
Crew	7
Passengers	130
Fuel capacity	3,600 l
Water capacity	1,000 l
Operational speed	36 kts

Propulsion: The vessel is powered by two Deutz MWM TBD 616V16 diesels rated at 1,107 kw AT 2,165 rpm, each driving a KMW 50S11 water-jet via a Reintjes WLS 430 reduction gearbox.

UPDATED

SOUTH AUSTRALIAN SHIPS PTY LTD

Ocean Steamers Road, Port Adelaide, South Australia, Australia 5015

Tel: +61 8 341 3030
Fax: +61 8 341 2228

D G Williams, *Chairman*

South Australian Ships was incorporated in 1994 with the objective of providing a dedicated facility for the construction of very large aluminium fast catamaran cargo vessels. The company has constructed a number of trawlers and is currently building a small fast passenger catamaran ferry. The technology and designs for the current build and other proposed vessels are supplied by InCat Designs of Sydney, Australia.

Artist's impression of the fast catamaran cargo vessel ***1996***

FAST CATAMARAN CARGO VESSEL (DESIGN)
Two versions of this concept design are being marketed at present, a 122 m version with a cargo capacity of 1,300 tonnes and a 160 m version with a capacity of 3,500 tonnes. Both craft have an operational speed of 40 knots and a range of up to 3,000 n miles.
Specifications

Length overall	160 m
Beam	33 m
Hull beam	6.0 m
Draft	4.5 m
Payload	3,500 t
Fuel capacity	1,375 t
Water capacity	5 t
Operational speed	40 kts
Range	3,000 nm

Classification: DnV
Propulsion: The vessel is powered by eight Wärtsila 18W38 diesel engines each rated at 12,500 kW. A pair of these diesels drive one of four Niigata KA1605 water-jets.

NEW ENTRY

WAVEMASTER INTERNATIONAL PTY LTD

Lot 500, Cockburn Road, Henderson, Western Australia 6166, Australia

Tel: +61 (9) 410 1422
Telex: 93356 AA
Fax: +61 (9) 410 2089

Glen Williams, *Director*

WaveMaster International, a leading designer and manufacturer of fast ferries, is owned by the Penang Shipbuilding Corporation of Malaysia. WaveMaster was originally established in 1983 and has since delivered over 30 commercial craft in the range 30 m to 50 m.

32 m PASSENGER CATAMARAN

This vessel was the first catamaran built by WaveMaster and was delivered in 1989 to a Hong Kong operator.

Yin Shan Hu
Specifications

Length overall	32 m
Beam	9.5 m
Draught	1.2 m
Payload	30 t
Crew	6-8
Passengers	252
Propulsive power	2 × 1,089 kW
Max speed	32 kts
Operational speed	28 kts

Classification: Z C China Classification Society, DnV + 1A1 R45 EO.
Propulsion: Engines: 2 × MTU 12V 396 TB 83, 1,089 kW each (32°C air, 32°C water) MCR 1,940 rpm; driving 2 × KaMeWa 63 S water-jet units
Electrical system: Power for this is supplied by 2 ×

WaveMaster International 380-seat Nansha 28 **1995**

WaveMaster 44 m catamaran Negeen **1993**

Mercedes-Benz/Stamford alternator sets, 92 kW each.
Navigation and communications: 72 and 48 mile colour radars, gyrocompass, echo-sounder, SSB and VHF radios.

35 m PASSENGER CATAMARAN
Zhen Xing

Specifications

Length overall	34.5 m
Beam	9.8 m
Draught	1.3 m
Payload	38 t
Crew	8
Passengers	310
Propulsive power	2 × 1,458 kW
Max speed	35 kts
Operational speed	30 kts

Classification: Z C China Classification Society, DnV + 1A1 R45 EO.
Propulsion: Engines: 2 × MTU 16V 396 TB 83, 1,458 kW each (32°C air, 32°C water) MCR 1,940 rpm; driving 2 × KaMeWa 63 S62.60 water-jet units.
Electrical system: 2 × Mercedes-Benz/Stamford alternator sets, 92 kW each.
Navigation and communications: 72- and 48- mile colour radars, gyrocompass, echo-sounder, SSB and VHF radios.

Peng Jiang

Delivered in August 1993, this vessel has been designed to meet restrictive low wash requirements imposed by the operator.

Specifications

Length overall	34.6 m
Length waterline	29.5 m
Beam	9.8 m
Draught	1.4 m
Crew	12
Passengers	193
Propulsive power	2 × 1,960 kW
Operational speed	40 kts
Range	250 n miles

Classification: ZC, DnV +1A1 HSLC Pass Cat R3.
Propulsion: Main engines: 2 × MTU 16V 396 TE 74L at 1,960 kW at 1,950 rpm.
Water-jets: 4 × KaMeWa 63SII.

40 m PASSENGER CATAMARAN
Peng Lai Hu

A catamaran delivered early in 1993 to a Chinese operator.

Specifications

Length overall	39 m
Beam	11.4 m
Draught	1.35 m
Crew	14
Passengers	354
Fuel capacity	8,800 l
Water capacity	1,500 l
Propulsive power	2 × 1,580 kW
Operational speed	30 kts

Classification: China Classification Society, ZC or DnV.
Propulsion: Engines: 2 × MTU 16V 396 TE 74 diesels, 1,580 kW each at 1,975 rpm; driving 2 × KaMeWa 71S water-jets.

WaveMaster 44 m Car/Passenger ferry general arrangement **1996**

42 m PASSENGER CATAMARAN
Nansha 18, Nansha 28
Andromeda

Delivered in August 1993, June 1994 and August 1995 respectively, these are the fastest passenger catamarans delivered by Wavemaster to date. Full load speeds of over 43 knots were achieved with a lightship speed of approximately 48 knots.

Specifications

Length overall	42 m
Length waterline	36 m
Beam	12 m
Draught	1.5 m
Displacement	175 t
Crew	8
Passengers	378
Propulsive power	4 × 1,960 kW
Operational speed	43.5 kts
Range	185 n miles

Classification: ZC, DnV +1A1 HSLC Pass Cat R3.
Propulsion: Engines: 4 × MTU 16V 396 TE 74L at 1,960 kW at 1,950 rpm; driving 4 × KMW 63SII water-jets. (Andromeda was powered by four MWM TBD 620V16 diesel engines each driving a KaMeWa water-jet via a Reintjes reduction gearbox).

44 m PASSENGER/CARGO CATAMARAN
Negeen

A symmetrical hull catamaran for a Middle East customer, Valfajre & Shipping Co, delivered in late 1993.

Two further vessels have been ordered by the

Craft built	Yard No	Delivered	Seats	Engines	Delivered to
Yin Shan Hu	020	July 1989	252	2 × MTU 12V 396R TB 83	Sanfu
Zhen Xing Hu	022	March 1990	310	2 × MTU 12V 396R TB 83	Jiangmen
Mystique	027	August 1991	150	2 × Perkins T 63544	Boat Torque Cruises
Wu Yi Hu	028	November 1991	354	2 × MTU 16V 396 TE 74	Jiangmen Hong Kong Macao
Peng Lai Hu	037	December 1992	354	2 × MTU 16V 396 TE 74	Jiangmen Hong Kong Macao
Nansha 11	046	December 1992	300	2 × MTU 8V 396 TE 74L	Panyu Nansha Port Passenger Transportation Co
Peng Jiang	035	July 1993	193	2 × MTU 8V 396 TE 74L	Jiangmen Hong Kong Macao
Nansha 18	047	August 1993	386	2 × MTU 8V 396 TE 74L	Panyu Nansha Port Passenger Transportation Co
Negeen	032	November 1993	244	2 × MTU 16V 396 TE 74L	Valfajre 8 Shipping Co
Fei Long	048	March 1994	485	2 × MTU 12V 183 TE 72	Yick Fung Ship & Enterprises Co Ltd
Fast Craft	049	November 1993	218	2 × MTU 12V 183 TE 72	Fastcraft Pty Ltd
Seaflyte	051	December 1993	160	2 × MTU 8V 183 TE 72	Fullers Ferries
Nansha 28	068	June 1994	380	4 × MTU 16V 396 TE 74L	Panyu Nansha Port Passenger Transportation Co
White Dolphin II	052	February 1995	320	2 × Wartsila UD23	Boat Torque Cruises
Andromeda	126	August 1995	380	4 × MWM TBD 620 V16	AT Cruises, Greece
Rivercat 7 (Nicole Stevenson)	130	August 1995	230	2 × Detroit 8V92TA	Sydney Ferries
Not named	134	(January 1997)	236 + 10 cars	2 × MTU 16V 396 TE 74L	Valfajre 8 Shipping Co
Not named	135	(January 1997)	236 + 10 cars	2 × MTU 16V 396 TE 74L	Valfajre 8 Shipping Co
Not named	140	(November 1996)	600	—	Auckland, New Zealand

same operator for delivery in January 1997 which carry 236 passengers, 10 cars and 16 pallets.

Specifications

Length overall	44 m
Length waterline	37.6 m
Beam	12.4 m
Hull beam	2.7 m
Draught	1.4 m
Displacement	169 t
Payload	36.15 t
Crew	8 (9 berths)
Passengers	244
Fuel capacity	14,000 l
Water capacity	4,000 l
Propulsive power	2 × 1,940 kW
Operational speed	30.6 kts continuous
Range	400 n miles

Classification: DnV +1A1 R3 HSLC, Passenger, EO.
Structure: Hull material: welded aluminium.
Propulsion: Engines: 2 × MTU 16V 396 TE 74L, 1,940 kW each at 2,000 rpm.
Transmissions: 2 × Reintjes VLJ 930 gearboxes.
Thrust devices: 2 × water-jets KaMeWa 71S.
Electrical system: Engines: 2 × MTU 6V 183 TA51; generators: 2 × Stamford UC 1274 135 kVA.

WaveMaster 44 m catamaran Andromeda **1996**

50 m PASSENGER CATAMARAN
Fei Long

Delivered in March 1994, *Fei Long* is the largest catamaran ferry built by Wavemaster to date. The craft operates with other catamarans on the Bohai Sea in northern China on a route linking Dalian and Yantai.

Specifications

Length overall	49 m
Length waterline	41 m
Beam	13.6 m
Draught	1.5 m
Passengers	485
Operational speed	40.5 kts
Range	390 n miles

Classification: DnV +1A1 HSLC R3 passenger.
Propulsion: Engines are two MTU 16V 396 TE 74L, driving reduction gearboxes to Kamewa 71S water-jets.

UPDATED

CHILE

ASENAV MR

Fidel Oteiza 1956 P 13, Santiago 9, Chile

Tel: +56 (2) 274 1515
Telex: 240841 EKOS CL
Fax: +56 (2) 204 9118

Astilleros y Servicios Navales (ASENAV) delivered its first catamaran, the *Patagonia Express*, in 1991. Since then it has delivered a further two aluminium craft and one steel version (slow speed). All these designs have been the result of collaboration between ASENAV and Batservice Holding, using the standard Sea Lord 28 design as the basis.

29 m CATAMARAN
Patagonia Express, Pacifico Express
Luciano Beta

Although all these catamarans have slightly differing specifications they are all based on the same standard vessel and are grouped here for convenience. The *Patagonia Express* was originally built to carry 220 passengers but was refitted to accomodate 60 passengers in comfort for 10 hour trips through the

Pacifico Express **1996**

channels of Southern Chile. *Pacifico Express* was designed to transport smolts (small live fish) from the cultivation centres to the remote breeding grounds in the fiords of southern Chile. The smolts are carried in six removable tanks on the vessel's working deck. *Luciano Beta* was designed to carry 130 passengers for charter, again in the extreme south of the country. All vessels are constructed of aluminium.

Specifications

Length overall	29.0 m
Beam	8.3 m
Draught	1.6 m
Fuel capacity	12,000 l
Water capacity	2,000 l
Max speed	30 kts
Operational speed	24 kts

Propulsion: The vessels are all powered by two Detroit Diesel 12V 149TI (*Luciano Beta* DD 16V 92 TA) each driving a Lips or Kamewa water-jet via a Reintjes reduction gearbox.

UPDATED

Luciano Beta
1996

CHINA, PEOPLE'S REPUBLIC

HANG TONG HIGH SPEED SHIP DEVELOPMENT CO LTD

Fenjiang Road, Xinhui City, Guangdong Province, People's Republic of China 529100

Tel: +86 (0750) 669 0966 / 663 2967
Fax: +86 (0750) 669 0966 / 666 6547

Hang Tong, a joint venture company, is specialised in the development of aluminium alloy high-speed craft. At present they are developing hydrofoils, catamarans and other high-speed ships, co-operating with partners in Australia and Russia. They are also producing sophisticated hovercraft backed by advanced technology and the research of the aerospace industry in China.

The repair of high-speed ships and welding of aluminium alloy and stainless steel structures are undertaken also.

The yard are licensed builders of Australian AMD catamaran designs, and are currently building a AMD 150.

AMD 150 Wave Piercing Catamaran Ferry

Construction of this vessel commenced in September 1995 with delivery scheduled for mid-1996.

Specifications

Length overall	25 m
Beam	10.65 m
Draught	1.8 m
Passengers	170
Operational speed	28 kts

Classification: Chinese Classification Society.

Propulsion: The main engines are 2 × Detroit 16V-92 TA high-speed diesels.

UPDATED

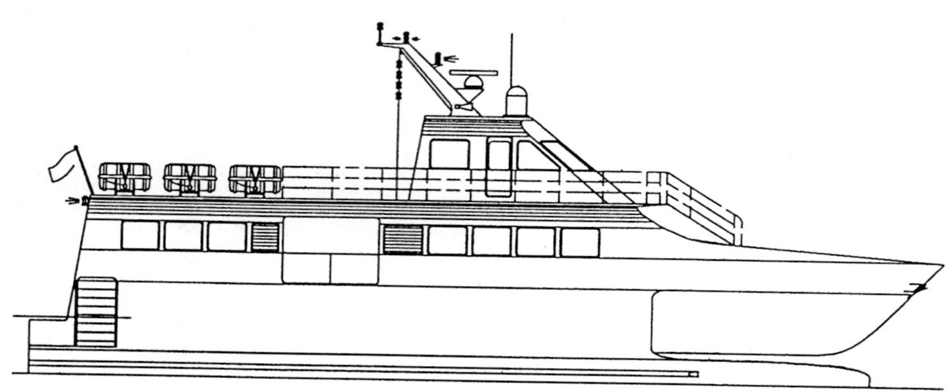

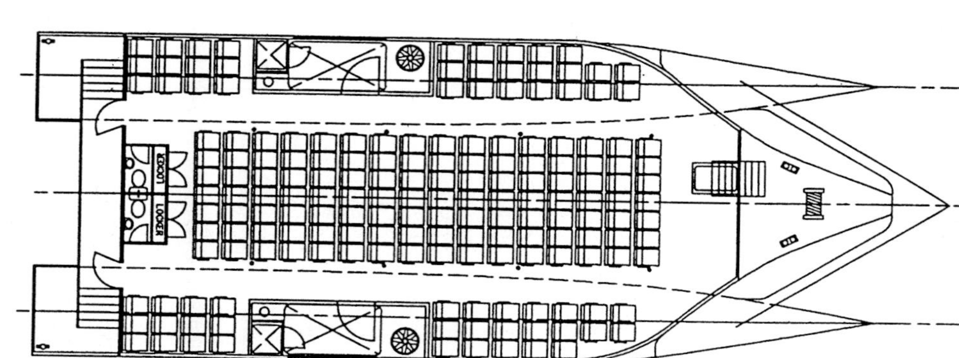

General arrangement of AMD150
1995

COMMONWEALTH OF INDEPENDENT STATES

SUDOEXPORT

11 Sadovaya Kudrinskaya, Moscow 123231, Russia, CIS

Tel: +7 (095) 252 4401
Telex: 411116 KURS
Fax: +7 (095) 200 2250

Vladimir A Chmyr, *General Director*
Vjacheslav V Yanchenko, *Director of Imports*
Yuri I Fomichev, *Director of Exports*

In 1995 three catamaran designs were being marketed by Sudoexport in the range of 31.8 to 49.3 m, and aimed at the river and coastal route markets.

ANDROMEDA (DESIGN)

Specifications

Length overall	31.8 m
Beam	10 m
Draught	1.8 m
Passengers	180
Propulsive power	2 × 809 kW

Max speed	30 kts
Operational speed	27 kts
Range	300 n miles

Propulsion: The main engines are 2 × Zvezda M401 A-2 diesels, 809 kW max each, at 1,550 rpm.

IMPULSE (DESIGN)

Specifications

Length overall	35 m
Beam	12.5 m
Draught	2.6 m
Passengers	400
Max speed	36 kts
Operational speed	33 kts
Range	300 n miles

Propulsion: The main engines are 2 × MTU 16V 396 TB 84.

PERSEUS (DESIGN)

Specifications

Length overall	49.3 m
Beam	10 m
Draught	2 m
Passengers	140
Propulsive power	2 × 3,675 kW
Max speed	40 kts
Operational speed	37 kts
Range	250 n miles

Propulsion: The main engines are 2 × Zvezda M504B-3 diesels, 3,675 kW each at 2,000 rpm.

VERIFIED

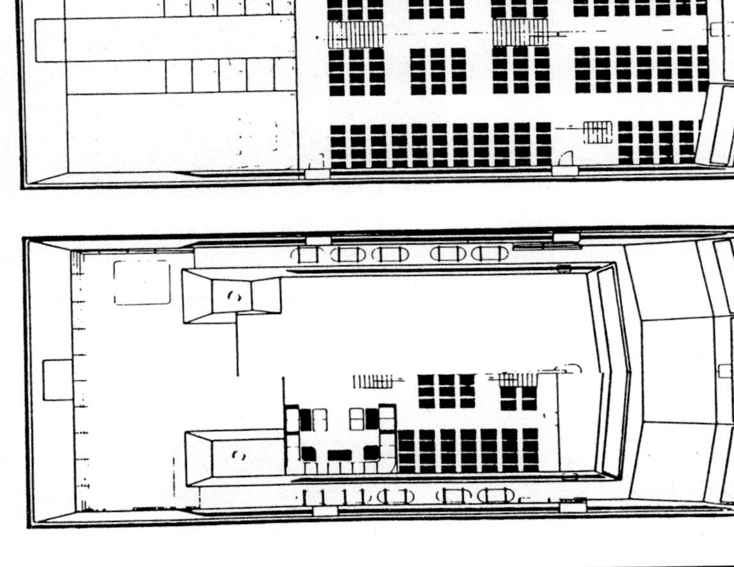

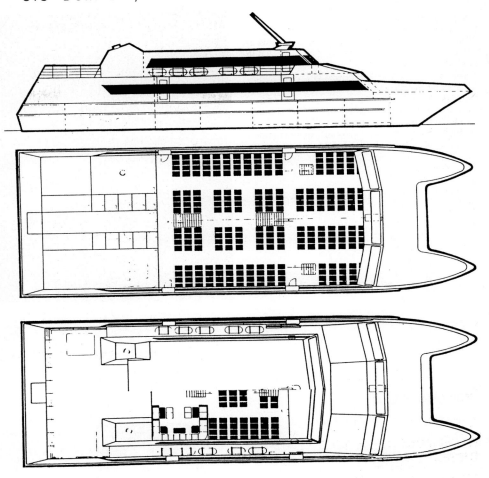

General arrangement of Impulse

DENMARK

DANYARD A/S

Kragholmen 4, PO Box 719, DK-9900 Frederikshavn, Denmark

Tel: +45 (98) 422299
Fax: +45 (98) 432930

Jens Viskinge Jensen, *President and CEO*
Gunnar Lage, *Executive President*
Christian Rodin-Nielson, *Vice President, Sales*
Niels Knudsen, *Vice President, Project Design*

Danyard has developed a series of fast ferries designated Seajet. The series consist of vessels from 60 to 96 m in length capable of carrying a deadweight in the range from 100 to 535 t. In addition to passengers the ferries are designed to carry cars, mobile homes, buses and trucks, depending on the Seajet specification. The Seajet is driven by water-jets connected to either gas turbines or high speed diesel engines.

Seajet is a lightweight aluminium construction and is designed on the basis of the innovative semi-SWATH hull form developed by Danyard in co-operation with NQEA Australia Pty Ltd. The semi-SWATH design minimises the heave and pitch movements, and lowers the acceleration forces imposed on passengers. The result is a ferry with excellent sea-keeping properties that ensure passengers a smooth ride, with the best possible comfort.

SEAJET 250

Two Seajet 250s were ordered by the Danish ferry operator Mols-Linen in 1994 for delivery in Spring 1996. The vessel is designed to operate on a route between Zeeland and Jutland. The high service speed allows one hour operation (45 minute transit time and 15 minute turn around time). To ensure the fast turn around time the vessel has been optimised to very short time in harbour by means of a large card deck allowing for unloading and loading simultaneously, and a large passenger deck fitted with large stairways to the card deck.

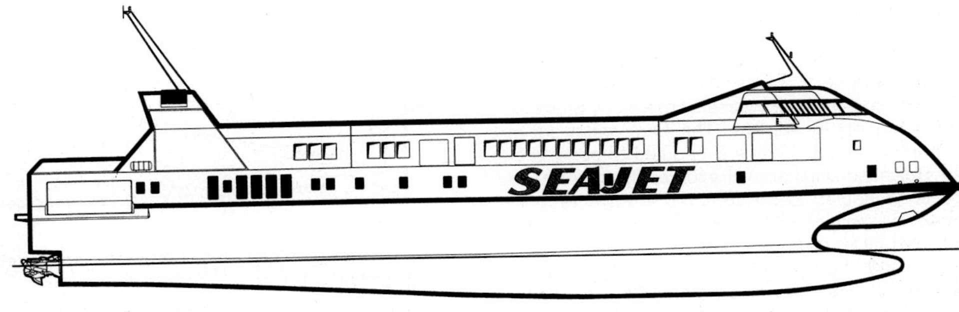

Seajet 250 side elevation

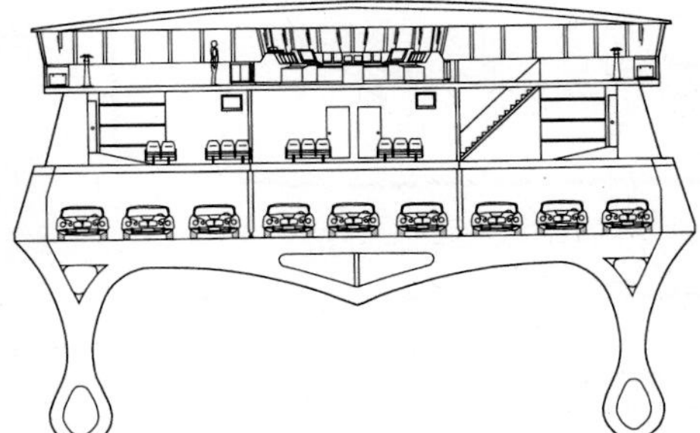

Seajet 250 transverse section

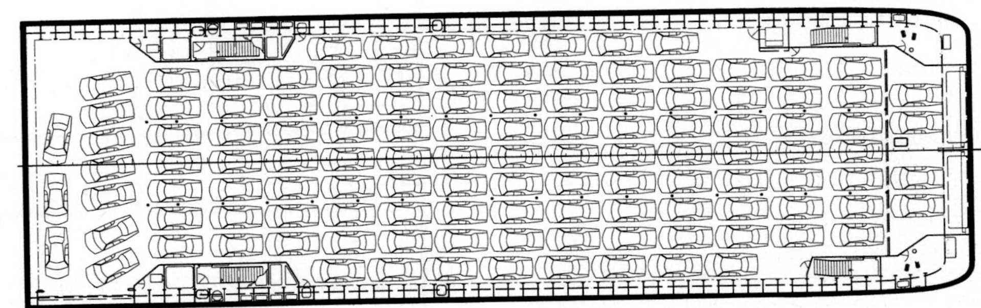

Seajet 250 car deck arrangement

1996

Specifications

Length overall	76 m
Beam	23.4 m
Draught	3.4 m
Passengers	450
Vehicles	120
Operational speed	43.6 kts

Classification: DnV R3 EO.
Propulsion: The main engines are 2 × LM 1600 gas-turbines; driving four KaMeWa water-jets.
Control: Ride control optional, recommended above significant 2.5 m wave height.

UPDATED

Artist's impression of Seajet 250
1994

FINLAND

FINNYARDS LTD

PO Box 139, SF-261 01 Rauma, Finland

Tel: +358 (38) 83611
Telex: 65117 FYARD SF
Fax: +358 (38) 836 2366

Aarno Mannonen, *President*

Finnyards Ltd was incorporated and became operational in January 1992, combining the total resources and facilities of Rauma Yards and Hollming Ltd, two leading shipyards located adjacent to one another in the city of Rauma, Finland. Since 1992 the company has invested heavily in new dry-dock and aluminium production facilities with an aluminium handling capability of 2,000 tonnes per annum and a steel capacity of 35,000 tonnes per annum. The shipyard employs some 1,900 people.

In July 1993 Finnyards received an order for two of the largest high-speed catamaran ferries to date. Ordered by Stena AB, the contract was worth in excess of $200 million. The design of the vessel was undertaken by Stena Rederi and is codenamed Stena HSS (High-speed Sea Service). A third craft was ordered in 1994 with an option for a further vessel.

Stena HSS

There have been three vessels ordered by Stena AB for operation in the UK. The first vessel to be delivered in early 1996 is scheduled to operate on the Holyhead-Dun Laoghaire route. The second vessel is scheduled to be delivered in April 1996 for operation between Stranraer and Belfast and the third vessel is currently scheduled to be delivered in Spring 1997.

The hull design is of a patented narrow hulled catamaran semi-Swath form designed to DnV certification with a service speed of 40 knots in a significant wave height of 5 m.

Specifications

Length overall	120 m
Beam	40 m
Passengers	1,500
Vehicles	375 cars or 50 lorries + 100 cars
Operational speed	40 kts

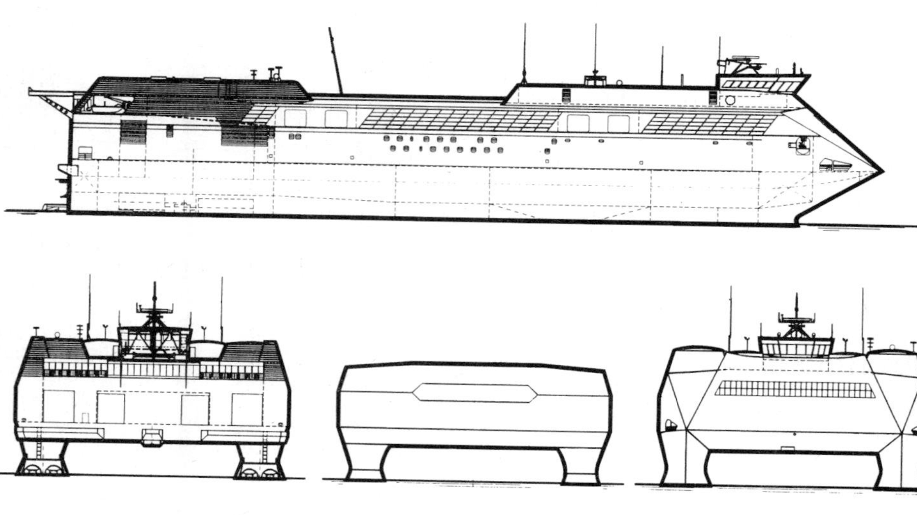

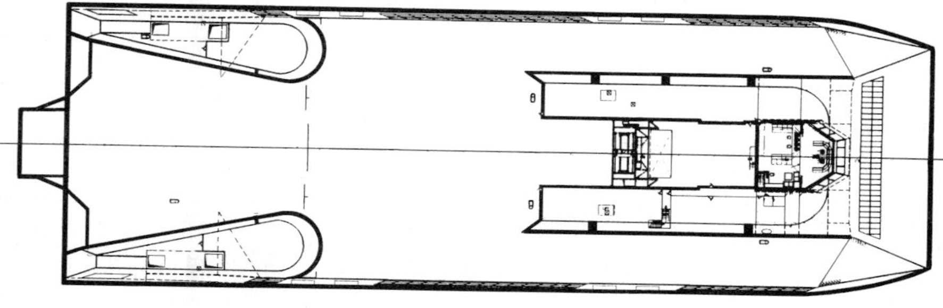

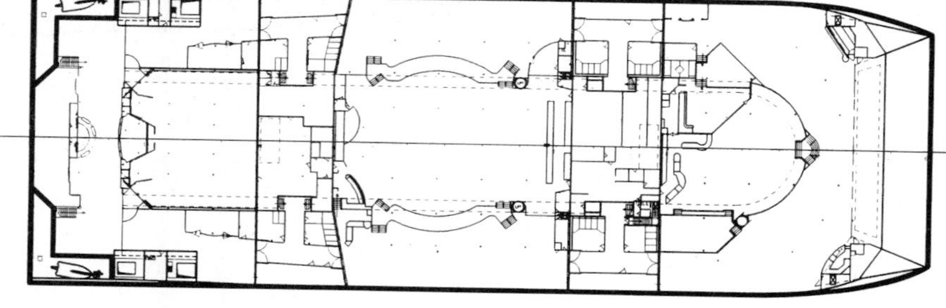

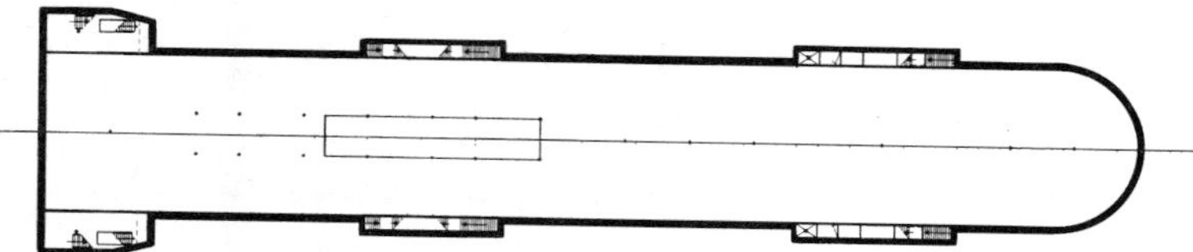

General arrangement of the Stena HSS
1996

Propulsion: The vessel is fitted with four gas-turbines, one General Electric/Kværner LM 1600 and one LM 2500 turbine in each hull. The turbines will drive through a MAAG gearbox to two KaMeWa 760 SII water-jets. This arrangement of the gas-turbines allows the vessel to cruise at 24 knots on the two LM 1600s, at 32 knots on the two LM 2500s and at 40 knots on all four.

102 m FAST FERRY (DESIGN)

Finnyards is currently marketing a new range of catamaran ferries from 100 to 170 m in length with speeds of between 30 and 45 knots. Besides its own research and development work, Finnyards is actively taking part in two development programmes, the Shipyard 2000 Ultralight vessel study in Finland and the Nordic dynamically loaded light construction programme.

The 102 m vessel is one variant of their design study and is capable of carrying 920 passengers and 266 cars at speeds of up to 40 knots with a power requirement of 33 MW.

UPDATED

Stena HSS on trials **1996**

Stena HSS main saloon showing the full height windows and combined structural cross bracing **1996**

Stena HSS under construction showing the main aluminium hull and composite bow structure **1996**

FRANCE

CONSTRUCTIONS ALUMINIUM NAVALES SARL

Quatali de la Cabaude, F-85100 les Sables d'Olonne, France

Tel: +33 93 47 30 30
Telex: 710 775 F
Fax: +33 51 21 20 06

Fabrice Epaud, *Commercial Director*

Ville de Toulon III

A 200-passenger, 20 knot vessel (length 25 m, beam 8 m) launched in 1987. The superstructure is of interest in that it is built up with tubular frames. Principal material of construction is aluminium AG 4 MC 5086. The craft is classified by Bureau Veritas.

Ville de Toulon III, *one of three catamaran ferries built to a design by Constructions Aluminium Navales sarl* **1992**

VERIFIED

IRIS CATAMARANS

Zone Industrielle, F-17290 Aigrefeuille, France

Tel: +33 46 35 70 40
Fax: +33 46 35 50 10

Jean François Fountaine, *Director*

The IRIS (InteR Islands Shuttle) project is a new multipurpose catamaran concept for the transportation of passengers, containers, or special cargo services for relatively short voyages.

The catamaran design consists of an open platform suspended between the two hulls, with the bridge situated at the forward end of this platform. Passenger modules having the dimensions of 40 ft containers, or of course containers, can be mounted on this platform.

Three designs are offered, all using the same hulls but different bridgedeck structures and propulsion packages.

IRIS 4.1

This version can carry four container-sized modules.

Specifications

Length overall	40 m
Length waterline	38 m
Beam	10.4 m
Draught	1.27 m
Payload	35 t (includes modules)
Passengers	160
Fuel capacity	5,060 l
Water capacity	750 l
Propulsive power	2 × 960 kW
Max speed	32 kts
Operational speed	26.6 kts
Range	300 n miles

Classification: DnV +1A1 HSLC R2 Passenger.
Structure: The main construction material is vacuum bagged GRP-Sandwich. This method is used to construct the hulls, control station, after deck and passenger modules; but all shock sensitive areas are single skin laminate. The transverse beams that support the bridgedeck structure are to be built from aluminium alloy and joined to the hulls on heavily reinforced watertight bulkheads.
Propulsion: The main engines are 2 × Deutz MWM TBD 616 V16 diesels, each producing 960 kW; driving 2 × Lips LJ 64 DL water-jets.

IRIS 6.1

This version can carry six container-sized modules.
Specifications

Length overall	40 m
Length waterline	38 m
Beam	12.74 m
Draught	1.48 m
Payload	51 t (includes modules)
Passengers	240
Fuel capacity	5,060 l
Water capacity	1,100 l
Propulsive power	2 × 1,524 kW
Max speed	33 kts
Operational speed	30 kts
Range	300 n miles

Classification: DnV +1A1 HSLC R2 Passenger.
Structure: The construction is similar to the IRIS 4.1.
Propulsion: The main engines are 2 × Deutz MWM TBD 620 V12 diesels, each producing 1,524 kW; driving 2 × Lips LJ 70 DL water-jets.

IRIS 6.2

This version can carry six container-sized modules, with two floors.
Specifications

Length overall	40 m
Length waterline	38 m
Beam	12.74 m
Draught	1.68 m
Payload	72 t (includes modules)
Passengers	384
Fuel capacity	10,600 l
Water capacity	1,800 l
Propulsive power	2 × 2,032 kW
Max speed	36 kts
Operational speed	31.6 kts
Range	300 n miles

Classification: DnV +1A1 HSLC R2 Passenger.
Structure: The construction is similar to the IRIS 4.1.
Propulsion: The main engines are 2 × Deutz MWM TBD 620 V16 diesels, each producing 2,032 kW; driving 2 × Lips LJ 70 DL water-jets.

NEW ENTRY

GERMANY

ABEKING AND RASMUSSEN SHIPYARD

PO Box 1160, D-27805 Lemwerder, Germany

Tel: +49 421 6733 532
Fax: +49 421 6733 115

This yard was established in 1907 and has since then become well known for its construction of high-quality fast military patrol vessels and minesweepers and a range of special utility craft and large motor and sailing yachts.

In 1995 the company signed an agreement with Lindstøls Skips of Norway to jointly build two 27.5 m catamarans to a Lindstøls design for operation in Germany. Brief details of these craft are given under the Lindstøls Skips entry.

NEW ENTRY

HDW

Howaldtswerke-Deutsche Werft AG

PO Box 6309 Werftstrasse 112-114, D-24143 Kiel, Germany

Tel: +49 (431) 700 2799/2314
Telex: 292288-0 HDW D
Fax: +49 (431) 700 3374/3388

Howaldtswerke-Deutsche Werft AG is a member of the Preussag Group and one of the largest shipbuilding companies in Germany. The production programme covers all types of merchant ships especially large container ships, ferries and cruise liners, LPG and LNG carriers and crude oil tankers. As well as conversions and repairs the naval construction covers the production of submarines, frigates and corvettes. The yard participates in substantial research and development projects in which it has gained a thorough knowledge of advanced marine technologies. It is currently participating in the European research programme 'Eurofast' for flexible advanced sea transportation.

Artist's impression of HDW Cargo Cat (design) ***1992***

CARGO CAT (DESIGN)

The Cargo Cat project was launched at the beginning of 1991 as part of a three-year research project on fast multihull vessels. This joint industry project is supported by the German Ministry of Research and Development and HDW is focusing on cargo and combined passenger cargo transport. The basic design features symmetrical hard-chined hulls, built in aluminium; the use of steel is being examined. Propulsion will be achieved by gas-turbine or diesel-driven water-jet installations. The engine room will be fully automated.

The deck will give enough space for ro-ro or lo-lo cargo, with a payload capacity of about 400 tonnes, depending on service speed and route distance. The basic design can be easily adapted for passenger/car ferry service.
Specifications

Length overall	78 m
Beam overall	26 m
Draught	2.5 m
Payload	400 t
Operational speed	36 kts

VERIFIED

ULTIMAR GmbH & Co KG

Am Seedeich 39, D-27572 Bremerhaven, Germany

Tel: +49 (203) 597893
Fax: +49 (203) 511212

Rolf Verson, *Director*

ULTIMAR 62

The Ultimar 62 is a fast catamaran in a pleasure craft configuration with a range of 600 n miles and a service speed of 35 knots. In June the vessel completed the trip from London to Monte Carlo in the record time of 89 hours total and a running time of 75 hours, averaging 29 knots.

The Ultimar is a deep V catamaran with excellent sea-keeping and outstanding economy due to its hydrofoil system.

The hull deck and superstructure are built in carbonfibre honeycomb composite at a total hull weight of only 7.5 tonnes.

Propulsion consists of 2 MAN diesel engines connected directly via propshafts to Hamilton water-jets.

Specifications

Length overall	19.6 m
Beam	6 m
Draught	1 m
Draught, foilborne	0.5 m
Displacement, max	27 t
Max speed	40 kts

HYSUCAT OFFSHORE

Nordblitz

This fast ferry was launched in 1994 and is of a similar design to the Ultimar 62, and uses the same patented hydrofoil system. These foils are arranged to carry 50 per cent of the ship's weight, and have no controllable flaps or other such moveable surfaces. The foils increase the hull's efficiency and also improve the seakeeping of the craft.

Specifications

Length overall	21.55 m
Length waterline	18.80 m
Beam	7.50 m
Draught	1.35 m
Passengers	118
Propulsive power	2 × 750 kW
Max speed	40 kts
Operational speed	36 kts

Classification: The craft is designed to the IMO code for high-speed craft.

Propulsion: The main engines are 2 × high-speed diesels each producing 700 kW at 2,000 rpm, driving 2 × controllable pitch propellers. The propellers operate in tunnels in the hull's underside, which increases the propulsion efficiency and allows a shallower draught, (the draught was limited to 1.5 m at the design stage).

The Ultimar 62 **1993**

HYSUCAT RIVER

Rheinjet

This 70 passenger fast ferry was launched in 1994 and also uses the Hysucat patented foil system, although simplified for river operations.

Specifications

Length overall	17.80 m
Length waterline	15.00 m
Beam	6.00 m
Draught	1.30 m
Passengers	60
Propulsive power	2 × 450 kW
Max speed	40 kts
Operational speed	38 kts

Propulsion: The main engines are 2 × high-speed diesels each producing 450 kW, driving 2 × controllable pitch propellers operating in tunnels.

UPDATED

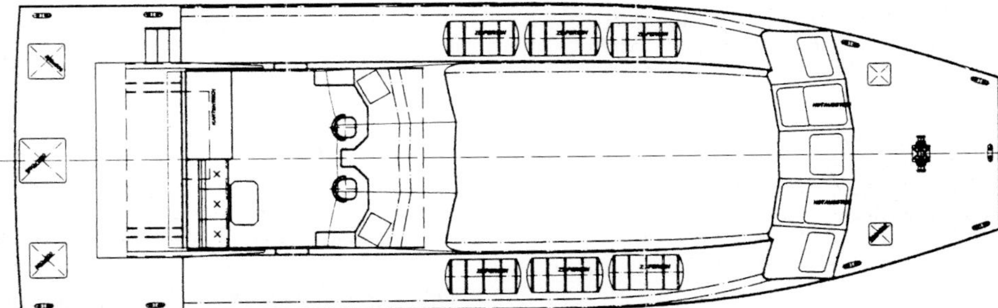

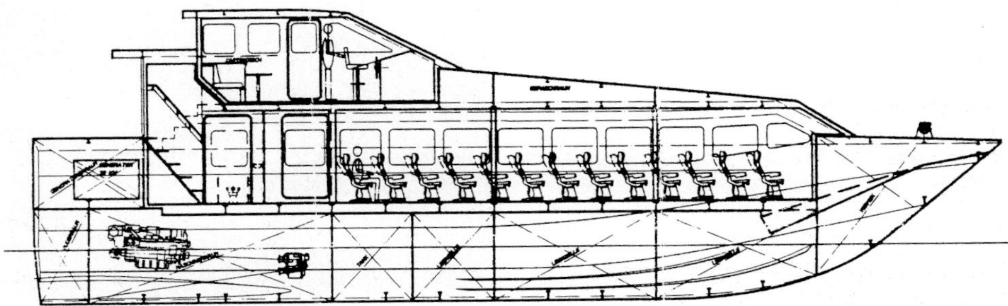

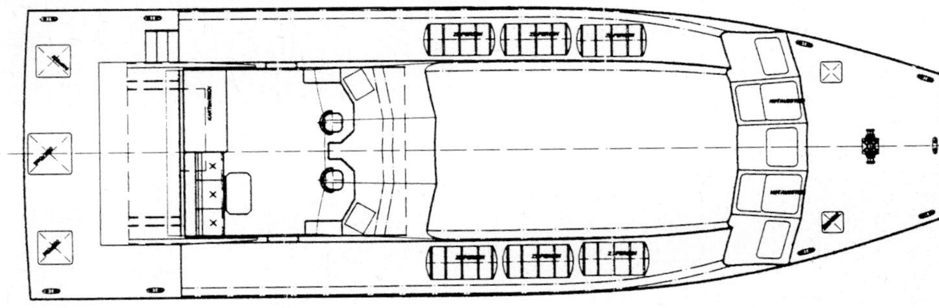

Layout of the Nordblitz **1995**

HONG KONG

A FAI HIGH PERFORMANCE SHIPS LTD

NKML31, Lai Chi Kok, Kowloon, Hong Kong

Tel: +852 741 0981
Telex: 45517 AFES HX
Fax: +852 786 2414
E-mail: afai@iohk.com

Vitus Szeto, *General Manager*

A Fai has been an InCat licensee since the early 1980s and has built 13 catamarans to their design. Since 1990 the company has concentrated on fast catamaran vessels designed by Advanced Multihull Designs Pty Ltd (AMD).

CA3 AIRPORT RESCUE BOAT

A Fai delivered an InCat 23 m airport rescue catamaran to the Hong Kong Government's Civil Aviation Department in July 1990. In addition to providing rescue services at Kai Tak airport, the vessel is also equipped for firefighting duties. Standard crewing is seven men.

Intended to be normally operated only within class I and II waters, it is designed to withstand minimum wave heights of 1.2 m at speeds of at least 25 knots. Forward there is a wheelhouse with a floor 1 m above the main deck level to give the crew a good all-round view. A firefighting monitor is mounted on the roof of the wheelhouse.

An emergency recess with two stairways is provided on each side of the vessel, the length of the rescue recess platforms being at least 2.5 m to facilitate the easy handling of stretchers. Aluminium fold-up panels with non-skid steps are fitted at each side of the recesses to allow survivors in the water to climb on board.

An awning aft of the wheelhouse is high enough to provide ample headroom for two tiers of stretchers and not restrict rearward visibility from the wheelhouse. Below the awning, there are three floodlights on each side to illuminate the deck area after dark.

Six rows of seats located port and starboard adjacent the outer awning supports are used as weathertight lockers for rescue equipment. Total rescue capability of the design is 32 people on stretchers, 64 on the seats and at least 154 standing. With the two diesels operating at their continuous rating of 550 kW at 2,000 rpm and leaving base with 2,400 litres of fuel on board, endurance is 4.5 hours.

Craft built	Completed	Seats	Speed	Delivered to	Route
21 m *Mingzhu Hu*	January 1982	150	29 kts	Ning Bo Hua Gang Co Ltd, Zhe Jiang Province, China	Hong Kong to Inland River
21 m *Yin Zhou Hu*	March 1982	150	29 kts	Ning Bo Hua Gang Co Ltd, Zhe Jiang Province, China	Hong Kong to Inland River
21 m *Liuhua Hu*	September 1982	150	29 kts	Guangdong Province, Hong Kong, Macao Navigation, China	Hong Kong to Taiping
21 m *Li Jiang*	June 1983	150	29 kts	Kwai Kong Shipping Co Ltd, Hong Kong	Hong Kong to Wuzhou
16 m *Kwong Fai*	June 1984	40	21 kts	Castle Peak Power Co Ltd, Hong Kong	Hong Kong
21 m *Yue Hai Chun*	October 1984	169	29 kts	Shen Zhen Shipping, China	Shekou to Zhu Hai
21 m *Shen Zhen Chun*	July 1985	169	29 kts	Shen Zhen Shipping, China	Shekou to Zhu Hai
21 m *Zhu Hai Chun*	December 1986	169	29 kts	Shen Zhen Shipping, China	Shekou to Zhu Hai/Macau
22 m *Gong Bian 153*	August 1988	-	33 kts	Guang Zhou Custom Dept, China	Whampo and Pearl River Area (Patrol Boat)
22 m *Ling Nan Chun*	November 1988	187	28 kts	Shen Zhen Shipping, China	Shekou to Zhu Hai
22 m *Nan Hai Chun*	March 1989	187	28 kts	Shen Zhen Shipping, China	Shekou to Zhu Hai
23 m *CA3*	June 1990	250 rescue places	28 kts	Civil Aviation Department, Government (Airport Rescue Boat)	Hong Kong Class 1 and 2 Limit Area Hong Kong
23 m *Dong Fang Chun*	April 1991	197	28 kts	Shen Zhen Shipping, China	Shekou to Zhu Hai
28 m AMD200 *Jin Xing*	Early 1993	235	28 kts	Shen Zhen Shipping, China	Shekou to Zhu Hai
24 m AMD170 *Wuzhou*	Mid-1994	150	29 kts	Wuzhou Guangxi Navigation	-
17 m AMD60	Early 1995	72	27.5 kts	Fei Dong Shipping, China	-
14 m *Harbourjet 5*	April 1995	60	25 kts	Harbourjet Shipping Ltd	-
14 m *Harbourjet 6*	May 1995	60	25 kts	Harbourjet Shipping Ltd	-
15 m Aluminiumcat	Nov 1995	70	24 kts	-	-
15 m Aluminiumcat	Dec 1995	70	24 kts	-	-
14 m Aluminiumcat	Dec 1995	60	25 kts	-	-

The vessel is the 13th InCat design built by A Fai at its Hong Kong yard since 1982.

AMD200 *Jin Xing*

Constructed by A Fai to an AMD design for a Chinese customer, this 28 m AMD design was delivered in June 1993.

Specifications

Length overall	28 m
Beam	10.3 m
Draught	1.8 m
Passengers	242
Fuel capacity	8,000 l
Water capacity	1,000 l
Operational speed	25 kts

Classification: Chinese ZC (CCS).

Propulsion: Engines: two Deutz MWM TBD 604B V8, 840 kW each at 1,800 rpm (other engine options available).

Transmissions: two Reintjes WVS 430 gearboxes.

Thrust devices: two FP Propellers.

Electrical system: 380 V AC 3-phase, 220 V AC single phase, 24 V DC.

Generators: two 75 kVA.

Civil Aviation 3 *airport rescue boat*

1991

AMD170 Wuzhou **1995**

AMD170 *Wuzhou*
Constructed by A Fai Engineers to an AMD design for the Wuzhou Guangxi Navigation Co, this vessel was delivered in mid-1994.

Specifications

Length overall	24 m
Beam	8.9 m
Draught	1.8 m
Passengers	150
Fuel capacity	8,000 l
Operational speed	29 kts

Classification: Chinese ZC (CCS).
Propulsion: 2 × Issotta Fraschini ID 36SS12 diesels each driving a fixed-pitch propeller via a ZF BW460 reverse reduction gearbox.

UPDATED

AMD200 Jin Xing

1994

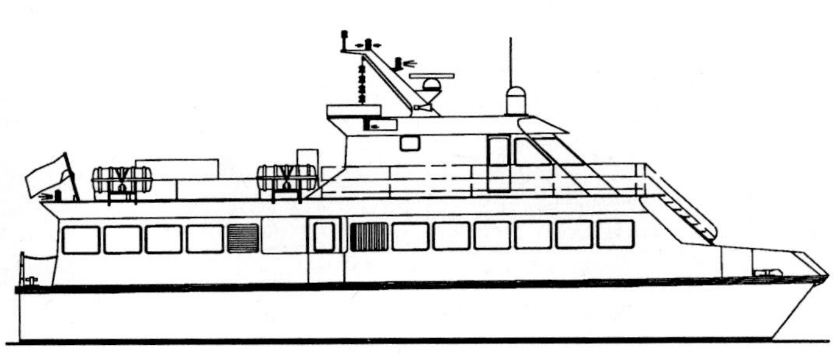

AMD170 PROFILE

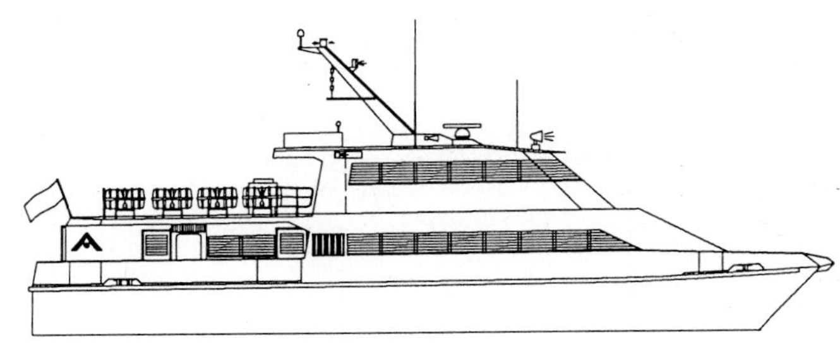

AMD200 PROFILE

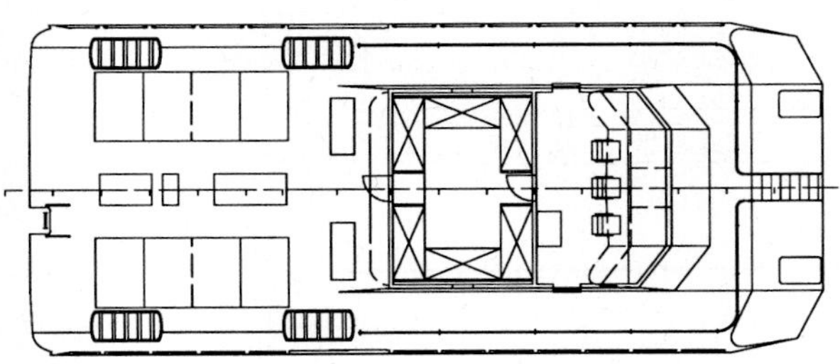

UPPER DECK

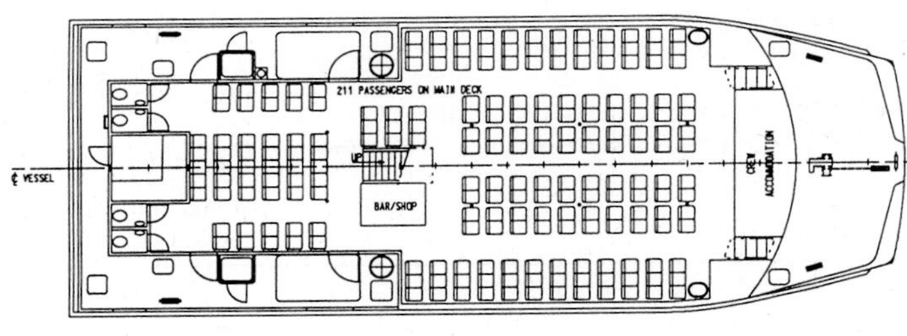

MAIN PASSENGER DECK : 211 PASSENGERS

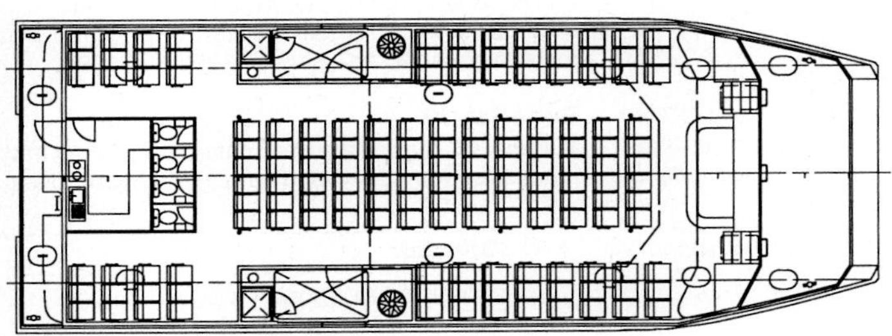

MAIN DECK : 150 PASSENGERS

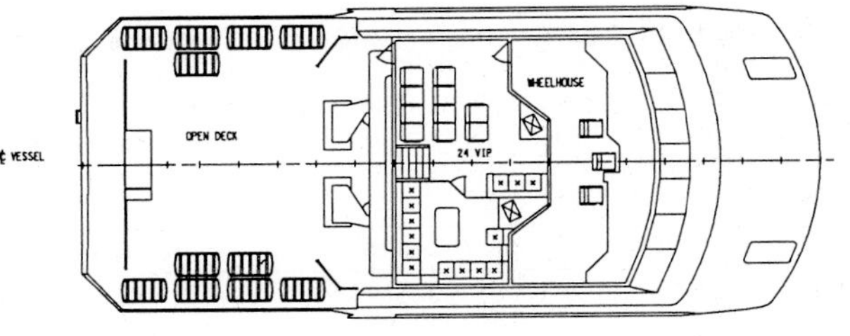

VIP LOUNGE AND UPPER DECK : 24 PASSENGERS

Layout of AMD170 conventional catamaran ***1994***

AMD200 built by A Fai Engineers, Hong Kong ***1994***

ITALY

MOSCHINI

Cantieri Ing Moschini SpA

Via De Nicola, 5, I-61032 Fano (PS), Italy

Tel: +39 (721) 854236/854484
Fax: +39 (721) 854934

Moschini are builders of high-speed monohull and catamaran vessels in Kevlar fibre and GRP structures.

21 m PASSENGER CATAMARAN (DESIGN)

Specifications

Length overall	21.2 m
Beam	7 m
Displacement, max	58 t
Passengers	200
Operational speed	23 kts

VERIFIED

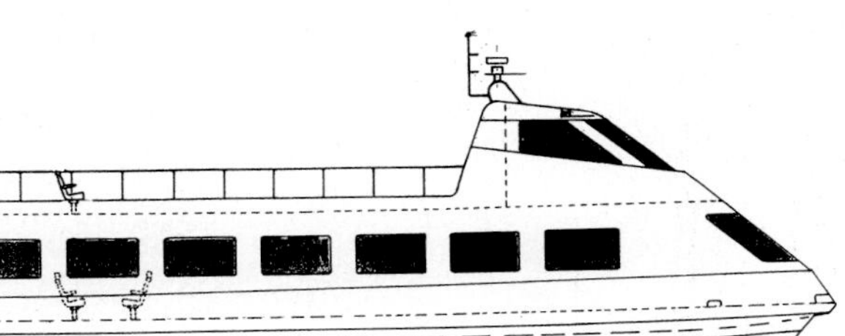

Moschini 21 m passenger catamaran (design)

RODRIQUEZ CANTIERI NAVALI SpA

Via S Raineri 22, I-98122 Messina, Italy

Tel: +39 (90) 7765
Telex: 980030 RODRIK I
Fax: +39 (90) 675294

Barbasso Gattuso, *President*
Giovanni Morace, *Managing Director*
Alcide Sculati, *Technical Manager*
Diego Mazzeo, *Sales and Marketing*

Seagull 400

1994

SEAGULL 400

Achernar

The Seagull 400 catamaran is based on extensive Rodriquez background in high-speed vessels and a study carried out since 1978. The vessel is built in light alloy, mostly welded but riveting is used wherever possible. The hulls are of symmetrical form.

The first vessel of this type was ordered by CAREMAR SpA and delivered to this Naples based operator in February 1993. The vessel is operated on the company's route from Naples to Capri.

Specifications

Length overall	43.25 m
Length waterline	36.4 m
Beam	10.9 m
Draught	1.45 m
Displacement, min	115 t
Displacement, max	150 t
Passengers	354
Propulsive power	2 × 2,000 kW
Max speed	34 kts
Range	200 n miles

Propulsion: Engines: 2 × MTU 16V 396 TE 74L, 2,000 kW each at 2,000 rpm, driving 2 × Kamewa 71 SII water-jets.

VERIFIED

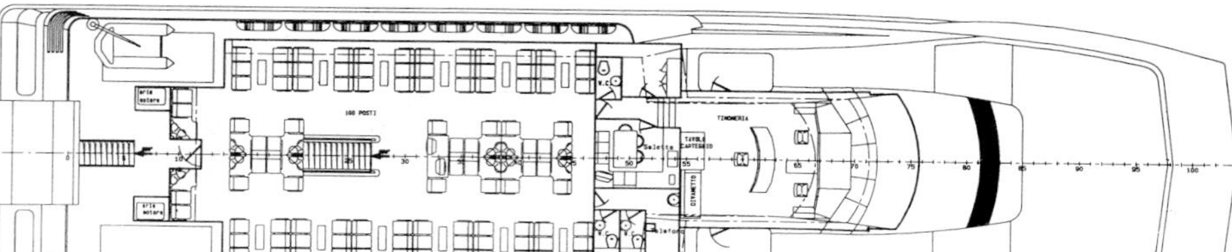

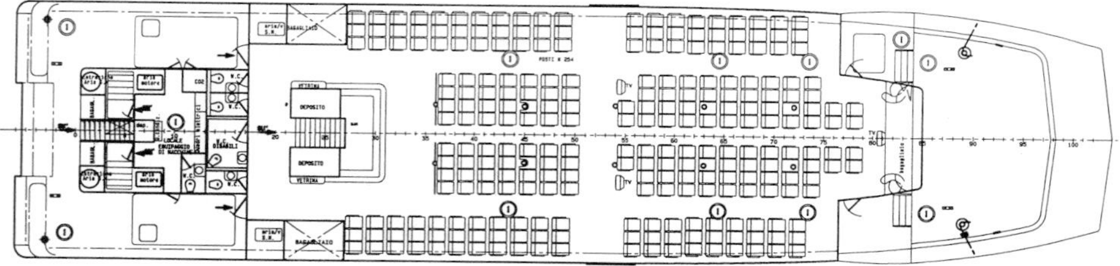

Seagull 400 deck layouts

1994

JAPAN

HITACHI ZOSEN CORPORATION

Head Office: 3-28 Nishi Kujo 5-chome, Konohana-ku, Osaka, 554 Japan

Tel: +81 (6) 466 7500
Telex: 63376 SHIPYARD J
Fax: +81 (6) 466 7572

T Arii, *General Manager*

Hitachi Zosen constructed a large number of PT-50 hydrofoils between 1960 and 1985 based on their technology license with Supramar of Switzerland.

The experience gained with these vessels lead to the development of the foil assisted Superjet-30 catamarans constructed between 1993 and 1994.

Superjet-30

Superjet-30 is a foil-assisted catamaran with a maximum speed of 40 knots. The hull is a hybrid design

Craft built (Superjet-30)	Yard No	Delivered	Seats	Operator
Trident Ace	7306	September 1993	160	Airport Awaji Aqualine Co Ltd
Artemis	7307	November 1993	160	Airport Awaji Aqualine Co Ltd
Apollon	7308	August 1994	160	Airport Awaji Aqualine Co Ltd
Dogo	7310	December 1993	156	Setonaikai Kisen Co Ltd
Miyajima	7312	April 1994	156	Setonaikai Kisen Co Ltd
Zuiko	7309	November 1993	156	Isizaki kisen Co Ltd
Shoko	7311	March 1994	156	Isizaki kisen Co Ltd

Superjet-30 Miyajima

1995

consisting of a catamaran and fully submerged foils. The lift of hydrofoils supports more than 80 per cent of the ship's weight. The control system of flaps and ailerons on the hydrofoils offers high sea-keeping capability.

Seven Superjet-30s were constructed at Hitachi Zosen Kanagawa Works.

Specifications

Length overall	31.5 m
Beam	9.8 m
Draught	1.9 m
Draught, hullborne	2.8 m (including foils)
Displacement	190 GRT
Passengers	200
Propulsive power	2 × 3,729 kW
Max speed	40 kts

Propulsion: The main engines are two high-speed diesel engines driving two water-jets.

Control: Motion control system provided.

UPDATED

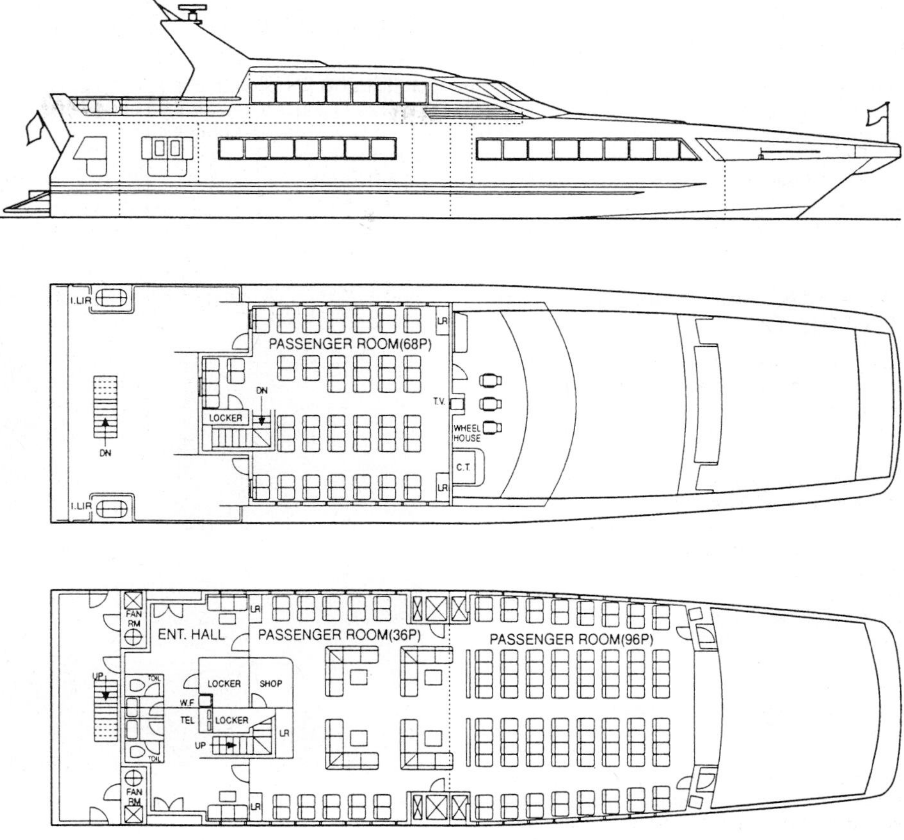

General arrangement of the Superjet-30 ***1994***

IHI

Ishikawajima-Harima Heavy Industries Company Ltd

Tokyo Chuo Building, 6-2 Marunouchi 1-chome, Chiyoda-ku, Tokyo 100, Japan

Tel: +81 (3) 3286 2353
Telex: 24104 IHISEN J
Fax: +81 (3) 3286 2435

Mikuni Komatsu, *General Manager*
Kenichiro Kondo, *Assistant Manager*

The Super Slender Twin Hull (SSTH) concept has been developed by IHI over the past five years. In 1991 the first SSTH project was launched called the SSTH 30. The concept has the benefits of displacement hulls, large loading deck space and, apart from the very high length-to-beam ratio of the hulls the design incorporates a double stage bow and a motion damping foil

SSTH 30 ***1993***

SSTH 90 (design) ***1995***

SSTH 30

This craft experiences vertical accelerations less than 0.1 g measured in head sea of 40 m wave length and 1 m significant wave height.

Specifications

Length overall	30.4 m
Beam	5.6 m
Passengers	68
Propulsive power	2 × 440 kW
Max speed	28.2 kts
Operational speed	21 kts

Propulsion: Engines: 2 × MTU 8V 183 TE 92 diesels, 440 kW (MCR) each.

SSTH 50 (DESIGN)

Specifications

Length overall	49.9 m
Beam	8 m
Draught	1.2 m
Passengers	320
Propulsive power	2 × 1,820 kW
Max speed	35 kts
Range	150 n miles

Structure: Hull material: welded aluminium.

Propulsion: Engines: 2 × 1,820 kW (MCR) diesels, driving 2 × water-jets.

SSTH 90 (DESIGN)

Specifications

Length overall	92.4 m
Beam	19.4 m
Draught	2.1 m
Payload	170 t
Passengers	400
Vehicles	80 cars
Propulsive power	4 × 5,150 kW
Max speed	42 kts
Range	200 n miles

Structure: Hull material: welded aluminium.

Propulsion: Engines: 4 × 5,150 kW high-speed diesels, driving water-jets.

SSTH 150 (DESIGN)

Passenger/car carrying high-speed ferry designed with steel hull and aluminium superstructure.

Specifications

Length overall	153.5 m
Beam	27.5 m
Draught	3.5 m
Passengers	1,000
Vehicles	300 cars
Propulsive power	2 × 20,600 kW
Max speed	37 kts
Range	400 n miles

Propulsion: 2 × gas-turbine engines each driving a water-jet unit.

SSTH 200 (DESIGN)

The SSTH 200 is a new all-steel design arranged for cargo and passenger operations.

Specifications

Length overall	199.9 m
Beam	29.8 m
Draught	4.9 m
Passengers	500
Propulsive power	2 × 20,600 kW
Max speed	32 kts
Range	600 n miles

Propulsion: 2 × LM 2500 19,800 kW gas-turbine engines each driving a water-jet propulsor.

VERIFIED

KAWASAKI HEAVY INDUSTRIES LTD SHIP GROUP

Tokyo Head Office: World Trade Center Building, 4-1 Hamamatsu-cho 2-chome, Minato-ku, Tokyo 105, Japan

Tel: +81 (3) 3435 2186
Telex: 2424371 KAWAJU J
Fax: +81 (3) 3436 3038

Kobe Works: 1-1 Higashi Kawasaki-cho 3-chome, Chou-ku, Kobe 650-19, Japan

Tel: +81 (78) 682 5120
Telex: 5623931 KHIKOB J
Fax: +81 (78) 682 5512

Ryunosuke Kawazumi, *Managing Director and Senior General Manager of Ship Group*

AMD1500 Kawasaki Jet Piercer, Hayabusa

1995

The concept design of wave piercing catamarans was introduced from Advanced Multi-Hull Designs Pty Ltd in 1990. Since then Kawasaki has been developing the design by conducting a wide range of tank tests, structural analysis and fire tests of aluminium structures.

Kawasaki Heavy Industries Ltd executed a construction contract between Maritime Credit Corporation of Japan and Kyushi Ferry Boat Co Ltd for a Kawasaki Jet Piercer AMD1500 in March 1994.

The keel of the vessel was laid at KHI's Kobe yard on 2 April 1994. The vessel, *Hayabusa*, was on trials by November 1994 and was delivered in December 1994. The vessel will be introduced on the route between Yawatahama, on the west coast of Shikoku, and Usuki, on the east coast of Kyushi by Kyushi Ferry Boat Company. The trip time will be reduced from 130 minutes to 90 minutes.

The design of the AMD1500 allows for two modes of operation. In car/passenger mode the vessel will carry 460 passengers and 94 cars at a maximum speed of 35 knots. In Freight mode the single vehicle deck can accomodate up to 24 twelve tonne freight trucks or 32 eight tonne freight trucks. This freight capacity results in a maximum deadweight of 570 tonnes. Such capacity provides flexibility for the operator allowing low season or night freight services for additional revenue.

AMD1500 KAWASAKI JET PIERCER
Hayabusa

Specifications

Length overall	100 m
Beam	19.98 m
Draught	3.1 m
Passengers	460
Vehicles	94 cars
Max speed	35.5 kts

Propulsion: 2 × Caterpillar 3616 and 2 × Caterpillar 3612 engines, driving 4 × Kawasaki KPJ-169A water-jets.

VERIFIED

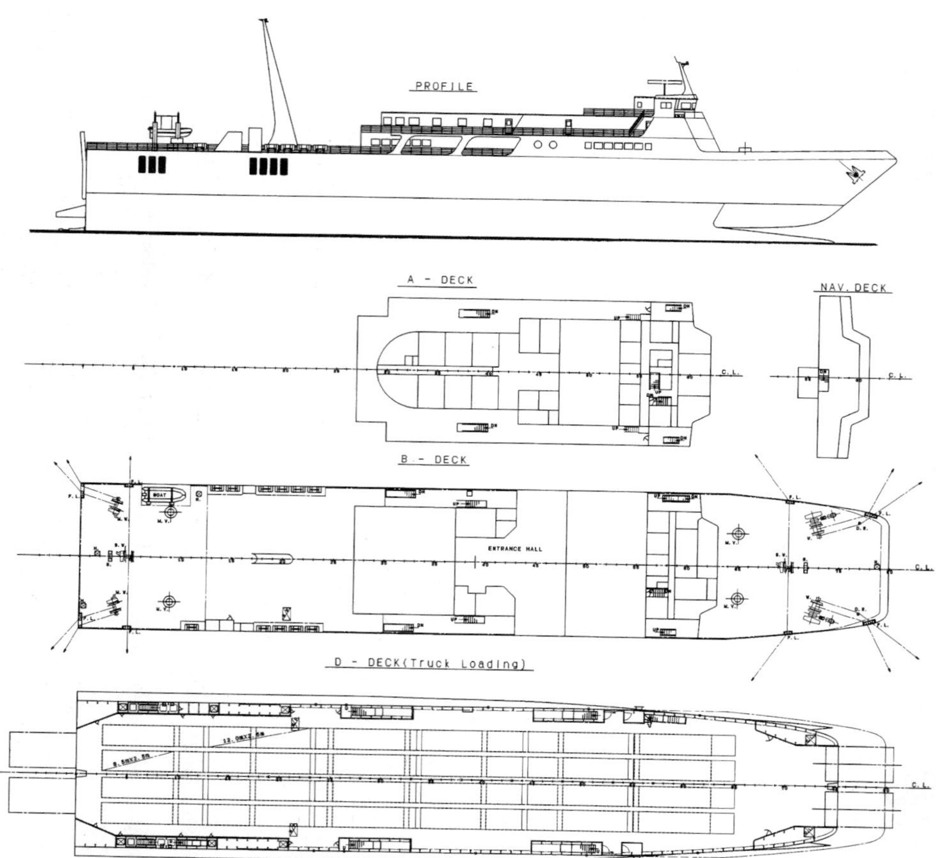

AMD1500 Kawasaki Jet Piercer

1995

MITSUBISHI HEAVY INDUSTRIES LTD

5-1 Maranouchi 2-chome, Chiyoda-ku, Tokyo, Japan

Tel: +81 (3) 3212 3111
Telex: 22443J
Fax: +81 (3) 3212 9822

HI-STABLE CABIN CRAFT (HSCC)
Ukishiro

Completed by Mitsubishi in the autumn of 1987 this prototype catamaran craft features a passenger cabin mounted on hydraulically actuated autostabilising rams. The cabin is centrally mounted on top of a 200 mm diameter central hydraulic jack having a stroke of 1 m. This supporting member is attached by a ball and socket joint to the hulls and positions the cabin completely clear of the hulls. Four other 85 mm hydraulic rams, attached with shock absorbers, support the cabin's four corners.

When motion of the basic catamaran craft occurs in heave, yaw, surge or sway, all hydraulic rams are activated simultaneously by an onboard computer (a 16 bit personal computer) with a rapid response

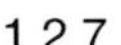

The Mitsubishi HSCC at sea **1989**

capability to monitoring sensors, thereby almost eliminating or minimising cabin motion. Trials have demonstrated reductions of cabin motion to one-third of the motion of the basic supporting catamaran structure.

The catamaran type was chosen as the basic vehicle because of its good stability characteristics and cabin width advantages. It is reported that the computer software required for the system was developed in a five-year study programme initiated by MHI and supported by the semi-governmental Japan Foundation for Shipbuilding Advancement.

Specifications

Length	12.7 m
Beam	5.4 m
Displacement	17 t (GRT)
Max speed	20 kts

Propulsion: 2 × Mitsubishi 239 kW diesels.
Operator: Higashi Chugoku Ryoju Kosan.

HI-STABLE CABIN CRAFT (HSCC)

Voyager

Following the prototype HSCC *Ukishiro* completed in 1987, Mitsubishi, in July 1990, completed a 200-passenger HSCC delivered to Nishi-Nippon Kaiun Kaisha Ltd

Specifications

Length overall	26.5 m
Beam	9 m
Draught	1.4 m
Displacement	132 (GRT)
Passengers	200
Max speed	18 kts

Propulsion: 2 × DDC 16V 92TA engines, 843 kW each.

SUPER SHUTTLE 400

Rainbow

Mitsubishi Supershuttle 400 *Rainbow* is the world's first diesel-driven hydrofoil catamaran. It was delivered to Oki Shinko Ltd in March 1993 and entered service in April 1993. Main engines, water-jets, foils and computerised ride control system were newly developed and manufactured by Mitsubishi Heavy Industries Ltd for this project.

Specifications

Length overall	33.3 m
Beam overall	13.2 m
Foil width	12.8 m
Displacement	302 t (GRT)
Passengers	341
Max speed	45.4 kts

Propulsion: 4 × Mitsubishi S16R-MTK-S diesel engines, 2,125 kW each, driving 2 × Mitsubishi MWJ-5000A water-jets
Operator: Oki Kisen Ltd

VERIFIED

Voyager

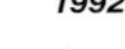
1992

Super Shuttle 400 Rainbow **1993**

MITSUI ENGINEERING & SHIPBUILDING COMPANY LTD

6-4 Tsukiji 5-chome, Chuo-ku, Tokyo 104, Japan

Tel: +81 (3) 3544 3462
Telex: 22821 J, 22924 MITZOSEN J
Fax: +81 (3) 3544 3031

Hiroshi Kitashima, *Director and General Manager, Ship and Ocean Project Division*
Yutaka Ikeda, *General Manager, Marine Department*

In 1978 Mitsui, employing its own design team, developed the Supermaran CP20HF, seating 195 passengers and with a cruising speed of about 30 knots. This craft has been redesigned for better seaworthiness and to operate in a maximum wave height of 2.5 m when comfortable service can be provided with no loss of speed. There were two delivered in March and June 1979.

The Supermaran CP30 was delivered to the Nankai Ferry Company Limited in Japan in July 1983. It carries 280 passengers at a cruising speed of 28 knots. The maximum operable wave height is 3 m and comfortable service is assured at a wave height of 2.5 m.

The Supermaran CP30 Mk II, *Marine Shuttle*, was introduced into service by the Tokushima Shuttle Line Company Ltd in February 1986. The vessel has a higher service speed than its predecessor the CP30, 32 knots against 28.1 knots.

A new type, the Supermaran CP10, *Marine Queen*, was delivered to the Sanzo Kigyo Company Ltd in April 1987, for cruising service in the Seto Inland Sea.

The two 280-seat Supermaran CP30 Mk IIIs, *Blue Star* and *Sun Rise*, entered service in 1987 with Tokushima, and a Supermaran CP30 Mk III, *Coral*, entered service in 1988 on the coastal route of the Shikoku Island facing to the Pacific Ocean.

They have a service speed of 32 knots and the improved seaworthiness and superior propulsive performance over the earlier CP20HF resulting from the improved hull form and their greater size.

Mitsui has, in addition, completed other high-speed catamarans, the Supermaran CP25 *Queen Rokko*, the Supermaran CP20 *Wakashio*, the Supermaran CP25 *New Tobishima*, the Supermaran CP5 *Mon Cheri* and the Supermaran CP15 *Aquajet I, II, III* and *IV* with water-jet propulsion. Five craft of the latest version Mightycat 40 with a maximum speed of over 40 knots have been completed, and a further CP15 and Mightycat 40 are currently under construction and scheduled to be delivered in March and June 1995 respectively.

Mitsui Supermaran CP20 Mk II Queen Rokko **1991**

Mitsui Mightycat 40 Neptune **1996**

Craft built (CP types)	Yard No	Completed	Seats	Delivered to
26.46 m CP20 Super Westamaran (ex-*Blue Hawk*)	-	1975	162	
26.46 m CP20 Super Westamaran (ex-*Marine Star*)	-	1976	180	
26.4 m CP20 Super Westamaran (ex-*Sun Beam*)	-	1978	188	
32.8 m CP20HF Supermaran *Sun Shine*	1600	March 1979	195	Tokushima Kosokusen Co Ltd
32.8 m CP20HF Supermaran *Blue Sky*	1601	June 1979	195	Tokushima Kosokusen Co Ltd
40.9 m CP30 Supermaran *Marine Hawk*	1603	July 1983	280	Nankai Ferry Co Ltd
41 m CP30 Mk II Supermaran *Marine Shuttle*	1604	February 1986	280	Tokushima Shuttle Line Co Ltd
21.67 m CP10 Supermaran *Marine Queen*	1607	April 1987	88	Kyowa Kisen KK
41 m CP30 Mk III Supermaran *Blue Star*	1605	June 1987	280	Tokushima Kosokusen Co Ltd
41 m CP30 Mk III Supermaran *Sun Rise*	1606	July 1987	280	Tokushima Kosokusen Co Ltd
41 m CP30 Mk III Supermaran *Coral*	1608	July 1988	250	
33.2 m CP25 Supermaran *Queen Rokko*	1609	June 1988	250	Awaji Ferry Boat Co Ltd
19.9 m CP5 Supermaran *Mon Cheri*	1610	July 1988	53	Tenmaya Marine Corporation
39 m CP25 Supermaran *New Tobishima*	1611	May 1989	300	Sakata City
33.2 m CP20 Supermaran *Wakashio*	1612	March 1989	96	Chiba Prefecture
34.2 m CP15 Supermaran *Aquajet I*	1613	March 1989	198	Kyodo Kisen Co Ltd
34.2 m CP15 Supermaran *Aquajet II*	1614	June 1989	198	Kyodo Kisen Co Ltd
34.2 m CP15 Supermaran *Aquajet III*	1616	November 1990	190	Kyodo Kisen Co Ltd
34.2 m CP15 Supermaran *Aquajet IV*	1617	January 1991	190	Kyodo Kisen Co Ltd
43.2 m Mightycat 40 *Sun Shine*	1618	June 1991	300	Tokushima Kosokusen Co Ltd
43.2 m Mightycat 40 *Soleil*	1619	September 1991	300	Tokushima Kosokusen Co Ltd
21.7 m CP10 Supermaran *Fusanami*	1620	February 1991	-	Chiba Prefecture
34.2 m CP20 Supermaran *Yumesaki*	1621	March 1992	83	Osaka City
43.2 m Mightycat 40 *Argo*	1622	December 1992	300	Nankai Ferry Co Ltd
43.2 m Mightycat 40 *Polar Star*	1623	March 1993	300	Tokushima Kosokusen Co Ltd
43.2 m Mightycat 40 *Venus*	1624	July 1993	300	Tokushima Kosokusen Co Ltd
43.2 m Mightycat 40 *Neptune*	1625	June 1995	300	Tokushima Kosokusen Co Ltd
30.3 m CP15 Supermaran *Marine Bridge*	1626	March 1995	235	Bantan Renraku Kisen Co. Ltd.

SUPERMARAN CP15
Aquajet I, II, III and IV
These catamaran passenger ferries have water-jet propulsion and were built for Kyodo Kisen Company Ltd. They entered service in 1988 to ply the route between Osaka, Kobe and Awaji Island.

Specifications

Length overall	34.2 m
Beam	8 m
Draught	1.2 m
Max speed	35 kts
Operational speed	31 kts

Propulsion: 2 × MTU 16V 396 TB 83, 1,469 kW (1,970 hp) each, at 1,940 rpm. These drive 2 × Kamewa water-jets S63.

SUPERMARAN CP15
Marine Bridge
This is the fifth CP15 passenger ferry although it differs in specification from the other four.

Specification

Length overall	30.33 m
Beam	8.30 m
Draught	1.3 m
Passengers	235
Max speed	32.8 kts
Operational speed	24 kts

Propulsion: The vessel is powered by two Niigata 12V16Fx diesel engines each rated at 1,324 kW at 1,900 rpm. Each engine drives a fixed pitch propeller via a reverse reduction gearbox.

SUPERMARAN CP20 Mk II
Queen Rokko
This is the catamaran double-decker cabin cruiser built for Awaji Ferry Boat Company in 1988.

Specifications

Length overall	33.2 m
Beam	9 m
Draught	1.5 m
Displacement	217 t
Passengers	250
Max speed	30 kts
Operational speed	25 kts

Propulsion: Two Deutz MWM 604B V12 engines, 1,278 kW (1,714 hp PS) each, at 1,800 rpm. These drive two fixed-pitch propellers through Niigata Converter MGN 433 EW gearboxes with electric variable propeller speed control device (reduction ratio 2.06:1).

Mitsui Supermaran CP15 Aquajet III **1990**

Mitsui Supermaran CP15 Marine Bridge **1996**

CATAMARANS	**Supermaran CP5**	**Supermaran CP10**	**Supermaran CP15**	**Supermaran CP20 Mk II**
Dimensions				
Length overall	19.9 m	21.67 m	34.2 m	33.2 m
Breadth	6 m	7.2 m	8 m	9 m
Draught	1.1 m	1.23 m	1.2 m	1.5 m
GRT, approx	50	80	154	–
Passengers	58	88	198	250
Crew	4	3	5	5
Main engines	GM 6V-92 TA	2 GM 12V-92 TA	2 MTU 16V 396 TB 83	2 MWM 604B V12
Max continuous rating, each	332 kW at 2,170 rpm	615 kW at 2,170 rpm	1,469 kW at 1,940 rpm	1,278 kW at 1,800 rpm
Continuous rating, each	–	492 kW	1,320 kW at 1,870 rpm	–
Max speed, approx	21 kts	26.6 kts	35 kts	30 kts
Service speed, approx	17 kts	21.8 kts	31 kts	25 kts
Endurance, approx	8 h	20 h	9 h	9 h

CATAMARANS	**Supermaran CP30**	**Supermaran CP30 Mk II**	**Supermaran CP30 Mk III**	**Mightycat 40**
Dimensions				
Length overall	40.9 m	41.9 m	41 m	43.2 m
Breadth	10.8 m	10.8 m	10.8 m	10.8 m
Draught	1.37 m full load	1.39 m full load	1.39 m full load	1.3 m
GRT, approx	283	268	270	300
Passengers	280	280	280	300
Crew	4	4	4	4
Main engines	2 × Ikegai 16PA4V185-VG	2 × Fuji Pielstick 16V 190 ATC	2 × Fuji Pielstick 12 PA4V 200 VGA	2 × Niigata 16 PA4V 200 VGA
Max continuous rating, each	1,801 kW at 1,475 rpm	2,050 kWs at 1,450 rpm	1,961 kW at 1,475 rpm	2,685 kW at 1,475 rpm
Continuous rating, each	1,700 kW at 1,475 rpm	1,700 kW at 1,425 rpm	1,845 kW at 1,400 rpm	2,550 kW at 1,450 rpm
Max speed, approx	31.1 kts	34 kts	35.1 kts	41 kts
Service speed, approx	28.1 kts	32 kts	32 kts	37 kts
Endurance, approx	10 h	8 h	8 h	5 h

SUPERMARAN CP30 Mk III

Sun Rise

This is a catamaran passenger ferry and the fourth one of the CP30 series built for Tokushima Kosokusen Company Ltd in 1987.

Specifications

Length overall	41 m
Beam	10.8 m
Depth	3.4 m
Draught	1.3 m
Passengers	280
Max speed	35 kts
Operational speed	32 kts

Propulsion: Two Fuji-Pielstick 12 PA4V 200 VGA engines, 1,961 kW each, at 1,475 rpm. The craft is propelled by two fixed-pitch propellers.

MIGHTYCAT 40

This is the latest catamaran class of passenger ferry of the CP30 series having the highest speed of all Japanese catamarans.

Six craft were built for Tokushima Kosokusen Company Ltd, Kyosho Kisen Company Ltd, Kobe Senpaku Company Ltd and Nankai Ferry Company Ltd.

Specifications

Length overall	43.2 m
Beam	10.8 m
Passengers	300
Max speed	41 kts

Propulsion: Two Niigata 16 PA4V 200 VGA engines, driving Kamewa 71S II water-jets.

UPDATED

NKK CORPORATION

Shipbuilding and Offshore Division:
1-1-2 Marunouchi, Chiyoda-Ku, Tokyo 100, Japan

Basic Ship Design Department:
2-1, Suehiro-Cho, Tsurumi-Ku, Yokohama 230, Japan

Tel: +81 (45) 505 7522
Fax: +81 (45) 505 7521

Kazuo Hayashi, *Product Development Manager*

In early 1991 the NKK Corporation announced the development of a high-speed catamaran project, the V-CAT. The company has built over 40 catamarans and has engaged in extensive research and development work on ultra-high-speed ships. Since July 1991 a 10 m sea-going test craft has been available for development trials.

The V-CAT is designed as a displacement vessel with special attention being given to the cross-sectional areas near the water surface, the upper side hull areas being particularly thin in order to reduce wave forces.

V-CAT vessels would be built in aluminium alloy, have water-jet propulsion and be powered with high-speed diesel engines; there are two versions proposed.

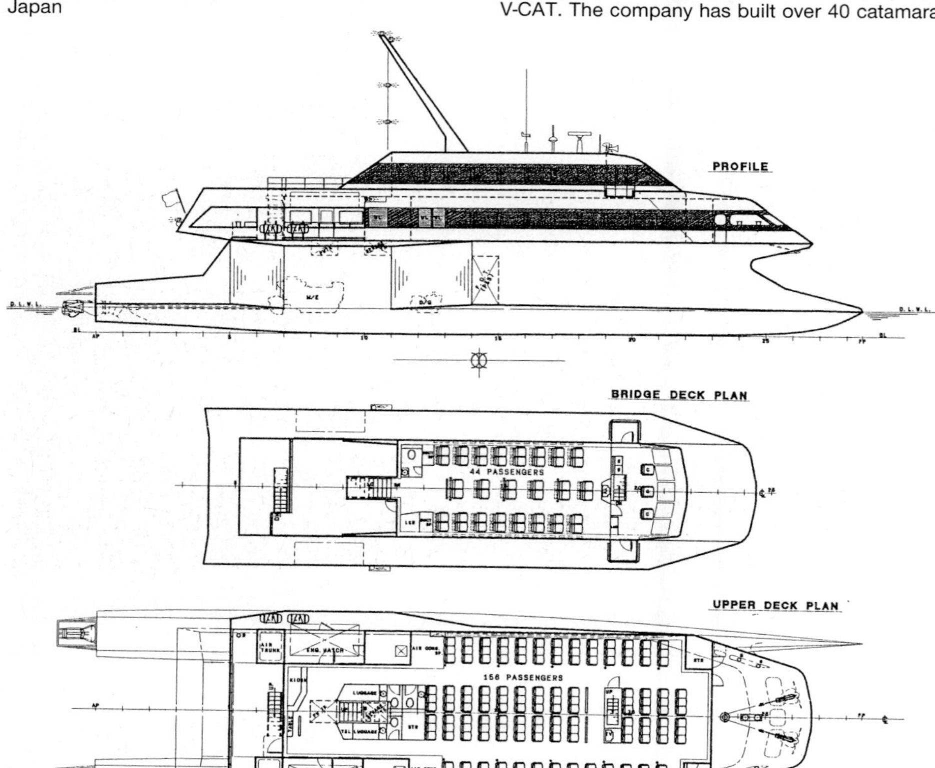

V-CAT (DESIGN)

200-passenger version

Specifications

Length overall	42 m
Beam	10.8 m
Draught	1.4 m
Passengers	200
Operational speed	40 kts

Propulsion: Main engines: 2 × high-speed diesels, MCR 2,386 kW.

V-CAT (DESIGN)

400-passenger version

Specifications

Length overall	52 m
Beam	15 m
Draught	1.6 m
Passengers	400
Propulsive power	2 × 3,878 kW
Max speed	40 kts

Propulsion: Main engines: 2 × high-speed diesels, MCR 3,878 kW.

VERIFIED

V-CAT 200-passenger ferry (design)

YAMAHA MOTOR COMPANY LTD

(Gamagori Shipyard) 2500 Shingai, Iwata, 438, Japan

Tel: +81 (538) 321145
Telex: 59645 J
Fax: +81 (538) 374250

29.1 m CATAMARAN TYPE 291

Two of these vessels were delivered in March 1989 to Tokyo Blue Cruises.

Built in GRP, they are powered by two DDC 16V 92TA 895 kW diesels driving five-blade propellers employing skew blades.

The most recent delivery of the Type 291, also to Tokyo Blue Cruises, was named *Bay Dream.*

Bay Dream

Yard No S-250.

Specifications

Length overall	29.1 m
Beam	8.1 m
Draught	2.05 m
Displacement, min	98.2 t
Crew	5
Passengers	182
Fuel capacity	5,000 l
Water capacity	2,000 l
Propulsive power	2 × 895 kW
Max speed	30.7 kts
Operational speed	23 kts (95% MCR, 70% load)
Range	200 n miles

Classification: J G certified for limited coastal water operation.

Propulsion: The main engines are 2 × DDC 16V 92TI, 895 kW each at 100% MCR.

Electrical system: Auxiliary engines: 4-stroke diesels, 1 × 48.5 kW at 1,800 rpm, 1 × 61 kW at 1,800 rpm; alternator: 3-phase AC, 1 × 50 kVA, 1 × 60 kVA.

Bay Bridge
Bay Frontier

Specifications

Details as for *Bay Dream* except as follows:

Displacement, 70% load	82 t
Passengers	230
Max speed	33 kts
Operational speed	25 kts

Electrical system: The auxiliary engines are 4-stroke diesels, 1 × 37.5 kW at 1,800 rpm, 1 × 35.2 kW at 1,800 rpm.

Alternator: 3-phase AC, 1 × 34.1 kVA, 1 × 20 kVA.

VERIFIED

Yamaha Motor Company Ltd catamaran Type 291 Bay Bridge ***1990***

KOREA, SOUTH

DAEWOO HEAVY INDUSTRIES LTD

541, 5-GA Namdaemun-ro-Jung-Gu, Seoul, Korea

Tel: +82 (2) 726 1911
Fax: +82 (2) 778 5423

Daewoo's Okpo shipyard has recently completed a 42 m 40 knot passenger catamaran for operation from Koje island to Pusan in South Korea. This is the first such craft constructed by Daewoo and the company is now marketing a range of vessels including a 37 m SES and an 80 m passenger/car ferry.

F-CAT 40 *Royal Ferry*

This all-aluminium vessel has been developed by Daewoo for Korea's domestic market. In order to achieve the high speed with acceptable sea-keeping qualities the design incorporates a foil extending between the two hulls. The vessel was delivered in late 1994.

Specifications

Length overall	40.25 m
Length waterline	37 m
Beam	9.3 m
Draught	1.48 m
Passengers	350
Vehicles	8
Fuel capacity	2 × 2,500 l
Water capacity	1,400 l
Propulsive power	2 × 2,000 kW
Max speed	40 kts
Operational speed	36 kts
Range	400 n miles

Classification: Korean Register.

Propulsion: 2 × MTU 16V 396 TE 74L diesels, producing 2,000 kW each at 2,000 rpm. Each drives a Kamewa 63 SII water-jet.

Electrical system: 2 × Cummins 6BT5.9G1(M) generators, 2 × Onan-Newage 75 kW alternators.

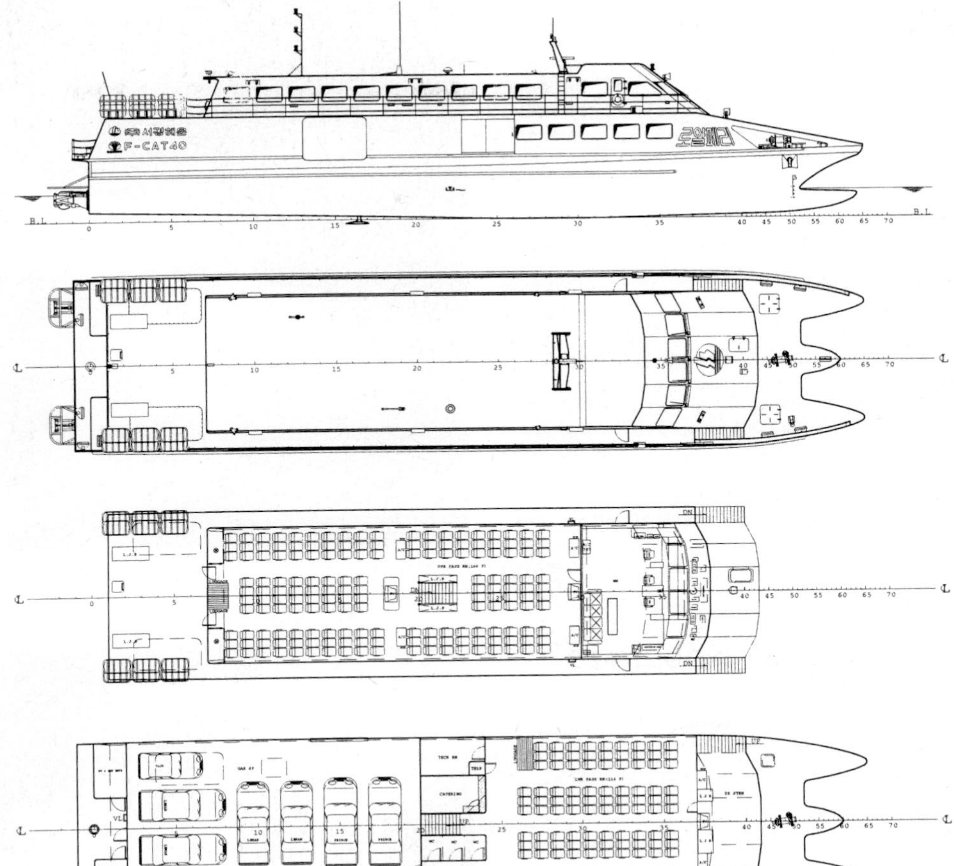

General arrangement of the F-CAT 40

1995

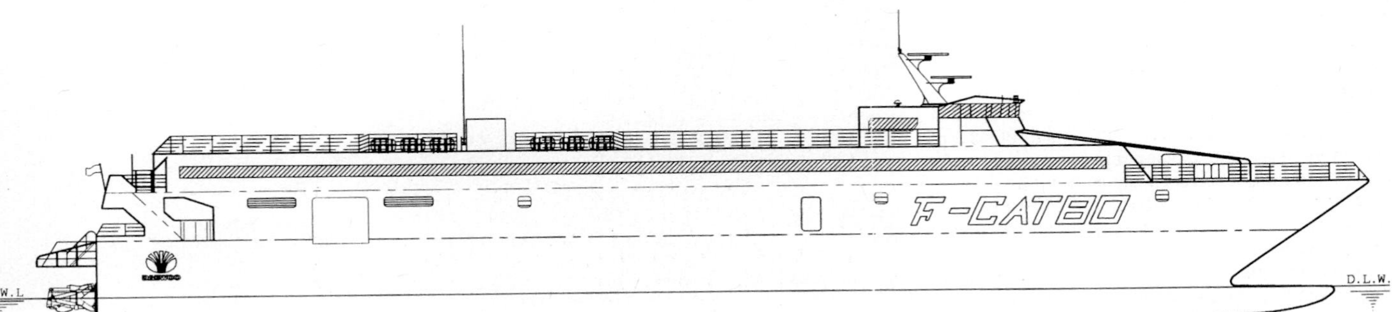

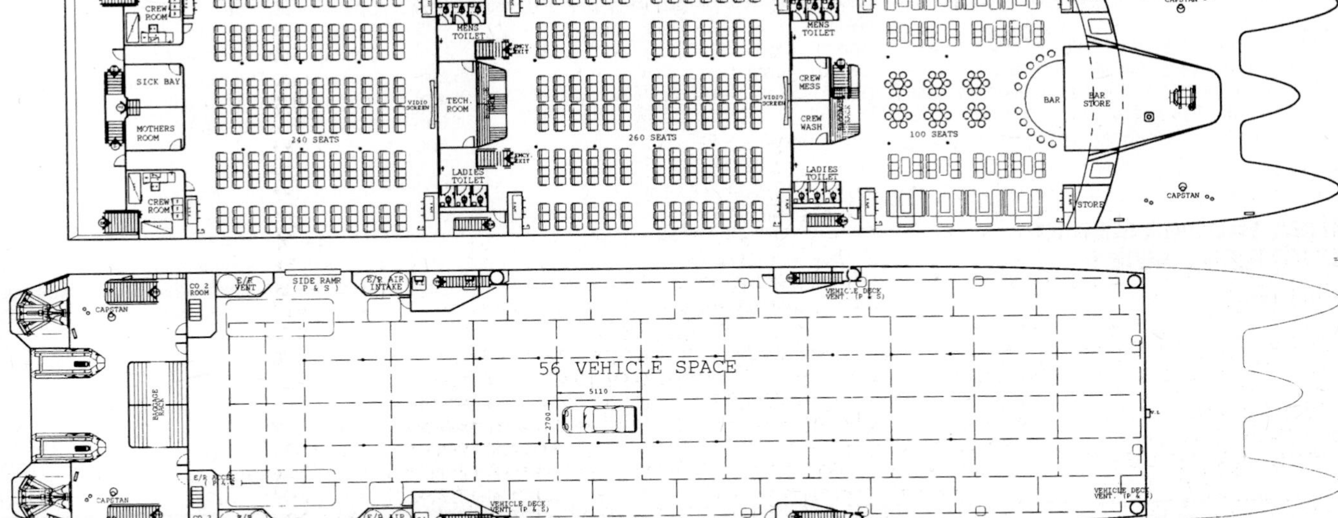

General arrangement of the F-CAT 80

1995

F-CAT 80 (DESIGN)

This 78 m catamaran design is based on the F-CAT 40 vessel but with the capability of transporting vehicles as well as passengers.

Specifications

Length overall	78 m
Length waterline	70.0 m
Beam	16.40 m
Draught	2.30 m
Payload	113 t
Crew	12
Passengers	600
Vehicles	56 cars
Fuel capacity	4 × 14000 l
Water capacity	6,350 l
Propulsive power	2 × 5,257 kW
Max speed	36 kts
Operational speed	33 kts

Classification: DnV +1A1 HSLC, Car ferry A, R1, EO.

Propulsion: The main engines are 2 × Caterpillar CAT3616 DITA, each producing 5,420 kW at 1,000 rpm, driving 2 × LIPS, LJ 140 DL water-jets via a reduction gearbox.

Electrical system: A Ssangyong-Cummins NT-855-GC6(M) generator, 250 kW, 450 V AC, 60 Hz, 3PH.

UPDATED

Royal Ferry ***1995***

HYUNDAI HEAVY INDUSTRIES COMPANY LTD

Head Office and Ulsan Works: 1 Cheonha-Dong, Dong-Ku, Ulsan, South Korea

Tel: +82 (522) 302841
Telex: 52452 HHIYARD K
Fax: +82 (522) 330491

Seoul Office and Special and Naval Shipbuilding Division:
140-2 Kye-Dong, Chongro-Ku, Seoul, South Korea

Tel: +82 (2) 746 4671/2
Telex: 28361/27496 HHIYARD K
Fax: +82 (2) 741 1152

45.5 m CATAMARAN FERRY

Han Ma Um Ho

A demand from a domestic customer for a high-speed passenger vessel for a 700 n mile round trip with more than 300 passengers was received in 1990. A comprehensive survey was undertaken of existing catamaran designs which motivated Hyundai to develop a design which could meet the long-range requirement and corresponding sea-keeping requirement. The sea-keeping capability has been met by incorporating a two-foil ride control system, the foils being positioned beneath the hulls at extreme forward and aft locations, and spanning the distance between the hulls. The company has previous experience of foil technology from their involvement in the build of an RHS 70 hydrofoil, Angel IX in 1985.

The design work began in August 1990 and was completed in mid-1991, supported by a large number of model tests both within and outside Hyundai Heavy Industries. The vessel with and without foils fitted, underwent instrumented sea trials throughout 1994. Data from this vessel are understood to be the basis of a much larger craft being developed by Hyundai.

Hyundai 45.5 m catamaran on trials (without foils fitted) ***1994***

Specifications

Length overall	45.5 m
Beam	11.4 m
Draught	1.6 m
Passengers	300
Propulsive power	3,061 kW
Operational speed	35 kts
Range	600-700 n miles

Classification: DnV +1A1 R170, EO, HSLC.

Propulsion: The main engines are 2 × Paxman Valenta 18RP 200CM, 3,061 kW each at 1,540 rpm, driving 2 × water-jets.

VERIFIED

KOREA TACOMA MARINE INDUSTRIES LIMITED

Hanjin Group

PO Box 339, 974-15 Yangduck-dong, Masan, South Korea

Tel: +82 (551) 551181/551188
Telex: 53662 KOTAMAN K
Fax: +82 (551) 949449/949903

Choong-Hoon Cho, *Chairman*
Yi-Taek Chim, *President*
Chul-Kyu Chun, *Vice President*
Shin-Doo Kang, *Executive Managing Director*

KTMI entered the catamaran market in 1995/96 with four designs, the Seacat 30 40, 50 and 80. The Seacat 30 and 40 are passenger carrying craft offering a 200 passenger and 300 passenger capacity respectively at speeds of up to 35 knots. The Seacat 50 and 80 are car and passenger carrying designs, again with speeds up to 35 knots. The Seacat 50 carries 250 passengers and 30 cars and the Seacat 80 carries 800 passengers and 30 cars. All craft are diesel/water-jet powered.

UPDATED

NETHERLANDS

SCHELDE SHIPBUILDING (ROYAL SCHELDE)

PO Box 16, 165 Glacisstraat, 4380 AA, Vlissingen, Netherlands.

Tel: +31 (118) 482118
Telex: 37815
Fax: +31 (118) 485010

Th P Winde, *Director of Shipbuilding*
E Buterijst, *Marketing and Sales*
A Van der Knapp, *Marketing and Sales*
B Oving, *Marketing and Sales*

Royal Schelde BV has developed a range of high-speed vessels in the past, starting with SES craft of which they built a 26 m demonstration vessel, *Seaswift 23*, which operated for a period between Southampton and the Isle of Wight in the UK. Subsequent to this vessel, Schelde Shipbuilding also developed a range of catamaran and monohulls, drawing on their experience of the building of naval frigates.

In view of the market developments the company has committed itself to the marketing of large high speed vessels, such as the Seaswift 60 air cushion craft, the CAT 70 HL catamaran design and the 90 and 128 m monohull designs.

70 m CATAMARAN - STANDARD (DESIGN)

This all-aluminium vessel is designed for car, bus, truck and passenger transportation. The standard version of the design can accommodate 432 passengers and 100 cars. The heavy lift (HL) version can accommodate 600 passengers and 154 cars or a combination of trucks, buses and cars.

Specifications

Length overall	70.70 m
Length waterline	62.50 m
Beam	22.40 m
Draught	2.74 m
Passengers	432
Vehicles	100 cars
Max speed	43 kts
Operational speed	41 kts
Range	325 n miles

Propulsion: Four Caterpillar 3616 engines each drive through reduction gearboxes to a Kamewa 100 water-jet unit.

Outfit: The car deck is arranged to allow for rapid loading/unloading using a drive-through system with combined ramp and doors aft and independent ramp and doors forward. The width of the car lanes is 2.35 m with a free height of 3.30 m.

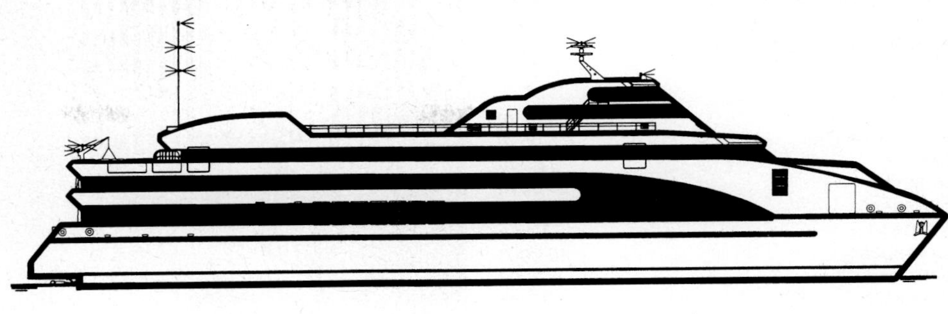

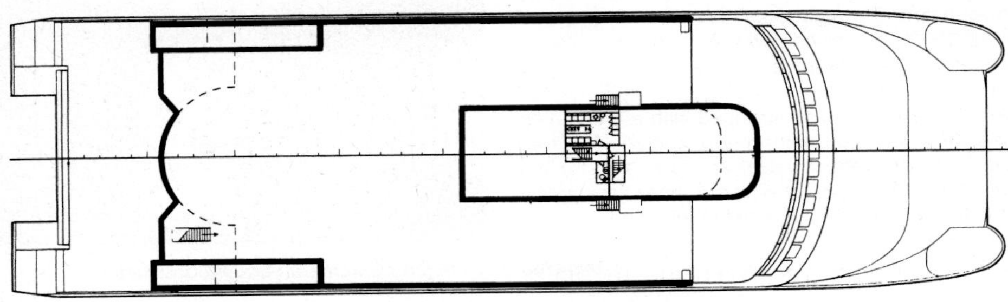

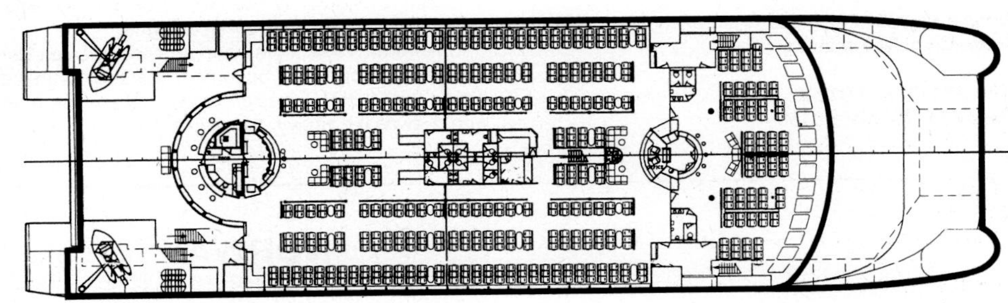

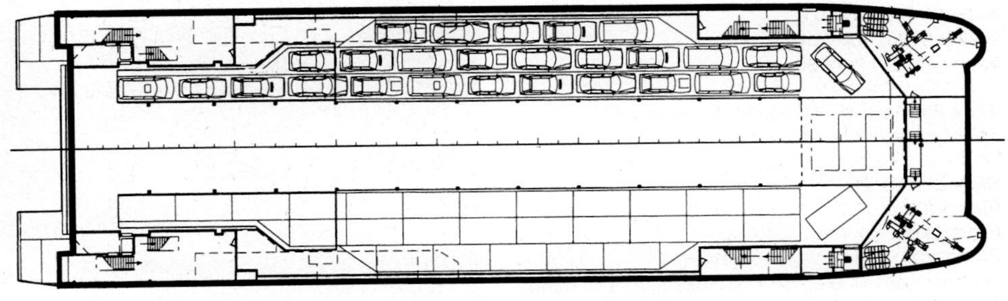

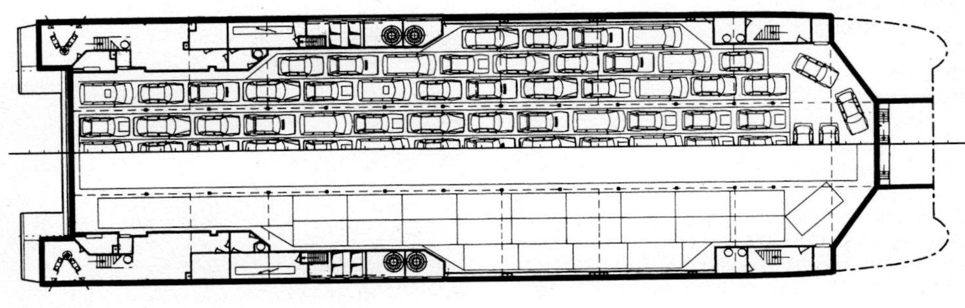

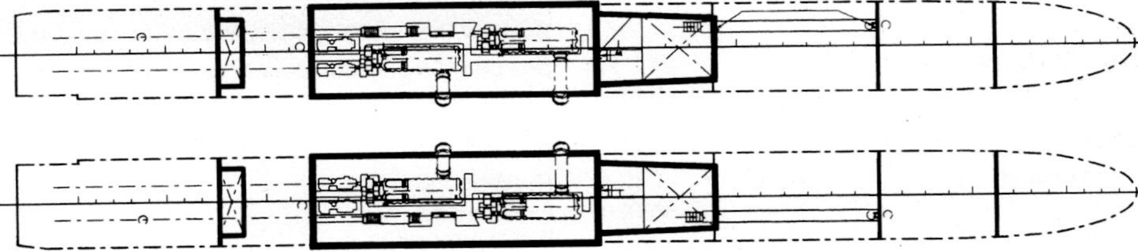

70 m (HL) Catamaran general arrangement
1996

70 m CATAMARAN - HEAVY LIFT (HL)

This design is similar to the standard design but incorporates increased passenger and vehicle loads with a higher superstructure. One vessel scheduled to be delivered to Catamaran Lines of Greece in mid-1996.

Specifications

Length overall	76.60 m
Length waterline	68 m
Beam	22.2 m
Draught	3.30 m
Passengers	600
Vehicles	154 cars
Fuel capacity	45,000 l
Water capacity	4,000 l
Max speed	36 kts
Operational speed	35 kts
Range	300 n miles

Propulsion: The main engines are 4 × MTU 20V 1163 TB 73 diesel engines each driving through reduction gearboxes to a Kamewa 112 S11 water-jet.

Outfit: The car deck is arranged with a mezzanine side deck and hoistable centre portion. The free height of the main car deck is 2.5 m and for the mezzanine deck is 2.0 m. The bus lanes have a total of 118 m length with a free height of 4.5 m.

UPDATED

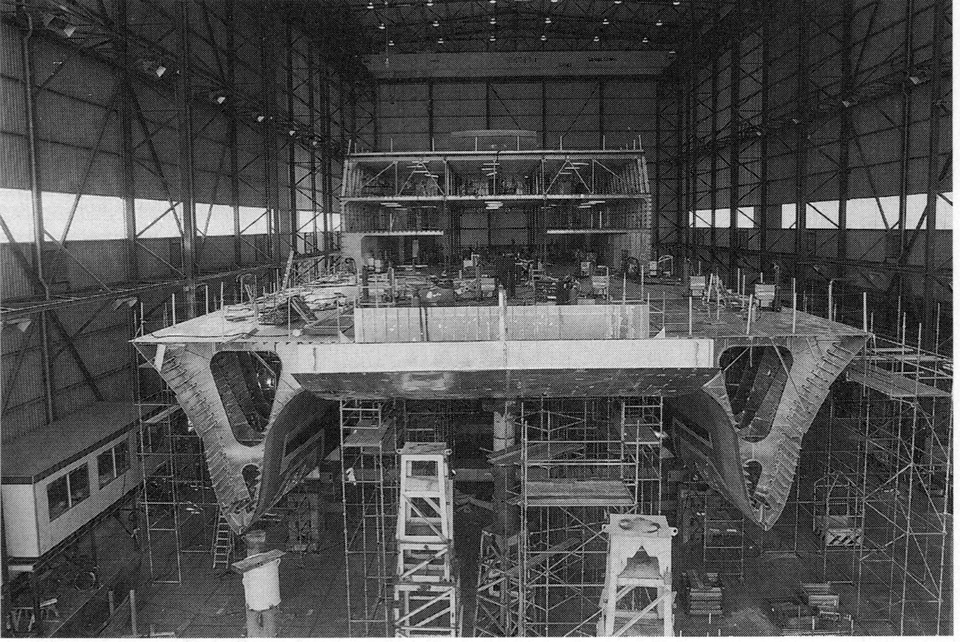

70 m (HL) Catamaran under construction ***1996***

VAN DER GIESSEN-DE NOORD

Schaardijk 23, 2921 LG Krimpen aan den Ijssel, Rotterdam, Netherlands

Tel: +31 (1) 807 91200
Fax: +31 (10) 8071 8180

This company has been licensed by Advanced Multi-Hull Designs Pty Ltd (AMD) of Sydney, Australia, to build their catamaran designs.

In Autumn 1992 it was announced that Van der Giessen-de Noord had become a shareholder in the Advanced Multi-Hull Designs company and together with Kawasaki Heavy Industries have joined the international advisory board of AMD. In 1995 the company was still actively engaged in promoting fast ships.

UPDATED

NORWAY

BÅTSERVICE HOLDING A/S

PO Box 113, N-4501 Mandal, Norway

Tel: +47 (38) 261011
Telex: 21862 YARD N
Fax: +47 (38) 264580

Bjorn Fjellhaugen, *Managing Director*
Jarl Mydland, *Sales Manager*

SEA LORD 28
Fjorddrott
Fjordbris
Fjordsol

In November 1990 Båtservice Holding A/S launched its first Sea Lord 28 high-speed catamaran. Two further vessels have now been delivered; all three are operated by Rogaland Trafikkselskap A/S.

Specifications

Length overall	28 m
Beam	8.3 m
Draught	2.3 m
Passengers	150
Fuel capacity	6,000 l
Water capacity	400 l
Propulsive power	2 × 1,500 kW
Max speed	37 kts
Operational speed	35 kts

Classification: DnV +1A1 R15 Light Craft - EO.

Propulsion: The main engines are 2 × MTU 12V 396 TE84, 1,500 kW each at 2,000 rpm (100% MCR), driving Servogear CP propellers, via ZF Type BW 465S gearboxes.

Auxiliary systems: 2 × MTU generators, 76 kW each.

Sea Lord 36 pollution control vessels for Aramco, Ain Dar 7 *and* Ain Dar 8 ***1994***

SEA LORD 32

Delivered to Rutelaget Askoy, Bergen, in December 1992.

Specifications

Length overall	32 m
Beam	9.24 m
Draught	1.5 m
Crew	4
Passengers	177
Fuel capacity	4,000 l
Water capacity	500 l
Operational speed	27 kts

Propulsion: The main engines are 2 × MTU 12V 183 TE92, 550 kW each, each driving a Servogear CPP via a ZF BW250 reduction gearbox.

SEA LORD 36 POLLUTION CONTROL
Ain Dar 7
Ain Dar 8

Early in 1991 Båtservice Industrier signed a contract with the Saudi Arabian company Aramco for the building of two 36 m Pollution Control Catamarans for operation out of the oil terminal at Ra's Tanurah. The contract was valued at US$15 million and was handled by the Aramco Overseas Company BV of the Netherlands.

The two vessels are equipped with MARCO Pollution Control Oil Recovery Filter belt systems. Produced by MARCO in Seattle, USA, since 1972, these systems employ a continuous mesh belt that allows water to pass through it but retains the collected oil. Oil and debris are carried towards the drive roller and collected in separate containers, the heavier material being scraped off first by a scraper blade.

Specifications

Length overall	36 m
Beam	11.8 m
Draught	1.85 m
Displacement, max	210 t
Crew	8
Fuel capacity	15.5 t
Water capacity	14.0 t
Propulsive power	2 × 1,630 kW
Max speed	33 kts
Operational speed	27 kts
Range	450 n miles

Structure: Hull material: aluminium.
Superstructure material: aluminium.

Propulsion: The main engines are 2 × Caterpillar 16V 3516 diesels, 1,630 kW each, driving 2 × VD802A Servogear CP propellers, via ZF gearboxes.

Auxiliary systems: Engines: 2 × 185 kW.

SEA LORD 38

The first Sea Lord 38 was delivered to Troms Fylkes Dampskibsselskap in April 1995.

Specifications

Length overall	38 m
Beam	11.2 m
Draught	1.6 m
Crew	5
Passengers	336
Fuel capacity	8,000 l
Water capacity	1,000 l
Operational speed	35 kts

Propulsion: The main engines are 4 × MTU 12V 183 TE 92 each rated at 625 kW at 2,300 rpm. Two pairs of diesels drive through a servogear 250 gearbox to servogear controllable pitch propellers.

SEA LORD 42 (DESIGN)

A 42 m, 380-passenger vessel was also being marketed in 1994. This design is classed to DnV +1A1 HSLC-EO R4.

Specifications

Length overall	42 m
Beam	11.8 m
Draught	1.7 m
Crew	4
Passengers	380
Fuel capacity	6,000 l
Operational speed	34 kts

Propulsion: The main engines are 4 × GM92 V16.

UPDATED

Fjordrott, Fjordbris *and* Fjordsol *Sea Lord 28 catamarans* **1996**

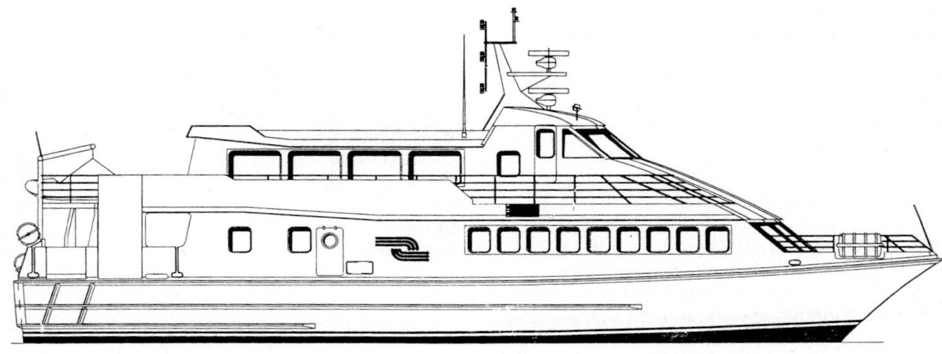

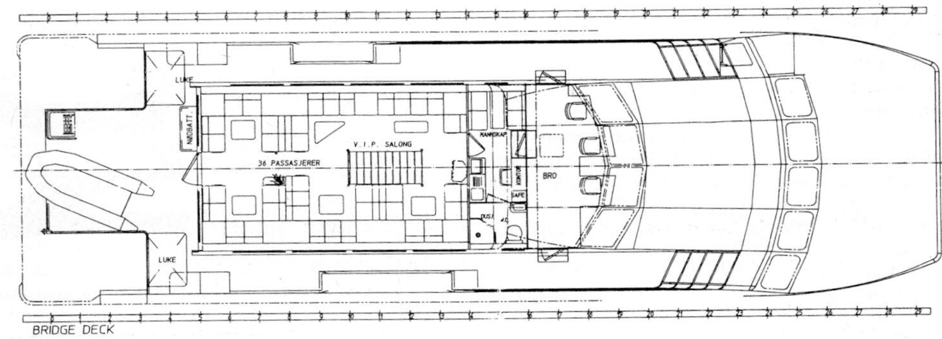

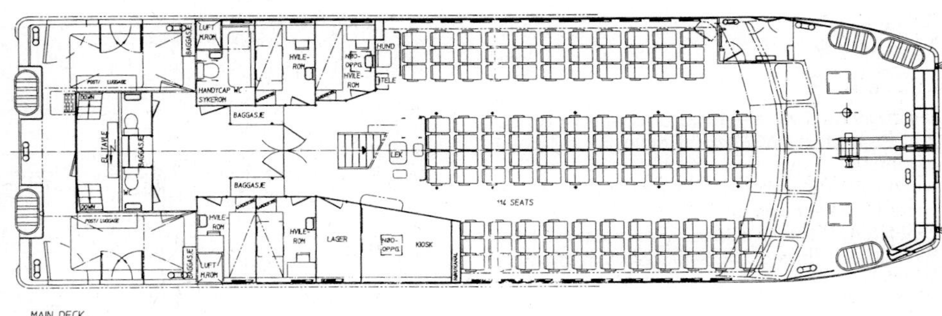

General arrangement of Sea Lord 28

CPS PRODUCTION A/S

Støperi GT 7, PO Box 724 Tangen, N-3002J Drammen, Norway

CPS DRIVE A/S

Dr Natvigs vei 4, N-1315 Nesøya, Norway

Tel: +47 (66) 982007
Fax: +47 (66) 982085

Jørgen Selmer, *Chairman*
Ragnar T Zachariassen, *General Manager*

CPS Mk III HIGH-SPEED CATAMARAN *Citius*

An innovative project completed in 1993, the CPS Mk III High-Speed Catamaran combines a number of

Citius *on trials* **1995**

unique features, particularly in relation to the machinery and propulsion system of the craft.

A large number of small engines (four in each hull) enables slender hulls to be used for this type of craft. An unusual transmission system is employed which permits for easy coupling and uncoupling of engines and rapid acceleration to cruise speed. An internal gantry crane arrangement allows for engine removal to be carried out without impinging on payload deck area. Engines may be engaged and disengaged depending on the output power required.

The basic version is a flat deck transporter but by adding various superstructures it is possible to configure the vessel for a wide range of applications.

Special attention has been paid to the aerodynamics of the superstructure and to crew visibility. Modular construction is employed for ease of manufacture and transport to an assembly area. Considerable care has been taken to provide a low-weight, high-strength structure, by the introduction of carbon fibre shafts, a pre-impregnated kevlar/epoxy superstructure and aluminium hull profiles.

Propulsion is provided by controllable-pitch surface-piercing propellers with a low drag drive and manoeuvring system.

Trials have taken place throughout 1994 and production of these craft is scheduled for 1996.

Specifications

Length overall	20.8 m
Beam	5.7 m
Draught	0.9 m
Displacement, min	19 t (basic version)
	19.5 t (passengers)
Displacement, max	24 t (basic version)
	31.5 t (passengers)
Crew	2
Passengers	68
Fuel capacity	3-5 × 1,200 l
Water capacity	500 l
Propulsive power	8 × 257 kW
Max speed	60 kts
Operational speed	50 kts

Propulsion: The main engines are 8 × Sabre 350C diesel, 257 kW each at 2,600 rpm, driving 2 × CPS controllable-pitch surface drive units with Rolla propellers.

VERIFIED

HOLEN MEK VERKSTED A/S

PO Box 20, N-6030 Langevaag, Norway

Tel: +47 (701) 92578
Fax: +47 (701) 93584

Capt. S Gudmundset, *Director*

Holen mek Verksted A/S specialises in the construction of high-speed vessels in welded aluminium, of up to 60 m in length. Comprehensive facilities for conversion and repair work on both aluminium and steel craft are also available at the yard, which is located close to Ålesund on Norway's west coast.

New buildings in aluminium include two 26 m catamaran passenger tenders carrying four hundred passengers.

MM 24 PC
Baronessa
Baronen

These are two identical high-speed catamarans which were delivered to Hardanger Sunnhordlandske Dampskipsselskap A/S on the west coast of Norway, in May and August 1994. They have been designed for operation at high speed in adverse weather conditions.

Specifications

Length overall	24 m
Length waterline	22 m
Beam	8.25 m
Draught	1.23 m
Passengers	125
Fuel capacity	5,000 l
Water capacity	1,000 l
Propulsive power	2 × 735 kW
Max speed	32 kts

Classification: DnV +1A1 HSLC Passenger R3 EO, IMO Resolution A373(X), Norwegian Maritime Directorate.

Structure: The hull and superstructure are constructed from aluminium.

Propulsion: The main engines are 2 × MTU 12V 183 TE92 diesels; driving 2 × Servogear variable pitch propellers.

MM 21 PC
Ibis III

Three of these craft are being constructed for Scavfer International S.A. to be operated by Interoil Services Limited as crew boats on the west coast of Nigeria. The vessels are all aluminium with a passenger saloon for 62 and crew facilities for 4. The first craft was launched on 20 September 1995.

Specification

Length overall	21.0 m
Length waterline	19.0 m
Beam	7.75 m
Draught	1.23 m
Passengers	62
Fuel capacity	5,000 l
Water capacity	2,000 l
Max speed	34 kts

Classification: DnV +1A1 HSLC Passengers R3

Propulsion: The vessels are powered by two MAN D2842 LE 402 diesel engines each driving a Servogear variable pitch propeller via a Mekanord V gearbox.

UPDATED

Baronessa at speed ***1995***

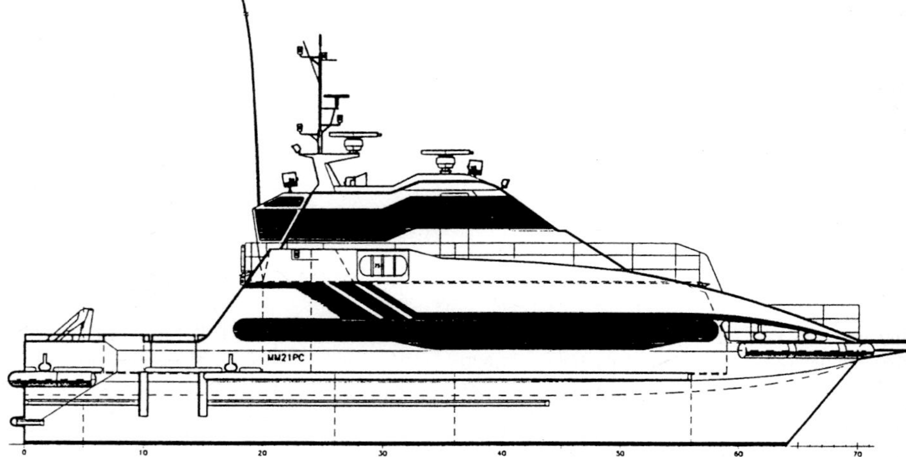

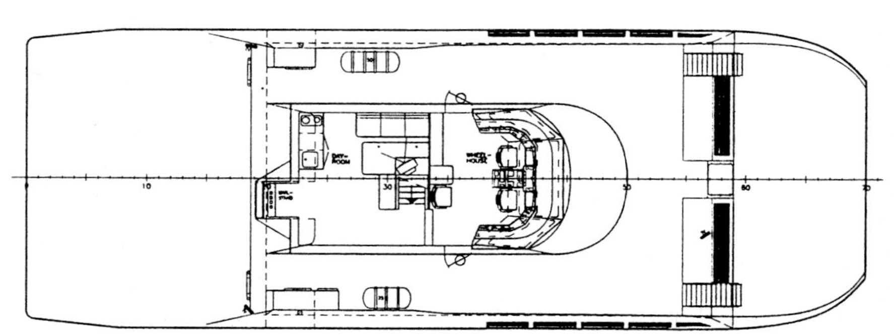

BRIDGEDECK

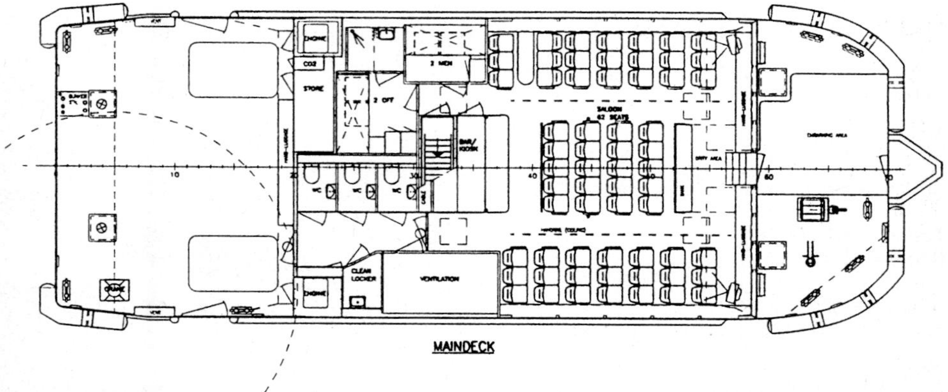

General arrangement of MM 21 PC ***1996***

HYDROCAT TECHNO A/S
HYDROCAT PRODUKSJON A/S

Wergelandsweien 2, N-6500 Kristiansund N, Norway

Tel: +47 7167 3322
Fax: +47 7167 3353

J Helseth, *Director*

HYDROCAT 2000 AC (DESIGN)

This project began in 1983 and since about 1986 has proceeded as a joint venture under Hydrocat Produksjon A/S with Mjosundet Båtbyggeri A/S, which delivered a 24 m, 72-seat, 20 knot catamaran ferry to Fosen Trafikklag A/S in 1991.

The Hydrocat 2000 AC concept is aimed at the provision of a craft of moderate size, having the capability of operating in rougher seas than would only normally be reasonable with a craft of larger size. With fixed surface-piercing foils it is seen by the Hydrocat company as a simple solution.

Due to the roll stability available in the catamaran configuration, the spanwise extent of the foil surfaces is relatively less than for a conventional surface-piercing hydrofoil vessel. This further contributes to a lower foil system weight than for the hydrofoil vessel.

The lines and materials of Hydrocat 2000 AC were established by late 1991. Propulsion will be by conventional propeller, and an all-hydraulic transmission system developed by Rexroth and Hydromarine may be used.

A quarter scale (6.6 m) manned model has been engaged in trials at speeds around 25 knots.

VERIFIED

KVÆRNER FJELLSTRAND A/S

N-5632 Omastrand, Norway

Tel: +47 (56) 554100
Fax: +47 (56) 554244

War Myklebost, *President*
Kjartan Stensønes, *Marketing Manager*
Alf Steine, *Financial Manager*

Fjellstrand was founded in 1928 in Omastrand, which is on the west coast of Norway. In January 1988 Fjellstrand merged with Kværner to form Kværner Fjellstrand A/S. A Singapore yard, Kværner Fjellstrand Pte Ltd, was opened in November 1991. Since February 1992 Kværner's high-speed craft activities have operated as Kværner a.s. Fast Ferries.

Kværner Fjellstrand has achieved the most extensive and sustained export penetration of the world high-speed ferry market, both in terms of number of vessels sold and number of countries sold into. By 1996, Kværner Fjellstrand had delivered high-speed catamarans to 21 different countries.

Following the delivery of nearly 400 aluminium vessels starting in 1952, Fjellstrand built its first catamaran (25.5 m) in 1976, the Alumaran 165 type. A further four vessels of this size followed up to 1981. The first 31.5 m passenger catamaran was delivered to a Norwegian operator. Between 1981 and 1985 a further twelve 31.5 m catamarans were delivered worldwide for passenger ferry work and crew/supply operations in the offshore oil industry. Design work on a larger 38.8 m type, the Advanced Slender Catamaran (ASC), started in 1983 and by June 1991, Fjellstrand had delivered 33 of this type. Please see earlier editions of this book for details of the 25.5, 31.5 and 38.8 m catamarans. The 40 m Flying Cat type is an extension of the 38.8 m ASC.

Kværner Fjellstrand now offers three main types of advanced high-speed catamarans to the market, the 79 m Jumbo Cat, Foil Cat and 40 m Flying Cat.

60 m JUMBO CAT

The Jumbo Cat design is currently available in two sizes, at 60 m and 81 m overall length. A 60 m version was ordered by Emeraude Lines in 1995 in a

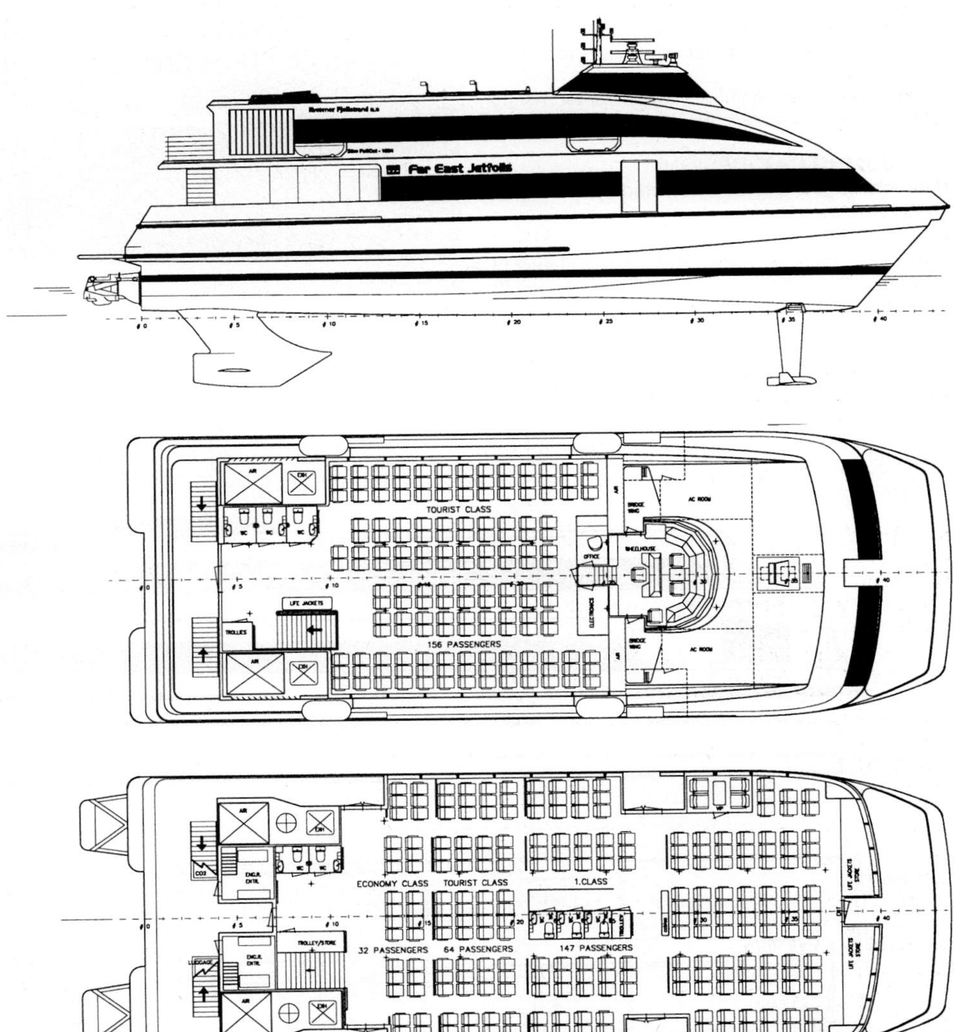

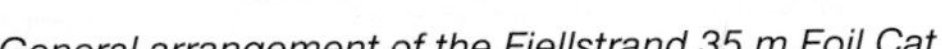
General arrangement of the Fjellstrand 35 m Foil Cat

1996

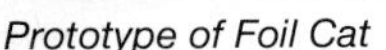
Prototype of Foil Cat **1994**

Fjellstrand 35 m Foil Cat delivered to Far East Hydrofoil Co **1996**

contract worth FRF 100 million for delivery in May 1996. The vessel (Yard No 1630) is scheduled to operate between St Malo in France and the Channel Islands.

Specifications

Length overall	59.2 m
Beam	16.5 m
Draught	2.9 m
Passengers	427
Vehicles	46
Fuel capacity	30,000 l
Water capacity	3,000 l
Propulsion power	10,800 kW
Operational speed	33 kts

Classification: DnV +1A1 HSLC Car Ferry A, R3, EO

Propulsion: The vessel is powered by two MTJ 20V 1163 TB73 diesel engines each rated at 5,400 kW at 1,200 rpm driving through reduction gears to a KMW 100 SII water-jet.

Control: The vessel is fitted with a Kværner motion damping system and two 60 kW bow thrusters.

81 m JUMBO CAT (DESIGN)

This is the largest fast ferry marketed by Fjellstrand.

Specifications

Length overall	81.0 m
Beam	25.8 m
Draught	3.3 m
Passengers	700
Vehicles	180
Fuel capacity	40,000 l
Water capacity	5,000 l
Propulsion power	25,000 kW
Operational speed	36 kts

Classification: DnV +1A1 HSLC Car Ferry A, R1, EO

Propulsion: This vessel is powered by four MTU 20V 1163 TB73L diesel engines each rated at 6,500 kW at 1,200 rpm driving through reduction gears to four separate steerable water-jets.

FOIL CAT

Development of this concept was undertaken with the assistance of a large-scale manned test craft enabling full-scale service speeds up to 50 knots

40 m Flying Cat New Arcadia **1996**

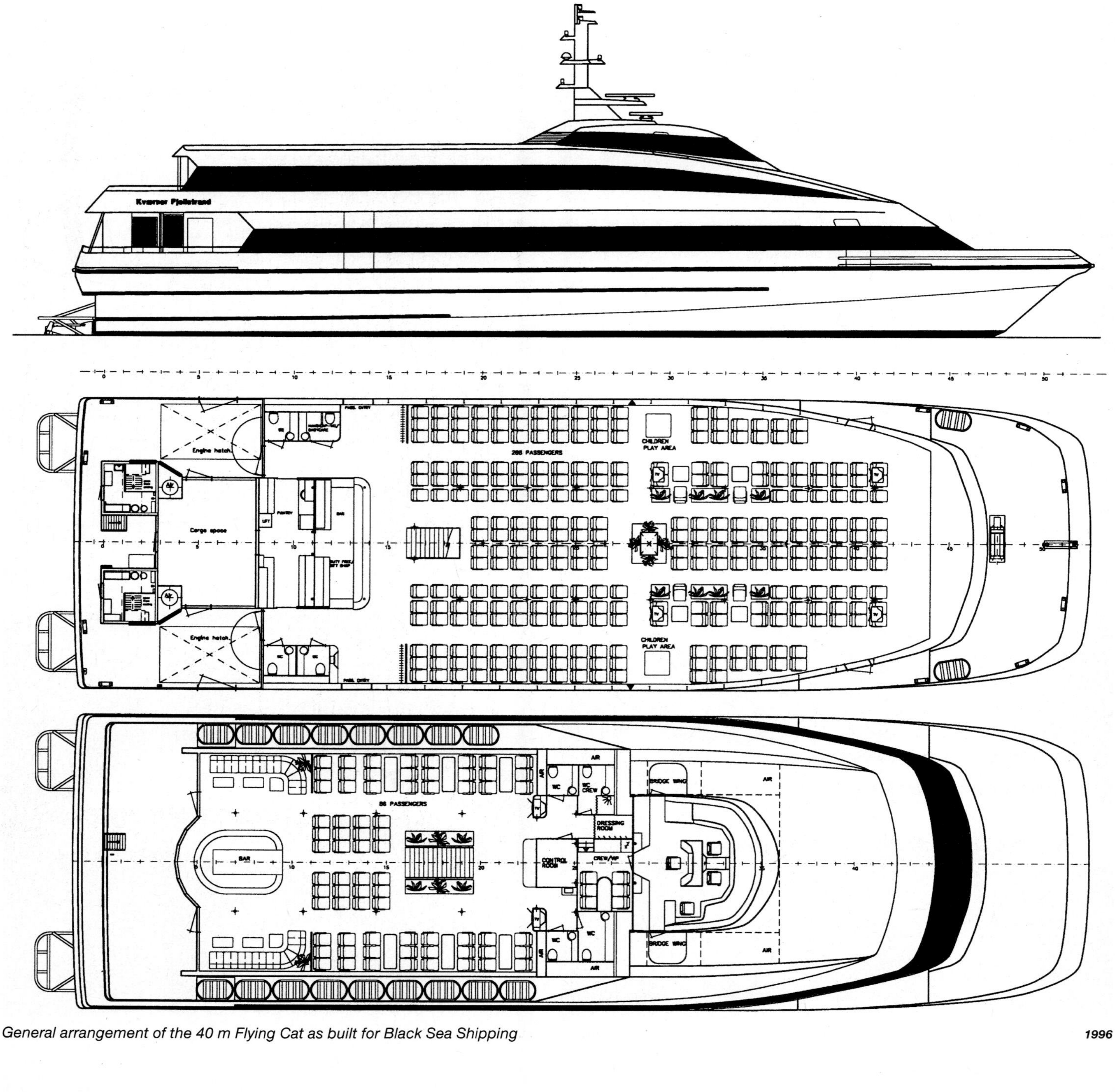

General arrangement of the 40 m Flying Cat as built for Black Sea Shipping **1996**

to be explored. While the simplicity of the catamaran construction is maintained in this new concept, the addition of the lifting and stabilising foil system enables considerably higher speeds at the level of 50 knots to be achieved economically and in rougher seas. In comparison with comparable vessels of other types the transport efficiency is significantly higher, leading to fuel consumption figures 50 per cent less than, for example, conventional high-speed catamarans. In addition, speed loss in waves is much reduced and vertical accelerations can be reduced to less than half those for comparable craft of other types.

After launching the 40 m prototype, comprehensive testing and improvements have been carried out. The next generation of the Foil Cat (Foil Cat 2/s) has been based on the wide experience gained from the prototype testing programme. Although the next model is shorter in length it has improved capacities and performance. Two of these improved craft (Yard Nos 1624 and 1625) were delivered in June 1995 to Far East Hydrofoil for its Hong Kong to Macau route. The prototype, Ahinora, was purchased by Black Sea Shipping in October 1995.

Specifications

Length overall	35 m
Beam	12 m
Draught, hullborne	4.7 m (max)
Draught, foilborne	2.55 m (min)
Crew	4
Passengers	407
Fuel capacity	20,000 l
Water capacity	3,000 l
Maximum speed	50 kts
Operational speed	45 kts
Range	300 n miles

Classification: DnV +1A1 HSLC passenger, R2, EO.

Propulsion: The main engines are 2 × GE LM 500 gas-turbines, driving 2 × Kamewa S80II, water-jets.

Navigation and communications: Arpa radars, gyrocompass, log, autopilot, electronic map system, GPS, echo-sounder; VHF radiotelephones, PA/intercom, CCTV, mobile telephone.

Control: Foil system: fully submerged foil system, active flap control.

Automatic control system: Kværner Fjellstrand AFCS.

40 m FLYING CAT

This Kværner Fjellstrand design was launched in 1989. By 1996 38 craft had been built, 20 from the Omastrand yard and 18 from the Singapore yard.

Victoria Clipper IV, Yard No 1615

Delivered March 1993 to Clipper Navigation Inc of the USA, the vessel operates between Seattle in the USA and Victoria in Canada. With a capacity of 324 passengers, the vessel employs water-jets to give a service speed of 33 knots with a 25.42 tonne load. A Clipper MDS will be installed.

Clipper Navigation Inc has operated a 38.8 m ASC from Kværner Fjellstrand, *Victoria Clipper*, since 1986. In April 1992 a Clipper MDS was installed on this vessel.

Evridika

This 40 m Flying Cat was ordered by Black Sea Shipping in Varna, Bulgaria in a contract worth US$6 million. The craft was delivered in October 1995 and operates on the Varna to Istanbul route. This particular 40 m Flying Cat is 2 m wider than the standard and consequently offer more room per passenger than normal.

Specifications

Length overall	40.55 m
Beam	12.0 m
Draught	1.8 m
Crew	6
Passengers	374
Fuel capacity	18,000 l
Water capacity	3,000 l
Propulsive power	4,000 kW
Operational speed	32 kts

Classification: DnV +1A1 HSLC, R90, EO, Light Craft.

Propulsion: The vessel is powered by two MTU 16V 396 TE74L diesel engines each rated at 2,000 kW at 2,000 rpm. Each engine drives through a ZF BW 755 reduction gearbox to a Kamewa S80II water-jet.

Fjellstrand 40 m Flying Cat delivered to Black Sea Shipping **1996**

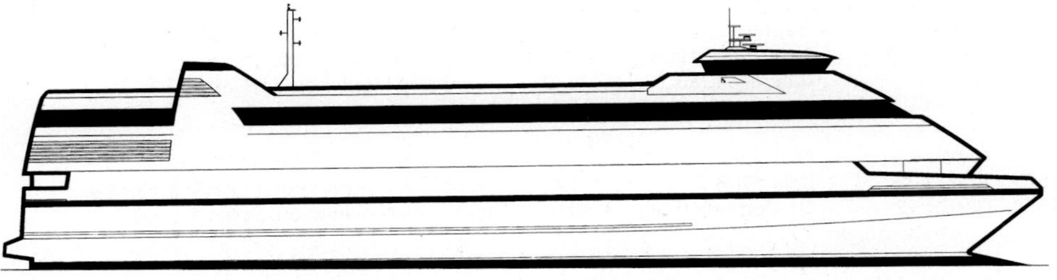

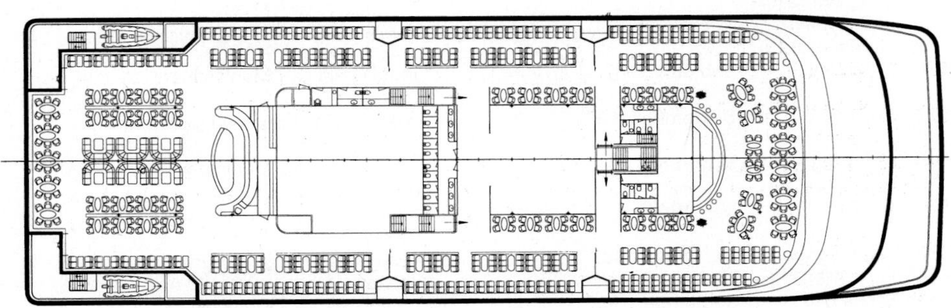

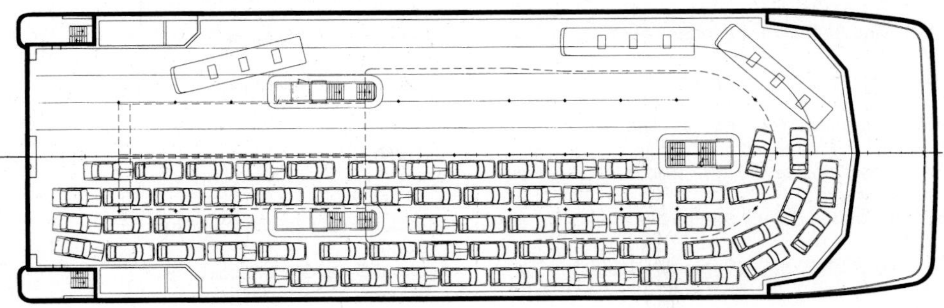

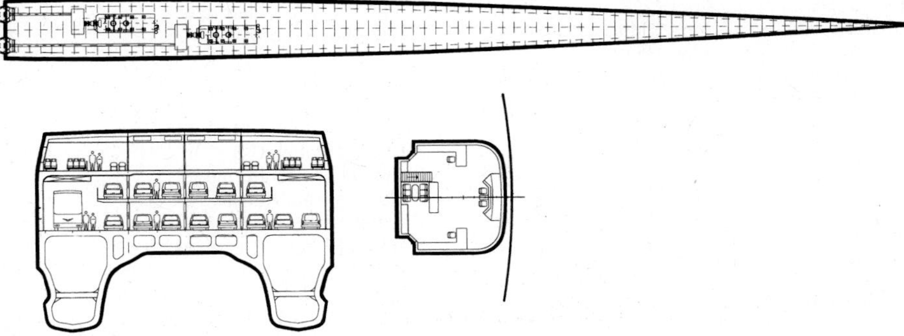

Fjellstrand 81 m Jumbo Cat general arrangement (design) **1996**

40 m Flying Cat Craft built or on order to 1996

Yard No	Name	Completed	Seats	Delivered to
1597	*Kommandøren*	April 1990	252	Fylkesbaatane i Sogn og Fjordane, Norway
1602	*Flying Cat I*	November 1990	372	Ceres Hellenic Shipping Co, Greece
1603	*Jet Cat*	December 1990	272	Seatran Travel, Malaysia
1605	*Alicone*	June 1991	352	CAREMAR SpA, Naples, Italy
1607	*Royal Vancouver*	October 1991	302	Royal Sealink Express, Vancouver, Canada
1609	*Royal Victoria*	November 1991	302	Royal Sealink Express, Vancouver, Canada
1610	*Orca Spirit*	May 1992	296	Nanaimo Express, Vancouver, Canada
1611	*Søløven*	May 1992	296	KatExpress, Århus, Denmark
1612	*Xin Shi Ji*	May 1993	300	Yantai Marine Shipping Co, China
1613	*Søløven II*	May 1993	292	Dampskibsselskabet Øresund, Denmark
1614	*Hai Ou*	January 1993	400	Dalian Steamship Co, Dalian, China
1615	*Victoria Clipper IV*	February 1993	324	Clipper Navigation Inc, Seattle, USA
1618	*Hai Yan*	December 1993	447	Dalian Marine Transport (Group) Company
1620	*Kraka Viking*	June 1994	168	DSØ, Denmark
1621	*Sifka Viking*	June 1994	168	DSØ, Denmark
1623	*Vargøy*	June 1994	230	Fylkesrederi og Ruteselskap, Norway
1624	*Fjordkongen*	December 1994	320	Troms Fylkes Dampskibsselskap, Norway
1628	*New Arcadia*	May 1995	300	Seo Kyung Shipping Co. Ltd, South Korea
1604	*Evridka*	October 1995	374	Black Sea Shipping, Bulgara
1626	–	January 1996	449	Eagle Ridge SA, Panama

ADVANCED SLENDER CATAMARANS (38.8 m) Craft built or on order 1985 to December 1991

Yard No	Name	Completed	Seats	Delivered to
	Tian Lu Hu	September 1985	326	Zhen Hing Enterprises Co Ltd, China
1570	*Yong Xing*	November 1985	312	Ningbo Huagang Ltd, China
1571	*Mexico* (ex-*Can Cun*)	January 1986	370	Cruceros Maritimos del Caribe SA, Mexico
1572	*Victoria Clipper*	May 1986	330*	Clipper Navigation Inc, USA
1573	*Anne Lise***	July 1986	195	Hardanger Sunnhordlanske A/S, Norway
1574	*Sevilla 92* (ex-*Caribbean Princess*)	31 October 1986	310	Islena de Navegacion, Spain
1575	*Rapido de Algeciros* (ex-*Bahamian Princess*)	February 1987	310	Islena de Navegacion, Spain
1576	*Caka Bey*	February 1987	449	Istanbul Great City Municipality, Turkey
1577	*Fjordprins*	September 1987	201	Fylkesbaatane i Sogn og Fjordane, Norway
1578	*Umur Bey*	May 1987	449	Istanbul Great City Municipality, Turkey
1579	*Yeditepe*	May 1987	449	Istanbul Great City Municipality, Turkey
1580	*Sognekongen*	December 1987	201	Fylkesbaatane i Sogn og Fjordane, Norway
1581	*Sarica Bey*	September 1987	449	Istanbul Great City Municipality, Turkey
1582	*Ulbatli Hasan*	October 1987	449	Istanbul Great City Municipality, Turkey
1583	*Uluc Ali Reis*	January 1988	449	Istanbul Great City Municipality, Turkey
1584	*Nusret*	March 1988	449	Istanbul Great City Municipality, Turkey
1585	*Karamürsel Bey*	March 1988	449	Istanbul Great City Municipality, Turkey
1586	*Sea Cat/Blue Manta*	April 1988	249	n/k
1587	*Hezarifen Celebi*	September 1988	449	Istanbul Great City Municipality, Turkey
1588	*Cavli Bey*	September 1988	449	Istanbul Great City Municipality, Turkey
1589	*Sleipner*	April 1989	243	Flaggruten, Norway
1590	*Draupner*	April 1989	243	Flaggruten, Norway
1591	*Dae Won Catamaran*	November 1988	396	Dae Won Ferry Co Ltd, South Korea
1592	*Nordlicht*	April 1989	272	AG EMS Emden, Germany
1593	*Leopardo*	June 1989	290	Cat Lines SA, Spain
1594	*Jetcat*	June 1988	213	n/k
1595	*Eyra*	August 1989	290	Cat Lines SA, Spain
1596	*Nam Hae Star*	October 1989	350	Nam Hae Express, South Korea
1598	*Mercury*	March 1990	288	AKP Sovcomflot, CIS
1599	*Solovki*	March 1990	246	AKP Sovcomflot, CIS
1600	*Varangerfjord*	June 1990	164	Finnmark Fylkesrederi og Ruteselskap, Norway
1601	*Løberen*	September 1990	256	Dampskibsselskabet Øresund, Denmark
1608	*Springaren*	June 1991	255	Svenska Rederi AB Øresund, a subsidiary of Dampskibsselskabet Øresund, Denmark

*of which 30 are external
**converted from freighter layout March 1991 having been bought from God Trans A/S, Norway in 1991.

Control: A Kværner motion dampening system is installed on the vessel.

40 m FLYING CAT - M2 VERSION

Kværner Fjellstrand after carefully studying the changes in the market, is continually developing its products. Alterations in the high-speed ferry market have influenced Kværner Fjellstrand to develop a new Flying Cat design. The new and more cost-effective version, Flying Cat M2, maintains the high quality of the original Flying Cat with regard to safety, seaworthiness and reliability.

UPDATED

LINDSTØLS SKIPS- & BÅTBYGGERI A/S

Solsiden 1, N-4950 Risør, Norway

Tel: +47 3715 0344
Fax: +47 3715 2060

Einar K Lindstøl, *Director*
Arne Lindstøl, *Manager*

Lindstøls Skips- & Båtbyggeri A/S was founded in 1870 by Erik K Lindstøl. Through the years Lindstøls Skips has acquired a broad experience in the construction of various types of vessels in the size range up to 60 m in length. A large number of sailing cargo vessels, rescue vessels, research, arctic, fishing and pleasure vessels were delivered to customers in several countries.

One of the most famous of these vessels was delivered in 1917 and named *Quest*; it travelled the oceans with Captain Shackleton on Antarctic expeditions for many years.

Erik K Lindstøl's son, Arne K Lindstøl, headed the yard for 40 years, up to 1952, when Einar K Lindstøl changed the building material from wood to steel. The company began using aluminium in construction in 1960.

Since that time Lindstøls Skips has built a number of fast catamaran craft. The yard signed an agreement with Abeking and Rasmussen of Germany in 1995 for the joint construction of two 27.5 catamarans designed by Lindstøls Skips for delivery in June 1996.

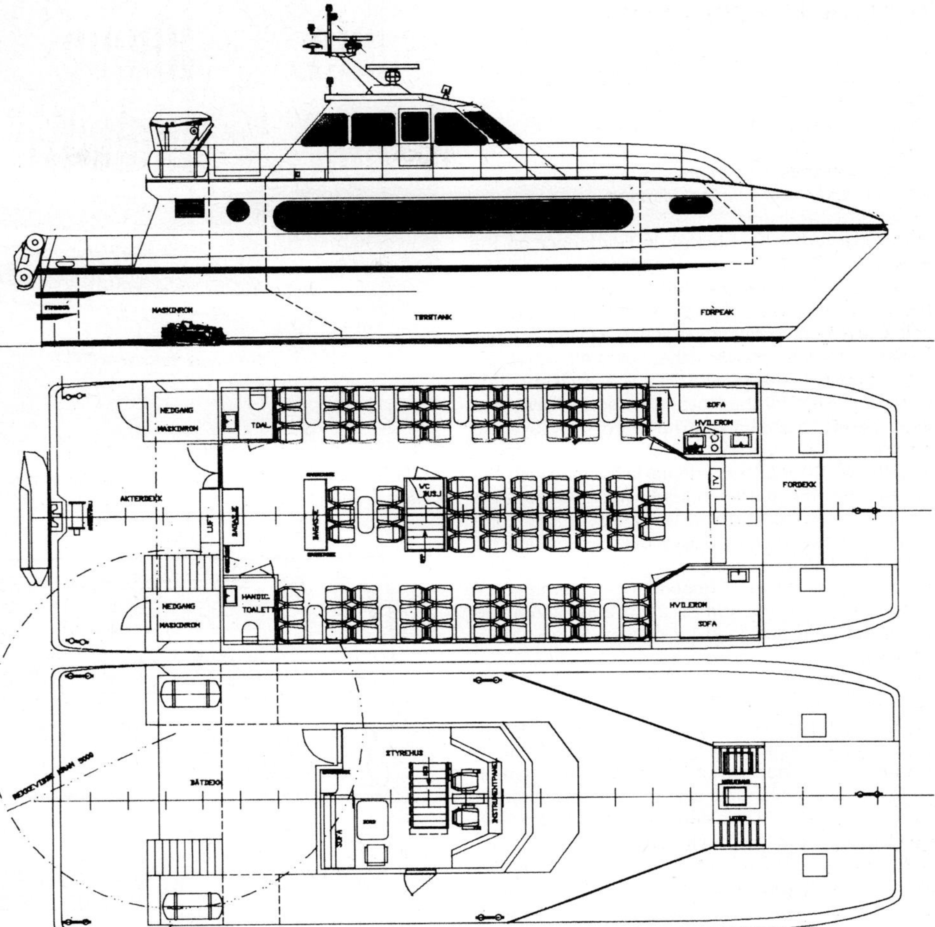

General arrangement of Lindstøl's Light 22.5 m catamaran

LIGHT 22.5 m CATAMARAN

The first Light 22.5 m catamaran built by Lindstøl Skips A/S, *Namdalingen*, was delivered from the yard in August 1990. Ordered by A/S Namsos Trafikkselskap the vessel has entered the rough coastal service route between Namsos and Rorvik/Leka in mid-Norway, north of Trondheim.

The Light 22.5 m is a 100 per cent Lindstøl-designed concept based on the first Norwegian built slender catamarans with symmetric hulls developed and built by Lindstøl Skips A/S in 1983 to 1985.

Namdalingen is the latest design in a continuous line of deliveries since the first sailing ship was built in 1870.

Lindstøl Skips A/S has been in aluminium constructions since the beginning of the 1960s and is today equipped with the most advanced CAD/CAM systems available, in order to offer the customer the best service during the projecting and building period.

Consideration has been given to ensure the possibility of changing a main engine within 8 hours. The reason for this is that *Namdalingen* is the only high-speed passenger vessel covering the Namsos - Rorvik and Leka area, and the vessel has to be in traffic 360 days a year. The owner, A/S Namsos Trafikkselskap, therefore has one spare engine in stock for replacing when routine overhauls are necessary.

Model tests indicated that when operating in 30 knots in a significant wave height of 1 m (maximum wave height of 2 m), accelerations in the passenger saloon will be 0.1 *g*. The wash at 30 knots is measured to 0.3 m, 30 m from the side of the vessel.

Special attention has been given to passenger and crew visibility, the wheelhouse has 360° visibility.

Fosningen

1992

Namdalingen, Yard No 296

Specifications

Length overall	22.5 m
Beam	7.6 m
Draught	1.1 m
Crew	2
Passengers	110
Fuel capacity	2 × 1,700 l tanks
Water capacity	400 l
Propulsive power	2 × 672 kW
Operational speed	30 kts
Range	440 n miles

Classification: DnV +1A1 R5, EO Light-Craft Passenger Catamaran.

Structure: Aluminium alloy, decks and superstructure of Lindstøl aluminium alloy sandwich profile.

Propulsion: The main engines are 2 × MTU 12V 183 TE 92, 672 kW each, at 2,300 rpm; driving Servogear CP propellers type 800 A, V drive gear VD 250 B.

Electrical system: Auxiliary engine: Mitsubishi/ Mustang A 372-22, 16 kW, 20 kVA.

Fosningen, Yard No 298

This is the second light 22.5 m catamaran built by Lindstøls Skips and was delivered on 25 June 1991. This vessel has 118 seats and is in service with Fosen Trafikklag A/S of Trondheim on an 8.3 n mile route between Skansen and Vanvikan. *Fosningen* is similar in many respects to *Namdalingen,* the main differences being large 1.1 m diameter four-bladed CP propellers to give good starting, stopping and manoeuvring qualities, and a change of saloon layout with the inclusion of a kiosk and office section. Some changes have also been made to the hull form below the waterline.

27.5 m CATAMARAN

Two of these vessels are under construction at a total contract value of £5.0 million. They are being produced jointly by Lindstøls Skips and the German yard Abeking and Rasmussen. The crafts seat 210 passengers each and are powered by two MTU 8V 936 diesels at speeds of up to 35 knots. The vessels are scheduled to operate from Hamburg in Germany in late 1996.

UPDATED

ROSENDAL VERFT A/S

PO Box 55, N-5470 Rosendal, Norway

Tel: +47 53481322
Fax: +47 53481934

Hallgeir Skjelnes, *Chairman*
Ronald Hellenes, *Technical Manager*

Rosendal Verft A/S, situated in Hardanger on the west coast of Norway, was established in 1989. The history of the yard reaches back to 1855 and during the intervening years a great number and range of ships have been built and launched: fishing vessels, ferries, research vessels, inspection craft, naval vessels, chemical tankers, lifeboats, ice-breakers, tugs and minelayers for the Royal Norwegian Navy, and high-speed catamarans. The yard employs 60 people.

With over 30 years experience in building with aluminium the yard started in 1986 with a subcontract for Fjellstrand A/S. The work included complete production of five 38.8 m passenger catamarans for delivery in Turkey.

The current range of Rosendal catamarans consists of two types, the Admiral 29 m, and the Admiral 36 m, both are designed for clearly defined operational areas.

In February 1991, Rosendal Verft started a development project for a 36 m catamaran.

The first Rosendal 36 m was delivered to Rederij Doeksen for operation between the Dutch Frisland islands and the northern coast of the Netherlands. The company, which was also the launch customer for the Rosendal 29 m catamaran, specified a 300-seat variant of the twin deck design.

In December 1994 the yard signed a contract for two Admiral 36 (plus two in option) with a Chinese company. The first vessel *Xunlong No 1* was put in service between Hong Kong and Shekou in 1995. *Xunlong* is the first 36 m with the four engine arrangement. Rosendal Verft have also started development of a 38 m craft to accomodate the large markets in Asia.

Xunlong No 1*, an Admiral 36 m passenger catamaran delivered in July 1995 to Shenzen Xunlong, China* **1996**

Admiral 29 m

The Admiral 29 m passenger catamaran has been designed to operate on coastal routes. The recommended service speed is 32 to 40 knots.

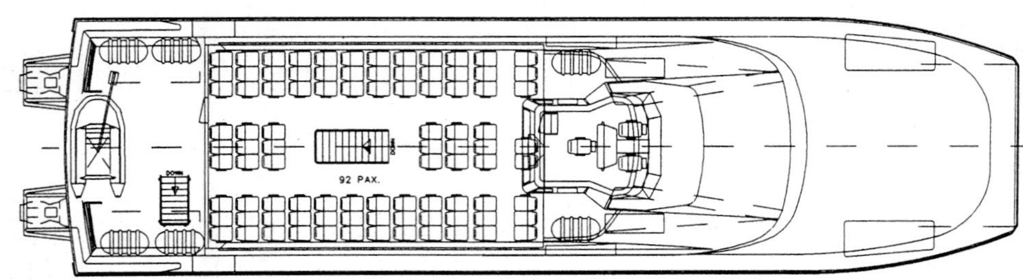

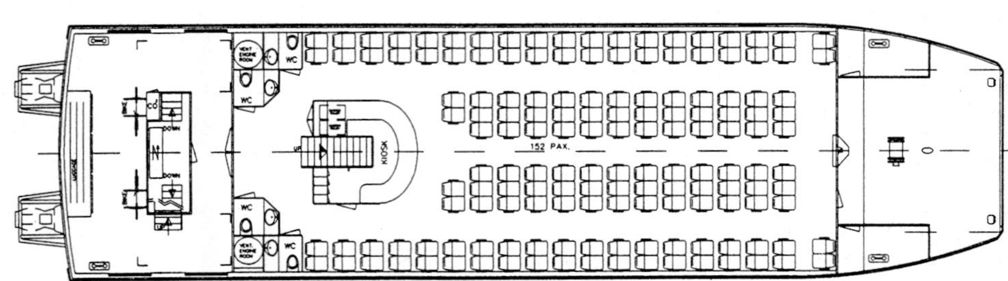

Admiral 29 m 250 passenger catamaran general arrangement **1995**

Recent Rosendal Verft 28 m and 29 m Catamarans (See 1992-93 edition for details of 28 m *Stuifdijk*)

Name	*Prinsessen*	*Skogøy*	*Agdenes*	*Tedno*
Built	1990	1991	1991	1992
Type	Slender-hull passenger catamaran	Slender-hull passenger/ cargo catamaran	Slender-hull passenger catamaran	Slender-hull passenger catamaran
Owner/Operator	Nesodden Bundefjord, Norway	Salten Dampskipselskap, Norway	Fosen Trafikkselskap, Norway	Hardanger Sunnhordlandske, Norway
Classification	DnV+1A1 Light Craft Passenger Catamaran (R20, EO)	DnV+1A1 Light Craft Passenger Catamaran (R15, EO)	DnV+1A1 Light Craft Passenger Catamaran (R15, EO)	DnV+1A1 HSLC Passenger Catamaran (R2, EO)
Hull	Aluminium	Aluminium	Aluminium	Aluminium
Dimensions				
Length	28 m	28.75 m	28.75 m	29 m
Beam	9 m	8 m	8 m	8 m
Draught	1.9 m incl propeller	2.1 m incl propeller	2.1 m incl propeller	2.4 m
Capacities				
Fuel oil	2 × 3,000 l	2 × 3,000 l	2 × 2,000 l	2 × 3,000 l
Fresh water	500 l	500 l	500 l	1,500 l
Lube oil	300 l	300 l	200 l	300 l
Accommodation				
Passenger seats	175	130	210	173
Facilities	Non-reclinable seats. Entertainment system: Television, radio, music. One toilet accessible for disabled persons.	Reclinable seats. Kiosk. Entertainment system: Television, video, radio, music. Hot and cold meals. Telephone. Three toilets, one for disabled persons.	Reclinable seats and sitting groups. Kiosk. entertainment system: 5 channels for CD, video music and radio. Hot and cold meals. Telephone. Three toilets, one for disabled persons.	Non-reclinable seats. Kiosk. Entertainment system: 5 channels for CD, video, music and radio. Hot and cold meals. Telephone. Four toilets, one for disabled persons.
Main engines	2 × Detroit Diesel 16V 92 TA; 566 kW each	2 × Detroit Diesel 16V 149 TIB; 1,324 kW each	2 × Deutz MWM TBD 604 BV12; 1,260 kW each	2 × MTU 12V 396 TE 74L 1,500 kW each
Propulsion	Twin controllable-pitch propeller	Twin controllable-pitch propeller	Twin controllable-pitch propeller	Twin controllable-pitch propeller
Performance				
Speed max	28 kts	36.3 kts	36 kts	36.5 kts
Speed service	25 kts at 85% MCR	33.3 kts at 85% MCR	33 kts at 85% MCR	34 kts at 85% MCR
Fuel consumption	280 l/h	565 l/h	510 l/h	653 l/h

Koegelwieck *1993*

Admiral 29 m Tedno *1993*

Passengers are seated in two compartments on two decks with restaurant and entertainment facilities provided.

Since 1989, Rosendal Verft has delivered eight 29 m catamarans to owners in Norway and Holland.

Specifications

Length overall	29 m
Beam	8 m
Passengers	250
Propulsive power	4 × 550 kW
Max speed	35 kts
Operational speed	33 kts

Propulsion: The main engines are 4 × MTU 12V 183 TE 62. There will be two engines in each engine room, connected to a common gearbox. This is the most economical installation regarding investment costs and safety. The installation will also implicate higher regularity, which will lead to substantial savings in maintenance, fuel consumption, spare parts, purchase price, and the vessel total operations economy.

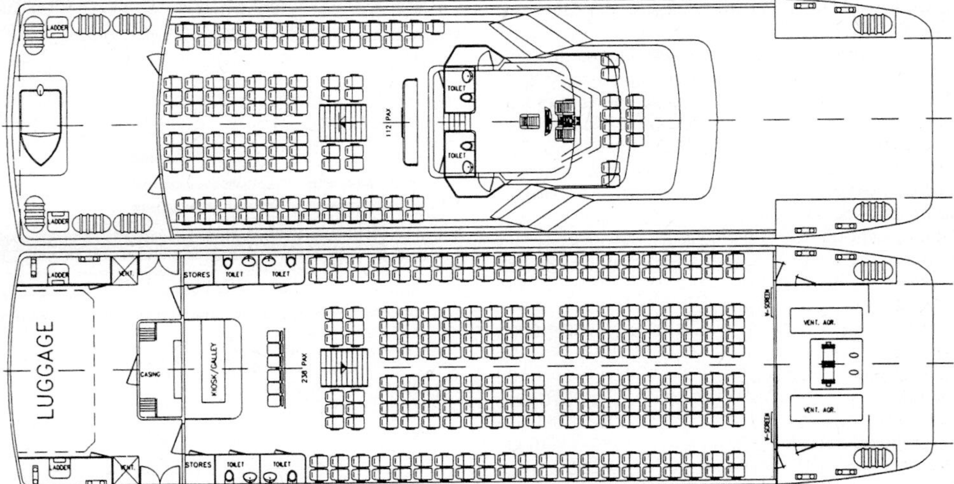

Admiral 36 m 400 passenger catamaran general arrangement *1995*

Admiral 36 m

The Admiral 36 m passenger catamaran has been designed to operate on coastal and open water routes. The reccommended service speed is 32 to 40 knots. Passengers are seated in three compartments on two decks with restaurant and entertainment facilities provided.

Specifications

Length overall	36 m
Beam	9.6 m
Passengers	350
Propulsive power	4 × 735 kW
Max speed	36 kts
Operational speed	34 kts

Propulsion: The main engines are 4 × MTU 12V 183 TE 92. There will be two engines in each engine room, connected to a common gearbox. This is the most economical installation regarding investment costs and safety. The installation will also implicate higher regularity, which will lead to substantial savings in maintenance, fuel consumption, spare parts, purchase price, and the vessel total operations economy.

UPDATED

HIGH-SPEED CATAMARAN CRAFT BUILT 1987 TO THE PRESENT

Yard No	Type	Name	Delivered	Seats	Delivered to	Route
242* Fjellstrand	38.8 m	*Umur Bey*	May 1987	450	Istanbul Great City Municipality, Turkey	Istanbul, Bosphorus
243* Fjellstrand	38.8 m	*Ulbatli Hasan*	Nov 1987	450	Istanbul Great City Municipality, Turkey	Istanbul, Bosphorus
244* Fjellstrand	38.8 m	*Uluc Ali Reis*	Feb 1988	450	Istanbul Great City Municipality, Turkey	Istanbul, Bosphorus
245* Fjellstrand	38.8 m	*Karamursel Bey*	Apr 1988	450	Istanbul Great City Municipality, Turkey	Istanbul, Bosphorus
246* Fjellstrand	38.8 m	*Cavli Bey*	Sep 1988	450	Istanbul Great City Municipality, Turkey	Istanbul, Bosphorus
256 Admiral	26 m	*Havstril*	Jun 1989	150	PEMEX, Mexico	Mexico
257 Admiral	29 m	*Lauparen* (ex-*Stuifdijk*)	Jun 1990	250	More og Romsdal, Norway	Keistiansuno - Trundheim
258 Admiral	29 m	*Prinsessen*	Nov 1990	175	Nesodden Bundefjord	Oslofjorden
259 Admiral	29 m	*Skogøy*	Apr 1991	130+ cargo	Salten Dampskipselskap, Norway	Svolvær - Narvik
260 Admiral	29 m	*Agdenes*	Jul 1991	210	Fosen Trafikklag, Norway	Trondheim - Sula
262 Admiral	35 m	*Koegelwieck*	Jun 1992	300	Rederij Doeksen, Holland	Terschelling - Harlingen
263 Admiral	29 m	*Tedno*	Nov 1992	173	Hardanger Sunnhordlanske, Norway	Bergen - Stavanger
264 Admiral	29 m	*Vegtind*	Dec 1994	100 + cargo	Torghatten Trafikk, Norway	North Norway
265 Admiral	29 m	*Thorolf Kveldulfsøn*	Mar 1995	100 + cargo	Helgeland Trafikk, Norway	North Norway
266 Admiral	36 m	*Xunlong No 1*	July 1995	312	Shenzhen Xunlong	China
267 Admiral	36 m	*Xunlong No 2*	Jan 1996	312	Shenzhen Xunlong	China

*Subcontract for Fjellstrand A/S

WESTAMARIN A/S

Andøyveten 23, PO Box 115, Vågsbygd, N-4602 Kristiansand, Norway

Tel: +47 (38) 088200
Telex: 21514 WRIN N
Fax: +47 (38) 085012

Westamarin A/S is a subsidiary of the Swedish company Swedish Addum Industri Group which is owned by Securum. The shipyard was established in 1855 and has been associated with the design and production of ships and offshore structures since that time. With a prior association with Westamarin West A/S, the yard has been developing large fast catamaran craft since 1990. The company holds the ISO-9001 quality assurance standard. In 1995 the company was awarded a contract by Stena Line for two HSS 900 fast catamaran passenger vehicle ferries, worth a total of £70 million. Few details of this vessel have been released.

Westamaran-12000 TC (design) artist's impression **1995**

WESTAMARAN 12000 OCEAN FLYER
(DESIGN)

The Westamaran 12000 was announced towards the end of 1990. Originally designed to carry up to 1,200 passengers and 275 cars, the current design is for a vessel with a maximum vehicle capacity of 550 cars and seating for 1,500 passengers. The design now allows for commercial traffic with various combinations of cars, trucks, trailers and buses to be carried.

Specifications

Length overall	124.5 m
Beam	34 m
Draught	4.5 m
Payload	750-1,000 t
Crew	20
Passengers	1,500
Vehicles	520 cars
Propulsive power	40,000-50,000 kW
Operational speed	40 kts
Range	600 n miles

Structure: Hull material: high-tensile steel. Superstructure material: aluminium alloy.
Propulsion: Engines: 2 or 4 gas-turbines, 40,000-50,000 kW.

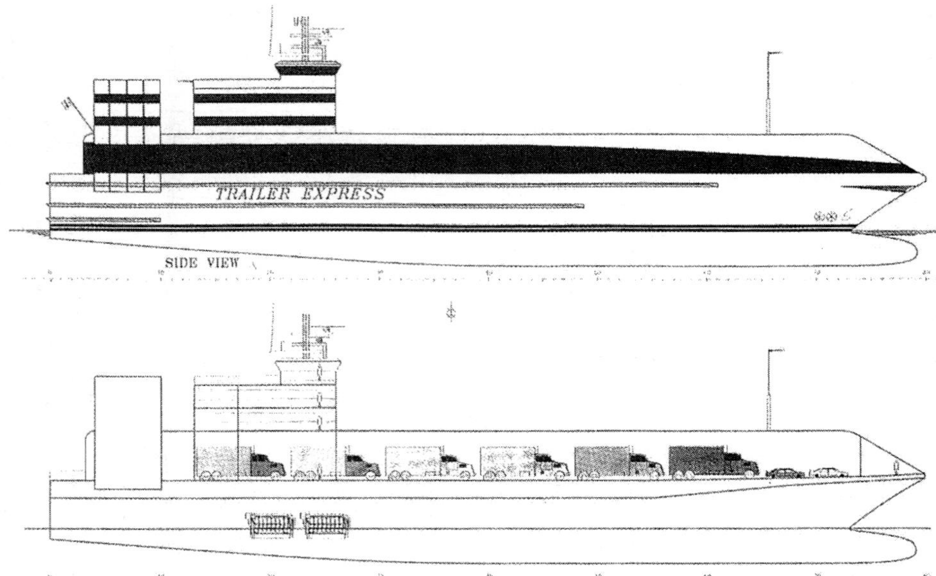

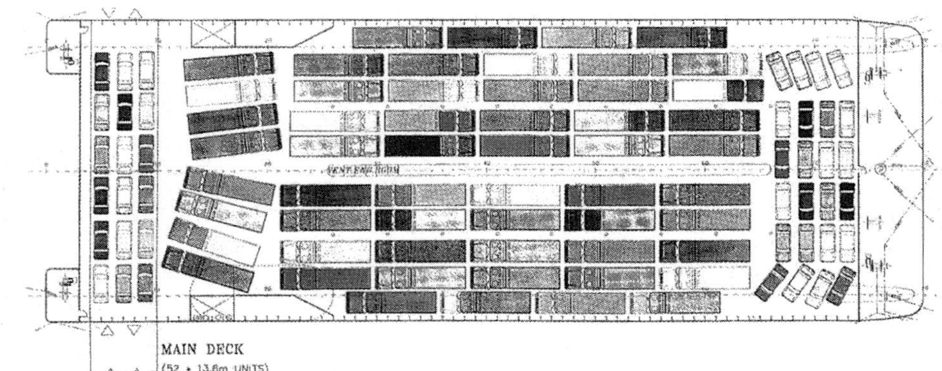

Westamaran 9600 ro-ro ferry (design) general arrangement **1995**

WESTAMARAN 12000 TC
(DESIGN)

Specifications

Length overall	124.6 m
Length waterline	107.6 m
Beam	40 m
Draught	5.5 m
Crew	20
Fuel capacity	400,000 l
Water capacity	10,000 l
Max speed	30 kts
Operational speed	23-30 kts

Classification: DnV +1A1-HSLC, R1 A - EO NAUT.
Structure: High-tensile steel and seawater-resistant aluminium.
Propulsion: The propulsion arrangement is configured with either two diesel or two gas-turbine engines, each driving CP propellers, depending on the operational speed requirements. Water-jets can also be accommodated for the higher speeds.

WESTAMARAN 9600 RO-RO FERRY
(DESIGN)

Specifications

Length overall	95.8 m
Beam	34 m
Draught	4 m
Crew	12
Vehicles	730 lane m
Fuel capacity	150 m³
Max speed	44 kts
Operational speed	35-44 kts
Range	600 n miles

Propulsion: The main engines are either diesels or gas-turbines.

WESTAMARAN 9500 OCEAN FLYER
(DESIGN)

Announced in the latter half of 1991 the Westamaran 9500 is another large high-speed passenger/car ferry being offered by Westamarin A/S. The two symmetrical hulls and bridging structure are to be made of high-tensile steel with the rest of the construction in aluminium. A ride control system will be employed and the engine room will be fully automated.

Specifications

Length overall	95 m
Beam	29 m
Draught	4.5 m
Payload	450-500 t
Crew	20
Passengers	1,000
Vehicles	320
Propulsive power	40,000/50,000 kW
Operational speed	45 kts
Range	600 n miles

Structure: Hull material: high-tensile steel. Superstructure material: aluminium alloy.
Propulsion: Engines: gas-turbine.

WESTAMARAN 8700
(DESIGN)

Specifications

Length overall	87 m
Beam	26 m
Draught	3.4 m
Crew	115 max
Passengers	950
Fuel capacity	75 m³
Water capacity	10 m³
Propulsive power	24,000 kW
Operational speed	35 kts

Artist's impression of the Stena HSS 900 catamaran ferry **1996**

Classification: DnV +1A1, HSCL, R2 Passenger vessel - EO NAUT or equivalent recognised classification society.

WESTAMARAN 7500 (DESIGN)

Specifications

Length overall	75 m
Beam	25.5 m
Draught	3.4 m
Crew	15
Passengers	900
Vehicles	187 cars
Fuel capacity	40,000 l
Water capacity	6,000 l
Propulsive power	22-30 mw
Operational speed	35-40 kts

WESTAMARAN 7100 OCEAN FLYER (DESIGN)

This design is offered in two versions; an all-aluminium construction or high tensile steel hulls with aluminium superstructure. Various stowage arrangements for cars with fixed/hoistable tween decks are offered to accommodate vehicles of double-decker/commercial trailer size. A choice of diesel or gas-turbine propulsion is available.

Specifications

Length overall	72.53 m
Beam	22.6 m
Draught	3.44 m
Payload	230-250 t
Crew	12
Passengers	450
Vehicles	128-144
Operational speed (depends on structural material)	33-40 kts
Range	350 n miles

Structure: Hull material: aluminium or high-tensile steel.

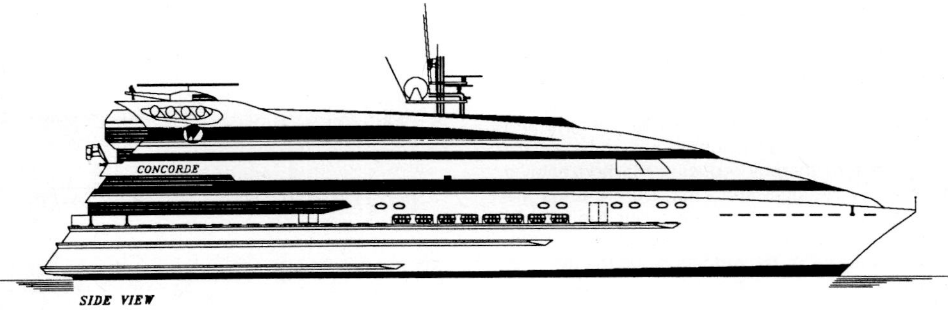

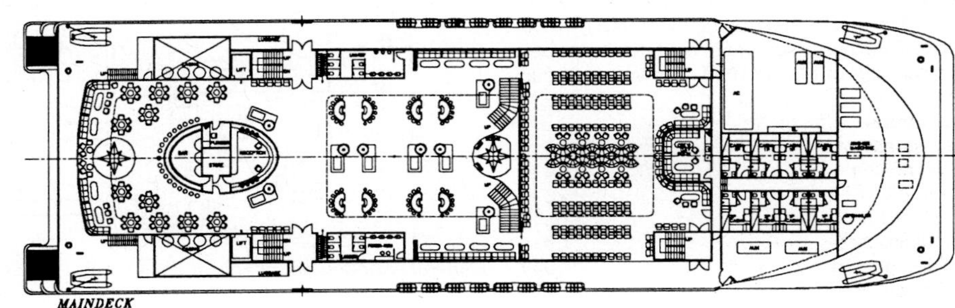

Westamaran 8700 (design) general arrangement **1995**

Superstructure material: aluminium alloy.
Propulsion: Engines: gas-turbine or diesel.

STENA HSS 900

Two of these vessels have been ordered by Stena Line and are currently under construction. These craft are designed to carry 900 passengers and 210 cars at speeds of up to 40 knots. The vessels are to be powered by ABB gas turbines.

Whilst few details have been released on the design of their caft, it is known that the first vessel is scheduled to operate on the Göteborg to Fredrikshavn route in mid-1996.

UPDATED

WESTAMARIN WEST A/S

A member of the Swede Ship Invest AB Group

PO Box 143, Vågsbygd, N-4501 Mandal, Norway,

Tel: +47 (38) 262222
Telex: 21514 WRIN N
Fax: +47 (38) 262302

Svein Berntsen, *Technical Manager*
Gowart Askildsen, *Purchasing Manager*
John Ihme, *Production Manager*

Westamarin West A/S in Mandal was established in 1961, under the name of Westermoen Hydrofoil A/S, to produce, develop, design and market high-speed vessels for commercial and military purposes. A number of Supramar PT hydrofoil craft were built in the 1960s.

In 1970-71 the first catamaran of an assymetric-hull type, the Westamaran, was introduced. The

Foilcat 2900 **1994**

catamaran was based on a semi-planing hull form of welded marine aluminium. This design was the first high-speed catamaran to enter ferry operations. In 1988 the yard delivered its first catamaran with symmetrical, slender hulls and in 1991 Westamarin West A/S departed from pure catamaran development with its latest vessels, FOILCAT 2900 and FOILCAT 3000, which are foil-assisted catamarans. Recently an South-east Asian owner placed an order for one FOILCAT 3000 with options for two more.

Since 1986 Westamarin West A/S has been part of the Swede Ship Invest AB group of companies which includes Oskarshamns Varv AB, Swede Ship Composite AB and an electrical contractor, Electro Swede AB.

FOILCAT 2900 (Yard No 107)

Foilcat 2900 is a hydrofoil-assisted catamaran initially jointly developed with Hardanger Sunnhordlandske Dampskibsselskap (HSD) operators of hydrofoils and catamarans since 1961. Model testing has been carried out by the Norwegian Marine Technology Research Institute A/S (MARINTEK) and by the Institut fur Schiffs- und Meerestechnik, Technical University, Berlin.

The Foilcat 2900 combines the best properties of the slender-hull catamarans with the speed capability of hydrofoil craft fitted with fully submerged foils. The foils are not surface-piercing and do not give self-stabilisation.

At a certain combination of rudder control and speed, a banking angle is introduced automatically during the turn thereby reducing the horizontal *g* forces on passengers and craft. During turns the outer hull is not raised thereby avoiding the harmful effects of propeller and foil aeration. Maximum rudder angles are ±25°, the rudders being the front foil struts.

The Foilcat 2900 entered service between Århus and Copenhagen (2.5 hour journey time) towards the end of November 1992 being chartered by DSØ and Difko Shipinvest A/S, and continued in operation to the end of March 1993. The vessel is currently operating in Indonesia.

Specifications

Length overall	29.25 m
Length waterline	26.4 m
Beam	8.36 m
Draught, hullborne	3.65 m
Draught, foilborne	1.9 m
Displacement, min	104 t
Displacement, max	123 t
Passengers	140
Fuel capacity	5,000 l
Water capacity	500 l
Propulsive power	2 × 2,000 kW
Max speed	50 kts
Operational speed	45 kts

Classification: DnV 1A1 R90 light craft passenger catamaran EO.

Structure: Hull material: plates Al. AA 5083, profiles Al. AA 6082. Superstructure material: aluminium alloy. Foils: stainless steel.

Propulsion: The main engines are two MTU 16V 396 TE 74L, 2,000 kW each at 2,000 rpm.

These drive two propellers, Ulstein-Liaaen Speed-Z Type CPZ 60/42 -125C (1.25 m diameter, 4-blade, Newton Rader blade sections, at 800 rpm)

Control: The vessel is fitted with three foils, two separate front foils (turntable-mounted) and a single transverse rear foil. Spanwise variation of angle of attack and camber have been incorporated to avoid downwash induced cavitation on the rear foil. The front foils are fitted with winglets to increase lift/drag ratio and during development tests a speed increase of approximately 7.5 knots was obtained.

Active foil stabilisation system equipped with trailing edge flaps actuated hydraulically (Movator actuators) via electric control valves working through an electronic control system named Flight Control System (FCS). Software for this system was provided by Camo A/S, supported by MARINTEK A/S which supplied the basis for this development.

At a speed of approximately 10 knots (at which the hull is still providing stability) the FCS is activated, the stabilisation is automatic and the trim is kept at +1° and roll is damped by the lifting forces generated by the foils. The FCS has control of the stabilisation long before it is possible to enter the lifting height at which insufficient hull stabilisation would result; this would occur at approximately 28 knots. The transition stability between the hullborne and the foilborne condition is therefore fully controlled.

Auxiliary systems: The auxiliary systems are powered by: two Mitsubishi S6F-T diesels, 56 kW each at 1,500 rpm; and two Newage Stamford UCM224G generators, 65 kVA, 230 V 3-phase 50 Hz.

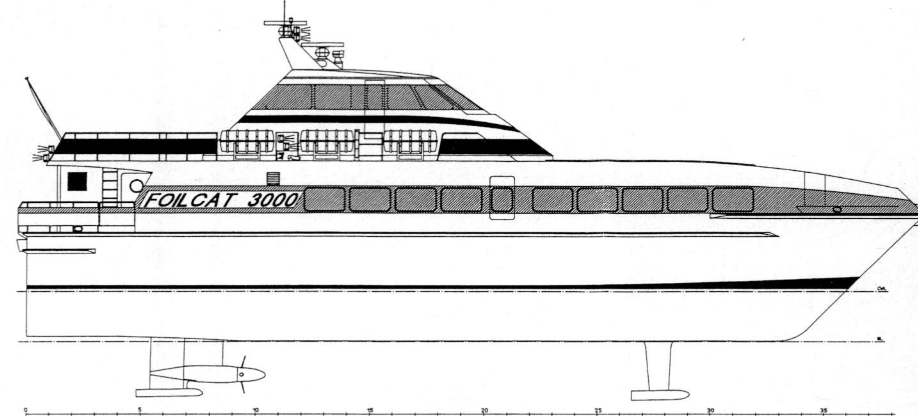

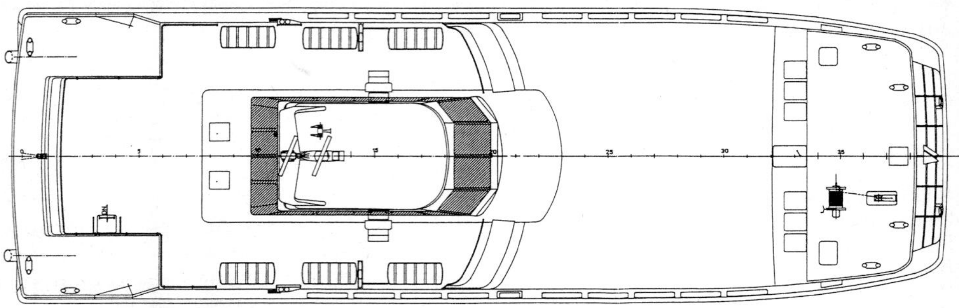

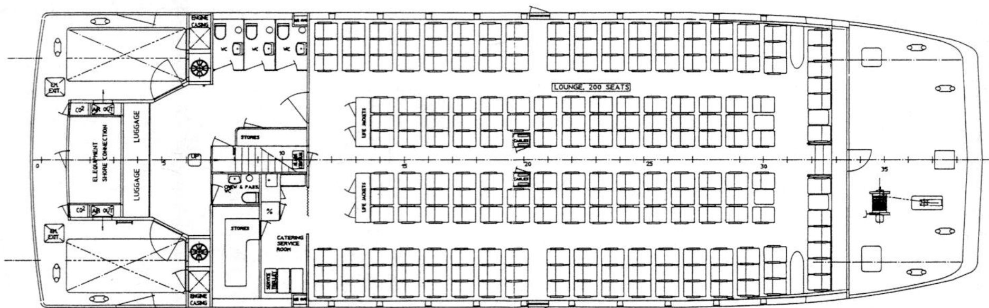

General arrangement of Foilcat 3000 **1995**

FOILCAT 3000

This design is a direct development of the 2900 design and provides increased passenger capacity. One vessel is currently under construction with two further craft under negotiation.

Specifications

Length overall	30 m
Length waterline	27 m
Beam	9.55 m
Draught, hullborne	3.8 m (including foils)
Payload	15 t
Passengers	200
Fuel capacity	5,000 l
Water capacity	1,000 l
Propulsive power	2 × 2,000 kW
Max speed	47 kts
Operational speed	44 kts

Classification: DnV +1A1 HSLC R2 Passenger, EO; IMO Code of Safety for Dynamically Supported Craft.

Structure: The hull is to be built in seawater-resistant aluminium. Alternately, deckhouse/wheelhouse to be built in plastic composites. The foils and struts to be built in steel of quality S165M. Three flap sets to be mounted on aft foil and one set on each of front foils. Flaps and similar parts can alternately be built in titanium or similar.

Propulsion: High-speed marine diesel engines (two), make 16V 396 TE 74L; driving two Ulstein Speed-Z CPZ-60/42-125L-HC units, with controllable-pitch propellers. Reduction gears are included.

Electrical system: 380 V AC, 50 Hz, 3 phase +N with supply from two motor aggregates.

220 V AC, 50 Hz, 1 phase.

24 V DC with supply from batteries.

The motor aggregates (2) are each 65 kVA.

Control: The forward foil struts are to be used as rudders. The struts/rudders are to be electrically synchronised.

WESTAMARAN 5000
Anne Lise

This vessel originally delivered as a thermo-cargo catamaran has been converted by Oskarshamns Varv to a passenger/car ferry; please see Oskarshamns entry for details. For details of the vessel in its original form please see the 1992-93 edition of this book.

WESTAMARAN W86

A total of 23 Westamarin W86s were built up to 1979 with speeds in the range of 24 to 28 knots. Details of these craft are given in earlier editions of this book.

WESTAMARAN W95

This longer version of the W86, of which 14 were delivered, can carry up to 248 passengers. Details of these craft are given in earlier editions of this book.

WESTAMARAN 3000 (ex-*W88*)

A faster but slightly smaller capacity craft than the W86 or W95 and replacing the W86, four W88s were sold, the last, *Fjordsol*, being slightly longer at 29.4 m. Details of these craft are given in earlier editions of this book.

Westamaran 3700 S Maria *1991*

WESTAMARAN 3000

Fjordsol

Specifications

Length overall	29.4 m
Length waterline	25.4 m
Beam	9 m
Draught	2.2 m
Payload	10 t (additional)
Passengers	202
Fuel capacity	2 × 2,800 l tanks
Water capacity	600 l
Propulsive power	2 × 1,150 kW
Operational speed	30 kts
Range	270 n miles

Propulsion: 2 × MTU 12V 396 TB83, 1,150 kW each at 1,940 rpm, ZF BW 455S gearboxes. Auxiliary engines: 2 × Daimler Benz OM 352A driving Stamford MSC 234F generators, 3 × 230 V, 50 Hz.

Structure: aluminium AA 5083.

WESTAMARAN W100

Specifications

Length overall	32.9 m
Beam	9.8 m
Draught	2.0 m
Passengers	300
Operational speed	28 kts

Propulsion: Main engines: 2 × MTU 16V 396 TB 83 or similar.

Catamaran craft built (W100) 1980 to 1982

Yard No	Name	Delivered
75	*Gibline I* (*W100D*) (ex-*Gimle Belle*, ex-*Condor 6*)	April 1980
76	*Independencia* (ex-*Gimle Bird*)	September 1981
77	*Porec* (ex-*Gimle Bay*)	January 1982
83	*Nearchos* (ex-*Venture 83*)	May 1982

WESTAMARAN 3700 SC

(Yard Nos 93 and 94)

In 1988 these craft were operated by Saltens Dampskibsselskap, and Ofotens Dampskibsselskap.

Specifications

Length overall	36.5 m
Length waterline	31.1 m
Beam	9.5 m
Draught	1.47 m
Payload	15 t (additional cargo)
Passengers	195
Fuel capacity	2 × 4,000 l tanks
Water capacity	600 l
Operational speed	35 kts
Range	280 n miles

WESTAMARAN 3700 SC

***Pilen* (ex-*Vindile*)**

(Yard No 95)

Specifications

Length overall	37 m
Length waterline	31.1 m
Beam	9.5 m
Draught	1.47 m
Passengers	322
Propulsive power	2 × 2,040 kW

Classification: DnV +1A1, R45, light craft passenger vessel.

Structure: Hulls, superstructure and deckhouse with wheelhouse built in seawater corrosion-resistant aluminium plates AA5083 (D54S 1/4H), profiles in AA 6081 WP (B 51 SWP).

Catamaran craft built (W86) 1971 to 1979

Yard No	Name	Originally delivered	Seats
21	*Fjordglytt*	June 1971	140
22	*Ar Vo* (ex-*Trident 1*, ex-*Belle de Dinard*, ex-*Karmsund*)	January 1972	
24	*Fjordtroll*	May 1972	140
25	*Supercats* (ex-*Sauda*)	June 1972	148
26	*Mayflower*	October 1972	134
27	*Kongsbussen*	April 1973	
28	*Hertugbussen*	May 1973	
29	*Tedno*	June 1973	140
32	*Flycat* (ex-*Koegelwieck*)	September 1973	135 + cargo
34	*Olavsbussen*	February 1974	
35	*Tjelden* (ex-*Haugesund*)	November 1973	94 + cargo
41	*Hilde* (ex-*Fjordbris*, ex-*Storesund*)	September 1974	165
42	*Stilbris* (ex-*Carib Link*, ex-*Fjordkongen II*)	January 1975	140
44	*Brynilen*	June 1975	94 (+ 6 t freight)
45	*Øygar*	September 1975	140
46	*Fjorddronningen*	January 1976	174
47	*Trident 2* (ex-*Highland Seabird*)	May 1976	
48	*Ternøy* (ex-*Fjorddrott*)	June 1976	167
49	*Fjordprinsessen*	March 1977	163
65	*Bornholm Express* (ex-*Steigtind*)	June 1977	182
54	*Mediteran*	June 1978	
67	*Marina I*	July 1978	
66	*Hornoy*	October 1979	136

Catamaran craft built (W95) 1974 to 1982

Yard No	Name	Originally delivered	Seats
36	*Trident 5* (ex-*Vingtor*)	May 1974	240
37	*Tranen* (ex-*Sleipner*)	June 1974	
38	*Rapido de Formentera* (ex-*Sunnhordland*)	April 1975	180
	Nasstro Azzurro (ex-*Martini Bianco*, ex-*Amarischia*, ex-*Martini Bianco*)	May 1975	
43	*Alisur Azul* (ex-*Westjet*) (W95T)	December 1976	
51	*Salem* (ex-*Tryving*) (ex-*Draupner*)	April 1977	
52	*Tunen*	May 1977	180
50	*Pegasus*	June 1977	
53	*Tranen*	June 1978	180
68	*Siken* (ex-*Tumleren*)	April 1979	180
79	*Trident 6* (ex-*Azur Express*, ex-*Alisur Amarillo* (W95D))	April 1981	211
80	*Tromsprinsen*	July 1981	210
81	*Trident 4* (ex-*Celestina*)	June 1981	218
84	*Trident 3* (ex-*Venture 84*)	July 1982	205

Catamaran craft built (W88) 1981 to 1986

Yard No	Name	Delivered	Seats
78	*Haugesund*	March 1981	180
82	*Midthordland*	November 1981	170
88	*Skogøy*	May 1985	132 + 10 t cargo
91	*Fjordsol*	June 1986	202

Propulsion: 2 × MTU 16V 396 TB 84 engines, 2,040 kW each, at 1,940 rpm. These drive two Kamewa 63S water-jet units.
Auxiliary systems: 2 × Mercedes OM 352 driving Stamford MSC 234 E70 kVA, 250 V, 50 Hz, 3-phase generators.

WESTAMARAN 3700 S
Maria
(Yard No WM 101- OV 527)
Specifications

Length overall	37 m
Beam	9.5 m
Draught	1.7 m
Passengers	318
Fuel capacity	13,000 l
Water capacity	1,200 l
Propulsive power	2 × 2,000 kW
Max speed	41 kts
Operational speed	38 kts

Classification: DnV
Propulsion: Engines: 2 × MTU 16V 396 TE 74L, 2,000 kW each at 1,980 rpm. These drive two Kamewa 63S II water-jet units.
Auxiliary systems: 2 × Mercedes-Benz OM 352A generators.

Catamaran craft built (W3600, ex-W120) 1987

Yard No	Name	Seats	Delivered	Operator
89	*Zi Liang*	354	January 1987	Nantong Hi-Speed Passenger Ship Co, China

Catamaran craft built (W3700 SC) 1988

Yard No	Name	Seats	Delivered	Owner
93	*Salten*	195 + 30 m² cargo hold	April 1988	Saltens Dampskibsselskap A/S
94	*Ofoten*	195 + 30 m² cargo hold	May 1988	Ofotens Dampskibsselskap A/S

Catamaran craft built (W3700 S) 1988

Yard No	Name	Seats	Delivered	Owner
95	*Pilen* (ex-*Vindile*)	300	1988	
101	*Maria*	318	June 1990	Brudey Frères

Catamaran craft built (W4100 S) 1990

Yard No	Name	Seats	Delivered	Owner
103	*Kyrmskaya Strela*	292	1990	Black Sea Shipping Co
104	*Golubayaa Strela*	300	Mar 1990	Black Sea Shipping Co
105	*Irbis*	292	Aug 1990	Novorossiysk Shipping Co
106	*Sirius*	292	Sep 1990	Novorossiysk Shipping Co

Catamaran craft built or on order (W4200 S) 1990 onwards

Yard No	Name	Seats	Delivered	Owner
108	*Westamaran 4200 S*	230	June 1991	Mitsui Company, Japan
109	*Mahatani Express*	304	1992	PT Pelni, Indonesia
–	*Seajet 1*	400	1995	Seajet, Greece

WESTAMARAN 3600 (ex-W120)
Zi Liang
Specifications

Length overall	36.2 m
Length waterline	32.26 m
Beam	9.77 m
Passengers	354
Fuel capacity	2 × 5,000 l tanks
Water capacity	1,200 l
Speed	25-27 kts
Range	270 n miles

Classification: DnV + 1A1, R45.
Structure: aluminium AA5083.
Propulsion: Main engines: 2 × MTU 16V 396 TB 83, each 1,540 kW at 1,940 rpm.
Gearboxes: ZF BU 755S, ratio 3.07:1.
Auxiliary engines: 2 × Mercedes-Benz OM 352A.
Auxiliary systems: 2 × Stamford MSC 234F

WESTAMARAN 4100 S
Kyrmskaya Strela
Golubaya Strela
Irbis
Sirius
On 9 May 1989 Westamarin A/S announced an order from AKP Sovcomflot for two catamaran ferries of a new type, the Westamarin 4100 S, for delivery to the Soviet Union Black Sea Shipping Company together with an option for a further two. This option was taken up in June 1989. The value of the first order was given as approximately NOK80 million for the two vessels.
Specifications

Length overall	42.5 m
Length waterline	37.2 m
Beam	10 m
Draught	1.6 m
Passengers	292
Fuel capacity	13,260 l
Water capacity	2,000 l
Max speed	38 kts
Operational speed	35 kts
Range	400 n miles

Classification: USSR Register of Shipping (RS) KM 2 II A3 pass CAT.
Propulsion: Engines, main: 2 × MTU 16V 396 TB 84, 2,040 kW each at 1,940 rpm; driving 2 × Kamewa 71 S water-jet units.
Auxiliary systems: 2 × Mercedes-Benz OM 366A.

WESTAMARAN 4200 S
Westamarin 4200 S
The first vessel of this type was delivered to Japan in June 1991 and named after the type. Two further vessels of this type were delivered to Japan in 1991 and 1992 and built by Oskarshamns Varv AB, Sweden. (See Oskarshamns Varv AB entry under Sweden).
Specifications

Length overall	42.23 m
Beam	10 m
Draught	1.6 m
Crew	4
Passengers	230
Propulsive power	2 × 2,000 kW
Max speed	38 kts
Operational speed	35 kts

Classification: NKK (NS * AI Catamaran Passenger Ship, MNS * Restricted Coastal Service)
Propulsion: Engines: 2 × MTU 396 V16 TE 74L, 2,000 kW each; driving Kamewa 71S II water-jets through 2 × ZF BU 755 gearboxes, ratio 2.333:1.
Auxiliary systems: 2 × Mitsubishi S6 FT diesels, 56 kW each driving Stamford Generators UCM 224 G23, 380 V AC, 50 Hz, 65 kVA.

UPDATED

Westamaran 4200 S
1992

SINGAPORE

ALUMINIUM CRAFT (88) PTE LTD

A division of Singmarine Industries Ltd

55 Gul Road, Singapore 2262

Tel: +65 862 4800
Fax: +65 862 4803

Chang Seak Foo, *Director and General Manager*
Fong Weng Meng, *Technical Manager*
Gabriel Tan, *Marketing Manager*

Singmarine's aluminium specialist, Aluminium Craft (88) Pte Ltd has accumulated over 24 years of experience in the building and repair of aluminium craft and industrial structures. Apart from its own proven monohull it also offers other hull designs such as the SWATH (Small Waterplane Area Twin Hull) and SES (Surface Effect Ship), Lock Crowther catamaran design, and construction of any designs of owners' choice.

Island Pearl *1993*

SS23

The first of these vessels, the *Glory of Singapore*, was launched in July 1989; both are for service on the Singapore to Batam route and have seating for 130 passengers. They are powered by two 671 kW high-speed diesel engines, giving a service speed of 25 knots.

The hulls of these vessels are of asymmetrical form, backed up by research and development with support from the Singapore Economic Development Board which provided a grant for the design.

Island Pearl
Sea Pearl

These semi-displacement hull catamarans were delivered in 1991 for service between Singapore and Tioman Island. Air conditioning is fitted.

Specifications

Length overall	34.5 m
Beam	9.82 m
Draught	1.55 m
Crew	6
Passengers	228
Fuel capacity	9,000 l
Water capacity	3,000 l
Propulsive power	2 × 1,260 kW
Speed	25 kts

Classification: GL + 100A4K.

Propulsion: Engines: 2 × Deutz MWM TBD 604B V12, MCR 1,260 kW each, driving two nickel aluminium-bronze 5-blade fixed-pitch propellers, left- and right-handed.

Auxiliary systems: 2 × Perkins/Stamford 80 kVA.

Tai An
Dong Qu Er Hao

Ordered by Humen Lungwei Passenger Transportation of Guandong in mid-1992, *Tai An* was delivered in July 1993. The craft was designed by Lock Crowther of Australia.

A repeat order was contracted in late 1993 and *Dong Qu Er Hao* was delivered in mid-1994.

Dong Qu Er Hao *1995*

Specifications

Length overall	35 m
Beam	11 m
Draught	1.5 m
Crew	8
Passengers	270
Fuel capacity	10,000 l
Propulsive power	2 × 1,260 kW
Max speed	29 kts

Propulsion: The main engines are two MTU 12V 396 TE 74L each driving conventional fixed pitch propellers via a reverse reduction gearbox.

Auxiliary systems: Generators: 2 × 100 kVA MTU 6R 099 TE51.

38 m CATAMARAN

Tai King

Ordered by Humen Transportation Co in 1994, this 360 passenger, 15 crew vessel is similar to *Tai An* and was delivered in mid-1995.

UPDATED

KVÆRNER FJELLSTRAND (S) PTE LTD

29 Tuas Crescent, Singapore 2263

Tel: +65 861 4180
Fax: +65 861 4181

Are D Dahl, *President*
P P Wee, *Senior Marketing Manager*
Aage Christensen, *Senior Operations Manager*

With over 60 high-speed catamaran vessels sold to 21 countries, Kværner Fjellstrand began construction in 1990 of a building yard in Singapore. Centrally placed in the Asia-Pacific region, the

Kværner Fjellstrand (S) Pte Ltd Shipyard in Singapore *1995*

Singapore yard is engaged in building the same range of vessels as the Norwegian yard and provides immediate after sales services in the region for existing and future operators of their vessels.

UPDATED

40 m Flying Cat Damania I *1996*

Catamaran vessels built or under construction by Kvaerner Fjellstrand (S) Pte

Type	Name	Seats	Delivered	Owner
40 m Flying Cat	*Perdana Ekspres*	352	April 1992	Inlandpark Sdn Bhd,
40 m Flying Cat	*Mabua Express*	248	November 1992	PT Mabua Intan Express,
40 m Flying Cat	*Universal Mk I*	259	December 1992	Woolaston Holdings Ltd,
40 m Flying Cat	*Universal Mk II*	259	December 1992	Woolaston Holdings Ltd,
40 m Flying Cat	*Universal Mk III*	258	October 1993	Woolaston Holdings Ltd,
40 m Flying Cat	*Universal Mk IV*	266	February 1994	Universal Mk IV Ltd,
40 m Flying Cat	*HKF I*	449	September 1993	HKY Ferry Co Ltd
40 m Flying Cat	*HKF II*	449	August 1993	HKY Ferry Co Ltd
40 m Flying Cat	*Universal Mk V*	266	February 1994	Universal Mk V Ltd,
40 m Flying Cat	*Paradise*	380	April 1994	Won Kwang Shipping
40 m Flying Cat	*Nam Hae Queen*	350	March 1994	Nam Hae Express Co
40 m Flying Cat	*Indera Bupula*	312	June 1994	Damania Shipping Ltd
40 m Flying Cat	*Damania I*	392	September 1994	Damania Shipping Ltd
40 m Flying Cat	*HKF III*	433	December 1994	HKY Ferry Co Ltd
40 m Flying Cat	*Aria Bupula*	270	January 1995	Bintan Resort Ferries
40 m Flying Cat	*Aremiti*	449	October 1994	Aremiti Pacific Cruises
40 m Flying Cat	To be named		1995	-
40 m Flying Cat	To be named		1995	-
40 m Flying Cat	To be named		1995	-
40 m Flying Cat	To be named		1995	-
40 m Flying Cat	To be named		1995	-
40 m Flying Cat	To be named		1995	-
40 m Flying Cat	*JumboCat I*	441	November 1995	Transtur-Aerobarcos
40 m Flying Cat	*JumboCat II*	441	November 1995	Transtur-Aerobarcos

MARINTEKNIK SHIPBUILDERS (S) PTE LTD

31 Tuas Road, Singapore 2263

Tel: +65 861 1706
Fax: +65 861 4244

Patrick Cheung, *Managing Director*
Priscilla Lim, *Financial Director*
Hans Erikson, *Director, Marketing and Sales*
Andrew Yeo, *Director, Project and Design*
Sölve Mårdh, *Director, Production*
Clas Norrstrand, *Director, Research and Development*

Marinteknik Shipbuilders (S) Pte Ltd was established in 1984 as FBM Marinteknik (S) Pte Ltd, for the building of high-speed vessels. To date, the yard has built more than 30 vessels for customers worldwide, of both monohull and catamaran type as passenger vessels and crew boats. Current craft under construction include passenger ferries with

Catamaran vessels built or under construction by Marinteknik Shipbuilders (S) Pte Ltd

Type	Yard No	Craft name	Owner/operator	Delivered	Engines	Classification	Payload	Speed
34 CCB	101	*Hakeem*	Ocean Tug Services	1985	2 × MTU 12V 396 TP 62 880 kW each	DnV R-60	50 passengers + 2.7 t cargo	27 kts
34 CCB	103	*Layar Sinar*	M I S C	1986	2 × MTU 12V 396 TB 83 1,185 kW each	DnV R-150	70 passengers + 6 t cargo	29 kts
34 CCB	105	*Layar Sentosa*	M I S C	1987	2 × MTU 12V 396 TB 83 1,185 kW each	DnV R-150	70 passengers + 6 t cargo	29 kts
36 CPV	111	*Airone Jet*	Med Mar srl, Naples	1988	2 × MTU 16V 396 TB 84 1,940 kW each	RINA/DnV	318 passengers	35 kts
34 CPV	112	*Jiu Zhou* (ex-*Shun de*)	Shun Gang	1987	2 × MTU 12V 396 TB 83 1,180 kW each	Z C	250 passengers	27 kts
36 CPV	115	*Condor 8*	Condor Ltd	1988	2 × MTU 16V 396 TB 84 1,940 kW each	DnV R-150	300 passengers	35 kts
36 CPV	117	*Selesa Ekspres*	Kuala Perlis-Langkawi Ferry Services Bhd	1990	2 × MTU 12V 396 TE 74L 1,400 kW each	DnV R-30	350 passengers	30 kts
41 CPV	119	*Camoes*	Hongkong Macao Hydrofoil Co Ltd	1989	2 × MTU 16V 396 TB 84 1,940 kW each	DnV R-25	306 passengers	38 kts
41 CPV	120	*Estrela do Mar*	Hongkong Macao Hydrofoil Co Ltd	1990	2 × MTU 15V 396 TB 84 1,940 kW each	DnV R-25	306 passengers	38 kts
41 CPV	121	*Lusitano*	Hongkong Macao Hydrofoil Co Ltd	1990	2 × MTU 16V 396 TB 84 1,940 kW each	DnV R-25	306 passengers	38 kts
41 CPV	123	*Vasco da Gama*	Hongkong Macao Hydrofoil Co Ltd	1991	2 × MTU 16V 396 TB 84 1,940 kW each	DnV R-25	306 passengers	38 kts
27 CPV	126	*Marine Star II*	Samavest Sdn Bhd	1990	2 × MTU 12V 396 TB 83L 1,180 kW each	DnV R-25	215 passengers	30 kts
41 CPV	127	*Santa Cruz*	Hongkong Macao Hydrofoil Co Ltd	1991	2 × MTU 16V 396 TB 74L 1,940 kW each	DnV R-25	306 passengers	39 kts
41 CPV	128	*Magellan*	Hongkong Macao Hydrofoil Co Ltd	1991	2 × MTU 16V 396 TE 74L 1,940 kW each	DnV R-25	306 passengers	38 kts
41 CPV	129	*St Malo*	—	1991	2 × MTU 16V 396 TE 74L 1,940 kW each	Bureau Veritas	350 passengers	35 kts
41 CPV	130	*Saphir Express*	Antilles Trans-Express	1994	4 × MTU 12V 396 TE 74L	Bureau Veritas	387 passengers	39.5 kts
41 CPV	133	*Nam Hae Prince*	Nam Hae Express Co Ltd	1993	2 × MTU 16V 396 TE 74L 1,940 kW each	DnV R-90	359 passengers	36.5 kts
35 CPV	118		—	1995	2 × MTU 16V 396 TE 74L	DnV	300 passengers	37 kts
42 CPV	137	*Discovery Bay 1*	Discovery Bay	1995	2 × MWM 16V Diesels	DnV	500 passengers	33 kts
42 CPV	138	*Discovery Bay 2*	Discovery Bay	1995	2 × MWM 16V Diesels	DnV	500 passengers	33 kts
42 CPV	139	*Discovery Bay 3*	Discovery Bay	1996	2 × MWM 16V Diesels	DnV	500 passengers	33 kts
41 CPV	140	*Turquoise Express*	Antilles Trans-Express	1995	4 × MTU 12V 396 TE 74L	Bureau Veritas	387 passengers	40 kts
45 CPV	136	Under construction	Antilles Trans-Express	(1996)	4 × MTU 16V 396 TE 741	Bureau Veritas	445 passengers	42 kts

potential speeds of up to 50 knots and passenger capacities of up to 500.

An associated company, Marinteknik Verkstads AB of Sweden, ceased trading in 1994 and details of their craft are included in this entry in a separate table.

36 m CATAMARAN
Selesa Ekspres

Selesa Ekspres is a 36 m passenger catamaran vessel and was delivered to its owner in November 1990. Its route of operation is between Penang/Pulau Langkawi and Penang/Medan.

Specifications

Length overall	36.5 m
Beam	9.4 m
Draught	1.2 m
Displacement, max	109.2 t
Payload	26.8 t
Crew	6
Passengers	350
Fuel capacity	9,000 l
Water capacity	1,000 l
Propulsive power	2 × 1,400 kW
Max speed	32 kts
Operational speed	30 kts
Range	300 n miles

Classification: DnV +1AZ1 R-30 EO, Catamaran Light Craft.

Propulsion: 2 × MTU 12V 396 TE 74L high-speed marine diesel engines, each giving 1,400 kW at 2,000 rpm coupled to 2 × Kamewa 63-SII water-jets.

MARINJET 41 m CATAMARAN
Camoes

Camoes is one of a series of catamarans built by Marinteknik Shipbuilders (S) Pte Ltd. The Jumbocat Class as it is known, has proved to have good and efficient hull characteristics. The ride comfort for passengers is noted to be exceptional with the installation of a pitch damping system. To date, seven such craft owned by Hongkong Macau Hydrofoil Company Ltd have been put into service for the route between Hong Kong and Macau.

The 41 m vessel has a total seating capacity for 306 passengers in a single-deck seating arrangement.

Turquoise, a CPV 41 delivered to Antilles Trans-Express in 1995 **1996**

Specifications

Length overall	41.5 m
Beam	11 m
Draught	1.2 m
Displacement, max	130 t
Payload	27.11 t
Crew	8
Passengers	306
Fuel capacity	7,000 l
Water capacity	1,000 l
Propulsive power	2 × 1,940 kW
Operational speed	38 kts
Range	240 n miles

Classification: DnV +1A1 R-25 EO, Catamaran Light Craft

Propulsion: 2 × MTU 16V 396 TB 84 high-speed marine diesel engines, each giving 1,940 kW at 1,940 rpm coupled to 2 × MJP J650R-DD water-jets.

Fast catamaran craft built by Marinteknik Verkstads AB of Sweden which ceased trading in 1994

Yard No	Type	Marinteknik Designations Old	Marinteknik Designations New	Engines	Craft name	Cruise speed, full load, kts	Delivered to	Originally delivered	Application	Seats	Loaded displacement, tonnes
42	29 m	JC-F1	—	2 × MTU 12V 396 TC 82, 1,175 kW	*Formentera Jet* (ex-*Jaguar*, ex-*Jaguar Prince*, ex-*Mavi Hali*, ex-*Aliterreno 1*)	27	Spain	Nov 1980	Ferry	197	85
46	29 m	JC 3000	—	2 × MTU 12V 396 TB 83, 1,225 kW	*Apollo Jet*	29	Hongkong Macao Hydrofoil Co Ltd	Jan 1982	Ferry	215	86
47	29 m	JC 3000	—	2 × MTU 12V 396 TB 83, 1,225 kW	*Hercules Jet*	29	Hongkong Macao Hydrofoil Co Ltd	1982	Ferry	215	86
48	29 m	JC 3000	—	2 × MTU 12V 396 TB 83, 1,225 kW	*Janus Jet*	29	Hongkong Macao Hydrofoil Co Ltd	Oct 1982	Ferry	215	86
50	29 m	JC 3000	—	2 × MTU 12V 396 TB 83, 1,225 kW	*Duan Zhou Hu* (ex-*Triton Jet*)	29	Zhao Gang Steamer Navigation Co of China	1983/ 23 Sep 1986	Ferry	215	86
51	33.71 m	PV 2400	Marinjet 33 CPV	2 × MTU 12V 396 TB 83, 1,225 kW	*Alize Express* (ex-*Nettuno Jet*)		SURF, Congo	May 1984	Ferry	218	86
54	33.71 m	PV 2400	Marinjet 33 CPV	2 × MTU 12V 396 TB 83, 1,225 kW	*Jet Kat Express* (ex-*Jetkat I*)		ATE	1984	Ferry	240	93.67
55	33.71 m	PV 2400	Marinjet 33 CPV	2 × MTU 12V 396 TB 83, 1,225 kW	*Giove Jet*		Alilauro SpA	1985	Ferry	276	96
56	34 m	PV 3100 (Jumbo)	Marinjet 34 CPV-D	2 × MTU 16V 396 TB 83, 1,540 kW	*Lommen*	32	Dampskibsselskabet Øresund A/S	Dec 1985	Ferry	235	97.58
59	34.1 m	PV 3100	Marinjet 34 CPV-D	2 × MTU 16V 396 TB 83, 1,540 kW	*Ørnen*	32	Dampskibsselskabet Øresund A/S	Jul 1986	Ferry	235	97.68
60	34.1 m	CV 3400	Marinjet 34 CCB	2 × MTU 16V 396 TB 93, 1,700 kW	*Emeraude Express*	40	Chambon (SURF)	Jan 1986	Crew boat	240	99.8
61*	34 m	—	Marinjet 34 CCB	2 × MTU 16V 396 TB 83, 1,180 kW	*Layar Sentosa*	30	on charter to Shell Sarawak	1986	Crew boat	—	90
62	34 m	—	Marinjet 34 CPV-D	2 × MTU 16V 396 TB 84, 1,935 kW	*Giunone Jet*		Alilauro SpA	—	Ferry	—	—
69	34 m		Marinjet 34 CPV PV-D	2 × MTU 16V 396 TB 84, 1,935 kW	*Acapulco Jet*	34	Alilauro SpA	Apr 1989	Ferry	300	96
70	34 m	—	Marinjet 34 CPV	—	*Nettuno Jet*		Alilauro SpA	1988	Ferry	—	—
74	41.5 m	—	Marinjet 41 CPV-SD	2 × MTU 16V 396 TB 84, 1,935 kW	*Öregrund*		Hongkong Macao Hydrofoil Co Ltd	28 Nov 1988	Ferry	306	130
73	34 m	—	—	2 × MTU 16V 396 TB84	*Saud*	32.5	Yasmine Line	Nov 1990	Ferry	255	—
82	41.5 m	—	CPV	4 × MTU 12V 396 TE 74L	*Jet Kat Express II*	40	Compagnie Maritime des Caraibes	1991	Ferry	380	—
86	34 m	—	CPV	2 × MTU 16V 396 TE 74L	*Antilles Express*	—	Antilles Trans-Express	1992	Ferry	297	—
88	41 m	—	CPV	—	*Saint Malo*	—	Channiland	1993	Ferry	350	—

Selesa Ekspres *1993*

Magellan *1993*

CPV 41 CATAMARAN
Saphir Express
Turquoise Express

Saphir Express is a 42 m catamaran of Marinteknik standard and a sister vessel to *Jet Cat Express II*, earlier delivered from Marinteknik Verkstads in Sweden. *Saphir Express* was delivered to Antilles Trans-Express, Guadeloupe, in September 1994.

A further vessel, *Turquoise Express*, of the same size but with different superstructure styling was delivered to Antilles Trans-Express in mid-1995.

Specifications

Length overall	41.5 m
Beam	11 m
Draught	1.2 m
Crew	4
Passengers	387
Propulsive power	4 × 1,415 kW
Operational speed	40 kts

Classification: Bureau Veritas

Propulsion: The main engines are 4 × MTU 12V 396 TE 74L diesel engines, each rated 1,415 kW at 2,000 rpm; each driving an MPJ J650R water-jet; via ZF 465 gearboxes.

Saphir Express *in service with Antilles Trans-Express* *1995*

CPV 42 CATAMARAN

Three craft were ordered by Hong Kong Resort Co in 1994, all of the same type and were designed to offer a 20 minute shuttle service from Discovery Bay to central Hong Kong. The first vessel was delivered in January 1995, the second in July 1995 and the third in January 1996.

Specifications

Length overall	42 m
Beam	11.5 m
Draught	1.3 m
Passengers	500
Operational speed	33 kts

CPV 45 CATAMARAN

Antilles Trans-Express ordered one CPV 45 catamaran in 1995 for delivery in October 1996. Whilst this vessel is powered by four high speed diesel engines, it is envisaged that higher speeds of over 50 knots will be achieved with gas-turbine arrangements.

Specifications

Length overall	45.0 m
Length waterline	37.0 m
Beam	11.0 m
Draught	1.3 m
Displacement, min	180 tonnes
Crew	8
Passengers	445
Operational speed	41.5 kts

Propulsion: The vessel is powered by four MTU 16V TE 74L diesel each driving a water-jet unit via a reduction gearbox.

UPDATED

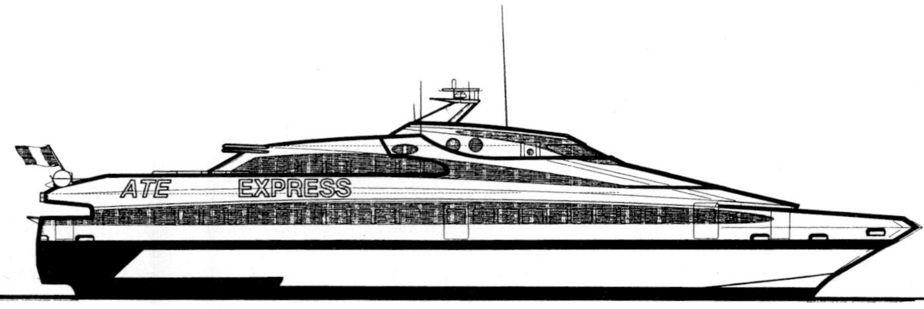

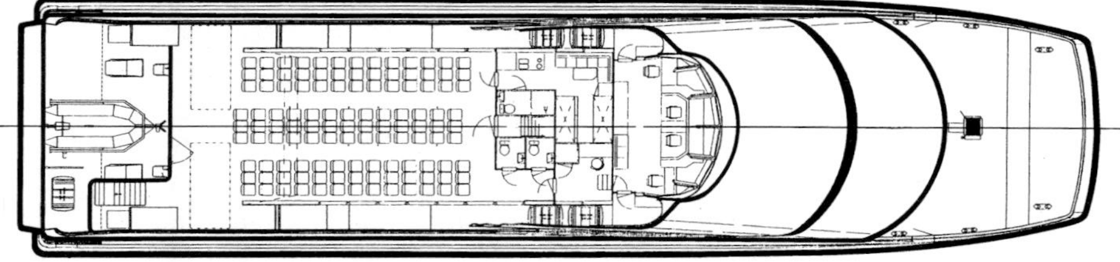

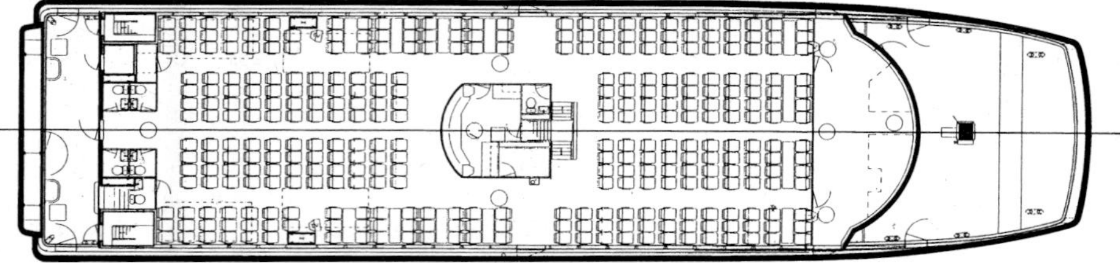

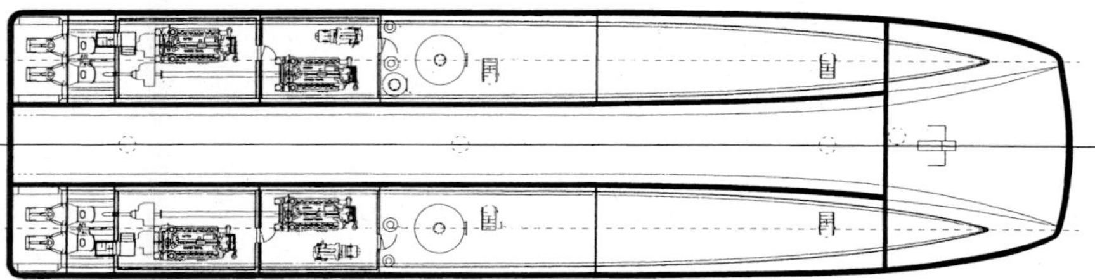

CPV 45, 445 seat catamaran
1996

SINGAPORE TECHNOLOGIES SHIPBUILDING & ENGINEERING LTD

PO Box 138, Jurong Town Post Office, Singapore 9161

Tel: +65 861 2244
Telex: 21206*SINGA RS
Fax: +65 861 3028/1601

R James Leo, *Executive Chairman*
See Leong Teck, *Senior Vice President*
Wong Kin Hoong, *Vice President*
Tan Pheng Hock, *Vice President*
Col Ting Tong Koi, *Vice President*
Tan Ching Eng, *Senior Manager*
Frankie Tan, *Senior Manager*
Han Yew Kwong, *Senior Manager*

Tai Ping **1993**

Singapore Technologies Shipbuilding & Engineering Ltd (STSE), a member of Singapore Technologies, announced in 1990 a contract to build a 282 passenger, 34.6 m high-speed catamaran ferry for operation between Hong Kong and the Pearl River Delta of Kwangtung Province, China.

Completely designed by STSE engineers, this vessel marks a significant move into the high-speed catamaran ferry business.

The company has, to date, built and on order, more than 100 aluminium high-speed vessels (with a length of 12 m or more) with speeds in excess of 20 knots.

34 m CATAMARAN
Tai Ping

Specifications

Length overall	34.6 m
Beam	10.5 m
Draught	2.1 m
Crew	10
Passengers	282
Fuel capacity	7,000 l
Water capacity	1,000 l
Propulsive power	2 × 1,412 kW
Max speed	29 kts
Operational speed	28 kts

Structure: Each hull is divided into seven separate watertight compartments by means of watertight bulkheads and has a forepeak, store void space, main engine room, auxiliary engine room and steering compartment. The accommodation cabin is sited above the main deck. The wheelhouse is arranged at the forward end of the upper deck.

Outfit: Immediately aft of the foredeck is the passenger saloon which also houses the toilets, a pantry and a kiosk.

The passenger saloon accommodates 272 passengers in aircraft style seats (non-reclinable type) with a fold-down plastic table. The VIP saloon, sited at the aft of wheelhouse on upper deck accommodates 10 VIPs in settee-seating. There are two cabins, provided on the upper deck, one for two officers and the other for eight crew.

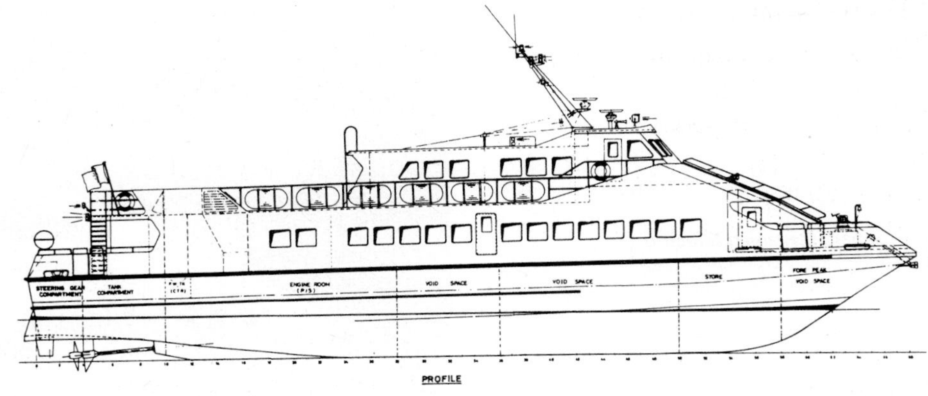

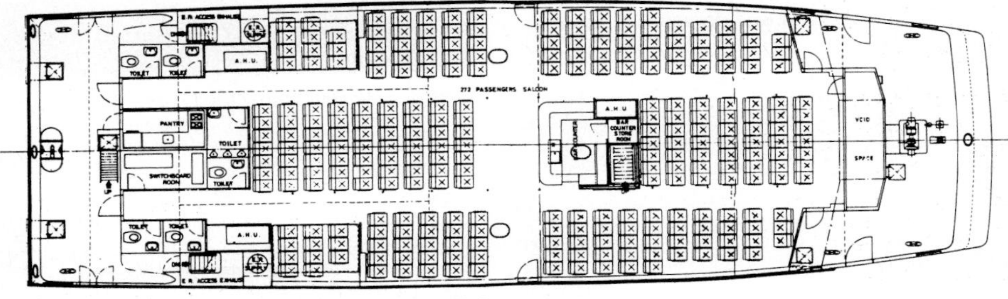

General arrangement of Tai Ping

All accommodation spaces are air conditioned.

Propulsion: The main engines are 2 × MTU 12V 396 TE 74L diesels, each producing 1,412 kW at 2,000 rpm MCR; driving fixed-pitch propellers through stern tube and shaft bearings; via ZF BW 465 gearboxes.

Electrical system: The primary system is 2 × 100 kVA, 380 V, 50 Hz, 3-phase; the secondary system is 230 V, 50 Hz, single-phase by 380/230 V transformers.

The emergency and engine starting use 24 V DC battery banks.

UPDATED

SOUTH AFRICA

TEKNICRAFT DESIGN

PO Box 381, Paarden Eiland 7420, South Africa

Tel: +27 (21) 790 1295
Fax: +27 (21) 790 4817

N De Waal, *Managing Director*
R Kalley, *Marketing*

The company PINI (Pty) Ltd was established in 1984 and since 1992 has been trading as Teknicraft Design. The company specialises in the design of waterborne craft, in particular medium- and high-speed catamarans.

Teknicraft Design currently deals with clients in South Africa, the United Kingdom, Europe, the

Sea Shuttle *during trials*
1994

Middle East and Australia and is constantly expanding its client base.

The company also offers a technical consulting service as well as assisting boatyards in project management and the streamlining of manufacturing processes.

Teknicraft and a finance company Competitive Concepts (Europe) Ltd have jointly constructed the 22.5 m foil-assisted catamaran ferry called *Sea Shuttle* and are marketing this and other vessels worldwide.

Sea Shuttle

The vessel is constructed in GRP foam sandwich to Lloyd's Register HCC(SC) service group 2.

Specifications

Length overall	22.5 m
Length waterline	19.6 m
Beam	7.2 m
Draught	1 m
Displacement	36 t
Payload	12 t
Crew	3
Passengers	117
Max speed	40 kts
Operational speed	30 kts
Range	250 n miles

Propulsion: 2 × MWM Deutz 234 TBD V16 diesels, driving 2 × Hamilton 422 water-jets, through 2 × Reintjes reduction gearboxes.

50 m SUPER SHUTTLE FERRY (DESIGN)

Specifications

Length overall	50 m
Length waterline	15.9 m
Displacement, min	185 t
Displacement, max	300 t
Passengers	360
Vehicles	57 cars
Fuel capacity	15 t
Water capacity	3t
Operational speed	35 kts
Range	270 n miles

Structure: Aluminium alloy.

Propulsion: Main engine: 2 × LM 500 gas-turbines, driving water-jets.

UPDATED

SWEDEN

OSKARSHAMNS VARV AB

A member of the Swede Ship Invest AB Group

PO Box 704, S-572 28 Oskarshamn, Sweden

Tel: +46 (491) 85500
Fax: +46 (491) 15312

Curt Tappert, *Managing Director*
Olle Johansson, *Technical Manager*
Ronnie Petersson, *Repair and Production Manager*

Part of the Swede Ship Invest AB Group of Rönnäng, Sweden, Oskarshamns Varv AB has been involved in the building of Westamarin catamarans.

Seajet 1, a Westamaran 4200 built by Oskarshamns Varv AB ***1996***

W-4200
Seajet 1

This vessel is a four engine development of the proven W-4200S class, and was delivered to Seajet in Greece in 1995.

Specifications

Length overall	42.0 m
Length waterline	37.4 m
Beam	10.0 m
Draft	1.8 m
Crew	6
Passengers	400
Fuel capacity	14,800 l
Water capacity	2,000 l
Propulsion power	5,940 kW
Max speed	42 kts
Operational speed	38 kts
Range	400 nm

Classification: DnV +1A1, HSLC, RZ, Passenger, EO.

Propulsion: The vessel is powered by four MTV 12V 396 TE74L diesel engines each driving a Kamewa 56S water-jet via a Reintjes VLJ 730H reduction gearbox.

Auxiliary systems: Two Stamford VCM 274E generators rated at 104 KVA each, with each generator being powered by a Scania 90 kW diesel engine. The vessel is fitted with a Maritime Dynamics T-foil/trim tab active ride control system.

W-4200 S
Mirage

Oskarshamns Varv's NB 531 *Mirage* was delivered to Northwest Shipping Ltd on 25 June 1991 and is a sister vessel to the Westamarin A/S NB 108 *Westamarin 4200 S* delivered to Mitsui, Japan, in June 1991. *Mirage* was later sold to Japan leaving the yard in August 1991. The vessel is the result of a co-operation between the two sister yards in the Swede Ship Group, Oskarshamns Varv AB and Westamarin West A/S.

Specifications

Length overall	42.23 m
Beam	10 m
Draught	1.6 m
Passengers	408

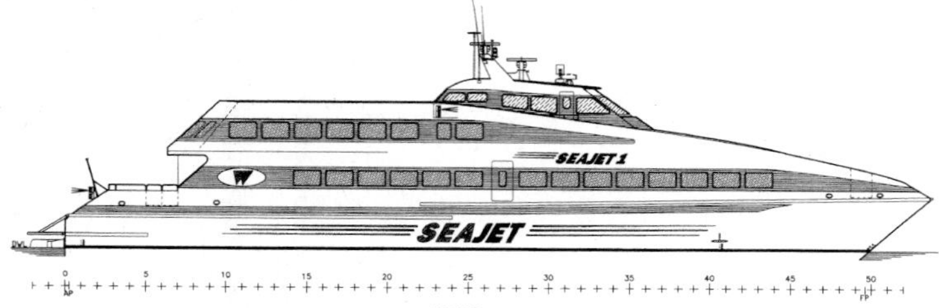

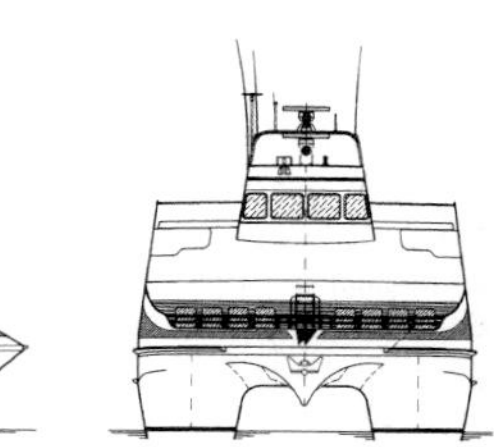

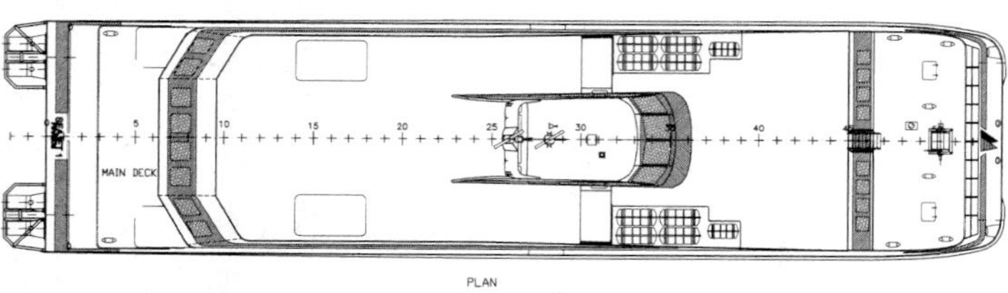

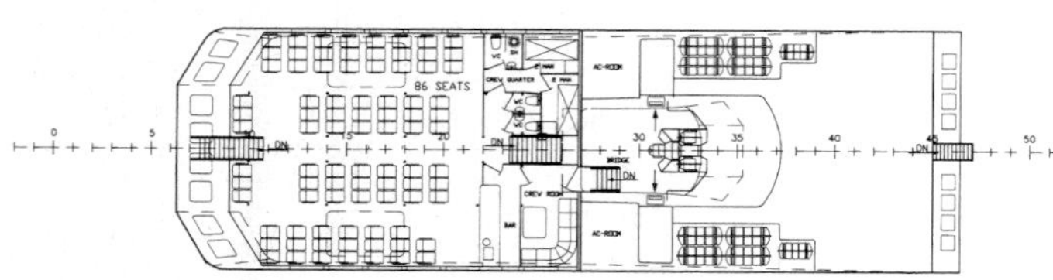

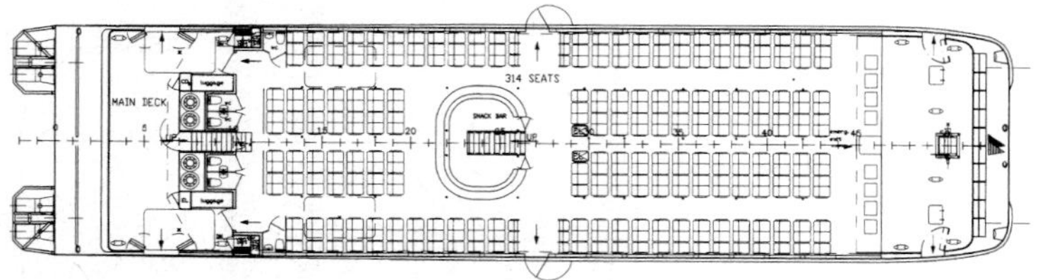

General arrangement of Seajet 1, a four engined 4200 class craft ***1996***

Fuel capacity	13,200 l
Water capacity	2,000 l
Propulsive power	2 × 2,000 kW
Max speed	38 kts
Operational speed	35 kts

Classification: DnV +1A1 R90 LC EO.
Propulsion: The main engines are 2 × MTU 396 V16 TE 74L, 2,000 kW each, at 2,000 rpm; driving 2 × Kamewa 71S II water-jets; via 2 × ZF BU 755 gearboxes, ratio 2.333:1.
Electrical system: 2 × Mitubishi S6 FT 56 kW diesels driving Stamford UCM 224 G23 generators.

Pelni Ekspres Satu

Delivered in 1992 to Jakarta this Westamarin 4200 S is very similar to the *Mirage* except for different auxiliary engines, which are Volvo Penta TAMD 71A, 110 kW at 1,500 rpm, and the main engines are rated at 1,830 kW, 1,940 rpm (tropical).

W-5000 CF
Madikera (Ex-Anne Lise)

This vessel is a car ferry conversion of the original W-5000 *Anne Lise,* the 49.5 m thermo-cargo catamaran which was delivered in August 1987, Yard No 92. Details of the vessel in its old configuration are given in the 1992-93 edition of this book.

This car ferry conversion was ordered by Brudey Frères for operation on a Guadeloupe to Martinique route with a trip time of about 3 hours. She was delivered in May 1993.

The vessel is equipped with two MacGregor Navire hydraulically operated ramps, port and starboard on the aft car deck.

Specifications

Length overall	49.45 m
Length waterline	43.6 m
Beam	14 m
Draught	2.6 m
Crew	8
Passengers	450
Vehicles	35 cars
Fuel capacity	40,000 l
Water capacity	2,000 l
Propulsive power	4 × 2,000 kW
Operational speed	30 kts

Classification: DnV +1A1 R280 LC Car Ferry A-EO.
Structure: Hull material: aluminium alloy.
Superstructure material: aluminium alloy.
Propulsion: The main engines are 4 × MTU 396 16V TE 74L, 2,000 kW each at 2,000 rpm; driving 4 × four Kamewa 63S II water-jets; via 4 × ZF BU 755 reduction gearboxes.
Electrical system: 2 × Volvo Penta/Stamford generators or similar, 130 kVA, 380 V 50 Hz 3-phase.

W-5600 CF (DESIGN)

This design is based on the proven W-5000 CF Class.

Specifications

Length overall	56 m
Beam	16 m
Draught	2.6 m
Payload	100 t
Passengers	450
Vehicles	50
Fuel capacity	2 × 26,000 l
Water capacity	1 × 2,000 l
Propulsive power	2 × 5,420 kW
Max speed	40 kts
Operational speed	36 kts

Classification: DnV +1A1, R2, HSLC, Car Ferry A, EO.
Structure: Seawater-resistant aluminium (marine grade).
Propulsion: The main engines are 2 × Caterpillar 3616 each producing 5,420 kW at 1,000 rpm; driving 2 × Kamewa 100S II or 4 × Kamewa 71S II water-jets.
Electrical system: 2 × Stamford/Volvo Penta or similar each 130 kVA, 3 × 380 V, 50 Hz or similar.
Control: One motion damping system with active flaps for damping of pitch, heave and roll. Regulation system type Robertson Tritech with software from Camo.

W-7500 (DESIGN)

Specifications

Length overall	75 m
Beam	25.50 m
Draught	3.40 m
Payload	350 t
Passengers	900
Vehicles	190 cars or 158 cars + 8 buses
Fuel capacity	40,000 l
Water capacity	6,000 l
Propulsive power	4 × 5,500 kW
Operational speed	36 kts

Classification: DnV +1A1, R1, HSLC, Car Ferry A, EO.
Structure: Seawater-resistant aluminium (marine grade).
Propulsion: The main engines are 4 × Ruston 16 RK270 diesels, each producing 5,500 kW at 1,000 rpm; driving 4 × Kamewa 112SII or similar; via 4 × reduction gears.
Electrical system: 4 × generator sets each 150 kVA, 3 × 380 V 50 Hz or similar.

UPDATED

THAILAND

ITALTHAI MARINE LTD

Italthai House, 11th Floor, 2018 New Petchburi Road, Bangkok, Thailand

Tel: +66 (2) 314 6101/7578/7246
Telex: 21225 ITELECT TH
Fax: +66 (2) 314 6385

Dr Chaijudh Karnasuta, *Chairman*
Angelo Gualtieri, *Managing Director*

Dou Men (Yard No 78)
Zhong Shan Hu (Yard No 80)

Two catamaran ferries were delivered in June and July 1990 to Yuet Hing Marine Supplies, Hong Kong, for the Hong Kong to Tao Mun, China route. These vessels are powered by two MWM TBD 604B V12 1,250 kW high-speed diesel engines driving Kamewa 63 S water-jet units.

VERIFIED

Dou Men
1993

UNITED KINGDOM

ALUMINIUM SHIPBUILDERS LTD

Fishbourne Quay, Ashlake Copse Road, Fishbourne, Isle of Wight PO33 4EE, UK

Tel: +44 (1983) 884719
Fax: +44 (1983) 884720

J A Davies, *Managing Director*
M J Love, *Chairman*
P D P Kemp, *Deputy Chairman*
M J Peters, *Production Director*
P Owen, *Contracts Manager*

Aluminium Shipbuilders was formed in 1983 by the current Managing Director and principal shareholder, John Davies. Initially, ASL undertook a design contract for the Belgian Shipbuilders Corporation for a new Bridge Erection Boat (BEB).

In early 1985 ASL was instrumental in the sale of two Australian designed and built 30 m catamarans to Sealink (UK) Ltd for service on the Portsmouth to Isle of Wight route. These craft, designed by International Catamaran Designs Pty Limited (InCat) were built at their yard in Hobart, Tasmania.

The first InCats built in Europe were the result of an initiative in late 1985 whereby, in association with McTay Marine Limited, the company responded to a Ministry of Defence (Navy) MoD(N) enquiry for the supply of Towed-Array Recovery/Deployment Vessels (TARVs). In December 1985 this joint venture resulted in the award of a contract for three TARVs and ASL undertook the fabrication and assembly of these vessels for fitting out by McTay Marine on Merseyside.

In 1986 ASL was awarded a contract for a 16 m Catamaran Riverbus from Thames Line plc. Subsequently, and after successful proving trials with the first craft named the *Daily Telegraph*, a further seven slightly larger 17.5 m craft were built in the succeeding two years, all for Thames Line.

Early in 1989 ASL obtained a £5 million contract from Condor Limited to build a 49 m wave piercing catamaran of InCat design.

Condor 9 was delivered in August 1990 and operated a daily service from March to November on the arduous Western Channel route from St Malo to Weymouth and return, via the Channel Islands. This

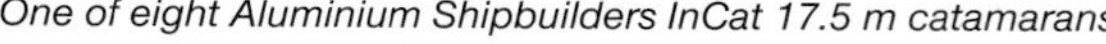

One of eight Aluminium Shipbuilders InCat 17.5 m catamarans **1992**

Condor 9 *built by Aluminium Shipbuilders Ltd* **1992**

vessel, which carries 450 passengers in two air conditioned saloons at a service speed of 35 knots, was built to the classification requirements of Det Norske Veritas Light Craft rules.

During the last quarter of 1991 the company received a contract for the fabrication of a novel high-speed trimaran passenger ferry. The craft is the prototype of a 70-seat variant which, with its inherent low-wash characteristics and economical propulsion arrangement, is intended as the next generation of smooth water fast river ferries.

In 1992 ASL expanded its high-speed craft repair facilities to cater for the increasing volume of specialised repair work associated with the entry into service of further SeaCats.

The company is currently in the process of acquiring construction facilities large enough to accommodate the next generation of SeaCat (of 78 m and above) for an ever growing marketplace.

RIVER 50

In August 1987, the first of a series of eight lightweight, high-speed passenger catamarans was delivered to Thames Line plc for operation between Charing Cross Pier and West India Dock on the River Thames. The vessel is powered by twin Volvo Penta TAMD 71A engines driving Riva Calzoni water-jets. Delivery was completed in 1988.

Specifications

Length overall	16.35 m
Beam	5.4 m
Draught	0.6 m
Fuel capacity	2 × 320 l
Water capacity	100 l
Propulsive power	2 × 228 kW
Operational speed	23-25 kts

Classification: UK DoT Class V smooth water limits.

Propulsion: The main engines are 2 × Volvo Penta TAMD 71A, 228 kW each at 2,500 rpm; driving Riva Calzoni IRCL 39 D water-jets; via MPM IRM 301 PL-1 gearboxes.

17.5 m CATAMARAN

A total of seven vessels was ordered by Thames Line plc for delivery during 1988. The vessels are 17.5 m long and have revised interior arrangements which allow for a spacious cabin for 62 passengers.

Specifications

Length overall	17.5 m
Beam	5.4 m
Draught	0.6 m
Passengers	50-70
Max speed	30 kts

Propulsion: water-jets.

49 m WAVE PIERCING CATAMARAN

Condor 9

The order by Condor Ltd for a 49 m InCat wave piercing catamaran was announced on 18 April 1989. Designed to carry 450 passengers, *Condor 9* replaced two hydrofoil vessels. The vessel was handed over in late August 1990.

Specifications

Length overall	48.7 m
Length waterline	40.5 m
Beam	18.2 m
Hull beam	3.3 m
Draught	1.9 m
Crew	15
Passengers	450
Fuel capacity	2 × 7,200 l
Water capacity	2 × 1,000 l tanks
Operational speed	35 kts

Classification: DnV +1A1 Light Craft (CAT) R45 Passenger Ship EO. Also surveyed under UK Department of Transport category Class 2, Short International Voyage vessel.

Structure: welded aluminium

Propulsion: The main engines are 4 × MWM TBD 604BV 16, 1,682 kW each at 1,800 rpm; driving 4 × MJP J650R-DD water-jet units.

If one engine should break down a speed of 30 knots can be maintained; each engine with its water-jet unit is entirely independent of the other three in its operation.

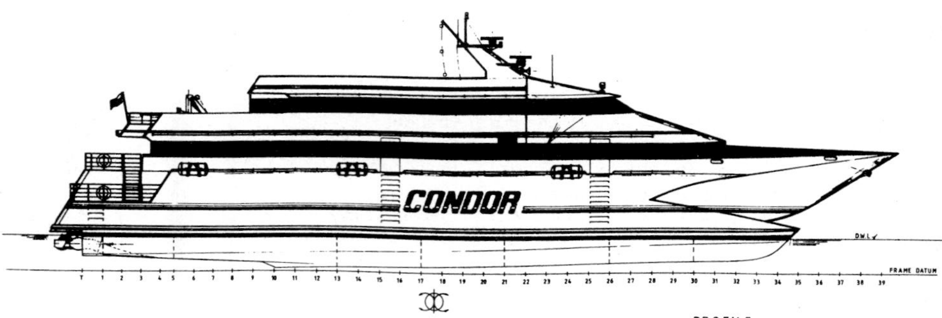

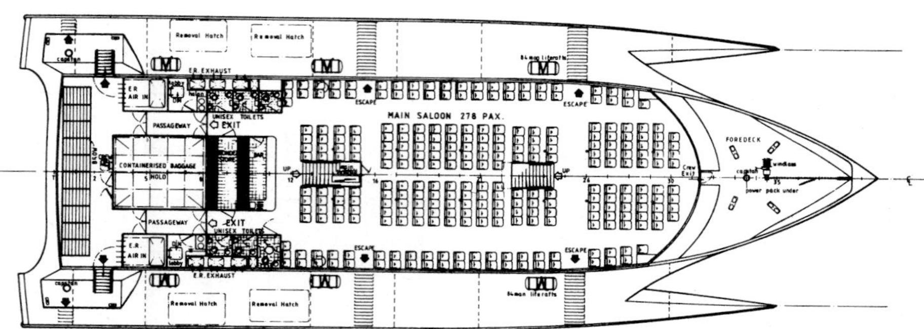

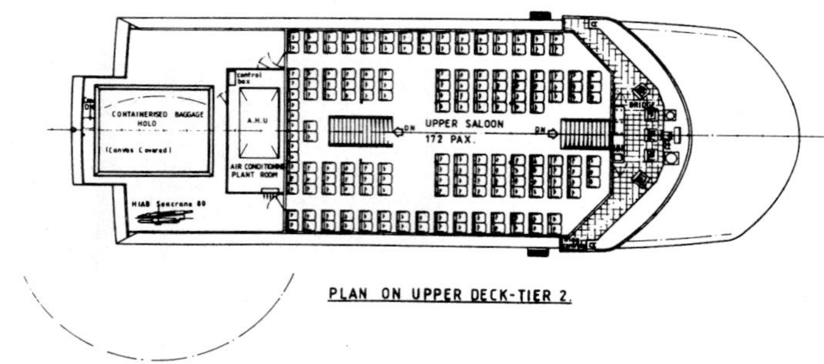

Condor 9

Craft built		Seats	Date
InCat 17.5 m	*Barclays Bank*	51	1987
InCat 17.5 m	*London Docklands*	62	April 1988
InCat River 50	*Le Premier* (ex-*Daily Telegraph*)	62	May 1988
InCat 17.5 m	*Chelsea Harbour*	62	May 1988
InCat 17.5 m	*Debenham Tewson and Chinnocks*	62	Aug 1988
InCat 17.5 m	*Harbour Exchange*	62	Aug 1988
InCat 17.5 m	*Daily Telegraph*	62	1988
InCat 17.5 m	*London Broadcasting Company*	62	1989
InCat WPC 49 m	*Condor 9*	450	1990

VERIFIED

FBM MARINE GROUP

Cowes Shipyard, Cowes, Isle of Wight, UK

Tel: +44 (183) 297111
Telex: 86466 FAMBRO G
Fax: +44 (183) 299642

Michael Roberts, *Deputy Chairman*
John Warbey, *International Sales Director*
Malcolm Keith, *Managing Director*
Nigel Warren, *Chief Designer*

The FBM Marine Group, formerly Fairey Marinteknik and Fairey Marine, builds of a wide range of monohull and catamaran vessels for many applications. FBM Marine has also produced the first UK-built Swath, the Atlantic Class Fast Displacement Catamaran. Details of this 36.4 m vessel are given in the *Swath Vessels* section of this book.

THAMES CLASS CATAMARAN (RTL HYDROCAT)

There have been three of these 62-seat minimum-wash high-speed ferries delivered. The concept originated with Robert Trillo Ltd (RTL) and was introduced to Fairey Marine Ltd (now FBM Marine Ltd) in 1986. It combines a number of features specifically aimed at optimising a design of a relatively high-speed vessel for river use. Of particular importance in such applications is the minimisation of wash disturbance and noise. Both of these aspects are inherent in the RTL concept, coupled with minimum water and air draughts.

The remarkably low wash of the concept is of particular value in rivers such as the Thames where very shallow conditions occur at low tide in many areas. The Riverbus Partnership took delivery of three Thames Class catamarans from January 1992 onwards and operated them on the Thames as commuter ferries.

Specifications

Length overall	25 m
Length waterline	23 m
Beam	5.7 m
Draught	0.75 m
Crew	2
Passengers	62
Fuel capacity	1,000 l
Max speed	25 kts

Structure: The hull structure is an FRC sandwich laminate with the bridge platform, box beams and salon constructed in low-maintenance marine grade aluminium alloy.

Propulsion: Two 6-cylinder in-line, turbocharged, heat exchange-cooled Scania DSI 11 marine diesel engines fitted with flanged-mounted MPM 320 reverse gearboxes drive the two Riva Calzoni IRC 390 water-jet units, via Aquadrive Cardan shafts.

FBM Marine Thames Class catamaran (RTL Hydrocat) in service on the Thames **1993**

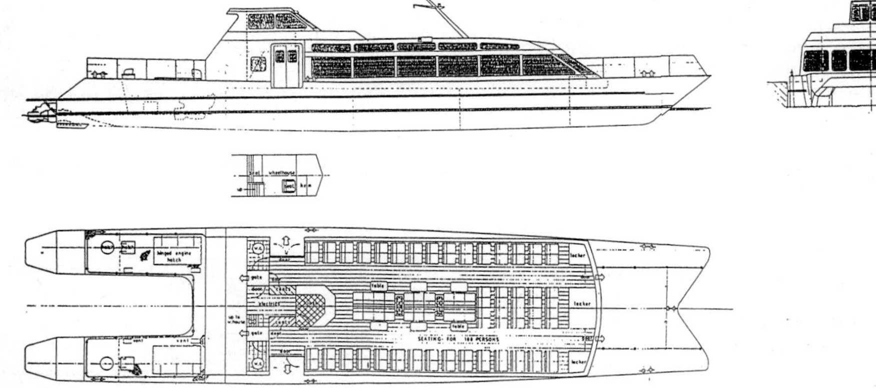

General arrangement of 29 m Thames Class catamaran (design)

30 m CITY SLICKER CATAMARAN (DESIGN)

The 30 m city slicker is an ultra low wash aluminium catamaran specifically designed for high-speed operation on riverine and harbour ferry routes.

Designed for medium- and high-speed passenger routes this variation of the 30 m City Slicker is capable of carrying 100-135 passengers at speeds up to 35 knots.

Specifications

Length overall	32.4 m
Length waterline	30 m
Beam	8 m
Draught	1 m
Passengers	100-135
Operational speed	30 kts

Structure: Aluminium hull and superstructure.

Propulsion: Main engines: 2 × MWM TBD 234 V12, driving a pair of water-jets.

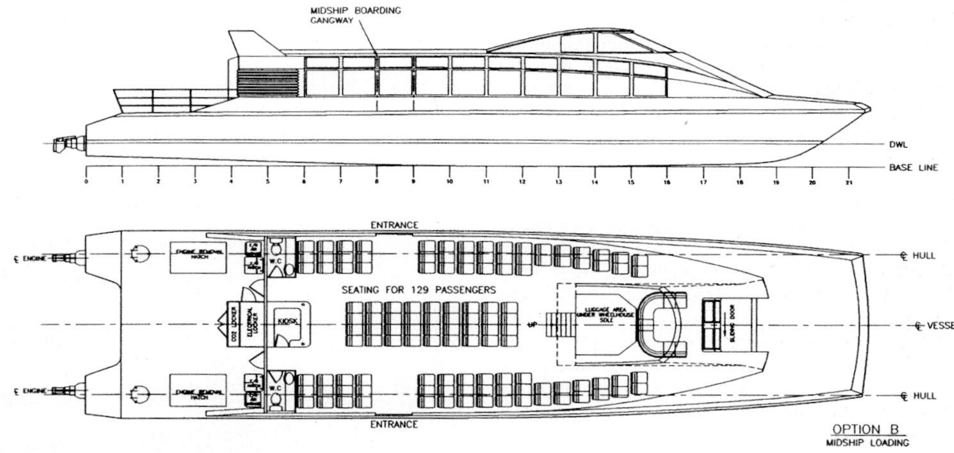

General arrangement of FBM's 30 m City Slicker catamaran (design) **1995**

SUBMARINE SUPPORT VESSEL *Adamant*

This vessel delivered in 1983 to the Ministry of Defence is based on the symmetrical hulls of the Solent Class range of passenger catamarans. The water-jet-propelled aluminium catamaran craft features a constant tension brow/gangway arrangement and large hydraulically operated fenders to facilitate 'at sea' transfers to and from submarines lying offshore.

The transfer system consists of an 8.1 m long aluminium brow pivoted at the inboard end to the base of an Effer Model 9600/3S hydraulic crane. A constant tension winch fitted on the crane supports the brow, allowing its outboard end, which is fitted with wheels and rubber tyres, to rest on the submarine. Relative movement between the two vessels is compensated by the automatic operation of the constant tension winch.

To prevent any possibility of damage to the submarine hull during such operations, two large foam filled fenders, each 2.5 m long × 1.25 m diameter, can be deployed on each side of the SSV. These fenders are normally stowed in deck cradles and are lowered and maintained in position by locally controlled hydraulic winches and an endless belt which passes through an eye located at water level.

Specifications

Length	30.8 m
Beam	7.8 m
Draught	1.1 m
Propulsive power	2 × 507 kW
Max speed	23 kts
Range	250 n miles

Propulsion: Engines: 2 × Cummins KTA19M diesels. Transmissions: 2 × ZF gearboxes.
Thrust device: 2 × MJP water-jets.

SOLENT CLASS CATAMARAN *Red Jet 1* and *Red Jet 2*

Another low-wash catamaran design, the 31.5 m Solent Class is in service with Red Funnel; the first of two was delivered in February 1991, following its launching on 4 December 1990.

The Solent Class catamarans are specifically designed for operations on coastal routes, rivers and urban environments.

During trials, *Red Jet 1* in full load condition (that is, 120 passengers, baggage, full fuel, water and three crew) achieved the following results:

Speed, maximum (measured mile): 38.3 knots at 100% MCR

FBM 30.8 m submarine support vessel Adamant **1993**

FBM Marine Solent Class catamaran ferry Red Jet 1 *operated by Red Funnel* **1996**

Speed, contract: 32.5 knots at 63% MCR
Speed, single engine: 24 knots
Acceleration: 35 knots in 47 s in 520 m
Fuel consumption: 375 l/h at 32.8 knots

The 30 m Solent Class Catamaran can maintain cruising speed of 38 knots in a 1 m head sea, and is well within the vertical acceleration limits prescribed for normal passenger comfort.

Specifications

Length overall	31.5 m
Beam	8.4 m
Draught	1.1 m
Displacement, max	65 t
Passengers	120
Fuel capacity	1,685 l
Water capacity	250 l
Propulsive power	2 × 1,360 kW
Operational speed	32.5 kts

Classification: DnV +1A1, R15, EO and UK Department of Transport Class IV for Solent use only.

Structure: Hull: marine grade aluminium, BS 1470 N8 plate, H30 TF extrusions.

Propulsion: Engines: 2 × MTU 12V 396 TE 84, 1,360 kW each, at MCR, 1,940 rpm; driving two MJP 650 water-jet units, driven via ZF gearboxes.

Control: The craft responds very quickly to the steering control at all speeds. The maximum rate of turn at 1,800 rpm is 6.6°/s. The turning circle under full helm becomes progressively tighter and the speed falls away to about 20 knots after a full circle. The diameter of this circle is approximately 325 m.

The craft can rotate about its own axis at the rate of 7.5°/s.

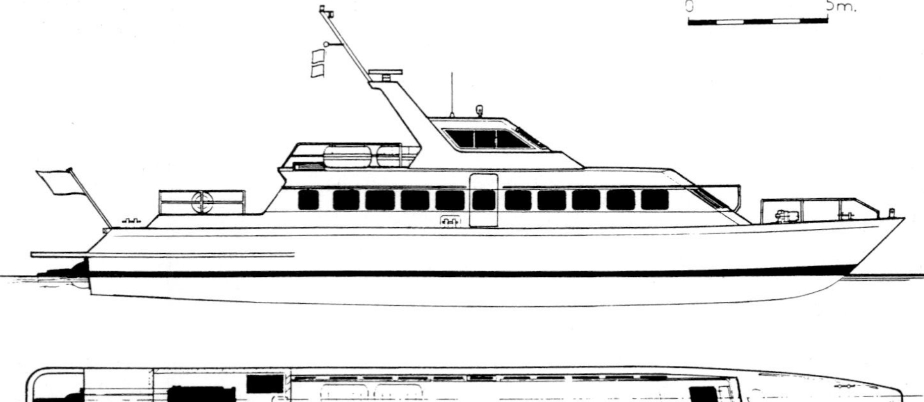

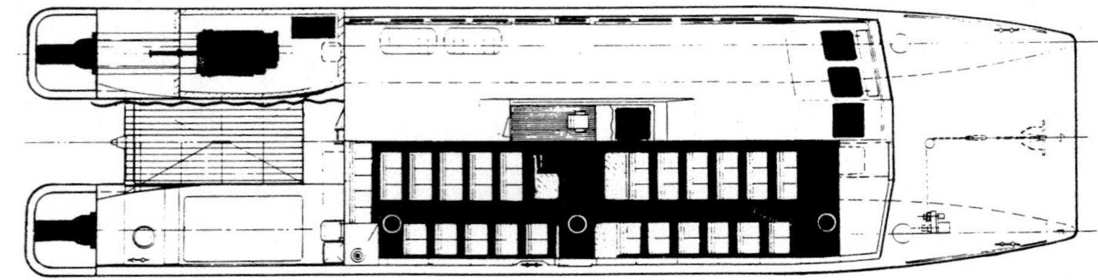
General arrangement of FBM Marine Solent Class catamaran ferry

35 m TRICAT CLASS CATAMARAN

Delivered in January 1994 this development of the well proven Solent Class catamaran transports passengers on the increasingly popular route from Hong Kong to the new airport at Shenzhen on the Chinese mainland.

This 35 m catamaran is designed for use in coastal and sheltered waterways and is particularly suitable for operation in busy harbours due to its manoevrability, shallow draught and low wash characteristics.

Specifications

Length overall	35.1 m
Length waterline	29.5 m
Beam	8.3 m
Draught	1.2 m
Passengers	160
Max speed	34 kts

Structure: Hull and superstructure material is aluminium.

Propulsion: Engines: 2 × MTU 12V 396 TE74.
Thrust devices: 2 × MJP water-jets.

35 m Tricat Class catamaran during sea trials **1994**

45 m TRICAT CLASS CATAMARAN

FBM's 45 m Tricat Fast Passenger has been specifically designed in association with one of the world's leading designers of luxury yachts and mini cruise liners, Terry Disdale.

This 312-seat catamaran is the result of FBM's extensive research and development programme to build a passenger catamaran which can achieve very high speeds with good passenger comfort without recourse to foils or air cushioned systems.

This 45 m fast passenger catamaran is designed to meet the requirements of the Hong Kong Marine Department for short international voyages out of

45 m Tricat Class catamaran on trials **1995**

Hong Kong under a Hong Kong flag and DnV Classification R1 for High-Speed Light Craft.

Five of these Tricats have been delivered to CTS-Parkview Ferry services for the route between Hong Kong and Macau. Two Tricats were built under licence by Babcock Rosyth (Fabricators) Ltd at the Rosyth Royal Dockyard. The first Tricat was launched on 8 September 1994 and delivered to Hong Kong in January 1995.

A further five Tricats were ordered in November 1995 for delivery to the same owner.

Specifications

Length overall	45 m
Length waterline	40 m
Beam	11.80 m
Draught	1.45 m
Payload	36.1 t
Passengers	312
Fuel capacity	7,500 l
Propulsive power	2 × 4,200 kW
Max speed	47 kts
Operational speed	44 kts
Range	125 n miles

Classification: DnV Classification R1 for High-Speed Light Craft.

Structure: The hull is constructed with aluminium and the superstructure is aluminium with lightweight FRP cladding.

Propulsion: The Tricat is powered by two Caterpillar Solar Taurus gas-turbines each rated at 4,200 kW at 13,000 rpm. These engines drive via separate rigidly mounted reduction gearboxes to Kamewa water-jets. The turbines and gearboxes are mounted on a raft rigidly bolted to the ship's structure.

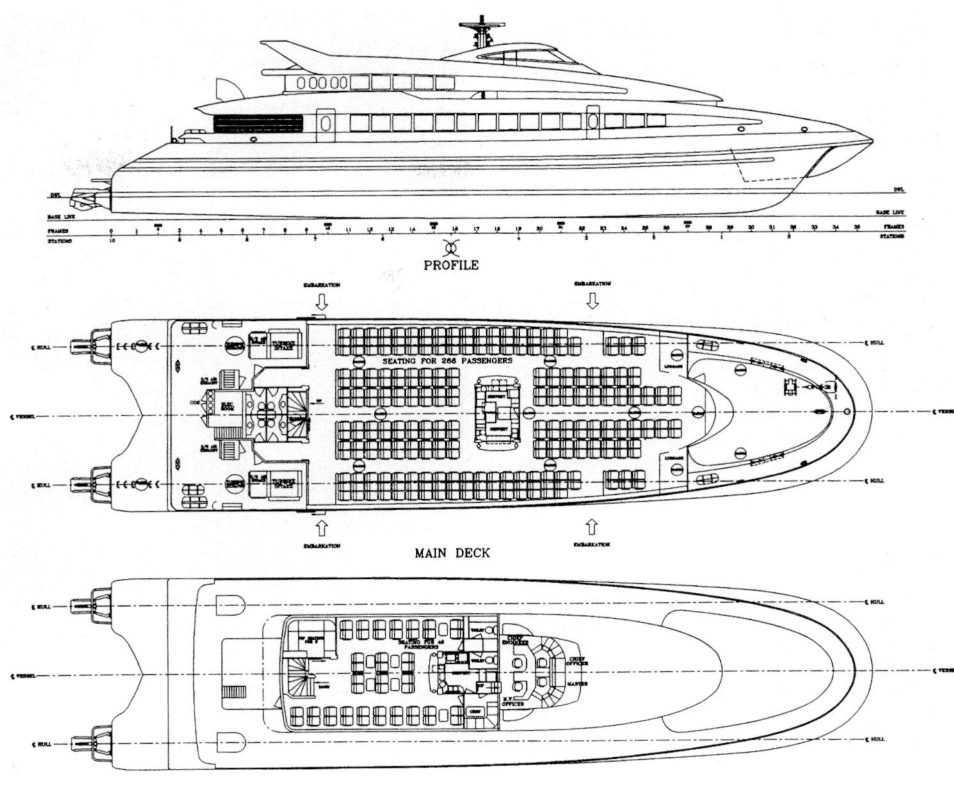

General arrangement of 45 m Tricat Class catamaran **1995**

FBM 45 m RIVER CAT

This passenger ferry is intended for intensive commuter passenger services within shallow harbours and sheltered routes. The River Cat specifically addresses the requirements for low fuel consumption and low wash. This catamaran incorporates the latest requirements of the IMO code for safety and incorporates the FBM TriCat unique futuristic styling.

Four of these craft were constructed for service on the River Tagus in Lisbon, Portugal. Two of these catamarans were subcontracted to a Portugese yard. The first craft was delivered in August 1995.

Specifications

Beam	11.8 m
Draught	1.38 m
Passengers	500
Fuel capacity	4,000 l
Water capacity	1,000 l
Operational speed	25 kts

Classification: IMO code for Safety of High-Speed Craft.

Structure: The hull is constructed of aluminium, and the superstructure is aluminium with lightweight FRP cladding.

Propulsion: The main engines are twin MWM TBD 616 V16s. These drive twin LIPS water-jets LJ76DL.

UPDATED

FBM 45 m River Cat Algés **1996**

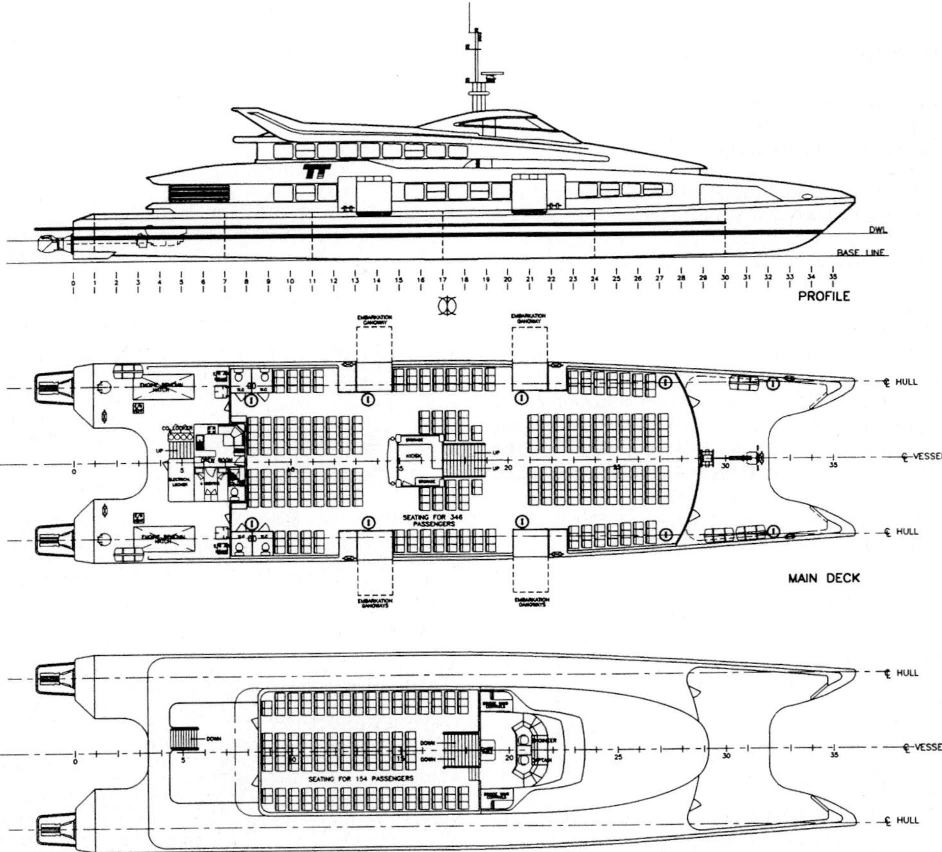

General arrangement of 45 m River Cat **1995**

LAY CONSTRUCTION LIMITED

65 Victoria Road, Swindon, Wiltshire, SN1 3BB

Tel: +44 1793 618566
Fax: +44 1793 488428

H P Lay, *Director*

Lay Construction Limited is an associated company to White Horse Ferries which operates fast passenger ferries on the river Thames in London. The company has recently completed its first 60 passenger fast trimaran vessel and started construction of the second. The helmsman's position and the berthing arrangements of these craft, and the earlier 12 seat prototype, *Ebeneezer Scrooge,* have been designed for single crew operation. Whilst the vessel is required by regulation to carry two crew when operating with more than 12 passengers, only one crew is actually required for all activities associated with the operation of these vessels.

12/60 PASSENGER FERRY

These craft were designed to operate fully laden at speeds up to 25 knots with low wash characteristics and simplified berthing arrangements. The first vessel, *Martin Chuzzlewit,* is powered by a 140 kW Perkins-Sabre diesel giving a speed of 12 knots. The second vessel is powered by a Deutz BF8M 350 kW diesel giving speeds of up to 20 knots.

Specifications

Length overall	17.5 m
Beam	5.5 m
Draught	0.8 m
Displacement, max	15 t
Crew	2
Passengers	60
Propulsive power	350 kW
Operational speed	20 kts

Martin Chuzzlewit *under construction* **1996**

Propulsion: The vessel is powered by a single Deutz BF8M 1015C diesel engine rated at 350 kW driving a single water-jet unit.

NEW ENTRY

UNITED STATES OF AMERICA

ALLEN MARINE, INC

Sitka, Alaska, USA

Alaskan Dream

Built in five months in 1988 for transport of miners to an island off Juneau, Alaska.

Specifications

Length overall	30 m
Displacement, max	72 t
Crew	3
Passengers	150
Operational speed	33 kts

Propulsion: Main engines: 4 × Caterpillar 3412 560 kW (750 hp) at 2,100 rpm, driving 4 × Hamilton 422 water-jet units, driven via a pneumatic clutch.

Golden Spirit

This 23.8 m catamaran, built in 1987 and designed by E A Drake Ltd of Seattle, was given a 222 per cent increase in installed power in 1992 to give a speed of 25 knots. Two MAN D2842 diesels, 746 kW each, were installed forward of the original engines, two DDC 8V71 diesels. Each new engine drives a 1 m diameter propeller via a ZF VW 165 reduction gearbox. The propellers are 2.78 m forward of the Hamilton water-jet inlets of the original installation. The water-jet inlets have been modified to straighten out the rotational component of the propeller slipstream. The modifications were carried out by the Union Bay Shipbuilding Corporation of Seattle. The vessel is now operated by Alaska Travel Adventures for wildlife tours from Sitka, Alaska.

VERIFIED

Golden Spirit *powered by two MAN and two DDC diesel engines* **1993**

DERECKTOR SHIPYARDS

311 East Boston Post Road, Mamaroneck, New York 10543, USA

Tel: +1 (914) 698 5020
Fax: +1 (914) 698 4641

Paul Derecktor, *President*
Mary Clerkin, *Marketing Manager*

Primarily a builder of fast monohull luxury yachts, Derecktor received an order in 1995 for two fast catamaran ferries for operation in New York Harbour. The company has two shipyards, one in Florida and one at the above address.

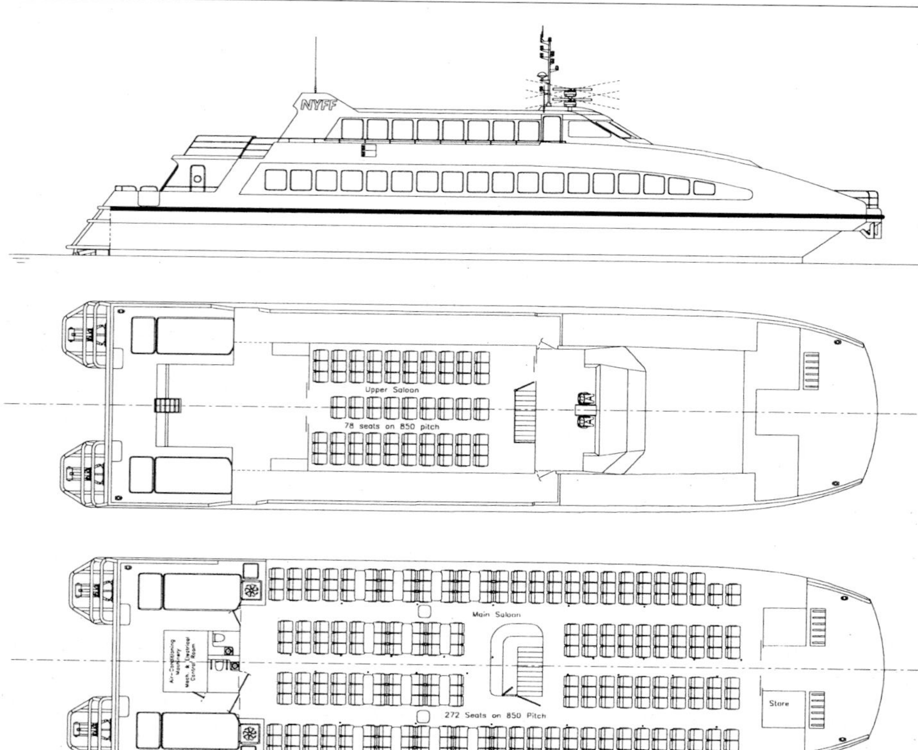

General arrangement of Derecktor 38 m Passenger Catamaran **1996**

38 m PASSENGER CATAMARAN

Two of these vessels are currently under construction. Designed by N Gee and Associates Ltd, these 35 knot craft feature slender hulls in order to reduce wash propagation at high and intermediate speeds.

Specification

Length overall	37.7 m
Length waterline	33.0 m
Beam	10.0 m
Draught	1.6 m
Displacement, max	140 t
Passengers	350
Propulsive power	4,000 kW
Max speed	35 kts

Classification: American Bureau of Shipping

Structure: All aluminium hull and superstructure.

Propulsion: Two MTU 16V 396 TE 747 diesels, one in each hull, each rated at 2,000 kW at 1,900 rpm and driving an MKP J650R-DD water-jet via a ZF BW 755 reduction gearbox.

NEW ENTRY

GLADDING-HEARN SHIPBUILDING

PO Box 300, One Riverside Avenue, Somerset, Massachusetts 02726-0300, USA

Tel: +1 (508) 676 8596
Fax: +1 (508) 672 1873

George R Duclos, *President*

This shipyard is a member of the Duclos Corporation and is well known for its range of commercial workboat and fast ferry craft. The yard has built a large number of small pilot craft as well as its well-known InCat catamaran ferries, (it is a licensed builder of International Catamarans Designs Pty Ltd, Australia).

Jet Cat Express **1992**

24 m CATAMARAN
Mackinac Express
Island Express

Two InCat catamaran ferries were built for the Arnold Transit Company for service from Upper and Lower Peninsulas of Michigan to the resort island in the Mackinac Straits. The vessels are powered by two MWM TBD 604B V8 diesel engines.

Specifications

Length overall	25.17 m
Length waterline	21.5 m
Beam	8.7 m
Hull beam	2.5 m
Draught	2.1 m
Passengers	365 (*Mackinac express*) 300 (*Island Express*)
Operational speed	31 kts

25 m CATAMARAN
Express II
(ex-Vineyard Spray)

Delivered September 1988.

Specifications

Length overall	25.17 m
Length waterline	21.51 m
Beam	8.7 m
Hull beam	2.5 m
Draught	2.1 m
Passengers	300
Fuel capacity	3,974 l
Propulsive power	2 × 1,290 kW
Operational speed	31 kts

Propulsion: The main engines are 2 × MWM 1,290 kW diesels.

Electrical system: 2 × 35 kW Lister generators.

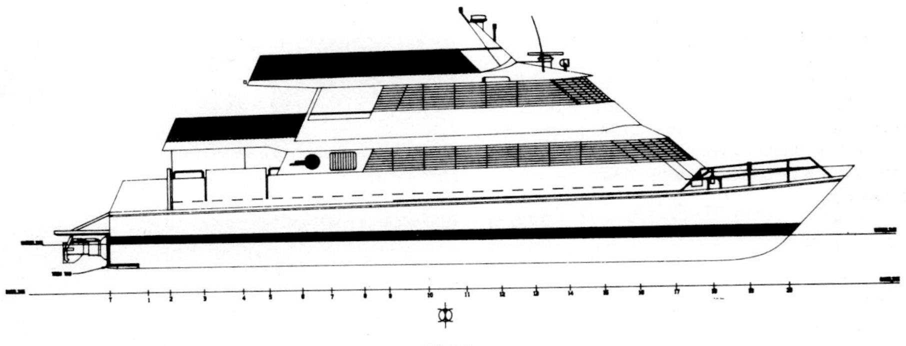

Jet Express II *general arrangement*

28 m CATAMARAN
Jet Cat Express

Delivered 15 April 1991 for service with *Catalina Channel Express.*

Specifications

Length overall	31.25 m
Beam	8.69 m
Draught	1.01 m
Crew	4
Passengers	368
Fuel capacity	7,570 l
Water capacity	757 l
Propulsive power	2 × 1,298 kW
Operational speed	31 kts

Propulsion: The main engines are 2 × DDC 16V 149TA, 1,298 kW each; driving 2 × Kamewa 63S2 water-jet units; via 2 × ZF BUK485 gearboxes.

28 m CATAMARAN Z-Bow
Friendship IV

The vessel is designed and certified to carry up to 149 passengers for distances of up to 100 miles offshore. Operating from Bar Harbor, Maine, the vessel *Friendship IV*, carries passengers on whale

Craft built (InCat) or on order		Originally delivered	Seats	Delivered To
24 m	*Makinac Express*	1987	365	Arnold Transit Co
24 m	*Island Express*	1988	300	Arnold Transit Co
25.17 m	*Express II* (*ex-Vineyard Spray*)	September 1988	380	Express Navigation
25.17 m	*Express I*	February 1989	260	Express Navigation
28.2 m	*Jet Express*	May 1989	380	Put-in Bay Boat Line Co
31.1 m	*Victoria Clipper III* (*ex-Audubon Express*)	1990	368	Clipper Navigation Inc
31.1 m	*Jet Cat Express*	1991	368	Doug Bombard Enterprises Catalina Channel Express
30 m	*Jet Express II*	May 1992	395	Put-in Bay Boat Line Co
28 m	*Friendship IV*	June 1993	149	Bar Harbor Whale Watch
32 m	*Friendship V*	June 1996	325	Bar Harbor Whale Watch
28.2 m	*Grey Lady*	November 1995	89	Hyannis Harbor Tours
20 m	XP 300	(1996)	149	-

watching/sightseeing excursions which last for approximately 3 hours. The craft was designed by InCat in 1993 and delivered by Gladding Hearn in June 1994.

Specifications

Length overall	28 m
Beam	9.0 m
Draught	1.7 m
Passengers	149
Fuel capacity	6,000 l
Propulsive power	2 × 607 kW
Max speed	28.6 kts
Operational speed	26 kts

Artist's impression of Gladding Hearn XP300 catamaran ferry

1996

28.2 m CATAMARAN

This vessel, delivered in November 1995, operates a fast ferry service between Hyannis and Nantucket taking less than 1 hour from centre to centre.

Specification

Length overall	28.2 m
Length waterline	23.6
Beam	8.7 m
Hull beam	2.75 m
Draught	1.0 m
Crew	2
Passengers	89
Fuel capacity	5,000 l
Water capacity	350 l
Operational speed	30 kts

Propulsion: This vessel is powered by two DDEC 16V 92 diesel engines each driving an MJP 550 water-jet via a reduction gearbox.

30 m CATAMARAN
Jet Express II

This craft is powered by two 1,298 kW MWM diesel engines driving Kamewa water-jets and can reach 32 knots fully loaded. The draught is 1 m.

32 m CATAMARAN
Friendship V

This all aluminium vessel is certified to carry up to 325 passengers with a fully loaded speed of 29 knots and a maximum speed of 35 knots. The vessel is to be used for whale watch tours and is scheduled to be delivered in June 1996.

Specification

Length overall	32.0 m
Length waterline	28.4 m
Beam	8.9 m
Hull beam	2.74 m
Draught	1.25 m
Passengers	325
Fuel capacity	10,000 l
Water capacity	890 l
Propulsive power	2,430 kW

Propulsion: The vessel is powered by four high-speed diesel engines each rated at 608 kW and each driving a water-jet.

Friendship IV

1995

XP 300 STANDARD CATAMARAN

This 20 m catamaran design of which one is currently under construction, is arranged for series production. The hulls are manufactured in epoxy FRP and the deck and superstructures in aluminium. It is understood that a large number of these craft are expected to be ordered.

Specification

Length overall	19.8 m
Beam	8.2 m
Draught	1.2 m
Passengers	149
Fuel capacity	3,000 l
Propulsive power	900 kW
Max speed	26 kts
Operational speed	25 kts

Structure: Epoxy FRP hulls and aluminium superstructure.

Propulsion: This proptotype vessel is powered by two DDEC 8V 92TA diesels driving via reverse reduction gearboxes to fixed pitch propellers. Each engine is rated at 450 kW at 2,100 rpm. The craft has been designed to accomodate larger engines and water-jet propulsors for speeds up to 30 knots.

UPDATED

MARINETTE MARINE CORPORATION

1600 Ely Street, Marinette, WI 54143-0198, USA

Tel: +1 (715) 735 9341
Fax: +1 (715) 735 3516

Peter Anderson, *Sales and Marketing*

Marinette Marine was incorporated in 1942 and proceeded to build a large number of slow and fast craft for the US Navy and other US Government organisations. The company currently handles large marine fabrications and has recently launched their final fast catamaran ferry, Straits Express.

Straits Express on trials

1996

30 m CATAMARAN
Straits Express

This is the first fast catamaran constructed by Marinette Marine. The vessel was delivered to Arnold Transit Co in May 1995 for operation on the Great Lakes.

Specification

Length overall	30.0 m
Length waterline	27.0 m
Beam	9.1 m
Draught	0.9 m
Crew	4
Passengers	400
Fuel capacity	7,600 l
Max speed	38 kts
Operational speed	35 kts

Structure: All aluminium construction

Propulsion: The vessel is powered by two Turbomeca Makila TI 1600 gas turbines each rated at 1,125 kW and each driving a Wadsworth 3000 waterjet via a ZF BW 465 reduction gearbox.

NEW ENTRY

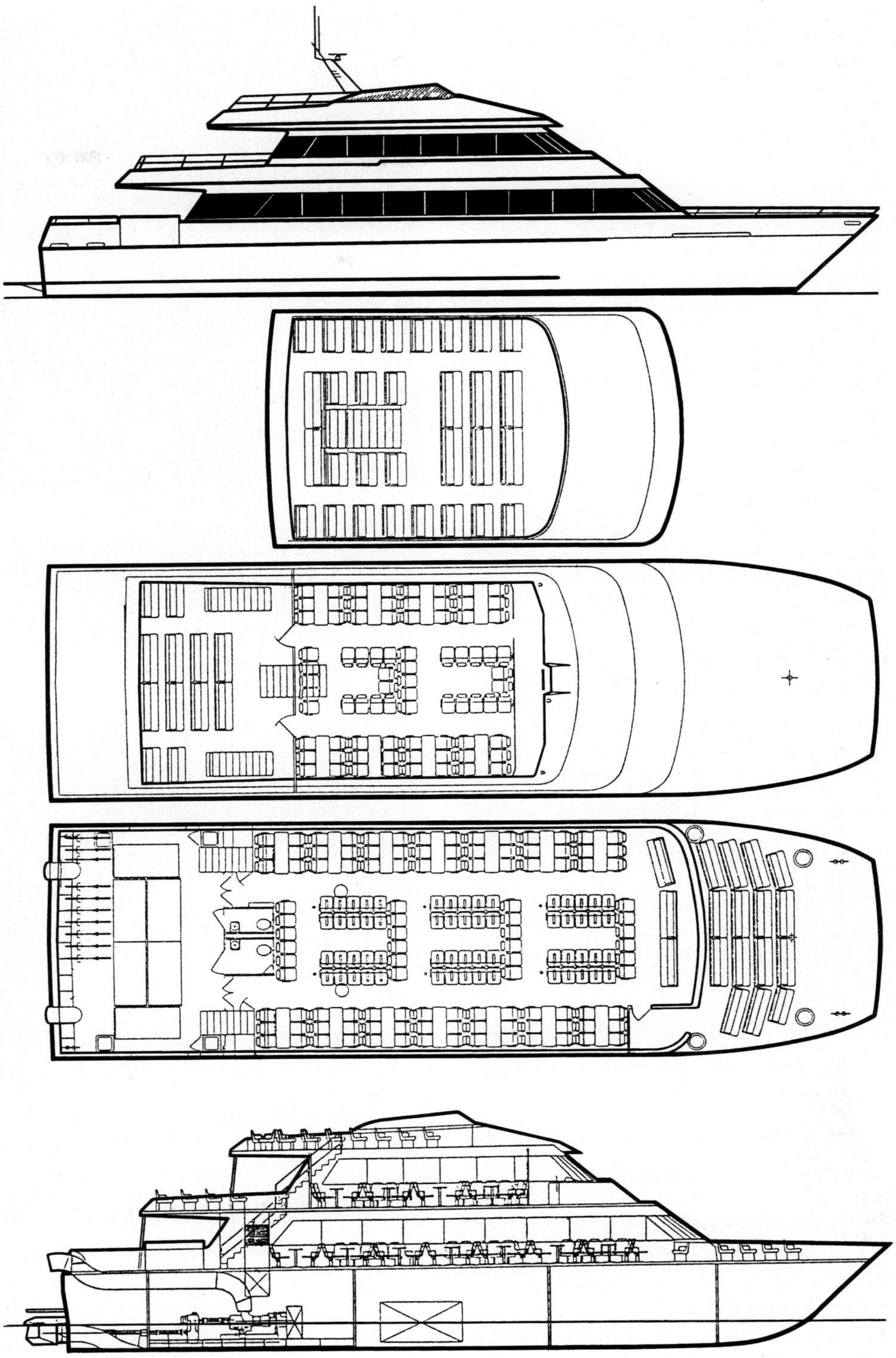

General arrangement of Straits Express
1996

NICHOLS BROTHERS BOAT BUILDERS INC

5400 S Cameron Road, Freeland, Whidbey Island, Washington 98249, USA

Tel: +1 (360) 331 5500
Fax: +1 (360) 331 7484

Matt Nichols, *President*
Archie Nichols, *Vice President*
Ken Schoonover, *Yard Supervisor*
Scott Murphy, *Financial Officer*
Bryan Nichols, *Marketing*

Licensed builder of International Catamaran Designs Pty Ltd, Australia.

The 400 passenger, 26 m Dolphin
1989

22 m CATAMARAN
Klondike

Eight of these craft have been delivered since 1984, the main order coming in 1988 for six identical craft for the Port of Puerto Rico. These vessels operate on a five mile route between old San Juan and the newer metropolitan area of Puerto Rico city.

Specifications

Length overall	21.98 m
Beam	8.69 m
Passengers	210
Fuel capacity	1,000 US gallons
Water capacity	1,000 US gallons
Operational speed	26 kts

Propulsion: *Klondike* is powered by 2 × Caterpillar 3412 TA diesels, 522 kW each; *Spirit of Alderbrook* by 2 × 12V-92TA diesels; and the Puerto Rico boats by 2 × DDC GM 12V71 diesels.
Gearboxes: Niigata MGN-80.

Propellers: Coolidge 5-blade.
Electrical system: Northern Lights 40 kW generator.
Control: The rudders are the curved dipping InCat type.

26 m CATAMARAN
Catamarin
Dolphin
Gold Rush
Klondike II (ex-Victoria Clipper, ex-Glacier Express, ex-Baja Express)

Specifications

Length overall	26.14 m
Beam	9.45 m
Draught	2.39 m
Fuel capacity	20,440 l
Water capacity	1,893 l (*Catamarin*) 1,515 l (*Klondike II*)
Propulsive power	2 × 1,004 kW
Operational speed	28 kts

Propulsion: The main engines are 2 × Deutz BAM 16M 816C diesels, each 1,004 kW continuous at 1,800 rpm; driving Coolidge 5-blade, 1.169 m × 1.194 m propellers; via Reintjes WVS 832 gearboxes, ratio 1:2.29.
Electrical system: Generators: 2 × John Deere 4275 engines and Northern Lights 50 kW generators. *Glacier Express* has Pacific Diesel units.

The 37 m InCat wave piercing catamaran Nantucket Spray, *renamed* SeaJet I **1991**

36 m CATAMARAN
Catalina Flyer

The largest capacity high-speed catamaran to be built in the USA, the 500-seat *Catalina Flyer* (delivered May 1988) is in service between Newport Harbor and Catalina Island in Southern California with Catalina Passenger Service.

Specifications

Length overall	36 m
Beam	12.2 m
Draught	2.44 m
Passengers	500
Fuel capacity	11,355 l
Water capacity	1,514 l
Propulsive power	2 × 1,490 kW
Max speed	30 kts
Operational speed	27 kts

Propulsion: The main engines are 2 × Caterpillar 3516 TA, 1,490 kW each, specially lightened diesels; driving 3-blade CuNiAl Bronze, 1.3 m diameter propellers; via 2 × Reintjes WS-1023, 2.538:1 gearboxes.
Electrical system: John Deere generators, 2 × 40 kW units.
Navigation and communications: Ross DR 600D flasher, 2 ICOM VHF radios, Furuno 1510D and 8030D radars, Sperry 8T autopilot, Furuno LC-90 Loran

Bow-loading ramp operation of Executive Explorer **1989**

Craft built (InCat)	Delivered	Seats	Operator	Owner
22 m InCat *Klondike*	June 1984	210	Yukon River Cruises, Inc	Brad Phillips
22 m InCat *Spirit of Alderbrook*	August 1984	240	Wes Johnson, Seattle Harbor Tours	
26 m InCat *Catamarin*	May 1985	400	Red and White Fleet	Crowley Maritime Corporation
26 m InCat *Gold Rush*	September 1985	400	Glacier Bay Yacht Tours	Robert Giersdorf
26 m InCat *Klondike II* (ex-*Victoria Clipper*, ex-*Glacier Express*, ex-*Baja Express*)	1985 January 1986	245*	Clipper Navigation Inc	
26 m InCat *Dolphin*	August 1986	400	Red and White Fleet	Crowley Maritime Corporation
30 m InCat *Executive Explorer*	June 1986	49 passengers in 25 staterooms	Glacier Bay Yachts Tours, Inc Catamaran Cruise Lines, Hawaii	
23 m InCat *Jera FB-816*	April 1988	232	US Army	US Army
36 m InCat *Catalina Flyer*	May 1988	500	California Cruisin'	Catalina Passenger Service
23 m InCat *Jelang K FB-817*	October 1988	232	US Army	US Army
37 m InCat (WPC) *SeaJet I* (ex-*Metro Atlantic*, ex-*Nantucket Spray*)	Spring 1989	400	Metro Marine Express	Metro Marine Express
22 m InCat *Martin Peña*	August 1989	167	Port of Puerto Rico	–
22 m InCat *Amelia*	November 1989	167	Port of Puerto Rico	–
22 m InCat *Covadonga*	December 1989	167	Port of Puerto Rico	–
22 m InCat *San Geronimo*	March 1989	167	Port of Puerto Rico	–
22 m InCat *Viejo San Juan*	May 1989	167	Port of Puerto Rico	–
22 m InCat *Cristobal Colón*	June 1989	167	Port of Puerto Rico	–
37 m InCat *Kona AggressorII*	December 1992	5 staterooms	Alaska Dive Boat, Inc	–
29 m InCat *Bay Breeze*	April 1994	250	City of Alameda	–
32 m Incat *Palau Aggressor III*	November 1994	49	Alaska Dive Boat, Inc	–
37 m SWATH Int *Cloud X*	due March 1995	365	Party Line Cruises Ltd	Martin Automatic Inc

*400 total with outside seating

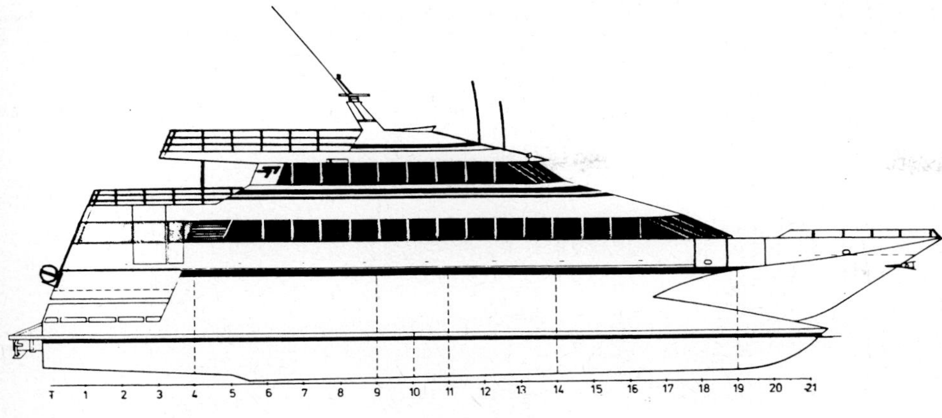

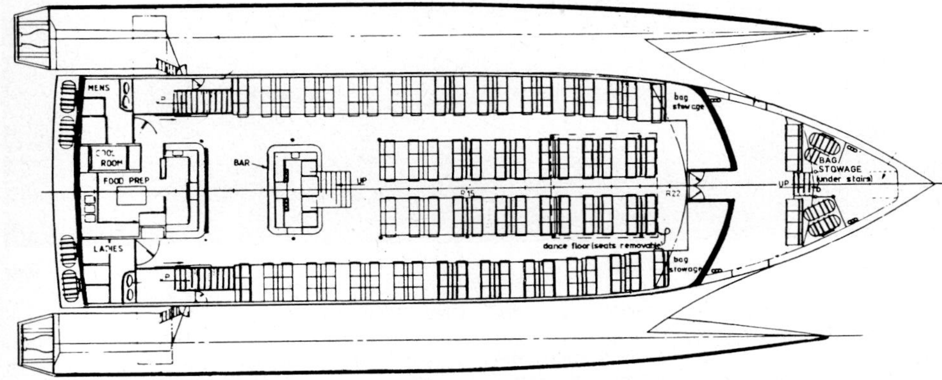

*General arrangement of the 37 m InCat wave piercing catamaran SeaJet I, ex-*Metro Atlantic, *ex-*Nantucket Spray

InCat Jelang K **1989**

Bay Breeze **1995**

30 m CATAMARAN

Executive Explorer

A 31.7 m cruising catamaran, built in 1986 for Alaskan and Hawaiian islands cruising.

Specifications

Length overall	30.03 m
Beam	11.2 m
Draught	2.51 m
Crew	20
Passengers	49
Fuel capacity	63,588 l
Water capacity	19,682 l
Propulsive power	2 × 1,004 kW
Operational speed	22 kts

Propulsion: The main engines are 2 × Deutz BAM 816, 1,004 kW continuous, each at 1,800 rpm; driving ISO class 1, 5-blade, Nicel 1.346 m × 1.422 m Columbia Bronze propellers; via 2 × Reintjes 842, 2.96:1 gearboxes.

Electrical system: The generator is a 120 kW, PDC 120 MB Mercedes-Benz W/OM-421.

38.6 m InCat WPC

Seajet I (ex-*Metro Atlantic*, ex-*Nantucket Spray*)

This $4 million vessel was ordered in June 1988 and entered service with Bay State Cruises, Boston.

Specifications

Length overall	38.6 m
Beam	15.6 m
Hull beam	2.6 m
Draught	1.3 m
Passengers	367
Fuel capacity	2 × 14,130 l
Water capacity	7,570 l
Propulsive power	2 × 1,768 kW
Max speed	36.4 kts
Operational speed	32 kts

Classification: USCG, SOLAS.

Propulsion: The main engines are 2 × MWM TBD 604 V16 1,768 kW each, at 1,800 rpm; driving 2 × Kamewa 63 S62/6 water-jet units.

Electrical system: 2 × John Deere; 55 kW generators.

Jera FB-816

Jelang K FB-817

There were two 23.17 m InCat catamarans built in 1988 for ferry service at the US Army's missile test range in the Marshall Islands. *Jera* was handed over to the Nichols Brothers Boatyard on 9 April 1988 and *Jelang K* on 7 October 1988.

Specifications

Length overall	23.17 m (*Jera*) 21.95 m (*Jelang K*)
Beam	8.94 m (*Jera*) 8.69 m (*Jelang K*)
Draught	1.8 m
Passengers	232
Fuel capacity	5,300 l (*Jera*) 4,164 l (*Jelang K*)
Water capacity	946 l
Propulsive power	2 × 715 kW
Operational speed	31 kts

Propulsion: The main engines are 2 × DDC GM 16 V92 TA, 715 kW each; driving 5-blade Osborne bronze propellers, 940 mm × 927 mm; via 2 × ZF BW 250, 2.03:1 ratio gearboxes.

Electrical system: 2 × 50 kW Northern Lights generators, John Deere 4276 engines.

Bay Breeze

Designed by International Catamarans, this craft was delivered in April 1994.

Specifications

Length overall	29 m
Beam	9 m
Draught	1.2 m
Passengers	250
Fuel capacity	4,166 l
Water capacity	2,840 l
Propulsive power	2 × 768 kW
Max speed	30 kts
Operational speed	28 kts

Propulsion: The main engines are 2 × Detroit Diesel 16V 92TA DDEC - 768 kW; driving 2 × Kamewa 50 water-jet units.

Electrical system: 2 × John Deere 4276 50 kW generators.

Palau Aggressor II

This second vessel purchased by the Alaska Dive Boat Company carries 16 overnight passengers and 49 day passengers. It is designed by InCat Designs Pty Ltd using their Z-Bow hull form.

Specifications

Length overall	32 m
Beam	9 m
Draught	1.3 m
Passengers	49
Fuel capacity	17,000 l
Water capacity	7,600 l
Propulsive power	1,570 kW
Operational speed	23 kts

Propulsion: The main engines are 2 × Caterpillar 3412 diesels each rated at 785 kW; driving 2 × Hamilton water-jets model 5711.

UPDATED

PETERSON BUILDERS INC

101 Pennsylvania Street, PO Box 650, Sturgeon Bay, Wisconsin 54235-0650, USA

Tel: +1 (414) 743 5574
Telex: 263423
Fax: +1 (414) 743 6089

Ellsworth L Peterson, *President*

Peterson Builders Inc (PBI) is a well established ship and patrol boat builder having been in continuous operation for over 62 years. Peterson is currently building three 14.6 m high-speed patrol craft. The first of the series completed trials exceeding all performance criteria, with speeds exceeding 45 knots. PBI has, over its 62 years, designed and constructed over 200 patrol craft ranging from 7m to 57 m. Speeds of PBI's patrol craft have exceeded 50 knots, driven by propulsion systems ranging from diesel to combination diesel/gas turbine. Propulsion includes fixed pitch, controlled reversible pitch, surface-piercing drives and water-jets.

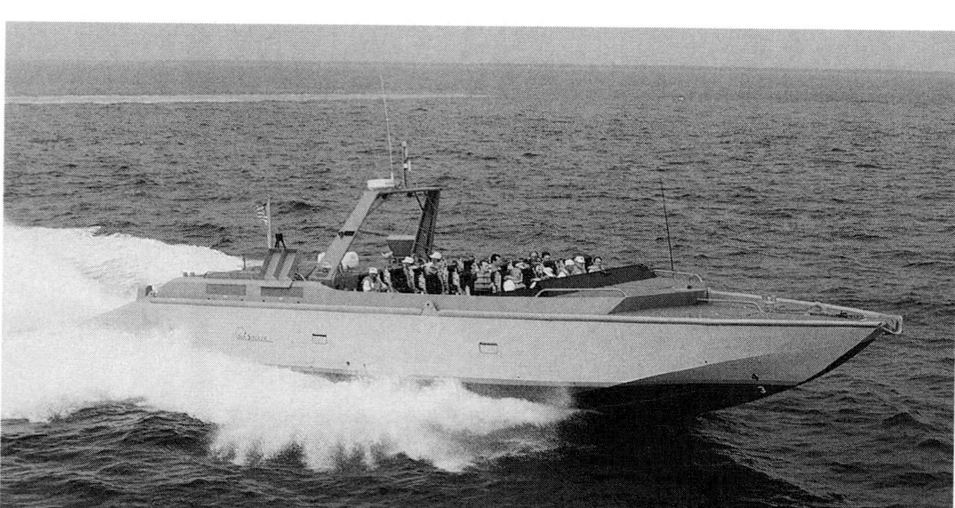

Peterson Builders Inc Sea Stalker Class ***1995***

SEA STALKER CLASS

In August 1993, PBI was awarded a contract by the United States Special Operations Command to construct the Sea Stalker. PBI's Sea Stalker Class patrol craft is an asymmetric catamaran based on the Cougar Cat 2100 Dark Moon Class patrol craft developed by Cougar Marine Ltd of Hamble, England.

PBI has also developed several variations of this high-speed craft for diverse operational requirements, including a closed cockpit version with a flying bridge for coastal patrol and search and rescue.

Specifications

Length overall	21.5 m
Propulsive power	2 × 2,610 kW
Max speed	>50 kts

Classification: DnV.
Propulsion: 2 × MTU 16V 396 TE 94 diesel engines, driving Rolla surface-piercing propellers.

Loitering propulsion will be provided by a dedicated diesel engine driving a Hamilton water-jet.

UPDATED

USA CATAMARANS INC

2541 State Rd 84, Fort Lauderdale, Florida 33312, USA

Tel: +1 (305) 944 1868
Fax: +1 (305) 792 9271

Builder of the first Air Ride Dual-Air Sea Coaster, a 20 m, 45 knot, 150 passenger ferry. See the Air Ride Craft Inc entry for details of the Dual-Air concept.

USA Catamarans Inc has also produced a 19.76 m, 140 seat catamaran ferry for Harbor Bay Express.

ANDROMEDA CLASS PASSENGER CATAMARAN

Harbor Bay Express II

Specifications

Length overall	19.76 m
Beam	7.3 m
Displacement, min	36.6 t
Crew	2
Passengers	148
Fuel capacity	3,000 l
Water capacity	600 l
Max speed	40 kts
Operational speed	30 kts

Harbor Bay Express II ***1996***

Classification: ABS and USCG approved.
Structure: All welded aluminium.
Propulsion: The vessel is powered by two MAN D2842 LYE diesel engines each rated at 750 kW at 2,300 rpm and each driving a 0.86 m diameter, 6 bladed surface propeller via a ZF 195 2.0:1 reverse reduction gearbox.

UPDATED

SMALL-WATERPLANE-AREA TWIN-HULL (SWATH) VESSELS

Company Listing by Country

Commonwealth of Independent States
Almaz Shipbuilding Company Ltd

Germany
Schichau Seebeckwerft AG

Japan
Mitsui Engineering & Shipbuilding Company Ltd

Korea, South
Hyundai Heavy Industries Company Ltd

Norway
Norsk Sisumaran KS/AS

United Kingdom
FBM Marine Group

United States of America
Navatek Ships Ltd
Nichols Brothers Boat Builders Inc
Swath Ocean Systems, Inc

COMMONWEALTH OF INDEPENDENT STATES

ALMAZ SHIPBUILDING COMPANY LTD

26 Petrovskij PR, 197042 St Petersburg, Russia, CIS

Tel: +7 (812) 350 1164
Fax: +7 (812) 235 7069

Lisa Kiznevion, *Marketing Manager*

Almaz Shipbuilding Company was founded in 1901 in St Petersburg by Alexander Zolotoff. Since that time over 1000 vessels have been delivered including fast patrol craft and passenger ferries.

In 1993 Almaz announced that a contract had been signed to construct two Swath craft designed by Marine Systems of Sukhoi. These were still under construction in 1996.

SUKHOI SWATH

Specifications

Length overall	32 m
Beam	11 m
Draught	2.3 m
Passengers	198
Operational speed	27 kts
Range	250 n miles

Propulsion: 2 × 1,500 kW diesels driving 2 × water-jets.

VERIFIED

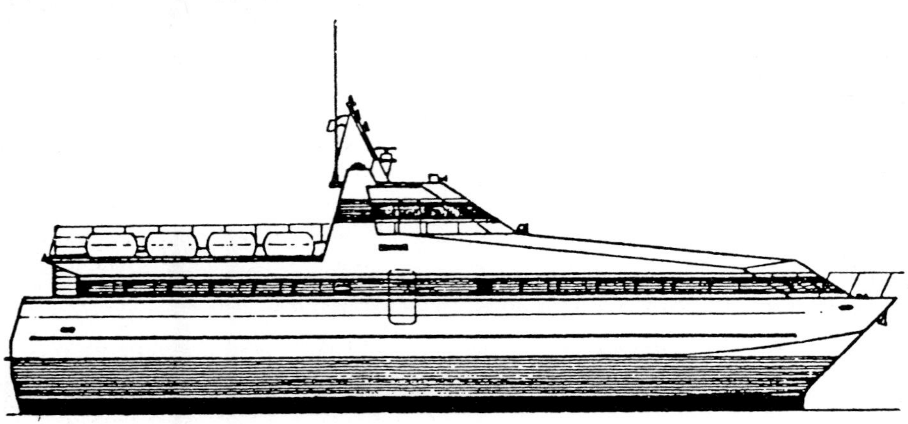

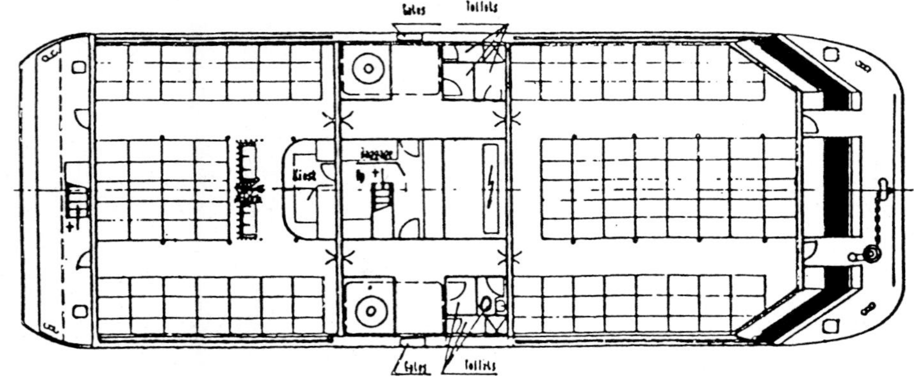

Sukhoi Swath profile and passenger deck layout
1994

GERMANY

SCHICHAU SEEBECKWERFT AG

PO Box 1240, Riedemannstrasse 1, D-27512 Bremerhaven, Germany

Tel: +49 (471) 3920
Telex: 238651 SISEW D
Fax: +49 (471) 392239

Josef Klar, *Chairman*
Dr Jürgen Gollenbeck, *Director*
Elmar Fritsche, *Director*
Hans Tempel, *Director*
Peter Güldensupp, *Director*

Schichau Seebeckwerft AG is a member of the Bremen Vulkan Group, the largest shipbuilder in reunited Germany. Schichau Seebeckwerft AG specialises in the construction of ro-ro ferries and other types of sophisticated craft.

SSW 320 A (DESIGN)

The SSW 320 A is the result of three years' effort in developing a high-speed Swath which is performance competitive with other types of craft in its class. Seating for over 600 passengers is provided with ample capacity to carry 100 cars or 75 cars and four large buses.

A high-deadweight fraction has been achieved through the application of advanced technology. Power and speed are competitive with other craft types. The sea-keeping is excellent with test results indicating less than 0.01 *g* (rms) midships vertical acceleration in 3 m significant seas. No fins are required for stabilisation.

Safety arrangements comply with the proposed amendments to the IMO High-Speed Craft Code. Auxiliary machinery is centrally located on the main deck to reduce service costs. Gas-turbines driving conventional CP propellers offer high-propulsion efficiency.

Swath designs of other capacities and speeds are available.

Specifications

Length overall	54.4 m
Beam	23 m
Draught	4.6 m
Passengers	600
Vehicles	100 cars
Fuel capacity	40 t
Operating speed	36 kts
Range	300 n miles

Structure: The hull is constructed from aluminium alloy.

Propulsion: The main engines are 4 × Allison 571-KF diesels; driving a CP propeller 2 × reduction gearboxes each with two inputs.

VERIFIED

JAPAN

MITSUI ENGINEERING & SHIPBUILDING COMPANY LTD

6-4 Tsukiji 5-chome, Chuo-ku, Tokyo 104, Japan

Tel: +81 (3) 3544 3462
Telex: 22821 J, 22924 MITZOSEN J
Fax: +81 (3) 3544 3031

Hiroshi Kitashima, *Director and General Manager, Ship and Ocean Project Division*
Yutaka Ikeda, *General Manager, Marine Department*

Mitsui began its high-speed Semi-Submerged Catamaran (SSC) development programme in 1970. Since 1976, the programme has been operated in conjunction with the Japanese Marine Machinery Development Association (JAMDA). In 1977 Mitsui built the experimental 18.37 tonne *Marine Ace* in order to obtain practical experience with this hull form. In 1979 the first SSC high-speed passenger vessel was launched under the provisional name *Mesa 80*. After extensive trials it was completed in 1981 and renamed *Seagull*. It has since been operated by Tokai Kisen Company Ltd on a passenger ferry service between Atami and Oshima island.

The company has also developed and built a SSC hydrographic survey vessel, *Kotozaki*, for the Fourth District Port Construction Bureau of the Japanese Ministry of Transport. This vessel was completed in 1981.

Marine Ace

Mitsui's first experimental SSC, *Marine Ace*, is built in marine grade aluminium alloy and can operate in Sea States 2 to 3.

Specifications

Length overall	12.35 m
Beam	6.5 m
Draught	1.55 m
Displacement, max	18.37 t*
Fuel capacity	1.45 m³
Operational speed	18 kts

* after modification in 1978

Propulsion: The main engines are two V-type four-cycle petrol engines, each developing 150 kW at 3,700 rpm. Each drives, via a vertical intermediate transmission shaft and bevel gear, a three-bladed fixed-pitch propeller.

Control: Four sets of fin stabilisers, driven by hydraulic servo motors, reduce ship motion in heavy seas.

Seagull

Developed jointly by Mitsui Engineering & Shipbuilding Company Ltd and the Japanese Marine Machinery Development Association (JAMDA), the 27 knot *Seagull* was the world's first commercial semi-submerged catamaran. Despite its small size, the overall length is just under 36 m, the vessel provides a stable ride in seas with 3.5 m waves.

During the first 10-month long commercial run in a service between Atami and Oshima, *Seagull* established an operating record of 97 per cent availability.

Specifications

Length overall	35.9 m
Beam	17.1 m
Draught	3.15 m
Crew	7
Passengers	446
Max speed	27 kts

Structure: Marine grade aluminium alloy.

Propulsion: Main engines are two Fuji-SEMT marine diesels, each developing 3,000 kW max continuous at 1,475 rpm. Each drives, via a vertical transmission shaft and bevel gear, a four-blade fixed-pitch propeller.

Electrical system: Two 206.25 kVA generators provide electrical power.

Control: Four sets of fin stabilisers driven by hydraulic servo motors reduce ship motion in heavy seas.

Mitsui SSC high-tech cruiser SSC 15 type, Marine Wave, *built in glass- and carbon-reinforced plastic* ***1986***

SSC 15
Marine Wave

The first Semi-Submerged Catamaran SSC 15 type cruiser *Marine Wave* built by MES for Toray Industries Inc was delivered in July 1985.

Marine Wave, which is only about 15 m in length, is relatively free from rolling and pitching by virtue of its SSC design which also allows a spacious deck to be provided and facilitates comfortable cruising. One of its most interesting features is the combination of its unusual shape with Toray's newly developed hull material incorporating carbon fibre composites. The SSC 15 has two sets of computer-controlled stabilising fins and two fixed fins.

Marine Wave is certificated by the Japan Craft Inspection Organisation for use in coastal waters. By August 1986 *Marine Wave* had operated over 860 hours including a voyage to West Japan in which it experienced waves 4.5 m in height.

Specifications

Length overall	15.1 m
Beam	6.2 m
Draught	1.6 m
Crew	2
Passengers	15
Fuel capacity	2,000 l
Water capacity	300 l
Max speed	18 kts
Operational speed	16 kts

Structure: Glass-reinforced plastic and carbon-reinforced plastic.

Propulsion: Two high-speed marine diesel Ford Sabre 5,950 cc engines, 200 kW each at 2,500 rpm, driving fixed-pitch propellers via Twin Disc MG 506 gearboxes, ratio 2.03:1.

Electrical system: Onan MDJJF-18R diesel unit.

Bay Star ***1993***

SSC 15
Sun Marina

The second of SSC 15 series, *Sun Marina* was built by Mitsui for San Marina Hotel, opened as a grand resort hotel in Okinawa in March 1987.

Sun Marina has a large luxurious party cabin which can accommodate 30 guests of the hotel, and sails round many coral reefs from the privately owned marina of the hotel.

Specifications

Length overall	15.1 m
Beam	6.4 m
Draught	1.6 m
Crew	3
Passengers	30
Fuel capacity	2 × 900 l
Water capacity	400 l
Max speed	20.5 kts
Operational speed	17 kts

Propulsion: The propulsive power is provided by two 170 kW marine diesels.

Electrical system: 15 kW generator.

SSC 20 Diana ***1991***

SSC 20
Bay Queen

Bay Queen is the seventh SSC vessel built by Mitsui since 1977. It can carry a maximum of 40 passengers and has entered service for operation in inspection tours, sightseeing, crew transportation and many other purposes in Tokyo Bay.

Bay Queen is the first and smallest commercialised SSC vessel in the world, made of aluminium to a design based on the concept of *Marine Wave* which was made of FRP.

Specifications

Crew	4
Passengers	40
Fuel capacity	2,400 l
Water capacity	1,000 l

Propulsion: 2 × high-speed marine diesel engines, 350 kW each at 2,000 rpm.

Electrical system: Yanmar 4JHL-TN diesel generator unit.

SSC 20
Diana

Diana is the second vessel of Mitsui SSC-20 series and was completed in the middle of March 1990. It is operated for day and night cruises as a party boat in Osaka Bay, a good application of the Mitsui SSC type, which can provide spacious deck area and a comfortable ride in rough sea conditions. It has an automatic motion control system to minimise ship motion.

Specifications

Length overall	20.7 m
Beam	6.8 m
Draught	1.6 m
Crew	3

Specifications of the high-speed SSC vessels built by Mitsui

Ship name	*Marine Ace*	*Seagull*	*Kotozaki*	*Marine Wave*	*Sun Marina*
Type	**Experimental vessel**	**High-speed passenger ferry**	**Hydrographic survey vessel**	**Cabin type luxury boat**	**Saloon type luxury boat**
Completion	1977	1979	1981	1985	1987
Length overall	12.35 m	35.9 m	27 m	15.1 m	15.05 m
Length waterline	11 m	31.5 m	25 m	11.95 m	11.9 m
Beam	6.5 m	17.1 m	12.5 m	6.2 m	6.4 m
Depth	2.7 m	5.85 m	4.6 m	2.75 m	2.75 m
Draught	1.55 m	3.15 m	3.2 m	1.6 m	1.6 m
GRT	-	670	250	19	19
Payload/passengers	20 passengers	402-446 passengers	approx 36 t	17 passengers	33 passengers
Strut type	twin/single	single	single	single	single
Hull material	Aluminium	Aluminium	Steel/Aluminium	FRP	FRP
Max speed	17.3 kts	27.1 kts	20.5 kts	18.2 kts	20.5 kts
Main engines	2 × gasoline 147 kW	2 × diesel 2,973 kW	2 × diesel 1,395 kW	2 × diesel 200 kW	2 × diesel 220 kW
Propeller	FPP	FPP	CPP	FPP	FPP
Fin control	automatic	automatic	manual	automatic	automatic

Ship name	*Bay Queen*	*Seagull 2*	*Diana*	*Bay Star*	*Cosmos*
Type	**Multipurpose boat**	**High-speed passenger ferry**	**Party boat**	**Multipurpose boat**	**Passenger ferry**
Completion	Feb 1989	Dec 1989	Mar 1990	Nov 1991	Oct 1995
Length overall	18 m	39.3 m	20.7 m	19.45 m	29.2 m
Length waterline	15.9 m	33.7 m	15.9 m	15.9 m	24.3 m
Beam	6.8 m	15.6 m	6.8 m	6.8 m	11.3 m
Depth	2.8 m	6.8 m	2.8 m	2.8 m	4.55 m
Draught	1.6 m	3.5 m	1.6 m	1.6 m	2.35 m
GRT	39	567	52	50	140
Payload/passengers	40 passengers	410 passengers	40 passengers	40 passengers	96 passengers
Strut type	single	single	single	single	single
Hull material	Aluminium	Aluminium	Aluminium	Aluminium	Aluminium
Max speed	20 kts	30.6 kts	19.2 kts	20 kts	24 kts
Main engines	2 × diesel 345 kW	4 × diesel 1,967 kW	2 × diesel 272 kW	2 × diesel 345 kW	2 × diesel 1,120 kW
Propeller	FPP	FPP	FPP	FPP	FPP
Fin control	automatic	automatic	automatic	automatic	automatic

Passengers	40
Max speed	19.22 kts

Structure: Marine grade aluminium alloy.
Propulsion: Main engines are two high-speed diesel engines, each developing 276 kW (370 hp) max continuous at 2,250 rpm.
Control: Maintenance-free sensors and a sophisticated fin control system are applied. One pair of canard fin stabilisers is automatically controlled by an electric motor.

SSC 30
Cosmos

Mitsui delivered the first SSC 30, *Cosmos,* to the Japanese Shipping Company in October 1995. The vessel is operated as a crew support ship for offshore transportation.

The SSC 30 has been developed as a medium sized standard SSC vessel. SSC 30 can give a comfortable ride in a 2 to 2.5 m wave height with a cruising speed of 20 knots.

Specifications

Length overall	29.2 m
Length waterline	24.3
Beam	11.3
Payload	5 t deck cargo
Crew	4
Passengers	96

Structure: Marine grade aluminium alloy.
Propulsion: The engines are two high-speed marine diesels, 1,120 kW.
Control: One set of forward fin stabilisers driven by hydraulic servo motors, and one set of fixed fins aft.

Cosmos

1996

SSC 40
Seagull 2

Seagull 2 has a capability of running at 30.6 knots at maximum continuous rating and 27.5 knots service speed with 410 passengers. According to the analysis of log book records, *Seagull 2* has better speed sustainability than *Seagull* in wave heights of 2.5 m and higher.

Specifications

Length overall	39.32 m
Beam	15.6 m
Draught	3.5 m
Crew	7
Passengers	410
Max speed	30.6 kts

SSC 40 Seagull 2

1991

Propulsion: Main engines are four MTU 16V 396 TB 84, each developing 2,000 kW max continuous at 1,940 rpm. Each pair of engines drives a four-blade fixed-pitch propeller, through a long straight tube shaft with two ZF reversible reduction gearboxes. A microcomputer-based remote-control system is applied.

Control: The ship control system is composed of a display of nautical information and ballast control. Nautical information includes draught, trim, heel, rudder angle, fin angle, ship speed, wind data, ship course and so on. A ballast control system displays ballast line layout and can operate ballast pumps and valves remotely.

Four fin stabilisers are automatically controlled by hydraulic rotary actuators.

UPDATED

KOREA, SOUTH

HYUNDAI HEAVY INDUSTRIES COMPANY LTD

1 Cheonha-Dong, Dong-Gu, Ulsan, Kyung-Nam, South Korea

Tel: +82 (522) 321307/302841
Telex: 52220 HYARD K
Fax: +82 (522) 324007

35 m SWATH VESSEL

Building of the 35 m Swath vessel started in 1991 and it was delivered in April 1993.

Specifications

Length overall	34.5 m
Length waterline	32.5 m
Beam	15 m
Draught	3.5 m
Propulsive power	2 × 2,000 kW
Operational speed	21.6 kts

Propulsion: The main engines are 2 × MTU 16V 396 TE84 2,000 kW at 1,940 rpm.

35 m Hyundai Swath vessel ***1994***

27.1 m (DESIGN)

For several years Hyundai Heavy Industries had been investigating coastal passenger Swath vessel designs, including eighth scale model testing before building the 35 m craft. However, among the variants investigated, a 27.1 m version was selected as satisfying the growing passenger accommodation requirements of the market.

Specifications

Length overall	27.1 m
Beam	12.4 m
Draught	2.6 m
Displacement, max	132 t
Passengers	254
Max speed	25.3 kts
Operational speed	24.7 kts

Propulsion: The main engines are 2 × 1,327 kW at 1,650 rpm (MCR).

VERIFIED

NORWAY

NORSK SISUMARAN KS/AS

Uno-Glaupa, PO Box 816, N-7001 Trondheim, Norway

Tel: +47 735 20615/701 25660
Fax: +47 735 35858/701 21595

Prof Arlid Rødland, *Director*
Per Kverndokk, *Director*

This company has produced a number of designs based on experience with an 11.4 m prototype. These designs include a 33 m 360 passenger Swath; a 28 m 250 passenger Swath, and a 30 m 304 passenger design.

STORMULK

This vessel is believed to be the first Norwegian Swath type and was launched on 20 June 1990. The STORMULK (Submerged Torpedo Multihull Craft) features an auxiliary bow hull which is designed to enhance static and dynamic behaviour of the Swath vessel concept without significant reductions in speed and economy.

STORMULK has completed successful testing off the mid-Norwegian coast at Froude numbers up to 1.202, corresponding to the anticipated service speed of 30 knots for a 20 m vessel.

Specifications

Length overall	11.4 m
Beam	6.4 m
Displacement, min	6.5 t
Passengers	32
Fuel capacity	2,400 l
Water capacity	1,370 l

Structure: Hull structure in marine grade aluminium, deck and superstructure in GRP sandwich construction.

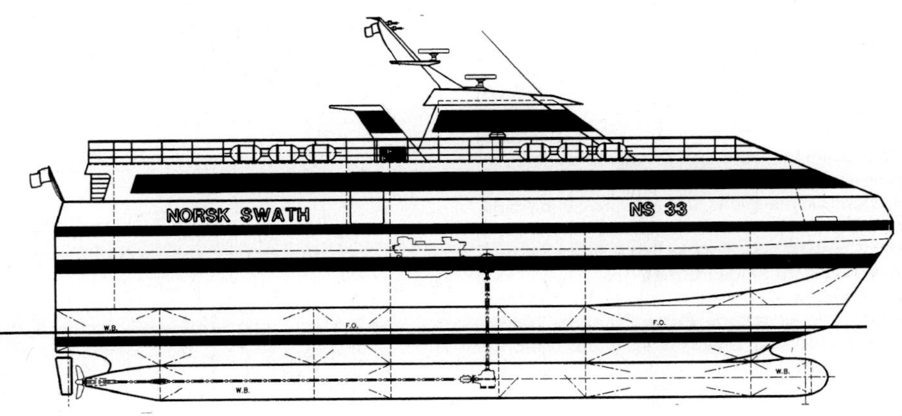

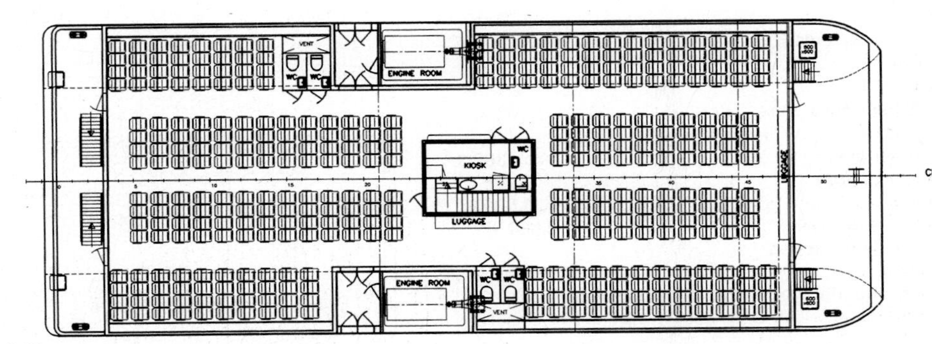

Norsk 33 m 360 passenger Swath (design) ***1995***

Propulsion: The main engines are 2 × Iveco 8061 SRM 27.

NORSK SWATH (DESIGN)

Based on the STORMULK prototype experience, a sequence of designs has now been made for modified Swath passenger ferries and/or combined passenger/cargo carriers in the LOA 23-33 m range with service speeds of 25 to 30 knots.

Specifications

Length overall	33 m
Beam	12.6 m
Passengers	360
Propulsive power	2 × 1,680 kW
Operational speed	25 kts

Propulsion: The main engines are 2 × MTU 16V 396 TE 74.

VERIFIED

UNITED KINGDOM

FBM MARINE GROUP

Cowes Shipyard, Cowes, Isle of Wight, UK

Tel: +44 (1983) 297111
Telex: 86466 FAMBRO G
Fax: +44 (1983) 299642

Michael Roberts, *Deputy Chairman*
John Warbey, *International Sales Director*
Malcolm Keith, *Managing Director*
Nigel Warren, *Chief Designer*

37 m ATLANTIC CLASS FAST DISPLACEMENT CATAMARAN (FDC) *Patria*

In August 1988 Fairey Marinteknik, now FBM Marine, announced the award of a contract for the supply of a 400-seat fast displacement catamaran to the Regional Government of Madeira, Portugal. Valued at £4 million the craft was delivered in early 1990.

First trials started in October 1989. On 5 October 1989 the vessel achieved a speed of 32.1 knots at two-thirds load, some 4 to 5 knots higher than the previous maximum recorded speed for a Swath type, therefore establishing a record.

In late January 1990 *Patria* was on trials in storm conditions and spent a total of 7 hours at sea averaging 28 knots in a fully loaded condition in wave heights of 2.5 to 3.5 m and windspeeds that seldom dropped below 70 knots and gusted, at times, above 90 knots. On Sunday 19 August 1990 *Patria* went into service.

Specifications

Length overall	36.5 m
Beam	13 m
Draught	2.7 m
Displacement, max	approx 180 t
Crew	8-10
Passengers	400
Fuel capacity	17,750 l
Propulsive power	2 × 2,040 kW
Operating speed	31.7 kts
Range	472 n miles
Operational limitations	wave height 3.5 m

Classification: DnV Passenger Ship Light Craft.

Propulsion: Main engines: 2 × MTU 16V 396 TB 84 rated at 2,040 kW (25°C air, 25°C sea) 1,940 rpm, driving twin shaft and 3-blade fixed-pitch Lips propellers via 3.23:1.0 ZF gearboxes.

Auxiliary systems: A ballast tank system is operated to adjust craft attitude: Pump: 50 m^3/h, 1.5 kW, 380 V on each of four ballast tanks in the platform, each of 7.5 t capacity.

Atlantic class FDC Patria *in service between Funchal and Porto Santo* **1991**

Mk 2 FDC (DESIGN)

A new fast displacement catamaran design was announced by FBM Marine Ltd in October 1990. This is a development of the *Patria* design which provides for water-jet propulsion.

Specifications

Length overall	38.75 m
Length waterline	31.7 m
Beam	13 m
Draught	2.7 m
Displacement, max	200 t
Payload	40 t
Passengers	396
Fuel capacity	7,000 l
Water capacity	1,000 l
Propulsive power	2 × 2,000 kW
Operational speed	30 kts
Range	222 n miles

Classification: DnV +1A1 R25 Light Craft EO.

Propulsion: Main engines: 2 × MTU 16V 396 TE 74L, 2,000 kW each at 2,000 rpm; driving a pair of water-jets.

UPDATED

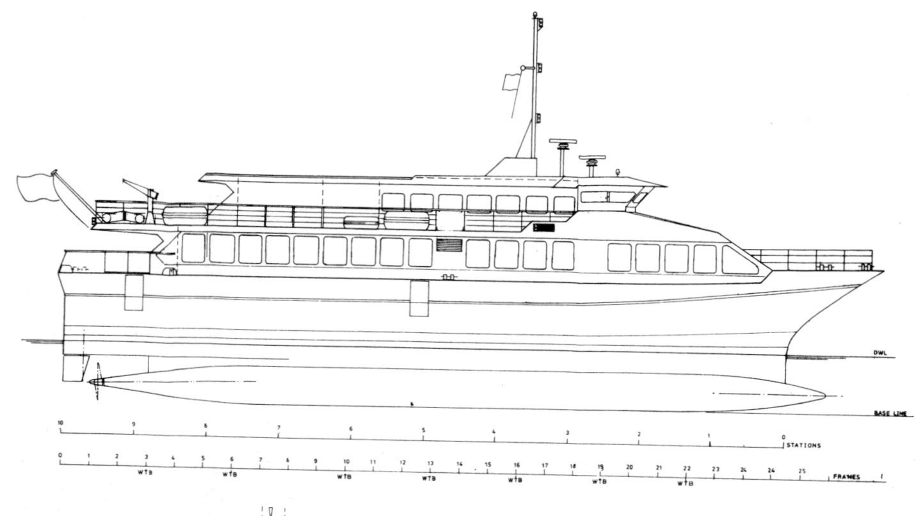

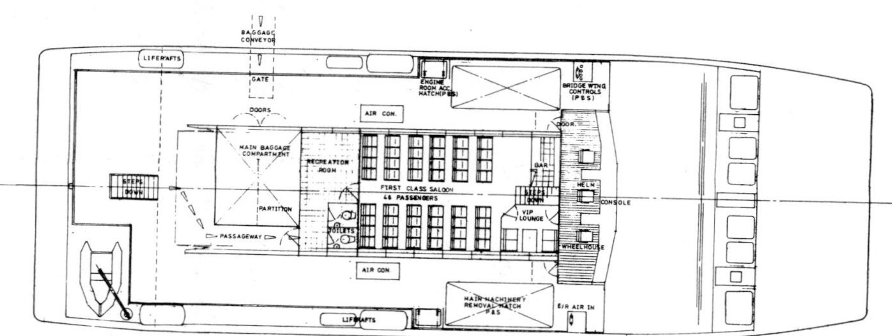

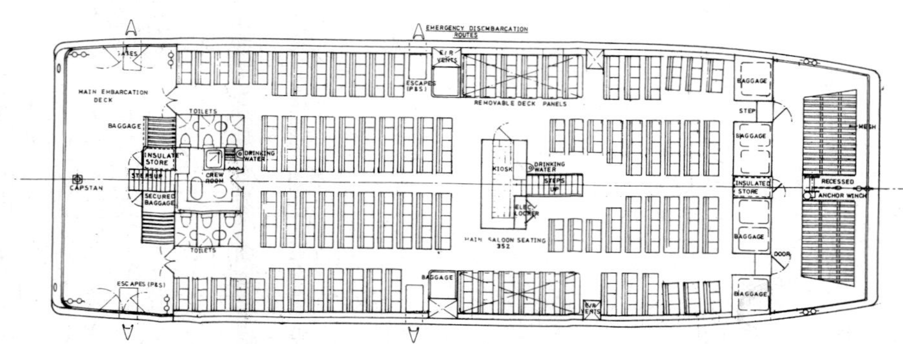

General arrangement of 37 m Atlantic class FDC **1990**

UNITED STATES OF AMERICA

NAVATEK SHIPS LTD

A subsidiary of Pacific Marine

Suite 1880, 841 Bishop St, Honolulu, Hawaii 96813, USA

Tel: +1 (808) 531 7001
Fax: +1 (808) 523 7668

William Clifford, *President*

Technology for the development of the first Pacific Marine Swath came from Dr Ludwig Seidl, Chairman of Department of Ocean Engineering, University of Hawaii. In 1977 Pacific Marine and Dr Seidl formed the Pacific Marine Engineering Science Company. In 1979 the company was granted patent (US Patent 4174671) covering its Swath design.

Pacific Marine invested $4.5 million to build a prototype vessel, the hull construction being subcontracted to Thompson Metal Fabricators, Vancouver, Washington.

Artist's impression of the 32 m SLICE prototype currently under construction ***1996***

Navatek I

The hull was launched in February 1989. After being outfitted at Northwest Marine, Portland, Oregon with a partial superstructure and pilot-house, sea trials commenced in May 1989. During those trials, *Navatek I* sailed 600 miles from Portland to San Francisco, California, then 2,100 miles across the Pacific to Honolulu, Hawaii. During the six day trip it averaged 15 knots, its design cruising speed, through seas of 1.8 to 3 m. It also demonstrated the ability to maintain 93 per cent of its speed through Sea State 5. *Navatek I* achieved a top speed of over 17 knots and its fuel consumption was 265 l/h at 1,600 rpm cruising speed. Its reduced ships motions were extremely good; waves up to 2.4 m produced almost no motion.

In July and August 1989 in the Molokai and Alenuihaha channels, *Navatek I* routinely ran all headings in average seas of 3.65 m, with occasional waves of just over 4.6 m. The largest wave it encountered during its trials was a 5.5 to 6.1 m wave set off Makapuu, Oahu. During that encounter, beer glasses sitting on tables in the forward lounge remained in place!

With the successful completion of sea trials in September 1989, Royal Hawaiian Cruises Ltd of Honolulu, Hawaii, signed a long-term lease on the vessel for use as a day excursion/dinner cruise boat serving the Hawaiian tourist trade. In October 1989, *Navatek I* sailed 6,500 miles via the Panama Canal to New Orleans, Louisiana, where Trinity Marine installed the rest of the two-deck superstructure.

In early 1990, the US Coast Guard certified *Navatek I* to carry 400 passengers on an ocean route. It thus became the first Swath to receive US Coast Guard approval as a commercial, passenger-carrying vessel.

Navatek I began commercial service in March 1990 and currently operates three scheduled cruises a day, seven days a week, in ocean waves ranging from 1.5 to 4.5 m.

In September 1991, the Coast Guard increased the passenger certification of *Navatek I* to 430 persons.

Royal Hawaiian Cruises has been able to command premium prices for places on these cruises due to the excellent stability and radically reduced motions of the Swath vessel. Despite operating daily in waves as high as 4.5 m, passenger reaction to the ride has been exceptional. During the initial three months of operation, Royal Hawaiian Cruises had its cabin crew report any incidence of passenger seasickness. Out of 17,430 passengers carried during this period only six were seasick. Since the start of service, operating days lost due to mechanical failure have been zero. Royal Hawaiian Cruises is able to offer tour wholesalers exclusive routes no other Hawaiian vessel can operate.

Navatek Ships Ltd began commercial production of its 40 m class Swath with the lease of *Navatek* in September 1989. It has licensed Kaiduan Offshore Sdn Bhd of Malaysia to build and market its Swath designs outside the USA on a non-exclusive basis.

Specifications

Length overall	43 m
Beam	16 m
Draught	2.44-4.27 m
Passsengers	430
Propulsive power	2 × 1,007 kW
Operational speed	15 kts
Max speed	18 kts

Propulsion: Main engines: twin Deutz MWM 16V-816CR diesels, continuous rating of 1,007 kW each, driving Ulstein reduction gears and Ulstein controllable-pitch 4-blade propellers.

Navatek I ***1993***

Navatek II *in operation*

1995

Electrical system: Twin Detroit Diesel 6-7 l generators rated at 99 kW each.

Navatek II

In 1991, Navatek Ships Ltd completed design, development and tank model testing in California of a proprietary, second-generation Swath design developed by engineers at Navatek Ships Ltd. In contrast to the original PAMESCO design, the new design features twin canted struts for which Navatek Ships Ltd itself holds patents pending.

Navatek's new, patented canted strut design offers several advantages over the vertical strut design employed in *Navatek I*. Inherent in any Swath design is the tendency of the bow to dive (monk moment), requiring fin stabilisation to overcome this phenomenon. But fin systems add resistance, requiring increased horsepower to move the vessel through the water. The twin, canted hull design of Navatek Ships Ltd produces a smaller bow down trimming moment, thus allowing smaller fins which results in less resistance and more speed per horsepower installed. Other advantages of canted struts include a larger damping effect in pitch, roll and heave, resulting in significantly better motion characteristics.

In November 1992, Navatek Ships Ltd began construction of its first twin, canted strut Swath, the *Navatek II*, at its Honolulu shipyard.

Navatek II was launched in January 1994 and began commercial service in April 1994 as a day cruise/adventure boat in the Hawaii tourist trade. Variations of this design for US Coast Guard duties have also been studied.

Specifications

Length overall	25 m
Beam	11.6 m
Draught	1.7 m
Passengers	150
Operational speed	23 kts
Range	750 n miles

Propulsion: Engines: 2 × MTU 12V 183.
Transmissions: 2 × ZF BW 250 gearboxes.
Thrust devices: 2 × 4-blade workboat style propellers.

Auxiliary systems: Generators: 2 × 45 kW Northern Lights.

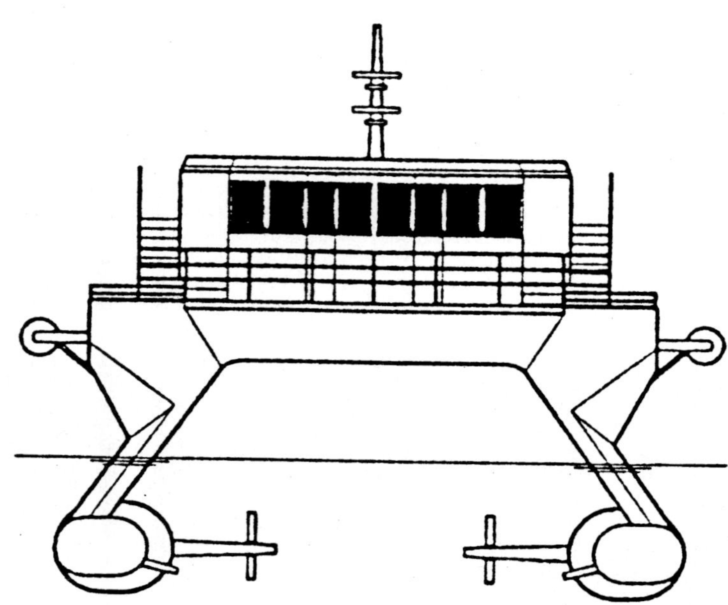
US Coast Guard patrol boat Swath (design)

1993

SLICE TECHNOLOGY PARTNERSHIP WITH LOCKHEED

In September 1993, Navatek Ships and the Marine Systems division of Lockheed Missiles & Space Company, Sunnyvale, California, announced that they had teamed up to commercialise Swath ship technology originally developed by Lockheed for the defence industry. Lockheed Missiles & Space Company, a leading defence contractor, has been involved in the development of many unique, high-technology marine vehicles. In addition to the world-recognised Polaris/Poseidon/Trident missile programmes, Lockheed developed one of the world's first deep diving manned vehicles, *Deep Quest*, followed by development of the Navy's submarine rescue submersibles, Deep Submergence Rescue Vehicles I and II. Lockheed's patented motion control system has been installed in the US Navy's T-AGOS 19 and T-AGOS 23 Swath surveillance ships. The company's high-technology Swath hull designs and computer-aided ship control systems continue to push the state of the art. In April 1993, the US Navy unveiled its Swath stealth ship *Sea Shadow*, designed and built by Lockheed. In addition to their collaboration on Swath design, Navatek and Lockheed are exploring other hull forms, first developed by Lockheed for the US defence industry, which may offer commercial potential. One of these hull forms, called SLICE, is a high-speed, 35 knot variant of Swath technology. By minimising wave-making resistance at high speeds, it produces significantly higher speeds for constant horsepower when compared to conventional Swath hull technology, yet it retains the sea-keeping of Swath technology. Navatek has negotiated worldwide rights to this technology, with Lockheed retaining military sales rights. In late 1993 the two companies received a $10 million advanced technology development grant from the US Navy to design and build a 177 tonne, 32 m SLICE prototype.

Design and tank testing work on the SLICE prototype was conducted at Lockheed's California facilities. Construction of the prototype began in early 1995 at Pacific Marine's shipyard in Hawaii with a target completion date of July 1996.

UPDATED

NICHOLS BROTHERS BOAT BUILDERS INC

5400 S Cameron Road, Freeland, Whidbey Island, Washington 98249, USA

Tel: +1 (360) 331 5500
Fax: +1 (360) 331 7484

Matt Nichols, *President*
Archie Nichols, *Vice President*
Ken Schoonover, *Yard Supervisor*
Scott Murphy, *Financial Officer*
Bryan Nichols, *Marketing*

Nichols Brothers received an order for a 37 m Swath vessel in late 1992, to be operated by Party Line Cruises of Miami. This vessel was constructed in the same facilities used for the shipyard's catamaran ferries.

37 m SWATH FERRY *Cloud X*

Designed by Swath International Limited, this craft was launched in May 1995 although it is understood that final delivery has been delayed until 1996. The craft is intended to operate from Miami to Key West in Florida as a passenger ferry with modern gambling facilities.

Specifications

Length overall	37.2 m
Beam	18 m
Draught	3.4 m
Passengers	365
Fuel capacity	16,000 l
Water capacity	3,000 l
Propulsive power	2 × 2,870 kW
Max speed	30 kts
Operational speed	28 kts

Propulsion: The main engines are 2 × Textron Lycoming TF40 gas-turbines rated at 2,870 kW each, driving 2 × Kamewa CPP propellers.

UPDATED

Launch of Cloud X in May 1995

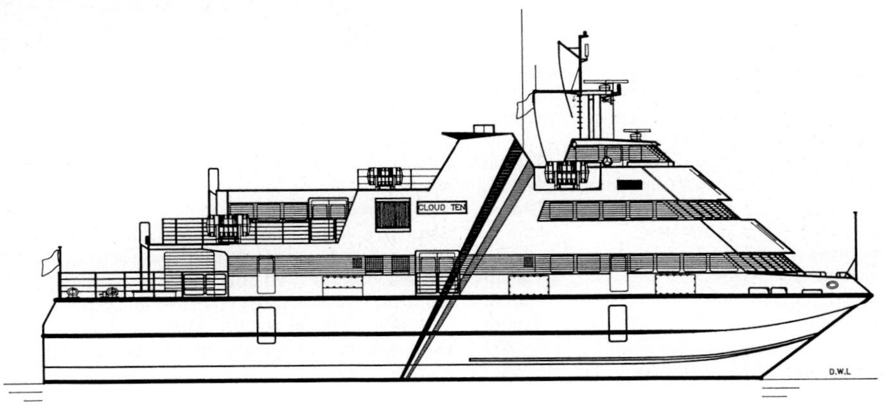

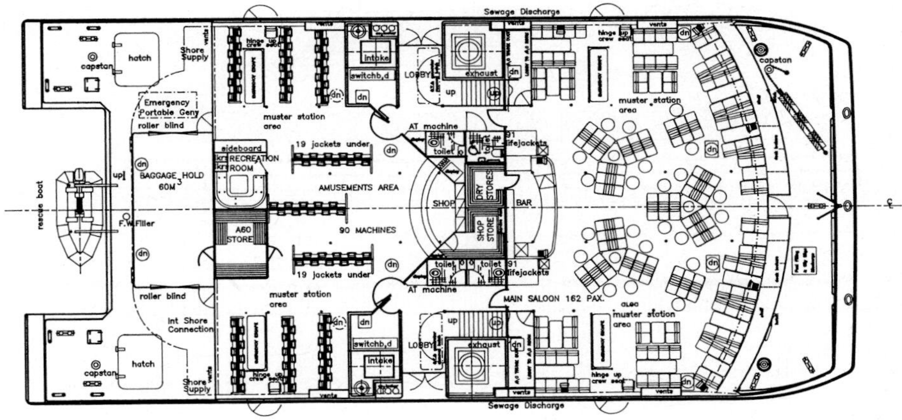

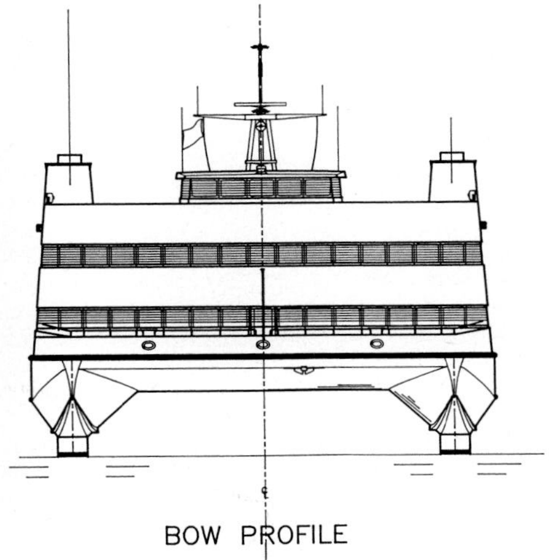

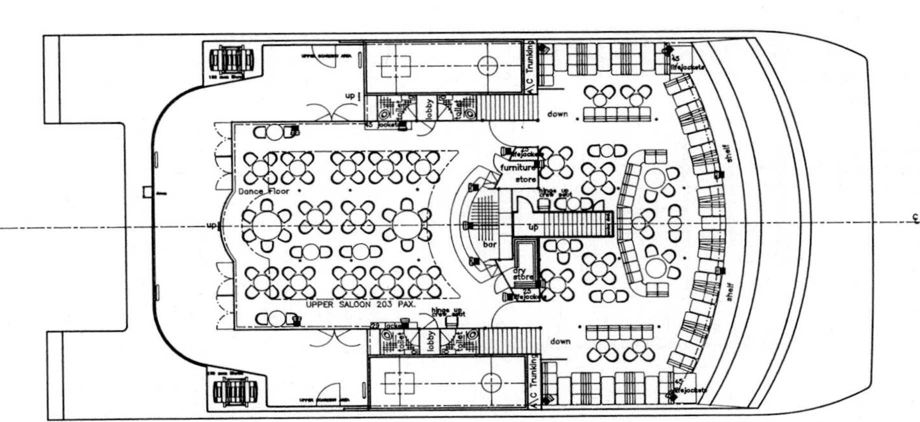

Profiles and plans of the Swath Ferry Cloud X

SWATH OCEAN SYSTEMS INC

1313 W 24th Street, National City, California 91950, USA

Tel: +1 (619) 336 4615
Fax: +1 (619) 336 4616

Nelson Hall, *General Manager*
Greg Smith, *Construction Manager*
Kurt Schmidt, *Engineering Manager*
Bill Shaw, *Yard Manager*
Michael Docker, *Design Manager*
Gary Prior, *Materials Manager*

Swath Ocean Systems (SOS) moved to a 5½ acre facility in July 1993. This new facility offers indoor construction with overhead crane handling equipment, outdoor yard with bayside launch capabilities and materials storage area. SOS has a complete in-house design and engineering department using the latest hydrostatics, resistance and CAD software.

SOS 4000 Class Chubasco 1 **1996**

Chubasco

Chubasco was launched 28 March 1987 by James Betts Enterprises of San Diego for Leonard Friedman for drift fishing. The design and building are under patents of Dr Thomas G Lang of the Semi-Submerged Ship Corporation.

She served as the official committee boat for the judges for the 1988 America's Cup races held at San Diego and in 1995 was sold to New Zealand Group, the winners of the Cup in that year.

Specifications

Length overall	21.95 m
Beam	9.45 m
Draught	3.05 m
Displacement, max	70 t
Fuel capacity	18,920 l
Water capacity	1,890 l
Propulsive power	2 × 559 kW
Max speed	21 kts
Operational speed	20 kts

Structure: Marine grade aluminium.
Propulsion: The main engines are 2 × DDC 8V 92 TI diesels, 559 kW (750 hp) each, turbocharged.
Control: Gyro-activated stabiliser fin system.

Steering station at stern, steering station at each wing outside pilot-house, bow thruster and controls at three stations.

Betsy (ex-*Suave Lino*)

Completed in 1981 for SOS as a fishing boat, *Betsy* was used as a tender by the Sail America Syndicate during the America's Cup defence off Fremantle, Australia.

The vessel is contructed of aluminium with a single strut configuration for each hull. Two high-speed diesels of 425 hp each, mounted at deck level, drive fixed-pitch propellers through bevel gears. Automatic fin control fitted.

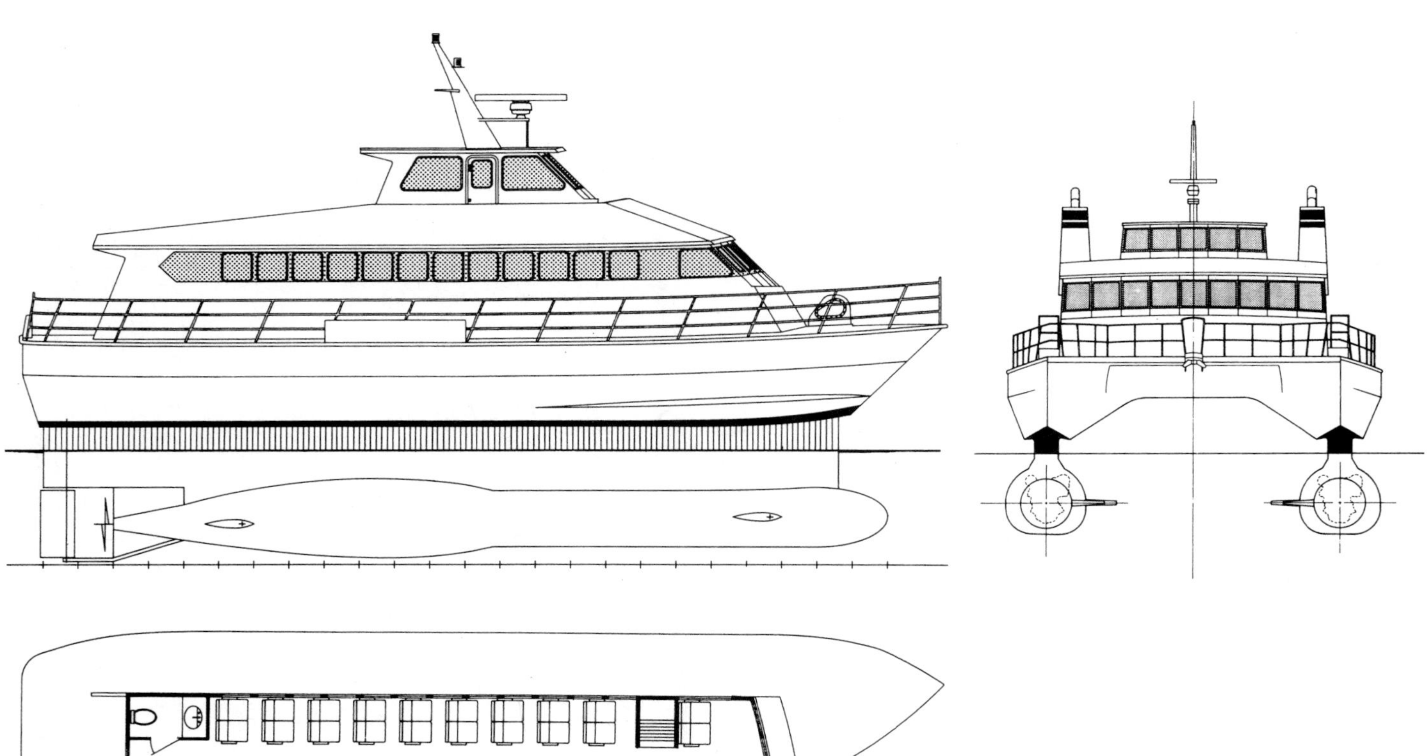

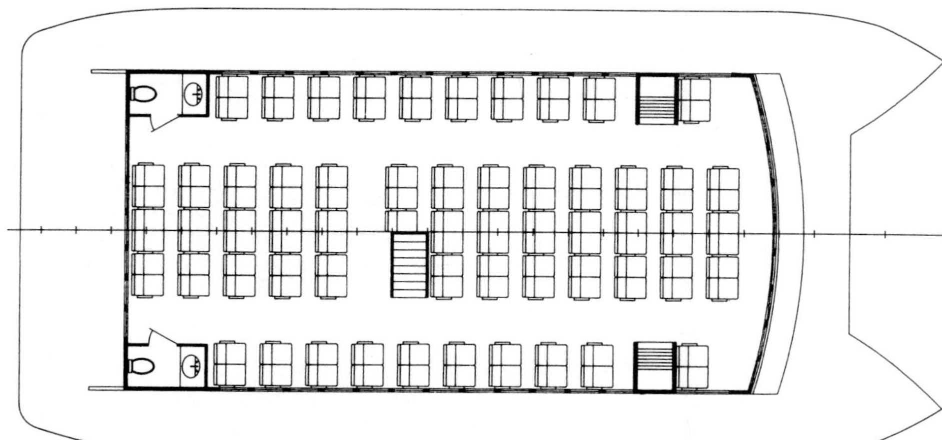

Swath Ocean 2000 class layout, Frederick G Creed **1991**

Houston Pilot Cutter ***1994***

Specifications

Length overall	19.2 m
Beam	9.1 m
Draught	2.13 m
Displacement, min	53 t
Payload	14 t
Max speed	18 kts

Propulsion: The main engines are 2 × DDC 8V 71, 317 kW (425 hp) each.

2000 CLASS

Frederick G Creed

A 20.4 m 80 tonne Swath vessel launched in November 1989 and made available for the Canadian Department of Fisheries and Oceans under a lease purchase contract for oceanographic and hydrographic service off the eastern coasts of Canada and the USA.

Specifications

Length overall	20 m
Beam	10.67 m
Draught	2.6 m
Displacement, max	80.26 t
Displacement, min	57.9 t
Passengers	125
Propulsive power	2 × 805 kW
Max speed	29 kts
Operational speed	25 kts

Propulsion: The main engines are 2 × DDC 12V 92TA 805 kW diesels.

HOUSTON PILOT CUTTER

A 20.4 m 80 tonne Swath vessel, based on the SOS 2000 class craft, was delivered to the Houston Pilots in early 1993. By December 1995 the vessel had logged over 14,000 hours and 24,000 pilot transfers.

Specifications

Length overall	20.4 m
Beam	11.28 m
Draught	2.44 m
Displacement, max	78 t
Displacement, min	57 t
Propulsive power	2 × 750 kW
Operational speed	23 kts

Propulsion: The main engines are 2 × Cat 3412 diesels rated at 750 kW each.

4000 CLASS

Chubasco 1

The vessel was launched in October 1993 and delivered to her owner Chubasco Charters of San Diego. It is currently used for long range fishing charters to the west coast of Maine.

Specification

Length overall	27.54 m
Beam	13.72 m
Displacement, max	182.8 t

Propulsion: Two Caterpillar 3516TA diesels each rated at 2,100 kW at 1,880 rpm and each driving a fix pitch propeller via a ZF BWK 755 reverse reduction gearbox.

UPDATED

HIGH-SPEED MONOHULL CRAFT

Company Listing by Country

Australia
Austal Ships Pty Ltd
Geraldton Boat Builders
Lloyd's Ships Holdings Pty Ltd
Oceanfast International Pty Ltd
SBF Engineering Pty Ltd
Sea Chrome Marine Pty Ltd
Transfield Shipbuilding (WA)
Wavemaster International Pty Ltd

Chile
Asmar Shipbuilding and Docking Co

Commonwealth of Independent States
Central Hydrofoil Design Bureau

Finland
Kværner Masa-Yards Inc

France
Ateliers et Chantiers du Havre
Guy Couach Constructions Navales
Leroux and Lotz
SBCN

Germany
Abeking and Rasmussen Shipyard
Blohm+Voss AG
Lürssen Werft GmbH & Co

Hong Kong
Cheoy Lee Shipyards Ltd
Chung Wah Shipbuilders Ltd

Italy
Azimut SpA
Cantieri Ing Moschini SpA
Cantieri Navali Italcraft Srl
Cantieri Navali Lavagna Srl
Cantieri Posillipo SpA
Cantieri Riva SpA
Crestitalia SpA
Fazioli Nautica Srl
Fincantieri Cantieri Navali Italiani SpA
Industrie Navales Meccaniche Affini SpA
Intermarine SpA
Rodriquez Cantieri Navali SpA
Tecnomarine SpA
Cantiere Nautico Versilcraft Srl
Sciomachen

Japan
Etoh Marine Corporation
Mitsubishi Heavy Industries Ltd
Mokubei Shipbuilding Company
Yamaha Motor Company Ltd

Korea, South
Semo Company Ltd

Malaysia
Chiong Brothers Shipyard
Wong's Shipbuilding Contractor & Designer

Netherlands
Damen Shipyards
Kees Cornelissen Shipyard
Royal Schelde BV

Norway
Båtutrustning A/S
Mjellem & Karlsen Verft A/S

Singapore
Aluminium Craft (88) Pte Ltd
Greenbay Marine Pte Ltd
Marinteknik Shipbuilders (S) Pte Ltd
Singapore Technologies Shipbuilding and Engineering Ltd

Spain
Bazan, Empresa Nacional

Sweden
Boghammar International AB
Oskarshamns Varv AB

Thailand
Technautic Intertrading Company Ltd

United Kingdom
Ailsa-Perth Shipbuilders Ltd
Berthon Boat Company Ltd
FBM Marine Group
McTay Marine
Vosper Thornycroft (UK) Ltd

United States of America
Admiral Marine Works Inc
Aluminum Boats Inc
Blount Marine Corporation
Bollinger Machine Shop & Shipyard Inc
Breaux's Bay Craft Inc
Christensen Motor Yacht Corporation
Denison Marine Inc
Derecktor Shipyards
Derecktor-Gunnell
Robert E Derecktor, Inc
Equitable Shipyards Inc
Gladding-Hearn Shipbuilding
Gulf Craft Inc
Halter Marine Inc
Magnum Marine Corporation
Munson Manufacturing Inc
Peterson Builders Inc
Swiftships Inc
Tempest Yachts Inc
Trinity Marine Group
Trinity Yachts Inc
Westport Shipyard Inc

AUSTRALIA

AUSTAL SHIPS PTY LTD

100 Clarence Beach, Henderson, Perth, Western Australia 6166, Australia

Tel: +61 (9) 410 1111
Fax: +61 (9) 410 2564

John Rothwell, *Managing Director*
Christopher Norman, *Director, Marketing*
Garry Heys, *Director and General Manager*
Kevin Stanley, *Director and General Manager*

48 m HIGH-SPEED MONOHULL PASSENGER FERRY

Ono-Ono

In December 1993, Austal won a $5.8 million contract to build a 48 m high-speed monohull ferry. The vessel was delivered in June 1994 and is operated by SPI Maritime from Tahiti's main port Papeete to the neighbouring islands of Huahine, Raiatea, Bora Bora and Tahea.

During delivery the vessel sailed under its own power from Western Australia to Tahiti covering over 7,000 n miles.

Specifications

Length overall	48 m
Length waterline	41.3 m
Beam	9 m
Draught	1.2 m
Crew	11
Passengers	450
Fuel capacity	20,000 l
Water capacity	2,000 l
Propulsive power	3 × 1,960 kW
Max speed	35 kts

Propulsion: The main engines are 3 × MTU 16V 396 TE 74L rated at 1,960 kW at 1,940 rpm, driving 3 × KaMeWa 63 water-jets via 3 × Reintjes VLJ930 gearboxes.

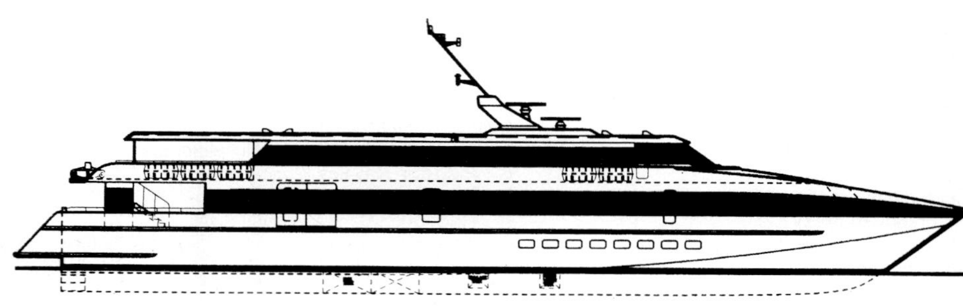

PROFILE

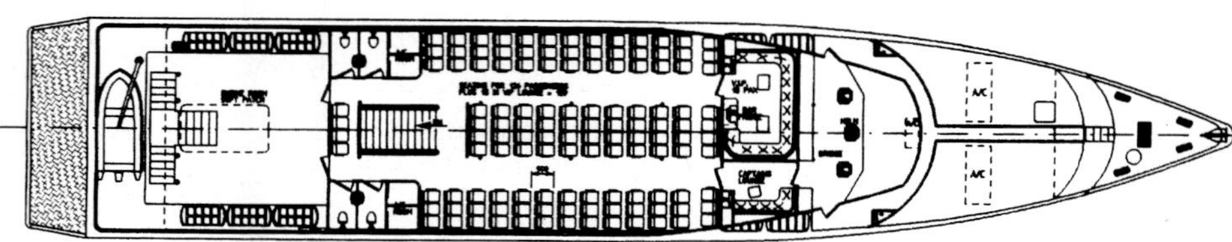

UPPER DECK

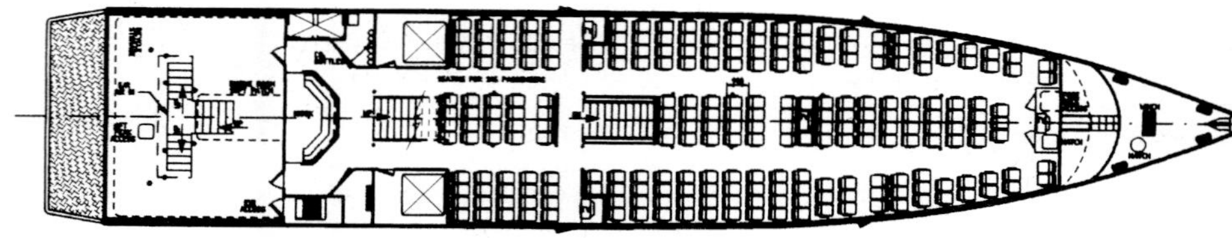

MAIN DECK

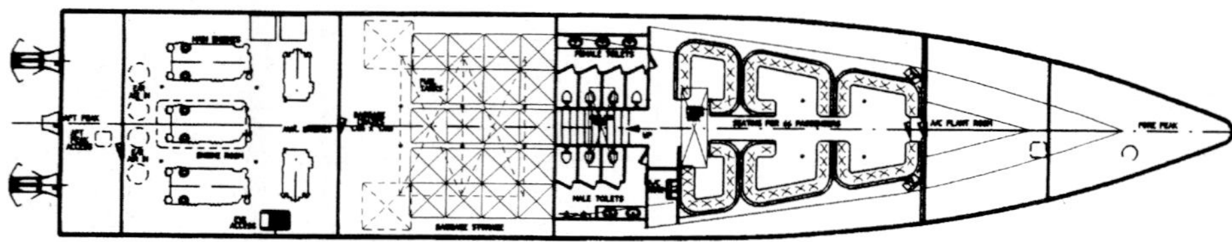

General arrangement of Ono-Ono **1995**

30 m MONOHULL FERRY

Ertugrul Gazi
Aksemseddin

These two 30 m monohull vessels were sold to the Turkish operator Istanbul Deniz Otobusleri in December 1994. The vessels operate between Istanbul and ports in the Marmara and Bosporus seas.

Specifications

Length overall	30 m
Length waterline	25.8 m
Beam	7.05 m
Draught	1.2 m
Crew	4
Passengers	155
Fuel capacity	4,000 l
Water capacity	400 l
Propulsive power	2 × 822 kW
Operational speed	25 kts

Propulsion: The vessel is powered by two MTU 8V 396 TE 74 diesels rated at 822 kW each. Each diesel drives through a ZF BU255 gearbox to an FFJet 550 water-jet.

UPDATED

Ono-Ono *on trials*
1995

GERALDTON BOAT BUILDERS

15 Larkin St, Geraldton, Western Australia 6530

Tel: +61 (099) 211288
Fax: +61 (099) 216404

Terry Bromley, *Director*

Geraldton Boat Builders specialises in building small fast patrol craft and commercial vessels, offering a range of both monohull and catamaran designs, all of a high-speed planing type. Hulls are manufactured from aluminium or GRP.

20 m PATROL VESSEL

Five of these vessels have been delivered to the Australian defence forces.

Specification

Length overall	20.0 m
Beam	5.7 m
Draught	1.5 m
Crew	7
Fuel capacity	5,000 l
Water capacity	1,000 l
Propulsive power	970 kW
Max speed	25 kts
Operational speed	21 kts
Range	650 n miles

Structure: Aluminium hull, deck and superstructure.

Propulsion: The vessels are powered by twin MTU 8V 183TE diesel engines each rated at 485 kW and driving via Twin Disc 5111A gearboxes to a three bladed propeller.

22 m PATROL VESSEL

This vessel was delivered to the Victorian State Government in Australia in late 1993.

Specifications

Length overall	22 m
Beam	6.6 m
Draught	1.6 m
Displacement, min	28 t
Displacement, max	43 t
Fuel capacity	14,000 l
Water capacity	200 l
	and 1,500 l/day desalinator
Propulsive power	2 × 1,500 kW
Max speed	28 kts
Operational speed	21.5 kts
Range	1,000 n miles

Propulsion: The vessel is powered by two MTU 12V 183 TF 92 diesel engines rated at 2,300 rpm each driving a fixed-pitch propeller via a ZF 193 reverse reduction gearbox.

UPDATED

LLOYD'S SHIPS HOLDINGS PTY LTD

41 Oxford Street, Bulimba, Queensland 4171, Australia

Tel: +61 (7) 3399 6866
Fax: +61 (7) 3395 5000

John Hardie, *General Manager*

Lloyd's Ships designs and constructs a range of luxury motor yachts and large catamaran ferry vessels with speeds up to 40 knots. All Lloyd's ships are constructed to 'Class'.

The company has Daikyo Australia Pty Ltd as its parent company, has 70 people directly employed and a turnover in excess of A$10 million per annum.

29.5 m MOTOR YACHT V102

Launched in July 1994, construction of this all-aluminium yacht recommenced in May 1993.

Specifications

Length overall	29.5 m
Length waterline	23.1 m
Beam	8.5 m
Draught	1.7 m
Displacement	130 t
Crew	6
Passengers	6 guests
Fuel capacity	26 t
Water capacity	6 t
Max speed	24 kts
Operational speed	17 kts

Lloyd's Ships 29.5 m motor yacht, V102 ***1995***

Classification: DnV +A1 High-Speed Lightcraft (Winter R280).

Propulsion: 2 × MTU 12V 396 TE 94 engines, powering 2 × Kamewa S71 water-jets.

UPDATED

OCEANFAST INTERNATIONAL PTY LTD

26 St George's Terrace, Perth, PO Box X2256, Western Australia, Australia

Tel: +61 (9) 325 8599
Telex: 94598 IAL AA
Fax: +61 (9) 325 6484/221 1813

Boat Factory: 15 Egmont Road, Henderson, Western Australia 6166, Australia

Tel: +61 (9) 410 1900
Fax: +61 (9) 410 2095

John Farrell, *Managing Director*

Oceanfast International is part of the Oceanfast Marine group which also includes International Shipyards, Motor Yacht International and Ferries Australia.

The Oceanfast Marine Group is one of Australia's largest shipbuilding operations, building a diverse range of craft from commercial fishing vessels and passenger ferries through to luxury motor yachts. The group operates under the ISO 9002 Quality Assurance code.

The most recent high- speed craft project, a 53 m, 20 knot propeller-driven semi-displacement luxury yacht, *Kremlin Princess,* was delivered in mid-1994.

Opal C

Specifications

Length overall	40.3 m
Beam	8.0 m
Draught	1.4 m
Displacement, min	140 t
Displacement, max	170 t
Crew	7
Passengers	7
Fuel capacity	35,000 l
Water capacity	7,000 l
Propulsive power	2 × 2,595 kW
Max speed	35 kts
Operational speed	30 kts
Range	900 n miles

Oceanfast Opal C ***1995***

Classification: DnV unlimited letter of compliance for hull construction and machinery installation.
Propulsion: The main engines are 2 × MTU 16V 396 TB 94 diesels each producing 2,595 kW, driving 2 × KaMeWa type 80 S62/6 water-jets via 2 × ZF BU755 non-reversible gearboxes.
Electrical system: The generator sets are 1 × 98 kW MTU/Mercedes, and 1 × 65 kW MTU/Mercedes.
Control: One pair of Koopnautic roll stabilisers and hydraulically operated trim tabs are fitted.

Antipodean

Specifications

Length overall	36 m
Beam	7.4 m
Draught	1 m
Displacement, min	95 t
Displacement, max	110 t
Fuel capacity	22,000 l
Water capacity	2,400 l
Propulsive power	2 × 1,461 kW
Max speed	30 kts
Operational speed	25 kts

Propulsion: The main engines are 2 × MTU 12 cylinder 396 TB 93 diesels, each producing 1,461 kW at 2,100 rpm, driving 2 × KaMeWa S62/6 water-jets.

Mystique

Specifications

Length overall	50 m
Beam	8.96 m
Draught	1.5 m
Displacement, min	210 t
Fuel capacity	93,000 l
Water capacity	10,000 l
Max speed	35 kts
Operational speed	28 kts

Propulsion: The main engines are 2 × MTU 16V 396 TB 94, and 1 × MTU 12V 396 TB 93, driving 3 × Kamewa type 80 S62/6 water-jets.
Electrical system: The power is supplied by 2 × 130 kVA Northern Lights generators.

Madiblue (ex-Parts VI)

Specifications

Length overall	46.69 m
Beam	8.36 m
Draught	1.25 m
Displacement, min	140 t
Crew	5
Fuel capacity	45,000 l
Water capacity	5,700 l
Propulsive power	3,896 kW
Max speed	30 kts

53 m high-speed displacement yacht, Kremlin Princess **1996**

Propulsion: The main engines are 2 × MTU 12 cylinder 396 TB 93, and 1 × MTU 8 cylinder 396 TB 93 diesels, driving 3 × KaMeWa 63S62/6 water-jets.
Electrical system: The power is supplied by 2 × 68 kVA Mercedes-Benz OM 352 220/380 V generator sets.

Sounds of Pacific

A 37.6 m cruising monohull vessel built for Island Cruise Line Pacific Inc. Now operating in Guam after its promotional trip to Japan.

Specifications

Length overall	37.6 m
Length waterline	31.4 m
Beam	7.5 m
Draught	1.05 m
Displacement, min	92 t
Crew	8
Passengers	100
Fuel capacity	6,000 l
Water capacity	2,500 l
Max speed	31 kts
Operational speed	27.5 kts

Propulsion: The main engines are 2 × MWM TBD 604B V16; driving 2 × Kamewa 71S 62/6 water-jets.

Kremlin Princess (ex-*Oceana*)

This all-aluminium motor yacht, launched in 1994, was designed by Jon Baunenburg and built by Oceanfast with Phil Curron as the naval architect.

Specifications

Length overall	53.5 m
Length waterline	45.66 m
Beam	10.0 m
Draught	2.34 m
Displacement, min	260 t
Fuel capacity	96,000 l
Water capacity	14,000 l
Propulsive power	7,136 kW
Max speed	22 kts
Operational speed	20 kts
Range	3,000 n miles (one engine)

Propulsion: The main engines are 2 × MTU 16V 396 TE 86, 2,050 kW each.

UPDATED

SBF ENGINEERING PTY LTD

Waters Edge, Lot 33 Cockburn Road, South Coogee, Western Australia 6166, Australia

Tel: +61 (9) 410 2244
Fax: +61 (9) 410 1807

Don Dunbar, *Managing Director, Designer*
Alan McCombie, *Director, Financial Controller*
Don Johnston, *General Manager*

SBF Engineering builds high-speed aluminium crew boats and passenger ferries, designed to meet the operational needs of individual shipping companies. Apart from the vessels detailed below, SBF Engineering has also built a 54 passenger, 35 knot, water-jet-propelled ferry, the *Fitzroy Reef Jet*.

Craft name	Payload	Engines	Delivery	Operating Country
Auto Batam 7	200 passengers	3 × MTU 12V 183 TE 62	March 1991	Singapore
Sea Dragon		2 × Cummins KT19	1991	Singapore
Satrya Express	62 passengers	2 × MTU 12V 396 TB 83		Indonesia
Sea Flyte	240 passengers	2 × MTU	1980	Singapore
Sundancer	160 passengers	3 × MWM TBD 234 V12		Singapore
James Kelly II	200 passengers	2 × GM 12V 92		Tasmania
Wilderness Seeker	100 passengers	2 × MWM TBD 234 V12	1985	Tasmania
Sing Batam 1	226 passengers	3 × MTU 12V 183 TE 62	December 1991	Singapore
Sea Dragon 3		2 × Cummins KT19-M	March 1992	Singapore
Tung Hsin	193 passengers	3 × MTU 12V 183 TE 72	February 1993	Taiwan
SBF 31 m	152 passengers	3 × MTU 12V 183 TE 72	July 1995	Singapore

Tung Hsin

This vessel is SBF's first export to Taiwan and was ordered by Tung Hsin Steamship Company Ltd. Operating in the south of Taiwan from Ping Tung to Hsiao Liu Chiu Island, *Tung Hsin* was designed and built to suit the client's operation. Consideration had to be given to the transport of motorbikes on the aft deck, therefore passengers are loaded forward and aft. The vessel was launched in January 1993 and delivered in February.

Specifications

Length overall	26.55 m
Length waterline	24.3 m

Auto Batam 7 **1993**

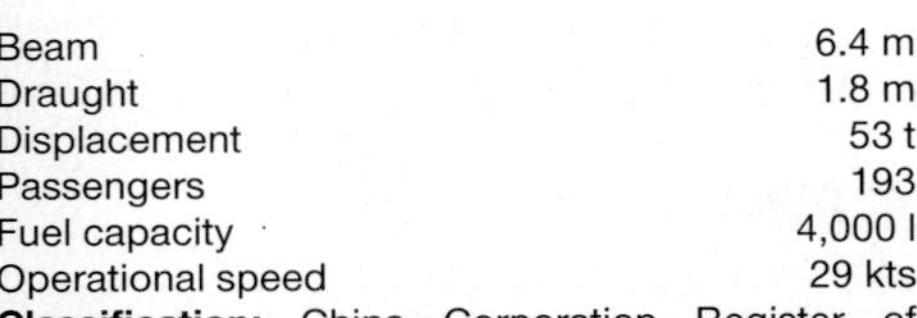

Beam	6.4 m
Draught	1.8 m
Displacement	53 t
Passengers	193
Fuel capacity	4,000 l
Operational speed	29 kts

Classification: China Corporation Register of Shipping.
Safety standards: Taiwan Marine Authority.
Structure: Hull material: aluminium.
Superstructure material: aluminium.
Propulsion: The main engines are 3 × MTU 12V 183 TE 72 diesels, driving 3 × Stone Marine 5-blade propellers via 3 × Niigata MGN 232 gearboxes.
Electrical system: Engine: 1 × Perkins 4.236 diesel. Generator: 1 × Lister 19 kVA.

Auto Batam 7

This monohull ferry (Yard No KP07) was delivered in March 1991 for service with Kalpin Shipping and Trading Company of Singapore for the Singapore to Batam Island route. She is a sister vessel of *Auto Batam 6*, delivered in 1990.

Specifications

Length overall	30 m
Length waterline	24.6 m
Beam	6.5 m
Draught	1.8 m
Displacement	54 t
Passengers	200
Fuel capacity	5,500 l
Operational speed	27 kts

Classification: Bureau Veritas.
Structure: Hull material: aluminium.
Superstructure material: aluminium.
Propulsion: The main engines are 3 × MTU 12V 183 TE 62 diesels, driving 3 × 5-blade propellers via 3 × ZF BW755 gearboxes.
Electrical system: 1 × Cummins 4B3.9 37 kVA 50 Hz 415/250 V generator, 1 × Lister-Petter 19 kVA air-cooled generator.

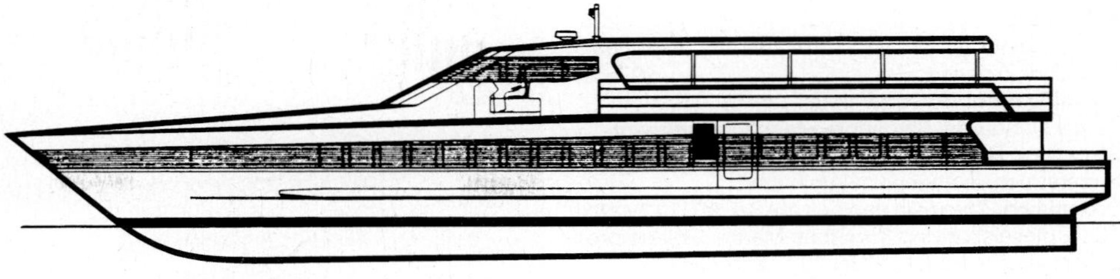

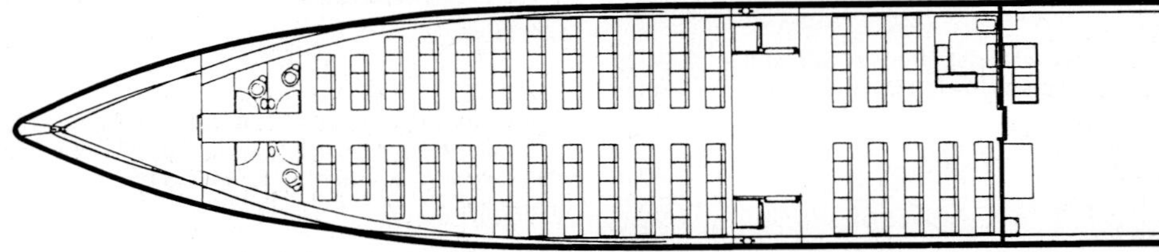

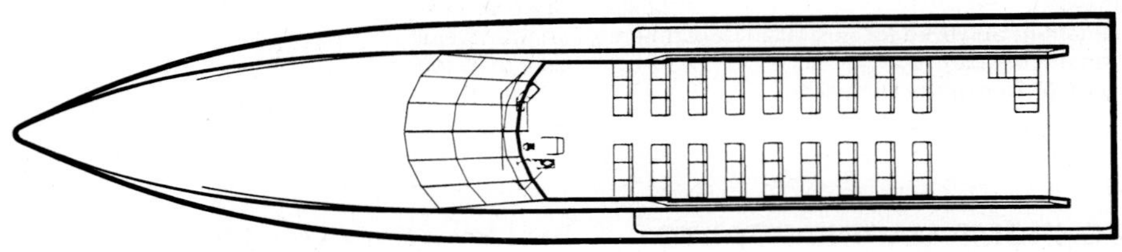

General arrangement of 31 m passenger ferry **1996**

Sea Dragon 2

A 23 m workboat for ship delivery and support work in Singapore harbour anchorage, delivered to Kalpin Shipping and Trading Company in late 1991.

Specifications

Length	23 m
Beam	6.2 m
Draught	1.3 m
Operational speed	22 kts

Propulsion: The main engines are 2 × Cummins KT19, 380 kW at 2,100 rpm.

Sea Dragon 2 *crew boat* **1993**

Sea Dragon 3

This vessel was ordered when the owners, Sea Dragon Marine Services Pte Ltd, took delivery of its sister vessel *Sea Dragon 2*. Launched and delivered in March 1992, the vessel was delivered under its own power.

Specifications

Length overall	22.55 m
Beam	6.2 m
Draught	1.3 m
Passengers	12
Propulsive power	2 × 3,171 kW

Structure: Hull material: aluminium.
Superstructure material: aluminium.
Propulsion: The main engines are 2 × Cummins KT19-M diesels, 317 kW each, driving 2 × 4-blade propellers, through 2 × Twin Disc 5111A gearboxes.

Sing Batam 1

This triple screw vessel (Yard No SB28) was ordered at the same time as *Sea Dragon 2* by the same owners but under the company name of Sing Batam Ferries Pte Ltd. This vessel is based upon *Auto Batam 7* delivered to Kalpin Shipping and Trading Company Pte Ltd earlier in 1991. The difference is that the upper deck is fully enclosed and air conditioned with the same interior seating as the main deck. This vessel was launched in Fremantle in December 1991 and delivered the same month, it took seven days under its own power to arrive in Singapore.

Specifications

Length overall	30 m
Length waterline	24.6 m
Beam	6.5 m
Draught	1.8 m
Displacement	54 t

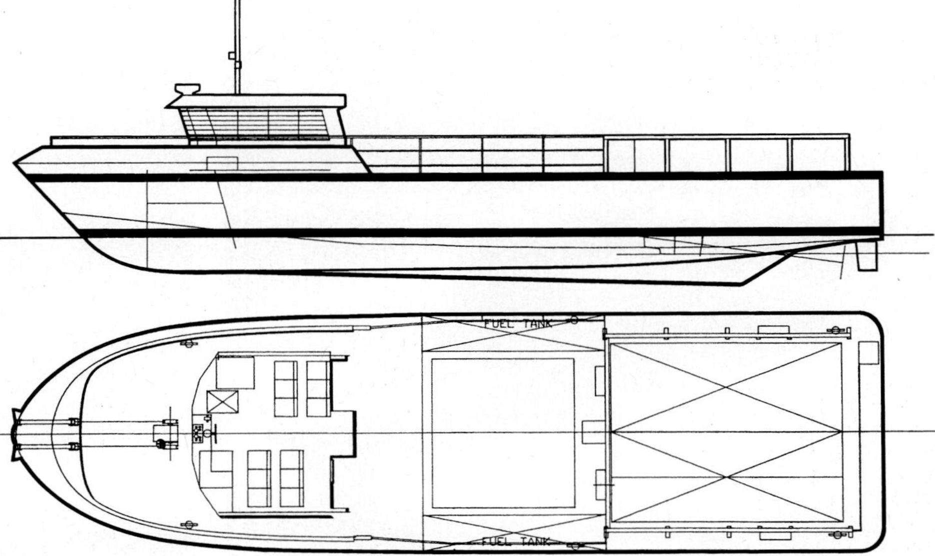

General arrangement of Sea Dragon 2 **1995**

Passengers	226
Fuel capacity	5,500 l
Operational speed	27 kts

Classification: Bureau Veritas.
Safety standards: Singapore Marine Department.
Structure: Hull material: aluminium.
Superstructure material: aluminium.
Propulsion: The main engines are 3 × MTU 12V 183 TE 62 diesels, driving 3 × Stone Marine 5-blade propellers via 3 × Niigata MGN 232 gearboxes.
Electrical system: Engines: 2 × Cummins 4B3.9 37 kVA 50 Hz 415/250 V generators.

MV Osprey V **1995**

Osprey

This vessel was delivered in September 1994 to Rottnest Express Pty Ltd for operation from Perth to Rottnest Island.

Specifications

Length overall	30 m
Length waterline	26.6 m
Beam	6.5 m
Draught	1.8 m
Passengers	257
Propulsive power	3 × 610 kW
Max speed	32 kts

Classification: Surveyed for Australian Department of Transport (Marine) 1D.
Structure: Marine grade aluminium.
Propulsion: The main engines are 3 × MTU 12V 183 TE 72 diesels, driving 3 × 5-blade Stone Marine propellers via 3 × Twin Disc MG 5141 reversing gearboxes.

SBF 31 m PASSENGER FERRY

This vessel was ordered by Auto Batam Ferry Services of Singapore and delivered in July 1995.

Specification

Length overall	31 m
Length waterline	27.6 m
Beam	6.5 m
Draught	1.8 m
Passengers	152
Propulsive power	1,830 kW
Max speed	32 kts

Propulsion: The vessel is powered by three MTU 12V 183 TE 72 diesels each rated at 610 kW at 2,100 rpm and each driving a fixed pitch propeller via a reverse reduction gearbox.

UPDATED

SEA CHROME MARINE PTY LTD

14 Rous Head Road, North Freemantle, Western Australia 6159, Australia

Tel: +61 (9) 335 1155
Fax: +61 (9) 430 5245

N Wilhelm, *Managing Director*
T Manners, *Sales and Marketing Manager*

Sea Chrome Marine Pty Ltd are builders of high-speed commercial vessels, specialising in FRP production. A range of fast fishing boats, ferries, pilot boats and patrol boats have been built, the largest being a 22 m, 30 knot lobster boat, *Desert Wind*.

22 m AQUACULTURE CRAFT

Desert Wind

Specifications

Length overall	22.2 m
Beam	6.1 m
Draught	1.45 m
Fuel capacity	4,600 l
Max speed	30 kts
Operational speed	25 kts

Structure: FRP construction.
Propulsion: The vessel is powered by two MTU 12V 193 diesel engines each driving a fixed pitch propeller via a reverse reduction gearbox.

NEW ENTRY

TRANSFIELD SHIPBUILDING

775 Cockburn Road, Henderson, Western Australia 6166, Australia

Tel: +61 (9) 437 0437
Telex: 93458AA
Fax: +61 (9) 410 2065

Formerly known as Australian Shipbuilding Industries WA Pty Ltd, Transfield Shipbuilding is continuing to build high-speed craft based on the original ASI 35 m patrol boat.

Developments of this design have now been supplied to the Royal Hong Kong Police (a total of six) and Kuwait Coast Guard (a total of four).

The company also has a license agreement with Rodriquez of Italy for the build and sales of the 102 m Aquastrada fast ferry design.

ASI 31.5 m PATROL BOAT

Australian Shipbuilding Industries won the contract to build patrol boats for the Pacific Patrol Boat Project. Participating countries and number of boats purchased are Papua New Guinea (4), Vanuatu (1), Western Samoa (1), Solomon Islands (2), Cook Islands (1), Tonga (3), Marshall Islands (1), Fiji (3), Kiribati (1), Tuvalu (1) and the Federated States of Micronesia (2). The craft undertake surveillance and enforcement of the Exclusive Economic Zones of the countries concerned. The craft listed in the accompanying table have been completed and handed over.

Specifications

Length overall	31.5 m
Length waterline	28.6 m
Beam	8.21 m
Draught	2.12 m
Displacement, max	165 t
Max speed	23 kts
Operational speed	21 kts
Range	2,500 n miles (at 12 kts)

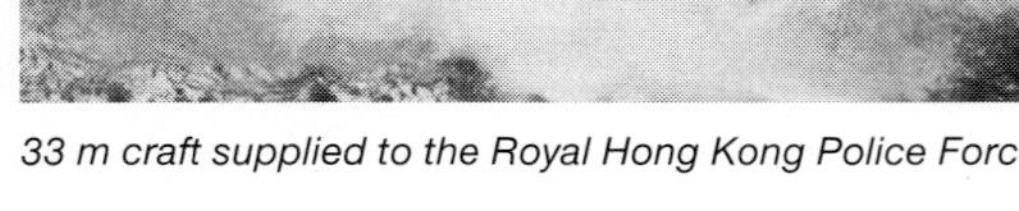

33 m craft supplied to the Royal Hong Kong Police Force **1994**

31.5 m craft supplied to the Kuwait Coast Guard **1994**

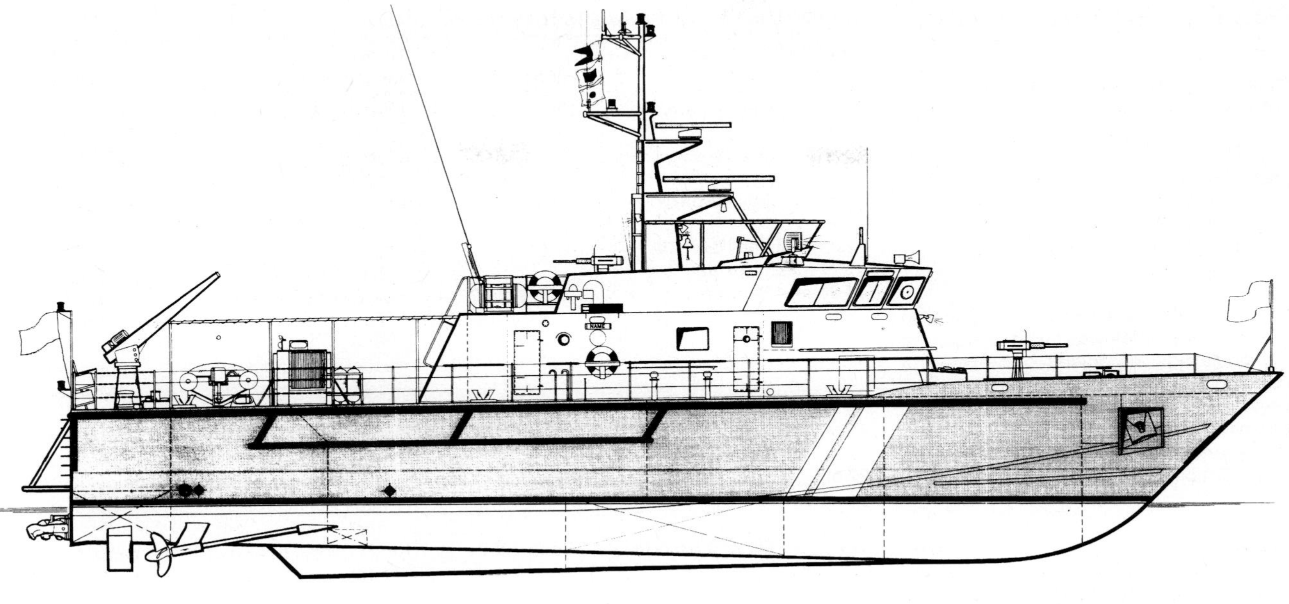

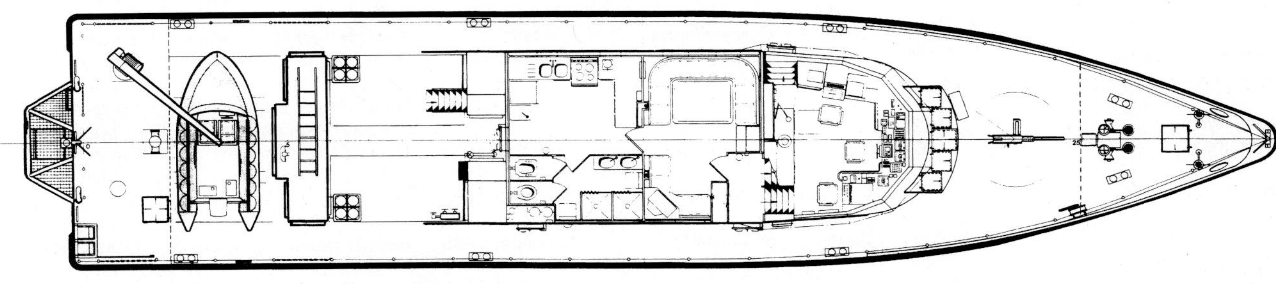

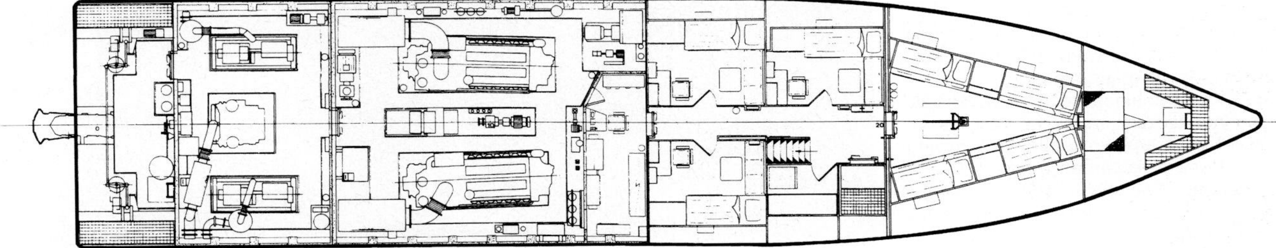

General arrangement of the Kuwait Coast Guard craft

1995

High-speed vessels built by Transfield Shipbuilding

Name	Country	Date
HMPNGS *Tarangau*	Papua New Guinea	16 May 1987
RVS *Tukoro*	Vanuatu	13 June 1987
HMPNGS *Dredger*	Papua New Guinea	31 October 1987
MV *Nafanua*	Western Samoa	19 March 1988
RSIPV *Lata*	Solomon Islands	7 July 1988
HMPNGS *Seeadler*	Papua New Guinea	29 October 1988
CIPPB *Tekukupa*	Cook Islands	1 September 1989
HMPNGS *Basilisk*	Papua New Guinea	1 July 1989
VOEA *Neiafu*	Tonga	28 October 1989
FSS *Palikir*	Micronesia	24 March 1990
VOEA *Pangai*	Tonga	30 June 1990
FSS *Micronesia*	Micronesia	3 November 1990
VOEA *Savea*	Tonga	23 March 1991
RMIS *Lomor*	Marshall Islands	22 June 1991
RSIPV *Auki*	Solomon Islands	2 November 1991
RKS *Teanoai*	Kiribati	22 January 1994
RFNS *Kula*	Fiji	28 May 1994
	Tuvalu	8 October 1994
RFNS *Kikau*	Fiji	27 May 1995
RFNS *Ruve*	Fiji	7 October 1995
PL 51 *Protector*	Hong Kong	
PL 52 *Guardian*	Hong Kong	
PL 53 *Defender*	Hong Kong	
PL 54 *Preserver*	Hong Kong	
PL 55 *Rescuer*	Hong Kong	
PL 56 *Detector*	Hong Kong	
P 301 *Inttisar*	Kuwait	January 1993
P 302 *Aman*	Kuwait	January 1993
P 303 *Maimon*	Kuwait	June 1993
P 304 *Mobark*	Kuwait	June 1993

31.5 m COAST GUARD BOAT

Four of these craft have been delivered to the Kuwait Coast Guard.

Specifications

Length overall	31.5 m
Length waterline	27.1 m
Beam	6.5 m
Draught	1.96 m
Displacement, max	150 t
Crew	11
Propulsive power	4,325 kW
Operational speed	28 kts
Range	300 n miles

Structure: Steel hulls, aluminium superstructure.

Propulsion: The main engines are 2 × MTU 16V 396 TB 94 diesels, driving propellers; and 1 × MTU 8V 183 TE 62 diesel, 550 kW, driving a Hamilton 422 water-jet. The third engine provides a loiter capability.

33 m POLICE BOAT

Six of these craft have been delivered to the Royal Hong Kong Police Force.

Specifications

Length overall	32.02 m
Length waterline	28.6 m
Beam	8.21 m
Draught	1.6 m
Crew	19

UPDATED

WAVEMASTER INTERNATIONAL PTY LTD

115 Egmont Road, Henderson, Western Australia 6166, Australia

Tel: +61 (9) 410 1422
Telex: 93356 AA
Fax: +61 (9) 410 2089

Trevor Kitcher, *Chairman*
John Mason, *Director*

WaveMaster International, a leading designer and manufacturer of fast ferries was taken over by the Penang Shipbuilding Corporation of Malaysia in 1994, providing a strong financial base for the planned expansion of their Western Australian yard. Formerly owned by Portmore Pty Ltd, WaveMaster was originally established in 1983 and has since delivered over 30 commercial craft in the range 30 m to 50 m.

Kita Ekspres

Launched November 1987.

Designed by WaveMaster to suit the demanding operational requirements in South-east Asian waters this vessel has triple water-jet units and air conditioned accommodation for 152 passengers.

Specifications

Length overall	30.4 m
Length waterline	27.5
Beam	6.1 m
Draught	0.8 m
Displacement, min	42 t
Displacement, max	60 t
Crew	8
Passengers	152
Fuel capacity	3,750 l
Water capacity	500 l
Max speed	33 kts
Operational speed	32 kts

Classification: Australian Uniform Shipping Laws Code IC, restricted offshore service (IMO).

Structure: Monohedron planing form. Construction in aluminium. Wheelhouse forward on forward deck, lower main cabin with aft engine room.

Propulsion: The main engines are three MWM TBD 234 V12 marine diesels rated at 605 kW at 2,200 rpm at 45°/32° ambient conditions driving Hamilton 402 water-jets via cardan shafts.

Electrical system: Two MWM D226-6 marine diesels driving Stamford 55 kVA alternators for 100 per cent redundancy.

Navigation and communications: Radar, Furuno 24 n mile range; VHF radio, Uniden MC 610; HF radio, Cidan 8525S; autopilot, Wagner SE.

Star Flyte

A Glen Williams design, delivered in October 1988.

Specifications

Length overall	41 m
Length waterline	35.2 m
Beam	8.5 m
Draught	2.05 m

Craft built in the last 10 years (high-speed monohulls)

Length overall	Vessel	Launched	Current owner/operator	Area of operation
32.4 m	*Sea Raider I*	1983	Boat Torque Cruises	Hillary's-Rottnest (Perth WA)
32.4 m	*Gordon Explorer*	1984	Morrison Tourist Services	Gordon River (Tasmania)
32.4 m	*Sea Raider II*	1984	Palayaran Bintan Baruna Sakti	Singapore-Batam Island
32.4 m	*Sea Raider III* (ex-*Sea Spirit*)	1985	Palayaran Bintan Baruna Sakti	Singapore-Batam Island
34.05 m	*Barbaros*	August 1987	Kuala Perlis-Langkawi Ferry Services Sdn Bhd	Langkawi Island Malaysia
30.4 m	*Kita Ekspres*	November 1987	Kuala Perlis-Langkawi Ferry Services Sdn Bhd	Langkawi Island Malaysia
41 m	*Star Flyte*	October 1988	Boat Torque Cruises	Fremantle-Rottnest (Perth WA)
27 m	*Suka Ekspres*	November 1988	Kuala Perlis-Langkawi Ferry Services Sdn Bhd	Langkawi Island Malaysia
27 m	*Senang Ekspres*	March 1989	Kuala Perlis-Langkawi Ferry Services Sdn Bhd	Langkawi Island Malaysia
37 m	*Jet Raider*	June 1990	Gulf Ferries Ltd	New Zealand
37 m	*Jet Raider II*	November 1990	Boat Torque Cruises Ltd	Rottnest (Perth WA)
37 m	*Jet Raider III*	March 1991	Palayaran Bintan Baruna Sakti	Singapore-Indonesia
39 m	*Ocean Raider*	July 1992	Seaflyte Ferry Services	Singapore
44.6 m	*Super Flyte*	January 1993	Boat Torque Cruises Ltd	Fremantle-Rottnest (Perth WA)
33 m	*Langkawi II*	November 1994	Kuala Perlis-Langkawi Ferry Services	Langkawi Island Malaysia
33 m	*Langkawi III*	November 1994	Kuala Perlis-Langkawi Ferry Services	Langkawi Island Malaysia
31.5 m	*Ocean Flyte*	November 1995	—	Singapore-Batam Island
35 m	*Sea Flyte II*	November 1995	Boat Torque Cruises Ltd	Fremantle-Rottnest (Perth WA)

Jet Raider **1995**

Super Flyte **1995**

Crew	5
Passengers	500
Fuel capacity	15,400 l
Water capacity	2,600 l
Operational speed	26 kts
Max speed	30 kts

Classification: DnV +1A1, R90 Light Craft. SF-LC, F-LC, Naut C, Naut B, ED-LG.
Propulsion: The main engines are two MTU 12V 396 TB 83 marine diesel engines driving custom-designed 4-blade propellers via ZF BW 465 2.025:1 reverse reduction gearboxes.
Electrical system: Two Perkins T6.3544 marine diesels driving 75 kW 415/240 V alternators.
Outfit: Passenger accommodation on three decks. The lower passenger cabin is forward with the engine room aft of midships and cargo hold aft of engine room. The main deck has a forward passenger cabin and main cabin with a bar for refreshments.

Star Flyte, *26 knots with up to 500 passengers*

1995

Suka Ekspres and *Senang Ekspres*

These 32 knot, 27 m high-speed ferries were delivered in November 1988 and March 1989 to Malaysia.

Specifications

Length overall	27 m
Length waterline	23 m
Beam	6.6 m
Draught	1.65 m
Crew	4
Passengers	140
Fuel capacity	5,500 l
Water capacity	750 l

Propulsion: The main engines are 2 × MWM 8V TBD 604B.
Electrical system: 1 × MWM D 226.6, 55 kW generator.

33 m Langawi II *and* III

1996

37 m JET RAIDER

A new project introduced in 1989, three of these craft have now been built. The first was delivered to New Zealand for operation by Fullers Gulf Ferries and the second completed towards the end of 1990 for Boat Torque Cruises, Rottnest (Perth WA).

Jet Raider II

Specifications

Length overall	37 m
Beam	7.2 m
Draught	1 m
Crew	5
Passengers	400
Fuel capacity	13,000 l
Water capacity	2,000 l
Propulsion	2 × 1,260 kW
Max speed	31 kts
Operational speed	36 kts

Classification: DnV + 1A1 R45 LC.
Propulsion: 2 × MWM 12V TBD 604B, 1,260 kW each, MCR, 1,800 rpm, driving 2 × Kamewa 56/S water-jet units.

31.5 m Ocean Flyte

1996

Jet Raider III

This all aluminium high-speed monohull was launched in March 1991 for operation by Palayaran Bintan Baruna Sakti.

Specifications

Length overall	36.5 m
Beam	7.2 m
Draught	1.1 m
Crew	6
Passengers	351
Fuel capacity	10,000 l
Water capacity	1,000 l
Propulsive power	2 × 1,180 kW
Operational speed	30 kts
Max speed	36 kts

Propulsion: The main engines are 2 × MTU 12V 396 TE 74, 1,180 kW each at 2,000 rpm, driving 2 × Kamewa 56S water-jets.
Electrical system: 2 × MTU 6R009 generators.

Super Flyte

A monohull delivered early in 1993.

Specifications

Length overall	44.6 m
Beam	9 m
Draught	2.3 m
Crew	5
Passengers	550

35 m Sea Flyte II *on trials*

1996

Fuel capacity	12,000 l
Water	2,500 l
Propulsive power	2 × 1,630 kW
Operational speed	27 kts

Classification: China Classification Society, ZC or DnV.

Propulsion: The main engines are 2 × MTU 16V 396 TE 74 diesels, 1,630 kW each at 2,000 rpm, driving 2 × propellers.

Ocean Flyte

Specifications

Length overall	31.5 m
Length waterline	26.6 m
Beam	6.5 m
Draught	0.95 m
Crew	5
Passengers	200
Fuel capacity	6,000 l
Water capacity	1,000 l
Propulsive power	3 × 610 kW
Max speed	29.5 kts
Range	360 n miles

Structure: Marine grade aluminium (MIG welded).

Propulsion: The main engines are 3 × MTU 12V 183 TE 72, each producing 610 kW at 2,100 rpm, driving Hamilton HM 521 water-jets via ZF gearboxes.

Electrical system: The power is supplied by 2 × MTU 6RO99 TA51 generators.

Sea Flyte II

Ordered by Boat Torque Cruises of Fremantle, Western Australia, this fast vessel has a novel power plant of two SACM diesels driving fixed pitch propellers.

Specifications

Length overall	35.4 m
Length waterline	31.6 m
Beam	7.0 m
Draught	2.1 m
Crew	4
Passengers	260
Operational speed	27 kts
Range	420 n miles

Propulsion: The vessel is powered by two Wärtsilä SACM UD23 V12 MSD MA3 diesels each rated at 720 kW at 1,860 rpm.

UPDATED

CHILE

ASMAR SHIPBUILDING AND DOCKING COMPANY

Rapa Nui Building, Prat 856, Valparaiso, Chile

Tel: +56 32 256373/259411
Fax: +56 32 214627

Jorge Swett, *Managing Director*
Sergio Garcia, *Commercial Manager*

ASMAR Shipbuilding and Docking Company has four main facilities in Chile, one at Valparaiso and at Talcahuano and two at Punta Arenas. The company builds a range of military and commercial high-speed vessels such as the Protector class pilot launches. Four 42.5 m patrol craft have recently been delivered to the Chilean Navy with two more on order. A 75 m patrol vessel for the Government of Mauritius Isles was launched in December 1995.

PROTECTOR CLASS PILOT LAUNCHES
Lep Hallef
Lep Alacalufe

Two 33 m 20 knot boats built under licence from FBM Marine Ltd entered service in September 1989. These vessels have a range in excess of 1,000 n miles and an endurance of up to 20 days and are powered by two MTU diesels. Both craft are permanently stationed in the Magellan Strait areas.

One of two FBM Marine-designed Chilean pilotboats ***1990***

Specifications

Length overall	32.7 m
Length waterline	29 m
Beam	6.7 m
Draught	2.1 m
Displacement, max	100 t
Crew	14
Fuel capacity	24,000 l
Water capacity	5,000 l
Propulsive power	2 × 900 kW
Max speed	20 kts
Operational speed	18 kts
Range	1,100 n miles

UPDATED

COMMONWEALTH OF INDEPENDENT STATES

CENTRAL HYDROFOIL DESIGN BUREAU

51 Svobody Street, Nizhny Novgorod 603003, Russia, CIS

B V Chubikov, *General Director*

In 1991 Sudoexport announced the availability of two high-speed monohull ferry designs, one for river use and one for open sea use. Since that time over 10 of the LINDA craft have been delivered.

In 1993 details of the 25 m landing craft Serna were released and it is understood that two of these craft have been constructed for operation on the Azov sea.

LINDA

Designed for passenger use on shallow rivers the vessel takes two basic forms: for long routes accommodation is provided for 50 passengers with a bar

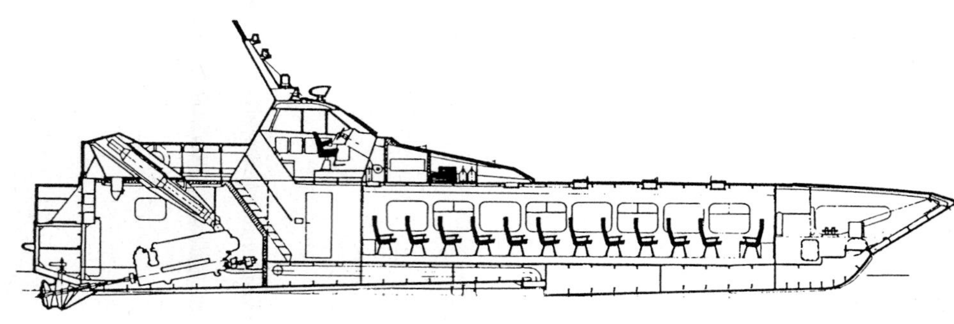

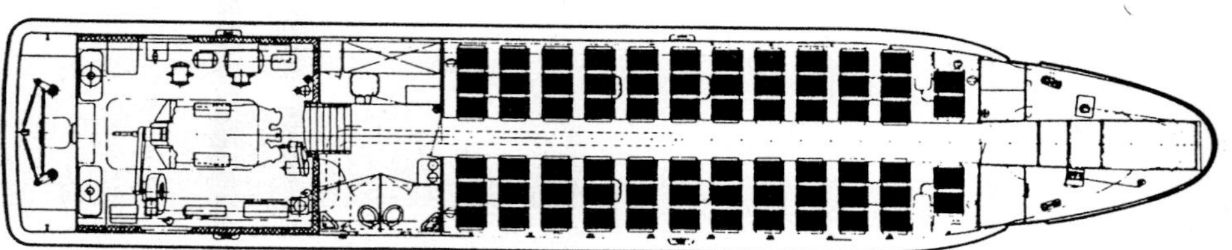

Linda
1993

and baggage space of 5 m³; on shorter routes the vessel is equipped with 70 seats with no bar and the same 5 m³ baggage space. Over ten of these craft have now been constructed with a continuing production planned for 20 craft. The high-calm water speed is achieved by a patented hull air lubrication system.

Specifications

Length overall	24.1 m
Beam	4.6 m
Draught	1 m
Passengers	50-70
Propulsive power	800 kW
Max speed	38 kts
Operational speed	30 kts
Range	215 n miles

Propulsion: The engine is a single M401A-2 rated at approximately 800 kW.

HERMES (DESIGN)

A design by the Central Hydrofoil Design Bureau.

Specifications

Length overall	50.2 m
Beam overall	12.6 m
Draught	2.6 m
Passengers	456
Max speed	43 kts
Operational speed	40 kts
Range	400 n miles

Propulsion: The main engines are 2 × MTU 20V 583 TB 91.

SERNA

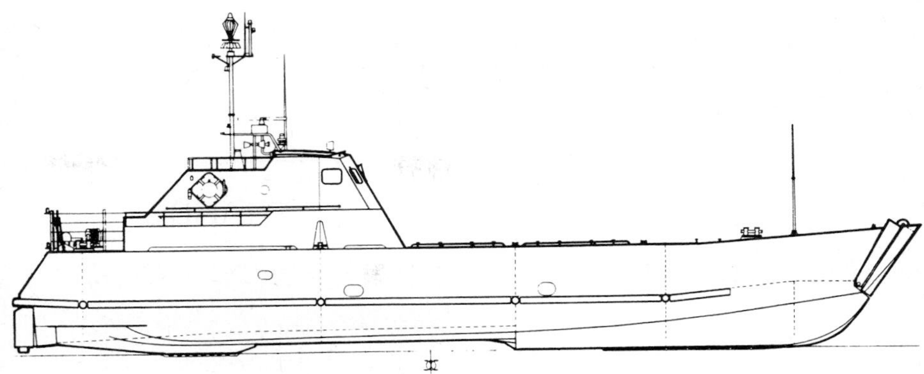

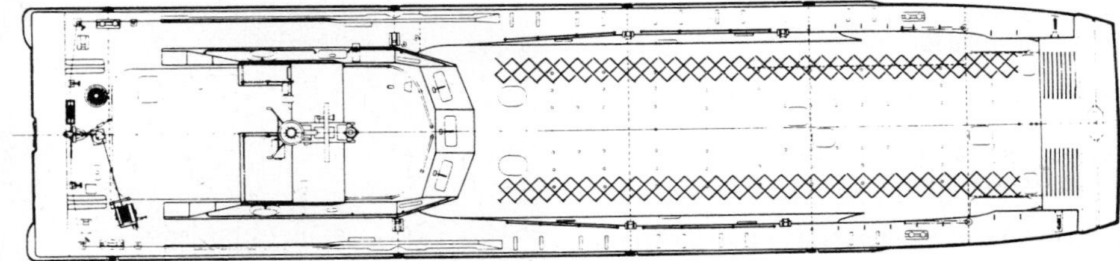

General arrangement of Serna

1994

Specifications

Length overall	25.35 m
Beam	5.85 m
Draught	1.58 m
Operational speed	30 kts
Range	600 n miles

Propulsion: Two M503A-Z Russian-built diesels drive two tunnelled surface propellers.

VERIFIED

FINLAND

KVÆRNER MASA-YARDS

PO Box 152, FIN-00151 Helsinki, Finland

Tel: +358 (0) 1941
Telex: 121246 MASAH SF
Fax: +358 (0) 650051

Martin Saarikangas, *President, CEO*
Ulf Jernstřom, *Senior Vice President, Sales*
Kaj Liljestrand, *Senior Vice President, Sales*
Kai Levander, *Senior Vice President, Technology*

EUROEXPRESS YARD 2000 PROJECT (DESIGN)

This project was included in a study programme funded 50:50 by the Finnish Government and the shipbuilding industry. Fast vessels and fast ships for operating in ice conditions were covered in the study, in particular, high-speed cargo ships linking Finland with the European market. A 40 knot Euroexpress concept has been designed around a deadweight capacity of approximately 4,000 tonnes and would be capable of executing a Finland to Germany trip in 24 hours (18 at sea, 6 turnround in port), halving existing times. KMY is concentrating on monohull solutions for such operations.

Kværner Masa-Yards has developed the fast monohull hullform suitable for both propeller and water-jet propulsion. The wave piercing 'whale back' bow reduces the impact loads and can therefore maintain high speed in heavy sea conditions.

These ships can have diesel or gas-turbine machinery depending on the speed requirements. Electric drive has been used in some applications to give freedom in machinery location. The slender monohull technique can be supplied in both cargo vessels, ferries and cruise liners ranging from 150 to 300 m in length and 5,000 to 50,000 tonne displacement.

In particular the KMY slender monohull concept has been designed to be integrated with fast loading and unloading port facilities.

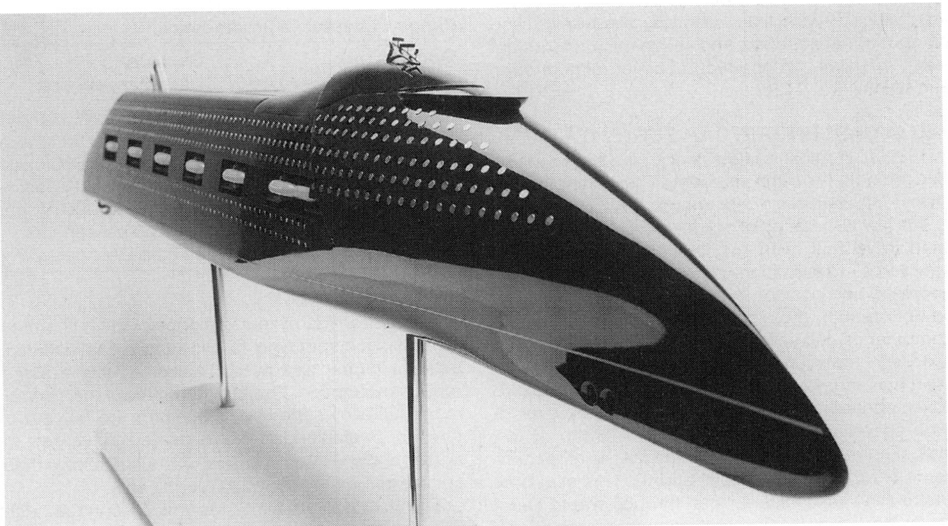

Kværner-Masa superliner concept for a 35 knot cruise vessel (design)

1995

Kværner-Masa slender monohull with outriggers (design)

1996

SLENDER MONOHULL WITH OUTRIGGERS (DESIGN)

The slender monohull with outriggers concept has been investigated by KMY for use at speeds in excess of 40 knots for both passenger, car and cargo carrying applications. A 175 m version of this craft has a beam of 34 m and a design draft of 5 m. With an installed power of 57,000 kW and carrying 1,500 passengers and 500 cars, speeds of over 40 knots are predicted. Used as a cargo carrier the equivalent payload would be fifty 30 tonne trailers or lorries. A total displacement of 5,000 tonnes is envisaged for this vessel.

UPDATED

FRANCE

ATELIERS ET CHANTIERS DU HAVRE

30 rue J.-J.-Rousseau, PO Box 1390, F-76066 Le Havre Cedex, France

Tel: +33 35 198000
Telex: 190 322 F
Fax: +33 35 198040

Gilbert Fournier, *ACH Group Chairman*
Alain Tessandier, *General Secretary*
François Faury, *Shipbuilding Manager*
Antoine Castetz, *Sales and Design Manager*

As a holding company Ateliers et Chantiers du Havre manages the activities of Société Nouvelle des Ateliers et Chantiers du Havre (SNACH), and Société Nouvelle des Chantiers de Graville (SNCG), as well as other companies operating in ship repairs, industrial or other activities.

The company runs two shipyards in Le Havre, the Graville yard which creates and realises fabrication drawings and builds hulls; and the Harfleur yard which is responsible for all outfitting.

Both shipyards specialise in medium-size high-technology ships, particularly prototypes, varying in length from 50 to 215 m.

Apart from shipbuilding, the company deals with marine, naval and offshore engineering, covering mechanics, hydraulics, robotics, electronics and computing, ship repair and mechanics, steel light and high-alloy constructions, boiler construction and so on.

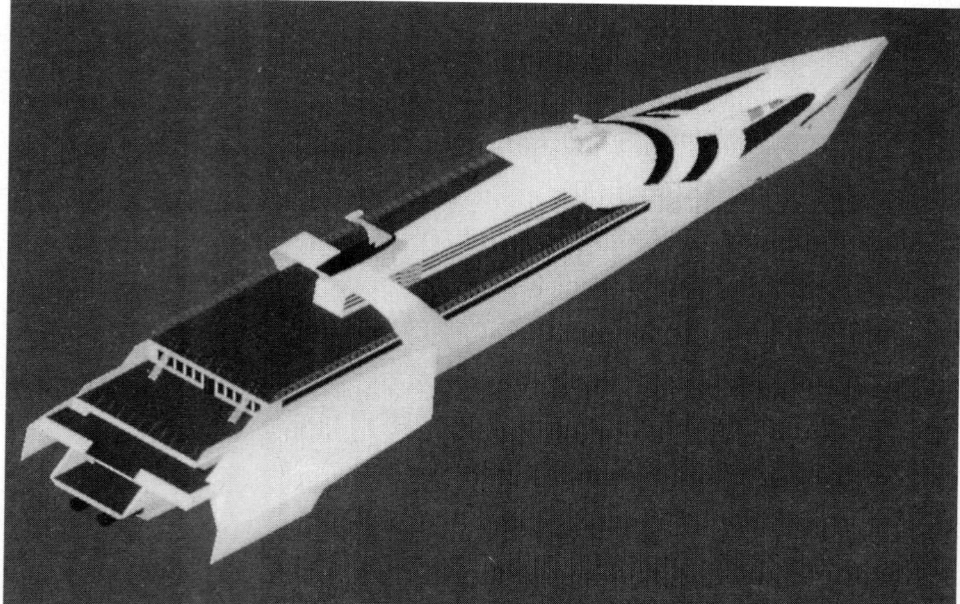

ACH 100 m passenger/car ferry (design) ***1993***

Range of Vessel Characteristics

Model	Capacity Cars/Passengers	Speed Full Load
150	550 vehicles/2,200 passengers	30-40 kts
120	300 vehicles/900 passengers	30-45 kts
100	180 vehicles/600 passengers	30-50 kts
76-400	80 vehicles/400 passengers	30-40 kts
76-300	60 vehicles/300 passengers	30-40 kts
45	300-400 passengers	20-35 kts
25	50-70 passengers	15-30 kts

100 m PASSENGER/CAR FERRY (DESIGN)

In 1992 ACH released details of a high-speed stabilised monohull design concept. The principles are given in the following description.

The hull is made up of one long and highly streamlined main hull, with two lateral wings providing transverse stabilisation. The specially designed geometry and position of the wings are the result of an optimisation process carried out during multiple computer calculations and towing tank tests by both head and transverse seas. The slenderness of the main hull and the shape of the lateral wings lead to advantageous propulsion characteristics over a wide speed range. The exceptional length of the main hull (which is more important than in other concepts of high-speed vessels) and the very slim bow shape allow the vessel to 'cut' through waves causing only a little pitching and minimum 'slamming'. Within this concept, the lateral sea-keeping and stability are adjusted precisely to the values which allow safety and comfort depending solely on the position and the dimensions of the lateral wings and these independently of the general architecture of the vessel and of the position of its load.

The hydrodynamic performance of the hull, which is of displacement type, is less sensitive to load variation, a higher deadweight causing only a slight reduction in speed. This characteristic of the slender monohull allows the use of steel for the hull structure, in particular for the larger sized vessel. In addition, the very slim shape of the hull allows high speeds to be maintained in rough seas.

The concept does not require, in contrast with SES, SWATH and hydrofoil types, any lifting, stabilisation systems and therefore presents little risk to the construction, offers reliability in use and only requires limited maintenance in operation. It is envisaged that the vessel is to be integrated into a total system which consists of special harbour equipment adapted to high-speed passenger transport, such as dock ramps or special landing pontoons, encompassing the entire mooring, loading and supply functions of the vessel.

Specifications

Length waterline	100 m
Beam	28 m
Draught	2.6 m
Passengers	450-600
Vehicles	150-180
Propulsive power	30,000 kW
Max speed	40 kts

Propulsion: Engines: 2 × gas-turbines, 15,000 kW each or 1 × gas-turbine 20,000 kW and 2 × diesel engines 5,000 kW each driving 2 × water-jets.

VERIFIED

GUY COUACH CONSTRUCTIONS NAVALES

215 Avenue Francis Tonner, F-06150 Cannes La Bocca, France

Tel: +33 93 47 11 22
Telex: 470737 F
Fax: +33 93 48 03 66

Guy Couach is the successor to Couach Ltd which has been famous in yachting since 1897. It has been

Guy Couach 2501 class ***1995***

MODELS 2500 to 3100

Type	**2501**		**2701**		**2901**	**3101**
Dimensions						
Length overall	25.5 m		27.77 m		29.8 m	31.2 m
Beam	6.3 m		6.34 m		6.3 m	7.0 m
Displacement, min	40 t		43 t		N/K	N/K
Main engines						
(largest installations)	2 × DDC 12V 71 TA 1,357 kW each	2 × DDC 16V 92 TA 2,177 kW each	2 × DGM 12V 71 TA 1,357 kW each	2 × DGM 12V 92 TA 2,118 kW each	2 × DDC 16V 92 TA 2,119 kW each	2 × MTU 12V 96 TB 93 1,461 kW each
Max speed	24 kts	32 kts	20 kts	30 kts	29 kts	32/33 kts

* Kevlar + Levi Drive Units (LDU) can increase performance by approx 3/4 knots

building motor yachts in glass fibre since 1962, and was the first to build a large motor yacht in Kevlar. The company now offers a range of 35 speed boats to luxury motor yachts of 6 to 30 m. Its shipyards currently build over 30 per cent of all French powerboat production with a turnover in 1994 of £18 million. The table above states models offered above 25 m.

VERIFIED

LEROUX AND LOTZ

10 rue des Usines, F-44100 Nantes, France

Tel: +33 40 959697
Fax: +33 40 46 52 06

Michell Breheret, *Commercial Director*
J Ninet, *Marketing Manager*

With seven building and repair yards located along the Atlantic and Channel coasts, and design and engineering offices in Nantes and Paris, the marine

Emeraude *on trials* ***1995***

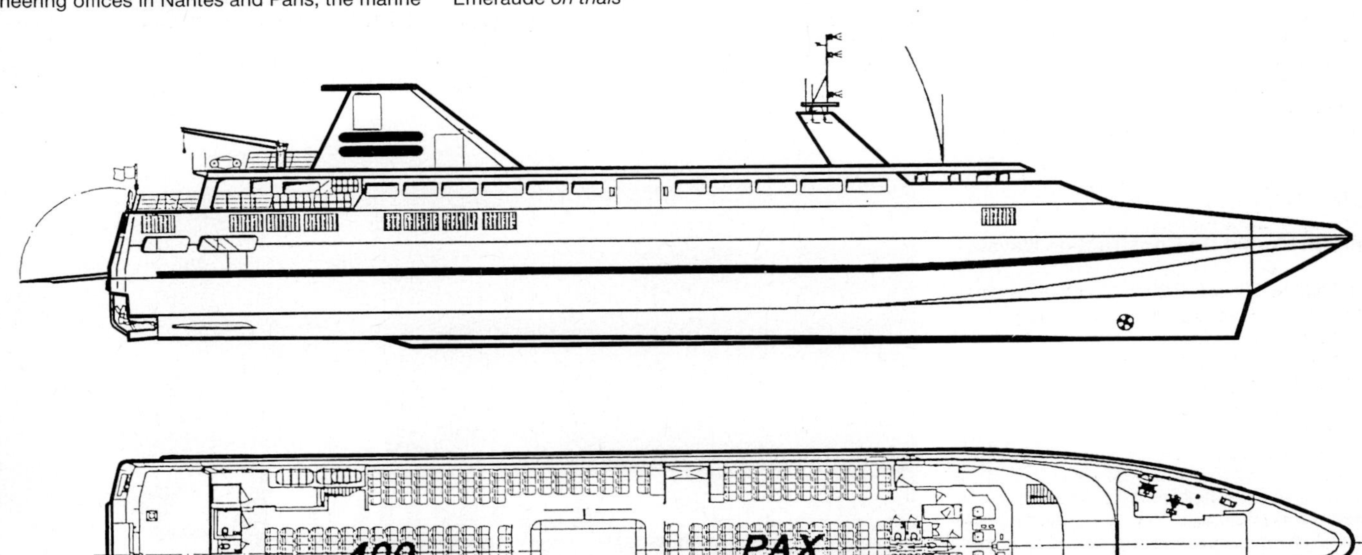

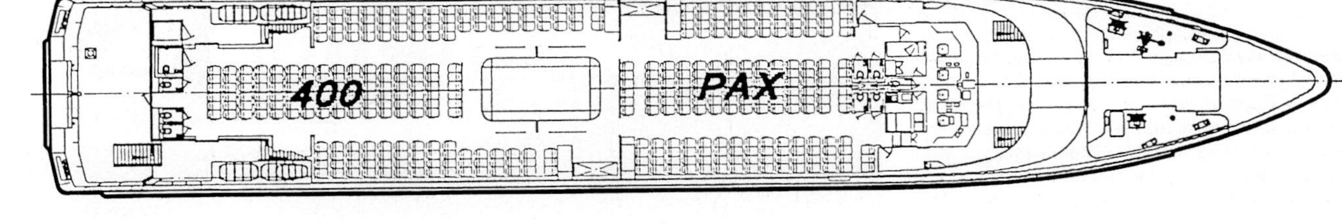

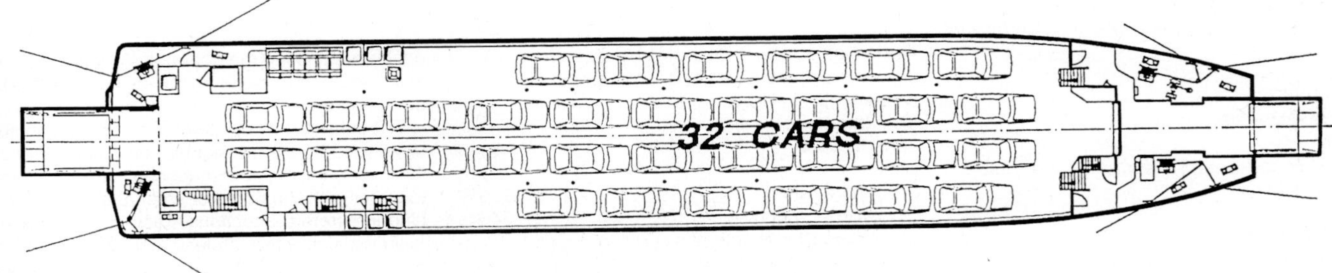

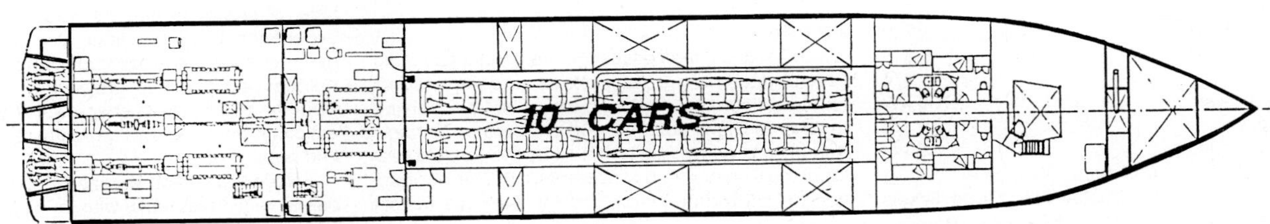

General arrangement of Emeraude ***1995***

division of the Leroux and Lotz Group is specialised in design and building of a wide range of medium sized civil and naval vessels.

The yard delivered its first fast ferry in 1994 and currently has one other under construction.

CORSAIRE 4500 (DESIGN)

Specifications

Length overall	50 m
Beam	7.8 m
Draught	1.6 m
Passengers	450
Fuel capacity	17 t
Water capacity	4,000 l
Propulsive power	6,103 kW
Max speed	37 kts
Operational speed	35 kts
Range	165 n miles

Propulsion: The main engines are 3 × Deutz-MWM 16V 620B diesels, each producing 2,034 kW, driving 2 × Kamewa S63 and 1 × Kamewa B63 water-jets.

Electrical system: 2 × 180 kW generating sets.

CORSAIRE 6000

The first vessel to this design, the *Emeraude*, was delivered to Emeraude Lines in Spring 1994 for service on the Saint Malo to Channel Island route.

Specifications

Length overall	66 m
Length waterline	58 m
Beam	10.9 m
Draught	2 m
Passengers	400
Vehicles	42 cars
Fuel capacity	30,000 l
Water capacity	8,000 l
Propulsive power	4 × 2,245 kW
Max speed	34 kts
Operational speed	32 kts
Range	150 n miles

Propulsion: The main engines are 4 × MWM 620B V16 diesels rated at 2,245 kW each; 3 × Kamewa water-jets, 2 × S80 and 1 × B90 units.

Control: The vessel is fitted with four roll stabilisation fins.

Corsaire 11000 after launch **1995**

CORSAIRE 11000
NVG ASCO

Construction of this vessel commenced in mid-1994 for delivery in 1996.

Specifications

Length overall	102 m
Beam	15.4 m
Draught	2.4 m
Passengers	550
Vehicles	148 cars or 108 cars + 4 coaches
Fuel capacity	84 t
Water capacity	8,000 l
Propulsive power	4 × 6,000 kW
Max speed	40 kts
Operational speed	37 kts
Range	300 n miles

Classification: Bureau Veritas I 3/3 E.

Structure: All aluminium hull and superstructure.

Propulsion: The main engines are 4 × MTU 20V 1163 TB 73L diesels, each producing 6,000 kW; driving 2 × Kamewa S112 and 2 × Kamewa B112 water-jets.

Electrical system: 3 × 400 kW generator sets.

Auxiliary systems: One 300 kW bow thruster.

VERIFIED

SBCN

Société Bretonne De Construction Navale

PO Box 20, Hent-Croas, F-29750 Loctudy, Brittany, France

Tel: +33 98 87 42 71
Telex: 941356 SBCN F
Fax: +33 98 87 91 40

Joel Ballu, *Principal*

SBCN specialises in high-speed craft built in cold moulded wood composite. The compound material is made up of very thin layers criss-crossed with hard mahogany fibres running in the same direction, vacuum-moulded in a matrix of epoxy resin. The resulting product is flexible, break-resistant and light, offers ease of maintenance and repair, good thermal and acoustic properties, avoidance of hull vibration and long-term maintenance of shape. The yard has a workshop area of 2,500 m². The yard is now manufacturing its own water-jets in copper aluminium alloy and glass epoxy casing under the name Centaur Jet.

Atlante (1985)
Amiral de Joinville
Tourville

For details of these craft please see the 1992-93 edition of this book.

Nicolas Bouchard

32 m fast passenger ferry. Delivered in September 1987 Société Anonyme Atlantic Armement for service between La Baule and Belle Ile.

Specifications

Length overall	32 m
Beam	6.8 m
Passengers	270
Propulsive power	1,790 kW
Max speed	37 kts
Operational speed	32 kts

Structure: Cold moulded wood composite.

Propulsion: 2 × MWM TBD 234 V16 marine diesels 895 kW each; driving 2 × MJP J550 water-jet units.

The new Atlante (Andrew N Smith) **1991**

Patriote

38 m patrol boat. Launched in November 1987.

Owners: Benin Navy.

Specifications

Length overall	38 m
Beam	6.9 m
Propulsive power	2,685 kW
Operational speed	34 kts

Structure: Cold moulded wood composite.

Propulsion: 3 × Baudouin 12P15-2 SR7 marine diesels, 895 kW each, driving 3 × Centaur Jet CJ600.

Atlante

A new French fast passenger ferry incorporating several interesting design concepts completed its first short summer holiday season in 1990 serving the Iles de Glenan off the southern coast of Brittany. *Atlante* was conceived and built by the Société Bretonne de Construction Navale (SBCN). The introduction of the vessel has halved the previous fastest journey time to the Iles de Glenan some 15 km offshore, enabling the operator, Vedettes de l'Odet, to schedule an extra return trip each day on this busy seasonal route.

The lightweight hull uses construction techniques developed by SBCN originally for fast military craft. Thin veneers of hard mahogany are sandwiched together with the fibres of each alternate layer running in different directions. Each layer is soaked in resin and finally the whole is vacuum-moulded in an epoxy matrix producing a lightweight structure which is resilient and durable, resistant to rot, waterproof in both directions and possessing a remarkable strength to weight ratio. Eight years of experience by the builder also indicate that the material is easy to repair and maintain, has excellent thermal and acoustic properties, is less prone to vibration and holds its shape well. For military applications it benefits from a greatly reduced magnetic and radar profile.

Unladen, the craft weighs 37 tonnes which compares very favourably with a disposable load of 24 tonnes of passengers and full tanks.

Specifications

Length overall	28 m
Beam	6.3 m
Draught	1.2 m
Displacement, min	37 t
Payload	24 t
Passengers	224
Propulsive power	1,683 kW
Operational speed	29 kts

Propulsion: The main engines are 2 × MWM V12, 634 kW each; 1 × MWM V8, 425 kW; each driving a PP170 water-jet, all identical except that the central jet has a different impeller and nozzle to ensure maximum thrust from the lower horsepower. All three jets have steering nozzles.

Soleil Royal

This passenger ferry was delivered to its owners (SOTEL, Cayenne, French Guyana) in 1989 for service between Kourou and Iles du Salut.

Specifications

Length overall	26.2 m
Beam	6.7 m
Passengers	105
Operational speed	21 kts

Structure: The hull material is cold moulded wood composite.

Propulsion: The main engines are 2 × MWM TBD 234 V12; driving 2 × Hamilton 402 water-jet units.

VERIFIED

GERMANY

ABEKING AND RASMUSSEN SHIPYARD

PO Box 1160, D-27805 Lemwerder, Germany

Tel: +49 (421) 6733532
Fax: +49 (421) 6733115

This yard was established in 1907 and has since become well known for its construction of high-quality fast military patrol craft and minesweepers, a range of special utility craft and large motor and sailing yachts.

In 1995 the company signed an agreement with Lindstøls Skips of Norway to jointly build two 27.5 m catamaran fast ferries and currently has designs for 100 m monohull passenger/car fast ferries.

Abeking and Rasmussen 37 m motor yacht ***1989***

37 m MOTOR YACHT

Specifications

Length overall	37 m
Displacement	200 t
Max speed	32 kts

Propulsion: Water-jet propulsion.

SAR 33 FAST PATROL BOAT

Fourteen craft have been built and are in service in Turkey.

Specifications

Length overall	34.6 m
Beam	8.6 m
Displacement	160 t
Operational speed	40 kts

Abeking and Rasmussen 34.6 m Coast Guard patrol boat, SAR 33 ***1989***

27 m MOTOR YACHT

Specifications

Length overall	27 m
Displacement	95 t
Operational speed	46.4 kts

CGV 26 FAST PATROL BOAT

Specifications

Length overall	26 m
Beam	5.8 m
Displacement	75 t
Operational speed	40 kts

Structure: Built in steel with an aluminium superstructure.

SAR 65/70 FAST PATROL CRAFT (DESIGN)

Specifications

Length overall	65-71 m
Beam	9-10 m
Displacement, max	650-850 t
Max speed	40 kts

BLOHM+VOSS AG

Hermann-Blohm-Strasse 3, D-20457 Hamburg, Germany

Tel: +49 (40) 3119 1803
Telex: 2 11 047-0 BV D
Fax: +49 (40) 3119 3300

Blohm+Voss has developed a variety of fast monohull (FM) vessels which all have in common a patented displacement type hull form. The hull shape comprises a very slender bow section and a semi-tunnelled stern, giving space for single or twin propellers of large diameters. This is understood to improve the overall hydrodynamic efficiency by up to 20 per cent compared to conventional hull forms.

The ability to take high payloads and to install medium-speed diesel engines makes the fast monohull concept versatile and economic for various applications.

Currently Blohm+Voss is marketing fast monohull container vessels, trailer carriers and passenger/ro-ro cargo ferries in the range of 100 m to 185 m with service speeds from 24 knots to 32 knots with

Blohm+Voss FM 130 (design) ***1995***

diesel engines, and for higher speeds with additional gas-turbines (CODAG).

FM 130 TRAILER CARRIER (DESIGN)

This fast trailer carrier is designed to transport 97 Euro semi-trailers, 30 t each, on two decks.

Specifications

Length overall	143.5 m
Length waterline	130 m
Beam	25 m
Draught	6.2 m
Payload	3,030 t
Crew	12
Vehicles	101
Propulsive power	2 × 16,000 kW
Operational speed	28.7 kts

FM 150 PASSENGER AND RO-RO CARGO FERRY (DESIGN)

This 150 m ferry is designed to carry 1,500 passengers and 100 cars and has a truck lane length of 1,500 m.

Specifications

Length overall	166 m
Length waterline	150 m
Beam	31.2 m
Draught	7.3 m
Crew	120
Passengers	1,500
Vehicles	100 cars
Propulsive power	2 × 18,900 kW
Operational speed	27.6 kts

FAST MONOHULL CONTAINER VESSELS (DESIGN)

Blohm+Voss has also developed a range of fast container vessels ranging from 130 m to 160 m with speeds up to 27 knots and container capacities from 720 to 1,050 TEU.

UPDATED

LÜRSSEN WERFT GmbH & CO

Friedrich-Klippert-Strasse 1, D-28759 Bremen, Germany

Tel: +49 (421) 66040
Telex: 0244484 A FLW D
Fax: +49 (421) 660 4443

Fast motor boats, motor cruisers and motor yachts have been built since 1890. Recent construction includes fast attack craft, small corvettes, mine combat vessels and fast yachts. In 1985 the rescue craft *Hermann Helms* was built followed by the rescue craft *Alfried Krupp* in 1988, *Arkona* in 1992 and *Bremen* in 1993.

It is understood that the shipyard signed an agreement in 1995 with IHI of Japan to market Japanese fast ferry designs in Europe.

Berlin and *Steppke*

These are rescue craft and are the first of a class of mother ship/daughter rescue craft designed.

Specifications

Length overall	27.5 m
Beam	6 m
Draught	1.63 m
Displacement	100 t
Crew	8
Propulsive power	2,350 kW
Operational speed	24 kts

Propulsion: The main engines are 1 × MTU 12V 396 TB 93 marine diesel developing 1,200 kW and 2 × MWM TBD 234 V12 wing engines each rated at 574 kW; driving 1 × 1,200 mm central propeller and 2 × 950 mm wing propellers (port and starboard).
Electrical system: Power is provided by 2 × Mercedes OM 352 diesels connected to Kaick generators, each set rated at 50 kVA.
Control: Steering gear is electrohydraulic to the three rudders, each having one emergency servo device.

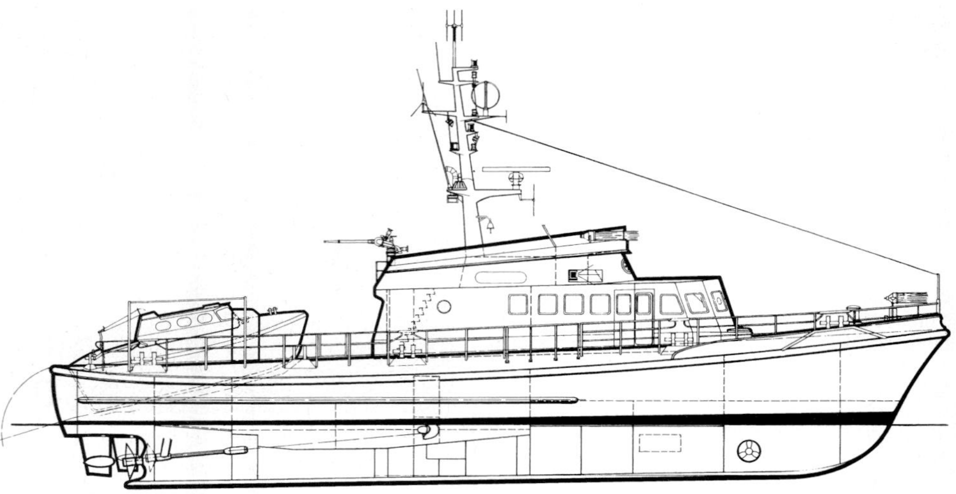

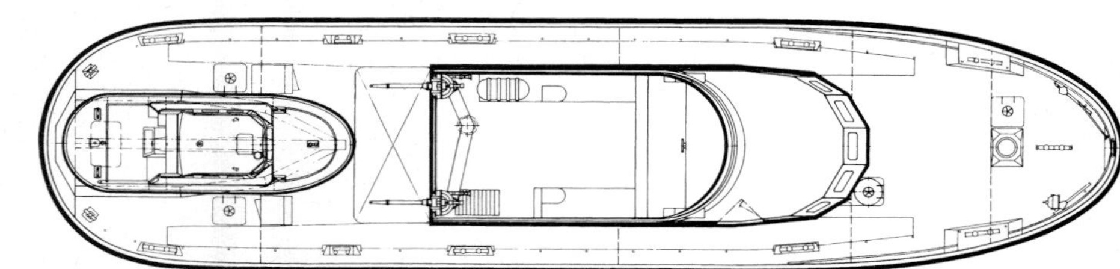

Sea rescue craft Berlin *with daughter vessel* Steppke ***1996***

Operations equipment: A daughter boat launched down stern ramp and through a hinged flap on the transom. Length 7.50 m, beam 2.29 m, draught 0.6 m, displacement 3.1 t. Power BMW D190 diesel of 121 kW output, driving a fixed-pitch propeller through reduction gearing, speed 15 knots.

UPDATED

HONG KONG

CHEOY LEE SHIPYARDS LTD

NKML 32-33, Lai Chi Kok, Po Lun Street, Kowloon, Hong Kong

Tel: +852 307 6333
Telex: 56361 CLS HX
Fax: +852 307 5577

Ken Lo, *Director*

The company was originally founded in Shanghai over a century ago. It moved to a small yard in Hong Kong in 1937, then to a much larger yard in 1940, and was occupied with building and repairing cargo ships. It diversified into building teak sailing yachts for export in 1956 and acquired a large site for a second yard on Lantau Island in 1960. The company commenced building motor yachts and building in GRP in 1961 and at present operates three divisions, one each for steel and composite commercial vessels, GRP workboats and GRP pleasure craft. The company has built over 4,000 vessels since the current records commenced in 1950.

Tanjung Bakarang

Harbour Inspection and Service Launch delivered in June 1988.
Owner: Marine Department, Bandar Seri Begawan, Brunei Darussalam.

Specifications

Length overall	25.84 m
Length waterline	22.2 m
Beam	6.43 m
Draught	1.82 m
Displacement	55 t
Crew	8
Passengers	65
Fuel capacity	13,620 l
Water capacity	2,630 l
Propulsive power	2 × 662 kW
Max speed	23.5 kts
Operational speed	19 kts

Classification: Lloyds ✠100A1 (Restricted Service) + LMC.
Propulsion: The main engines are 2 × MAN D2842 LXE, 662 kW each driving propellers through ZF BW 190 gearboxes.

Discovery Bay 17

Fast passenger vessel delivered October 1988 and followed by a second, delivered to Penguin Boat Services Pte Ltd, Singapore, in 1991.
Owner: Hong Kong Resort Company Ltd.

Specifications

Length overall	22.78 m
Length waterline	20.04 m
Beam	5.41 m
Draught	1.67 m
Displacement	36.1 t
Crew	4
Passengers	163
Fuel capacity	5,100 l
Water capacity	450 l
Propulsive power	2 × 737 kW
Max speed	25 kts
Operational speed	23 kts

Classification: American Bureau of Shipping 100 A1 + AMS.
Structure: Deep V constant deadrise construction in solid GRP. It has a two tier superstructure with a wheelhouse and short passenger saloon on the

upper deck forward half, after half and open under awning.
Propulsion: The main engines are 2 × Stewart and Stevenson Detroit Diesel Model 16V-92MCTAB, 737 kW each driving propellers through Nico MGN 273 gearboxes.
Electrical system: 1 × Mercedes-Benz/Stamford generator set, 32.5 kVA, 380 V, 50 Hz, 3-phase, 2 × 24 V 200 Ah starting battery sets, 1 × 24 V 120 Ah starting battery set.
Navigation and communications: 1 × Anritsu RA-72OUA daylight marine radar. Also 1 × Sailor VHF/RT 2048 compact VHF radiotelephone.

CHEOY LEE 70

Sport fishing yacht designed by American Naval Architect Tom Fexas.

Specifications

Length overall	21.59 m
Length waterline	18.49 m
Beam	6.32 m
Draught	1.57 m
Displacement, min	37.6 t
Fuel capacity	7,570 l
Water capacity	1,514 l
Propulsive power	2 × 805 kW
Max speed	24 kts
Operational speed	21 kts

Structure: Moderate V bottom form with sponson chines. Hull decks and superstructure in GRP with extensive use of foam core materials.
Propulsion: The main engines are 2 × Detroit Diesel 12V 71TA diesels each developing 805 kW.

CHEOY LEE 81

A sports yacht designed as Mr Tom Feseas (USA) and constructed of GRP/foam sandwich. This vessel is scheduled for delivery in July 1996.

Specification

Length overall	24.7 m
Beam	6.43 m
Draught	1.52 m
Fuel capacity	7,570 l
Water capacity	2,271 l
Max speed	27 kts

Propulsion: Two Caterpillar 3412TA diesel engines each rated at 932 kW driving a fixed pitch propeller.

CHEOY LEE 83

Presently sold as a cockpit motor yacht, the hull of this craft is also used as the basis of a 'sports fisherman' vessel.

Specifications

Length overall	25.27 m
Length waterline	22.29 m
Beam	6.42 m
Draught	1.62 m
Displacement, min	63.8 t
Fuel capacity	11,355 l
Water capacity	2,650 l
Propulsive power	2 × 650 kW
Max speed	24 kts
Operational speed	17-19 kts

Structure: Moderate V bottom form with sponson chines; hull, decks and superstructure in GRP with extensive use of foam-cored sandwich construction.
Propulsion: 2 × Detroit Diesel 12V 71TA 650 kW each driving propellers through ZF BW 195 reverse/reduction gearboxes; underwater exhausts with idling bypasses.

CHEOY LEE 92

An enlarged version of the Cheoy Lee 83 cockpit motor yacht with similar layout and machinery except generator sets of 25 kW and a more elaborate bathroom for the aft cabin.

Caterpillar 3412 746 kW engines are fitted in the later models for a maximum speed of 25 knots.

Specifications

Length overall	28.02 m
Length waterline	24.94 m
Beam	6.43 m
Draught	1.37 m
Displacement	67.85 t
Fuel capacity	15,000 l
Water capacity	2,650 l
Propulsive power	2 × 746 kW

20 m SURVEILLANCE VESSEL

This vessel was constructed for the Environment Protection Council of Kuwait in 1993.

Specifications

Length overall	19.8 m
Length waterline	17.65 m
Beam	5.54 m
Draught	1.57 m
Displacement	28 t
Crew	8
Fuel capacity	6,000 l
Water capacity	400 l
Propulsive power	2 × 820 kW
Max speed	30 kts
Operational speed	25-28 kts

Structure: The hull and superstructure material is GRP.
Propulsion: The main engines are 2 × MAN D2842 LZE diesels, 820 kW each, driving 2 × propellers via 2 × ZF 195 2:1 reduction gearboxes.
Electrical system: 2 × Onan MDGBA 30 kW generators.

Penguin Progress, *sister vessel to* Discovery Bay 17

1990

Recent version of Cheoy Lee 92 fast motor yacht *1995*

Cheoy Lee 83 cockpit motor yacht *1990*

44 m MOTOR YACHT

This is the largest GRP/foam sandwich vessel constructed by Cheoy Lee and was delivered in December 1995. The vessel was designed by Frank Mulder for an unspecified owner.

Specification

Length overall	44.1 m
Beam	8.8 m
Draught	2.0 m
Fuel capacity	91,600 l
Water capacity	13,400 l
Max speed	25 kts

Classification: ABS +A1 'Yachting Service' AMS Class.
Propulsion: Two MTU 12V 396TE84 diesels each rated at 1,450 kW and driving fixed pitch propellers.

VERIFIED

CHUNG WAH SHIPBUILDERS LTD

41 Yau Tong Marine Lot, Cha Kwo Ling Road, Kwun Tong, Kowloon, Hong Kong

Tel: +852 727 6333
Telex: 45803 WAHBU HX
Fax: +852 347 3446

Brenda Lui Yee Man, *Director*
Edward Poh Choo Chye, *Director*
David Cho Lai Tong, *General Manager*

The company was established in 1940, and business covers shipbuilding, ship repairing, mechanical and electrical engineering, ship brokerage and consultancy.

The company has built and repaired marine craft in steel ranging from salvage tugs, deck container vessels, firefighting boats, supply vessels and cargo vessels to police patrol boats.

The company has completed a total of 34 steel police patrol launches for the Royal Hong Kong Marine Police and three command launches for the Customs and Excise Department of the Hong Kong Government. The success of these craft has been due to the joint efforts of Damen Shipyards (in the Netherlands) responsible for the basic design of the hull, and Chung Wah Shipbuilders Ltd (formerly called Chung Wah Shipbuilding and Engineering Company Ltd) responsible for the construction of the vessels.

PL71, one of 15 Chung Wah-built high-speed launches for the Royal Hong Kong Marine Police **1986**

KING CLASS
King Lai

Police launch.

Specifications

Length overall	26 m
Length waterline	24.6 m
Beam	5.6 m
Crew	18
Max speed	26 kts
Operational speed	24 kts
Electrical engine loitering speed	9 kts.

Structure: Constructed in steel.

Propulsion: The main engines are 2 × MTU 12V 396 TB 83 each delivering 1,100 kW through ZF gearboxes; 1 × Benz 424A engine, with ZF gearbox.

2 × fixed-pitch propellers by SMM (MTU engines); 1 × Kamewa steerable water-jet (Benz engine).

Electrical system: This is powered by 2 × Kosan 60 kVA alternators.

Navigation and communications: RM1226C 12 in, with 9 in slave radar and EMY1/C speed log repeater supplied by Racal Decca; 1 × Simrad echo-sounder; 1 × S G Brown 1000 gyrocompass and repeater.

Control: Nautiservo BV electrohydraulic steering gear.

Operations equipment: An Avon sea rider launched or recovered by hydraulic crane operated from flying bridge.

VERIFIED

King class police launches built by Chung Wah **1990**

ITALY

AZIMUT SpA

Viale Dei Mareschi, 14-10051 Avigliana, Turin, Italy

Tel: +39 (11) 936 7271
Fax: +39 (11) 936 7270

Dr Paolo Vitelli, *President*
Ing Giuseppe Dilorenzo, *Technical Manager*
Dr Massimo Perotti, *Director*

Azimut SpA was founded in 1969 by Dr Paolo Vitelli and began by importing distinguished yachting marques. Later Vitelli decided to design his own boats and commission yards to build them. As the company grew so did its sales network. In 1978-80 it became the first company in Italy to manufacture fibreglass boats, and in 1982 launched the first ever yacht of over 30 m to be built in that material, the 105' *Failaka*.

In 1985 the company took over the Fratelli Benetti yard in Viareggio, renowned the world over for its 40-50 m steel-hulled megayachts. In 1988 it also acquired a yard for the production of 10-18 m fiberglass boats in Avigliana near Turin.

In 1996 the Group employed 220 people (135 in Avigliana and 85 in Viareggio) and, when its supplier network is taken into account, provides work for approximately a further 200 people. With an output of 110/115 boats a year, it is one of Europe's major boat yards.

The company's production is split into three distinct lines to meet the demands of a wide section of the market:

AZ 10-18 m fiberglass boats (AZ 36', 40', 43', 50', 54').
AZIMUT 18-36 m boats (65' Pininfarina, 78' Ultra, 90'-100' Jumbo).
BENETTI 40+ m aluminium-steel yachts.

The company markets its boats through a sales network of about 25 dealers, covering the European, North American, South-east Asian and Japanese markets. The group has also invested considerably in the setting up of an aftersales service network.

Details of the following motor yachts built by Azimut are given in the 1992-93 edition of this book: *Rima*, *Atlantic Challenger* and *Athina R.*

UPDATED

CANTIERI ING MOSCHINI SpA

Direzione e Cantieri di Bellocchi
Via De Nicola 5, I-1032 Fano, Pesaro, Italy

Tel: +39 (721) 854236
Fax: +39 (721) 854934

Cantieri del Porto
Lungomare Mediterraneo 2-4, I-1032 Fano, Pesaro, Italy

Tel: +39 (721) 809988

Cantieri Ing Moschini SpA has been building GRP boats in the Pesaro area of Italy since 1970. The company now operates three yards and employs 175 people.

The following are some of the high-speed vessels built in co-operation with SIAR SpA.

35 m ferry built by Cantieri Ing Moschini SpA and SIAR SpA **1992**

35 m FERRY

The hull and main deck of this vessel are built in GRP with the superstructure built in aluminium alloy. The passenger capacity is 350 and speed is 25 knots.

36 m FERRY
Ischiamar II

Launched in 1992 following experience gained with the 35 m ferry, this vessel is of all-GRP construction.

Specifications

Length overall	36 m
Beam	7.1 m
Displacement, max	134 t
Passengers	350
Operational speed	28 kts

Propulsion: The main engines are 2 × MTU 12V 396 TE 94 diesels.

Sunliner IX **1992**

Sunliner IX

This Andrea Bacigalupo-designed vessel was built in Kevlar fibres by Cantieri Ing Moschini and fitted out by SIAR for Amital of Zurich.

Specifications

Length overall	30 m
Beam	7.1 m
Displacement, max	120 t
Fuel capacity	40,000 l
Water capacity	4,000 l
Propulsive power	2 × 1,864 kW
Operational speed	32 kts

Propulsion: The main engines are 2 × MTU diesels, driving 2 × Kamewa water-jets.

Sunliner X

Also designed by Andrea Bacigalupo, this vessel has a range which allows Atlantic crossing.

Specifications

Length overall	35 m
Beam	7.1 m
Displacement, max	130 t
Fuel capacity	40,000 l
Water capacity	5,000 l
Propulsive power	2 × 2,610 kW
Operational speed	42 kts

Propulsion: The main engines are 2 × MTU diesels, driving propellers.

21 m PATROL BOAT (DESIGN)

Specifications

Length overall	21 m
Beam	6.1 m
Displacement, max	32 t

Structure: The hull and superstructure are constructed from Kevlar fibre.

Propulsion: The main engines are 2 × MTU 8V 396 TE 94 diesels, driving 2 × Levi surface drives.

VERIFIED

CANTIERI NAVALI ITALCRAFT Srl

Via di Villa Emiliani 11, I-00197 Rome, Italy

Tel: +39 (6) 807 5377/3650/0981
Telex: 613054 ITCRAF I
Fax: +39 (6) 808 2701

Aristide Abbati, *Marketing Manager*

Italcraft, with a covered area of over 12,000 m², has built more than 2,500 craft since 1953. Its latest design is the M78, at 56 knots one of the world's fastest production motor yachts, a development of its original 55 knot Drago class. The M78 is available in three yacht layout variations including an 'open' version with limited accommodation, named Ultra 70. There are also patrol craft and 100 passenger, 45 knot ferry versions. The patrol boat has a maximum speed of 52 knots and the ferry 45 knots.

56 knot Italcraft M78 **1989**

M78 AEROMARINA

Fast motor yacht.

Specifications

Length overall	22 m
Beam	5.45 m
Draught	1.2 m
Displacement, max	36 t
Max speed	56 kts
Operational speed	45 kts
Range	350 n miles

Structure: Hull and deck constructed in GRP with aramidic fibre (Kevlar 49 Du Pont), impregnated with isophthalic resin. The superstructure consists of GRP and isophthalic resin. Four transverse bulkheads subdivide the hull.

Propulsion: The main engines are 2 × MTU 12V 331 TC 92 diesels; 2 × reverse/reduction gearboxes are coupled by Aquamet 22 Armco shafts to 2 × surface-piercing Nibral propellers.

Electrical system: 1 × 12 kW diesel generator, 220 V AC 50 Hz, alternative by electric equipment 60 Hz standard USA.

Navigation and communications: Furuno or Vigil radar, 48 mile range; Loran C; echo-sounder; computerised electronic log; VHF, 55 channel 25 W.

Internal communications: Intercom between wheelhouse, flying bridge, forecastle and quarterdeck; intercom in cabins, saloon and bridge.

Control: A dual station hydraulic steering system is coupled to rudders patented by Italcraft. Steering positions are in the wheelhouse and flying bridge.

Outfit: Deckhouse; wheelhouse, main saloon and galley Below decks; 3 double cabins, owner's toilet/shower, guest toilet/shower, crew toilet/shower, double-berth crew cabin. All accommodation is air conditioned.

VERIFIED

CANTIERI NAVALI LAVAGNA Srl

Via Dei Devoto 197, I-16033 Lavanga (GE), Italy

Tel: +39 (185) 300341
Telex: 282693 CANACE I
Fax: +39 (185) 306601

Dr Aldo Ceccarelli, *Chairman and Manager*

Cantieri Navali Lavagna builds the Admiral line of luxury high-speed motor yachts in aluminium or wood with sizes ranging from 22 to 45 m.

Over the past few years a number of the following craft have been launched:

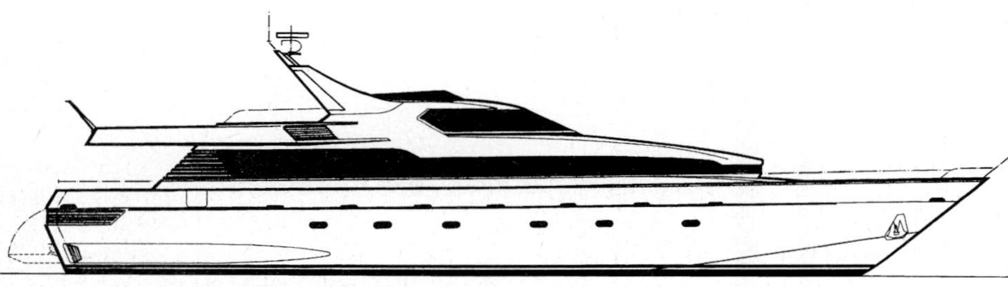

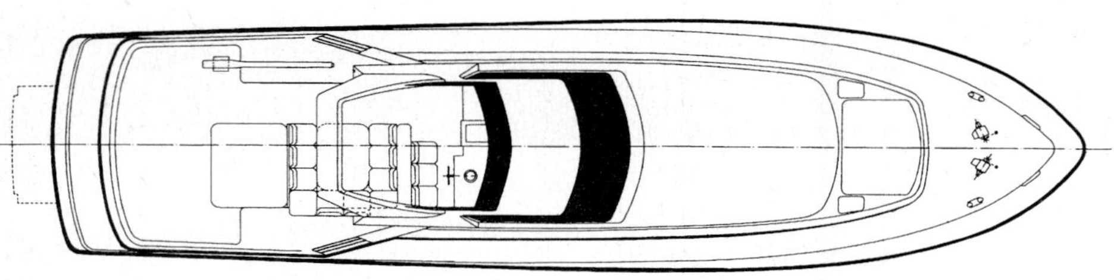

Admiral 27 **1995**

ADMIRAL 25

Specifications

Length overall	25 m
Beam	6.5 m
Draught	2 m
Displacement, max	70 t
Fuel capacity	15,000 l
Water capacity	3,500 l
Propulsive power	2 × 1,137 kW
Max speed	26 kts
Range	900 n miles

Propulsion: The main engines are 2 × MTU 8V 396 TE 94.

ADMIRAL 27

Specifications

Length overall	27 m
Beam	6.8 m
Draught	2.05 m
Displacement, max	80 t
Fuel capacity	15,000 l
Water capacity	3,500 l
Propulsive power	2 × 1,432 kW
Max speed	30 kts
Operational speed	28 kts
Range	800 n miles

Propulsion: The main engines are 2 × MTU 12V 396 TB 93.

ADMIRAL 28

Specifications

Length overall	28 m
Beam	7 m
Draught	2.05 m
Displacement, max	86 t
Fuel capacity	20,500 l
Water capacity	3,500 l
Propulsive power	2 × 1,704 kW
Max speed	31 kts
Operational speed	29 kts
Range	780 n miles

Propulsion: The main engines are 2 × MTU 12V 396 TE 94.

ADMIRAL 32

Specifications

Length overall	32 m
Beam	7.25 m
Draught	1.2 m
Displacement, max	97 t
Fuel capacity	18,000 l
Water capacity	4,000 l
Propulsive power	2 × 1,946 kW
Max speed	32 kts
Operational speed	28 kts
Range	695 n miles

Propulsion: The main engines are 2 × MTU 12V 396 TB 94.

VERIFIED

CANTIERI POSILLIPO SpA

Località Porto del Bufalo, I-4016 Sabaudia (LT), Italy

Tel: +39 (773) 57135
Telex: 680562 POS SA I
Fax: +39 (773) 57139

Ing Giovanni Arrabatio, *Hull design, engines and propulsion*
Paola Galeazzi & Giovanni Zuccon, *Superstructures design, interior layout and furnishings*

Posillipo has been crafting and building pleasure boats since 1948 from a base on the west coast of Italy. While its beginnings were with the production of high-performance mahogany runabouts, the company soon expanded its boundaries to meet the demands and tastes of an international market of boat enthusiasts.

In 1965, production began on larger day cruisers and cabin cruisers, fabricated in wood. This followed moving the shipyard from an area of natural caves of Cape Posillipo to Sabaudia between Rome and Naples. Soon after christening a new shipyard at Sabaudia where fibreglass construction was initiated, Posillipo directed its energies toward increasing its international markets, including the United States. Posillipo's principal contribution to the world of pleasure motor yachts is known as the 'Technema' line, ranging in size from 11 to 39 m.

In 1991 Cantieri Posillipo SpA was purchased by an American company, the first time an Italian shipyard has been sold to an American company.

TECHNEMA

A series of motor yachts ranging from 13 to 40 m in length with speeds from 29 to 50 knots and over. Propulsion options include direct drive, V-drive, Arneson drive and water-jets, with engine choices from Caterpillar, GM, MAN, MTU and Textron Lycoming.

VERIFIED

A 27 m Posillipo Technema motor yacht
1993

CANTIERI RIVA SpA

Via Predore 30, I-24067 Sarnico, Italy

Tel: +39 (35) 910202
Fax: +39 (35) 911059

Based on Lake Iseo in Northern Italy, Riva is the world's most prestigious manufacturer of luxury powerboats in the 27-70 ft range. Its customers include many Heads of State, senior industrialists and celebrities.

Riva has the capability to build between 30 and 40 powerboats each year. Its principal markets are in Europe and the Middle East, and the sales network is being expanded to take advantage of opportunities worldwide.

UK AGENTS: BK ElectroMarine Ltd, Hamble Point Marina, School Lane, Hamble, Hampshire SO31 4NB, UK

Tel: +44 (1703) 455112
Fax: +44 (1703) 455746

Brian Kaye, *Managing Director*

Black Corsair **1995**

BLACK CORSAIR

Specifications

Length overall	18.79 m
Beam	5.35 m
Draught	1.6 m
Fuel capacity	4,500 l
Water capacity	800 l
Passengers	6 guests
Crew	1
Propulsive power	2 × 809 kW
Max speed	37 kts
Range	543 n miles

Propulsion: 2 × MAN D2842 LZE diesels, 809 kW each.

Corsaro **1995**

CORSARO

A successor to the Black Corsair with increased space, more power and refined lines.

Specifications

Length overall	19.72 m
Beam	5.35 m
Draught	1.65 m
Fuel capacity	4,150 l
Water capacity	800 l
Crew	2
Passengers	8 guests
Max speed	32 kts
Range	507 n miles

Propulsion: 2 × MTU 183 TE 92 diesel engines, 735 kW each.

RIVA 29 m GRANDYACHT (DESIGN)

Specifications

Length overall	28.4 m
Beam	6.75 m
Draught	1.9 m
Fuel capacity	12,000 l
Water capacity	3,000 l, desalinator: 3,000 l/day
Propulsive power	2 × 1,670 kW
Max speed	28 kts
Operational speed	25 kts cruising

Propulsion: 2 × MTU diesel engines, 1,670 kW each.

VERIFIED

CRESTITALIA SpA

Via Armezzone, I-19031 Ameglia (SP), Italy

Tel: +39 (187) 670798
Telex: 283042 CRESTI I
Fax: +39 (187) 65282

A Melai, *Managing Director*
E Cossutta, *General Manager*

Crestitalia started building GRP craft in 1961 at Como and moved to a new shipyard at Ameglia (La Spezia) in 1971. The Ameglia yard has been equipped with a new launching deck and sheds capable of building five 40 m craft simultaneously. Principal customers are the Italian Navy and Police, and overseas military and police forces. All craft and constructed in GRP.

MV88 27 m multipurpose crew boat **1987**

MV115 PATROL TRAINING BOAT

Two of these vessels are under construction for the Italian Customs and are scheduled for delivery in 1997 and 1998. These are stretched versions of the Bigliani Class and can be used for both patrol and training purposes.

Specification

Length overall	35.5 m
Beam	7.2 m
Draught	1.2 m
Displacement, max	115 t
Crew	34 max
Propulsive power	5,120 kW
Max speed	35 kts
Operational speed	18.5 kts
Range	700 n miles

Structure: GRP

Propulsion: The vessel is powered by two MTU 16V 396 TB94 diesel engines each rated at 2,560 kW. Each engine drives a fixed pitch propeller via a reverse reduction gearbox.

MV100

Diving support and underwater exploration boat.

The MV100 is an enlarged version of the M85 (26 m), with a number of similarities in layout and equipment.

MV100 30 m diving support and underwater exploration boat

1988

Specifications

Length overall	30 m
Beam	6.9 m
Draught	1.05 m
Displacement, max	105 t
Max speed	27 kts
Range	560 n miles (16.5 kts)

Structure: Semi-planing V-shaped hull in GRP with a GRP sandwich superstructure.

Propulsion: Two MTU 12V 396 TB 93 marine diesels, driving twin screws.

Electrical system: Two Mercedes OM 421 diesel generators providing 96 kW each.

Navigation and communications: One magnetic compass and one Anschutz gyrocompass with two repeater compasses. One Sagem electromagnetic log, one RN 770 Decca radar, one Noak long-range searchlight, Elac LAZ51AT/LSE 133 echo-sounder, Zeiss Orion 80B night vision telescope and Decca Navigator Mark 21.

Control: Electric/hydraulic steering gear.

Outfit: Two twin-berth officers' cabins, two crew cabins, three berths in each, and one trainee cabin with six berths.

Operations equipment: Underwater exploration equipment is two Pluto RCVs equipped with search and identification sensors.

MV88

Multipurpose crew boat and quick deployment forces transport.

Specifications

Length overall	27.28 m
Beam	6.98 m
Draught	1.1 m
Displacement, min	82 t
Crew	4
Passengers	250
Water capacity	2,600 l
Propulsive power	2 × 1,193 kW
Max speed	28 kts
Operational speed	23 kts

Structure: GRP.

Propulsion: The main engines are 2 × 1,193 kW marine diesels, driving propellers or water-jets.

MV85 BIGLIANI CLASS

Fast patrol boat. Fourteen vessels have been delivered to the Italian Customs.

Specifications

Length overall	27 m
Beam	6.95 m
Draught	1.15 m
Displacement, max	91 t
Propulsive power	2 × 2,610 kW
Max speed	45 kts
Operational speed	40 kts
Range	850 n miles

MV85 27 m Bigliani Class fast patrol boat (second series)

1996

Serena Lauro

1990

Classification: Registro Italiano Navale (RINa).
Structure: GRP.
Propulsion: Two MTU 16V 396 TB 94 diesels, driving two three-bladed Nibral alloy propellers.
Electrical system: Two diesel generators of 50 kW/50 Hz output, each capable of providing normal full load requirements, one emergency diesel generator of 10 kVA/380 V.
Navigation and communications: One GEM 732 radar, one Anschutz gyrocompass, one Sagem electronic data log, one echo-sounder, and one ARPA radar; one complete radio station.
Control: remote engine room controls from wheelhouse and flying bridge
Outfit: Commanding Officer, four officers and eight ratings accommodated in single Commanding Officer's cabin, two double-berth officers' cabins and forward messdeck fitted with eight berths for ratings. Wardroom and galley situated in after part of wheelhouse structure.

MV84 27 m Corrubia series fast patrol boat (second series) ***1996***

MV 84 CORRUBIA CLASS

Based on the Bigliani prototype craft, four Corrubia class patrol craft were delivered by 1996 and a further nine vessels are on order for final delivery in 1999.

Specification

Length overall	26.8 m
Beam	7.65 m
Draught	1.2 m
Displacement, max	92 t
Max speed	43 kts
Operational speed	20 kts
Range	700 n miles

Structure: GRP
Propulsion: The vessels are powered by two MTU 16V 396TB94 diesel engines each rated at 2,600 kW driving fixed pitch propellers via a reverse reduction gearbox.

MV70

Fast patrol boat.

Specifications

Length overall	21.1 m
Beam	5.3 m
Draught	0.9 m
Displacement, max	40 t
Crew	4
Propulsive power	2 × 1,044 kW
Max speed	35 kts
Operational speed	31 kts

Structure: GRP.
Propulsion: 2 × 1,044 kW diesel engines, 2 × propellers.
Navigation and communications: Radar and echo-sounder, VHF-SSB-UHF.
Control: Mechanical remote controls to engines, hydraulic steering gear.

31 m PASSENGER FERRY
Serena Lauro

Built in GRP 1988-89.

Specifications

Length overall	31 m
Beam	6.9 m
Draught	0.9 m
Crew	3
Passengers	350
Propulsive power	2 × 820 kW
Max speed	24 kts
Operational speed	20 kts

Propulsion: The main engines are 2 × 820 kW high-speed diesels, driving propellers.

32 m PASSENGER FERRY (DESIGN)

Specifications

Length overall	32.4 m
Beam	6.9 m
Draught	2 m
Crew	4
Passengers	200
Propulsive power	2 × 1,339 kW
Max speed	30 kts
Operational speed	26 kts

Propulsion: The main engines are 2 × MTU 12V 396 TE 74L, driving propellers.

34 m PASSENGER FERRY (DESIGN)

Specifications

Length overall	33.8 m
Beam	7 m
Draught	2 m
Passengers	250
Crew	4
Propulsion	2 × 1,815 kW
Max speed	30 kts

Propulsion: The main engines are 2 × MTU 12V 396 TE 74, driving propellers.

37 m PASSENGER FERRY (DESIGN)

Specifications

Length overall	37.2 m
Beam	7.9 m
Draught	2.1 m
Crew	4
Passengers	252
Propulsive power	2 × 1,521 kW
Max speed	25.5 kts
Operational speed	22 kts

Propulsion: The main engines are 2 × MTU 12V 396 TE 74L, driving propellers.

UPDATED

FAZIOLI NAUTICA Srl

Via Della Scafa 135, I-00054 Fiumicino, Italy

Tel: +39 (6) 658 3838/0355
Fax: +39 (6) 652 3466

Previously known as Alfa Marine, this company builds a number of fast motor yachts, the largest of which is the Alfa 83.

ALFA 83 25 m FAST CRUISER

Specifications

Length overall	25 m
Beam	6 m
Draught	1.5 m
Displacement, min	40 t
Displacement, max	43.75 t
Fuel capacity	8,000 l
Propulsive power	1,460 kW
Max speed	38 kts
Operational speed	34 kts

Structure: Built in GRP with V-keel with longitudinal side fins.
Propulsion: Two MTU 12V 396 TB 93, 1,460 kW each driving propellers through BW 460 gearboxes.
Manoeuvring: Bow thruster.
Electrical system: 2 × diesel generators 25 kW, central control and distribution panel 24 V, batteries 500 Ah, 24 V.
Navigation and communications: 40 mg radar, echo-sounder with optical plotting, GPS, automatic

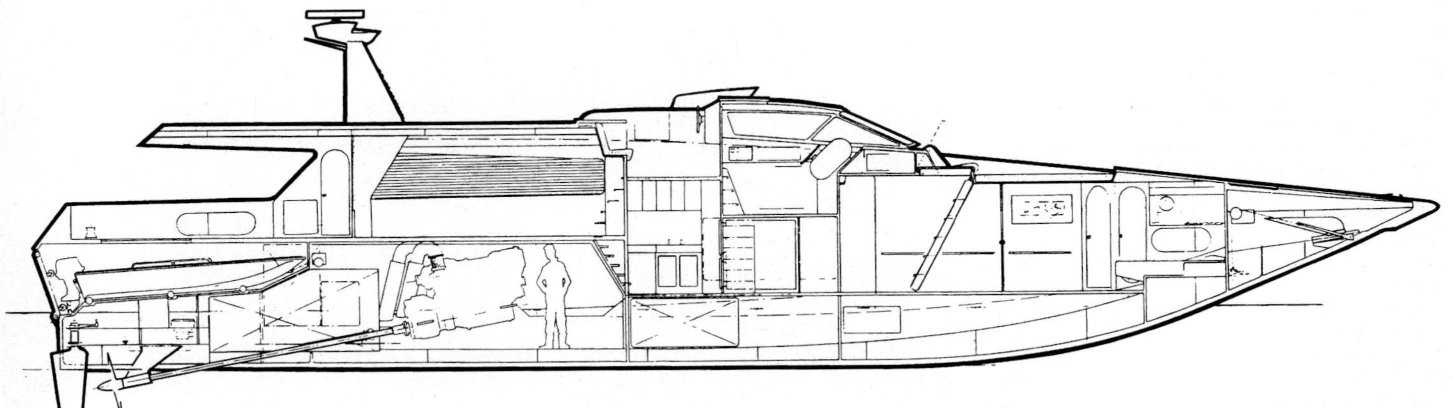

Interior arrangement of Alfa 83 25 m fast cruiser ***1995***

pilot. Communications are provided by a VHF 25 W 60-channel radio, SSB 1 828 MHz 220 W.
Outfit: Master cabin with bathroom and WC; 4 guest cabins, with bathroom and WC; kitchen, crew quarters, 2 bunk beds, piloting cabin, 2 seats, fly deck controls, 3 seats, fly sun deck, poop deck, lounge with bar, aft deck. Air conditioning fitted.

VERIFIED

Alfa Marine 25 m, 33 knot fast cruiser
1988

FINCANTIERI CANTIERI NAVALI ITALIANI SpA

Head Office: Via Genova 1, I-34121 Trieste, Italy
Naval Shipbuilding Division: Via Cipro, 11, I-16129 Genova, Italy

Tel: + 39 (10) 59951
Telex: 270168 FINC GE I
Fax: +39 (10) 599 5272

Mario De Negri, *Naval Shipbuilding Division General Manager*

Fincantieri is one of the major and most diversified shipbuilding and diesel engine manufacturing organisation in Europe.

The company designs, markets and builds merchant ships and naval vessels, offshore platforms and marine diesels and undertakes the largest ship repair and conversion contracts.

In 1995 this yard received orders for three 95 m, MVD 1200 Pegasus fast ferry designs and in November, an order for six slightly larger 100 m fast ferries for Sea Containers.

Few details of these latter vessels have been released so far.

Destriero

Destriero, which is owned by the Yacht Club Costa Smeralda, was built specifically to challenge the Blue Riband reward.

Destriero was built at the Fincantieri Yards of Riva Trigoso (Genova) and Muggiano (La Spezia).

The design of *Destriero* started in March 1990. The contract was signed in May 1990, the vessel was launched in March 1991 and the sea trials were completed by the end of May 1991. On trials *Destriero* has reached 62.8 knots.

Capacity is provided for 750 tonnes of fuel; each of the three engines burns up to 3.5 t/h.

Design and engineering of the vessel was undertaken by Fincantieri, hull forms by American naval architect Donald L Blount and styling by Pininfarina.

On 9 August 1992 *Destriero* broke the Blue Riband record for the fastest crossing of the Atlantic by more than 21 hours, completing the crossing from Ambrose lighthouse (New York) to Bishop Rock (Scilly Isles, UK), a distance of 3,106 n miles, in 58 hours 34 minutes and 50 seconds at an average speed of 53.09 knots.

It has been reported that on the initial westbound crossing of *Destriero* the starting displacement was 1,070 tonnes with a corresponding speed of 43 knots. As fuel was consumed speed increased, rising eventually to its maximum. The reported eastbound crossing time of 62 hours 7 minutes, together with the record westbound crossing time, also set a new double-crossing record of 159 hours 48 minutes and 15 seconds, a feat no other marine vessel has ever achieved.

Specifications

Length	67.7 m
Beam	12.9 m
Displacement, max	1,070 t
Fuel capacity	750 t
Propulsive power	44,742 kW
Max speed	65 kts, light load
Operational speed	40 kts, full load
Range	>3,000 n miles

Artist's impression of the Fincantieri 100 m fast ferry ordered by Sea Containers **1996**

MDV 1200 Pegasus *under construction* **1996**

The arrival of Destriero *at Bishop Rock, 9 August 1992*

1993

Classification: The vessel is classified according to DnV Light Craft Rules, DnV having co-operated closely with the designers during design and construction; also Registro Italiano Navale.
Propulsion: The craft is powered by three GE LM 1600 gas-turbines, 14,914 kW each, packaged in resiliently mounted MTU modules, driving three Kamewa 125 SII water-jets.
Reduction gears: Renk-Tacke Bus 255.
Structure: Aluminium alloy.
Control: Reverse thrust and steering affected by the 2 outer water-jets.

MDV 1200 *Pegasus*

The MDV 1200 *Pegasus* is a deep-V monohull fast ferry designed to maintain high speeds in exposed sea conditions. Three of these craft are currently on order from Ocean Bridge Investments for operation between Italy and Greece. The first hull section of the new MDV 1200 Pegasus was laid down on 10th July 1995 at Fincantieri's Riva Trigoso yard and is scheduled to be delivered in mid 1996. The hull, tested at the Danish Maritime Institute, was specifically optimised to ensure excellent sea-keeping performance.

The craft is capable of carrying 450 passengers and up to 150 cars at a speed of 40 knots.

Styling was defined jointly with Pininfarina.

Passenger and crew area subdivision into three main zones is protected by a sprinkler system. The hull is made of high-tensile steel and the superstructures of light alloy. The similar, but slightly larger vessels for Sea Containers are constructed in aluminium.

The propulsion system and generating sets are split into two compartments in order to give the ship a return capability in case of failure of one engine room.

Specifications

Length overall	95 m
Length waterline	82 m
Beam	16.5 m
Draught	10.25 m
Passengers	600
Vehicles	170 cars
Propulsive power	24000 kW
Operational speed	36 kts
Range	300 n miles

Classification: This design was developed in line with Category B of the new IMO Regulations for Fast Ferries, and classed by Registro Italiano Navale.
Propulsion: Four MTU 20V 1163 TB 73L diesel engines each drive a Kamewa water-jet via a reduction gearbox.
Electrical system: Three main diesel generators and one emergency generator are specified.

MDV 3000 *Jupiter* (DESIGN)

The MDV 3000 *Jupiter* is a deep-V monohull fast ferry designed to transport passengers, cars and trucks at high speed.

The flexibility of the vessel allows it to be used in two different operating conditions: in a touristic service, where the cargo capability of the vessel is 420 cars - 1,500 passengers (deadweight 800 t), with a speed of over 38 knots; and in a freight service, where the cargo capability of the vessel is 120 cars and 420 m of freight lanes (deadweight 1,200 t), with a speed of over 34 knots.

Specifications

Length overall	132.5 m
Beam	20.20 m
Passengers	1,500 max
Vehicles	420 cars
Propulsive power	2 × 27,000 kW

Classification: This design has been developed in compliance with Category B of new IMO regulations.
Propulsion: The propulsion system and generating sets are split into two compartments and consist of two LM 2500 gas-turbines and two diesel engines with a total power installed of 54,000 kW.

UPDATED

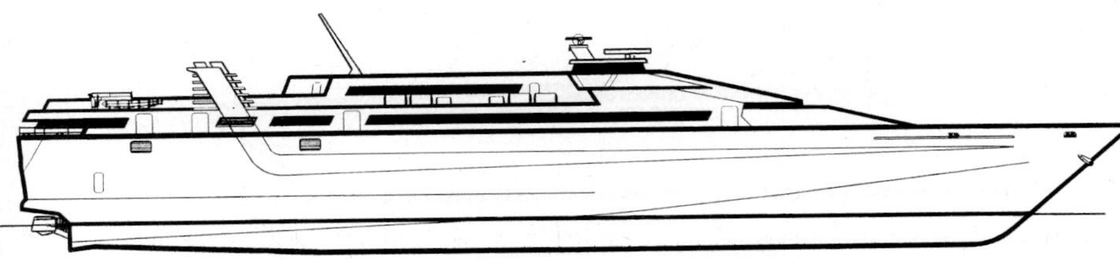

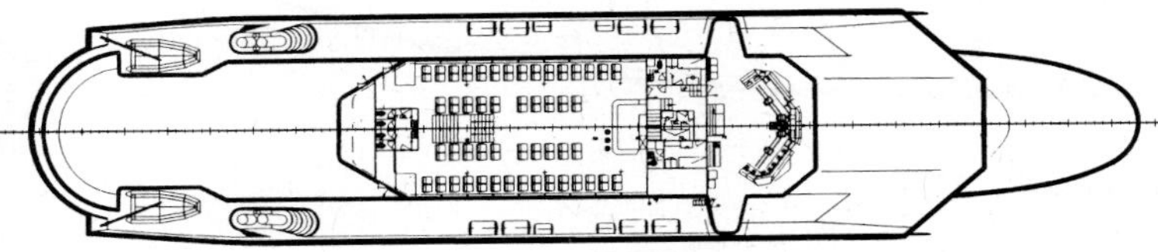

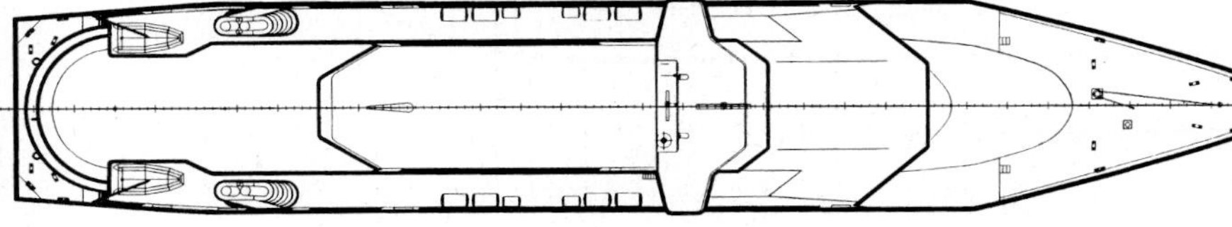

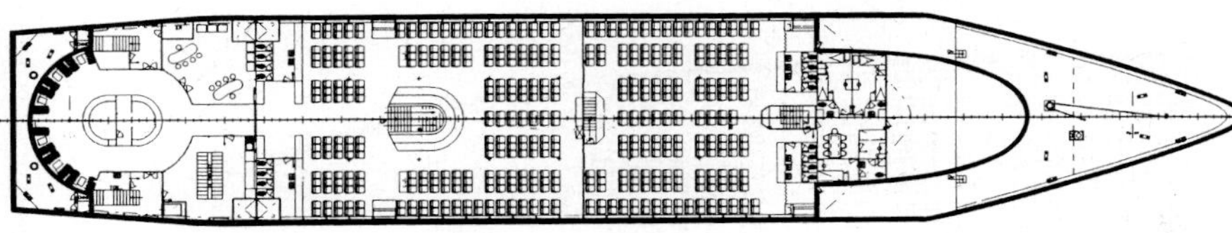

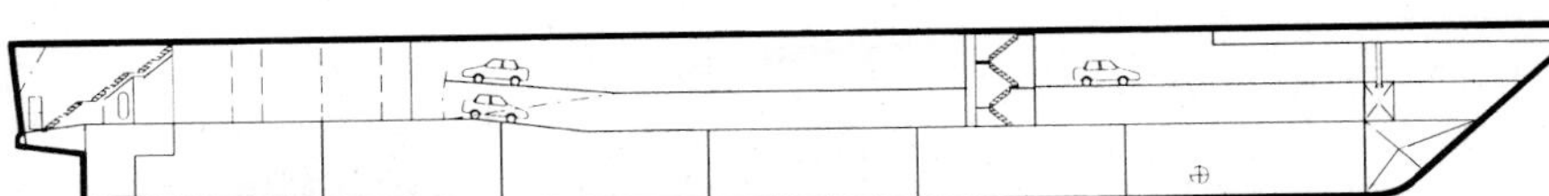

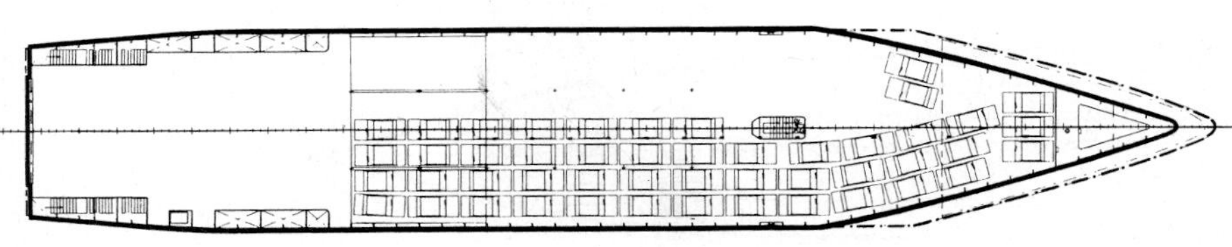

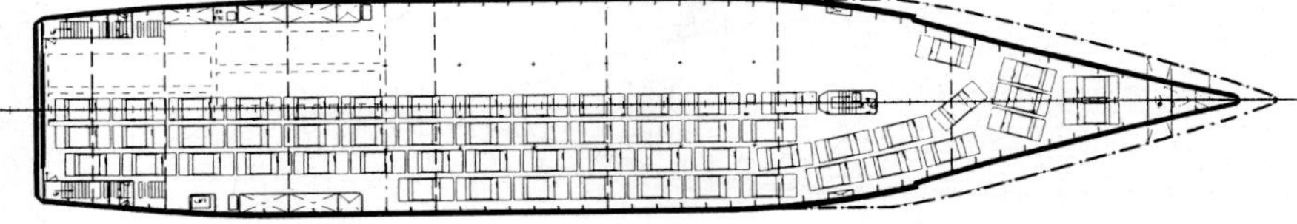

General arrangement of MDV 1200 Pegasus
1996

INDUSTRIE NAVALES MECCANICHE AFFINI SpA (INMA)

Viale F.Bartholomeo 362, 19100 La Spezia, Italy

Tel: +39 (187) 544111
Telex: 270297 IMAI
Fax: +39 (187) 524181

V Solinas, *Marketing Manager*

Industrie Navales Meccaniche Affini (INMA) is a licensee of Rodriquez Cantieri Navali and is currently building two FFM 1035 passenger/vehicle monohulls, this being the designation given by INMA for Aquastrada craft built under licence from Rodriquez. The company is also marketing larger monohull craft in association with Rodriquez.

FFM 1035 (AQUASTRADA)

Two of these Rodriquez Aquastrada craft are under construction for Corsica Ferries and are scheduled for delivery in March and June 1996.

Specifications

Length overall	103.5 m
Length waterline	86.0 m
Beam	14.5 m
Draught	2.05 m
Passengers	542
Vehicles	150 cars
Operational speed	35 kts
Range	370 n miles

Propulsion: The vessel is powered by four MTU 20V 1163 TB74L diesel engines, two arranged to power the central booster water-jet and the other two driving individual wing water-jets.

FFM 1418 (DESIGN)

This 142 m monohull vessel is designed to carry 1,500 passengers and 425 cars at speeds of up to 37.5 knots.

Specifications

Length overall	141.8 m
Length waterline	122.7 m
Beam	21.1 m
Draught	3.43 m
Displacement, min	2,000 t
Displacement, max	3,000 t
Passengers	1,500
Vehicles	425 cars
Fuel capacity	82,500 l
Water capacity	15,000 l
Propulsive power	45,000 kW
Max speed	37.5 kts
Operational speed	36.0 kts
Range	n miles

Structure: Steel hull, aluminium superstructure.

Propulsion: The vessel is designed to be powered by one GE LM 2500 gas turbine rated at 21,000 kW and four MTU 20V 1163 TB93 diesels each rated at 6,000 kW. The gas turbine drives a Kamewa 200BII water-jet whereas the diesels drive in pairs into two Kamewa 160 SII water-jets. The vessel is also offered without the gas turbine in which case speeds of approximately 25 knots are predicted. With only two diesels installed, speeds of approximately 18 knots are predicted.

NEW ENTRY

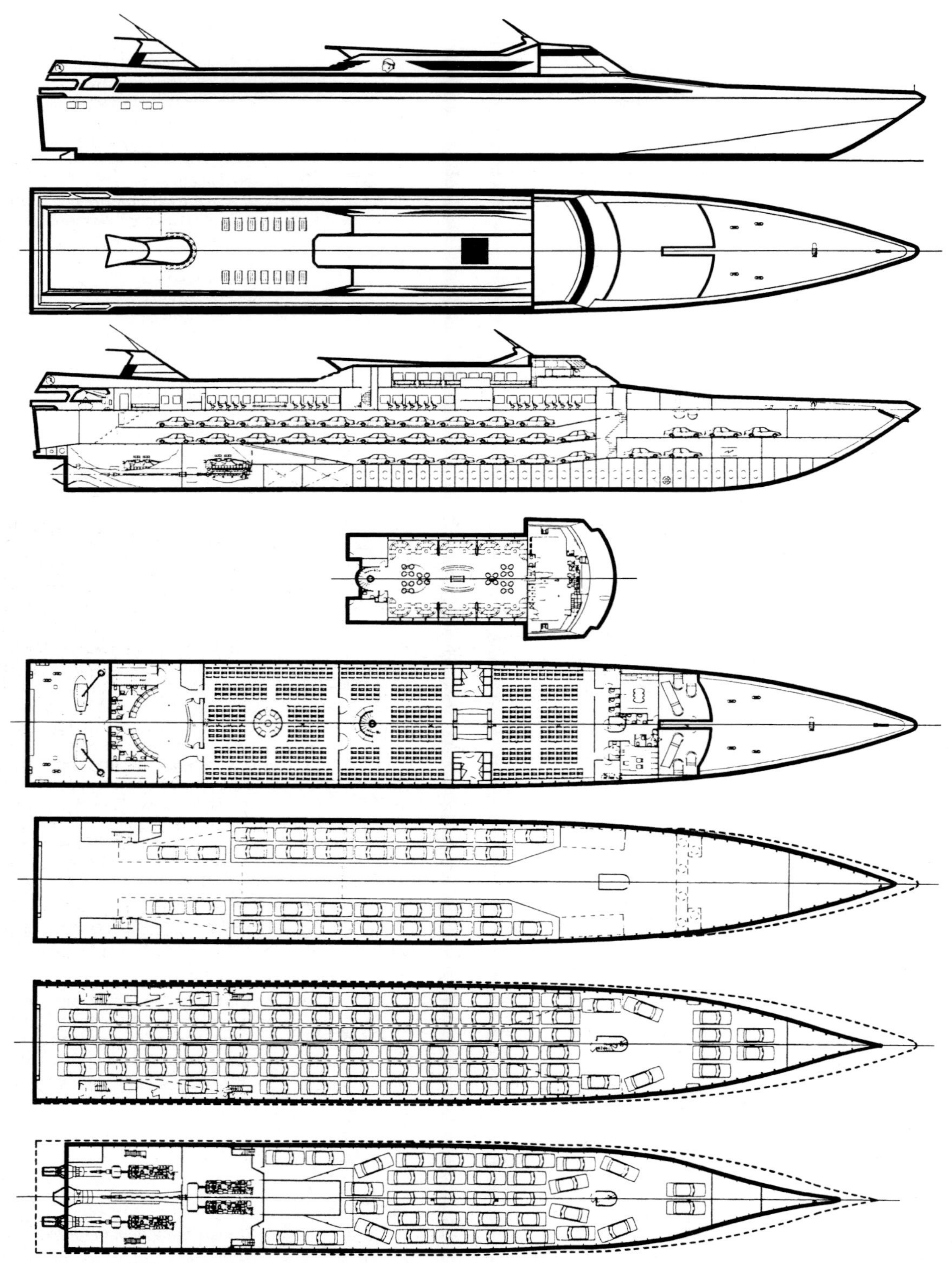

INMA FFM 1035 Aquastrada vessels for Corsica Ferries **1996**

INTERMARINE SpA

I-9038 Sarzana, La Spezia, Italy

Tel: +39 (187) 671800
Telex: 271062 IMARIN I

23 m PATROL CRAFT

Specifications

Length overall	23.8 m
Beam	8.4 m
Draught	1.2 m
Displacement	55 t
Crew	11
Propulsive power	2 × 1,925 kW
Max speed	40 kts
Operational speed	35 kts
Range	450 n miles

Structure: Constructed of GRP, the hull is of soft round form with fine entry forward, running into a hard chine constant deadrise aft.

Propulsion: The main engines are 2 × 1,925 kW diesels, driving 2 × 3-blade, fixed-pitch propellers.

27 m PATROL CRAFT

Specifications

Length overall	27.27 m
Beam	6.8 m
Draught	2.1 m
Displacement	85 t
Crew	15
Propulsive power	2 × 2,575 kW
Max speed	40 kts
Operational speed	36 kts
Range	1,000 n miles

Structure: Same material and form as the 23 m patrol craft.

Propulsion: 2 × 2,575 kW diesel engines, driving 2 × 3-blade, fixed-pitch propellers.

Electrical system: A generator of 76 kVA.

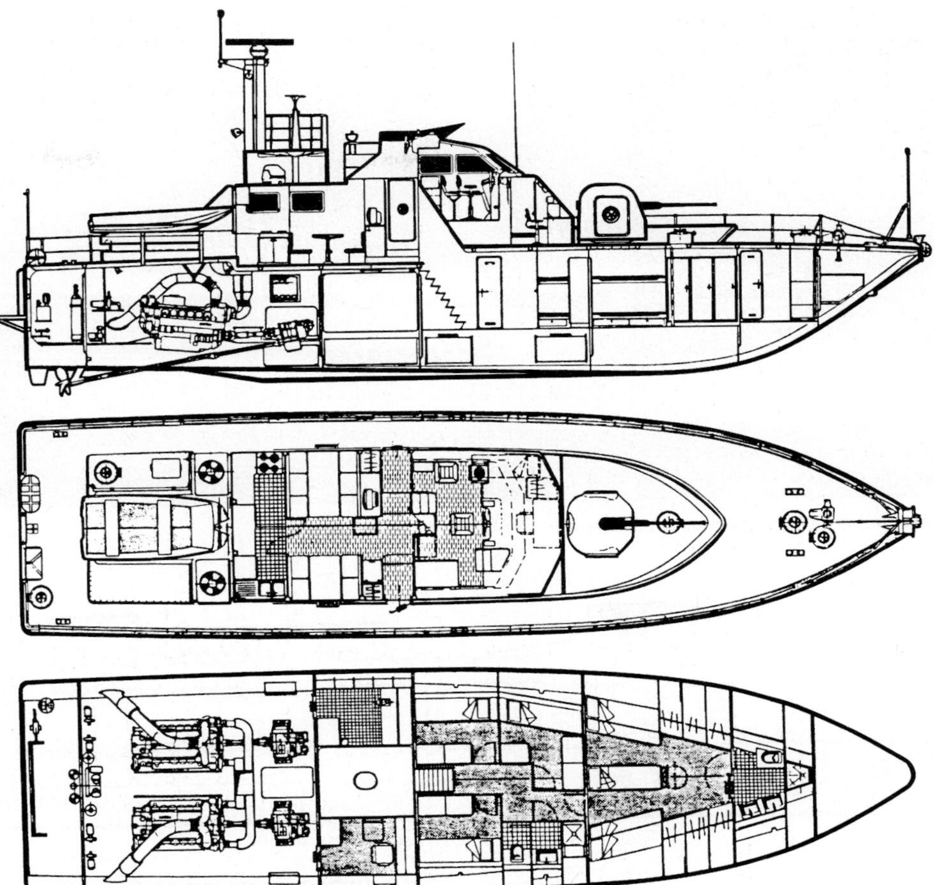

Intermarine 23 m patrol boat **1995**

27 MTS PATROL CRAFT

Supplied to African navies.

Specifications

Length overall	23.8 m
Beam	8.4 m
Draught	1.2 m
Displacement, max	55 t
Crew	11
Propulsive power	2 × 1,925 kW
Max speed	40 kts
Operational speed	35 kts
Range	450 n miles

Structure: Same material and form as the 23 m patrol craft.

Propulsion: The main engines are 2 × 1,925 kW diesel engines; driving 2 × 3-blade, fixed-pitch propellers.

Electrical system: 43 kVA generator.

VERIFIED

RODRIQUEZ CANTIERI NAVALI SpA

22 Via S Raineri, I-98122 Messina, Italy

Tel: +39 (90) 7765
Telex: 980030 RODRIK I
Fax: +39 (90) 675294

Basbasso Gattuso, *President*
Giovanni Morace, *Managing Director*
Alcide Sculati, *Technical Manager*
Diego Mazzeo, *Sales and Marketing*

37 m FOIL-ASSISTED MONOHULL (MONOSTAB)

This is a patented concept for a stabilised monohull vessel matching the characteristics of a semi-planing hull with two automatically controlled surface-piercing foils, the object being to achieve a better overall performance than that obtained with a pure monohull, especially at Froude numbers near unity.

If water-jet propulsion is used for a semi-planing monohull, it is almost inevitable that with engines and auxiliary machinery also being at the stern, the vessel will have a far aft centre of gravity with subsequently large changes in centre of gravity position from full load to light condition. Such machinery location also allows however for a hull shape with very fine entrance angles providing reduction in bow wave generation and good sea-keeping performance especially in head seas.

The foil-assisted monohull concept reduces the difficulties of an excessively rear centre of gravity position by the provision of a pair of surface-piercing foils connected to moving arms, manually or automatically controlled and positioned at the rear of the craft. The effect is to allow for a true dynamic relief of weight load from abaft, thereby reducing the amount of craft weight supported by the combined buoyant/planing lift of the hull and effecting a planing trim reduction substantially equivalent to a forward shifting of the craft centre of gravity. This in turn leads to an improvement of cruising performance, because of the higher efficiency of foils in relation to hull efficiency in the range of speeds under consideration and, of the indirect advantage of being able to trim the craft correctly for any load condition. Further, with a considerable improvement in directional stability, with the dihedral effect of the foils generating correct banking in turns and the possibility of regulating the planing trim angle of the craft in head seas to reduce slamming, a large reduction of the hull bottom deadrise can be obtained, leading in turn to a better hydrodynamic efficiency of the hull.

The 47 m foil-assisted monohull, in service with Adriatica SpA di Navigazione **1995**

Additional advantages of the concept, if trimmable foils are used, are that a strong roll and pitch damping effect is obtained, together with an increase in the transverse stability of the basic hull. These effects allow for a reduction in the waterline beam, improving hydrodynamic efficiency and rough water performance. With automatic control actuation of the moving arms a considerable

Aquastrada Guizzo *in service with Tirrenia* **1995**

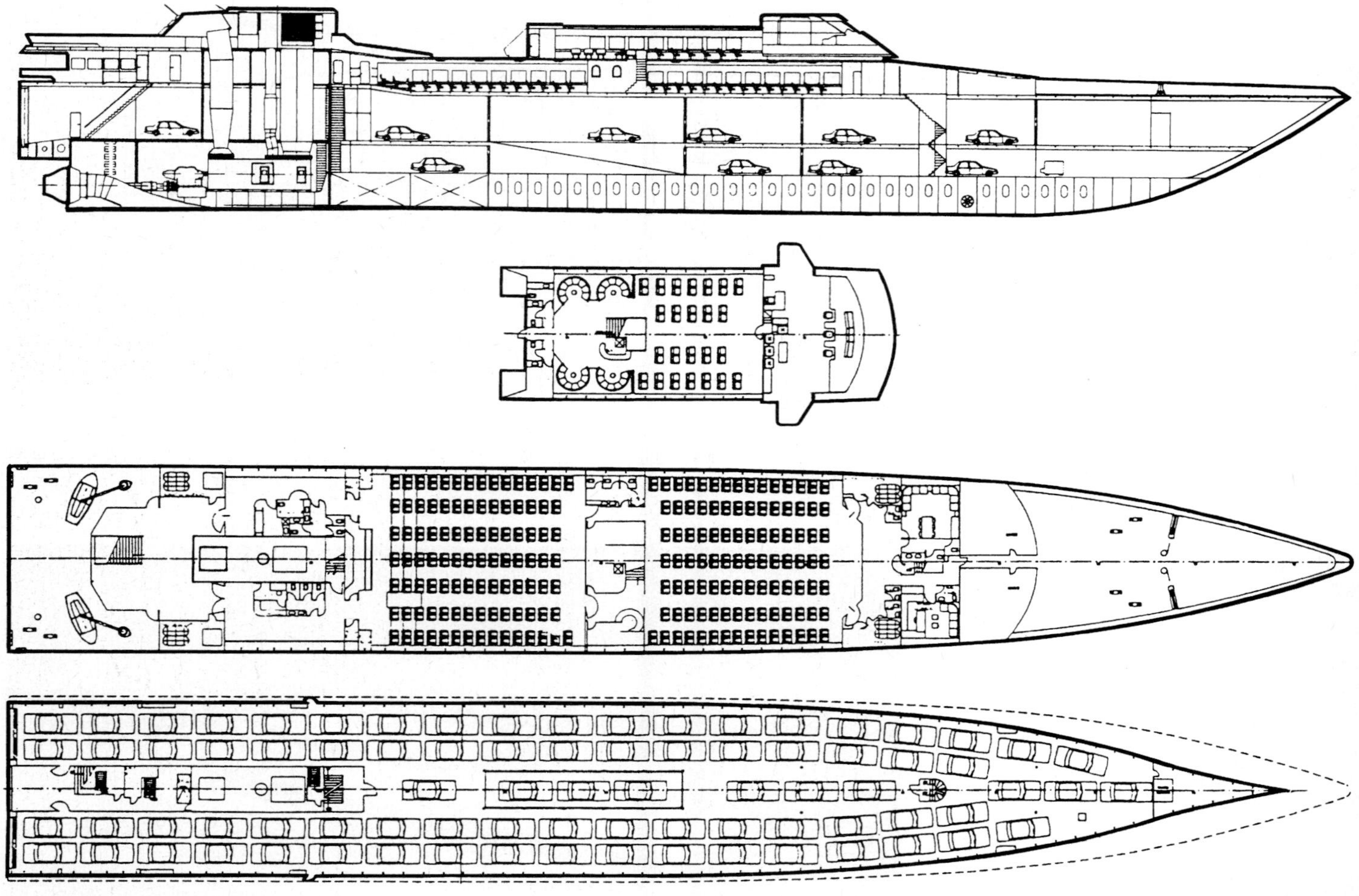

General arrangement of Aquastrada Guizzo **1995**

increase in rough water performance can be obtained without involving unduly fast arm movements.

The first craft to be built according to the above principles was launched in 1989 and entered service with Aliscafi SNAV in April 1990 on the Naples to Capri and Ischia routes.

Specifications

Length overall	37 m
Length waterline	30 m
Beam	7.5 m
Draught	1.05 m
Displacement, min	88 t
Displacement, max	125 t
Passengers	350
Propulsive power	2 × 1,920 kW
Operational speed	35 kts
Range	200 n miles

Propulsion: Engines: 2 × MTU 16V 396 TB 84 diesels, 1,920 kW each at 1,940 rpm

47 m FOIL-ASSISTED MONOHULL

Two of these vessels have been bought by Adriatica di Navigazione SpA, one by Saremar and one by an unknown operator. The first vessel *Marconi* was delivered in December 1991 and the second *Pacinotti* in June 1992. The third vessel *Isola di San Pietro* was delivered to Saremar, a state owned company, in June 1993. Following the introduction of the 37 m foil-assisted monohull, these larger vessels accommodate 400 passengers. Interior design is by Ennio Cantu who has been responsible for many Adriatica di Navigazione SpA vessels. The two passenger saloons are air conditioned. The third and fourth boats do not have aft stabilising foils but four Vosper Thornycroft stabilising fins, two forward and two aft.

Specifications

Length overall	46.9 m
Length waterline	37.2 m
Beam	7.6 m
Draught	1.3 m
Displacement, max	154 t
Passengers	400
Propulsive power	2 × 2,000 kW
Operational speed	34 kts
Range	200 n miles

Propulsion: Engines: 2 × MTU 16V 396 TE 74L, 2,000 kW each at 2,000 rpm.

Thrust devices: 2 × Kamewa water-jets (first two boats); 2 × Ulstein Propeller Speed-Z CPZ 60/42-125 CPP (third boat).

AQUASTRADA
Guizzo
Scatto

Two of these large fast monohull passenger/car ferries have been constructed for Tirrenia of Italy. They both have a similar arrangement although *Scatto* has a slightly greater capacity at 542 passengers and 150 cars. A third and fourth vessel of a very similar design under construction for Corsica Ferries are due for delivery in 1996 from the Rodriquez licencee, INMA of La Spezia.

The vessel's hulls are of a hard chine form and constructed of high tensile steel. The superstructures for the passenger accommodation are constructed of aluminium.

The capacities of the two Tirrenia vessels are similar although *Scatto* carries a slightly increased payload of 535 passengers and 156 cars as against 448 passengers and 126 cars. The performance penalty associated with this increased payload is small and equivalent to 1.5 knots of speed.

The Corsica Ferries vessel is slightly longer at 103.5 m as against 101.75 m and will be powered by four MTU 20V 1163 TB 74L diesel engines as opposed to the diesel/gas-turbine combination of the other vessels. The service speed of this vessel is understood to be 35 knots.

Specifications

Length overall	101.75 m
Length waterline	85.3 m
Beam	14.5 m
Draught	2.05 m
Displacement, max	1,057.5 t
Displacement, min	800.5 t
Passengers	450
Vehicles	126 cars
Propulsive power	24,065 kW
Operational speed	43 kts
Range	370 n miles

Propulsion: Engines: 2 × MTU 16V 595 TE 70, 3,565 kW each, 1 × GE LM 2500 gas-turbine, 20,500 kW; driving 2 × Kamewa 100 SII, 1 × Kamewa 180 SII.

UPDATED

TECNOMARINE SpA

Via Coppino 435, Viareggio, Italy

Tel: +39 (584) 380381/3801
Fax: +39 (584) 387630

Ms Anna Maria Marano, *President*

Tecnomarine was established in 1973 staffed with skilled labour and technicians from Picchiotti. The yard builds fast craft in wood, GRP, aluminium alloy and steel of from 14 to 120 m and is now one of the largest builders of luxury yachts in the world. Tecnomarine has a design staff of 45 and has longstanding working relationships with Sparkman and Stephens on engineering design, Paola D Smith & Associates on interior design and Stefano Righini Design on styling. The total area of the company's various yards is 16,752 m^2.

Tecnomarine T118 motor yacht Longitude Zero ***1989***

TECNOMARINE 118

Motor yacht.

Specifications

Length overall	36 m
Length waterline	31.16 m
Beam	7.33 m
Draught	2.25 m
Fuel capacity	14,000 l
Water capacity	4,000 l
Propulsive power	2 × 1,940 kW
Max speed	29-30 kts
Range	1,000 n miles

Structure: Construction in aluminium alloy or GRP.
Propulsion: 2 × MTU 16V 396 TB 93, 1,940 kW at 2,100 rpm each.

COBRA 76

Super Cobra

The first vessel of this new type named *Super Cobra* was launched in October 1990 for shipment to her owner in the USA.

Specifications

Length overall	22.9 m
Beam	5.176 m
Draught	1.5 m
Displacement, max	42 t
Crew	2
Passengers	6
Fuel capacity	5,000 l
Water capacity	2,000 l
Max speed	34 kts
Range	360 n miles

Classification: American Bureau of Shipping.
Structure: Hull and deck GRP, superstructure light alloy.
Propulsion: The main engines are 2 × GM 16V 92TA, DDC.

Tecnomarine T90 ***1993***

TECNOMARINE T90

The Tecnomarine T90 motor yacht is the latest vessel to come from this luxury yacht builder and was completed September 1991. With a GRP hull based on the proven 92 ft series and aluminium superstructure, speeds in excess of 30 knots are expected.

Specifications

Length overall	27 m
Beam	6.42 m
Draught	2 m
Crew	4
Passengers	8
Fuel capacity	10,500 l
Water capacity	2,300 l
Propulsive power	2 × 1,462 kW
Max speed	31 kts
Operational speed	25 kts
Range	430 n miles

Propulsion: The main engines are 2 × MTU 12V 396 TB 93.

TECNOMARINE T72

Motor yacht.

Specifications

Length overall	21.8 m
Length waterline	17 m
Beam	6.1 m
Draught	1.9 m
Displacement, max	45 t
Fuel capacity	4,800 l
Water capacity	2,000 l
Propulsive power	2 × 895 kW
Max speed	28 kts
Operational speed	25 kts
Range	350 n miles

Structure: GRP.
Propulsion: Main Engines: 2 × CAT 3412.

VERIFIED

CANTIERE NAUTICO VERSILCRAFT Srl

Via dei Pescatori 64, Viareggio (LU), Italy

Tel: +39 (584) 384946
Telex: 624198 VERSIL I

Marketing:
Versil Marine SA
Hinterbergstrasse 21, CH-6330 Cham-Zug, Switzerland

Tel: +41 (42) 418044
Telex: 865328 VEMA CH
Fax: +41 (42) 416723

Versil Marine France
64 La Croisette, Palais Mirimar, F-06400 Cannes, France

Tel: +33 93 43 56 66
Telex: 970836 VERSIL F

73 ft CHALLENGER

Specifications

Length overall	22.26 m
Beam	6.1 m
Draught	1.83 m
Displacement, max	45 t
Crew	2
Passengers	6-8
Fuel capacity	9,988 l
Water capacity	1,614 l
Max speed	26 kts
Operational speed	23 kts

Structure: GRP.
Propulsion: 3 × GM 12V 92 TI.

83 ft SUPER CHALLENGER
Marcalec

Specifications

Length overall	25.4 m
Beam	6.09 m
Draught	1.83 m
Displacement, min	40 t
Displacement, max	50 t
Crew	2-3
Passengers	6-8 berths
Fuel capacity	10,000 l
Water capacity	1,600 l
Max speed	25 kts
Operational speed	22 kts
Range	572 n miles

Structure: GRP.
Propulsion: 3 × GM 12V 92 TI diesel engines.

66 ft VERSILCRAFT
Earl Grey

Specifications

Length overall	19.8 m
Beam	5.6 m
Draught	1.5 m
Displacement, min	29 t
Crew	1-2
Passengers	6-8
Fuel capacity	5,000 l
Water capacity	800 l
Propulsive power	2 × 597 kW

Propulsion: The main engines are 2 × MAN 597 kW diesels.

VERIFIED

The Versilcraft 66 ft
1990

SCIOMACHEN

Via Ferrarese 3, I-40128 Bologna, Italy

Tel: +39 (51) 368846
Fax: +39 (51) 368413

Franco Sciomachen, *Director*
Ernesto Sciomachen, *Director*
Aldo Sciomachen, *Director*

The Sciomachen name has been associated with yachts and boats since 1951. After the early years devoted mainly to sailing craft, the company's projects today encompass a full range of marine designs from high-speed power yachts to fast ferries, excursion vessels, fishing vessels, displacement yachts, as well as racing and cruising sailboats. Construction materials include fibreglass, steel, aluminium and wood, with sizes from about 7 m to over 45 m.

The company's yacht design experience is reflected in the attractiveness of its commercial vessels, where practicality is matched with aesthetically pleasing lines.

Sciomachen's European headquarters are in Bologna, Italy, while an office in San Diego, California, serves the Pacific area.

Neocastrum

Delivered in May 1993, this 35 m fast ferry was constructed at Cantiere Foschi's facilities in Cesenatico, Italy, for Foderaro Navigazione. The owners are also planning to order a sister ship to replace a 30 m vessel of similar design out of the same facilities. A third vessel is to be built for another owner.

Hull No 1 is equipped with a pair of Mitsubishi 1,632 kW diesels for a top speed of 31 knots. Passenger capacity is 350 with about two-thirds seated in the main deck saloon and one-third in the upper deck saloon. The Captain's cabin and a crew cabin are located just aft of the bridge. Forward of the main deck saloon, a crew mess and galley have direct access to the fore deck.

Neocastrum
1993

The vessel is operated between the south-west coast of Italy and the islands off the north coast of Sicily. The daily round trip is approximately 160 n miles with about a three hour passage each way.

Specifications

Length overall	35.4 m
Beam	7.6 m
Displacement, min	85 t
Passengers	350
Fuel capacity	12,000 l
Water capacity	2,000 l
Propulsive power	2 × 1,632 kW
Max speed	31 kts

Propulsion: 2 × Mitsubishi diesels.

Two smaller ferries have also been built, the 19.5 m *Neptunus* and the 18 m *Siro*, both delivered June 1992.

Hipponion

Delivered in May 1990.

Specifications

Length overall	30.28 m
Beam	7.13 m
Displacement, min	52.15 t
Passengers	350
Propulsive power	2 × 1,044 kW
Operational speed	26 kts

Propulsion: 2 × diesels.

Hipponion *1993*

Golfo Di Arzachena

Delivered in May 1992.

Specifications

Length overall	23.68 m
Beam	6.11 m
Displacement, min	29.33 t
Passengers	200
Propulsive power	2 × 336 kW
Speed	22 kts

Propulsion: 2 × diesels.

37 m FAST FERRY

A new 37 m fast ferry is under construction at CN Fuschi in Cesenatico. The vessel is a development of *Neocastrum*.

Specifications

Length overall	37.4 m
Length waterline	31.2 m
Beam	7.65 m
Displacement, min	90 t
Passengers	350
Propulsive power	2 × 2,350 kW (diesels)
Fuel capacity	14,000 l
Operational speed	35-40 kts

40 m FAST FERRY (DESIGN)

Following the launching of two smaller vessels in 1994, Sciomachen developed an all-aluminium 40 m, 450 passenger fast ferry to IMO's International Code of Safety for High-Speed Craft (Category B).

The service speed is 35 knots full load, with a top speed in excess of 40 knots in trial conditions. This speed is achieved with a triple diesel configuration driving three water-jets, although a gas-turbine propulsion system is also being considered.

In order to comply with Category B of the rules, the engine room is split into two units, capable of functioning independently from each other. Passenger accommodation is also split into three areas, protected by sprinkler systems, and each passenger has at least two routes to reach an alternative location in case of fire. A full alarm and monitoring system is installed throughout the ship. Passenger seats are designed to withstand the accelerations arising from a full speed collision.

Specifications

Length overall	40 m
Beam	8.5 m
Draught	1.15 m
Passengers	450
Propulsive power	3 × 2,000 kW or 2 × 3,000 kW
Max speed	40+ kts

Structure: Aluminium alloy throughout.

Propulsion: 3 × diesels, or 2 × gas-turbines.

VERIFIED

JAPAN

ETOH MARINE CORPORATION

5-32 Shioya, Kurogawa-Cho, Imari City, Saga Prefecture, Japan 848-01

Tel: +81 (955) 271288
Fax: +81 (955) 271286

J Sireci, *Design Engineer*

Etoh Marine Corporation occupies a modern boat manufacturing facility in Imari City, completed in 1990 for the construction of aluminium craft. The company delivered the *Fuki 8*, a 232 passenger monohull ferry, in January 1994. The vessel will provide a service between Tomishima and Akashi in Japan.

Fuki 8 *at speed* *1994*

Specifications

Length overall	33.5 m
Length waterline	30.97 m
Beam	6.5 m
Draught	1 m
Fuel capacity	12,000 l
Water capacity	500 l
Operational speed	28 kts
Propulsive power	2 × 1,200 kW
Range	600 n miles

Propulsion: 2 × Yanmar V-16 Model 16LAK-STI diesel engines rated at 1,200 kW each, driving 2 × 5-bladed propellers, through Niigata MGM 433 gearboxes.

Electrical system: A Yanmar 4CHL-N generator rated at 40 kW.

VERIFIED

MITSUBISHI HEAVY INDUSTRIES LTD

5-1 Marunouchi 2-chome, Chiyoda-ku, Tokyo 100, Japan

Tel: +81 (3) 3212 3111
Telex: 22443J
Fax: +81 (3) 3212 9822

The following vessels have been built at the Shimonoseki Shipyard and Machinery Works in Hikoshima, Shimonoseki, Japan.

Seahawk *1992*

Seahawk

Please see the 1991 edition for an earlier built *Seahawk*.

Specifications

Length overall	48.5 m
Beam	8.2 m
Passengers	301
Propulsive power	2 × 2,051 kW
Max speed	29 kts

Propulsion: 2 × diesel engines, 2,051 kW each, 1,450 rpm.

Owner: Koshikishima Shosen Ltd.

Marine Star

Built in 1983 and originally in service with Oki Kisen Company Ltd, this craft has now been sold to a foreign owner.

Specifications

Length overall	48.5 m
Beam	8.2 m
Passengers	351
Propulsive power	2 × 1,805 kW
Max speed	30.7 kts

Propulsion: 2 × 1,805 kW (2,420 hp) high-speed diesels.

Seagrace

This vessel was delivered to its owner, Kyushu Shosen Ltd, in March 1993.

Specifications

Length overall	48.5 m
Beam	8.2 m
Draught	3.95 m
Passengers	286
Max speed	30.11 kts
Propulsive power	2 × 2,051 kW

Propulsion: 2 × diesels, 2,051 kW each, 1,450 rpm.
Control: Fin stabiliser, anti-pitching fin.

30 m FISHERY PATROL BOAT

Specifications

Length overall	31.5 m
Beam	6.3 m
Crew	12
Propulsive power	2 × 1,160 kW
Max speed	31 kts

Propulsion: 2 × 1,160 kW engines (1,520 hp) at 1,840 rpm.
Owner: Yamaguchi Prefecture.

Seagrace *1993*

26 m FISHERY PATROL CRAFT

Specifications

Length overall	26.03 m
Beam	5.73 m
Propulsive power	2 × 1,160 kW
Max speed	36 kts

Propulsion: 2 × 1,160 kW engines at 1,840 rpm.
Owner: Nagasaki Prefecture.

UPDATED

MOKUBEI SHIPBUILDING COMPANY

1-2-20 Imakatata, Otsu, Shiga Prefecture, Japan

Tel: +81 (775) 722101
Fax: +81 (775) 722111

Mamoru Nakano, *President*
Masaru Ikeda, *Naval Architect*

Lansing

A water-jet-propelled sightseeing tourist boat built in 1982 for operation by the Biwa Lake Sightseeing Company on the very shallow Biwa Lake. Built in aluminium, the vessel has seating for 86 passengers and two crew. The fully laden power-to-weight ratio is 41.5 hp/t.

Specifications

Length overall	22 m
Length waterline	19.8 m
Beam	4 m
Draught	0.55 m
Displacement, max	26 t
Crew	2
Passengers	86
Propulsive power	2 × 400 kW
Max speed	27 kts
Operational speed	30 kts

Propulsion: The main engines are 2 × MAN 254 MLE V12 diesels rated at 400 kW each, at 2,230 rpm; driving two Hamilton Model 421 type directly driven from engine flywheel via torsionally flexible coupling and Cardan shaft.

Control: The vessel is fitted with an auxiliary diesel AC generator which enables AC motor driven hydraulic power packs to be used for the water-jet unit controls. A tandem pump hydraulic power pack is used for the reverse ducts while a single pump hydraulic power pack operates the steering. At the helm, control for steering is via a wheel; the reverse is operated via a single electric joystick and two position indicators are fitted, one for the steering deflector angle and the other for the reverse duct position.

Mokubei Lansing *1987*

Kaiyo *1988*

ESCORT BOAT

Kaiyo

A 25.5 m, 21.5 knot steel hull firefighting boat equipped to carry foam liquid, launched 19 February 1986 and owned by Sanyo-kaiji Company Ltd and Nihon-kaiji-kogyo Company Ltd.

Designer: Dr M Ikeda.

Specifications

Length overall	25.5 m
Beam	5.6 m
Draught	1.1 m
Displacement, min	54.85 t
Crew	9
Propulsive power	2 × 746 kW

Takashima *1991*

Propulsion: The main engines are 2 × Yanmar 12LAAK-UT1, 746 kW each at 1,850 rpm, driving two fixed-pitch, 3-blade, aluminium bronze propellers, 1,000 mm diameter, 1,000 mm pitch, developed blade-area ratio: 0.90:1. Propeller shaft diameter: 99 mm, length 6,500 mm; via NICO-MGN 332 gearboxes, shaft output MCR: 1,000 hp at 907 rpm.

Mizusumashi II

Water quality research boat delivered 31 March 1989.

Specifications

Length overall	23.5 m
Beam	4.8 m
Displacement, max	39.12 t
Crew	30
Propulsive power	2 × 1,007 kW
Max speed	28 kts

Propulsion: 2 × DDC 16V 92TA, 1,007 kW each, MCR, 2,300 rpm; driving 2 × 5-blade propellers, 700 mm diameter, 884 mm pitch, developed area ratio: 1.0; via NICO MGN 332E reduction gearboxes, ratio: 1.42:1.

20 m COASTGUARD VESSEL

Takashima

Delivered on 31 October 1989 for operation on Lake Biwa, this vessel is owned by the Shiga police.

Specifications

Length overall	19.8 m
Beam	4.7 m
Draught	0.8 m
Propulsive power	2 × 775 kW
Max speed	30.3 kts

Propulsion: The main engines are 2 × GM 12V 92TA, 775.5 kW each at 2,300 rpm (100% MCR), 615 kW each at 2,170 rpm (normal service).

VERIFIED

YAMAHA MOTOR COMPANY LTD

2500 Shingai, Iwata, Shizuoka 438, Japan

Tel: +81 (538) 321145
Telex: YAMAHAMOTOR IWATA
Fax: +81 (538) 374250

The Tsugaru

This boat was designed to engage in supervision and survey operations in Matsu Bay, Aomori Prefecture.

Specifications

Length overall	19.55 m
Beam	4.4 m
Draught	0.8 m
Passengers	22
Fuel capacity	1,900 l
Water capacity	200 l
Propulsive power	2 × 410 kW
Max speed	33.5 kts
Operational speed	29 kts
Range	240 n miles

Structure: The hull material is FRP, and is single skin.

Propulsion: The main engines are 2 × GM 8V 92TA diesels, 410 kW at 2,240 rpm, 373 kW continuous at 2,170 rpm; driving 2 × surface step drives.

Electrical system: 1 × 18.2 kW generator.

24 m MOTOR YACHT

This GRP motor yacht (Yard No S-314) was delivered to a Yokohama owner in July 1995.

Yamaha 24 m motor yacht ***1996***

Specifications

Length overall	23.95 m
Beam	5.0 m
Draught	1.85 m
Displacement, min	36 t
Fuel capacity	4,000 l
Max speed	31.5 kts

Classification: J.G. certification for coastal water operation.

Propulsion: The vessel is powered by two MAN 12V diesel engines each rated at 800 kW and each driving a fixed pitch three bladed propeller via a reverse reduction gearbox.

UPDATED

The Tsugaru *in Matsu Bay* ***1993***

KOREA, SOUTH

SEMO COMPANY LTD

Shipyard: 1 Jangiri Donghaemyun, Kosung Kun, Kyung Nam, South Korea

Tel: +82 (556) 723535
Fax: +82 (556) 723570

Seoul Office: Sungwoo Building, 5th floor, 51-1 Dowhadong, Mapoku, Seoul, South Korea

Tel: +82 (2) 702 3535
Fax: +82 (2) 701 1780

SEMO 20 m PATROL BOAT

This boat type has been used by the Korean Office of Customs Administration for several years.

Specifications

Length overall	19.9 m
Beam	4.76 m
Draught	0.87 m
Crew	10
Propulsive power	2 × 485 kW
Max speed	26 kts
Operational speed	20 kts

Propulsion: The main engines are 2 × DDC 8V 92TA diesels, 485 kW each at 2,300 rpm, driving 2 × propellers.

VERIFIED

Semo 20 m patrol boat

1993

MALAYSIA

CHIONG BROTHERS SHIPYARD

and other yards, Sibu, Sarawak, East Malaysia

One of a number of builders of fast river ferries for Malaysian river services.

64 SEAT RIVER FERRY

Specifications

Length overall	27.44 m
Beam	3.2 m
Displacement, min	15-16 t
Passengers	64
Fuel capacity	600 l
Max speed	32 kts

Structure: Cabin skin: 1.5 mm galvanised steel. Frames: 3 mm steel strip.
Plating: 3 mm steel, 6 mm below engine room.
Hull weight of steel: 10 t.
Propulsion: Engine: can be MAN, 260 kW (350 hp), cruise 2,200 rpm, 87.5% of full power.

VERIFIED

WONG'S SHIPBUILDING CONTRACTOR & DESIGNER

3rd Floor, 27 Long Bridge, PO Box 497, 96007 Sibu, Sarawak, Malaysia

Tel: +60 (84) 322098/331582
Telex: 72186 HWAHUN MA
Fax: +60 (84) 331582/316310

Paul H L Wong, *Principal*

This yard delivered four fast monohull river ferries in 1995 and currently has three further craft under construction for delivery in 1996.

Jambo Jet 218

Built in 1995 for operation from Singapore and P. Tioman.

Specifications

Length overall	42.07 m
Beam	5.5 m
Passengers	231
Operational Speed	30 kts

Classification: NKK.
Structure: The main hull and superstructure are of mild steel construction.
Propulsion: The vessel is powered by two DDC 16V 149TI diesel engines, each rated at 1,340 kW at 1,900 rpm.

Labuan Express Tiger

This vessel was built in 1995 with a very similar specification to *Jambo Jet.* However with passenger numbers reduced to 207, the operational speed increased to 32 knots with the same engine power. The vessel operate from Labuan to Kota Kinabalu.

Bullet Xpress III

Built in 1995 for operation between Cebu, Ormocand and Tagbilaran.

Specifications

Length overall	39.5 m
Beam	4.4 m
Passengers	139
Operational speed	20 kts

Propulsion: The vessel is powered by two Yanmar 12LAK ST2 diesels each rated at 900 kW.

Jambo Jet 118

Built in 1995 for operation between Mersing and P. Tioman.

Specifications

Length overall	32.8 m
Beam	4.17 m
Passengers	96
Operational speed	26 kts

Propulsion: The vessel is powered by two MTU 12V 183 TC60 diesel engines.

47 m Monohull Ferry

Three of these craft are currently under construction for delivery in 1996. Two vessels are for Chinese control operation and one for Indonesian operations between Pontianak and Jakarta.

Specifications

Length	46.8 m
Beam	6.1 m
Passenger (approx)	300
Operational speed	28 kts

Propulsion: The two vessels for China are powered by two Mitsubishi S16R-MPTK diesels rated at 1,610 kW at 1,800 rpm and the Indonesian vessel by three Yanmar 16LAK STI diesels each rate at 1,120 kW at 1,900 rpm.

Ekspres Bahagia

Specifications

Length overall	41.16 m
Beam	5.18 m
Passengers	250
Propulsive power	2 × 1,490 kW
Max speed	40 kts
Operational speed	36 kts

Classification: NKK.
Structure: The hull material is mild steel.
Propulsion: The main engines are 2 × DDC 16V 149 TI, 1,490 kW each at 2,100 rpm, driving propellers.

Desa Intan

Operating area: Melacca and Dumai.

Specifications

Length overall	40.78 m
Beam	5.5 m
Passengers	282
Propulsive power	3 × 902 kW
Max speed	35 kts
Operating speed	32 kts

Classification: NKK.
Structure: The hull material is mild steel.
Propulsion: The main engines are 3 × Yanmar 12LAK ST2, 902 kW each at 1,910 rpm.

UPDATED

NETHERLANDS

DAMEN SHIPYARDS

Industrieterrein Avelingen West 20, PO Box 1, 4200 AA, Gorinchem, Netherlands

Tel: +31 (1830) 39911
Telex: 25335 DAME NL
Fax: +31 (1830) 32189

P H Noordenbos, *Director High-Speed Craft*

Damen Shipyards specializes in the design and construction of a wide range of work boats, dredgers and patrol craft up to 90 m in length and with installed powers up to 10,000 kW.

The shipyard started in 1927 and in 1969 began the construction of commercial vessels to standard designs by modular construction. Since 1969 more than 3,000 ships have been built and delivered worldwide to 117 countries.

The high-speed and naval craft department produces a wide range of high-speed craft for commercial, patrol and rescue operations. The largest of the Damen range are the 53 m, 27 knot firefighting craft.

NEW ENTRY

Damen Stan 2300 in series production ***1996***

Particulars of standard high-speed craft built by Damen Shipyards

Type	STAN 2100	STAN 2300	STAN 2600	STAN 3000	STAN 3400
Length overall	21.1 m	23.1 m	27.0 m	29.5 m	34.0 m
Beam	6.6 m	5.7 m	6.0 m	6.0 m	7.2 m
Draught	1.5 m	1.3 m	1.8 m	2.1 m	2.1 m
Crew	12	12	17	18	18
Max speed	31.7 kts	35 kts	31 kts	26.2 kts	34 kts
Operational Speed	26 kts	30 kts	29 kts	24 kts	25 kts
Range	500 n miles	500 n miles	800 n miles	700 n miles	800 n miles

KEES CORNELISSEN SHIPYARD

Waaldijk 11b, NL-6621 KG Dreumel, Netherlands

Tel: +31 (8877) 2880
Fax: +31 (8877) 2908

Kees Cornelissen, *Managing Director*

This shipyard was founded in 1978 and now employs a labour force of over 65. The yard builds fast aluminium yachts as well as larger low-speed vessels.

EUROSHIP 45.5 m MOTORYACHT

This all-aluminium motoryacht with transatlantic capability was delivered in 1994.

Specifications

Length overall	45.5 m
Length waterline	39.5 m
Beam	8.6 m
Draught	2.15 m
Passengers	14 (including crew)
Fuel capacity	40,000 l
Water capacity	10,000 l
Max speed	26 kts
Operational speed	23 kts

Propulsion: The main engines are 2 × MTU 16V 396 TE 94 diesels, driving propellers via 2 × ZF BW 755 gearboxes.

Electrical system: Two Northern Lights 90 kW generators, one 45 kW generator.

Euroship 26 m motoryacht ***1993***

EUROSHIP 26 m MOTORYACHT

Construction of this vessel began in February 1993 and it was delivered in 1994.

Specifications

Length overall	26 m
Length waterline	21.5 m
Beam	6.25 m
Draught	1.6 m
Passengers	8
Fuel capacity	12,000 l
Water capacity	2,500 l
Max speed	28 kts
Operational speed	24 kts
Range	1,800 n miles

Structure: The superstructure material is aluminium, and the hull material is steel.

Propulsion: The main engines are 2 × Deutz MWM diesels, driving propellers via 2 × ZF gearboxes.

Electrical system: Two 30 kW Northern Lights generators.

VERIFIED

SCHELDE SHIPBUILDING (ROYAL SCHELDE)

PO Box 16, 165 Glacisstraat, 4380 AA, Vlissingen, Netherlands

Tel: +31 118 482118
Telex: 37815
Fax: +31 118 485010

Th P Winde, *Director of Shipbuilding*
E Bilterijst, *Marketing and Sales*
A Van der Knapp, *Marketing and Sales*
B Oving, *Marketing and Sales*

Royal Schelde has developed a range of high-speed vessels in the past, starting with SES craft of which they built a 26 m demonstration vessel, Seaswift 23, which operated for a period between Southampton and the Isle of Wight in the UK. Subsequent to this vessel, Schelde Shipbuilding also developed a range of catamarans and monohulls, drawing on their experience of the building of naval frigates.

In view of the market developments the company has committed itself to the marketing of large high-speed vessels, such as the CAT 70 catamaran design and the 90 and 128 m monohull designs.

90 m PASSENGER/VEHICLE FERRY (DESIGN)

This vessel is designed as a slender monohull high-speed ferry intended for passenger, car and trailer transportation. The two car decks, one of which is hoistable, is laid out for a total of 144 cars.

Specifications

Length overall	103.4 m
Length waterline	90 m
Beam	15.0 m
Draught	2.9 m
Crew	14
Passengers	450
Vehicles	144 cars or 18 trailers
Fuel capacity	85,000 l
Water capacity	6,000 l
Max speed	38 kts
Operational speed	37 kts
Range	550 n miles

Classification: DnV +1A1 HSLC R1 Passenger Car Ferry A, EO.

Propulsion: The vessel is understood to be powered by six diesel engines, three in each of two engine rooms. The central engines in each engine room drive via a common gearbox to a booster water-jet whilst the other four engines drive via individual gearboxes to steering and reversing water-jets.

128 m PASSENGER/VEHICLE FERRY (DESIGN)

This vessel is designed as a monohull high-speed ferry intended for the transportation of passengers, cars and coaches. The car decks are laid out to accomodate 234 cars or 166 cars and 6 coaches. Two aft ramps will be fitted to allow the vessel to be loaded and unloaded using a drive round system. The accomodation areas are designed for a total of 778 passengers.

Specifications

Length overall	128 m
Length waterline	115.0 m
Beam	18.4 m
Draught	2.8 m
Passengers	778
Vehicles	234
Fuel capacity	85,000 l
Water capacity	7,000 l
Propulsive power	41250 kW
Operational speed	37.5 kts

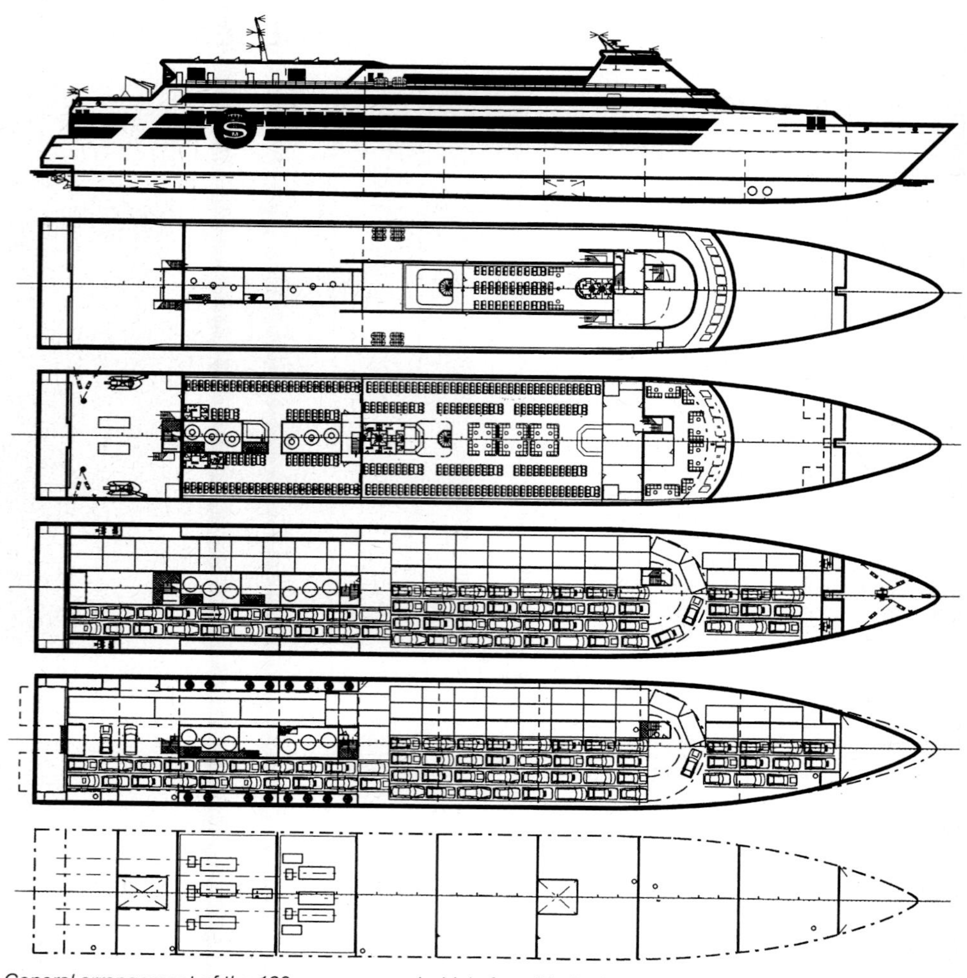

General arrangement of the 128 m passenger/vehicle ferry (design) **1996**

Classification: DnV +1A1 R1 HSLC Passenger Car Ferry B, EO.

UPDATED

NORWAY

BÅTUTRUSTNING A/S

Termetangen, N-5420 Rubbestadneset, Norway

Tel: +47 (5) 427111
Fax: +47 (5) 427602

Builder of many monohull vessels, Båtutrustning A/S was engaged in the construction of a 26 m 45 knot ferry in January 1989.

Askepott

Designed by Teknisk Modellcenter A/S, this three-engine 118 passenger 40 knot ferry was delivered to Per Vold in 1989. The vessel has an unusually high maximum speed capability of 47 knots.

Specifications

Length overall	25.30 m
Length waterline	21.45 m
Beam	6 m
Passengers	118
Fuel capacity	6,000 l
Propulsive power	872 kW
Max speed	47 kts
Operational speed	40 kts
Range	420 n miles

Structure: The hull is GRP sandwich construction.

Propulsion: The main engines are 3 × MWM TBD 234 V16, each 872 kW max, 780 kW continuous; driving 3 × Kamewa water-jet units, via Type 40S 3 × ZF BU250 gearboxes.

VERIFIED

Askepott (Alan Bliault) **1990**

MJELLEM & KARLSEN VERFT A/S

Thormøhlensgt 35/51, PO Box 2713 Møhlenpris, N-5026 Bergen, Norway

Tel: +47 (55) 542200
Fax: +47 (55) 542201

Paal Martens, *Vice President*
Steiner Draegebø, *Managing Director*

Mjellem & Karlsen signed a US$33 million contract in December 1993 with European Ferries Denmark AS to build a 95 m fast passenger and vehicle ferry in aluminium. This vessel was delivered in May 1995. A second ferry is now under construction for Starmarine Denmark AS for delivery in mid 1996. The vessel will be named M/F *Djursland* and will be operated on the same route.

The company is currently marketing two larger designs, a 115 m vessel which is a stretched version of the 95 m and carrying 800 passengers and 210 cars and a 135 m vessel, to be constructed in high-tensile steel, carrying 1,200 passengers and 400 cars.

Mjellem & Karlsen's 95 m passenger/car ferry M/F Kattegat **1996**

95 m PASSENGER/CAR FERRY
Kattegat

The ferry is hired from European Ferries Denmark AS on a long-term bare boat charter by Driftsselskabet Grenaa Hundested A/S, to provide ferry service between the two ports of Grenaa and Hundested in Denmark. The ferry commenced operations during Summer 1995.

Based on the company's extensive experience in the design and construction of military vessels, the 95 m ferry was constructed in a series of modules which were assembled at the Halsnøy Verft AS yard, which is part of the Mjellem & Karlsen group. Many of these modules were fabricated by other Norwegian subcontractors.

The ferry is equipped with a bow and stern ramp system that is compatible with conventional ferry terminals and allows quick unloading of cars, buses and trucks. The six vehicle lanes run the full length of the vessel. A combination of fixed and hoistable tween-decks ensures maximum flexibility without too much of a weight penalty. With the hoistable tween-decks in the upper position, two lanes with six buses in each lane are available together with 52 cars.

Specifications

Length overall	95 m
Length waterline	86.45 m
Beam	17.4 m
Draught	3.65 m
Crew	12
Passengers	600
Vehicles	160 cars +12 buses
Fuel capacity	196,000 l
Water capacity	27,000 l
Propulsive power	4 × 5,800 kW
Max speed	38 kts
Operational speed	35 kts

Structure: The hull and superstructure are constructed from seawater resistant aluminium. The hull structure combines the use of plates and stiffeners with extruded profiles, depending on local and general strength requirements.

Propulsion: The main engines are 4 × MTU 20V 1163 TB 73 diesels, each producing 5,800 kW at 1,200 rpm; each driving Kamewa 112 SII water-jets.

Control: All four water-jets are steerable, and two powerful bow thrusters have been fitted. Four computer-controlled fins are fitted for stabilisation. The vessel is controlled from an integrated bridge system.

Outfit: The passenger areas are located on one level, separated from the engine rooms by the car decks, so reducing noise from the machinery.

UPDATED

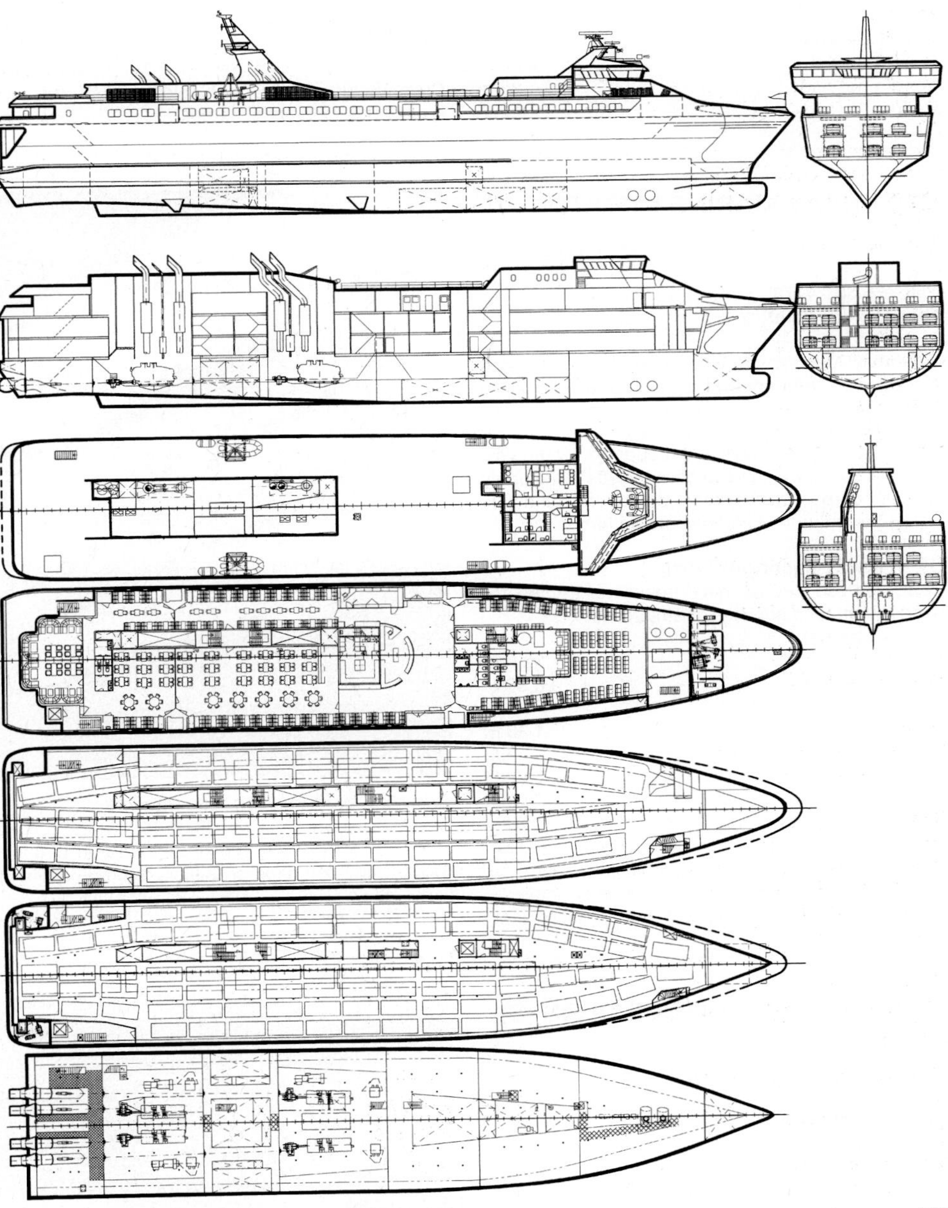

General arrangement of 95 m fast passenger/car ferry **1995**

SINGAPORE

ALUMINIUM CRAFT (88) PTE LTD

55 Gul Road, Singapore 2262

Tel: +65 862 4800
Fax: +65 862 4803

Chang Seak Foo, *Director and General Manager*
Fong Weng Meng, *Technical Manager*
Gabriel Tan, *Marketing Manager*

A subsidiary of Singmarine Industries Ltd (a member of the Keppel Group), Aluminium Craft (88) Pte Ltd has accumulated more than 30 years of experience in the building and repairs of aluminium craft and industrial structures. It has the expertise to build sophisticated vessels such as the Surface Effect Ship, Navatek Ltd's SWATH (Small-Waterplane-Area Twin-Hull) and Lock Crowther's catamarans. Apart from its own proven monohull, the company also has a design team capable of building vessels to meet the specific requirements of its clients. It also provides a comprehensive range of repair services including jumboisation and conversion.

27.5 m CREW BOAT

Borcos 112
Borcos 113

Specifications

Length overall	27.5 m
Length waterline	25 m
Beam	6.2 m
Draught	1 m
Crew	6
Passengers	68
Payload	6 t (additional)
Fuel capacity	6 t
Water capacity	2,000 l
Operational speed	18 kts
Range	400 n miles

Classification: Lloyd's ✠100A1 +LMC for local trade limits, personnel carrier.

Borcos 112 *crew boat* **1992**

28 m FERRY

Delivered in the first quarter of 1993 for a Chinese owner, this 138 passenger vessel was classed and surveyed by the China Classification Society (ZC). A service speed of 28 knots is achieved with 1,700 kW total output from two marine diesel engines.

VERIFIED

GREENBAY MARINE PTE LTD

4, Pioneer Sector 1, Jurong, Singapore 2262

Tel: +65 861 4178
Fax: +65 861 8109

Greenbay Marine was incorporated in 1980 as a shipbuilding company and has since that time built a wide range of vessels in steel and aluminium.

The company also, provides design, consultancy and full after sales service and support for the vessels it supplies which have covered offshore supply vessels, cargo vessels, tugs, patrol craft and fast passenger monohull and catamaran ferries.

32 m Fast Passenger Ferry

Four of these vessels have been constructed for *Auto Batam* ferry services of Singapore.

Specifications

Length overall	32.0 m
Length waterline	28.65 m
Beam	6.4 m
Draught	1.30 m
Passengers	200
Fuel capacity	5,000 l
Water capacity	2,000 l
Operational speed	26 kts
Range	250 nm

Classification: Singapore Marine Department.
Structure: All aluminium hull and superstructure.
Propulsion: The vessel is powered by three MTU 12V 183 TE72 diesel engines each rated 610 kW, two driving fixed pitch propellers and one driving a water-jet.

NEW ENTRY

Greenbay Marine's 32 m Auto Batam 9 **1996**

MARINTEKNIK SHIPBUILDERS (S) PTE LTD

31 Tuas Road, Singapore 2263

Tel: +65 861 1706
Telex: 53419 MARJET RS
Fax: +65 861 4244

David C H Liang, *Group Chairman*
Patrick Cheung, *Managing Director*
Andrew Yeo, *Director and Technical Manager*
Susan Sim, *Business Manager*

Marinteknik Shipbuilders (S) Pte Ltd was established in 1984 for the building of high-speed vessels. To date, the yard has built more than 30 vessels of

85 m Monohull Car/Passenger Ferry **1995**

Craft built (high-speed monohull)

Designation	Yard No	Craft name	Owner/operator	Delivered	Engines	Classification	Payload	Speed
30 MCB (CV900)	102*	*Hamidah*	Ocean Tug Service	1985	2 × MTU 6V 396 TC 62	DnV R-30 Crew boat, light craft	50 passengers + 6.8 t	19 kts cruise
31 MCB	104	*Zakat*	Black Gold (M), Sdn Bhd, Malaysia	1986	2 × MTU, 440 kW each	GL+100A2, 30 miles	38 passengers + 13.38 t	37 kts
31 MCB	106	*Amal*	Black Gold (M), Sdn Bhd, Malaysia	1986	2 × MTU, 440 kW each	GL+100A2, 30 miles	38 passengers + 13.38 t	
35 MPV	107*	*Discovery Bay 12*	Discovery Bay Co	April 1987	2 × MWM TBD 604B V8, 840 kW each	HK Navy Dept, Cl2, Protected Waters	256 passengers	25 kts
35 MPV	108	*Discovery Bay 15*	Discovery Bay Co	May 1987	2 × MWM TBD 604B V8, 840 kW each	HK Navy Dept, Cl2, Protected Waters	256 passengers	25 kts
35 MPV	109	*Discovery Bay 16*	Discovery Bay Co	June 1987	2 × MWM TBD 604B V8, 840 kW each	HK Navy Dept, Cl2, Protected Waters	256 passengers	25 kts
35 MPV	110	*Zhen Jiang Hu* (ex-*Wu Yi Hu*)	Jiangmen Jiang Gang Passenger Traffic Co, China	1987	2 × MTU 12V 396 TB 83, 1,180 kW each		265 passengers + 3.12 t	27 kts contract
40 MPV-D	116	*Celestina*	Alilauro SpA	1988	2 × MTU, 1,940 kW each	RINA/DnV	265 passengers	30 kts
35 MPV	122	*Discovery Bay 19*	Hong Kong Resort Co Ltd	1990	2 × MWM TBD 604B V8, 840 kW each	DnV R-25	256 passengers	25 kts
35 MPV	125	*Discovery Bay 20*	Hong Kong Resort Co Ltd	1990	2 × MWM TBD 604B V8, 840 kW	DnV R-25	256 passengers	25 kts
35 MPV	131	*Discovery Bay 21*	Hong Kong Resort Co Ltd	1992	2 × MTU 8V 396 TE 74 840 kW each	DnV R-3	300 passengers	25 kts
35 MPV	132	*Discovery Bay 22*	Hong Kong Resort Co Ltd	1993	2 × MTU 8V 396 TE 74 840 kW each	DnV R-3	300 passengers	25 kts

*hull built by Marinteknik Verkstads AB, Sweden and fitted-out by Marinteknik Shipbuilders (S) Pte Ltd, Singapore

Fast monohull craft built by Marinteknik Verkstads AB of Sweden which ceased trading in 1994

Designation	Yard No	Craft name	Owner/operator	Delivered	Engines	Payload	Speed
30 MCB (CV900)	58*	*Hamidah*	Ocean Tug Service	1985	2 × MTU 6V 396 TC82	50 passengers + 6.8 t cargo	19 kts cruise
MPV	64*	*Discovery Bay 12*	Discovery Bay	April 1987	2 × MTU, 840 kW each	22 t	25 kts
41 MPV	65	*Cinderella West*	City Jet Line Rederi AB	1987	4 × Scania DSI 14, 300 kW each	450 passengers	22 kts cruise
38 MPV	66	*Cosmopolitan Lady*	Private Cruise International I Ltd	1989	2 × MTU, 880 kW each	12 passengers	20 kts
41 MPV	68	*Europa Jet*	Alilauro SpA	1987	2 × MTU, 770 kW each	350 passengers	22 kts
41 MPV	71	*Rosario Lauro*, (ex-*Aurora Jet*)	Alilauro SpA	1988			
41 MPV	72	*Cinderella II*	City Jet Line	1989	2 × MTU 12V 396 TB 83	450 passengers	28 kts
41 MPV	76	*Iris*	Kværner Express	1989	2 × MTU 12V 396 TB 83	350 passengers	28 kts
41 MPV	78	*Cinderella*	City Jet Line	1990	2 × MTU 12V 396 TB 83	450 passengers	28 kts
42 MPV	77**	*Blue Crystal*	Fyneside Shipping Caraibes	1991	2 × MTU 12V TBD 604B	12 passengers	27 kts
41 MPV	79	*Diamant Express*	Compagnie Maritime des	1991	2 × MTU 12V 396 TE 74	400 passengers	29 kts
43 MPV	80**	*Northern Cross*	Lillbacka Shipping	1991	2 × Caterpillar 3512 D	12 passengers	27 kts
41 MPV	83	*Napoli Jet*	Navigazione Libera del Golfo	1992	2 × MTU 12V 396 TE 74	400 passengers	29 kts
43 MPV	84**		BM Marine	1992	2 × MTU 12V 396 TE 94 1 × Lycoming TF40	12 passengers	45 kts
41 MPV	87	*Adler Express*	Hallia-und Inselreederei	1993	2 × MTU 12V 396 TE 74	400 passengers	29 kts

*Fitted-out by Fairey Marinteknik Shipbuilders (S) Pte Ltd, Singapore, now Marinteknik Shipbuilders (S) Pte Ltd
**Mini-cruise vessels

both monohull and catamaran type as passenger vessels and crew boats for customers worldwide. The length of these vessels varies from 27 to 41 m and they have a speed range of 18 to 40 knots.

Marinteknik Verkstads AB of Sweden, an associated company, ceased trading in 1994 and details of its craft are included in this entry in a separate table.

In 1995 the company revealed plans for the construction of an 85 m monohull fast ferry although it is understood that no contract has, as yet, been signed.

35 m PASSENGER FERRY

A number of 35 m passenger ferries have been built to different operational requirements.

Owner: Yuet Hing Marine Supplies.

Specifications

Length overall	35 m
Beam	7.7 m
Draught	1.25 m
Crew	14
Passengers	265
Fuel capacity	6,000 l

The 265 seat, 27 knot Celestina **1989**

Water capacity	1,000 l
Propulsive power	2 × 1,180 kW
Max speed	30 kts
Operational speed	27 kts

Classification: ZC ✠100 A4K MCA and IMO code A373(x).
Structure: Deep-V forward and flat-V with flat chines aft. Constructed in marine grade aluminium T profile extrusions and plates welded by Robot MIG fully automatic welding machines. Provision is made for the main engines to be removed through two bolted access hatches.
Propulsion: The main engines are 2 × MTU 12V 396 TB 83 marine diesels, 1,180 kW at 1,940 rpm continuous each; driving 2 × Kamewa Type 63/S62/60 water-jet propulsion units.

85 m Monohull Car/Passenger Ferry (design)

Specifications

Length overall	85 m
Beam	15 m
Draught	3 m
Passengers	584
Vehicles	104 cars
	7 buses
Max speed	36 kts
Operational speed	35 kts
Range	750 n miles

Classification: The car deck is designed to the latest Scandinavian safety requirements.
Structure: The hull can be built from either high-tensile steel with aluminium superstructure, or using all aluminium construction.
Propulsion: The main engines are 3 × MTU 1163 or equivalent, each powering a Kamewa or MJP water-jet.
Control: The vessel will have an active stabiliser system to aid sea-keeping.

UPDATED

Rosaria Lauro *built at Öregrund* ***1989***

SINGAPORE TECHNOLOGIES SHIPBUILDING AND ENGINEERING LTD

7 Benoi Road, Singapore 916405

R James Leo, *Executive Chairman*
See Leong Teck, *Senior Vice President*
Wong Ken Hoong, *Vice President*
Tan Pheng Hock, *Vice President*
Col Ting Tong Koi, *Vice President*
Tan Ching Eng, *Vice President*
Frankie Tan, *Senior Manager*
Han Yew Kwang, *Senior Manager*

Tel: +65 861 2244
Telex: 21206*SINGA RS
Fax: +65 861 3028/1601

Singapore Technologies Shipbuilding and Engineering Ltd (STSE) was established in 1968 as a specialist shipyard. Current areas of expertise include the building of specialised commercial vessels, military engineering equipment fabrication and the reconstruction and modernisation of old vessels. STSE is located in a 30 acre site at the mouth of the Benoi Basin. In addition to the Swift class patrol boat described below STSE has built or have on order over 30 of its PT class patrol boats (14.54 m, 30 knots), 19 for the Singapore Marine Police, two for Singapore Customs and Excise Department and seven for the Royal Brunei Police Force; this last order was completed by the end of 1987. Please see the 1991 edition of this book for a general arrangement drawing of the Swift class patrol boat.

SSE has also completed a luxury motor yacht, 14.13 m, delivered to a Singapore owner.

SWIFT CLASS PATROL BOAT

A fast patrol boat, 12 of which were built over the period 1979 to 1980 (Yard Nos 152 to 163) for the Singapore Navy.

Specifications

Length overall	22.7 m
Length waterline	20 m
Beam	6.2 m
Draught	1.6 m
Displacement	47 t
Crew	12
Fuel capacity	7,000 l
Water capacity	2,000 l
Propulsive power	2 × 992 kW
Max speed	33 kts (Deutz)
	35 kts (MTU)
Operational speed	31 kts (Deutz)
	31 kts (MTU)
Range	550 n miles

Structure: Hard chine planing form, welded aluminium.
Propulsion: Two Deutz SBA 16M 816 diesels, 992 kW each, at 2,000 rpm or two MTU 12V 331 TC 92 diesels, 1,100 kW each, at 2,300 rpm.
Electrical system: Two diesel generating sets, each 440 V, 60 Hz, three-phase, can sustain 100 per cent ship's load.

VERIFIED

SPAIN

BAZAN, EMPRESA NACIONAL

Paseo de la Castellana 55, E-28046 Madrid, Spain

Tel: +34 (1) 441 5100
Fax: +34 (1) 441 5090

J C Sánchez Alvarez, *Commercial Manager, Fast Ferries*

Empresa Nacional Bazan is owned by the Spanish Government with its main activities being the design and construction of naval vessels for the Spanish Navy, but current collaboration also includes joint design and construction programmes with Germany (frigates), Holland (frigates) and France (submarines and minehunters), and the design and construction of the Royal Thailand Nany carrier. Bazan also continues to design and build a range of commercial vessels, many exported worldwide. The company has three shipyards, at Ferrol, Cartargena and San Fernando.

MESTRAL CAR FERRY

Late in 1992, two 96 m monohull car ferries were ordered by Compania Trasmediterranea from EN Bazan. The first vessel, *Albayzin*, was delivered from the San Fernando Shipyard in October 1994 and was immediately transferred to Buquebus. This Uruguayan company subsequently leased the vessel to the New Zealand operator Sea Shuttle in late 1994. The second vessel, *Alcántara*, was delivered in May 1995 to Compania Transmediterranea to be operated on the route between Palma de Mallorca and the Spanish Mainland. The vessel is constructed entirely of aluminium with a deep-V hull form providing the seakeeping and powering performance specified for the Trasmediterranea ferry routes.

A third vessel is scheduled for delivery to Trasmediterranea in May 1996.

Specifications

Length overall	96.2 m
Length waterline	84 m
Beam	14.6 m
Draught	2.1 m
Crew	16
Passengers	450
Vehicles	84 cars

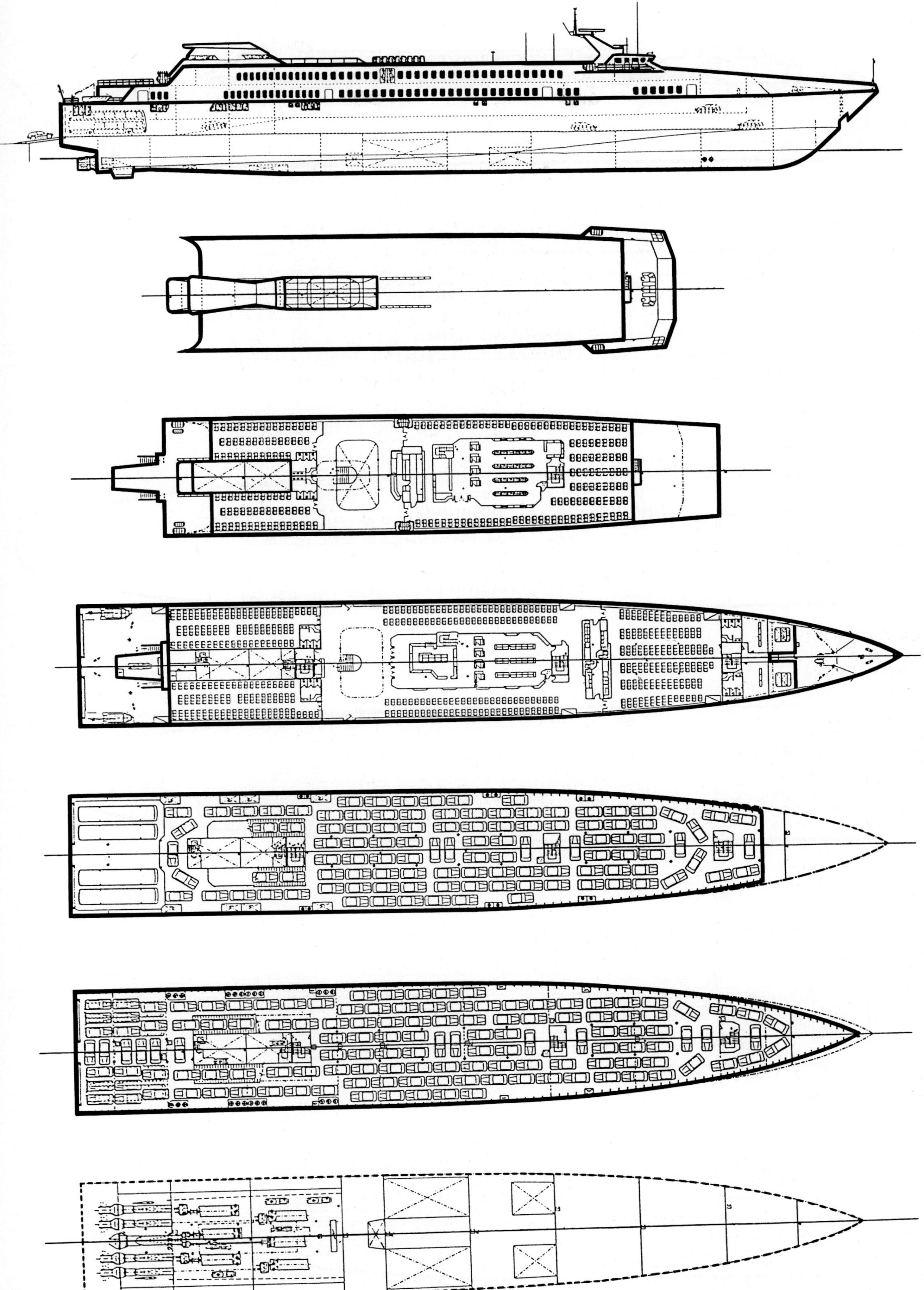

1996

General arrangement of Alhambra *car ferry*

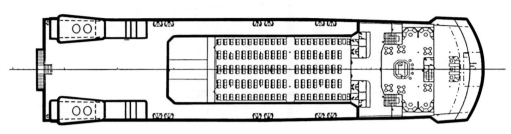

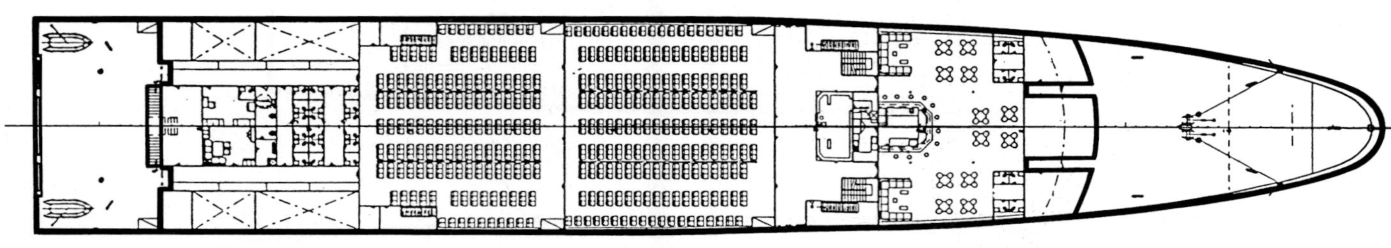

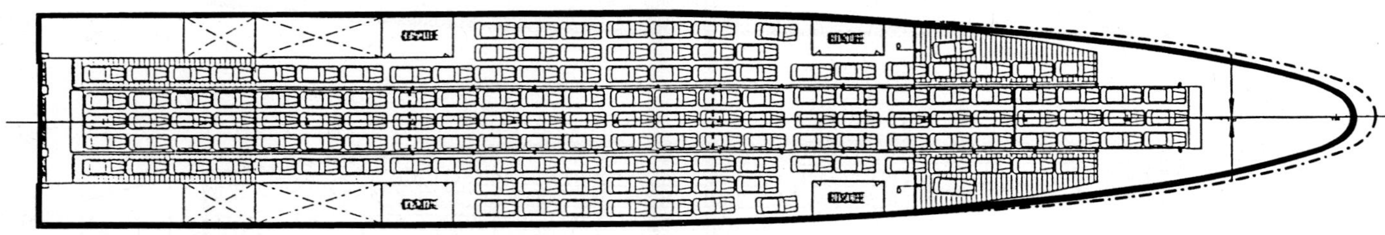

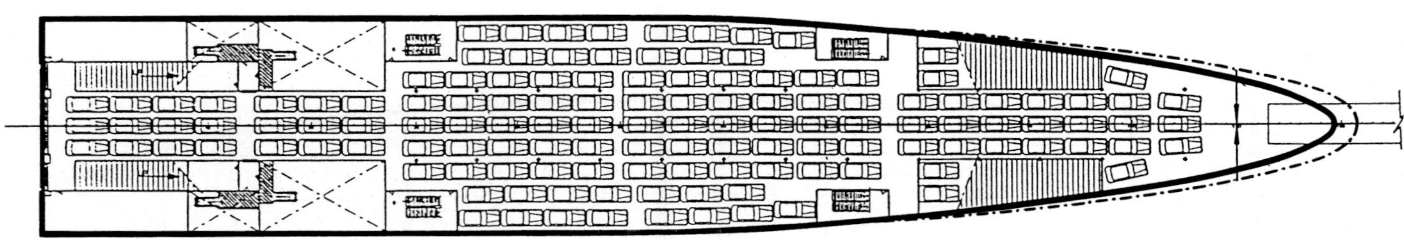

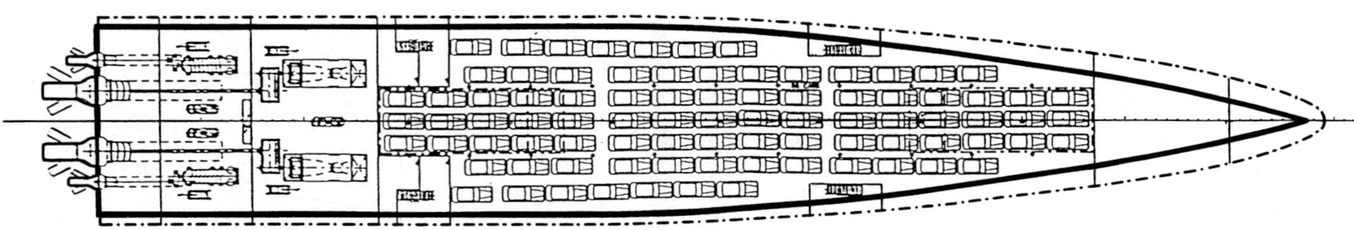

General arrangement of TF-130 car ferry (design)

The Mestral passenger/vehicle ferry Albayzin **1996**

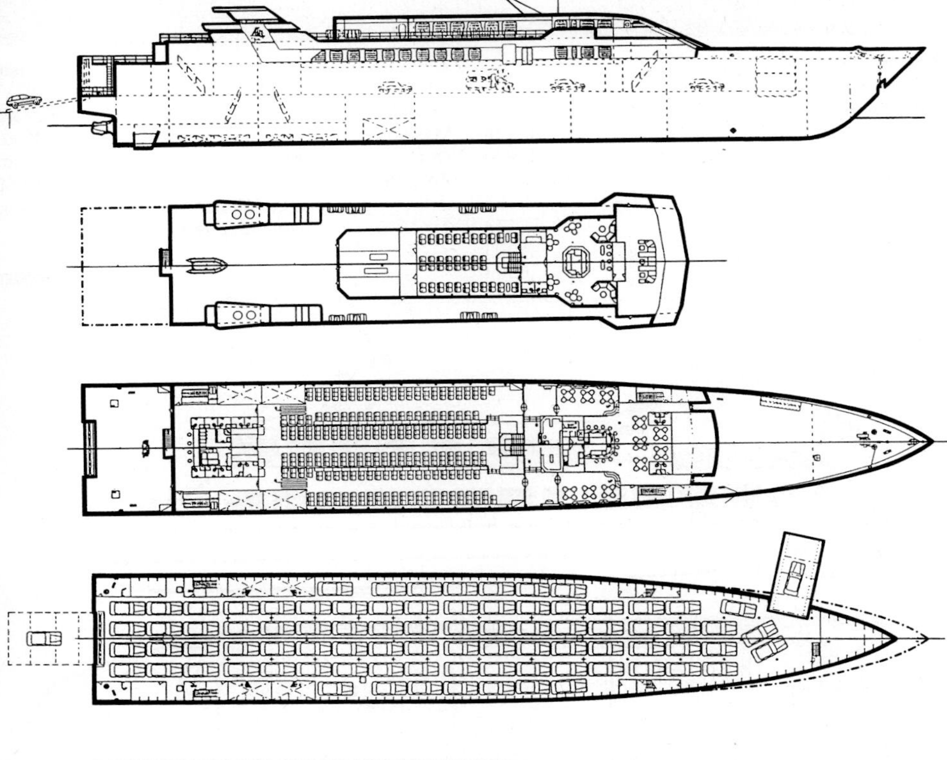

General arrangement of Mestral car ferry **1996**

Propulsive power	21,600 kW
Max speed	38 kts
Operational speed	37 kts
Range	300 n miles

Classification: DnV +1A1 HSLC R1 Car Ferry A EO.
Propulsion: The vessel is powered by 4 × Caterpillar 3616 diesel engines, each driving a size 100 KaMeWa water-jet, the outer two jets being of a steering and reversing type.
Electrical system: Power is provided by 3 × Caterpillar 3408 diesels each rated at 270 kW.
Auxiliary systems: An active ride control system is provided on all vessels, the *Albayzin* having four Vosper Thornycroft stabiliser fins and the other vessels having a system based on two active fins forward and two active transom flaps aft.

ALHAMBRA

The first Alhambra were ordered by Buquebus for delivery in October 1996 to be operated across the River Plate between Argentina and Uruguay.

This vessel is an enlarged version of the Mestral type in which all the shipyard experience has been utilised.

Specifications

Length overall	125Specif m
Length waterline	110 m
Beam	18.7 m
Draught	2.45 m
Crew	27
Passengers	1,228
Vehicles	244 cars
Propulsive power	33,900 kW
Max speed	40 kts
Operational speed	38 kts
Range	300 n miles

Classification: DnV +1A1 HSLC R1 Car Ferry A EO.
Propulsive: The vessel is powered by 6 × 5,650 kW diesel engines. The two central diesel engines drive a booster water-jet and each of the four lateral diesel engines drives a water-jet propulsor with steering and reversing capacity.
Electrical system: Power is provided by 3 diesel generators, each rated at 350 kW.
Auxiliary systems: An active ride control system is provided based on two active fins forward and two active transom flaps aft.

TF-130 (DESIGN)

This is the biggest fast ferry design of Bazán with capacity to transport coaches and lorries.

Specifications

Length overall	130.7 m
Length waterline	116.0 m
Beam	21 m
Draught	3 m
Crew	27
Passengers	1,100
Vehicles	370 cars
Propulsive power (CODAG)	52,300kW
Max speed	39 kts
Operational speed	37 kts
Range	400 n miles

Classification: DnV +1A1 HSLC R1 Car Ferry A EO.
Propulsion: The vessel will be powered by 2 × 5,400 kW diesel engines and 2 × 20,750 kW gas turbines. The two diesel engines will be coupled to two central water-jets and the two gas turbines to two central water-jets. All water-jets will be provided with steering and reversing mechanisms.
Electrical system: Electric power will be produced by 3 generator sets each rated at 500 kW.
Auxiliary systems: An active ride control system is provided based on two active fins forward and two active transom flaps aft.

SERBAL

Bazán is working on the design of a new car ferry that will be an intermediate version between Mestral and Alhambra.

Specifications

Length overall	107.5 m
Length waterline	95.0 m
Beam	16.4 m
Draught	2.25 m
Passengers	700
Vehicles	150
Max speed	42 kts

Propulsion: The vessel will be powered by 2 × Caterpillar 3616 diesel engines each driving a water-jet and one gas turbine LM2500 driving another water-jet.
Electrical system: Power will be provided by three main generator sets.
Auxiliary systems: An active ride control system will be provided.

UPDATED

SWEDEN

BOGHAMMAR INTERNATIONAL AB

Nysaetravagen 6-8, S-181 61 Lidingō, Sweden

Tel: +46 (8) 766 0190
Telex: 14149 BOGBOAT S
Fax: +46 (8) 766 1855

Boghammar International AB is situated at Lidingō just outside Stockholm, approximately 15 minutes by car from Stockholm city and only 40 minutes from Stockholm International airport.

The company was formed in 1984 and is the international selling company for Boghammar Marine AB. The yard was formed in 1906, it is family owned and is today headed by the third generation.

Close to 1,200 boats have been built over the years, some 90 per cent being of the yard's own design. Today the yard specialises in building all-aluminium constructed boats for commercial use such as high-speed monohull craft for patrol duty and day passenger transports.

The latest design of high-speed monohull craft for day passenger transports is the Kungsholm series. Three have now been built, *Gripsholm* in 1989, *Kungsholm* in 1990 and *August Lindholm* in 1992. The first two vessels are almost identical with some minor superstructure differences. The interior design of *Kungsholm* and its machinery and bridge are different to those of *Gripsholm*. *August Lindholm* also has two funnels instead of just one.

Gripsholm

Specifications

Length overall	26.5 m
Beam	5.6 m
Draught	1.85 m
Crew	5
Passengers	125
Propulsive power	3 × 744 kW
Max speed	36 kts
Operational speed	33 kts

Propulsion: The main engines are 3 × MAN V12 D2842 LXE-LYE, 744 kW each at 2,200 rpm; Servogear Petch VD propellers.

Kungsholm

Specifications

Length overall	27.5 m
Beam	5.6 m
Draught	1.85 m
Propulsive power	3 × 723 kW
Max speed	35 kts
Operational speed	30 kts

Propulsion: The main engines are 3 × MWM TBD 234 V12, 723 kW each at 2,300 rpm, driving 2 × Servogear CP propellers.

August Lindholm

This vessel (Yard No 1154) is the latest building from the Boghammar yard and is owned and operated by Stockholm Sightseeing, a subsidiary of Bore Lines, Sweden.

August Lindholm 1993

Specifications

Length overall	28.1 m
Beam	5.6 m
Draught	1.2 m
Displacement	41.5 t
Passengers	173
Fuel capacity	4,800 l
Water capacity	600 l
Propulsive power	2 × 723 kW
Max speed	30 kts
Operational speed	25 kts

Propulsion: The main engines are 2 × MWM TBD 236 V12 diesels, 723 kW each at 2,300 rpm, driving 2 × Michigan-Wheel propellers.

VERIFIED

OSKARSHAMNS VARV AB

A member of the Swede Ship Invest AB Group

PO Box 704, S-572 28 Oskarshamn, Sweden

Tel: +46 (491) 85550
Fax: +46 (491) 15312

Curt Tappert, *Managing Director*
Olle Johansson, *Technical Manager*
Ronnie Petersson, *Repair and Production Manager*

Located on the east coast of Sweden, the Swede Ship Oskarshamns Varv shipyard specialises in building aluminium and steel motor yachts, catamarans and military craft. Craft are built in construction halls 90 × 31.5 m, 83 × 12 m and 40 × 31.5 m with overhead cranes, lifting 80 tonnes capacity. There are also machine shop and repair facilities with one floating dock with a lifting capacity of 2,000 tonnes. Number of employees is about 170.

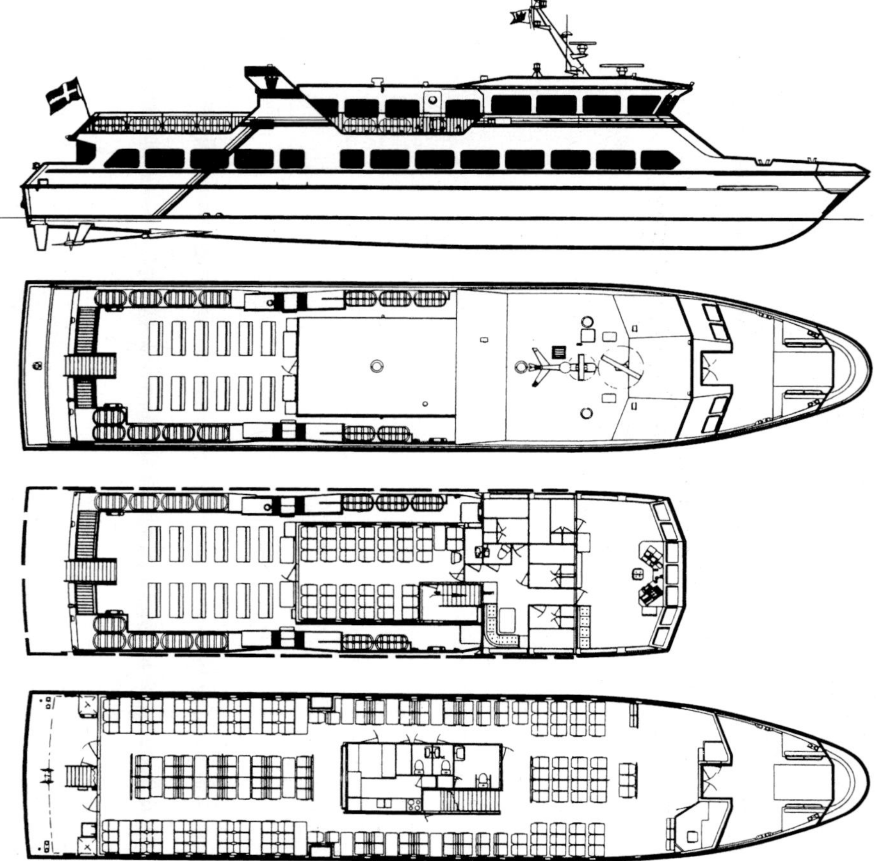

Swede Ship 3700

1995

Five Swede Ship 3700 class vessels **1995**

SWEDE SHIP 3700

Värmdö, Vånö, Väddö, Växo, Viberö

Five passenger vessels built for Waxholms Ångfartygs AB of Stockholm. The first vessel was delivered in 1990 and the last two were delivered in 1993.

Specifications

Length overall	37.7 m
Beam	7.5 m
Draught	1.28 m
Crew	4
Passengers	340
Fuel capacity	6,000 l
Water capacity	2,800 l
Propulsive power	3 × 600 kW
Operational speed	22 kts
Range	300 n miles

Classification: National Swedish Administration of Shipping and Navigation.

Structure: The hull and superstructure material is aluminium, AlMg 4.5Mn.

Propulsion: The main engines are 3 × MAN D 2842 LYE, 600 kW each at 2,150 rpm, driving 3 × Finnscrew fixed propellers via 3 × ZF BW 256 gearboxes.

Electrical system: One G&M 138 MDV generator, 126 kVA, one G&M 71 MDP 6T generator, 65 kVA.

UPDATED

THAILAND

TECHNAUTIC INTERTRADING COMPANY LTD

44/13 Convent Road, Silom, Bangkok 10500, Thailand

Tel: +66 (2) 340730/9368
Fax: +66 (2) 2376710

Capt Nirun Chitanon, *Director and General Manager*

The Technautic shipyard employs 150 people and has a total area of 7,944 m², the main building occupying 2,076 m². Over 52 craft in the 8 to 26 m range have been delivered, mainly patrol boats and workboats.

P86 surveillance craft ***1990***

P86

Surveillance craft.

Specifications

Length overall	26.2 m
Length waterline	22.6 m
Beam	6.3 m
Draught	1.1 m
Displacement, min	59,400 t
Displacement, max	70,000 t
Crew	14
Fuel capacity	18,050 l
Water capacity	2,545 l
Propulsive power	2,350 kW
Max speed	27 kts
Operational speed	25 kts

Structure: GRP sandwich with Airex PVC foam core.

Propulsion: Three Isotta Fraschini ID 36 8VSS engines, driving three Castoldi 07 water-jets.

VERIFIED

UNITED KINGDOM

AILSA-PERTH SHIPBUILDERS LTD

Harbour Road, Troon, Ayrshire KA10 6DN, UK

Tel: +44 (1292) 311311
Telex: 778027 AILSA G
Fax: +44 (1292) 317613

Gregory Copley, *Chairman*
W Reid, *Managing Director*
Tom Jenkins, *Director and Naval Architect*
Alan Macdonald, *Marketing Manager*

Ailsa-Perth Shipbuilders' shipyard at Troon in Scotland has built vessels since 1886, including warships for the navies of Canada, New Zealand, other Commonwealth states, Mexico and the UK Ministry of Defence.

The covered building hall has two building ways and a 5,860 m² (63,000 ft²) machine and fabrication shop for construction of vessels in steel, aluminium and GRP up to 114 m in length and 20.5 m beam. There is a 130 m long fitting-out quay with a lifting capacity of 50 tonnes and two dry docks.

There are comprehensive facilities for naval architects and in-house technical services and an extensive collaboration programme with associated companies including Australian catamaran builder ASD.

Ailsa-Perth Shipbuilders offers worldwide after sales support with a flying squad available for repair, refit, training or other needs. The company can co-operate with clients to meet technology transfer, co-production or licence production needs. Technical teams can plan mid-life programmes for naval vessels to extend their service life, or can modify them to meet newly emerging threats or tasks.

VERIFIED

FBM MARINE GROUP

Cowes Shipyard, Cowes, Isle of Wight, UK

Tel: +44 (1983) 297111
Telex: 86466 FAMBRO G
Fax: +44 (1983) 299642

Michael Roberts, *Deputy Chairman*
Malcolm Keith, *Managing Director*
John Warbey, *International Sales Director*
Nigel Warren, *Chief Designer*

PROTECTOR 26 CUSTOMS AND EXCISE CUTTER

UK Customs and Excise Marine Branch placed an order for three 26 m Protector fast patrol cutters which entered service during 1988. The craft are a development of the 33 m Protector class, designed to meet the needs of HM Customs and Excise for operation anywhere round the coastline of the United Kingdom. A fourth 26 m Protector for HM Customs and Excise was built under licence by Babcock Thorn at the Rosyth Royal Dockyard in 1993.

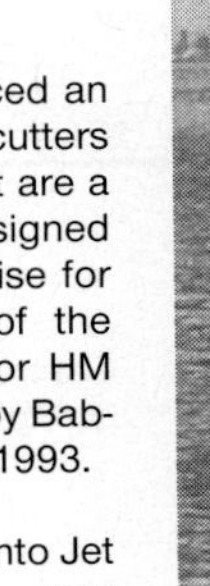

Sorrento Jet ***1991***

Specifications

Length overall	25.7 m
Beam	6.2 m
Draught	1.7 m
Crew	8
Propulsive power	2 × 1,074 kW
Max speed	25 kts
Operational speed	8 kts (loiter)

Structure: Hull, deck and superstructure in welded marine grade aluminium, with integral alloy fuel tanks.

Propulsion: Two Paxman 12 SET CW marine diesel engines of 1,074 kW each with ZF BW 460S gearboxes. These units drive two fixed-pitch propellers coupled to ZF BW 460S gearboxes via a V-drive. One single Perkins T6.3544 marine diesel engine of 159 kW driving a Hamilton 361 water-jet unit for cruise/loiter speeds.

Electrical system: Two 30 kW (continuous) diesel driven 240 V single-phase 50 Hz generator sets and engine driven alternators. Also a 24 V DC battery supplied system.

Navigation and communications: Equipment includes two navigational radars, one with ARPA plotter, gyro with repeaters, Decca Navigator Mk 53, direction-finder, log, echo-sounder, and autopilot.

One HF set and one marine 2,182 kHz UHF set, telex, navtex and internal communications.

Control: Power-assisted hydraulic steering system operating twin-linked balanced aerofoil spade rudders. Primary controls are from the wheelhouse, with a secondary position on the open bridge.

Auxiliary systems: A hydraulic knuckle boom crane mounted on main deck for launch and recovery of rigid inflatable boarding boat.

Outfit: Single cabins for commanding officer and seven crew. Four cabins are fitted with pipe-cots for visitors.

Protector 26 ***1992***

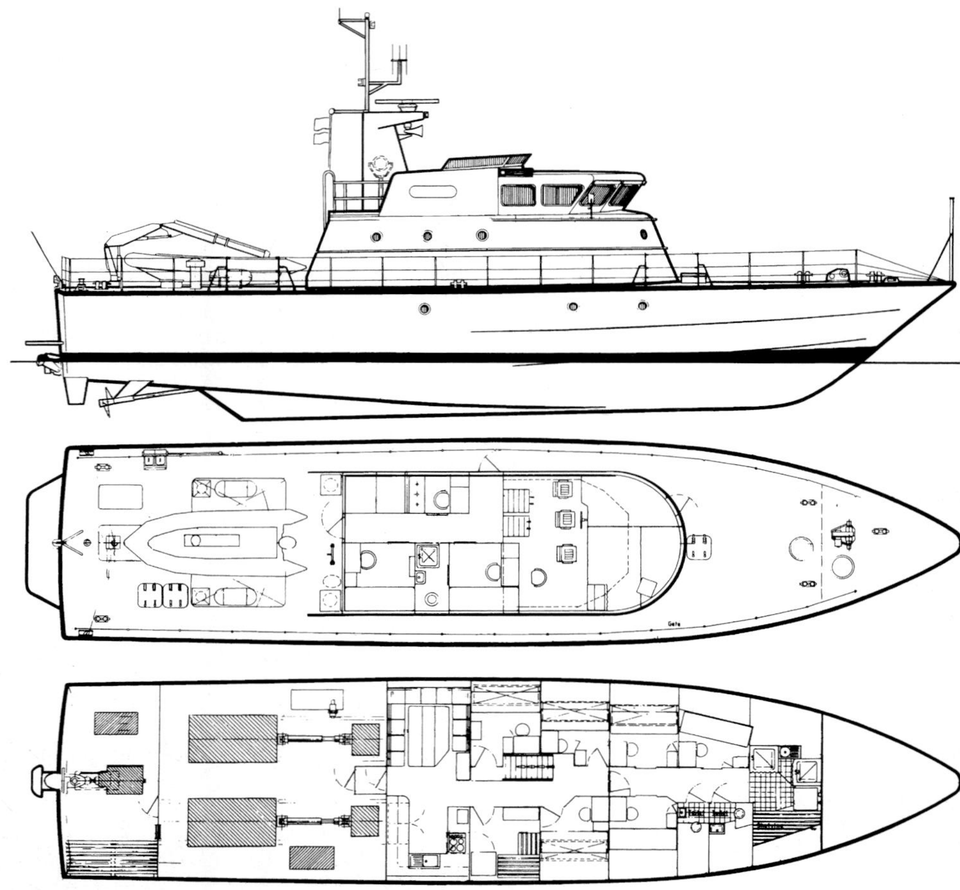

Protector 26 profile, deck plan and accommodation ***1995***

41 m PASSENGER FERRY
Capri Jet
Sorrento Jet

Designed by Marinteknik Verkstads AB and FBM Marine Ltd, *Capri Jet,* a 41 m passenger ferry, was completed in 1988 and operates on the Naples/Capri route.

A second similar vessel, *Sorrento Jet*, was ordered in May 1989 and was delivered in 1990.

Specifications

Length overall	41 m
Beam	7.8 m
Draught	1.1 m
Payload	27 t
Passengers	350
Fuel capacity	7,000 l
Water capacity	1,000 l
Propulsive power	2 × 1,180 kW
Capri Jet	
Max speed	33.5 kts
Sorrento Jet	
Operational speed	29 kts

Classification: Built to rules of the Code of Safety for Dynamically Supported Craft comparable to the SOLAS and Load Line Conventions, class notation RINa is *100-A (UL) 1.1-Nav. S-TP.

Structure: The superstructure and hull are built in welded marine grade aluminium, subdivided into seven watertight compartments. A semi-planing hull with a deep-V forward progressing to a shallow-V aft with hard chines.

The extruded profiles are of quality Alcan B51 S WP. The sheets are of quality Alcan B54 S1/2.

Propulsion: Two MTU 12V 396 TB 83 marine diesels giving minimum 1,180 kW each at MCR (1,045 kW for *Sorrento Jet*), 1,940 rpm at ambient air temperature of 27°C and seawater temperature at 27°C. Engines are coupled to ZF marine reduction gearboxes, and drive two MJP water-jet units, steering deflection angle is 30° port and starboard with an estimated reverse thrust of approximately half of the forward gross thrust.

Electrical system: Two Perkins 4.236M diesel generators each driving two 30 kVA alternators, Stamford MSC 234A.

Electrical supplies: 380 V AC, 50 Hz 3-phase, 220 V AC, 50 Hz single-phase, 24 V DC, shore supply connection.

Control: All controls and machinery instruments are within reach of the helmsman's seat. Steering and reversing buckets for the water-jets are controlled electrohydraulically from the wheelhouse. A retractable bow thruster unit is fitted.

UPDATED

McTAY MARINE

The Magazines, Port Causeway, Bromborough, Wirral, Merseyside L62 4YP, UK

Tel: +44 (151) 346 1319
Telex: 628052
Fax: +44 (151) 334 0041

M Brodie, *Managing Director*
R McBurney, *Commercial Director*

McTay Marine is a subsidiary of the Mowlem Group. Although high-speed craft have not in the past been the main output of the shipyard, the company has completed two fast monohull craft. The most recent vessel was a 47 m Customs craft for the Greek Ministry of Finance, delivered in late 1995.

Europatrol 250 on trials **1995**

Chartwell

A high-speed survey vessel for hydrographic survey duties in the Thames and Thames estuary. The vessel has a longitudinally framed steel hull with an aluminium superstructure. The hull form is based on the NPL high-speed, round bilge series. The survey duties include echo-sounding, sonar sweeping, wire sweeping, marking obstructions, tidal stream observations and search and rescue.

Specifications

Length overall	26.58 m
Beam	5.84 m
Propulsive power	2 × 1,074 kW
Max speed	22.8 kts

Propulsion: The main engines are 2 × Paxman Diesels 12 SETCWM, 1,074 kW each, 1,500 rpm.

2 × fixed-pitch 3-blade Brunton propellers, driven via ZF BW 460 gearboxes, ratio 1.509:1.0. One PP Jets PP170 water-jet unit (for improved control at low speed) driven by Volvo Penta AMD121D diesel, 283 kW, 1,800 rpm.

EUROPATROL 250

This 47 m Customs craft was delivered from the yard in November 1994. The design and build of this vessel was a result of a collaboration between McTay Marine and Vosper International. Vosper International provided the design of this vessel which is one of a family of offshore patrol and surveillance craft marketed by the company.

Specifications

Length overall	47.3 m
Length waterline	43.5 m
Beam	7.5 m
Draught	2.5 m
Displacement	240 t
Crew	21
Propulsive power	9,800 kW
Maximum speed	40 kts
Range	2,000 n miles

Structure: The hull and weatherdeck are of welded mild steel and the superstructure of welded aluminium alloy.

Propulsion: The vessel is propelled by three GEC Paxman diesels each driving a fixed-pitch propeller via a reverse reduction gearbox. The centre gearbox is fitted with a trolling valve to allow slow ship speeds of 2 to 4 knots.

UPDATED

VOSPER THORNYCROFT (UK) LTD

Victoria Road, Woolston, Southampton, Hampshire SO9 5GR, UK

Tel: +44 (1703) 445144
Telex: 47682 VTWOOL G
Fax: +44 (1703) 421539

Vosper Thornycroft (UK) Ltd continues the shipbuilding business established over a century ago by two separate companies, Vosper Ltd and John I Thornycroft and Company Ltd. These companies merged in 1966, were nationalised in 1977, returned to the private sector in 1985, and floated on the London Stock Exchange in 1988. The company has designed, built and repaired warships of all sizes, and has always specialised in high-speed craft. Since the early 1970s it has also developed the use of Glass-Reinforced Plastic (GRP) for warships, particularly Mine Countermeasures Vessels.

Within the past two years the company has invested in the extension and upgrading of its design and production facilities including the latest laser steel cutting and CAD/CAM equipment. Today, its shipyards at Southampton and Portsmouth on the southern coast of the UK are among the most modern in the world.

Diversified engineering work is also undertaken, including ship design consultancy for overseas builders, support services and the design and manufacture of roll damping fins, bow thrusters, water-jet propulsors and electronic control systems for marine and industrial use.

The company currently has under construction two 83 m corvettes for Oman and four 56 m fast attack craft for Qatar. Fast patrol craft designs range upwards from 30 m and the first of an updated 34 m patrol craft design has recently been completed for HM Customs and Excise.

30 m FAST PATROL BOAT HAWK CLASS

The 30 m Hawk class patrol boat is designed for prolonged operation at speed in EEZ offshore roles. Three of these craft have been delivered to Jordan.

Specifications

Length overall	30.45 m
Beam	6.87 m
Displacement	95 t
Crew	typical complement is 3 officers, 2 petty officers and 11 junior ratings
Max speed	28 kts

Structure: GRP and the superstructure is marine grade alloy both constructed to Lloyd's approved standards. Hull shape is hard chine with a moderately high deadrise, fine entry forward, and generous freeboard.

Propulsion: Two high-speed turbocharged marine diesels coupled to reverse reduction gearboxes, driving two fixed-pitch propellers; other configurations are optional.

Navigation and communications: Radar, electronic warfare and communications sets to suit operational requirements.

34 m FAST PATROL BOAT

Originally based on a 31 m Vosper Thornycroft design which was exported to many navies, the 34 m fast patrol boat has been developed using simplified

Vosper Thornycroft 30 m patrol boat on trials **1994**

34 m Customs Boat Sentinel **1995**

construction techniques to reduce costs and enable relatively inexperienced shipyards to build an effective craft and develop their own technology.

There have been 49 of these craft built under licence by Bollinger Machine Shop and Shipyard, Louisiana, USA, for the US Coast Guard. For details of these craft see under the Bollinger entry.

34 m CUSTOMS BOAT

Developed from the earlier 103 ft, 106 ft and 110 ft designs, over 100 of which were built for many navies, the 34 m has been designed to operate all year round in the demanding environment of the UK offshore waters. It has a much improved machinery layout compared with the earlier 110 ft design and meets modern accommodation standards.

The first vessel of this improved design, HMCC *Sentinel*, entered service with the UK Customs and Excise on 3 December 1993.

Specifications

Length overall	34.95 m
Length waterline	31.5 m
Beam	7.2 m
Draught	1.9 m
Displacement	155 t
Crew	17
Max speed	32 kts
Range	2,300 n miles

Structure: The main structure, up to and including the weatherdeck and all transverse watertight bulkheads, is constructed from welded mild steel. The superstructure is built from marine grade aluminium alloy and bonded to the hull by welding to an explosively bonded structural transition joint.

Propulsion: Two high-speed turbocharged marine diesels driving two fixed-pitch propellers via cardan shafts and reverse/reduction gearboxes. Trolling valves are fitted to the gearboxes to permit slow-speed main engine drive.

Auxiliary (Loiter) propulsion is provided and is a water-jet propulsor driven by an independent marine diesel.

Operations equipment: Light weapons, radar and passive sensors to suit operational requirements.

34 m Vosper Thornycroft designed US Coast Guard patrol boat **1990**

VERIFIED

UNITED STATES OF AMERICA

ADMIRAL MARINE WORKS INC

919 Haines Street, Port Townsend, Washington, WA 98368, USA

Tel: +1 (360) 385 4670
Telefax: +1 (360) 385 4256

D Wakefield, *President*
C McKinney, *Partner*
K Speer, *Partner*

Admiral Marine is a privately owned business specialising in the construction of high-performance pleasure craft up to 60 m in length. The shipbuilding facility is based in Port Townsend at the entrance to Puget Sound.

MY Evviva

This vessel is the largest to have been built at Admiral Marine Works and was delivered in late 1993.

Specifications

Length overall	48.8 m
Length waterline	40.2 m
Beam	9.2 m
Draught	2.4 m
Displacement, min	190 t
Displacement, max	245 t
Fuel capacity	74,000 l
Water capacity	4,900 l
Max speed	30 kts
Range	6,000 n miles (12 kts)

Structure: The craft superstructure and interior is constructed of fibre reinforced plastic with extensive use of Nomex honeycomb and Kevlar fibre reinforcement. The main hull construction uses Airex foam core with polyester resin and glassfibre reinforced skins.

Propulsion: The vessel is powered by two MTU 16V 396 TB 94 diesel engines each driving through a ZF reverse reduction gearbox to a Lips fixed-pitch propeller.

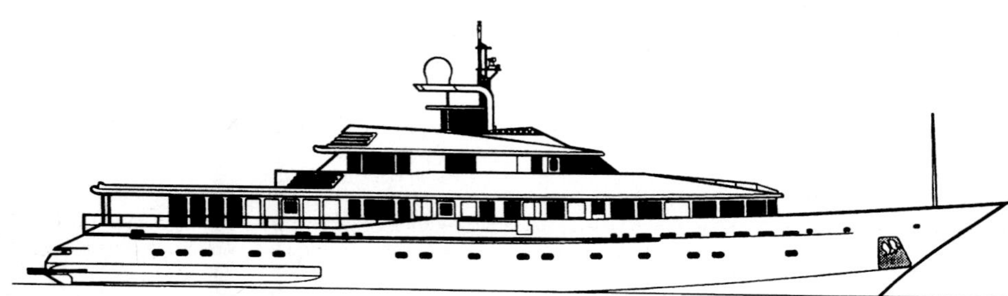

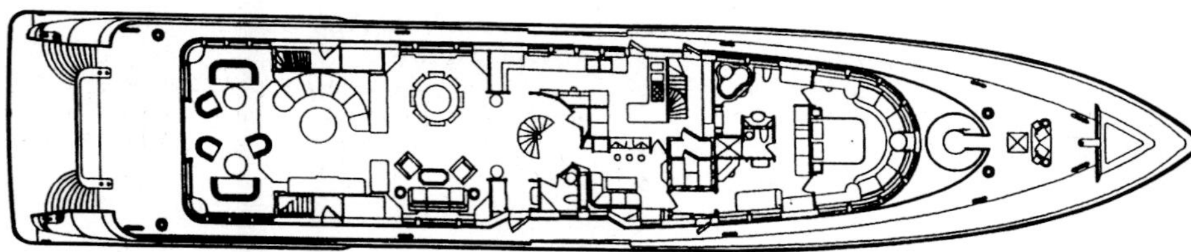

General arrangement of MY Evviva **1995**

UPDATED

ALUMINUM BOATS INC

A company of the Trinity Marine Group

Crown Point, Louisiana, USA

25.9 m CREW BOAT
Osco Satria
Osco Perkasa

These fast crew boats delivered in August and September 1991 will seat 15 passengers inside and carry drilling supplies on their aft decks. Each vessel is equipped with a pollution control system consisting of oil spill dispersant tanks and two 3 m dispersant spray arms. In addition to the internal carbon dioxide and foam systems, external firefighting capabilities are added by two fire monitors provided aft. The two vessels are to operate in Indonesia.

Specifications

Length overall	25.9 m
Length waterline	23.24 m
Draught	0.89 m
Beam	5.1 m
Displacement	43.4 t
Propulsive power	2 × 716 kW
Operational speed	30 kts

Propulsion: The main engines are 2 × DDC 16V 92TA diesels, 716 kW each, at 2,100 rpm, driving through ZF Mod. BW 255, ratio 2.33:1 gearboxes.

Oil Sagbama 1995

26 m CREW BOAT
Maleo

This vessel was delivered in 1994 and outfitted for crew support, firefighting and oil dispersing duties.

Specifications

Length overall	26 m
Beam	6.1 m
Draught	1.37 m
Payload	16 t
Crew	6
Passenger	45
Fuel capacity	15,000 l
Water capacity	2,700 l
Max speed	26 kts
Operational speed	21 kts

Propulsion: Two Caterpillar 3412 DITA 500 kW diesels each driving a fixed-pitch propeller via a Twin Disc MG 518 reverse reduction gearbox.

Auxiliary systems: The vessel is equipped with a 20,000 l foam tank and a 1,000 l oil dispersant tank with fire monitors and oil dispersant spray arms.

26 m crew boat Maleo 1995

26.2 m CREW BOAT
Abeer Three

Announced in October 1992 this vessel was the 25th designed and built by Aluminum Boats. *Abeer Three* is American Bureau of Shipping (ABS) certified and complies with US Coast Guard requirements. Delivered to Barberlines Arabian Navigation and Shipping Company Ltd of Saudi Arabia it replaces another Aluminum Boats vessel of the same name which was sold by its owners.

Specifications

Length overall	26.2 m
Beam	6 m
Draught	1.7 m
Propulsive power	2 × 820 kW

Propulsion: The main engines are 2 × DDC 16V 92TA diesels, 820 kW each, at 2,300 rpm; driving 2 × Rolla Nibral 5-blade propellers, through ZF gearboxes.

Electrical system: 2 × Kato 40 kW generators.

27 m PASSENGER FERRY
Greatland

This all-aluminium vessel was delivered to Kenai Tours, Seward, Alaska, in September 1992. The boat operates on the waterways and coastlines of national parks in Alaska as a sightseeing vessel.

Specifications

Length overall	27.1 m
Beam	7.3 m
Fuel capacity	13,250 l
Water capacity	1,900 l

Propulsion: The main engines are 2 × DDC 12V 92TA diesels, driving through ZF gearboxes.

Electrical system: The power is supplied by 2 × Northern Lights generators, 33 kW and 12 kW.

29 m PASSENGER FERRY
Caribe Cay

This vessel was delivered to Transport Services of St John, a tour operator based in the US Virgin Islands, in mid-1995.

29 m passenger ferry Caribe Cay 1996

Specification

Length overall	29.0 m
Beam	7.3 m
Draught	1.7 m
Passengers	276
Fuel capacity	10,600 l
Water capacity	950 l
Max speed	30 kts

Structure: All aluminium construction.

Propulsion: The vessel is powered by five Cummins KTA 19M3 diesel engines each rated at 520 kW at 2,100 rpm and each driving a fixed pitch propeller via a Twin Disc 1.92:1 reverse reduction gearbox.

30.5 m FERRY
Majestic Princess

Operated by the Boston Harbor Commuter Service, the *Majestic Princess* is a high-speed ferry during the day and a dinner cruiser at night. The middle row of seats on the main deck is easily removed to provide floor space for dancing, bar and buffet tables.

The present operation is a 9.8 mile route between Boston's old Hingham Shipyard and Rowes Wharf; a water shuttle to Boston's Logan Airport is also operated.

Specifications

Length overall	30.5 m
Beam	7.8 m
Passengers	325
Operational speed	30 kts

Propulsion: The main engines are 4 × DDC 12V 71TI diesels; Columbian Bronze propellers, via Twin Disc 514, 2:1 ratio gearboxes.

Electrical system: The generators are 2 × DDC 371, 75 kW.

32 m RESCUE BOAT
Oil Sagbama
Oil Siluko

These vessels were completed in late 1994, and delivered under their own power from the Aluminum Boats yard to Bonny in Nigeria where they operate. In addition to serving in an offshore role to accommodate 90 evacuees and seven crew members, the vessels are equipped to fight fires, disperse oil, tow up to 15 tonnes and rescue and retrieve people from the sea. Two 10 m spray arms can disperse 800 gallons/min of water and foam mixture from a 10,000 l foam tank.

The vessels are owned by O.I.L. Ltd of Woking, UK.

Specifications

Length overall	31.85 m
Beam	7.16 m
Draught	1.6 m
Crew	7
Passengers	90
Fuel capacity	22,000 l
Water capacity	4,800 l
Propulsive power	2 × 570 kW

Propulsion: The vessel is powered by two Caterpillar 3412 D1TA diesels developing 570 kW each at 2,100 rpm. Each engine drives a five-bladed fixed-pitch propeller via a Twin Disc MG 518 reverse/reduction gearbox.

UPDATED

BLOUNT MARINE CORPORATION

461 Water Street, Warren, Rhode Island 02885, USA

Tel: +1 (401) 245 8300
Fax: +1 (401) 245 8303

Luther H Blount, *President*
Marcia L Blount, *Executive Vice President*
Ronald Baer, *Works Manager*

Blount Marine Corporation was formed in 1952 and, as of December 1994, had designed and built 300 vessels ranging in size from 5 to 80 m. Among the many types built has been the world's first small stern trawler and a significant number of all types of passenger/commuter vessels including mini-cruise ships, making Blount Marine one of the best known small passenger-boat builders in the USA. The Hitech composite hull was invented by Luther Blount.

Hitech Express

Hull No 251, Design No P452

A multipurpose craft design started in 1983 and built in 1984. The vessel has been granted USCG Certification for 149 passengers. Two smaller versions have been built.

Hitech Express has been engaged in demonstrating reliable, fast economical commuting service in the USA. It has made five runs to New York City from Warren, Rhode Island, a distance of 150 miles, in just over five hours (November 1984, May 1985, June 1985). It has made the run from the Battery, New York, to Staten Island fully loaded in 10 minutes, against 28 minutes via conventional ferry; also crossed the Hudson at mid-Manhattan in 2 minutes 46 seconds (in November 1984 and June 1985).

Specifications

Length overall	23.48 m
Length waterline	22.66 m
Beam	6.1 m
Draught	1.12 m
Displacement, max	56.39 t
Displacement, min	23.87 t
Payload	15 t
Crew	2
Passengers	149
Fuel capacity	1,923 l
Propulsive power	2 × 380 kW
Max speed	27.8 kts
Operational speed	24.3 kts
Operational limitation	wave height 1.5 m Beaufort 4-5
Range	250 n miles

Structure: Aluminium structural frames, bulkheads and decks with polyurethane foam sprayed over and a layed up glassfibre skin ¼ to ⅛ in thick forming the outer hull covering.

Propulsion: 2 × GM 12V-71 TI, 380 kW at 2,300 rpm (each), driving 2 × 711 mm diameter, 622 mm pitch Columbian Bronze propellers.

Electrical system: Two 60 A alternators, one on each main engine providing 32 V DC power throughout vessel. Engine room area available for optional generator.

VERIFIED

Blount Marine Hitech Express ***1993***

BOLLINGER MACHINE SHOP & SHIPYARD INC

PO Box 250, Lockport, Louisiana 70374, USA

Tel: +1 (504) 532 2554
Telex: 584127

Donald T Bollinger, *Chairman and CEO.*
Richard Bollinger, *President*
Marc Stanley, *Executive Vice President*

Founded in 1946, Bollinger expanded from a machine shop/repair facility to building offshore workboats for the oil industry. In August 1984, the company was awarded a contract to build 16 of the Island class patrol boats for the US Coast Guard. The hull is the well proven 33.50 m patrol boat design by Vosper Thornycroft (UK) Ltd and the superstructure has been adapted to meet US Coast Guard operational requirements. All 16 vessels were successfully delivered by the end of June 1987.

In February 1987, Bollinger was awarded an additional 21 Island class (B class) patrol boats for the US Coast Guard. All 21 of these vessels were successfully delivered by January 1990. A further 12 vessels (C class) were ordered in January 1990 and all 12 vessels were successfully delivered by February 1992.

ISLAND CLASS 33 m PATROL BOAT

Specifications

Length overall	33.52 m
Beam overall	6.4 m
Draught	1.98 m
Displacement	167.76 t (A class) 153 t (B class) 137 t (C class)
Crew	18
Fuel capacity	39,295 l
Water capacity	6,661 l
Propulsive power	2 × 4,020 kW
Operational speed	26 kts
Max speed	26+ kts
Range	3,928 n miles

Structure: Designed by Vosper Thornycroft (UK) Ltd and built in steel with an aluminium superstructure.

Propulsion: A and B Class: Two Paxman Valenta 16RP 200M V type; 4,020 kW at 1,500 rpm (max), 2,170 kW at 802 rpm (max). Engines are coupled to ZF gearboxes, ratio 1.87:1. C Class: Two Caterpillar 3516 DITA V type; 2,088 kW at 1,900 rpm. Engines are coupled to ZF gearboxes ratio 2.333:1. These drive two Vosper Thornycroft 5-blade (skewed) propellers, 1,257 mm diameter, 1,066 to 1,549 mm pitch (0.7R).

Electrical system: Two Caterpillar 3304T, 99 kW generators.

Control: Vosper Thornycroft steering system. Paxman engine controls.

NAMED ISLAND CLASS 33 m PATROL BOATS

Forty-nine of these Vosper Thornycroft (UK) designed boats have now been named:

A-CLASS

1301	*Farallon*
1302	*Manitou*
1303	*Matagorda*
1304	*Maui*
1305	*Monhegan*
1306	*Nunivak*
1307	*Ocracoke*
1308	*Vashon*
1309	*Aquidneck*
1310	*Mustang*
1311	*Naushon*
1312	*Sanibel*
1313	*Edisto*
1314	*Sapelo*
1315	*Matincus*
1316	*Nantucket*

B-CLASS

1317	*Attu*
1318	*Baranof*
1319	*Chandeleur*

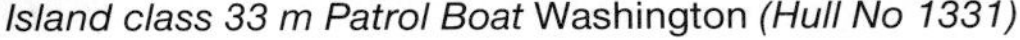

Island class 33 m Patrol Boat Washington *(Hull No 1331)* ***1994***

United States Navy Coastal Patrol Boat (Cyclone class) ***1994***

1320 *Chincoteague*
1321 *Cushing*
1322 *Cuttyhunk*
1323 *Drummond*
1324 *Key Largo*
1325 *Metomkin*
1326 *Monomoy*
1327 *Orcas*
1328 *Padre*
1329 *Sitkinak*
1330 *Tybee*
1331 *Washington*
1332 *Wrangell*
1333 *Adak*
1334 *Liberty*
1335 *Anacapa*
1336 *Kiska*
1337 *Assateague*
C-CLASS
1338 *Grand Isle*
1339 *Key Biscayne*
1340 *Jefferson Island*
1341 *Kodiak Island*
1342 *Long Island*
1343 *Bainbridge Island*
1344 *Block Island*
1345 *Staten Island*
1346 *Roanoke Island*
1347 *Knight Island*
1348 *Mackinac Island*
1349 *Galvaeston Island*

Vessel Nos 1344 to 1349 inclusive were launched between May and November 1991.

52 m COASTAL PATROL BOAT

Designated primarily to fulfil coastal patrol, surveillance and interdiction roles and special warfare missions, the PC class was originally awarded by Naval Sea Systems Command to Bollinger in August 1990, as an eight vessel contract. A further five vessels were ordered in July 1991.

Based on an existing Vosper Thornycroft patrol craft hull platform, this multimission ship was modified to suit US Navy operational requirements.

Specifications

Length overall	51.81 m
Beam	7.92 m
Draught	2.4 m
Displacement	334 t
Fuel	48,500 l
Max speed	35 kts
Range	2,500+ n miles at 12 kts
Operational limitation	Sea State 5

Structure: Hull: steel; Main deck: steel; Superstructure: aluminium.

52 m Coastal Patrol Boats built

Ship name	Hull no	Delivery
USS *Cyclone*	PC-1	19 Feb 1993
USS *Tempest*	PC-2	21 May 1993
USS *Hurricane*	PC-3	21 Jul 1993
USS *Monsoon*	PC-4	20 Sep 1993
USS *Typhoon*	PC-5	29 Nov 1993
USS *Sirocco*	PC-6	28 Feb 1993
USS *Squall*	PC-7	9 May 1994
USS *Zephyr*	PC-8	16 Aug 1994
USS *Chinook*	PC-9	11 Nov 1994
USS *Firebolt*	PC-10	2 Feb 1995
USS *Whirlwind*	PC-11	11 Apr 1995
USS *Thunderbolt*	PC-12	20 Jun 1995
USS *Shamar*	PC-13	5 Sep 1995

UPDATED

BREAUX'S BAY CRAFT INC

PO Box 306, Loreauville, Louisiana 70552, USA

Tel: +1 (318) 229 4246/7
Fax: +1 (318) 229 8332

Roy Breaux, Jr, *President*
Royce Breaux, *Chairman and Executive Vice President*
Hugh Breaux, *Vice President*
Jerry Lagrange, *Secretary*
Velta Breaux, *Treasurer*

Agathe

Crew boat.

Owner: Compagnie des Moyens de Surfaces Adaptes à l'Exploitation des Océans (SURF), serving ELF offshore Cameroon fields five times weekly since 1982.

Specifications

Length overall	34.9 m
Beam	7.32 m
Draught	1.93 m
Displacement, min	65 t
Displacement, max	100 t
Payload	33 t
Crew	3
Passengers	65
Fuel capacity	1,300 l
Propulsive power	3 × 545 kW
Max speed	24 kts
Operational speed	22 kts
Range	1,000 n miles

Classification: Bureau Veritas.

Structure: Aluminium.

Propulsion: Three GM 16V-92 marine diesels, max rating 545 kW each at 2,150 rpm; continuous 545 kW at 2,000 rpm; driving three four-blade propellers.

Mexico III ***1994***

Wildcat ***1994***

Electrical system: The auxiliary engines are two generators Type Delco-GM 3L 71, 30 kW.
Navigation and communications: Two radars, one autopilot and one echo-sounder; one SSB radio and two VHF radios.
Safety equipment: In accordance with SOLAS regulations. One Zodiac inflatable and outboard.

Miss Peggy Ann

Owner: John E Graham & Sons, Bayou LaBatre, Alabama, serving the oilfields of the Gulf of Mexico.

Specifications

Length overall	39.63 m
Beam	8 m
Draught	1.37 m
Crew	10
Passengers	64
Fuel capacity	36,336 l
Water capacity	70,969 l
Propulsive power	4 × 1,521 kW
Operational speed	23.5 kts
Range	2,160 n miles

Classification: USCG Certified for 200 miles offshore ABS Load-Line Assignment.
Structure: All-welded aluminium construction with transverse non-floating frames.
Propulsion: The main engines are four DDC 12V-71TI 1,521 kW (2,040 hp) at 2,100 rpm, driving 88.9 mm Aquamet No 17 stainless steel shafts and Michigan Nibral Dina Quad propellers 96.5 × 88.9 cm; via Twin Disc MG-514 gearboxes, with 2.5:1.0 reduction.
Electrical system: Auxiliary power is supplied by two 40 kW Detroit Diesel/Kato generator sets.
Navigation and communications: Radars, 2 × Furuno FR-810D; SSB, Stephens SEA 222; VHF, Cybernet CTX 2050; LORAN, Furuno LC-90; depth indicator, Datamarine 3000; loudhailer, Apelco HXL 1000.

Mexico III

This all-aluminium passenger ferry was delivered in April 1993 for use in rivers and protected waters.

Specifications

Length overall	45.7 m
Beam	9.14 m
Draught	2.13 m
Passengers	800
Fuel capacity	23,000 l
Operational speed	24 kts

Propulsion: The main engines are 4 × DDC 16V 92TA diesels, driving via 4 × Twin Disc MGN273EV gearboxes.

Wildcat

This all-aluminium crew boat was delivered to the Pennzoil Exploration Company in 1993.

Specifications

Length overall	46.33 m
Beam	8.99 m
Crew	8
Passengers	72
Payload	260 t
Fuel capacity	58,000 l

Propulsion: The main engines are 5 × Caterpillar 3412 diesels.

Miss Pearl Louise

This supply vessel was delivered in mid-1994 to John E Graham & Sons for operation in the Gulf of Mexico. Based on the earlier craft, *Miss Peggy Ann*, this vessel is slightly longer and faster.

Specifications

Length overall	41.15 m
Beam	8.0 m
Draught	1.53 m
Crew	5
Passengers	10
Payload	180 t
Fuel capacity	42,000 l
Operational speed	25 kts

Propulsion: The vessel is powered by four 12V 92TA marine diesels each driving a fixed-pitch propeller via a reverse reduction gearbox.

VERIFIED

CHRISTENSEN SHIPYARDS

4400 S E Columbia Way, Vancouver, Washington 98661, USA

Tel: +1 (360) 695 3238
Telex: 754607 CHRISTENSEN
Fax: +1 (360) 695 3252
E-mail: chrisship@aol.com

David H Christensen, *President*

The company builds custom motor yachts of double Airex cored GRP construction; Kevlar and carbon fibre materials are also used in areas of high stress. A standard mould is used for building hulls from 30 to 46 m in length, which can be widened for different lengths and engine power requirements. Alternative superstructures are installed to meet individual owners' requirements. Unless otherwise specified, Christensen yachts are built under ABS standard inspections to ABS +1A1-AMS.

The company established a 6,500 m² (70,000 ft²) building facility in 1986 and by March 1995 had built 21 yachts and were employing 150 people working for customers in Belgium, Italy, Japan and the USA.

Royal Oak ***1990***

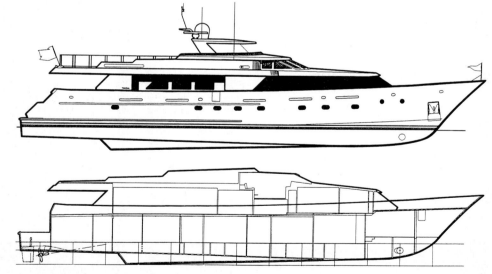

Christensen 120 ft raised pilot-house motor yacht ***1995***

Royal Oak

Launched October 1988; a pilot-house motor yacht for a Japanese owner.

Specifications

Length overall	39.6 m
Length waterline	35.7 m
Beam	8.2 m
Draught	1.8 m
Displacement, min	131.5 t
Displacement, max	172.3 t
Fuel capacity	30,280 l
Water capacity	5,677 l
Propulsive power	2,088 kW
Operational speed	20 kts

Propulsion: The engines are 2 × DDC 16V92TA, Model 8162-7400, dry weight 3,538 kg, each 1,044 kW at 2,300 rpm (gross power), 932 kW at 1,950 rpm cruising power.

120 ft MOTOR YACHT

Specifications

Length overall	35.1 m
Length waterline	34 m
Beam	7.9 m
Draught	2 m
Fuel capacity	30,280 l
Propulsive power	1,946 kW
Operational speed	22 kts

Propulsion: Engines: 2 × Deutz MWM TBD 604B V8 diesels, 973 kW each at 1,800 rpm.
Transmissions: 2 × ZF reduction gearboxes.
Electrical system: Generators: 2 × John Deere/Lima 50 kW.

UPDATED

DENISON MARINE INC

PO Box 805, 750 North East 7th Avenue, Dania, Florida 33004, USA

Tel: +1 (305) 920 0622
Fax: +1 (305) 920 6553

Christopher Denison, *President*
Ann Denison, *Vice President, Secretary, Treasurer*
Carl Bischoff, *Vice President of Operations*
Robert Langlois, *Chief Operations Officer*

Denison Marine Inc specialises in the design and construction of aluminium motor yachts from 20 to 50 m in length. At its inception in 1983, the company integrated modern automation technologies in shipbuilding with traditional craftsmanship and attention to detail. Both conventional and modern yachts are manufactured in the USA.

Denison Marine has pioneered the use of water-jet and surface-drive propulsion in yachts over 30.5 m

Recent motor yachts completed

	Dynamo V	*Lady Anna*	*Big Bad John*	*Patricia*	*Astra Dee*	*Pharaoh*
Launch date	1989	1990	1990	1990	1990	1991
Hull	Raised bridge cockpit motor yacht	Aluminium sports fisherman	Raised bridge cockpit motor yacht	Raised bridge cockpit motor yacht	Flush bridge motor yacht	Aluminium sports fisherman
Length overall	35.06 m	36.89 m	33.23 m	32.32 m	28.35 m	36.27 m
Beam	6.71 m	7.62 m	6.71 m	6.71 m	6.71 m	7.32 m
Draught	1.37 m	1.75 m	1.83 m	1.83 m	1.22 m	2.01 m
Engines	2 MTU 12V 396 TB 83 1,439 kW each	2 MWM TBD 604B 1,919 kW each	2 DDC 16V 149 1,790 kW each	2 MWM TBD 604B V12 1,439 kW each	2 DDC 16V 149 1,790 kW each	2 DDC 16V 149 1,790 kW each
Propulsion	2 × KaMeWa S63 water-jet units	2 × turned propellers	2 × turned propellers	2 × turned propellers	2 × Arneson ASD-16 units	Props
Displacement	102 t	102 t	102 t	96.5 t	86.4 t	90 t
Berths	8 + 3 crew	6 + 4 crew	6 + 3 crew	8 + 3 crew	6 + 6 crew	6 + 4 crew
Speed	34 kts	32 kts	32 kts	30 kts	36 kts	35 kts

that exceed 34 knots. Denison has also produced the largest sport fishing boat built in the United States and also one of the largest custom yachts, the *Miss Turnberry*.

For Your Eyes Only

Raised bridge motor yacht, built December 1985, Hull No 103, fitted with trim tabs and bow thrusters.

Specifications

Propulsive power	2 × 1,439 kW
Operational speed	30 kts

Structure: Welded aluminium.

Propulsion: The main engines are two MTU 12V 396 TB 93, 1,439 kW (1,930 bhp) each, at 2,100 rpm, fitted with ZF BW 455, 2.27:1 reduction gears, driving two KaMeWa type 63 water-jet units.

Outfit: Sleeps eight in four staterooms, four berths for crew. The three guest staterooms have twin or queen-size berths, hanging lockers, drawers and toilets with showers. Flybridge lounge area has over 8 m of seating, Mar Quipt hydraulic crane, 4.6 m Bayliner tender with 85 hp outboard and lighted helicopter landing pad. Push-button, automatic fold-forward mast to clear helicopter rotor blades. Fully equipped galley.

Quest

A bridge motor yacht completed in 1987, Hull No 116.

Specifications

Length overall	31.39 m
Beam	6.71 m
Draught	1.22 m
Displacement	101.59 t
Fuel capacity	28,387.5 l
Water capacity	5,677.5 l
Propulsive power	2 × 1,440 kW
Max speed	36 kts

Propulsion: The main engines are two MTU 12V 396 TB 93, 1,440 kW each, driving two KaMeWa 63 water-jets.

Electrical system: Two Northern Lights 55 kW and one Northern Lights 12 kW diesel generators.

Quest *1989*

Thunderball

Raised bridge motor yacht launched in August 1988, Hull No 114.

Specifications

Length overall	33.53 m
Beam	6.71 m
Draught	1.22 m
Displacement	113.78 t
Crew	6
Passengers	8
Fuel capacity	38,985.5 l
Water capacity	3,785 l
Max speed	46 kts

Structure: Marine grade aluminium.

Propulsion: The main engines are two MTU 16V 396 TB 94 marine diesels, driving via two KaMeWa 72 water-jets.

Thunderball *1989*

Miss Turnberry (ex-*Monkey Business II*)

Motor yacht delivered in 1990, Hull No 115.

Specifications

Length overall	42.67 m
Beam	8.23 m
Draught	1.83 m
Displacement, max	185 t
Fuel capacity	60,800 l
Propulsive power	2 × 2,088 kW
Max speed	26 kts
Range	4,800 n miles

Structure: Marine grade aluminium.

Propulsion: Two Caterpillar 3516 marine diesel engines 2,088 kW each, driving two Arneson ASD 18 drives with Rolla Nibral 5-blade surface-piercing propellers.

Electrical system: Two Northern Lights 100 kW diesel generating sets.

VERIFIED

DERECKTOR SHIPYARDS

311 E Boston Port Road, Mamaroneck, New York 10543, USA

Tel: +1 (914) 698 5020
Fax: +1 (914) 698 4641

Paul Derecktor, *President*
Mary Clerkin, *Marketing Manager*

There are two shipyards in the group: Robert Derecktor Inc of New York and Derecktor-Gunnell of Florida. They have built over 250 boats up to 36 m in length.

Dillinger 1992

Dillinger 74

This vessel, completed in the Autumn of 1990, was designed by Frank Mulder, the Dutch naval architect designer of *Octopussy. Dillinger 74* is built in advanced carbon fibre pre-impregnated materials.

Specifications

Length overall	22.66 m
Length waterline	18.5 m
Beam	5.24 m
Draught	1.09 m
Fuel capacity	7,570 l
Water capacity	1,893 l
Max speed	55 kts

Propulsion: The main engines are 2 × MTU 12V 396 TB 93; 2 × Kamewa S45 water-jet units.

MIT sea AH 1994

MIT sea AH

This vessel was designed by Richard Liebowitz Design with Sparkman & Stephens and is the third and largest sea AH for the same owner.

Specifications

Length overall	34.75 m
Length waterline	29.89 m
Beam	7.01 m
Draught	1.95 m
Propulsive power	2 × 1,700 kW
Operational speed	29 kts

Propulsion: The main engines are 2 × MTU 12V 396 TE 94, 1,700 kW each; driving 2 × propellers driven via ZF V-drive gearboxes, one Arneson surface drive.

S&S 105
Lady Francis

A high-speed water-jet-propelled motor yacht built in 1987, to American Bureau of Shipping ✠A1 for Yachting Service.

Designers: Sparkman & Stephens Inc, 79 Madison Avenue, New York 10016, USA.

Specifications

Length overall	32 m
Length waterline	27.66 m
Beam	7.01 m
Draught	1.22 m
Fuel capacity	22,710 l
Water capacity	6,056 l
Propulsive power	2 × 1,462 kW
Max speed	31 kts
Operational speed	25 kts

Structure: Aluminium alloy, 5086 series welded aluminium, 6061 aluminium extrusions, teak main deck and boat deck.

Propulsion: The main engines are two MTU 12V 396 TB 93 diesel engines 1,462 kW (1,960 hp) each, driving two Kamewa Series 63 water-jet units.

DERECKTOR 66
Wicked Witch III

High-speed motor yacht.

Specifications

Length overall	20.11 m
Length waterline	16.38 m
Beam	5.41 m
Draught	1.67 m
Displacement, max	29.51 t
Propulsive power	2 × 649 kW
Max speed	33 kts

Structure: Aluminium alloy, stepped surface hull form, skeg on centreline.

Propulsion: The main engines are two GM 12V-71 T marine diesels 649 kW each, coupled to 195 ZF, V-drive gearboxes; propeller shaft angle: 7°.

31 m MOTOR YACHT

Built in early 1989 this 31 m luxury yacht was designed by DIANA Yacht Design BV, Netherlands.

Specifications

Length overall	31 m
Length waterline	26 m
Beam	7.5 m
Draught	1.4 m
Displacement, max	120 t
Fuel capacity	25,000 l
Water capacity	6,000 l
Propulsive power	2 × 2,040 kW

Structure: All-aluminium fully planing deep-V hull

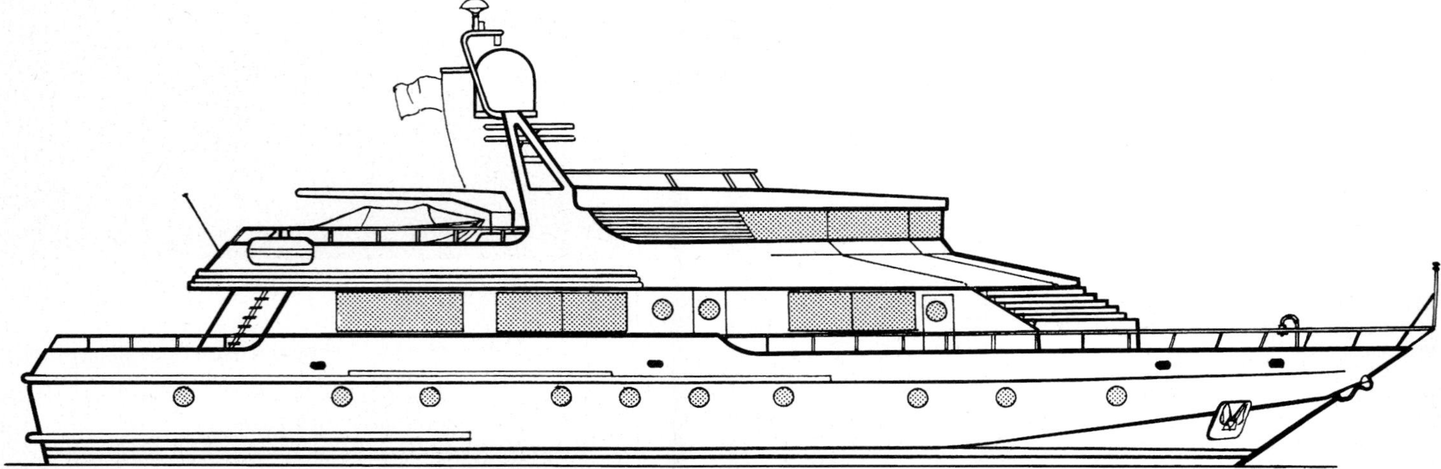

31 m (DIANA Yacht Design BV) water-jet luxury motor yacht built by R E Derecktor Shipyard 1995

with transom stern, trim wedge, 3 spray rails and chine rail each side on bottom, flared bow, 3 watertight bulkheads. Fuel, water, oil and sanitary tanks built in double bottom.

Material of hull plating and superstructure: aluminium alloy grade 5083; remaining parts of construction to be aluminium alloy grade 6082.

Propulsion: The main engines are two diesel engines MTU 16V 396 TB 84, rating to ISO 3046/i, 2,040 kW (2,775 hp) each, driving two Kamewa water-jet units Series 71.

Auxiliary systems: Two 40 hp thrusters, by Cramm (Holland) mounted in engine room for low speed propulsion and manoeuvring, Schottel Bow Thruster, two deck cranes by Cramm, two Steen Anchor Windlass, windows supplied by WIGO, Holland.

22 m FEXAS EXPRESS MOTOR YACHT
Transition

Designed by Tom Fexas Yacht Design Inc, Florida, this vessel was delivered towards the end of 1990.

Specifications

Length overall	22.6 m
Length waterline	19.5 m
Beam	5.8 m
Draught	0.92 m
Displacement, max	34.47 t
Fuel capacity	10,598 l
Water capacity	2,498 l
Propulsive power	2 × 746 kW
Max speed	35 kts
Operational speed	30 kts
Range	1,200 n miles

Propulsion: The main engines are two MAN D2842 LYE, 746 kW each.

Transition **1992**

20 m SPORT FISHING BOAT

Designed by Tripp Design, this all-aluminium vessel was delivered from the New York yard in 1995.

Specifications

Length overall	20 m
Length waterline	17.75 m
Beam	5.4 m
Draught	1.7 m
Propulsive power	Two 950 kW
Operational speed	40 kts
Range	900 n miles

Propulsion: 2 × MTU 8V 396 TE 94 rated at 950 kW each driving through a ZF BW 255S gearbox.

UPDATED

EQUITABLE SHIPYARDS INC

A company of the Trinity Marine Group

Industrial Canal, PO Box 8001, New Orleans, Louisiana 70182, USA

Tel: +1 (504) 286 2500
Fax: +1 (504) 286 2554

34 m FERRY
Kalama
Skagit

A contract valued at US$5 million was placed with Equitable Shipyards in 1988 for the supply of two air conditioned 25 knot, 250-commuter passenger vessels for the Washington State Department of Transportation for service in 1989 between Vashon Island, Bremerton and downtown Seattle.

The vessels were delivered in October 1989 but due to budget constraints they did not immediately enter service with Washington State Ferries but were chartered to the California Department of Transportation for use between San Francisco and the East Bay.

Specifications

Length overall	34.07 m
Beam	7.49 m
Draught	2.13 m
Fuel capacity	15,140 l
Water capacity	2,650 l
Propulsive power	4 × 716 kW
Operational speed	25 kts

Classification: USCG, sub-chapter T, ABS, under 100 GRT.

Structure: Aluminium.

Propulsion: 4 × DDA GM 16V 92TA, 716 kW each, at 2,100 rpm; driving via 4 × ZF, ratio 2.5:1.0.

Electrical system: 2 × Detroit Diesel 4.71 diesel engines driving two 60 kW generators.

Caribe Tide

An air conditioned 240 passenger ferry delivered in 1988 for serving cruise ship passengers in the US Virgin Islands.

Specifications

Length overall	19.82 m
Beam	7.32 m
Draught	1.68 m

Skagit *at speed* **1990**

Classification: USCG.
Structure: Aluminium.
Propulsion: 4 × Cummins KT 19M, 380 kW each, at 2,100 rpm; driving via Twin Disc MG 514, ratio 2:1.

24 m FAST PATROL BOAT

Equitable Shipyards Inc built and delivered eight of these fast patrol boats to the Philippine Navy. These boats formed part of contracts with Halter Marine Inc and the US Navy, with funding coming from the US Foreign Military Sales Programme. There were also 17 craft built and delivered to Saudi Arabia.

This fast patrol boat is a new design from Halter Marine Inc which was selected after a US national competition.

Specifications

Length overall	23.78 m
Beam	6.1 m
Draught	1.77 m
Displacement, max	57.3 t
Fuel capacity	18,925 l
Propulsive power	2 × 1,044 kW
Operational speed	24 kts
Range	1,200 n miles

Propulsion: The main engines are 2 × DD 16V 92TAB, 1,044 kW each.

EXTRA FAST PATROL BOAT TEST

Designed with Trinity Marine Group's expertise in patrol boat and offshore racing technology, the XFPB is an extremely stable, high-speed platform suitable for use as a pleasure craft or patrol craft. The XFPB hull cuts through water like a knife at a maximum speed of 62 knots and provides excellent handling and ride quality while minimising slamming.

The 21.7 knot, 240 passenger Caribe Tide **1993**

The XFPB's modular design makes it extremely versatile in its potential applications. It is available in GRP, Kevlar, marine grade aluminium alloys and lightweight high-strength steel.

Specifications

Length overall	25 m
Beam	5.5 m
Draught	1.06 m
Displacement, max	49.9 t
Crew	9
Max speed	62 kts

Structure: The hull is deep-V, FRP/Kevlar or aluminium.
Propulsion: The main engines are Triple Marine diesels, driving Arneson Surface-Piercing Drives or water-jets.

ISLA CLASS PATROL BOAT

Two Isla class Patrol Boats were delivered to the Mexican Navy in Autumn 1993. Others are under contract and in construction. Built at Equitable Shipyards, these boats are derivatives of the Extra Fast Patrol Boat.

Specifications

Length overall	25 m
Beam	5.5 m
Draught	1.06 m
Displacement, max	49.9 t
Crew	9
Max speed	50 kts
Range	700 n miles

Classification: ABS.
Structure: The hull is deep-V, FRP/Kevlar or aluminium.
Propulsion: The main engines are Triple Marine diesels, driving Arneson Surface-Piercing Drives.

Isla class Patrol Boat **1994**

25 m SPECIAL OPERATIONS CRAFT

This vessel was designed to meet the US Navy's special operations requirements and was selected from two trials craft, the other being the Peterson/Cougar catamaran. The hull is based on the XFPB trials craft.

Specifications

Length overall	24.75 m
Beam	4.72 m
Draught	1.07 m
Max speed	50 kts
Operational speed	35 kts
Range	675 n miles

Propulsion: The craft is powered by two MTU 12V 396 TE 94 diesels rated at 1,650 kW at 200 rpm, each driving a Kamewa 50S water-jet.

25 m Special Operations Craft **1995**

Fjordland

Built for Kenai Tours in 1990 this vessel is almost identical to the *Greatland* briefly described in the entry for Aluminum Boats Inc, of Trinity Marine Group.

VERIFIED

GLADDING-HEARN SHIPBUILDING

One Riverside Avenue, Box 300, Somerset, Massachusetts 02726-0300, USA

Tel: +1 (508) 676 8596
Fax: +1 (508) 672 1873

George R Duclos, *President*

This shipyard is a member of the Duclos Corporation and is known for its range of commercial workboats and fast ferry craft. The yard has built a large number of small pilot craft as well as its well-known Incat catamaran ferries.

19 m PILOT BOAT

This all-aluminium Hunt-designed pilot boat was delivered to the Lake Charles Pilots in September 1995.

Specifications

Length overall	19.3 m
Beam	5.56 m
Draught	1.73 m
Fuel capacity	3,800 l
Propulsive power	1,216 kW
Max speed	25 kts

19 m Gladding-Hearn pilot boat

1996

20 m PILOT BOAT

Delivered in July 1993 to the San Francisco Bar Pilots, the boat was designed jointly with C Raymond Hunt Associates.

The deep-V, twin-screw vessel is designed and equipped to run 24 hours a day at speeds over 25 knots. The rugged, all-aluminium hull and superstructure was built with heavy-duty, low-maintenance equipment, including keel-coolers and a 3,800 litre remote-controlled ballast tank.

Specifications

Length overall	20.42 m
Beam	5.33 m
Draught	1.83 m
Max speed	25.5 kts

24.5 m FERRY

Scheduled for delivery in May 1995, this craft is designed to run at 22 knots in 1.5 m of water.

Specifications

Length overall	24.5 m
Beam	6.4 m
Draught	0.9 m
Passengers	400
Propulsive power	1,823 kW
Operational speed	22 kts

30 m MONOHULLED FERRY

This is a new generation of monohulled fast ferries designed for fast offloading of passengers.

The first four all-aluminium vessels of this class, *Henry Hudson*, *Robert Fulton*, *Empire State* and *Garden State* were delivered to New Jersey-based Port Imperial Ferry Company for passenger service between New Jersey and New York City.

The vessel's unique bow-loading system safely offloads 100 passengers per minute.

Specifications

Length overall	29.56 m
Beam	7.77 m
Draught	1.83 m
Passengers	400
Propulsive power	2 × 500 kW
Max speed	18 kts

Monohulled passenger ferry Robert Fulton **1994**

Propulsion: The main engines are twin Caterpillar 3412 diesels, each rated at 500 kW at 1,800 rpm. The engines drive two 1.07 m bronze propellers via ZF 2.57:1 reverse/reduction gears.

UPDATED

GULF CRAFT INC

3904 HWY182, Patterson, Louisiana 70392, USA

Tel: +1 (504) 395 5254/6259

R Scott Tibbs, *President*

Gulf Craft Inc is a builder of high-speed aluminium conventional hull passenger ferries and crew boats. The *Caleb McCall* is a 44 m crew boat with a maximum speed of 27 knots. An interesting feature of this craft is that there are five engines which the owner claims give better manoeuvrability and make engine replacement or repair easier.

Caleb McCall

Crew boat.

Owner: McCall Boat Rental, Cameron, Louisiana, USA

Specifications

Length overall	44.2 m
Beam	8.5 m
Draught	2.4 m
Crew	6
Passengers	75
Fuel capacity	45,420 l
Water capacity	75,700 l
Max speed	27 kts
Operational speed	23 kts

Classification: USCG approved Gulf of Mexico, 200 miles offshore.

Structure: Superstructure and hull are built in aluminium. Hull plating is in 5086 grade, 15.8 mm thick over the propellers, the remainder of the bottom is 12.7 mm thick with 8.4 mm side plating, superstructure is in 4.8 mm plate.

Propulsion: Five Cummins KTA19-M diesel engines coupled to Twin Disc MG 518, 2.5:1 reduction gearboxes, driving five three-blade Columbian Bronze FP propellers.
Electrical system: Two Cummins 6B5.8, 56 kW generators.
Navigation and communications: Raytheon/JRC colour and Furuno FR 8100 radars, Si-Tex Koden Loran, Datamarine sounder, Decca 150 autopilot.
Motorola Triton 20 SSB, Raytheon 53A VHF.
Control: Orbitrol/Charlynn steering and Kobelt engine controls. Duplicate engine controls also fitted on the upper bridge allowing operator to face aft with a clear view while working cargo at rigs and oil platforms.
Outfit: Three two-berth cabins, galley and mess room.

Annabeth McCall
Norman McCall

Two of four very large crew boats delivered in 1989 to McCall Boat Rental of Cameron, Louisiana. These boats combine increase in size (48.78 m long) for improved sea-keeping with a reasonably high speed of around 25 knots.

Specifications

Length overall	48.78 m
Beam	9.15 m
Propulsive power	6 × 507 kW

Propulsion: The main engines are 6 × Cummins KTA19-M2 diesels, each 507 kW, giving a total power of 3,042 kW.

Blair McCall

The previous world's largest crew boat of 47.25 m in length and powered by five Cummins diesels of 507 kW each.

Specifications

Payload	200 t
Passengers	92
Propulsive power	5 × 507 kW
Max speed	23 kts

VERIFIED

HALTER MARINE INC

A company of the Trinity Marine Group

Formed in 1957, Halter Marine Inc has built over 1200 vessels since then and has designed and built more high-speed vessels than any other shipyard in the USA. The yard specialises in aluminium and high strength Corten steel hulls. The parent company is Trinity Industries of Dallas, Texas and the sister company is Equitable Shipyards.

The following craft descriptions represent some of the principal types of high-speed craft designed and built by Halter Marine Inc, having lengths of approximately 20 m or over with speeds over 20 knots.

HALMAR 65 (CREW BOAT TYPE)

This is a crew boat design but is also available in the following variants: customs launch, tanker service launch, pilot boat, ferry, communications launch, workboat and ambulance launch. The first of the type was designed and built in 1964 and over 120 of these craft have now been built. The craft have been classified by various authorities including USCG, ABS and Lloyd's. Most are in service with the offshore oil industry.

Specifications

Length overall	19.66 m
Beam	5.9 m
Draught	1.12 m
Crew	6
Fuel capacity	3,596 l
Propulsive power	380 kW
Max speed	21 kts (aluminium hull)
	18 kts (steel hull)
Operational speed	19 kts (aluminium hull)
	16 kts (steel hull)
Operational limitation	Sea State 3-4

Structure: Corten steel, longitudinally framed; aluminium 5086, transverse framed.
Propulsion: Various options, the most popular being two GM 12V-71 TI, producing 380 kW each at 2,100 rpm, driving 2 × Columbian Bronze propellers, 813 mm diameter, in Nibral.
Electrical system: 110/220 V AC, 60 Hz, generator 2-71 GM, 20 kW.
Control: Morse MD-24, manual, two stations. Steering hydraulic, 600 lb/sq in.
Outfit: 49 passengers and 2 crew (1 captain, 1 deckhand/engineer).

Halmar 101 Fraih Al-Fraih **1996**

Halmar 78 crew boat Oil Conveyor II **1987**

HALMAR 65 (PATROL BOAT TYPE)

Main particulars as for the Halmar 65 crew boat type but with the following differences:

Specifications

Displacement, max	34.54 t
Fuel capacity	4,546 l
Propulsive power	2 × 675 kW
Max speed	26 kts (aluminium hull)
	21 kts (steel hull)
Operational speed	22 kts (aluminium hull)
	18 kts (steel hull)

Propulsion: The most popular combination is two GM 12V-71 TI, 675 hp each at 2,300 rpm; driving 2 × Columbian Bronze propellers, 838 mm diameter, in Nibral.

HALMAR 78 (PATROL BOAT TYPE)

The first Halmar 78 was completed in 1982 and 23 had been built by August 1985.

Specifications

Length overall	23.78 m
Beam	5.64 m
Draught	1.43 m
Displacement	42.67 t
Payload	14 t
Fuel capacity	10,607 l
Propulsive power	503 kW
Max speed	22 kts
Operational speed	20 kts
Operational limitation	Sea State 4-5
Range	745 n miles

Classification: Lloyd's class 100 A-1, November 1982.
Structure: Corten steel, longitudinally framed.
Propulsion: 2 × GM 12V-71 TI, producing 503 kW each at 2,300 rpm; driving 2 × Columbian Bronze propellers, 864 mm diameter, in Nibral.
Electrical system: 220/440 V AC, 50 Hz, generator 2-71 GM, 20 kW.
Navigation and communications: Sailor RT-144 VHF and Decca 150 radar.
Control: Morse MD-24, manual, 2 stations.
Outfit: Captain, 2 officers, 8 crew. Below the main deck there are 4 staterooms, 3 toilets and a galley.

HALMAR 101 (CREW BOAT TYPE)

A crew boat design available in a full range of variants. Designed and first built in 1977-78, 38 had been delivered by December 1985, classified either by USCG or ABS. The latest vessel, *Fraih Al Fraih*, was delivered to Kuwait in 1995 for security services for offshore oil rigs.

Specifications

Length overall	31 m
Beam	6.48 m
Draught	1.68 m
Displacement, min	55.88 t

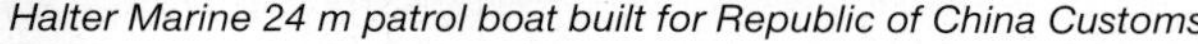

Halter Marine 24 m patrol boat built for Republic of China Customs ***1994***

The ATCO Hebah, *25 passenger, 25 tonne cargo, crew boat built by Halter Marine Inc* ***1990***

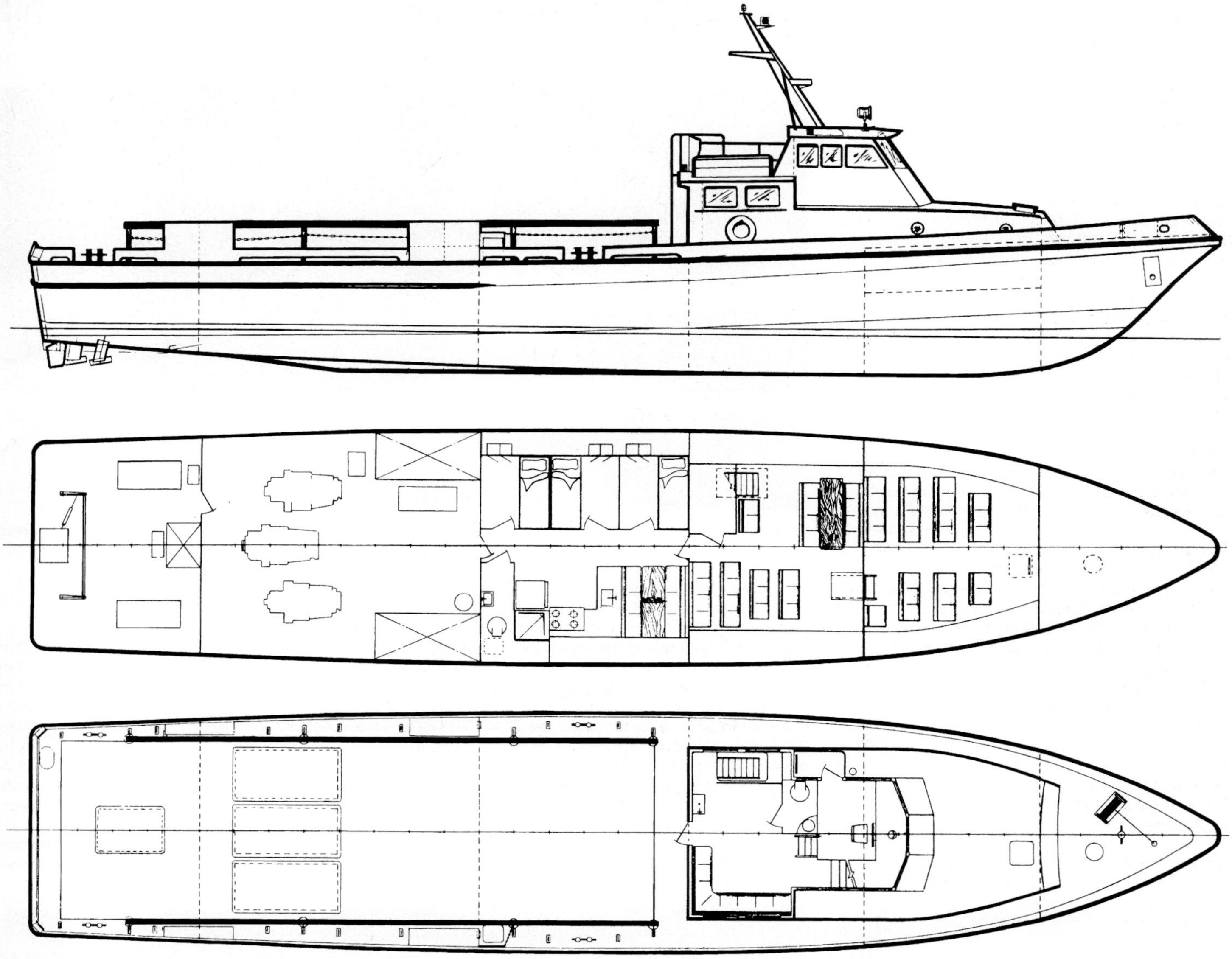

General arrangement of Halmar 101 ***1995***

Payload	30.48 t
Crew	6
Passengers	55
Fuel capacity	9,092 l
Propulsive power	3 × 380 kW
Max speed	22 kts
Operational speed	20 kts
Operational limitation	Sea State 5
Range	500 n miles

Structure: Aluminium 5086, transverse framed.

Propulsion: The main engines are 3 × GM 12V-71 TI, 380 kW each at 2,100 rpm, driving via Twin Disc 2:1 reduction gears to 3 × Columbian Bronze propellers, 864 mm diameter, in Nibral (one vessel is fitted with three Rocketdyne water-jet units, two 406.4 mm diameter driven by two GM 16V-92 TI diesel engines and one 609.6 mm diameter driven by one Allison 501 gas-turbine).

Electrical system: 2 × generators, GM 3-71, 30 kW each 110/220 V AC, 60 Hz.

Navigation and communications: VHF, Sailor 144, SSB, Motorola, Radar, Decca D-150 36 mile range.

Control: Kobelt, pneumatic, 2 stations.

34 m CREWBOAT
Hebah
Marwa
Daina

Three of these all-aluminium crew boats were built for Marine and Transportation Services, Saudi (Ltd) Damman, Saudi Arabia, and delivered in 1988 and 1989.

Specifications

Length overall	33.74 m
Beam	6.61 m
Passengers	25

Fuel capacity	12,870 l
Water capacity	3,785 l

Propulsion: The main engines are Detroit Diesel 12V-71 TI, 380 kW (510 hp) each, at 2,100 rpm; driving through Twin Disc MG 514, ratio 2:1.

24 m PATROL BOAT

This craft was built by Halter Marine for the Republic of China (Taiwan) Customs.

Specifications

Length overall	23.8 m
Beam	5.6 m
Draught	1.5 m
Crew	10
Operational speed	24 kts

Structure: The hull is aluminium.

Propulsion: The main engines are twin Marine diesels, driving 2 × Columbian Bronze propellers (4-bladed).

UPDATED

Halmar 122 deep-V hull crew boat
1986

MAGNUM MARINE CORPORATION

2900 Northeast 188th Street, North Miami Beach, Florida 33180, USA

Tel: +1 (305) 931 4292
Fax: +1 (305) 931 0088

Mrs Katrin Theodoli, *President and CEO*

Magnum Marine specialises in the construction of high-performance, offshore pleasure and patrol craft from 8 to 21 m in length.

Magnum patrol craft are in service with the US Marine Patrol, US Customs, US Coast Guard and many other non-US agencies.

MAGNUM 63

This boat is built in accordance with the requirements of Lloyd's Register of Shipping and the American Bureau of Shipping. By August 1989 a total of 14 had been built; the first was completed in 1985. In August 1986 the Magnum 63 won the 370 mile Miami to Nassau to Miami offshore race. In 1987 a new and faster version of this Magnum 63 was developed and Magnum again won the race. The craft can be fitted out as a patrol boat. A flybridge version was shipped to Japan in November 1987.

Specifications

Length overall	19.2 m
Length waterline	16.31 m
Beam	5.28 m
Draught	0.91 m
Crew	9
Fuel capacity	4,320 l
Water capacity	720 l
Propulsive power	2 × 1,074 kW
Max speed	52 kts
Range	400-500 n miles

Magnum 70
1992

Structure: The boat is basically a four-piece construction consisting of a hull, deck, forward inner liner and cockpit liner, all laminated in GRP or for additional weight-saving the lamination can be of Du Pont Kevlar. Interiors may be built of Kevlar and Nomex honeycomb composite materials. Deadrise aft is 24°.

Propulsion: The main engines are 2 × DD 16V 92TA, 1,074 kW each, driving 2 × Arneson surface drive SP2000 propeller units.

Electrical system: 8 × 12 V, 200 Ah batteries, four for each engine; 60 A engine driven alternators; 12 V and 24 V DC system; 100/220 V 60 Hz AC system; two automatic 60 A converters; Onan diesel generator, 7.5 kW.

MAGNUM 63 (1987 VERSION)
Maltese Magnum

Specifications

Length overall	19.2 m
Beam	5.18 m
Draught	0.91 m
Fuel capacity	4,542 l
Water capacity	946 l
Crew	6-10
Propulsive power	2 × 1,380 kW
Max speed	65.8 kts

Structure: Constructed in Du Pont Kevlar, superstructure to suit individual requirements.

Propulsion: The main engines are 2 × CRM marine diesels, 1,380 kW each at 2,075 rpm coupled to two

1987 version of Magnum Marine 63, Maltese Magnum, *winner of the 1987 Miami to Nassau to Miami sea race at an average of 51 knots over 314.77 n miles* ***1988***

Arneson drives via 1.18:1 reduction gearboxes, driving 2 × five-blade Nibral propellers, 838 mm diameter, 143 mm pitch.

MAGNUM 70

The largest boat displayed at the 1991 Miami International Boat Show was the 21.34 m Magnum 70 Superyacht. This boat is built in Kevlar and in the standard version is powered by two Detroit Diesel 16V 92TA diesels.

Specifications

Length overall	21.34 m
Beam	5.18 m
Draught	1.83 m
Crew	1-2
Passengers	6-8
Fuel capacity	4,543 l
Water capacity	946 l
Propulsive power	2 × 1,044 kW
Max speed	39 kts (standard shaft) 48 kts (Arneson)
Operational speed	35 kts (standard shaft) 44 kts (Arneson)

Propulsion: The standard engines are 2 × DDC 16V 92TA, 1,044 kW each.

MAGNUM 90

A 27 m production motor yacht delivered in Spring 1992 with the same performance as the Magnum 70. The standard version is equipped with three Detroit Diesel 16V 92TA diesels coupled to Arneson surface drives. Lycoming gas-turbines can also be installed in the Magnum 90.

VERIFIED

MUNSON HAMMERHEAD BOATS INC

PO Box 597, La Conner, Washington 98257, USA

Tel: +1 (360) 466 5925
Fax: +1 (360) 466 5921

Christopher D Barry, *Chief Naval Architect*

Munson Hammerhead Boats, a subsidiary of American Eagle Manufacturing, produces high-speed aluminium craft up to 25 m in length. In addition to high-speed ferry boats, the company also produce fast landing craft, police, patrol and rescue craft.

RIVER EXCURSION BOAT
Yukon Queen

Owned by Westours Inc the *Yukon Queen* operates on the Yukon River between Circle in Alaska and Dawson in Canada's Yukon Territory.

Specifications

Length overall	19.5 m
Beam	5.18 m
Draught	0.84 m
Passengers	49
Fuel capacity	4,353 l
Water capacity	1,325 l
Propulsive power	3 × 410 kW
Max speed	26.8 kts
Operational speed	23 kts

Propulsion: The main engines are 3 × Lugger 6140A, 410 kW each, 2,100 rpm, 6-cylinder turbocharged after-cooled in-line diesels, driving Hamilton 361 water-jets.

Yukon Queen *built by Munson Manufacturing Inc* **1992**

20 m PASSENGER VESSEL

This vessel is owned by Lake Chelan Boat Company of Chelan, Washington.

Specifications

Length overall	19.81 m
Beam	6.3 m
Draught	1 m
Displacement, max	40.64 t
Crew	100
Fuel capacity	1,893 l
Propulsive power	2 × 805 kW
Max speed	30 kts
Operational speed	24 kts
Range	113 n miles

Propulsion: The main engines are 2 × DDC 12V 92, 805 kW each, at 2,300 rpm.

UPDATED

PETERSON BUILDERS INC

101 Pennsylvania Street, PO Box 650, Sturgeon Bay, Wisconsin 54235-0650, USA

Tel: +1 (414) 743 5574
Telex: 263423
Fax: +1 (414) 743 6089

Ellsworth L Peterson, *President*

Peterson Builders Inc (PBI) is a well established ship and patrol boat builder having been in continuous operation for over 62 years. Peterson is currently building three 14.6 m high-speed patrol craft. The first of the series completed trials exceeding all performance criteria, with speeds exceeding 45 knots. PBI has, over its 62 years, designed and constructed over 200 patrol craft ranging from 7 m to 57 m. Speeds of PBI's patrol craft have exceeded 50 knots, driven by propulsion systems ranging from diesel to combination diesel/gas turbine. Propusion includes fixed pitch, controlled reversible pitch, surface piercing drives and water-jets.

Peterson Builders 14.6 m PCC **1996**

PBI Mk 1

The PBI Mk 1 launched in 1983 is a twin-screw diesel-powered high-performance coastal patrol craft, built of marine grade aluminium alloy.

Specifications

Length overall	20.17 m
Beam	5.48 m
Draught	1.64 m
Displacement	42.7 t
Crew	10
Fuel capacity	9,085 l
Water capacity	1,794 l
Propulsive power	1,790 kW
Max speed	27.5 kts
Operational speed	20.5 kts
Range	683 n miles
Operational limitation	Sea State 6

Propulsion: 2 × DDC 16V 92MTI, 1,790 kW total.

Electrical system: Onan 30 kW driven by Ford 4-cylinder diesel.

14.6 m PCC

In November 1994 Peterson was awarded a contract by US Naval Sea Systems Command to build three coastal patrol craft with an option for further vessels.

UPDATED

SWIFTSHIPS INC

PO Box 1908, Morgan City, Louisiana 70381, USA

Tel: +1 (504) 384 1700
Fax: +1 (504) 384 0914

Dennis R Spurgeon, *Chairman*
Robert W Ness, *President*
Calvin J LeLeux, *Executive Vice President*
Mark H Dearing, *Treasurer/Controller*
Leslie Lallande, *Business Development Manager*
A J Blanchard, *Marketing Manager*
C C Clark, *Purchasing Manager*

Swiftships produces aluminium alloy craft up to 38 m and steel vessels from 45 to 76 m long. Swiftships employs approximately 900 personnel and apart from its fast crew boats has supplied fast aluminium patrol craft ranging from 8 to 45 m in length. These craft are in service with US armed forces, naval coastguard and police forces in some 20 countries throughout the world.

Swiftships 65′ patrol boats **1987**

65′ PATROL BOAT

Patrol boats supplied to governments of Antigua, Dominica and St Lucia.

Specifications

Length overall	19.81 m
Beam	5.56 m
Draught	1.52 m
Fuel capacity	4,542 l

Structure: Superstructure and hull constructed in aluminium alloy.

Propulsion: 2 × GM 12V-71 TI marine diesel engines coupled to Twin Disc MG 514C reverse/reduction gearboxes, each to conventional propellers.

Control: Engine controls by Ponish with a Vickers/Charlynn steering system.

115′ CREW BOAT

Fast supply/crew boat.

Specifications

Length overall	35.05 m
Beam	7.62 m
Draught	2.2 m
Payload	75.55 t
Crew	6
Passenger	49
Fuel capacity	14,000 l
Propulsive power	3 × 596 kW
Speed	23 kts
Range	750 n miles

Propulsion: 3 × MTU 8V 396 TC 82 diesels providing 596 kW at 1,845 rpm each, driving a 4-bladed bronze propeller via ZF BW 255 2:1 reduction gearboxes and a 101 mm diameter Aquamet 17 shaft.

135′ CREW BOAT

Specifications

Length overall	41.15 m
Beam	7.92 m
Payload	100 t
Fuel capacity	38,600 l
Max speed	24 kts

Propulsion: 4 × MTU 12V 183 TE 72 diesel engines.

VERIFIED

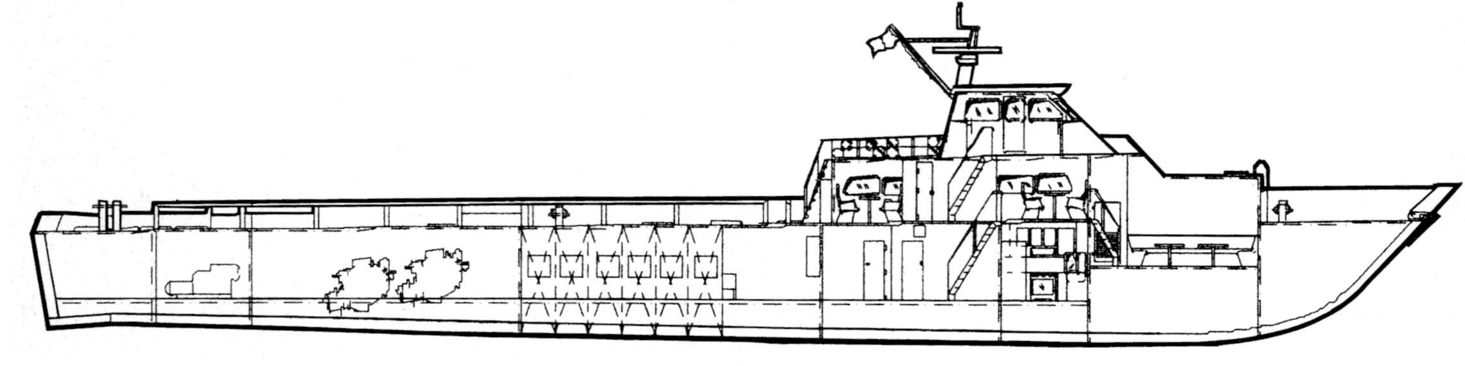

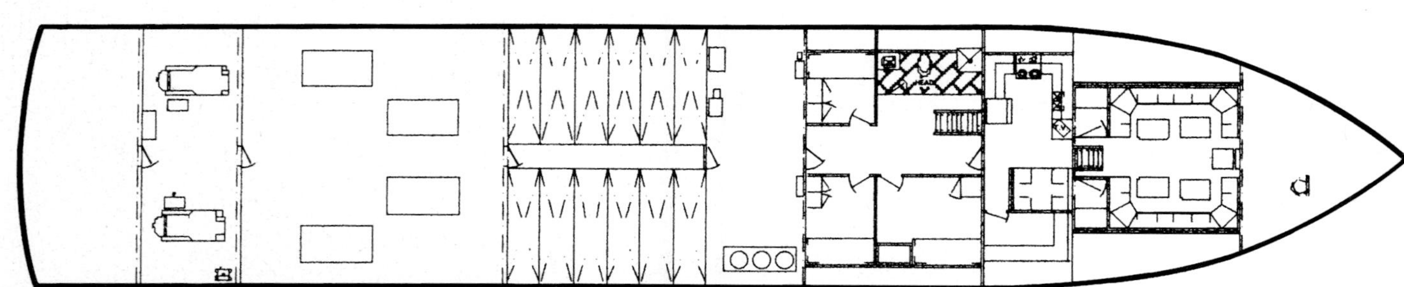

Swiftships 135′ crew boat, general arrangement **1995**

TEMPEST YACHTS INC

3333 North East 188th Street, North Miami Beach, Florida 33180, USA

Tel: +1 (305) 937 4400
Fax: +1 (305) 937 3752

Adam Erdberg, *President*

Tempest Yachts Inc has established a reputation as an innovative manufacturer of high-quality, diesel-powered vessels for a wide variety of applications. The company, with its new headquarters, is located on North Miami Beach, Florida where it currently produces 18 models ranging from 9.75 to 25.9 m in length. Tempest Yachts is a high-technology oriented, growing company. The constantly developing state-of-the-art technology is complemented with extensive offshore experience and enables Tempest to produce vessels that are comfortable, practical and well designed for their particular application.

Due to its capabilities, Tempest Yachts was selected from among all American boat builders to design and construct an offshore Fast Coastal Interceptor (FCI) craft for the US Coast Guard. These patrol boats, 13.4 m in length, are currently operated in various areas in most weather conditions for a variety of applications ranging from rescue missions to anti-drug warfare.

Propulsion is provided by Tempest's T-Torque (US Patent 4919630) surface-piercing drive system.

TEMPEST 44 (FCI)

Fast Coastal Interceptor (FCI) craft first delivered to the US Coast Guard in April 1987.

Specifications

Length overall	13.4 m
Beam	2.9 m
Draught	0.1 m
Displacement, max	8 t
Fuel capacity	11,750 l
Propulsive power	2 × 317 kW
Operational speed	45 kts

Propulsion: 2 × Caterpillar 3208 TA 317 kW diesels each driving a T-Torque surface-piercing propeller.

TEMPEST 60

High-speed offshore performance craft available for both pleasure and commercial applications.

Specifications

Length overall	18.29 m
Beam	4.8 m
Draught	1.07 m
Displacement, max	22.68 t
Fuel capacity	3,785 l
Water capacity	1,060 l
Propulsive power	2 × 783 kW
Max speed	50 kts

Structure: FRP, ABS class.

Propulsion: The main engines are 2 × Caterpillar 3412 TA diesels, 783 kW (1,050 hp) each; driving Tempest's own T-Torque surface-piercing drive system.

Electrical system: 220 V AC, 110 V AC, 24 V DC, 12 V DC.

Navigation and communications: VHF, Loran, radar, autopilot, depthsounder.

Control: Kobelt mechanical engine controls, single station hydraulic power steering system.

TEMPEST 74

Added to the Tempest range in 1991, the Tempest 74 is an ocean-going cockpit motor yacht, also available for various commercial applications.

Specifications

Length overall	22.55 m
Beam	6.1 m
Draught	1.07 m
Displacement, max	43.13 t
Fuel capacity	8,327 l
Water capacity	1,135 l
Propulsive power	2 × 783 kW
Max speed	26 kts

Structure: The hull material is FRP, ABS class; the deck material is Aluminium 5086.

Propulsion: 2 × Caterpillar 3412 TA diesels, 783 kW each; driving Tempest T-Torque surface-piercing drive system.

Electrical system: 220 V AC, 110 V AC, 24 V DC, 12 V DC.

Control: Dual station, hydraulic power steering system, Vosper stabilisers.

TEMPEST 80

Ocean-going enclosed sport yacht, also available in various commercial applications.

Specifications

Length overall	24.39 m
Beam	6.1 m
Draught	1.22 m
Displacement, max	36.28 t
Fuel capacity	7,570 l
Water capacity	1,135 l
Propulsive power	2,912 kW
Max speed	36 kts

Structure: The hull and deck are FRP.

Propulsion: The main engines are 2 × Detroit Diesel 16V 92TA, 1,081 kW each plus 1 × Lycoming Y-53 gas-turbine of 750 kW; driving T-Torque surface-piercing drive system (US Patent 4919630).

Electrical system: 220 V AC, 110 V AC, 24 V DC, 12 V DC.

TEMPEST 84

Ocean-going sky lounge motor yacht, also available in various commercial applications.

Tempest 74 cockpit motor yacht **1992**

Tempest 84 sky lounge motor yacht **1994**

Tempest 80' enclosed motor yacht **1994**

Specifications

Length overall	25.61 m
Beam	6.1 m
Draught	1.3 m
Displacement, max	56.69 t
Fuel capacity	8,705 l
Water capacity	1,135 l
Propulsive power	2,912 kW
Max speed	26 kts

Structure: The hull is FRP and the deck is aluminium 5086.
Propulsion: The main engines are 2 × Detroit Diesel 16V 92TA, 1,081 kW each plus 1 × Lycoming T-53 gas-turbine of 750 kW; driving T-Torque surface-piercing drive system (US Patent 4919630).
Electrical system: 220 V AC, 110 V AC, 24 V DC, 12 V DC.

TEMPEST 85

Ocean-going raised pilot-house motor yacht also available in various commercial applications.
Specifications

Length overall	25.91 m
Beam	6.4 m
Draught	1.52 m
Displacement, max	61.22 t
Fuel capacity	13,248 l
Water capacity	2,650 l
Propulsive power	2 × 783 kW
Max speed	30 kts

Structure: The hull is FRP, ABS class, and the deck is aluminium 5086.
Propulsion: The main engines are 2 × Caterpillar 3412 TA diesels, 783 kW (1,050 hp) each; driving 4-blade Nibral propellers.
Electrical system: 220 V AC, 110 V AC, 24 V DC, 12 V DC.
Navigation and communications: VHF, Loran, radar, autopilot, depthsounder, SATNAV, SATCOM, facsimile, SSB.
Control: Kobelt pneumatic, 2 stations, hydraulic power steering system, hydraulic bow thruster.
Fire extinguishing system: Halon 1301.

VERIFIED

TRINITY MARINE GROUP

A Trinity Industries Company

PO Box 3029, 13085 Industrial Seaway Road, Gulfport, Mississippi 39503, USA

Tel: +1 (601) 896 0029
Telex: 6821246 HALMAR
Fax: +1 (601) 897 4866

John Dane III, *President*
Vince Almerico, *Snr Vice President, Operations*
Harvey Walpert, *Snr Vice President, Administration*
James G Rivers, *Vice President, International Sales*
Anil Raj, *Vice President, Government Projects*
Sidney Mizell, *Vice President, Sales*

Details of high-speed vessels built in the Trinity Marine Group are given in the entries for the relevant shipyards.

Shipbuilding companies within the group:
Halter Marine Inc
Moss Point Marine Inc
Trinity Yachts Inc
Aluminum Boats Inc
Equitable Shipyards Inc
HBC Barge Inc
Gretna Machine and Iron Works Inc

Shipbuilding Facilities:
Trinity Marine Panama City, Florida, USA
Trinity Beaumont, Beaumont, Texas, USA
Equitable Halter, New Orleans, Louisiana, USA
Trinity Madisonville, Madisonville, Louisiana, USA
Halter Moss Point, Moss Point, Mississippi, USA
Halter Lockport, Lockport, Louisiana, USA
Moss Point Marine, Escatawpa, Mississippi, USA
Moss Point Marine South, Escatawpa, Mississippi, USA
Aluminum Boats Inc, Crown Point, Louisiana, USA
Gretna Machine and Iron Works, Gretna, Louisiana, USA
Trinity Brownsville, Brownsville, Pennsylvania, USA
Trinity Marine Gulfport, Gulfport, Mississippi, USA
Trinity Marine Carothersville, Carothersville, Missouri, USA
Platzer Shipyards Inc, Houston, Texas, USA
Port Allen Marine, Baton Rouge, Louisiana, USA.

VERIFIED

TRINITY YACHTS INC

A company of the Trinity Marine Group

Leda

Trinity Yachts Inc delivered the 29.5 m motor yacht *Leda* in March 1991. It was designed by naval architect Gerhard Gilgenast.

Although *Leda* is under 30 m and has a sleek hull and low profile, she offers expansive, luxurious accommodation including four double staterooms with private baths and a unique formal dining salon with a panoramic view over the bow. *Leda's* most impressive feature is her exceptional low noise and vibration level, previously not considered possible on a yacht with her performance and equipment.
Specifications

Length overall	29.57 m
Length waterline	25.3 m
Draught	1.4 m
Fuel capacity	26,495 l
Water capacity	3,028 l
Max speed	20 kts
Operational speed	18 kts

Propulsion: The main engines are 2 × MTU 8V 396 TB 93, driving 2 × 4-bladed skew propellers.

22 m SPORT YACHT

This sport fishing yacht was delivered in 1994.
Specifications

Length overall	22.13 m
Beam	6.04 m
Draught	1.4 m
Fuel capacity	10,500 l
Water capacity	1,000 l
Max speed	32 kts
Operational speed	27 kts
Range	750 n miles

22 m Sport Yacht **1995**

Propulsion: Two DDEC 16V 92TA diesels rated at 1,100 kW at 2,300 rpm.

VERIFIED

WESTPORT SHIPYARD INC

PO Box 308, Westport, Washington 98595, USA

Tel: +1 (206) 268 0117
Fax: +1 (206) 268 0119

Randy Rust, *General Manager*

Westport Shipyard was established in 1964 and sold to the present owners in 1977. The yard has a workforce of 110 and consists of 5,110 m² (70,000 sq ft) of covered building sheds and workshops plus 4 acres of fenced storage space. The range, in length, of craft built is from 10.4 to 36.6 m. Hulls of the larger craft are built with a sandwich-type construction of Airex PVC and GRP, which the builder claims yields a tougher and lighter hull than an all-GRP type. Hull moulds are adjustable for length and beam enabling craft to be built in the following length ranges: 16.15 to 19.8 m, 19.8 to 29 m and 27.4 to 36.6 m. The company has built over 50 vessels to USCG 'S' classification since 1977.

Westship Lady

Designed by Jack Sarin, this vessel was delivered in Spring 1993. Four other vessels to this design have been delivered: *Norwegian Queen, Lady Lee, Rain Maker* and *Black Sheep. Black Sheep* was 2 m longer overall.
Specifications

Length overall	32.33 m
Beam	6.91 m
Draught	1.68 m
Displacement, max	95 t

Crew	14
Fuel capacity	18,950 l
Water capacity	2,840 l
Max speed	28 kts
Operational speed	25 kts
Range	2,000 n miles

Structure: The hull is FRP/Airex core and the superstructure is FRP/composite.

Propulsion: The main engines are 2 × MTU 8V 396 TE 94.

Kenai Explorer

Delivered in the Spring of 1993, *Kenai Explorer* operates as a tour vessel in the Kenai Fjords area of Alaska and is certified to operate within 20 miles of a harbour of safe refuge. The hull is built with Airex core and fire retardant resin with plywood bulkheads and stringers of fibreglass and foam. The superstructure is of fibreglass and core type construction.

Specifications

Length overall	27.44 m
Beam	6.71 m
Passengers	149
Fuel capacity	11,355 l
Water capacity	1,135 l
Propulsive power	2 × 969 kW
Operational speed	26 kts

Propulsion: The main engines are 2 × DDC 16V 92TA diesels, 969 kW each at 2,300 rpm.

Chugach

Delivered in May 1992 this vessel, designed by Jack Sarin, is owned and operated by Stan Stephens Charters, Valdez, Alaska.

Specifications

Length overall	24.4 m
Beam	6.4 m
Draught	1.5 m
Passengers	149
Fuel capacity	7,570 l
Water capacity	416 l
Propulsive power	626 kW
Max speed	22.6 kts
Operational speed	18 kts

Propulsion: The main engines are 2 × Lugger L6170A diesels, 626 kW each at 2,100 rpm.

WESTSHIP 98

Lady Kathryn

Designed by Jack Sarin, this vessel was delivered at the end of 1992.

Specifications

Length overall	29.88 m
Beam	6.91 m
Draught	1.73 m
Displacement, min	74.83 t
Passengers	10
Fuel capacity	17,000 l
Water capacity	2,840 l
Max speed	23 kts
Operational speed	19 kts
Range	1,720 n miles

Structure: Hull: FRP/Airex core.
Superstructure: FRP/composite.

Propulsion: The main engines are DDC 12V 92.

Westship Lady

1996

Northstream *1992*

Northstream

Delivered in Spring 1990, this Sports fisherman type was designed by Jack Sarin, with acoustic engineering by Joe Smullin.

Specifications

Length overall	32.7 m
Beam	7.32 m
Displacement, min	80 t
Displacement, max	93 t
Fuel capacity	22,330 l
Max speed	27 kts
Operational speed	22 kts

Kenai Explorer *1995*

Lady Kathryn *1993*

Structure: Hull: double-cored Airex bottom, single-cored Airex sides; superstructure: composite with Airex core.
Propulsion: The main engines are 2 × DDC 16V 92TA with DDEC system.
Control: Stabilisers: Naiad 301s with 0.56 m² fins. Bow thruster: Wesmar 12.2 kW.

Heritage

An ocean-going motor yacht, built in advanced plastics. The hull construction is in fibreglass with vacuum-bonded 1 in Airex core on the sides and a double layer of ¾ in Airex on the bottom. Where appropriate unidirectional and biaxial materials are used extensively. All structural bulkheads, lower soles, exterior decks and superstructure are fibreglass composite. All stringers are foam and fibreglass. The exterior skin is laid up with isophthalic resin for added blister resistance. The bottom is triple-coated with International Paint 2000 epoxy and then double-coated with Hysol antifouling paint.

Specifications

Length overall	29.88 m
Beam	6.71 m
Displacement, min	65.3 t
Displacement, max	83 t
Propulsive power	2 × 805 kW
Max speed	26 kts
Operational speed	22.5 kts

Propulsion: The main engines are 2 × DDC 12V 92TAB, 805 kW each at 2,300 rpm, driving 2 × Michigan Wheel Dynaquad, 4-blade, 1067 × 91.4 mm Nibral Alloy propellers.

Tahiti

Delivered in Spring 1991, this is the second in the Westship Series and was designed by Jack Sarin.

Specifications

Length overall	29.12 m
Beam	6.91 m
Draught	1.68 m
Displacement	74.83 t
Passengers	10
Fuel capacity	13,250 l
Water capacity	2,840 l
Max speed	24 kts
Operational speed	18 kts

Structure: The hull is FRP/Airex core, and the superstructure is FRP/composite.
Propulsion: The main engines are Caterpillar 3412.

Bluefin

This boat was delivered to California Fish and Game in Spring 1991.

Specifications

Length overall	19.77 m
Beam	5.84 m
Passengers	9
Fuel capacity	9,463 l
Water capacity	1,135 l
Max speed	30 kts

Structure: The hull is FRP/Airex core, and the superstructure is wood/fibreglass.
Propulsion: The main engines are 2 × DDC 12V 92TAB.

30 m FERRY
Catalina Express
Islander Express

Delivered in 1994 these two vessels operate off the coast of Southern California for Catalina Express Lines. Licensed for coastwise service (20 miles from harbour of safe refuge), the boats will carry 149 passengers at speeds of up to 32 knots.

The hull form features modified propeller tunnels for increased propeller efficiency.

Specifications

Length overall	30 m
Beam	6.71 m
Passengers	149
Fuel capacity	9,500 l
Water capacity	418 l
Propulsive power	2 × 1,491 kW
Operational speed	32 kts

Structure: The vessels are constructed from Fibre Reinforced Plastic (FRP) sandwich with an Airex core and fire retardant resin. The vessels were the first to be built in a new Westport adjustable hull mould.
Propulsion: The main engines are 2 × 16V 149TIB DDEC Detroit diesels, driving propellers.
Electrical system: The electrical power is supplied by two Northern Lights generators.

Catalina Express *1995*

Alaskan Explorer *1996*

Alaskan Explorer
Glacier Explorer
Nunatak

Alaskan Explorer was delivered to Kenai Fjords Tours in Spring 1995. The vessel is based in Seward, Alaska, for day tours to the scenic Kenai Fjords national park area.

The hull form incorporates propeller tunnels, and was designed by Jack Sarin based on Westport's 8500 series high-speed hull mould.

Glacier Explorer and *Nunatak* are both scheduled to be delivered in mid-1996.

Specifications

Length overall	30 m
Beam	6.71 m
Passengers	149
Fuel capacity	11,360 l
Water capacity	1,135 l
Propulsive power	2 × 1,305 kW
Operational speed	28 kts

Propulsion: The main engines are 2 × Caterpillar 3512 DITA diesels, each producing 1,305 kW at 1,800 rpm; driving propellers via a ZF460 gearbox.
Electrical system: The power is supplied by 2 × Northern Lights generators, 40 kW and 20 kW.

UPDATED

WING-IN-GROUND-EFFECT CRAFT

Company Listing by Country

China, People's Republic
CSSRC
Maric

Commonwealth of Independent States
Central Design Bureau of Hydrofoils

Germany
Botec Ingenieursozietät GmbH
Rhein-flugzeugbau GmbH (Rfb)

Japan
Dr Shigenori Ando
Tokushima Buri University
Tottori University

CHINA, PEOPLE'S REPUBLIC

CSSRC

China Ship Scientific Research Centre

Wuxi, Jiangsu, People's Republic of China

Tel: +86 (510) 6702131
Telex: 362016 CSSRC CN
Fax: +86 (510) 6701164

RAM-WING VEHICLE 902

A single-seat test vehicle.

The research plan behind the development of the 902 was begun in 1979 and a programme of theoretical and wind tunnel experimental research was carried out which provided solutions for the particular problem of longitudinal stability encountered by such craft when operating in and out of ground-effect. The 902 was built in 1983 and first flew on 12 November 1984.

Take-off can be achieved in waves up to 0.4 or 0.5 m with winds of Beaufort 6 to 7. The craft can be flown in and out of ground-effect and in the surface-effect region of 0.6 to 8 m altitude it can fly safely without any automatic stabilising device.

Specifications

Length overall	9.55 m
Span	5.8 m
Weight, max	0.4 t
Weight, min	0.3 t
Payload	0.1 t
Take-off distance	150 m
Take-off speed	40.5 kts
Operational speed	65 kts
Operational limitation	wave height 0.5 m Beaufort 6-7

Propulsion: The main engines are 2 × HS-350A, 15 kW each, aircraft piston engines, driving 2 × fixed-pitch, aircraft type propellers.

XTW-1 in cruising flight

1991

XTW-1

Following the success of the 902 a larger ram-wing craft was built, the XTW-1, for lake and river communications duties. This craft has a weight of 950 kg and is powered by two 30 kW piston engines giving it a cruise speed of 70 knots, with four people on board. A retractable undercarriage is incorporated for slipway handling.

Wing-in-ground-effect craft built by China Ship Scientific Research Centre (XTW-2) **1996**

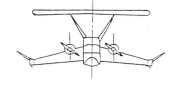

XTW-2

With the experience gained with the 902 and XTW-1, a much larger project was embarked upon in 1988. The XTW-2 was built in 1990 and performance testing was completed in 1992. Operations commenced in 1993. The main centre hull is fitted with a passenger cabin with 14 seats. Provision is made for two pilots as long distance operations are envisaged. The aisle width in the passenger cabin is 40 cm and ceiling height allows for standing of passengers when entering and disembarking.

Specifications

Length overall	18.5 m
Span	12.72 m
Weight, max	3.6 t
Payload	1.2 t
Propulsive power	448 kW (take-off)
Operational speed	80-100 kts
Flight altitude	1 m
Range	485 n miles
Operational limitation	Sea State 3

Propulsion: The main engines are 2 × IO-540 K1B5 aircraft piston engines.

UPDATED

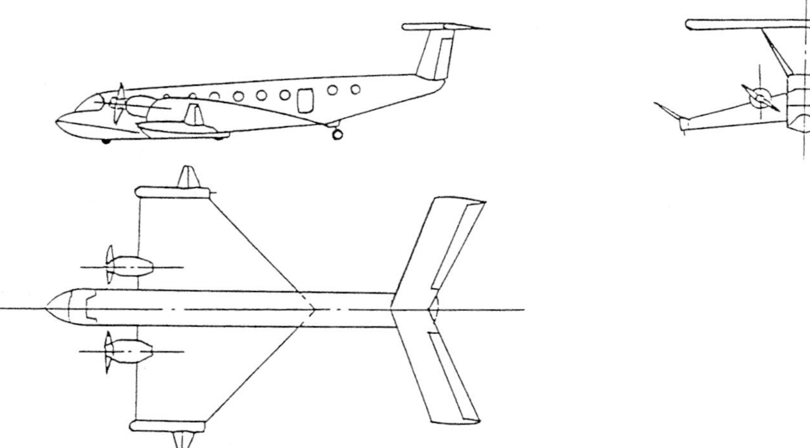

XTW-2 in flight over the China Sea **1996**

MARIC

Marine Design and Research Institute of China

314 Sichuan Road, Central, PO Box 002-053, Shanghai, People's Republic of China

Tel: +86 (21) 321 5044
Telex: 33029 MARIC CN
Fax: +86 (21) 329 0929

Sun Songhe, *Director*
Yun Liang, *Deputy Chief Naval Architect*

PAR WIG TYPE 750

This two-seat experimental Power-Assisted Ram-Wing-In-Ground-effect (PAR WIG) craft was completed in 1985, and over the period March 1985 to June 1987 over 40 trial flights were performed, exploring various operating conditions.

Over-water behaviour: can take-off and fly steadily in wave heights of 0.5 to 0.7 m with Beaufort 4 to 5 and gust 6 wind conditions. In horizontal flight, average pitch is 0.3° and roll, 0.53°.

Specifications

Length overall	8.47 m
Span	4.8 m
Weight, max	0.8 t
Payload	0.2 t
Propulsive power	4 × 22 kW
Take-off distance	160 m
Take-off speed	24 kts
Max speed	71 kts
Flight altitude	0.5 m
Range	70 n miles

Structure: Built in GRP with aircraft construction techniques.

Propulsion: Four 22 kW piston engines driving four ducted propellers Type DT-30.

PAR WIG TYPE 751 (AF-1)

This 20 passenger PAR WIG is currently under construction and expected to be completed during 1994.

Reference: *20-Passenger Power-Augmented-Ram-Wing-In-Ground-Effect Craft (PAR WIG) Type AF-1* by Hu An-ding and Wang Gou-zhong, MARIC, Second International Conference for High-Performance Vehicles. CSNAME, Shenzhen, China 12-15 November 1992.

VERIFIED

MARIC PAR WIG Type 750 coming ashore

1991

MARIC PAR WIG Type 750

1991

COMMONWEALTH OF INDEPENDENT STATES

CENTRAL DESIGN BUREAU OF HYDROFOILS

51 Svobody Street, Nizhni Novgorod, Russia, CIS

Tel: +7 (831) 225 1037
Telex: 151348
Fax: +7 (831) 225 0248

B V Chubikov, *General Director, Chief Designer*
V V Sokolov, *Chief Designer, Ekranoplan Programme*

and

KRYLOV SHIPBUILDING RESEARCH INSTITUTE

44 Moskovskoye Street, 196158 St Petersburg, Russia, CIS

Tel: +7 (812) 293 5482

Prof V M Pashin, D Sc (Tech), CMAS, *Director*

The above two organisations are working in co-operation on wing-in-ground-effect designs.

SDVPs

SDVP is a Russian abbreviation for Dynamic Air Cushion Vehicles.

In 1990 first details were published in the USSR, on a series of designs of wing-in-ground-effect craft developed under the direction of Dr R Ye Alekseev of the Central Design Bureau of Hydrofoils. The need for these craft arises from the speed limitations of hydrofoils and the appreciable draught and limited speed of catamarans in long distance river operations. The type of wing-in-ground-effect craft under development employ the power-assisted-lift principle, or PAR WIG (Power-Assisted Ram-Wing-In-Ground-effect) as it is sometimes known. The designs have over-hard-surface as well as over-water capability.

The first design to be built is the Volga-2.

VOLGA-2

This craft can overcome uneven surfaces and obstacles up to 0.4 m in height. The engines for Volga-2 are two VAZ-413 'rotor-piston' engines, believed to be rotary engines. Experimental data gained during trials of Volga-2 show propulsion economics to be on a level with existing hydrofoils. Further details of this craft are given in the table that follows.

An interesting aspect of the SDVP designs is the use of soft balloon-type structures to give the craft amphibious capabilities; the main structures are built in light alloys.

The Gorky Institute of Water Transportation Engineers (GIIVTOM), together with the Scientific Industrial Society (NPO) of the Central Design Bureau of Hydrofoils and the United Volga River Shipping Line (VORP), have carried out research appraising the technical possibilities and economic expediency of using these wing-in-ground-effect craft. As an example it was found that the route Nizhni Novgorod to Kazan, 432 km, could show positive economic results if wing-in-ground-effect craft were to be used for passenger-carrying services.

In the accompanying table the Raketa, Meteor, Kometa and Vykhr craft are design studies; Volga-2 has been built.

A.90.150 EKRANOPLAN

There were five of these craft built, with three remaining. Working prototypes of cargo versions have been built enabling the economics of future passenger-carrying versions to be predicted. The fuselage is of a relatively simple girder and stringer design and, like the wings, is divided into watertight

Craft Type Name

Characteristics	Volga-2	Raketa-2	Raketa-2.2	Meteor-2	Kometa-2	Vykhr-2 (Whirlwind)
Passenger capacity	8	50	90	120	150	250
RF River Register class	R	O	O	O	M	M
Weight	2.5 t	16 t	31 t	32 t	42 t	105 t
Length	11.3 m	26.2 m	34.8 m	36 m	25 m	54 m
Width	7.63 m	14.9 m	19.8 m	20 m	N/K	28 m
Draught	0.2 m	0.35 m	0.5 m	0.45 m	0.5 m	0.7 m
Engine	2 VAZ-413 RPD 2 × 95 kW	2 TVD-10 Type M601 turboprop 2 × 662 kW	3 TB7-117C turboprop 3 × 1,795 kW	2 AP-24 turboprop 2 × 1,840 kW	2 D-36 turbofan 2 × 6,500 kg thrust	2 D-36 turbofan 2 × 6,500 kg thrust
Speed	120 km/h 65 kts	150 km/h 80 kts	150-180 km/h 80-97 kts	170 km/h 92 kts	185 km/h 100 kts	280 km/h 150 kts
Range	500 km (270 n miles)	500 km (270 n miles)	800 km (432 n miles)	800 km (432 n miles)	930 km (500 n miles)	1,500 km (800 n miles)
Seaworthiness (wave height)	0.5 m	1.25 m	1.25 m	1.5 m	Beaufort 4	Beaufort 5
Crew						
watch	1	3	3	4	4	6
total aboard	2	6	6	8	8	12

Volga-2 8 passenger, 65 knot wing-in-ground-effect craft (A Belyaev) **1995**

compartments so that the craft will float while at rest. The fuselage is divided into three parts; the nose section with the flight deck and crew service area, a middle section containing the cargo or passenger area, and the tail section which houses auxiliary machinery.

The nose-mounted jet engines have pivoted exhaust nozzles; during take-off the jet exhaust streams are directed beneath the wing to boost the ram-air pressure beneath the wing. On changing to cruising flight the nozzles are redirected to provide horizontal thrust, accelerating the craft until cruising speed is reached; the take-off jet units are then shut down. The same procedure is used when landing the craft to reduce hydrodynamic loading. The fuselage nose location of the jet units allows their intakes to be positioned in the contours of the nose in such a way as to minimise aerodynamic resistance.

In cruising flight the craft is propelled by the NK-12 turboprop installation mounted high at the fin and tailplane intersection in order to keep the intake away from sea spray as far as it is feasible.

Pitching stability is more difficult to achieve for a craft operating in ground-effect mode than in normal free flight, because it is influenced by the flight altitude as well as the angle of attack. The Ekranoplan has a very large tailplane to counter this problem, which is greater increased in efficiency by the propeller slipstream.

A.90.150 Ekranoplan in flight (A Belyaev) **1995**

A.90.150 Ekranoplan loading cargo **1992**

A.90.150 Ekranoplan taking off **1995**

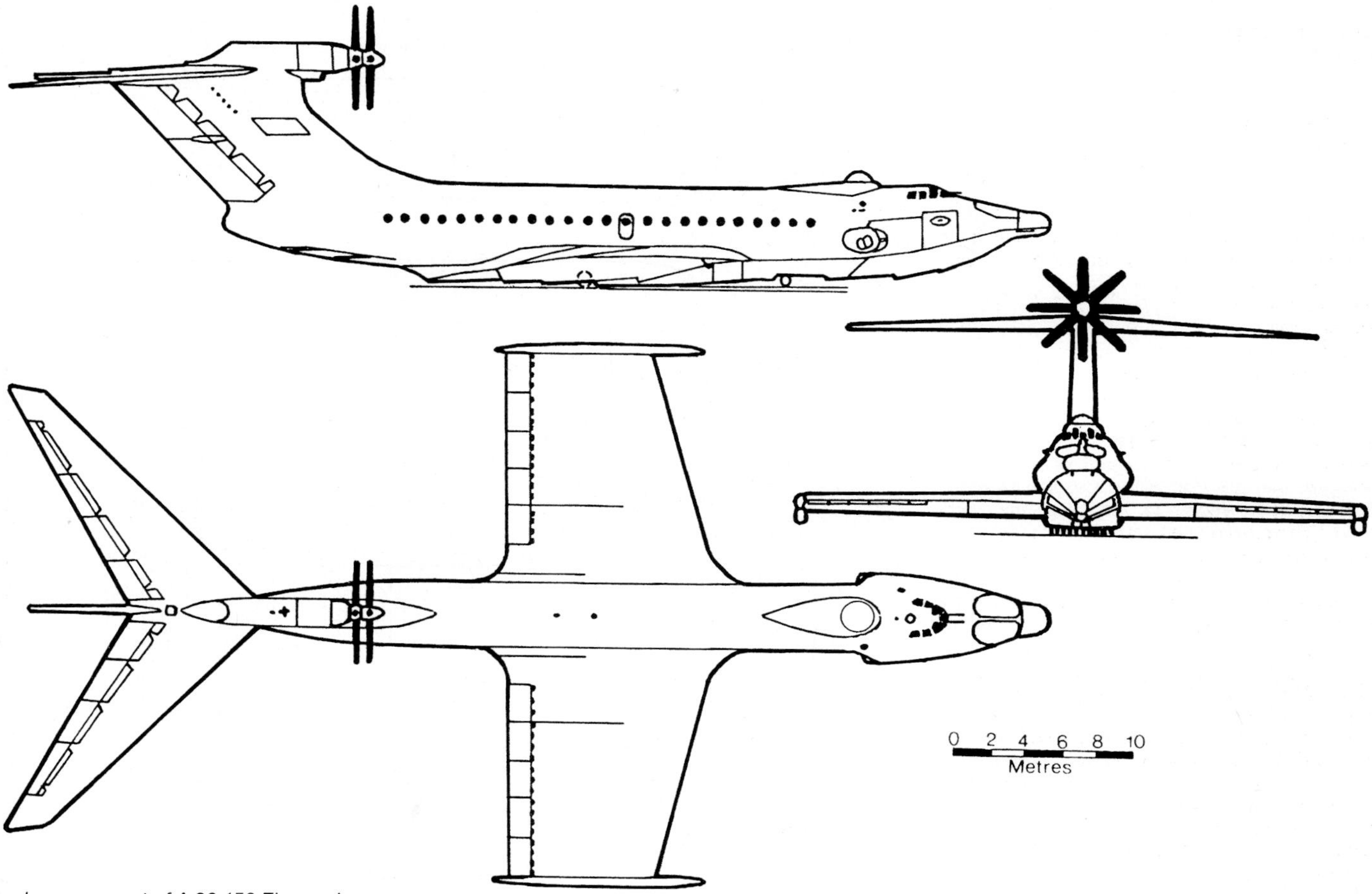

0 2 4 6 8 10
Metres

General arrangement of A.90.150 Ekranoplan **1995**

Caspian Monster at speed (A Belyaev) **1995**

Specifications

Length overall	58 m
Span	31.5 m
Height	15 m
Weight, normal take-off	110 t
Weight, max	125 t
Passengers	100-150 (single-deck version)
	350 (twin-deck version)
Fuel capacity	33,000 l (max)
	17,650 l (normal)
Propulsive power	11,000 kW
Operational speed	216 kts
Range	1,080 n miles
Operational limitation	Beaufort 4-5

Propulsion: The main engines are 2 × Kuznetsov NK-8 turbofan engines, up to 10.5 t thrust, for take-off, and 1 × Kuznetsov NK-12, 11000 kW, turboprop for sustained cruising.

Outfit: Passenger cabin length: 25 m
width: 3.3 m
height: 3 m
volume: 240 m^3.

Raketa-2 design, a 90 passenger, 90 knot craft

1992

A.90.150 EKRANOPLAN, CARGO VERSION

During the development of the cargo model, a version was designed to have the fuselage split in two vertically, in order to facilitate loading. It is a unique project, with no equivalent known of anywhere else.

Specifications

Payload	30 t
Range	540 n miles

Outfit: Cargo section length: 25 m
width: 3.3 m
height: 3 m.

70 m HAWK

Three of these craft are reported to have been constructed, with production of passenger-carrying versions scheduled to start in 1995.

Specifications

Length overall	70 m
Beam	35 m
Weight, max	160 t
Max speed	300 kts

LUN (CASPIAN MONSTER)

The Russians built the first large-scale WIG craft in the 1960s; the 500 t, so called Caspian Monster, which remained secret to the West until very recently. There have been several (at least five), of these military craft built to various designs since, with at least two protoypes completed in 1982, and one craft of the Lun design currently building at the Central Design Bureau of Hydrofoils. The original Caspian Monster prototype is reported to have crashed and sunk in the Caspian Sea in 1980.

The craft are ideally suited for rapid transportation of forces, with a greater payload capacity, greater range, and less fuel consumption than conventional aircraft, whilst operating at a comparable speed.

The Caspian Monster Lun design apparently went into military service in 1989, but all of these craft are now reported to have been withdrawn from military activities. The craft and associated technology are reportedly now up for sale.

The craft is propelled by eight turbofan engines, and the craft is armed with six anti-ship missiles.

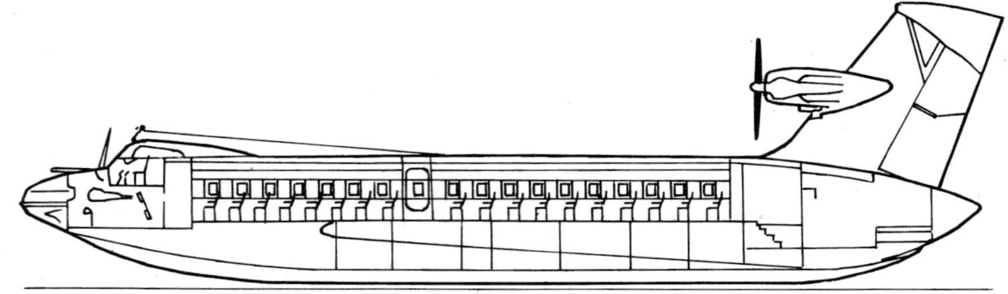

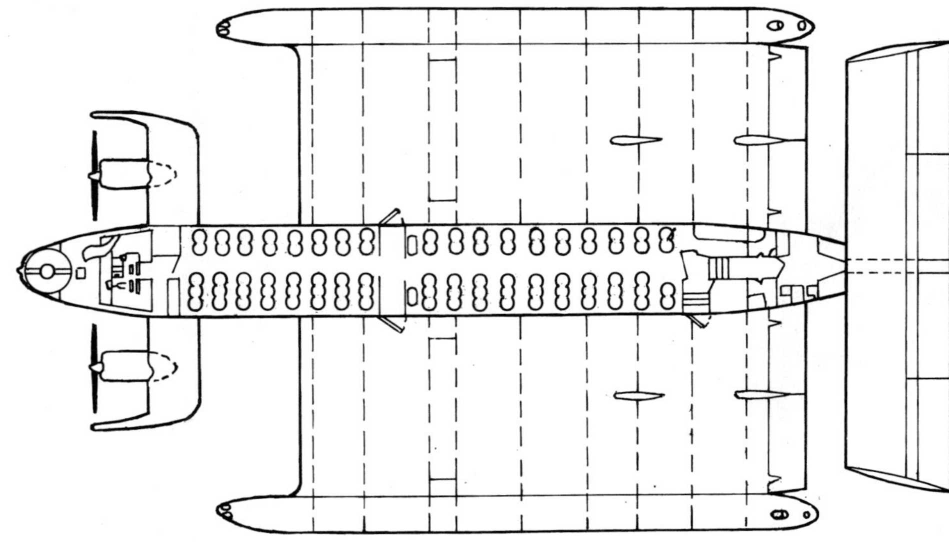

Caspian Monster SM-8 development craft (A Belyaev)

1995

Specifications

Length overall	75 m
Span	41 m
Weight	400 t
Flight altitude	4 m
Max speed	300 kts
Range	1,620 n miles

VERIFIED

GERMANY

BOTEC INGENIEURSOZIETÄT GmbH

Odenwaldring 24, D-64401 Gross-Bieberau, Germany

Tel: +49 (6162) 3624/1013
Fax: +49 (6162) 1014

Günther W Jörg, *Principal*
Reiner A Jörg, *Assistant*

Günther W Jörg was for a number of years a constructor, works manager and development engineer for various West German Vertical Take-Off and Landing (VTOL) projects. He sees his Aerodynamic Ground-Effect Craft (AGEC) concept as a means of providing fast, economical and comfortable long distance travel. His experiments began in the 1960s with a series of radio-controlled models. The first Günther Jörg ram-wing, a two-seater powered by a modified Volkswagen engine, was designed in 1973 and first flew in 1974. After an extensive test programme, Jörg II was designed, performing its first flight in 1976. This incorporated more than 25 design improvements and has travelled more than 10,000 km. During 1978 and 1979, Jörg designed a glassfibre-hulled four- to six-seater Jörg III. The first prototype was completed in 1980. Designs are being prepared for larger and faster craft capable of carrying heavier loads over greater distances.

Stabilisation about the pitch and roll axes and maintaining the flying height of the AGEC can be regulated independently by the ground/water surface reaction and therefore requires only a simple steering control for movement around the vertical axis. This basic requirement led to the development of a tandem wing configuration, the handling characteristics of which were first tested on models and then on two-seat research craft. Tests showed that the tandem wings had good aerodynamic qualities, even above turbulent water, with or without water contact.

AGECs have ample buoyancy and are seaworthy, even while operating at low-speed (cruising in displacement condition). After increasing speed the craft lifts off the surface of the water and the resulting air cushion reduces the effects of the waves.

After losing water contact the boat starts its ram-wing flight at a height of 4 to 8 per cent of the profile depth. A two-seater with a wing span of 3.2 m and a profile length of 3.05 m will have a flying height above the water surface of up to 0.9 m at a speed of 140 km/h. The low power requirement of this type of craft is achieved through the improved lift-to-drag ratio of a wing-in-ground-effect as compared to free flight.

A craft of more than 300 tonnes would have a wing chord of 36 m and fly under ground-effect conditions between 3.5 and 7 m. It would have a wing span of 40 m and a length of 100 m, requiring engine thrust of 40,000 kW. Cruising speed would be 250 km/h from 7,350 kW and craft of this size could travel all year round over 90 per cent of the world's sea areas.

The following operational possibilities are foreseen:

Inland Waterways and Offshore Areas: Suitable for rescue boats, customs, police, coastguard units, patrol boats, high-speed ferries, leisure craft.

Coastal Traffic: Large craft would be operated as fast passenger and passenger/car ferries and mixed traffic freighters.

TAF VIII-2 in service in Asia **1995**

TAF VIII-4S during ground test **1992**

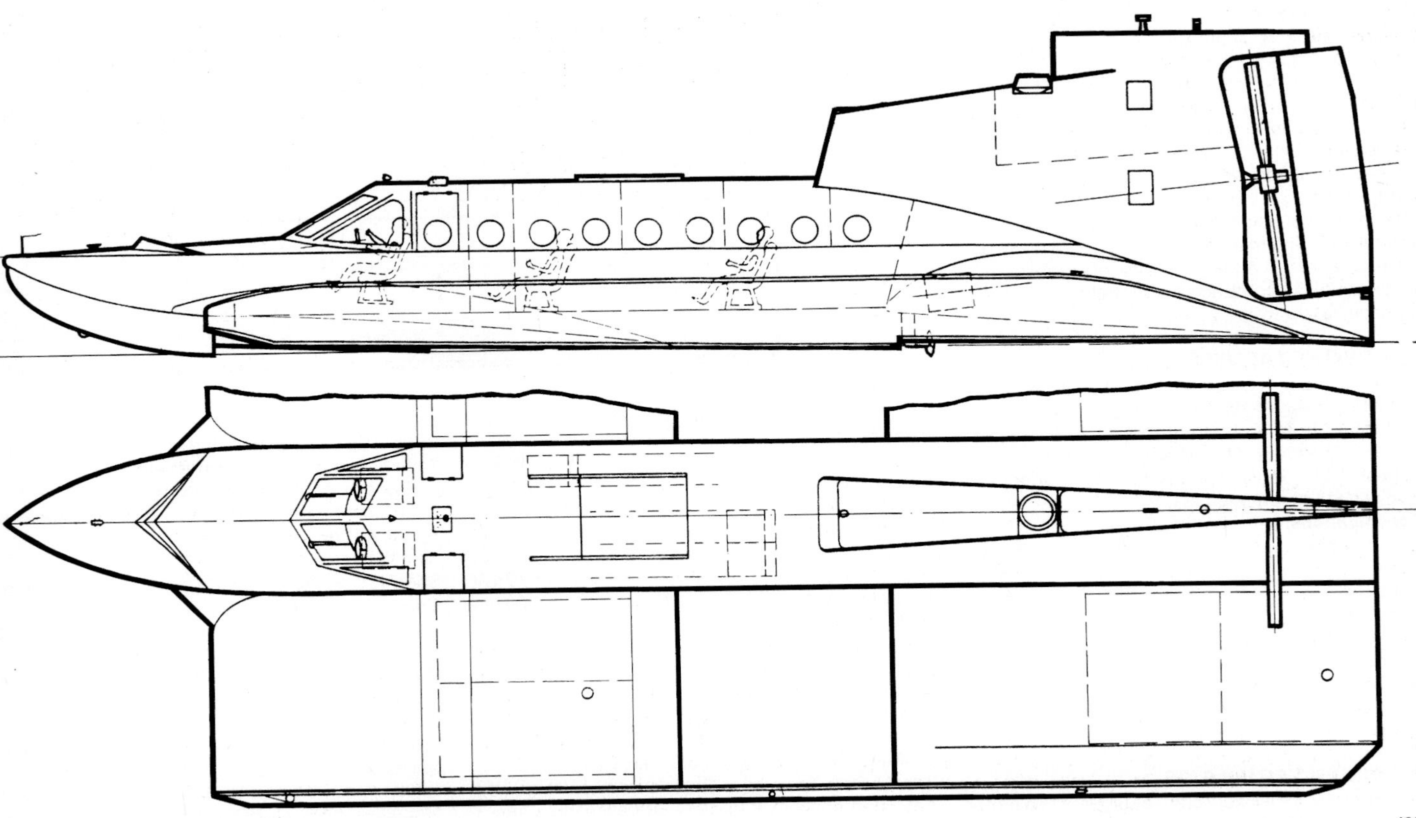
General arrangement of Jörg TAF VIII-5 Flairboat **1995**

Overland: Suitable for crossing swamps, flat sandy areas, snow and ice regions. Another possible application is as a high-speed tracked skimmer operating in conjunction with a guide carriage above a monorail.

Small craft, displacing 1 tonne or more, can travel over the supporting surface at a height of 304 mm or more at a speed of 96.6 to 144.8 km/h.

Larger craft, weighing 10 to 50 tonnes will be able to fly at a height of 914 mm to 1.98 m at a speed of 129 to 177 km/h.

Coastal craft displacing more than 100 tonnes will fly at a height of 3 m or more.

The basic advantage of the AGEC is its ability to transport passengers and freight far quicker than conventional ship, rail or road transport. The ratio between empty weight and service load is approximately 2:1 but can certainly be improved. Fuel consumption is 80 to 85 per cent lower than that of a boat of similar construction. A high degree of ride comfort is achieved with these craft.

The Airfoil-Flairboats of Jörg design are designed in accordance with International marine standards.

Details of early Jörg craft can be found in the 1992-93 edition of this book.

A Jörg Airfoil Flairboat at high-speed showing condensation trails, not spray **1992**

JÖRG V
TAF VIII-4S

This new Jörg craft underwent its first ground tests in September 1986. Open sea tests in the North Sea started in September 1987.

Specifications

Length overall	17.95 m
Weight, max	3.5 t
Passengers	5-8
Propulsive power	485 kW
Operational speed	45-90 kts
Flight altitude	0.6 m
Range	269 n miles

Propulsion: The main engine is 1 × 485 kW Textron Lycoming LTX 101 turboshaft with water-methanol injection available for 10% power increase for take-off. One diesel engine driving a retractable marine propeller, MT-P 4-blade, 2.9 m diameter, cable/hydraulically controlled; via 9 × V-belts transmissions (Optibelt, Höxter, Germany).

Jörg TAF VIII-3 with engine cover raised **1992**

FLAIRBOAT TAF VIII-5

Intended for river and inter-island traffic. The first TAF VIII-5 was under construction on the Oder River in Autumn 1991.

Specifications

Length overall	19.8 m
Span	8.5 m
Draught, hullborne	0.4 m
Weight, max	9.2 t
Payload	1.5 t
Crew	2
Passengers	12-15
Propulsive power	2 × 550 kW
Max speed	108 kts
Operational speed	95 kts
Range	200 n miles

Structure: Aluminium and composite plastics.

Propulsion: The main engines are 2 × 550 kW petrol engines or 1 × 1,200 kW 12-cylinder diesel. Water propulsion: retractable propeller for harbour manoeuvring.

FLAIRBOAT TAF VIII-3

Construction of this new project began in Germany at the beginning of 1991. It is being built as an eight-seat patrol boat and is due to go into series production. The first craft was launched at the end of August 1991 and high-speed tests on the Oder River followed in September 1991.

Specifications

Length overall	14 m
Span	5.85 m
Hull beam	1.6 m
Weight, min	2.2 t
Take-off speed	39 kts
Operational speed	76 kts
Max speed	84 kts
Flight altitude	0.35 m

Propulsion: The engine is a 7.8 l, V8.

FLAIRSHIP TAF VIII-5/25

This design is for a luxury craft (equivalent to a motor yacht specification) carrying up to 10 people. The craft is scheduled for delivery in 1996.

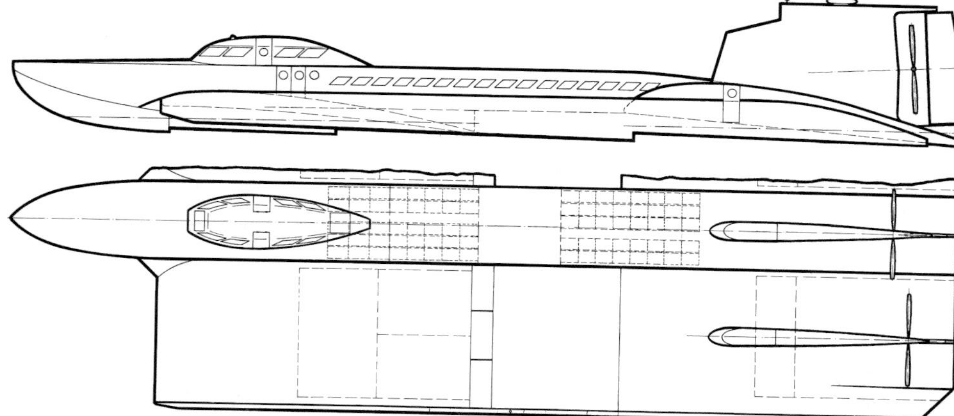

Flairship TAF VIII-7/3D **1996**

Specifications

Length overall	25.2 m
Length waterline	24.2 m
Span	13.4 m
Weight, max	15 t
Crew	3
Propulsive power	1,540 kW
Operational speed	90 kts
Flight altitude	0.75-0.93 m
Range	432 n miles

Propulsion: The engine is 1 × 18-cylinder diesel, 1,540 kW, driving 1 × 4.5 m diameter air propeller, 2 × steerable, retractable water propellers.

FLAIRSHIP TAF VIII-7/3D (DESIGN)

The TAF VIII-7 design is Botec's largest design and has been conceived to carry 80 passengers and 3 crew at speeds up to 124 knots in sea conditions up to 2.5 m significant wave height. With two of the three engines running the speed is reduced to 119 knots and a 1.5 m wave height limitation. With only one of the three engines running the speed and wave limitation are 92 knots and 0.5 m respectively.

Specification

Length overall	45.7 m
Span	18.6 m
Crew	3
Passengers	80
Fuel capacity	6,000 l
Max speed	124 kts
Range	750 n miles
Operational limitation	2.5 m significant wave height

Propulsion: The vessel is powered by three high-speed air cooled diesel engines each rated at 1,700 kW and each driving a variable pitch air propeller.

UPDATED

RHEIN-FLUGZEUGBAU GmbH (RFB)

Head office and main works: Flugplatz, PO Box 408, D-4050 Mönchengladbach 1, Germany

Tel: +49 (2161) 682243
Fax: +49 (2161) 682273

Other works: Flugplatz, D-2401 Lübeck-Blankensee, Germany

Dipl-Ing Hartmut Stiegler, *President*

RFB X-113 Am during flight demonstration over Wattenmeer **1987**

RFB is engaged in the development and construction of airframe structural components, with particular emphasis on wings and fuselages made entirely of glassfibre-reinforced resins. Research and design activities include studies for the Federal German Ministry of Defence.

Current manufacturing programmes include the series production of Fantrainer 400/600 and components and assemblies made of light alloy, steel, glass and carbon fibre-reinforced resins for aircraft and quantity production; manufacturing and maintenance of ejection seats and energy-absorbing armoured seats for helicopters; emergency overhead oxygen boxes for airliners.

As a result of Dr Lippisch's work on the wing-in-ground-effect machine X-112 in the USA, RFB bought several of his patents and further developed the wing-in-ground-effect technology in close co-operation with Dr Lippisch.

After elaborate towing and wind tunnel tests supplemented by radio control model tests, the X-113 was derived, a 1:1.7 scaled down version of a four-seat craft. This single seat trimaran-type craft, built of composite materials in a special sandwich construction developed by RFB, successfully underwent tests on Lake Constance in October 1970.

During additional trials, which were performed in Autumn 1972 in the Weser estuary and the North Sea coastal region over rough water, the X-113's design and the chosen composite construction method proved fully effective.

The flight performance measurements confirmed the analytically expected improvements with respect to lift and drag resulting in gliding angles of 1:23 close to the surface. Even flights out of ground-effect were successfully performed with gliding angles of 1:7 because of the low aspect ratio during this flight phase.

The X-113 showed inherent stabilities even with respect to altitude keeping. Speeds of 97 knots (180 km/h) were achieved with a power of 28 kW (38 hp) in ground-effect. The ability to achieve bank attitudes permits very small curve radii and excellent manoeuvrability. Remarkably good sea behaviour was shown from the outset. Take-offs and landings in wave heights of about 0.75 m presented no problem.

RFB X-114 Aerofoil boat with hydrofoils extended **1987**

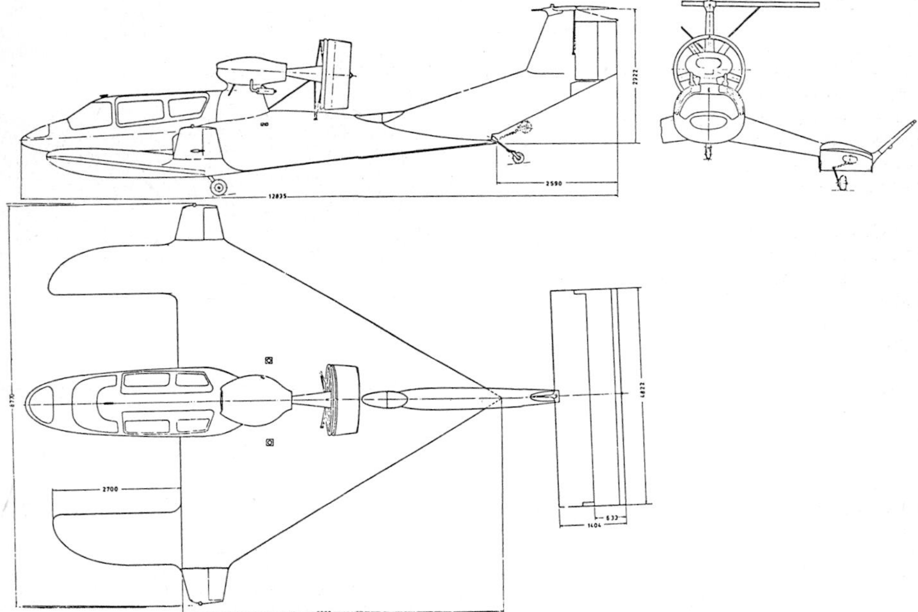

General arrangement of RFB X-114 **1987**

RFB X-114 AND -114H AEROFOIL BOATS

Evolved from the X-113, this six- to seven-seater has a maximum take-off weight of 1,500 kg and is fitted with a retractable wheel undercarriage, enabling it to operate from land or water.

Power is provided by a 200 hp Lycoming IO-360 four-cylinder, horizontally opposed air-cooled engine driving a specially designed RheinFlugzeugbau ducted fan. Range, with 100 kg of fuel, is more than 1,000 km. Operational speed is 75 to 200 km/h.

An initial trials programme was successfully completed in 1977. A new series of trials is now being undertaken after hydrodynamic modifications which included the fitting of hydrofoils beneath the sponsons, raising maximum take-off weight to 1,750 kg. In this configuration it is known as the X-114H.

The vehicle is designed to operate over waves up to 1.5 m in ground-effect and can therefore be used without restriction during 80 per cent of the year in the Baltic Sea area and 60 per cent of the year in the North Sea. In high seas of more than 1.5 m, take-off and landing takes place in waters near the coast. Flying is virtually unrestricted, providing due allowance is made for the loss in economy.

Fuel consumption costs, while flying in ground-effect, are lower than those for cars. RFB states that its economics cannot be matched by any other form of transport aircraft.

Although built primarily as a research craft to extend the experience gained with the X-113 Am single seater, Aerofoil boats of the size of the X-114 are suitable for air taxi work along coastlines, the supervision of restricted areas, patrol, customs and coastguard purposes, and search and rescue missions.

Without any significant new research the construction of a vehicle with a take-off weight of approximately 18,000 kg is possible. On a vehicle of this size, the ratio of empty weight to take-off weight is less than 50 per cent.

Specifications

Length overall	12.8 m
Span	7 m
Weight, max	1,500 kg (X-114)
	1,750 kg (X-114H)
Payload	500 kg
Max speed	108 kts
Operational speed	81 kts
Range	1,160 n miles

AIRFISH FF1/FF2

Further application of the ground-effect technology resulted in a prototype for a new two-seat sports vehicle, the Airfish FF1/FF2. Unlike the X-113 and X-114, which were operational out of ground-effect in free flight, the FF1 and FF2 are solely operational in ground-effect. These craft were developed and successfully tested in 1988 with the objective of optimising the handling of the craft as a 'boat' in ground-effect.

AIRFISH 3

The first preproduction craft Airfish 3 successfully passed all function tests in September/October 1990 and proved all performance data.

Built from composite plastics, metal and fabric, an interesting feature of this craft is the incorporation of a retractable water rudder integrated with an electrically driven propeller with two forward and one reverse gears for maximum manoeuvrability in harbour areas. The two-cylinder BMW Boxer engine with an output of 60 kW (75 hp) drives the

The RFB Airfish FF-2 showing its inflated wing structure ***1989***

ducted reduction gear-controlled six-bladed propeller.

By virtue of its specific aerodynamic layout the vehicle always stays close to the surface over which it is operating, but permitting single 'dynamic jumps' over obstacles. This capability is made possible by using the stored kinetic energy but which does not, however, permit continued free flight out of ground-effect. Thus the vehicle, like a hovercraft, can be considered as a boat thereby avoiding the necessity of applying aircraft regulations and having a licensed pilot for its operation.

To make the boat more manoeuvrable in ports its width may be reduced by 1.5 m by pivoted winglets folded electrically by a push-button in the cockpit.

For road transport the Airfish loaded on a boat trailer can be towed by a motor car.

Specifications

Weight, min	425 kg
Weight, max	650 kg
Fuel capacity	35 kg
Take-off speed	39 kts
Operational speed	65 kts
Max speed	78 kts
Flight altitude	0.1-1 m
Range	175 n miles

VERIFIED

Airfish 3 engaged in performance tests in September 1990 ***1991***

JAPAN

TOKUSHIMA BURI UNIVERSITY

School of Engineering, Shido-Town, Kagawa Prefecture, Japan 769-21

Fax: +81 878 94 4201

with

DR SHIGENORI ANDO

Motoige 17-75, Iwasaki, Nissin-Cho, Aichi Prefecture, 470-01 Japan

Tel: +81 (5617) 33246

Dr Ando has developed a number of designs for Power-Assisted Ram-Wing-In-Ground-effect (PAR WIG) craft. Radio-controlled models have been built of several configurations, these developments following his earlier work with Nagoya University.

Reference: *PAR-WIG Performance Prediction during Acceleration from Water-Borne to Air-Borne,* by Dr Shigenori Ando and Michiyo Kato. Transactions of the Japan Society for Aeronautical and Space Sciences 1991 and 1995.

UPDATED

PAR WIG model development by Dr Shigenori Ando ***1992***

TOTTORI UNIVERSITY

Department of Applied Mathematics and Physics, Faculty of Engineering, Koyama, Tottori 680, Japan

Tel: +81 (857) 280321
Fax: +81 (857) 310882

Syozo Kubo, *Professor*

μSKY I AND μSKY II (MARINE SLIDER PROGRAMME)

This ram wing project was first announced by Mitsubishi on 1 February 1990. Both prototypes were aimed at the eventual production of a commercial craft for leisure use but it is understood that this work has now been suspended.

μSky I

μSky I first flew in December 1988. The structure is rigid; an earlier craft, Rameses I (USA built), employed a flexible structure.

Specifications

Length overall	4.4 m
Span	3.5 m
Weight, min	0.2 t
Weight, max	0.3 t
Crew	1
Propulsive power	48 kW
Take off speed	35 kts
Max speed	44 kts

Propulsion: The engine is a water-cooled gasoline engine 48 kW (Rotax 532), driving a 4-blade, fixed-pitch propeller.
Structure: Hull: GFRP.
Wing: GFRP.
Tail: aluminium plus cloth.

μSky II

μSky II first flew on 8 February 1990 at Kobe, Hyogo Prefecture.

The prototype craft obtained the Ship Inspection Certificate on 17 July 1990, and five preproduction craft on 11 September 1991 from the Japanese Government.

Specifications

Length overall	5.95 m
Span	4.32 m
Weight, min	0.3 t
Weight, max	0.4 t
Crew	2
Propulsive power	48 kW
Take off speed	33.5 kts
Max speed	46 kts
Flight altitude	0.5 m

Propulsion: The engine is a water-cooled gasoline 48 kW (Rotax 532); propeller diameter: 1.54 m.
Propeller number of blades: 3.
Propeller pitch: fixed.
Propeller material: GFRP.
Structure: Hull: GFRP.
Wing: aluminium plus cloth.
Tail: aluminium plus cloth.
Control: Air and water rudders are fitted.
The vehicle may be dismantled for transportation.

VERIFIED

μ*Sky I* ***1992***

μ*Sky II* ***1992***

CIVIL OPERATORS OF HIGH-SPEED CRAFT

Company Listing by Country

Argentina
Ferry Lineas

Australia
Boat Torque Cruises Pty Ltd
Fantasea Cruises
Gordon River Cruises Pty Ltd
Great Adventures
Great Keppel Island Tourist Services Ltd
Hayman Resort
Mackenzies Marine
Peel's Tourist and Ferry Services Pty Ltd
Pure Pleasure Cruises
Queensland Government
Quicksilver Connections Ltd
Rottnest Express Pty Ltd
Roylen Cruises
State Transit Authority of New South Wales
Tangalooma Island Resort Ltd
White Dolphin Cruises

Bahrain
Coastguard Directorate

Belgium
Eurosense Hoversounding NV
Oostende Lines

Bolivia
Crillon Tours SA

Brazil
Norsul Offshore SA
Transtur

Bulgaria
Black Sea Shipping plc
Navibulgar

Canada
Canadian Coast Guard Hovercraft Units
West Coast Canada
Eastern Canada
Cominco Snip Operation

Chile
Patagonia Travelling Service

China, People's Republic
Cactec
Changjiang Shipping Corporation
Chongqing Shipping Companies
Dalian Steamship Co
Dalian Yuan Feng Ferry Company
Guangdong Province Navigation Company
Nantong High-Speed Passenger Ship Company
Ningbo Fast Ferries Ltd
Sanfu Shipping China
Shanghai Free Flying Transport
Shen Zhen Shipping
Shen Zhen Xun Long Transportation
Wan Shan District Company
Wuzhou Navigation Company
Yantai Marine

Commonwealth of Independent States
Black Sea Shipping Company
Far Eastern Shipping Company
Northern Shipping Company
Novorossiysk Shipping Company
Soviet Danube Shipping Company

Croatia
Atlas Turistička Plovidba
Kvarner Express International DD
Jadrolinija

Denmark
Cat-Link
Dampskibsselskabet (Dsøresund Ø) A/S
Gråhunbus
Grenna- Hundested
Supply-Trans A/S

Estonia
Sukkula
Tallink Express

France
Bateaux Gallus
Channiland
Corsica Ferries
Emeraude Lines
Naviland
Société National Corse Mediterranée (SNCM)
Surf SA

French Polynesia
Aremiti Pacific Cruises (Bora Bora Navette)
Ferry Transport
Leprado
SPI Maritime

Germany
AG EMS
Hallig und Inselreederi
Köln-Düsseldorfer Deutsche Rheinschiffahrt AG (KD)
Schiffahrtskontor Altes Land
TT-Line

Greece
Advanced Technology Cruises
Catamaran Lines
Ceres Hydrofoil Services
Dodecanese Hydrofoils
Giaimar Lines
Hermes
Ilio Lines
Nomikos
Paraskevas Shipping Company (Takistours)
Renatour SA
Santa Lines
Seajet Shipping

Guadeloupe
Antilles Trans-express
Société de Transports Maritimes Brudey Frères

Guam
Island Cruise Line Pacific Inc

Hong Kong
Castle Peak Power Company Ltd
China Merchant Development Company
Chu Kong Shipping Company Ltd
CTS-Parkview Ferry Services
Customs and Excise Department
Discovery Bay Transportation Services Ltd
Far East Hydrofoil Company Ltd
Hong Kong Hi-Speed Ferries Ltd
The Hong Kong & Yaumati Ferry Company Ltd
Royal Hong Kong Police Force, Marine Region
Panyu Nan Sha Shipping
Yuet Hing Marine Supplies Company Ltd

Hungary
Mahart Passnave Passengers Shipping Ltd

India
Damania Shipping
New India Business House Ltd
Shipping Corporation of India

Indonesia
Bahtera Segara Persanda
Bali Hai Cruises
Citra Bahari Nustraindo
PT Hover Maritim Semandera
PT Mabua Intan Express (PT Mahasara Buana)
Pulau Seribu Marine Resort
Quicksilver

Iran
Valfajre 8 Shipping

Italy
Adriatica di Navigazione SpA
Albadria
Alilauro-Gru.So.N. SpA
Alilauro SpA
Alimar SpA
Aliscafi Snav SpA
Caremar
Elba Ferries
Foderaro Navigazione
Linee Lauro Srl
Ministero Dei Trasporti
Misano Alta Velocita' Srl
Navigazione Lago di Como
Navigazione Libera Del Golfo SpA
Navigazione Lago Maggiore
Navigazione Sul Lago di Garda
Ocean Bridge Investments
Saremar
Siremar
Tirrenia Navigazione
Toremar
Vetor Srl

Japan
Awaji Ferry Boat Company
Awashima Kisen Company Ltd
Bantan Renraku Kisen
Biwako Kisen Company Ltd
Diamond Ferry Company
Fuke Kaiun Company Ltd
Goto Ryokaykusen Company Ltd
Hankyu Kisen Company Ltd
Higashi-Nihon Ferry Company
Hiroshima Imabari Kosokusen Company Ltd
Imabari Kosokusen Company Ltd
Ishizaki Kisen Company Ltd
Iwakuni Hashirajima Kosokusen Company Ltd
Kagoshima Shosen Company Ltd
Kaijo Access Company
Kato Kisen Company Ltd/Kansai Kisen Company Ltd Jet Line
Koshikishima Shosen Ltd
Kumejima Ferry Company Ltd
Kyodo Kisen Kaisha Ltd
Kyushi Ferry Boat Company
Kyushu Railway Company
Kyushu Shosen Company Ltd
Kyushu Yusen Company Ltd
Maritime Safety Agency of Japan
Marunaka Kisen Company Ltd
Meitetsu Kaijo Kankosen Company Ltd
Nankai Ferry Company Ltd
Oita Hover Ferry Company Ltd
OKI Kisen KK
Ryobi Unyu
Sado Kisen Kaisha
Sea-Com Cruise Corporation
Setonaikai Kisen Company Ltd (Seto Inland Sea Lines)
Shikoku Ferry Company (Bridge Line)
Tenmaya Marine Company Ltd
Third District Port Construction Bureau
Tokai Kisen
Tokushima Shuttle Line Company Ltd
Yaeyama Kanko Ferry Company
Yasuda Sangyo Kisen Company Ltd

Jordan
Arab Bridge Maritime Co
Jordan Ports Corporation

Korea, South
Dae-A Ferry Company Ltd
Dong Yang Express
Geo Je Haewoon
Government
Jung Ahang Express Company
Kang Won Hungup
Kumsan Hungup
Nam Hae Express Company
Semo Company Ltd Marine Craft
Seo Kyung Haewoon
Won Kwang Shipping

Company Listing by Country *continued*

Malaysia
Kuala Perlis Langkawi Ferry Service Sdn Bhd
Lada Langkawi Holdings
MISC
Sriwani Tours and Travel

Malta
Gozo Channel Company Ltd
Virtu Ferries Ltd

Mexico
Cruceros Maritimos del Caribe SA De CV
Pemex

Netherlands
Rederij G Doeksen en Zonen BV

New Zealand
Fiordland Travel Ltd NZ
Fullers Cruises Northland Ltd
Gulf Ferries Ltd
Interisland Line
Stewart Island Marine
Wanaka Lake Services Ltd

Norway
North Cape Minerals A/S
Finnmark Fylkesrsrederi og Ruteselskap
Fosen Trafikklag A/S
Fylkesbaatane i Sogn og Fjordane
Helgeland Trafikkselskap A/S
HSD
L Rødne and Sønner A/S
Møre og Romsdal Fylkesbåtar A/S
Namsos Trafikkselskap A/S
Nesodden-Bundefjord Dampskipsselskap A/S
Rogaland Trafikkselskap A/S
Saltens Dampskipsselskap A/S
Simon Møkster Shipping A/S
Sørlands Cruise
Torghatten Trafikkselskap A/S
TFDS
Vest-Trafikk A/S

Pakistan
Pakistan Water and Power Development Authority

Paraguay
Aliscafos Itaipu SA

Philippines
Aboitez Supercat
Grand Seaway Ferries Inc
Universal Aboitiz

Poland
Zegluga Gdanska

Portugal
Regiao Autonoma da Madeira Direcçao Regional de Portos

Puerto Rico
Puerto Rico Ports Authority

Saudi Arabia
Dery Shipping Lines
Saudi Aramco

Sierra Leone
Sierra Link

Singapore
Auto Batam Ferries
J & N Cruise Pte Ltd
Pelayaran Bintan Baruna Sakti
Resort Cruises (S) Pte Ltd
Shell Eastern Petroleum (Pte) Ltd
Sinba Shipping
Tian San Shipping Pte Ltd
Yang Passenger Ferry Service

Slovakia
Slovenská Plavba Dunajská Závod Osobnej Lodnej Dopravy (Passenger Transport Division)

Slovenia
Kompas International DD

Spain
Compañia Trasmediterranea SA
Flebasa Lines
Lineas Fred Olsen
Trasmapi
Islena de Navegacion SA

St Pierre Et Miquelon
Armement Borotra Frères

Sweden
Justin Management AB
Koster Marine
Pilen (Köpenhamnspilen AB)
Sea Containers Sweden AB
Stena Line

Taiwan
Tien Peng Yang Hovertravel Corporation
Tung Hsin Steamship Company Ltd

Thailand
Fast Ferry Siam Ltd
Jet Cat Tour Company Ltd
Thai General Transport Ltd

Tunisia
Sea Bus SA

Turkey
Istanbul Deniz Otobüsleri

United Kingdom
Condor Ltd
Hoverspeed Ltd
Hovertravel Ltd
Hoverwork Ltd
Isle of Man Steam Packet Company
Red Funnel Ferries
Sea Containers Ltd
Sea Containers Scotland Ltd
Stena Sealink Line
White Horse Ferries Ltd
Wightlink Ltd

United States of America
Alaska Travel
Arnold Transit Company
Bar Harbor Whale Watch
Blue and Gold Fleet
Bottom Time Adventures
Catalina Channel Express Lines
Catalina Passenger Services
Clipper Navigation Inc
Cross Sound Ferry Services
Express Navigation Inc
Florida Cruise
Golden Gate Ferry
Harbor Bay Maritime
Hawaiian Cruises Ltd
Hy-Line Cruises
Kenai Fjords Tours
New York Fast Ferries Services Inc
NY Waterway
Party Line Cruise Company
Phillips Cruises & Tours (Yukon River Cruises)
Put-In-Bay Boat Line
Red and White Fleet
Sayville Ferry Service Inc
Sea Jet Cruise Line
Sea Princess (Guam) Corporation
Shepler's Mackinac Island Ferry
Star Line
Washington State Ferries

Uruguay
Aliscafos
Buquebus
Transportes Anfibios SA

Virgin Islands (US)
Azam Marine
Nautical Trading Ltd
Virgin Hydrofoil Service
Zanzibar

CIVIL OPERATORS OF HIGH-SPEED CRAFT

The following abbreviations are used in this section:

ALH	Air-Lubricated-Hull craft
CAT	CATamaran vessel
FAMH	Foil-Assisted MonoHull vessel
F-CAT	Foil-CATamaran vessel
HOV	HOVercraft, amphibious capability
HYD	HYDrofoil, surface-piercing foils, fully immersed foils
MH	MonoHull vessel
SES	Surface-Effect Ship or sidewall hovercraft (non-amphibious)
SWATH	Small-Waterplane-Area Twin-Hull vessel
TRI	TRImaran
WPC	Wave Piercing Catamaran

ARGENTINA

FERRY LINEAS

Darsena Sud, Puerto Buenos Aires, Argentina

Tel: +54 (361) 4161/0346/3140
Telex: +54 (361) 5921

High-speed craft operated

Type	Name	Seats	Additional Payload	Delivered
CAT InCat Australia 74 m	*Atlantic II (ex-Sea Cat Calais, ex-Sea Cat Tasmania)*	432	80 cars	1993

(*Atlantic II* is chartered from Sea Containers Ltd, UK.)

Operations
Buenos Aires to Colonia, Uruguay (32 n miles).

VERIFIED

AUSTRALIA

BOAT TORQUE CRUISES PTY LTD

PO Box 189, South Perth, Western Australia 6151, Australia

Tel: +61 (9) 474 1497
Fax: +61 (9) 368 1656

Trevor A Kitcher, *Managing Director*

High-speed craft operated

Type	Name	Seats
MH WaveMaster 41 m	*Star Flyte*	506
MH WaveMaster 45 m	*Super Flyte**	585

*Operated by Kangaroo Island Fast Ferries, an associate company of Boat Torque Cruises.

Operations
Perth and Fremantle to Rottnest Island.

UPDATED

FANTASEA CRUISES

PO Box 616, Airlie Beach, Queensland 4802, Australia

Tel: +61 (79) 466999
Fax: +61 (79) 467278

D G Hutchen, *Managing Director*

High-speed craft operated

Type	Name	Seats	Delivered
CAT NQEA InCat 24 m	*Quickcat II*	195	1985
CAT InCat 31 m WPC	*2000*	226	March 1988
CAT NQEA InCat 29 m	*Monarch* (ex-*South Molle* and *Telford Capricorn*)	332	1994
CAT NQEA InCat 22 m	*Princess* (ex-*South Molle* and *Telford Reef*)	195	1994

Operations
Specialising in cruises to the Great Barrier Reef daily from Hamilton, Daydream, South Molle, Club Med Lindeman and Long Islands as well as mainland resorts.

UPDATED

GORDON RIVER CRUISES PTY LTD

PO Box 40, Strahan, Tasmania 7468. Australia

Tel: +61 (004) 717187/7281
Telex: 59284 AA
Fax: +61 (004) 717317

R F Kearney, *Proprietor*
J A Kearney, *Proprietor*

High-speed craft operated

Type	Name	Seats	Delivered
MH SBF Eng 27.7 m	*James Kelly II*	200	1983
MH WMI Eng 32.3 m	*Gordon Explorer*	250	1985
MH SBF Eng 22.5 m	*Wilderness Seeker*	100	1986

Operations
High-speed cruising in Macquarie Harbour and Gordon River World Heritage area, 4½ hour trips.
The three vessels have been carrying 90,000 passengers annually to the Gordon River.

VERIFIED

Wilderness Seeker ***1989***

GREAT ADVENTURES

PO Box 898, Cairns, Queensland 4870, Australia

Tel: +61 (70) 515644
Telex: 48284 GRTADV AA
Fax: +61 (70) 517556

John Finnin, *General Manager*
Jeff Sharp, *Sales and Marketing Manager*

High-speed craft operated

Type	Name	Seats	Delivered
CAT InCat (Hobart) 20 m	*Fitzroy Flyer*	169	June 1981
CAT NQEA InCat 22 m	*Green Island Express*	200	June 1982
CAT NQEA InCat 22 m	*Reef Adventure III*	214	March 1984
CAT NQEA InCat 30 m	*Reef Cat*	309	June 1986
CAT NQEA InCat 30 m	*Reef King*	390	December 1987
CAT Lloyd's 35 m	*Reef Queen*	390	February 1993
CAT Lloyd's 38 m	*Reef Prince*	393	October 1995

Sun Paradise *and* Sun Goddess 1992

Operations (daily from Cairns City)
Two outer Barrier Reef destinations:
Norman Reef via Green Island
Moore Reef via Fitzroy Island
Two Island destinations
Green Island
Fitzroy Island
300,000 passengers annually

UPDATED

Reef Cat *at the Norman Reef Pontoon* 1993

Reef Queen 1993

GREAT KEPPEL ISLAND TOURIST SERVICES LTD

168 Denison Street, Rockhampton, Queensland, Australia

Tel: +61 (079) 336744/272948

Claude Diehm, *Director*
Claude Diehm Jr, *Director*
David Diehm, *Director*
Andrew Diehm, *Director*
Helen Jackson, *Director/Secretary*

High-speed craft operated

Type	Name	Seats	Delivered
CAT SBF Engineering	*Victory III*	448	1985
MH SBF Engineering	*Aqua Jet*	48	1985

Operations
Rosslyn Bay (Yeppoon) to Great Keppel Island
Rosslyn Bay (Yeppoon) to Carricornia Section, Great Barrier Reef, 90 minutes.

VERIFIED

HAYMAN RESORT

A Division of Ansett Transport Industries

Hayman Island, Queensland 4801, Australia

Tel: +61 (79) 469100
Telex: 48163 AA
Fax: +61 (79) 469410

Akos Niklai, *Managing Director*
T A Klein, *General Manager*

High-speed craft operated

Type	Name	Seats	Delivered
MH Wavemaster 35 m	*Sun Goddess*	146	1984
MH Oceanfast 34.75 m	*Sun Paradise*	96	1987
MH Precision 22 m	*Reef Goddess*	60	1987
MH Steber 15 m	*Sun Aura*	18	1989
CAT NQEA Seajet P35	*Sun Eagle*	—	1996

Operations
Hayman Island to Great Barrier Reef
Hayman Island to Hamilton Island.

UPDATED

MACKENZIES MARINE

Esperance, Western Australia

High-speed craft operated

Type	Name	Seats	Delivered
CAT SBF 20 m	*Seabreeze*	116	1994

Operations
Esperance to Woody Island.

VERIFIED

PEEL'S TOURIST AND FERRY SERVICES PTY LTD

PO Box 197, Lakes Entrance 3909, Victoria, Australia

Tel: +61 (051) 551246

Barrie Peel, *Managing Director*

High-speed craft operated

Type	Name	Seats	Delivered
CAT InCat (Hobart) 20.4 m Bulls Marine Pty Ltd	*Thunderbird*	190	December 1984

Operations
Three routes are operated on Gippsland Lakes. These range from 35 to 70 km with journey times between 2 and 2½ hours.

VERIFIED

Peel's InCat Thunderbird 1987

PURE PLEASURE CRUISES

PO Box 1831, Townsville, Queensland 4810, Australia

Tel: +61 77 213555

High-speed craft operated

Type	Name	Seats	Delivered
WPC InCat, 31 m WPC	*2001*	196	1989

Operations
Townsville to Kelso Reef, Magnetic Island and Orpheus Island.

UPDATED

QUEENSLAND GOVERNMENT

Department of Harbours, Marine Boating and Fisheries Patrol, Thursday Island, Queensland, Australia

High-speed craft operated

Type	Name	Delivered
CAT NQEA InCat, 22 m Cheetah Class	*Wauri*	1988

VERIFIED

QUICKSILVER CONNECTIONS LTD

PO Box 171, Port Douglas, North Queensland 4871, Australia

Tel: +61 (070) 995455
Telex: 48969 LOWISL AA
Fax: +61 (070) 995525

Mike Burgess, *Managing Director*
John F Lergessner, *Operations Manager*

High-speed craft operated

Type	Name	Seats	Delivered
WPC InCat 37.2 m	*Quicksilver V*	340	November 1988
WPC InCat 37.2 m	*Quicksilver VII*	340	September 1989
WPC NQEA/InCat 45 m	*Quicksilver VIII*	400	May 1995

Operations
Port Douglas to Agincourt Reef North, 39 n miles, 1 hour 30 minutes
Port Douglas to Cairns, 36 n miles, 1 hour 10 minutes
Port Douglas to Low Isles.

UPDATED

45 m wave piercing catamaran operated by Quicksilver Connections **1996**

ROTTNEST EXPRESS PTY LTD

Lot 33, Cockburn Road, South Coogee, Western Australia 6166, Australia

High-speed craft operated

Type	Name	Seats	Delivered
MH SBF 30 m	*Osprey V*	257	1994

Operations
Fremantle to Rottnest Island.

VERIFIED

Osprey V operated by Rottnest Express Pty Ltd. **1996**

ROYLEN CRUISES

A Division of McLean's Roylen Cruises Pty Ltd

PO Box 169, Mackay, Queensland 4740, Australia

Tel: +61 (79) 553066
Fax: +61 (79) 553186

Barry J Dean, *Manager*

High-speed craft operated

Type	Name	Seats	Delivered
CAT InCat (Hobart) 29 m	*Spirit of Roylen*	290	1982
CAT InCat (NQEA) 24 m	*Roylen Sunbird*	240	1987

Operations
Mackay to Great Barrier Reef (140 km return)
Mackay to Hamilton Island (120 km return)
Mackay to Brampton Island (40 km return)
Mackay to Lindeman Island (100 km return)

Fares (one day excursion)

Destination	Fare
Great Barrier Reef	A$90, includes lunch and coral viewing
Brampton Island	A$45, includes lunch
Hamilton Island	A$40
Lindeman Island	A$90, includes lunch

Fares (one way transfers)

Destination	Fare
Brampton Island	A$25
Hamilton Island	A$36
Lindeman Island	A$35

UPDATED

STATE TRANSIT AUTHORITY OF NEW SOUTH WALES

Level 29, 100 Miller Street, North Sydney, NSW 2059, Australia

Tel: +61 (2) 956 4770
Fax: +61 (2) 956 4771

L Bartolomeo, *Chief Executive*
G Slee, *Chairman*

High-speed craft operated

Type	Name	Seats	Delivered
CAT NQEA 36 m InCat	*Blue Fin*†	250	March 1990
CAT NQEA 36 m InCat	*Sir David Martin*†	280*	December 1990
CAT NQEA 36 m InCat	*Sea Eagle*†	280*	April 1991
CAT NQEA 35 m RiverCat	*Dawn Fraser*††	172**	May 1992
CAT NQEA 35 m RiverCat	*Betty Cuthbert*††	172**	May 1992
CAT NQEA 35 m RiverCat	*Shane Gould*	172**	January 1993
CAT NQEA 35 m RiverCat	*Marlene Matthews*	172**	January 1993
CAT NQEA 35 m RiverCat	*Evonne Goolagong*	172**	September 1993
CAT NQEA 35 m RiverCat	*Marjorie Jackson*	172**	September 1993

* 250 inside, 30 outside
** 150 inside, 22 outside

Operations
†Sydney (Circular Quay) to Manly, 7 n miles, 15 minutes
Fare, single: A$4.60
††Sydney (Circular Quay) to Parramatta, 14 n miles, 60 minutes
Fare, single: A$4.00

UPDATED

36 m Jetcat Blue Fin *1995*

35 m Low-Wash RiverCat Evonne Goolagong *1995*

TANGALOOMA ISLAND RESORT LTD

PO Box 1102, Eagle Farm, Queensland 4007, Australia

Tel: +61 (7) 268 6722
Fax: +61 (7) 268 6106

Brian Osborne, *Director*

High-speed craft operated

Type	Name	Delivered
CAT InCat 20 m	*Tangalooma*	December 1981

Operations
Brisbane to Moreton Island, 26 n miles, 1 hour 10 minutes
During the period 1 July 1994 to 30 June 1995, 49,000 passengers and 1,200 tonnes of cargo were carried each way between Brisbane and Moreton Island.

UPDATED

WHITE DOLPHIN CRUISES

PO Box 189, South Perth 6151, Western Australia, Australia

High-speed craft operated

Type	Name	Seats	Delivered
Cat Fast Craft Int.26 m	*White Dolphin II*	320	1995

Operations
Fremantle to Rottnest Island

NEW ENTRY

White Dolphin II *1996*

BAHRAIN

BAHRAIN COASTGUARD DIRECTORATE

Ministry of the Interior, Public Secretary, PO Box 13, Bahrain

Tel: +973 700000
Telex: 9572 CGD BN
Fax: +973 700728

Col Abdul Aziz A Al-Khalifa, *Director*

High-speed craft operated
HOV Air Vehicles Tiger

Operations
General purpose search and rescue.

UPDATED

BELGIUM

EUROSENSE HOVERSOUNDING NV

Main office: Nervierslaan 54, B-1780 Wemmel, Belgium

Tel: +32 (2) 460 7000
Telex: 26687 B
Fax: +32 (2) 460 4958

E Maes, *Managing Director*
J Van Sieleghem, *Project Leader*

Zeebrugge office: New-Yorklaan, B-8380 Zeebrugge, Belgium

Tel: +32 (50) 546438
Telex: 26687 B
Fax: +32 (50) 547486

High-speed craft operated

Type	Name	Delivered
BHC SR. N6 Mk 6	*Beasac III*	November 1989

Operations
Eurosense Hoversounding NV employs a converted BHC SR. N6 Mk 6 for Belgian coast hydrographic survey and remote sensing work. The craft is based at Zeebrugge on behalf of the Ministry of Works.

VERIFIED

The Eurosense SR. N6 Mk 6, Beasac III *1991*

OOSTENDE LINES

Madouplein 1, B-1030 Brussels, Belgium

Tel: +32 (2) 219 5555
Fax: +32 (2) 223 0309

E Depraetere, *Managing Director*
R Beyen, *Technical Director*
F Engelen, *Commercial Director*
J Carlier, *Nautical Director*

High-speed craft operated

Type	Name	Seats	Delivered
HYD Boeing Jetfoil 929-115	*Princesse Clémentine*	280	May 1981
HYD Boeing Jetfoil 929-115	*Princesse Stephanie*	280	July 1981

Operations
Ostend to Ramsgate, 67 n miles, 1 hour 45 minutes
Passengers carried in 1989: 326,641
Passengers carried in 1990: 351,400
Passengers carried in 1991: 360,605
Passengers carried in 1992: 334,170
Passengers carried in 1993: 286,315
Passengers carried in 1994: 264,076

UPDATED

Princesse Clémentine *1995*

BOLIVIA

CRILLON TOURS SA

PO Box 4785, Avenida Camacho 1223, La Paz, Bolivia

Tel: +591 (2) 350363/374566/374567/372970
Telex: 2557 CRITUR BV
Fax: +591 (2) 391039

Darius Morgan, *President*
Elsa Morgan, *General Manager*
Helmut Kock, *Hydrofoil Designer and Consultant*

USA office: 1450 South Bayshore Drive 815, Miami, Florida, USA

Tel: +1 (305) 358 5353
Fax: +1 (305) 372 0054

Crillon Tours SA was founded in 1958 by Darius Morgan and started its hydrofoil services on Lake Titikaka in 1966. The company's first craft was the *Inca Arrow,* an Albatross type built by the Ludwig Honold Manufacturing Company. Three more hydrofoils were added in the next 10 years, followed in 1979 by the Italian-built *Sun Arrow*. Later in 1990 a Russian hydrofoil was added to the fleet, a gift from the Soviet President L. Breznev to US President R. Nixon.

A sister operation is undertaken on Lake Itaipu in Paraguay by Darius Morgan's other company, Aliscafos Itaipu SA. Since 1991 the fleet has been serving the 'Andean Roots' cultural complex and Inca Utama hotel on the sacred lakes.

High-speed craft operated

Type	Name	Delivered
HYD Ludwig Honold Manufacturing Co	*Inca Arrow*	1966
HYD Ludwig Honold Manufacturing Co	*Copacabana Arrow*	1964
HYD Ludwig Honold Manufacturing Co	*Andes Arrow*	1965
HYD Ludwig Honold Manufacturing Co	*Titikaka Arrow*	1963
HYD Ludwig Honold Manufacturing Co	*Bolivia Arrow*	1976
HYD Seaflight SpA H.57	*Sun Arrow*	1979
HYD Batumi Ship Building Plant, CIS	*Glasnost Arrow*	1990

Operations
Lake Titikaka, serving La Paz, Huatajata, Sun Island, Copacabana, Juli, Puno, Tiahuanacu, Guaqui, Suriqui and Kalauta Islands. Daily national and international itineraries (Bolivia/Peru).

UPDATED

BRAZIL

NORSUL OFFSHORE SA

Av. Augusto Severo, 8-5th floor, Rio de Janeiro, RJ CEP 20021-040, Brazil

Tel: +55 (21) 292 0122
Telex: (021) 22115
Fax: +55 (21) 252 8881

Carlos Temke, *Managing Director*
Aristido Reichert, *Administrative and Financial Director*
Americo Oliveira, *Contract Manager*
Mauro Sergio, *Technical Manager*

High-speed craft operated

Type	Name	Seats	Delivered
MH Swiftships	*Parintins*	70	1972
MH Swiftships	*Penedo*	70	1972
MH Breaux's Bay	*Piracicaba*	56	1975
MH Halter Marine	*Atalaia*	70	1980
MH Halter Marine	*Capela*	70	1980
MH Inace	*Norsul Paracuru*	60	1986
MH Inace	*Norsul Parnaiba*	60	1986
MH Inace	*Norsul Propria*	60	1986

Operations
Offshore support along Brazilian coast with bases in Rio, Macaé, Natal, Fortaleza and Aracaju.

UPDATED

Atalaia *operated by Norsul Offshore SA* *1993*

TRANSTUR

Aerobarcos do Brasil, Transportes Maritimos e Turismo SA

Praça Iaiá Garcia, 3 Ribeira, Rio de Janeiro, Brazil

Tel: +55 (21) 396 3567/2282/5940
Fax: +55 (21) 396 3965

Hamilton Amarante Carvalho, *Director President*
Luiz Paulo Amarante Carvalho, *Superintendent*
Vicente Oliveros Perez, *Director of Administration and Finance*

High-speed craft operated

Type	Name	Seats	Delivered
HYD Rodriquez PT 20	*Flecha do Rio*	85	1970
HYD Rodriquez PT 20	*Flecha de Niterói*	85	1970
HYD Rodriquez PT 20	*Flecha das Ilhas*	85	1971
HYD Rodriquez PT 20	*Flecha de Itaipú*	85	1971
HYD Rodriquez PT 20	*Flecha Fluminense*	85	1971
HYD Rodriquez PT 20	*Flecha de Ipanema*	83	1977
HYD Rodriquez PT 20	*Flecha de Icaraí**	83	1977
HYD Rodriquez PT 20	*Flecha da Ribeira*	83	1978
CAT Fjellstrand(s) 40 m	–	–	1996
CAT Fjellstrand(s) 40 m	–	–	1996

*Laid up

Operations
Rio de Janeiro to Niterói, 5 minutes, 2.8 miles
Rio de Janeiro to Paquetá Island, 20 minutes, 9.2 miles.

UPDATED

Rodriquez PT 20 operated by TRANSTUR *1993*

BULGARIA

BLACK SEA SHIPPING PLC

46 Tzaribrode Street, 9000 Varna, Bulgaria

High speed craft operated

Type	Name	Seats	Delivered
CAT Fjellstrand 40 m	*Ahinora*	—	1995

Operations
Varna to Burgas and Istanbul

NEW ENTRY

NAVIBULGAR

Navigation Maritime Bulgare

1 Chervenoarmeiski Blvd, 9000 Varna, Bulgaria

Tel: +359 (52) 222474
Telex: 77525/77352 NAVIBULGAR
Fax: +359 (52) 222491

Dimitar Mavrov, *Director General*
Ivan Borisov, *Managing Director*
Stefan Gramatikov, *Passenger Department Manager*

High-speed craft operated

Type	Name	Seats	Additional Payload	Delivered
HYD S Sormovo	*Kometa 1*	108	0.7 t	1978
HYD S Sormovo	*Kometa 2*	108	0.7 t	1979
HYD S Sormovo	*Kometa 3*	108	0.7 t	1980
HYD S Sormovo	*Kometa 7*	108	0.7 t	1974
HYD S Sormovo	*Kometa 8*	108	0.7 t	1974
HYD S Sormovo	*Kometa 12*	108	0.7 t	1977

Operations
Varna to Bourgas to Sozodol, 66 n miles, 3 hours

VERIFIED

CANADA

CANADIAN COAST GUARD HOVERCRAFT UNITS

Headquarters Administration: Fleet Aviation Office, Fleet Systems Directorate, Canadian Coast Guard (CCG), 8th Floor, Tower 2, Canada Building, 344 Slater Street, Ottawa, Ontario K1A 0N7, Canada

Tel: +1 (613) 998 1617
Fax: +1 (613) 995 4700

C D O'Halloran, *Manager*

Operations
The (CCG) operates two Hovercraft Units, administered from CCG Headquarters in Ottawa, with operational tasking controlled by the region in which they are based.

VERIFIED

WEST COAST CANADA

Canadian Coast Guard Hovercraft Unit: PO Box 23968, AMF, Vancouver International Airport, British Columbia V7N 1T9, Canada

Tel: +1 (604) 273 2556

J McGrath, *Officer in Charge*

High-speed craft operated

Type	Delivered
HOV BHC SR. N6, Serial No 039, CH-CGB, purchased from BHC	1977
HOV BHC SR. N6, Serial No 030, CH-CCG, rebuilt by Unit	April 1986

(HOV BHC SR. N5, Serial No 021, was retired and scrapped in April 1986 and No 031 was withdrawn from service in November 1992)

Operations
The Canadian Coast Guard Hovercraft Unit in Vancouver was formed in 1968 for hovercraft evaluation in search and rescue and other coastguard duties.

The patrol area is the Straits of Georgia and Gulf Islands (500 sq miles), although search and rescue duties are undertaken outside this area. The average patrol distance is 80 miles.

The Unit commenced operations with SR. N5 021 in 1968 in the search and rescue role and quickly established itself. Within five years it was responding to over 900 calls per year. The craft's speed and versatility made it ideal for other CCG roles, amongst which are light station servicing, buoy maintenance, ship inspections, shore patrols, pollution control and emergency work with other agencies. In 1977, the additional work justified a second craft and SR. N6 039 was purchased. Soon afterwards new fishing fleet activities resulted in a northward extension of the SAR cover provided. In 1980-81, the first of two old SR. N6 craft previously purchased was completely rebuilt and commissioned by Unit personnel, enabling a sub-base at Parkesville 90 km north of Vancouver to be built and equipped with one SR. N6, becoming operational in early 1982. This sub-base was closed in November 1992 and SR. N6, Serial No 031 was removed from service.

VERIFIED

EASTERN CANADA

Laurentian Region ACV Unit: 850 Nun's Island Boulevard, Nun's Island, Québec H3E 1H2, Canada

Tel: +1 (514) 283 0681

D L'Heureux, H Goulet, *Craft Captains*

High-speed craft operated

Type	Name	Delivered
HOV BHC AP1-88/200 Serial No 201, registration CH-CGC	*Waban-Aki*	September 1987

Operations
This Unit started operations by evaluating the potential of hovercraft in the Montreal District of the Laurentian Region, and in 1980 was integrated into the CCG Fleet operating in that region. In 1974-75, the *Voyageur* demonstrated remarkable capabilities for ice-breaking in the St Lawrence and its tributaries, and has been used extensively every winter to break and manage ice in shallow water and for flood relief.

Voyageur was replaced in September 1987 with a BHC AP1-88/200, designed with a forward well-deck and equipped with an easily removable crane, together with a hydraulic capstan and winch. As well as ice-breaking in winter, *Waban-Aki* maintains marine aids to navigation along 350 miles of the St Lawrence river and also responds to SAR incident calls.

VERIFIED

Waban-Aki *breaking ice in a tributary of the St Lawrence, to prevent flooding* **1991**

COMINCO SNIP OPERATION

Bag 9000, Smithers, British Columbia V0J 2N0, Canada

Tel: +1 (604) 662 0800
Fax: +1 (604) 662 0847

Merlyn Royer, *Project Manager*
Paul Morrison, *Chief Pilot*

Cominco Metals acquired an AP1-88 in 1990 (built by NQEA Australia) for the transport of diesel fuel, supplies and ore at its gold mining operations at Bronson Creek in north-west British Columbia. The craft was first on site 11 July 1990. Conversion of the AP1-88 *Hover Mirage II* was undertaken by NQEA Australia to a 10 t freighter version AP1-88/300. The craft operates over a 70 mile route mostly on the unnavigable Iskut and Stikine rivers.

UPDATED

Cominco AP1-88/300 operating in north-west British Columbia (R Wade) **1994**

CHILE

PATAGONIA TRAVELLING SERVICE

Chile

High-speed craft operated

Type	Name	Seats	Delivered
CAT AYSN Båtservice Sea Lord 28	*Patagonia Express*	60	1991

Operations
Puerto Montt to Termas de Puyuhvapi to San Rafael Lagoon.

VERIFIED

CHINA, PEOPLE'S REPUBLIC

CACTEC

China Air Cushion Technology Development Corporation

9 Qi Xiang Nan Li, Binhu Road, Tianjin, People's Republic of China and 171 Gaoxion Road, Shanghai, People's Republic of China

Tel: +86 (22) 331859/333339
Cable: 3333

Telex: 770539

Formed in 1984, CACTEC, subordinated to China State Shipbuilding Corporation (CSSC), is a specialised business corporation. The corporation deals, jointly with MARIC, with a wide variety of applications of the air cushion principle, and lays emphasis on the research, development, design and production of both amphibious hovercraft and sidewall hovercraft.

High-speed craft operated

Type	Seats	Delivered
SES MARIC 7203	81	September 1982
SES MARIC 719	186	1984
HOV MARIC 716 II	32	1985

VERIFIED

CHANGJIANG SHIPPING CORPORATION

Shanghai, People's Republic of China

High-speed craft operated

Type	Delivered
SES Vosper Hovermarine HM 218, Serial No 129*	1983
SES Vosper Hovermarine HM 218, Serial No 130*	1983

*purchased from The Hong Kong & Yaumati Ferry Company Ltd

Operations
Shekou (China) to Pearl River and Aberdeen (Hong Kong).

VERIFIED

CHONGQING SHIPPING COMPANIES

Head Office: Chongqing Shipping Company, 21 DaoMenKou, Chongqing, People's Republic of China

High-speed craft operated

Type	Name	Seats	Delivered
SES Dong Feng MARIC 717 III	*Ming Jiang*	54-60	September 1984
SES Dong Feng MARIC 717 III	*Jin Sha Jiang*	54-60	1987
SES Dong Feng MARIC 717 III	*Jin Ling Jiang*	54-60	1989
SES Dong Feng MARIC 717 II	*Chong Qing*	70	October 1984
SES Dong Feng MARIC 717 II	*Yu Xiang*	70	1989

Operations
Chong Qing to Yi Bin, 200 n miles
Chong Qing to Lu Zhou, 135 n miles
Yangtze River between Chong Qing and Fu Ling, 65 n miles

Yu Xiang, delivered in September 1989, operates from Hang Zhou to Chong Qing, 1,512 n miles along the Great Canal and Yangtze River through the spectacular 'Three Gorge' area.

VERIFIED

DALIAN STEAMSHIP CO

People's Republic of China

High-speed craft operated

Type	Name	Seats	Delivered
CAT Fjellstrand (S) Flying Cat 40 m	*Hai Ou*	400	January 1993
CAT Fjellstrand (S) Flying Cat 40 m	*Hai Yan*	400	January 1993

Operations
Dalian to Nantai.

VERIFIED

DALIAN YUAN FENG FERRY COMPANY

People's Republic of China

High-speed craft operated

Type	Name	Delivered
CAT Fjellstrand 38.8 m	*Fei Yu*	1993
CAT Wavemaster 49 m	*Fei Long*	1994

Operations
Dalian to Yantai.

VERIFIED

GUANGDONG PROVINCE NAVIGATION COMPANY

People's Republic of China

High-speed craft operated

Type	Name	Seats	Delivered
CAT A Fai InCat 21.9 m	*Mingzhu Hu*	150	1982
CAT A Fai InCat 21.9 m	*Yin Zhou Hu*	150	1982
CAT A Fai InCat 21.9 m	*Liuhua Hu*	150	1982

Operations
Taiping and Jiangmen to Hong Kong.

VERIFIED

NANTONG HIGH-SPEED PASSENGER SHIP COMPANY

Nantong, People's Republic of China

High-speed craft operated

Type	Name	Seats	Delivered
CAT Austal Ships 36 m	*Tong Zhou*	430	1990

Operations
Shanghai to Nantong.

VERIFIED

NINGBO FAST FERRIES LTD

305 Jiangdong Road North, Ningbo, People's Republic of China

Tel: +86 574 7757493
Fax: +86 574 7708400

Yong DA *operated by Ningbo Fast Ferries* ***1996***

Yong Xing *operated by Ningbo Fast Ferries* **1987**

Yong Wang *operated by Ningbo Fast Ferries* **1996**

This company also operates travel agencies, fast craft repair yards and other tourist cruise organisations.

High-speed craft operated

Type	Name	Seats	Delivered
CAT Fjellstrand 38.8 m	*Yong Xing*	312	1985
CAT Fjellstrand 31.5 m	*Yong Wang* (ex-*Lygra*)	306	1995
CAT Fjellstrand 25.7 m	*Yong DA* (ex-*Manger*)	186	1995

Operations
Ningbo to Shanghai, Suzhou and Putuo.

UPDATED

SANFU SHIPPING CHINA

People's Republic of China

High-speed craft operated

Type	Name	Seats	Delivered
CAT A Fai InCat 21 m	*Jin San Hu*	150	1985
CAT WaveMaster 32 m	*Yin San Hu*	252	July 1989

VERIFIED

SHANGHAI FREE FLYING TRANSPORT

People's Republic of China

High-speed craft operated

Type	Name	Seats	Delivered
SES Wu-Hu Shipyard MARIC 719 II	—	257	August 1988
CAT Austal 40 m	*Free Flying*	—	1994

Operations
Shanghai to Ningbo.

VERIFIED

MARIC 719 II 257 seat, 28 knot SES built by Wu-Hu Shipyard **1989**

SHEN ZHEN SHIPPING

People's Republic of China

High-speed craft operated

Type	Name	Seats	Delivered
CAT A Fai InCat 21 m	*Yue Hai Chun*	169	1984
CAT A Fai InCat 21 m	*Shen Zhen Chun*	169	1985
CAT A Fai InCat 21 m	*Ling Nan Chun*	169	1987
CAT A Fai InCat 21 m	*Nan Hai Chun*	169	1989
CAT A Fai InCat 21 m	*Dong Fang Chun*	169	1991
CAT A Fai InCat 21 m	*Zhu Hai Chun*	169	1986
CAT A Fai AMD 28 m	*Jin Xiang*	242	1993

Operations
Shen Zen to Zhu Hai.

VERIFIED

SHEN ZHEN XUN LONG TRANSPORTATION

People's Republic of China

High-speed craft operated

Type	Name	Seats	Delivered
CAT Rosendal Verft 36 m	Xunlong I	350	1995
CAT Rosendal Verft 36 m	Xunlong II	350	1996

Operations
She Kou to Hong Kong.

NEW ENTRY

WAN SHAN DISTRICT COMPANY

People's Republic of China

High-speed craft operated

Type	Name	Seats	Delivered
MH Aluminium Craft (88) 28 m	Tong Chi Yi Hao	138	1993
CAT Aluminum Craft (88) 35 m	Dong Qu ER Hao	270	1994

Operations
Local Services in Guangdong Province.

NEW ENTRY

WUZHOU NAVIGATION COMPANY

People's Republic of China

High-speed craft operated

Type	Name	Seats	Delivered
CAT A Fai InCat 21 m	*Lijiang*	150	1983
CAT A Fai AMD 170	*Wuzhou*	150	1994

Operations
Wuzhou to Hong Kong.

VERIFIED

YANTAI MARINE

2 Huanhai Road, Yantai, People's Republic of China

High-speed craft operated

Type	Name	Seats	Delivered
CAT Fjellstrand 40 m	*Xin Shi Ji*	—	1993

VERIFIED

COMMONWEALTH OF INDEPENDENT STATES

BLACK SEA SHIPPING COMPANY

1 Lastochkina Str, Odessa 270026, CIS

Telex: 232711, 412677

Kolkhida craft at Odessa **1988**

High-speed craft operated

Type	Name	Seats	Delivered
HYD S Ord Kometa	*Kometa 27*	116	1975 (Yalta)
HYD S Ord Kometa	*Kometa 32*	116	1977 (Yalta)
HYD S Ord Kometa	*Kometa 37*	116	1978 (Odessa)
HYD S Ord Kometa	*Kometa 40*	116	1979 (Yalta)
HYD S Ord Kometa	*Kometa 41*	116	1979 (Yalta)
SES Sosnovka Rassvet	—	80	—
HYD-Feodosia Tsiklon	—	—	November 1987
CAT Westamarin W 4100S	*Krymskaya Strela*	298	April 1990
CAT Westamarin W 4100S	*Golubaya Strela*	300	April 1990
CAT Fjellstrand 40 m	*Ahinora*	350	1995

Operations
Daily services, Odessa to Ochakov, Kherson and Nikolaev. Services also from Yalta to Istanbul and Piraeus.
Black Sea Kometas carry over 1.5 million passengers a year and are mostly based in the ports of Sochi, Tuapse, Novorossiysk, Yalta, Odessa and Izmail.

UPDATED

FAR EASTERN SHIPPING COMPANY

ul 25-go Oktyabrya 15, Vladivostok 690019, CIS

High-speed craft operated

Type	Name	Seats	Delivered
HYD Kometa	*Kometa 20*	116	1973
HYD Kometa	*Kometa 29*	116	1976
HYD Kometa	*Kometa 31*	116	1977

Operations
Vladivostok to Nakhodka to Preobrazhemie to Olga to Rudnaya Pristan (264 n miles)
Vladivostok to Slavyanka (60 n miles).

UPDATED

NORTHERN SHIPPING COMPANY

Archangelsk, CIS

High-speed craft operated

Type	Name	Seats	Delivered
CAT Fjellstrand 38.8 m	*Solovki**	230	March 1990
HOV BHC AP1-88/100	*North Wind* (ex-*Siverko*)	68	September 1991

*Currently leased to another operator

Operations
Archangelsk to Petrominsk to Solovetskiy.

VERIFIED

NOVOROSSIYSK SHIPPING COMPANY

1 ul Svobody, Novorossiysk 353900, CIS

Tel: +7 (86134) 51276
Telex: 279113
Fax: +7 (86134) 64255

High-speed craft operated

Type	Name	Seats	Delivered
HYD Kometa	*Kometa 19*	116	1973
HYD Kometa	*Kometa 22*	116	1974
HYD Kometa	*Kometa 24*	116	1975
HYD Kometa	*Kometa 33*	116	1976
HYD Kometa	*Kometa 53*	116	1982
CAT Westamarin W 4100S	*Irbis*	292	August 1990
CAT Westamarin W 4100S	*Sirius*	292	September 1990

Operations
Novorossiysk to Pertominsk to Solovetskiy, 188 n miles
Novorossiysk to Solovetskiy, 166 n miles
Novorossiysk to Istanbul and Pireaus.

VERIFIED

Westamarin W 4100S prior to delivery to Novorossiysk Shipping Company (Alan Bliault) ***1991***

SOVIET DANUBE SHIPPING COMPANY

2 Pr Suvorova, Izmail 272630, CIS

Telex: 412699, 232817

High-speed craft operated

Type	Name	Delivered
HYD Kometa	*Kometa 34*	1977
HYD Kometa	*Kometa 35*	1978
HYD Kometa	*Kometa 36*	1978

VERIFIED

CROATIA

ATLAS TURISTIČKA PLOVIDBA

20,000 Dubrovnik, Pile 1, Croatia

Tel: +385 20 44222
Telex: 27517, 27583 CRO
Fax: +385 20 411100/442720

Owned by leading Croatian Travel Agency Atlas, Turistička Plovidba operates three Kometa and two Kolkhida hydrofoils for passenger and tourist services on the Adriatic sea.

High-speed craft operated

Type	Name	Seats	Delivered
HYD Ord Kometa	*Krila Dubrovnika*	—	1971
HYD Ord Kometa	*Krila Hvara*	—	1982
HYD Ord Kometa	*Krila Braca*	—	1982
HYD Ord Kometa	*Krila Istre*	—	1994
HYD Ord Kometa	*Krila Dalmacije*	—	1994

UPDATED

JADROLINIJA

Po Box 123, Riva 16, 5100 Rijeka, Croatia

High-speed craft operated

Type	Name	Seats	Delivered
CAT Westamaran 95	*OLEA*	—	1994

Operations
Zadar to Adriatic Islands.

NEW ENTRY

KVARNER EXPRESS INTERNATIONAL DD

Marsala Tita 186, 51410 Opatija, PO Box 92, Croatia

Tel: +385 (51) 271111
Fax: +385 (51) 271549/741

Radomir Premuš, *Managing Director*

In 1985 Kvarner Express introduced high-speed daily ferry services from Opatija to the Island of Rab and to Venice.

High-speed craft operated

Type	Name	Seats	Delivered
HYD Ord Kolkhida	*Magnolija*	145	1985
HYD Ord Kolkhida	*Kamelija*	145	1985
HYD Ord Kolkhida	*Mirta*	145	1986
MH Marinteknik 41 MPV	*Iris*	350	1989

Operations
Opatija to Rab, 50 n miles, Mali Losin, 53 n miles
Opatija to Venice and in Spring 1987 to Ancona and Rimini
Istrian Peninsula to Venice, Kornati Islands, Rimini, Ravenna, Pesaro
Rab and Mali Losin to Venice, Rimini, Zadar
Rueica to Venice, Silba and Rimini
Zadar to Sirenic and Ancona.

UPDATED

Marinteknik Iris ***1995***

DENMARK

CAT-LINK

Hallandsgade 2, DK-8000 Århus C, Denmark

High-speed craft operated

Type	Name	Seats	Additional Payload	Delivered
WPC InCat Australia 78 m	*Cat-Link I*	600	120 cars	1995

Operations
Århus to Kalundborg.

NEW ENTRY

DAMPSKIBSSELSKABET (DSØRESUND Ø) A/S

Havnegade 49, PO Box 1509, DK 1020 Copenhagen K, Denmark

Tel: +45 3314 7770
Fax: +45 3393 1330

Finn Zoega Olesen, *Managing Director*
Jens Nygaard, *Director*

High-speed craft operated

Type	Name	Seats	Delivered
CAT Marinteknik Marinjet	*Lommen* (Yard No 56)	235	December 1985
CAT Marinteknik 33 m	*Ørnen*	235	May 1986
CAT Fjellstrand 38.8 m	*Løberen*	256	September 1990
CAT Fjellstrand 38.8 m	*Springaren*	256	July 1991
CAT Fjellstrand 40 m Flying Cat	*Saelen*	288	May 1993
CAT Fjellstrand 40 m Flying Cat	*Søbjørnen*	288	May 1993
CAT Fjellstrand 40 m	*Kraka Viking*	160	July 1994
CAT Fjellstrand 40 m	*Sifka Viking*	160	July 1994

UPDATED

GRÅHUNBUS

Denmark

High-speed craft operated

Type	Name	Seats	Delivered
MH Boghammar 29.5 m	*Grasoelen*	—	1993

VERIFIED

GRENAA-HUNDESTED

Faergevej 2, 3390 Hundested, Demark

High-speed craft operated

Type	Name	Seats	Additional Payload	Delivered
MH Mjellem & Karlsen 95 m	*Kattegat*	600	160 cars +12 buses	1995
MH Mjellem & Karlsen 95 m	*Djursland*	600	160 cars +12 buses	(1996)

Operations
Grenaa to Hundested

NEW ENTRY

Kattegat *1996*

SUPPLY-TRANS A/S

Wholly owned by Temdex A/S

Kongevejen 64, DK-3450 Allerød, Denmark

Tel: +45 4814 3515
Fax: +45 4814 0515

Peter Krumbak, *Director*

Operator of specialised high-speed craft for the construction industry.

High-speed craft operated

Type	Name	Seats	Delivered
MH	*Kato I*	30	–
MH	*Nanok*	30	–
MH	*Imera*	30	–
MH	*Fremad II*	30	December 1994

VERIFIED

ESTONIA

SUKKULA

Estonia

High-speed craft operated

Type	Name	Seats	Delivered
CAT Teknicraft 22 m	*Sea Shuttle I*	–	1994

Note: It is not clear where this vessel will operate in 1996/97.

Operations
Tallin to Helsinki.

VERIFIED

TALLINK EXPRESS

Ädala 4A, Tallin, EE 0006, Estonia

High-speed craft operated

Type	Name	Seats	Delivered
HYD Morye Cyclone	*Liisa*	–	1992
HYD Morye Olympia	*Laura*	–	1993
HYD Morye Olympia	*Jaanika*	–	1994

Operations
Tallin to Helsinki.

UPDATED

FRANCE

BATEAUX GALLUS

24 quai Lunel, F-06300 Nice, France

Fax: +33 93 26 54 60

Salvatore Lauro, *Managing Director*

High-speed craft operated

Type	Name	Seats	Delivered
HYD Ord Kolkhida	*Gallus 6*	155	1991
HYD Ord Kolkhida	*Gallus 7*	155	1991
HYD Ord Kolkhida	*Gallus 8*	155	1991

Operations
Cote d'Azur (Monaco, Nice, Cannes, St Tropez, San Remo) and between Nice and Calvi, Corsica.

VERIFIED

CHANNILAND

3 rue Georges Clémenceau et Gare Maritime, BP 319, F-50400 Granville, France

High-speed craft operated

Type	Name	Delivered
CAT Westamaran 86	*Brittania*	1992
CAT Marinteknik 42 m	*Saint Malo*	1993

Operations
Granville to Jersey (April to October)
Jersey to Sark and Guernsey (April to September)
Jersey to Guernsey (April to November)
St Malo to Jersey (April to November).

VERIFIED

CORSICA FERRIES

A member of the Tourship Group

5 Bis Rue Chanoine Leschi, Po Box 239, F-20294 Bastia, Corsica, France

High-speed craft operated

Type	Name	Seats	Additional Payload	Delivered
MH INMA/Rodriquez 103 m	—	600	150 cars	(1996)
MH INMA/Rodriquez 103 m	—	600	150 cars	(1996)

Operations
Bastia and Calvi to Nice

NEW ENTRY

EMERAUDE LINES

BP 16, Gare Maritime, F-35401 Saint Malo Cedex, France

Tel: +33 99 40 48 40
Fax: +33 99 40 04 43

Pierre Legras, *Chairman*
Jean-Luc Griffon, *Commercial Director*
Jean-Francois Negre, *General Manager*

High-speed craft operated

Type	Name	Seats	Additional Payload	Delivered
CAT Westamarin W95	*Trident 3*	205	—	—
CAT Westamarin W95	*Trident 4*	218	—	May 1988
CAT Westamarin W95	*Trident 5*	200	—	—
CAT Westamarin W95 D	*Trident 7*	201	—	1990
CAT Westamarin W95 D	*Trident 8*	201	—	
MH SBCN Hydro Jet	*Mont Orgueil*	140	—	January 1991
CAT Fjellstrand Jumbocat	—	437	46 cars	(May 1996)

Note: *Trident 6* was sold in 1994

Operations
Saint Malo to Jersey to Guernsey to Sark
Granville to Jersey to Guernsey
Carteret to Jersey to Guernsey
Portbail to Jersey.

UPDATED

Trident 3 *in service with Emeraude Lines* ***1992***

NAVILAND

Parc du Golfe, F-56000 Vannes, France

Tel: +33 97 46 6000

Naviland was formed in 1993 by Sealink SNAT and took over the Navix SA fleet.

High-speed craft operated

Type	Name	Seats	Delivered
MH SFCN 28 m	*Nicholas Bouchard* (Navijet)	262	1988

Operations
Belle Ile en Mer to La Trinité, Port Navalo and Vannes.

UPDATED

SOCIÉTÉ NATIONAL CORSE MEDITERRANÉE (SNCM)

France

High-speed craft operated

Type	Name	Seats	Additional Payload	Delivered
MH Lerouse and Lotz Corsaire 11000	—	550	148 cars	(1996)
MH Lerouse and Lotz Corsaire 11000	—	550	148 cars	(1996)

Operations
Nice to Calvic (Corsica)

NEW ENTRY

SURF SA

Cie des Moyens de Surfaces Adaptes a l'Exploitation des Oceans

148 rue Sainte, F-13007 Marseilles, France
Po Box 48, F-13262 Marseilles Cedex 7, France

Tel: +33 91 54 92 29
Telex: 401042 SURF F
Fax: +33 91 33 85 70

High-speed craft operated

Type	Name	Seats	Delivered
MH SFCN 34.9 m	*Aida*	90	April 1986
MH SFCN 34.9 m	*Angelica*	90	April 1986
CAT Marinteknik Verkstads 40 m	—	—	January 1992

Operations
Offshore support, off Congo coast and Cameroon, Pointe Noir to Emeraude North and South oilfields and to the Likouala oilfield.

VERIFIED

SURF's Angelica *and* Aida ***1989***

FRENCH POLYNESIA

AREMITI PACIFIC CRUISES (*BORA BORA NAVETTE*)

French Polynesia

High-speed craft operated

Type	Name	Seats	Delivered
CAT Sabre Catamarans, 17 m	*Aremiti*	—	1990
CAT Sabre Catamarans, 29 m	*Aremiti II*	288	1992
CAT Fjellstrand 40 m	—	300	1994

Operations
Papeete to Moorea.

VERIFIED

FERRY TRANSPORT

BP 3917 Papeete, Tahiti, French Polynesia

High-speed craft operated

Type	Name	Seats	Delivered
WPC InCat Tasmania 37 m	*Tamahine Moorea II*	350	1993
SES Oceanfast UT 928	*Tamahine Moorea II B*	350	1993

Operations
Popeete to Moorea

NEW ENTRY

LEPRADO

French Polynesia

High-speed craft operated

Type	Name	Delivered
CAT InCat 23 m	*Tamahine Moorea*	1992
WPC InCat 37 m	*Tamahine Papeete* (ex-*Seaflight*)	1993

Operations
Tahiti to Moorea.

VERIFIED

SPI MARITIME

French Polynesia

High-speed craft operated

Type	Name	Seats	Delivered
CAT Austal 48 m	*Ono-Ono*	–	1994

Operations
Papeete to Bora Bora.

VERIFIED

GERMANY

AG EMS

PO Box 1154, Am Borkumkai, D-26691 Emden 1, Germany

Tel: +49 (21) 890722
Fax: +49 (21) 890742

High-speed craft operated

Type	Name	Seats	Delivered
CAT Fjellstrand 38.8 m	*Nordlicht*	272	March 1989

Operations
Emden to Borkum.

VERIFIED

Nordlicht *operated by AG Ems* ***1992***

HALLIG UND INSELREEDERI

D-25980 Westerland, Sylt, Germany

Tel: +49 4651 98700
Fax: +49 4651 26300

High-speed craft operated

Type	Name	Delivered
MH Marinteknik 42 m	*Adler Express*	1993

UPDATED

KÖLN-DÜSSELDORFER DEUTSCHE RHEINSCHIFFAHRT AG (KD)

Frankenwerft 15, D-50667 Köln, Germany

Tel: +49 (221) 20880
Fax: +49 (221) 208 8229

High-speed craft operated

Type	Name	Seats
HYD Sormovo Raketa	*Rheinpfeil* (*Rhine Arrow*)	64

Raketa, Rheinpfeil, *operated by Köln-Düsseldorfer (KD) German Rhine Line* ***1992***

Operations
Cologne to Koblenz to Bingen to Mainz and many intermediate stops, 9 April to 24 October.

VERIFIED

SCHIFFAHRTSKONTOR ALTES LAND

Buergerei 29, D-2170 Steinkirchon, Germany

High-speed craft operated

Type	Name	Seats	Delivered
CAT Lindstøl Ships 27.5 m	–	–	1995
CAT Lindstøl Ships 27.5 m	–	–	1995

Operations
River Elbe (Standersand to Landungsbrücken (Hamburg))

NEW ENTRY

TT-LINE

Mattentwiete 8, D-20457 Hamburg, Germany

High-speed craft operated

Type	Name	Seats	Additional Payload	Delivered
CAT Austal Auto Express 82	–	600	175 cars	(1996)

Operations
Traevmunde (Germany) to Trelleborg (Sweden)

NEW ENTRY

GREECE

ADVANCED TECHNOLOGY CRUISES

67 Iroon Polytechniou Avenue, GR-18536 Pireas, Greece

Tel: +30 (1) 451 1017/418 0341/4181263
Fax: +30 (1) 452 3876/4181266

Michail Theocharis, *Managing Director*

High-speed craft operated

Type	Name	Seats	Additional Payload	Delivered
SES Polyship 30 m	*Manto*	200	–	1993
SES Polyship 33 m	*Alexandros**	250	–	1994
CAT Wavemaster	*Andromeda*	400	–	1995
CAT Wavemaster	*Nefeli*	500	50 cars	(1996)
CAT Wavemaster	*Sirius*	600	50 cars	(1996)

*Transferred to West Coast 1994

Operations
Services from Pasei to Corfu to Brindisi.

UPDATED

CATAMARAN LINES

Greece

High-speed craft operated

Type	Name	Seats	Additional Payload	Delivered
CAT Royal Schelde 70 HL	unknown	600	154 cars	(1996)

Operations
Igovmenitsa to Brindisi

NEW ENTRY

CERES HYDROFOIL SERVICES

8 Akti Themistokleus, Freattys, Piraeus, Greece

Tel: +30 (1) 428 0001
Telex: 240107 HYDR GR
Fax: +30 (1) 428 3526

Services started in 1975 with the Piraeus to Hydra route.

High-speed craft operated

Type	Name	Seats*	Delivered
HYD S Ord Kometa-M	*Flying Dolphin I*	132	1975
HYD S Ord Kometa-M	*Flying Dolphin II*	132	1975
HYD S Ord Kometa-M	*Flying Dolphin III*	132	1976
HYD S Ord Kometa-M	*Flying Dolphin V*	132	1976
HYD S Ord Kometa-M	*Flying Dolphin VI*	132	1976
HYD S Ord Kometa-M	*Flying Dolphin VII*	132	1976
HYD S Ord Kometa-M	*Flying Dolphin IV*	132	1977
HYD S Ord Kometa-M	*Flying Dolphin VIII*	132	1977
HYD S Ord Kometa-M	*Flying Dolphin IX*	132	1978
HYD S Ord Kometa-M	*Flying Dolphin X*	132	1978
HYD S Ord Kometa-M	*Flying Dolphin XI*	132	1979
HYD S Ord Kometa-M	*Flying Dolphin XII*	132	1979
HYD S Ord Kometa-M	*Flying Dolphin XIV*	132	1981
HYD S Ord Kometa-M	*Flying Dolphin XV*	132	1981
HYD S Ord Kometa-M	*Flying Dolphin XVI*	132	1981
HYD S Ord Kolkhida	*Flying Dolphin XVII*	155	1986
HYD S Ord Kolkhida	*Flying Dolphin XVIII*	155	1986
HYD S Ord Kometa	*Flying Dolphin XX*	132	1988
HYD S Ord Kometa	*Flying Dolphin XXI*	132	1988
HYD S Ord Kometa	*Flying Dolphin XXII*	132	1989
HYD S Ord Kometa	*Flying Dolphin XXIII*	132	1989
HYD S Ord Kometa	*Flying Dolphin XXIV*	132	1989
HYD S Ord Kometa	*Flying Dolphin XXV*	132	1989
HYD S Ord Kolkhida	*Flying Dolphin XIX*	155	1990
CAT K Fjellstrand Flying Cat	*Flyingcat I*	352	1990
HYD S Ord Kometa	*Flying Dolphin XXVI*	132	1991
HYD S Ord Kometa	*Flying Dolphin XXVII*	132	1991
HYD S Ord Kometa	*Flying Dolphin XXVIII*	132	1991
HYD S Ord Kolkhida	*Flying Dolphin XXIX*	155	1993

(*Flying Dolphins IV, V* and *XII* are owned by Ceres Hydrofoils Shipping and Tourism SA. *Flying Dolphins VIII, IX* and *X* are owned by Ceres Hydrocomets Shipping and Tourism SA. *Flying Dolphins VI, VII, XI* and *XXIX* are owned by Ceres Express Ways Shipping and Tourism SA. *Flying Dolphins XIV, XV, XVI* and *XVII* are owned by Ceres Hydrolines Shipping Company.)
*MTU engines are being fitted to all Ceres Kometas enabling seat numbers to be increased to 132

Operations
Aghios Konstantinos to Volos to Skiathos to Glossa to Skopelos to Aionissos
Piraeus (Zea) Aigina to Poros to Hydra to Ermioni to Spetsai to Porto Heli to Leonidi to Kiparissi to Monemvassia to Kythira and Neapoli
Macedonia to Thessaloniki
Halkidiki to Moudania and Marmaras.

VERIFIED

Fjellstrand Flying Cat I *in service 1990 with Ceres Hydrofoil Services* ***1991***

DODECANESE HYDROFOILS

56 Panepistimiou Street, GR-10678 Athens, Greece

High-speed craft operated

Type	Name	Seats	Delivered
HYD Kometa	*Marilena*	–	1981
HYD Kometa	*Tzina*	–	1981
HYD Kometa	*Marilena II*	–	1993
HYD Kometa	*Georgios M*	–	1993
HYD Kometa	*Aristea M*	–	1993
HYD Kometa	*Tzina II*	–	1993

Operations
Inter-Dodecanese islands.

VERIFIED

GIAIMAR LINES

35A Vouliagmenis Avenue, 16675 Glyfada, Greece

High-speed craft operated

Type	Name	Seats	Delivered
HYD Feodosia Kometa	*Cyclades*	102	1994
HYD Feodosia Kometa	*Samos*	102	1994

Operations
Island link in Eastern Aegean Sea.

NEW ENTRY

HERMES

143 Koloktroni Street, GR-18536 Piraeus, Greece

High-speed craft operated

Type	Name	Seats	Delivered
HYD Rodriquez RHS 70	*Nikos*	–	1993
HYD Rodriquez RHS 70	*Iptamenos Hermes II*	–	1993
HYD Rodriquez RHS 140	*Iptamenos Hermes I*	–	1993
HYD Rodriquez RHS 160	*Iptamenos Hermes III*	–	1994

VERIFIED

ILIO LINES

1 Makras Stoas Street, GR-18531 Piraeus, Greece

High-speed craft operated

Type	Name	Seats	Delivered
HYD Kometa	*Delfini I*	102	1992
HYD Kometa	*Delfini II*	102	1992
HYD Kometa	*Delfini III*	102	1992
HYD Kometa	*Delfini IV*	102	1992
HYD Kometa	*Thraki I*	102	1992
HYD Kolkhida	*Delfini V*	–	1992
HYD Kometa	*Delfini VII* (ex-*Kometa 42*)	102	1992
HYD Kometa	*Delfini VIII*	102	1992
HYD Kometa	*Thassan Dolfin*	102	1992
HYD Kometa	*Delfini XVIII*	102	1992
HYD Kometa	*Delfini XX*	102	1992
HYD Kolkhida	*Delfini XXI*	–	1992
HYD Kolkhida	*Delfini XXII*	–	1992

Delfini XVI ran aground and sank in gale conditions on 18 August 1993
Delfini V was damaged in a collision in 1994

VERIFIED

NOMIKOS

Greece

High-speed craft operated

Type	Name	Delivered
HYD Kometa	*Flying Ikaros I* (ex-*Wanda*)	1990
HYD Kometa	*Flying Ikaros II* (ex-*Maria*)	1990
HYD Kometa	*Flying Ikaros III*	1990

VERIFIED

PARASKEVAS SHIPPING COMPANY (TAKISTOURS)

Bouboulinas 6, Dapia, GR-18050 Spetsai, Greece

Tel: +30 (298) 73025/72888
Telex: 214528
Fax: +30 (298) 74315

Takis Paraskevas, *Owner, Managing Director*

High-speed craft operated

Type	Name	Seats	Delivered
CAT Westamarin W86	*Keravnos*	168	1990

Operations
Pireaus to Agistri, Aegina and Epidaurus.

UPDATED

RENATOUR SA

Rethimniaki Naftiliaki Touristiki

250 Arkadiou Rethymno, Crete, Greece

Telex: 291226 GR

High-speed craft operated

Type	Name	Seats	Delivered
CAT Westamarin W100D	*Nearchos* (ex-*Venture 83*, launched as *Rosario*)	245	May 1982

Operations
Réthimnon to Santorini (Thira).

VERIFIED

SANTA LINES

Greece

High-speed craft operated

Type	Name	Delivered
HYD Kometa	*Santa*	1992
HYD Kometa	*Santa II*	1993
HYD Kometa	*Santa III*	1993

Operations
Kavala to Thassos and Limenaria.

VERIFIED

SEAJET SHIPPING

Greece

High-speed craft operated

Type	Name	Seats	Delivered
CAT Westamarian 4200S	Seajet I	—	1995

Operations
Rafina to Cyclade Islands.

NEW ENTRY

GUADELOUPE

ANTILLES TRANS-EXPRESS

Gare Maritime, Quai Gatine, 97110 Pointe à Pître, Guadeloupe

Tel: +590 911343
Fax: +590 911105

C H Munier, *General Manager*
L Labatut, *Operating Manager*

High-speed craft operated

Type	Name	Seats	Delivered
CAT Marinteknik 41 m CPV	*Jetkat Express II*	380	1992
CAT Marinteknik 34 m CPV	*Emeraude Express*	242	1986
CAT Marinteknik 34 m CPV	*Antilles Express*	297	1992
CAT Marinteknik 41 m CPV	*Saphir Express*	—	1994
CAT Marinteknik 42 m	*Turquoise Express*	385	1995

Operations
Pointe à Pître to Marie Galante, 45 minutes
Pointe à Pître to Les Saintes, 45 minutes
Pointe à Pître to Dominique to Martinique, 3 hours 45 minutes
Pointe à Pître to Dominica (Roseau), 1 hour 30 minutes
Transit in Roseau 30 minutes
Dominica to Martinique (Fort de France), 2 hours
Pointe à Pître to Martinique, 2 hours 50 minutes

High-speed sea transport of passengers between Guadeloupe and its dependencies Marie Galante and Les Saintes, as well as the neighbouring islands of Dominica and Martinique. In addition to its regular lines ATE organises charter trips and other activities.

UPDATED

SOCIÉTÉ DE TRANSPORTS MARITIMES BRUDEY FRÈRES

Quai de la Darse 78, Centre St John Peroe, 97110 Pointe à Pître, Guadeloupe

Tel: +590 900448
Telex: 919810 GL
Fax: +590 821562

Brudey Doenis, *Shipowner*
Vala Claude, *Commercial Director*

High-speed craft operated

Type	Name	Seats	Delivered
MH Esterel 35 m	*Tropic*	250	1988
CAT Westamarin 3700S 37 m	*Maria*	320	1990
CAT Westamarin 27 m	*Flycat* (ex-*Kogelwieck*)	140	1992
SES	*Atlantica*	350	1995

Operations
Pointe à Pître to Dominique to Port de France, 2 hours 50 minutes
Pointe à Pître to Les Saintes, 21 miles, 45 minutes
Pointe à Pître to Marie Galante, 25 miles, 55 minutes.

UPDATED

GUAM

ISLAND CRUISE LINE PACIFIC INC

Guam

High-speed craft operated

Type	Name	Seats	Delivered
MH Oceanfast 37.6 m	*Sounds of Pacific*	100	1991

Operations
Tourist excursions from Guam.

NEW ENTRY

HONG KONG

CASTLE PEAK POWER COMPANY LTD

Hong Kong

High-speed craft operated

Type	Name	Seats	Delivered
CAT A Fai InCat 16 m	*Kwong Fai*	40	June 1984

VERIFIED

CHINA MERCHANT DEVELOPMENT COMPANY

152 Connaught Road, Central, Hong Kong

High-speed craft operated

Type	Name	Seats	Delivered
SES Hovermarine HM 218	*Yin Bin 1*	84	1986
SES Hovermarine HM 218	*Yin Bin 2*	84	1986
CAT Mitsui CP 20	*Yin Bin 3*	250	1987
SES Huangpu MARIC 7211	*Yin Bin 4*	162	1993
CAT Cougar 32 m	*Yin Bin 5*	—	1993
CAT Fjellstrand 38.8 m	*Heng He*	—	1994

Operations
Shekou to Hong Kong Central.
Fu Yong to Hong Kong Central.

UPDATED

CHU KONG SHIPPING COMPANY LTD

7/F 28 Connaught Road West, Hong Kong

Chu Kong Shipping Company Ltd is registered in Hong Kong but owned by a People's Republic of China organisation. It acts as the general manager in Hong Kong for all the transportation companies in the ports around Guangdong Province. These transportation companies include:

Hui Yang County
Jiang Men Passenger Shipping
Jiuzhou Port Administration
Ping Gang Transportation Corporation
San Fu Shipping Company
Shun Gang Passenger Transport
Taishan Guanghai Port Corporation
Xin Gang Passenger Transport
Zhon Gang Steamer Navigation Company
Zhong Shan Shipping
Zhu Hai Jiuzhou Port Administration

High-speed craft operated

Type	Name	Seats	Delivered
CAT Fjellstrand 31.5 m	*Hai Shan* (ex-*Bei Xiu Hu*)	289	1984
CAT Fjellstrand 31.5 m	*Li Wan Hu*	289	1984
CAT Fjellstrand 31.5 m	*Hai Tian* (ex-*Peng Lai Hu*)	291	1985
CAT Marinteknik 34 m	*Jiu Zhou*	250	1987
CAT Narinteknik 34 m	*Zhen Jiang Hu*	262	1987
CAT Precision Marine 40 m	*Shun Feng*	352	1988
CAT Precision Marine 40 m	*Xin Ning*	280	1988
CAT WaveMaster 32 m	*Yin Shan Hu*	252	1989
CAT Italthai Marine 32.5 m	*Dou Men*	252	1990
CAT WaveMaster 34.5 m	*Zhen Xing Hu*	310	1990
CAT Austal 40 m	*Hai Wei* (ex-*Shun Shui*)	354	1991
CAT Singapore Shipbuilding 35 m	*Tai Ping*	300	1991
CAT WaveMaster 39 m	*Wu Yi Hu*	358	1992
CAT Austal 40 m	*Xin Duan Zhou*	338	1992
CAT Austal 40 m	*Hai Bin* (ex-*Shun De*)	354	1992
CAT Austal 40 m	*Hai Zhu*	338	1992
CAT Austal 40 m	*Nan Gui*	338	1992
CAT Austal 40 m	*Kai Ping*	368	1992
CAT Austal 40 m	*Lian Shan Hu*	338	1992
CAT Austal 40 m	*Cui Heng Hu*	338	1992
CAT WaveMaster 39 m	*Peng Lai Hu*	354	1992
CAT Austal 40 m	*Nan Xing*	338	1993
CAT Austal 40 m	*Hai Chang*	338	1993
CAT Aluminium Craft (88) 35 m	*Dong Tai An*	250	1993
CAT Austal 40 m	*Hui Yang*	368	1993
CAT Austal 40 m	*Tai Shan*	338	1993
CAT Austal 40 m	*Gang Zhou*	318	1993
CAT Austal 40 m	*Gao Ming*	338	1993
CAT Austal 40 m	*Gui Feng*	318	1993
CAT Austal 40 m	*San Bu*	368	1993
CAT WaveMaster 39 m	*Peng Jiang*	193	1993
CAT Austal 40 m	*Shunjing*	355	1994
CAT Austal 40 m	*Lian Gang Hu*	355	1994
CAT Austal 40 m	*Yi Xian Hu*	355	1994
CAT Austal 40 m	*Xin He Shan*	300	1994
CAT Austal 40 m	*Zhong Shan*	355	1994
CAT Aluminium Craft 38 m	*Tai Kang*	—	1995
CAT Austal 40 m	*Shun De*	—	1995
CAT Austal 40 m	*Hai Yang*	—	1995

Vessels are ordered through the subsidiary company Yuet Hing Marine Supplies Company Ltd.

CTS-PARKVIEW FERRY SERVICES LTD

CTS-Parkview Shipyard Building, NKML 36, Po Lun Street (Extension), Lai Chi Kok, Kowloon, Hong Kong

Tel: +852 810 5511
Fax: +852 810 0667

L Baum, *Vice President*

High-speed craft operated

Type	Name	Seats	Delivered
CAT Marinteknik 41 m	*Lusitano*	306	1991
CAT Marinteknik 41 m	*Vasco Da Gama*	306	1991
CAT Marinteknik 41 m	*Santa Cruz*	306	1991
CAT K Fjellstrand (S) FlyingCat 40 m	*Universal Mk I*	266	Dec 1992
CAT K Fjellstrand (S) FlyingCat 40 m	*Universal Mk II*	266	Jan 1993
CAT K Fjellstrand (S) FlyingCat 40 m	*Universal Mk III*	266	Oct 1993
CAT K Fjellstrand (S) FlyingCat 40 m	*Universal Mk IV*	266	Jan 1994
CAT FBM Tricat 35 m	*Universal Mk VI*	160	Dec 1993
CAT FBM Tricat 45 m	*Universal Mk 2001*	303	Feb 1995
CAT FBM Tricat 45 m	*Universal Mk 2002*	303	Jun 1995
CAT FBM Tricat 45 m	*Universal Mk 2003*	303	Jul 1995
CAT FBM Tricat 45 m	*Universal MK 2004*	303	1996
CAT FBM Tricat 45 m	*Universal MK 2005*	303	1996

Universal Mk 2001 *1995*

Operations
Hong Kong Central to Macau
Kowloon to Macau
Hong Kong to Shenzhen Airport, China.

UPDATED

CUSTOMS AND EXCISE DEPARTMENT

8th Floor, Harbour Building, 38 Pier Road, Central, Hong Kong

Tel: +852 2852 3386
Telex: 65092 CUSEX HX
Fax: +852 2854 1959

Raymond Li, *Assistant Commissioner (Operations)*
Lawrence Wong, *Head of Command, Marine and Land Enforcement*

High-speed craft operated

Type	Name
MH Chung Wah Shipbuilding and Engineering Co Ltd King Class Yard No 204	*Customs 6 Sea Glory*
MH Chung Wah Shipbuilding and Engineering Co Ltd King Class Yard No 205	*Customs 5 Sea Guardian*
MH Chung Wah Shipbuilding and Engineering Co Ltd King Class Yard No 206	*Customs 2 Sea Leader*

UPDATED

Hong Kong Customs and Excise fleet ***1991***

DISCOVERY BAY TRANSPORTATION SERVICES LTD

Hong Kong Resort Company

2nd floor, Pier Office, Discovery Bay, Lantau, Hong Kong

Tel: +852 2987 7351
Fax: +852 2987 5246

Eric Chu, *Executive Director*
Andrew Kwong, *Executive Director*

High-speed craft operated

Type	Name	Seats	Delivered
SES Hovermarine HM 218	*RTS 201*	100	October 1986
SES Hovermarine HM 218	*RTS 202*	100	March 1987
SES Hovermarine HM 218	*RTS 203*	100	December 1986
MH Marinteknik Sweden/Singapore 35 MPV	*Discovery Bay 12*	300	May 1987
MH Marinteknik (S) 35 MPV	*Discovery Bay 15*	300	May 1987
MH Marinteknik (S) 35 MPV	*Discovery Bay 16*	300	June 1987
MH Marinteknik (S) 35 MPV	*Discovery Bay 19*	300	January 1990
MH Marinteknik (S) 35 MPV	*Discovery Bay 20*	300	May 1990
MH Marinteknik (S) 35 MPV	*Discovery Bay 21*	300	June 1992
MH Marinteknik (S) 35 MPV	*Discovery Bay 22*	300	March 1993
MH Cheoy Lee 22.8 m	*Discovery Bay 18*	170	January 1989
MH Cheoy Lee 19.7 m	*Discovery Bay 23* (ex-*Discovery Bay 3*)	100	August 1982
MH Cheoy Lee 19.7 m	*Discovery Bay 8*	100	July 1983
MH Cheoy Lee 19.7 m	*Discovery Bay 9*	100	September 1983
CAT Marinteknik (S) 42 m	*Discovery Bay 1*	500	Jan 1995
CAT Marinteknik (S) 42 m	*Discovery Bay 2*	500	July 1995
CAT Marinteknik (S) 42 m	*Discovery Bay 3*	500	Jan 1996

Note: Discovery Bay 10, 11 and 17 were sold in 1995

Discovery Bay 1 ***1996***

Operations

Discovery Bay, Lantau to Central, Hong Kong, 9 n miles, 25 minutes
Approximately 600,000 passenger trips per month.

UPDATED

FAR EAST HYDROFOIL COMPANY LTD

Member of Shun Tak Group

Penthouse, 39th Floor, Shun Tak Centre, 200 Connaught Road, Central, Hong Kong

Tel: +852 2859 3111
Telex: 74200 SEDAM HX
Fax: +852 2559 6471

Stanley Ho, *Group Executive Chairman*
David Hill, *Executive Director*
Andrew Tse, *Director*
Jenning Wang, *Engineering Manager*
Edmund Cheng, *Fleet Operations Manager*

The company started hydrofoil service in 1963 with a PT 20 and gradually built up to a total of 14 surface-piercing hydrofoils. The Far East Hydrofoil Company began the world's first commercial Jetfoil service in April 1975. Subsequently the Jetfoils took over the bulk of the traffic due to passenger demand and the surface-piercing hydrofoils were gradually phased out and additional Jetfoils purchased. All surface-piercing hydrofoils were removed from service by the end of 1983 and subsequently sold. In 1994 FEH Jetfoils carried 80 per cent of all Hong Kong to Macau passenger traffic with 49,116 crossings and 10.4 million passengers. By June 1994 FEH Jetfoils had carried a total of 109,369,784 passengers. The fitting of new seats and interior decoration to the entire FEH fleet began in April 1993 and was completed in 1995.

Funchal, *Jetfoil Model 929-115* ***1990***

São Jorge (Paul Beaver) ***1995***

High-speed craft operated

Type	Name	Seats	Delivered
STEC			
HYD Boeing Jetfoil 929-100	*Madeira*	268	1975
HYD Boeing Jetfoil 929-100	*Santa Maria*	268	1975
HYD Boeing Jetfoil 929-100	*Flores* (ex-*Kalakaua '78*)	268	1978
HYD Boeing Jetfoil 929-100	*Corvo* (ex-*Kamehameha*)	268	1978
HYD Boeing Jetfoil 929-100	*Pico* (ex-*Kuhio*)	268	1978
HYD Boeing Jetfoil 929-100	*São Jorge* (ex-*Jet Caribe I* '80, ex-*Jet de Oriente '78*)	268	1980
HYD Boeing Jetfoil 929-100	*Acores* (ex-*Jet Caribe II*)	268	1980
HYD Boeing Jetfoil 929-100	*Ponta Delgada* (ex-*Flying Princess II*)	268	1981
HYD Boeing Jetfoil 929-115	*Terceira* (ex-*Normandy Princess*)	268	1981
HYD Boeing Jetfoil 929-100	*Urzela* (ex-*Flying Princess*)	268	1981
HYD Boeing Jetfoil 929-115	*Funchal* (ex-*Jetferry One '83*)	268	1983
HYD Boeing Jetfoil 929-115	*Horta* (ex-*Jetferry Two*)	268	1983
HYD Boeing Jetfoil 929-115	**Lilau* (ex-*HMS Speedy*)	268	1987
HYD Boeing Jetfoil 929-100	*Guia* (ex-*Okesa*)	268	1990
HYD Boeing Jetfoil 929-115	*Taipa* (ex-*Princesa Guaeimara*)	268	1991
HYD Boeing Jetfoil 929-115	*Cacilhas* (ex-*Princesa Guayarmina*)	268	1991
HYD China Shipbuilding PS-30	*Balsa*	290	1994
HYD China Shipbuilding PS-30	*Praia*	290	1995
F-CAT Fjellstrand Foilcat 35 m	*Barca*	–	1995
F-CAT Fjellstrand Foilcat 35 m	*Penha*	–	1995

*converted 929-320

Operations

Hong Kong to Macau, 38 to 40 n miles, 24 hour service since March 1989
Services operate four times per hour each way between 07.00 and 20.00 and twice an hour from 20.00 to 02.30 and then two more sailings at 04.00 and 06.00.

UPDATED

HONG KONG HI-SPEED FERRIES LTD

Member of Shun Tak Group

13/F, V Huen Building, 138 Queen's Road, Central, Hong Kong

Tel: +852 815 2789
Telex: 89846 HKHPF HX
Fax: +852 543 0324/544 4392

Dr Stanley Ho, *Chairman*
Captain P N Parashar, *General Manager*

High-speed craft operated

Type	Name	Speed	Seats	Delivered
MH Vosper Thornycroft 62.5 m*	*Cheung Kong*	26 kts	659	May 1985
MH Vosper Thornycroft 62.5 m*	*Ju Kong*	26 kts	659	May 1985

*Note: These vessels are due to be sold in 1996.

Operations

Hong Kong to Macau, journey time approximately 105 minutes.
Seven departures on weekends and holidays, six departures on weekdays.

Fares

Weekends and public holidays: HK$58 to HK$95
Weekdays: HK$35 to HK$71
Exclusive of embarkation fee of HK$26 from Hong Kong and HK$22 from Macau

UPDATED

Cheung Kong ***1989***

THE HONG KONG & YAUMATI FERRY COMPANY LTD

Central Harbour Services Pier, 1st Floor, Pier Road, Central, Hong Kong

Tel: +852 542 3081
Telex: 83140 HYFCO HX
Fax: +852 542 3958

Colin K Y Lam, *Chairman*
Peter M K Wong, *President and Chief Executive Officer*
David C S Ho, *General Manager*

The world's largest operator of sidewall hovercraft (SES).

High-speed craft operated

Type	Name	Seats	Delivered
SES Hovermarine HM 216 (HM 2 Mk III)	*HYF 103*	74	1975
SES Hovermarine HM 216 (HM 2 Mk III)	*HYF 104*	74	1975
SES Hovermarine HM 218 (HM 2 Mk IV)	*HYF 105*	100	1976
SES Hovermarine HM 218 (HM 2 Mk IV)	*HYF 106*	100	1976
SES Hovermarine HM 218 (HM 2 Mk IV)	*HYF 107*	100	1976
SES Hovermarine HM 218 (HM 2 Mk IV)	*HYF 111*	105	1979
SES Hovermarine HM 218 (HM 2 Mk IV)	*HYF 112*	105	1979
SES Hovermarine HM 218 (HM 2 Mk IV)	*HYF 113*	105	1980
SES Hovermarine HM 218 (HM 2 Mk IV)	*HYF 114*	105	1980
SES Hovermarine HM 218 (HM 2 Mk IV)	*HYF 115*	105	1980
SES Hovermarine HM 218 (HM 2 Mk IV)	*HYF 116*	74	1980
SES Hovermarine HM 218 (HM 2 Mk IV)	*HYF 117*	105	1980
SES Hovermarine HM 218 (HM 2 Mk IV)	*HYF 118*	105	1980
SES Hovermarine HM 218 (HM 2 Mk IV)	*HYF 119*	105	1980
SES Hovermarine HM 218 (HM 2 Mk IV)	*HYF 120*	105	1980
SES Hovermarine HM 218 (HM 2 Mk IV)	*HYF 121*	105	1980
SES Hovermarine HM 218 (HM 2 Mk IV)	*HYF 122*	105	1980
SES Hovermarine HM 218 (HM 2 Mk IV)	*HYF 123*	105	1980
SES Hovermarine HM 218 (HM 2 Mk IV)	*HYF 124*	105	1980
SES Hovermarine HM 218 (HM 2 Mk IV)	*HYF 125*	105	1980
SES Hovermarine HM 218 (HM 2 Mk IV)	*HYF 126*	105	1980
SES Hovermarine HM 218 (HM 2 Mk IV)	*HYF 127*	105	1980
SES Hovermarine HM 218	*HYF 128*	105	1985
SES Hovermarine HM 218	*HYF 130*	74	1982
SES Vosper Hovermarine HM 527	*Tejo*	200	1983
SES Vosper Hovermarine HM 527	*Douro*	200	1983
SES Vosper Hovermarine HM 527	*Sado*	200	1983
SES Vosper Hovermarine HM 527	*Mondego*	200	1983
CAT Kværner Fjellstrand 40 m	*HKF I*	422	1993
CAT Kværner Fjellstrand 40 m	*HKF II*	422	1993
SES Vosper Hovermarine HM 218	*HYF 129*	105	1994
CAT Kværner Fjellstrand 40 m	*HKF III*	422	1994

Operations	Crossing time
Hong Kong Central to:	
Tuen Mun	42 min (SES)
	30 min (CAT)
Tsuen Wan	22 min
Goad Coast	45 min
Tsim Sha Tsui East	5-8 min
Mui Wo/Peng Chau	35 min
Cheung Chau	35 min
Macau	80 min
Shekou	70 min
Whampoa	175 min
Wanchai to Tuen Mun	45 min

UPDATED

ROYAL HONG KONG POLICE FORCE, MARINE REGION

25 Salisbury Road, Tsim Sha Tsui, Kowloon, Hong Kong

Tel: +852 366 5827
Telex: 65367 HX
Fax: +852 311 5564

A J Ferrige, *Regional Commander, Assistant Commissioner*
Hui Chiu-Yin, *Deputy Regional Commander, Chief Superintendent*
P H Cummings, *Chief Staff Officer, Chief Superintendent*

High-speed craft operated

Type	Name
MH Chung Wah Shipbuilding 26.3 m Mk II	*PL 57 Mercury*
MH Chung Wah Shipbuilding 26.3 m Mk II	*PL 58 Vulcan*
MH Chung Wah Shipbuilding 26.3 m Mk II	*PL 59 Ceres*
MH Chung Wah Shipbuilding 26.5 m Mk I	*PL 60 Aquarius*
MH Chung Wah Shipbuilding 26.5 m Mk I	*PL 61 Pisces*
MH Chung Wah Shipbuilding 26.5 m Mk I	*PL 62 Argo*
MH Chung Wah Shipbuilding 26.5 m Mk I	*PL 63 Carina*
MH Chung Wah Shipbuilding 26.5 m Mk I	*PL 64 Cetus*
MH Chung Wah Shipbuilding 26.5 m Mk I	*PL 65 Dorado*
MH Chung Wah Shipbuilding 26.5 m Mk I	*PL 66 Octans*

High-speed craft operated continued

Type	Name
MH Chung Wah Shipbuilding 26.5 m Mk I	*PL 67 Vela*
MH Chung Wah Shipbuilding 26.5 m Mk I	*PL 68 Volans*
MH Chung Wah Shipbuilding 26.5 m Mk III	*PL 70 King Lai*
MH Chung Wah Shipbuilding 26.5 m Mk III	*PL 71 King Yee*
MH Chung Wah Shipbuilding 26.5 m Mk III	*PL 72 King Lim*
MH Chung Wah Shipbuilding 26.5 m Mk III	*PL 73 King Hau*
MH Chung Wah Shipbuilding 26.5 m Mk III	*PL 74 King Dai*
MH Chung Wah Shipbuilding 26.5 m Mk III	*PL 75 King Chung*
MH Chung Wah Shipbuilding 26.5 m Mk III	*PL 76 King Shun*
MH Chung Wah Shipbuilding 26.5 m Mk III	*PL 77 King Tak*
MH Chung Wah Shipbuilding 26.5 m Mk III	*PL 78 King Chi*
MH Chung Wah Shipbuilding 26.5 m Mk III	*PL 79 King Tai*
MH Chung Wah Shipbuilding 26.5 m Mk III	*PL 80 King Kwan*
MH Chung Wah Shipbuilding 26.5 m Mk III	*PL 82 King Yan*
MH Chung Wah Shipbuilding 26.5 m Mk III	*PL 83 King Yung*
MH Chung Wah Shipbuilding 26.5 m Mk III	*PL 84 King Kan*
MH Transfield Shipbuilding 32.6 m	*PL 51 Protector*
MH Transfield Shipbuilding 32.6 m	*PL 52 Guardian*
MH Transfield Shipbuilding 32.6 m	*PL 53 Defender*
MH Transfield Shipbuilding 32.6 m	*PL 54 Preserver*
MH Transfield Shipbuilding 32.6 m	*PL 55 Rescuer*
MH Transfield Shipbuilding 32.6 m	*PL 56 Detector*

This organisation also operates a smaller range of high-speed craft including 3 × 9.5 m and 7 × 7 m RHIB 40 kts interceptors and five 50 knot anti-smuggling vessels.

UPDATED

26.5 m Chung Wau Patrol Boat Mk III ***1996***

PANYU NAN SHA SHIPPING

58th Floor, Bank of China Tower, 1 Garden Road, Central, Hong Kong

High-speed craft operated

Type	Name	Delivered
HYD PTS 75 Mk II	*Nan Sha No 1*	1992
HYD Rodriquez RHS 140	*Nan Sha No 3*	1992
HYD Rodriquez RHS 140	*Nan Sha No 5*	1993
CAT WaveMaster 39 m	*Nan Sha No 11*	1992
CAT WaveMaster 42 m	*Nan Sha No 18*	1994
CAT WaveMaster 42 m	*Nan Sha No 28*	1994
CAT NewTech	*Nan Sha No 38*	(1996)
CAT NewTech	*Nan Sha No 68*	(1996)

Operations
Hong Kong to People's Republic of China.

UPDATED

YUET HING MARINE SUPPLIES COMPANY LTD

25/F Yardley Commercial Building, 1-3 Connaught Road West, Hong Kong

Tel: +852 815 0333
Telex: 65317 YHMSC HX
Fax: +852 815 2188

Liang Jian Tao, *Managing Director*
Lin Zao Yu, *Director and Deputy General Manager*

Yuet Hing Marine Supplies Company Ltd is an associate company of Chu Kong Shipping and has ordered the building of over 50 various high-speed passenger vessels in aluminium alloy since 1980 for companies in the ports of Guangdong Province.

UPDATED

HUNGARY

MAHART PASSNAVE PASSENGERS SHIPPING LTD

1056 Budapest, Belgrád rakpart, Nemzetközi Hajóállomás, Hungary

Tel: +36 (1) 118 1953
Telex: 225412
Fax: +36 (1) 118 7740

Jenö Vajas, *Managing Director*
Zsolt Krucsai, *Director*

MAHART Passnave Ltd introduced three Raketa hydrofoils on the River Danube between Hungary and Austria in 1962. Since the mid-1970s the Raketas have been replaced by Meteor and Voskhod hydrofoils. In 1993 four Polesye type vessels were introduced on the same routes, these craft have a very low draft of 0.40 m on foils. The cruise speed of all vessels is between 38 and 42 knots. MAHART carries between 40,000 and 50,000 passengers a year. Hydrofoils and traditional boats are also available for private hire.

High-speed craft operated

Type	Name	Seats	Delivered
HYD Sormovo Meteor	*Sólyom I*	104	1975
HYD Sormovo Voskhod	*Vöcsök I*	62	1977
HYD Sormovo Voskhod	*Vöcsök II*	62	1986
HYD Sormovo Voskhod	*Vöcsök III*	62	1987
HYD Sormovo Voskhod	*Vöcsök IV*	62	1987
HYD Sormovo Meteor	*Solyom II*	104	1988
HYD Polesye	*Bíbic I*	44	1992
HYD Polesye	*Bíbic II*	44	1992
HYD Polesye	*Bíbic III*	44	1993
HYD Polesye	*Bíbic IV*	44	1993

Operations
Between Budapest and Vienna, 282 km, 5 or 6 hours (downstream or upstream), April to October, daily. Budapest to Esztergom, June to August weekends, 73 km, 1 hour.

UPDATED

Vöcsök III operated by MAHART **1996**

INDIA

DAMANIA SHIPPING

Passenger Terminal, No 2 New Ferry Wharf, Mallet Bunder Road, Bombay 400 009, India

High-speed craft operated

Type	Name	Seats	Delivered
CAT Fjellstrand 40 m	*Damania I*	–	1994

Operations
Bombay to Goa.

NEW ENTRY

NEW INDIA BUSINESS HOUSE LTD

Arvind Complex Plot No 156, Opp. Maharashtra Nagar, Lokmanya Tilak Road, Boivali (West), Bombay 400092, India

High-speed craft operated

Type	Name	Seats	Delivered
HOV Griffon 4000 TD	*Shri Bajarangtasbapa*	51	1992
HOV Griffon 4000 TD	*Shri Saibaba*	51	1992

VERIFIED

SHIPPING CORPORATION OF INDIA

Nehru Centre, Discovery of India Building, Dr Annie Besant Road, Worli, Bombay 400018, India

Tel: +91 22 493 1461
Fax: +91 22 495 0356

High-speed craft operated

Type	Name	Seats	Delivered
CAT Tille Shipyards 31.9 m	*Khadeeja Beevi*	100	1990
CAT Tille Shipyards 31.9 m	*Hameedath Bee*	100	1990

Operations
Lakshadweep area of South West India.

UPDATED

INDONESIA

BAHTERA SEGARA PERSANDA

Indonesia

High-speed craft operated

Type	Name	Delivered
CAT Precision 31 m	*Bahtera Princess*	1990
CAT 26 m	*Bahtera Express*	1991
MH Aluminium Craft 88	*Penguin Success*	1992

Operations
Sekupang to Singapore.

UPDATED

BALI HAI CRUISES

PO Box 548, Den Pasar 80001, Bali, Indonesia

High-speed craft operated

Type	Name	Seats	Delivered
CAT Austal 34 m	*Bali Hai I*	300	1989
CAT Austal 36 m	*Bali Hai II*	332	1994

Operations
Benoa to Lembongan Island.

UPDATED

CITRA BAHARI NUSTRAINDO

JLRE Martatinata, Sukupang Pulau Datam, Jakarta, Indonesia

High-speed craft operated

Type	Name	Seats	Delivered
CAT NQEA 24 m InCat	*Supercat II*	180+	1990

VERIFIED

PT HOVER MARITIM SEMANDERA

Jalan Gondangdia Lama 26, Jakarta 10350, Indonesia

Tel: +62 (21) 325608/310 3358
Telex: 45746 SHARCO IA
Fax: +62 (21) 310 3357

Air Marshal, Suharnoko Harbani Rtd, *Chairman*
H M Suharnoko, *Vice Chairman*
H Wijaya, *Commissioner*
Ir A W Suharnoko, *President, Director*
Isamaya P Asrah, *Director*

High-speed craft operated

Type	Name	Seats	Delivered
SES Vosper Hovermarine HM 218 Mk IV	*Semandera Satu*	78	1986
SES Vosper Hovermarine HM 218 Mk IV	*Semandera Dua*	78	1986

Operations
Tanjung Priok (Port of Jakarta) to P Kotok Besar and P Antuk Timur (Holiday resort islands north-west of Jakarta), distance 40 to 45 n miles, trip time 1 hour 20 minutes, commercial service started February 1987, one and occasionally two trips per day, four days per week. Departures: Jakarta 07.00, Islands 16.00, contract with resort operator (subsidiary of Japan Airlines).

Vosper Hovermarine HM 218 Mk IV Semandera Satu *1989*

Hover Maritim Semandera is also offering a two day cruise package to the Ujung Kulon National Park from Jakarta, distance 135 n miles, trip time 4 hours 25 minutes, service started September 1987, major holidays only. Departures: 07.00 from Jakarta.

Since November 1989, the company has provided offshore crew transfer services.

VERIFIED

PT MABUA INTAN EXPRESS (PT MAHASARA BUANA)

Jakarta, Indonesia

High-speed craft operated

Type	Name	Seats	Delivered
CAT K Fjellstrand (S) Flying Cat 40 m	*Mabua Express*	248	1992
F-CAT Westamarin 2900	*Foilcat*	—	1995

Operations
Bali to Lombok.

UPDATED

PULAU SERIBU MARINE RESORT

Indonesia

High-speed craft operated

Type	Name	Delivered
MH Yamaha 19.5 m	*Lumba-Lumba*	1989
MH Yamaha 20 m	*Pantara VII*	1993

Operations
Jakarta to Pulau Seribu.

VERIFIED

QUICKSILVER

Bali

High-speed craft operated

Type	Name	Delivered
WPC NQEA InCat 37 m	*Quicksilver Beluga*	1992

Operations
Benoa to Nusa Penida.

VERIFIED

IRAN

VALFAJRE 8 SHIPPING

Karimkhan-Zand Avenue, Abyar Alley, 15875 Tehran, Iran

High-speed craft operated

Type	Name	Seats	Additional Payload	Delivered
CAT WaveMaster 44 m	*Negeen*	242	—	1994
CAT WaveMaster 44 m	—	160	10 cars	(1996)
CAT WaveMaster 44 m	—	160	10 cars	(1996)

Operations
Khoramshahr to Kuwait city.

UPDATED

ITALY

ADRIATICA DI NAVIGAZIONE SpA

PO Box 705, I-30123 Venice, Italy

Tel: +39 (41) 781611
Telex: 410045 ADRNAV I
Fax: +39 (41) 781894

P Chenda, *Managing Director*
F Luis, *Commercial and Operations Director*

High-speed craft operated

Type	Name	Seats	Delivered
HYD Rodriquez RHS 160	*Diomedea* (launched as *Flying Phoenix*)	168	1975
HYD Rodriquez RHS 160F	*Monte Gargano*	212	1989
Rodriquez Monostab 47	*Marconi*	400	1991
Rodriquez Monostab 47	*Pacinotti*	400	1992

Operations
Pacinotti: Manfredonia to Vieste, 1 hour
Vieste to Rodi, 40 minutes
Rodi to Tremiti, 50 minutes
Marconi: Operations on longer routes along Adriatic coast
Diomedea: Ortana to Tremiti, 1 hour 40 minutes
Monte Gargano: Termoli to Tremiti, 45 minutes.

UPDATED

Marconi *operated by Adriatica di Navigazione* *1992*

ALBADRIA

Italy

High-speed craft operated

Type	Name	Seats	Delivered
SES Cirrus 120P	*La Vikinga*	—	1993

Operations
Bari to Kerkira and Durres.

VERIFIED

ALILAURO-GRU.SO.N. SpA

Piazza Marinai d'Italia, Sorrento, Naples, Italy

Tel: +39 (81) 8781430
Fax: +39 (81) 8071221

Captain Salvatore Di Leva, *Chairman*

High-speed craft operated

Type	Name	Seats	Delivered
MH Marinteknik 34 MPV	*Europa Jet*	350	1988
CAT Marinteknik 34 CPV	*Giunone Jet*	300	1988
MH Crestitalia	*Freccia Del Golfo*	290	1989

Operations
Sorrento to Capri
Naples to Sorrento

NEW ENTRY

ALILAURO SpA

Via F Caracciolo 11, I-80122 Naples, Italy

Tel: +39 (81) 761 1004/4249
Telex: 720354 ALILAR I
Fax: +39 (81) 761 4250

Captain Salvatore Lauro, *President*
Dott Nicola D'Abundo, *Managing Director*

High-speed craft operated

Type	Name	Seats	Delivered
HYD Sormovo Kometa-M	*Alivenere* (ex-*Aligiglio*)*	116	1972
HYD Sormovo Kometa-M	*Alisorrento**	116	1972
HYD Sormovo Kometa-M	*Alivesuvio**	116	1973
HYD Kolkhida	*Aligea*	155	1987
CAT Marinteknik Marinjet 33 CPV	*Giove Jet*	280	1989
HYD S Ord Kolkhida	*Aliatlante*	155	1986
HYD S Ord Kolkhida	*Alieolo*	155	July 1986
HYD Sormovo Kometa-M	*Freccia Vulcano*	116	1987
CAT FBM Marinteknik Shipbuilder (S) Pte Ltd Marinjet 34 CPV	*Acapulco Jet*	300	1989
MH FBMM (S)	*Celestina*	350	1988
CAT Marinteknik Verkstads AB	*Nettuno Jet*	300	1988
MH Marinteknik Verkstads AB 41 MPV	*Rosaria Lauro*	350	1988
CAT Marinteknik Verkstads 36 CPV	*Airone Jet*	316	1988
HYD Kolkhida	*Alikenia*	115	1989
HYD Kolkhida	*Aliflorida*	115	1988
HYD Kometa	*Alieros*	116	1973
HYD Kometa	*Alisaturno*	116	1972
HYD Kometa	*Alischia*	116	1977
HYD Kometa	*Alicapri*	116	1983
HYD Kolkhida	*Aliantares*	115	1991
HYD Kolkhida	*Allaturo*	115	1991
HYD S Ord	*Aliarturo*	147	1991
HYD S Ord	*Aligiulia*	147	1991

Operations
Naples to Ischia Porto
Naples to Forio
Sorrento to Fiumicino
Capri to Ischia
Salerno to Amalfi to Positano to Capri to Napoli
Naples to Capri and the ports of the Cilento coast
Naples to Positano
Formia to Ischia to Capri to Sorrento to Napoli
Sorrento to Ischia
Fiumicino to Ponza to Ventotene to Ischia to Capri to Sorrento
Trapani to Egadi
Lampedusa to Linosa.

UPDATED

Nettuno Jet ***1992***

ALIMAR SpA

Calath Deglizingari, Stazione Marittima, 16126 Genova, Italy

High-speed craft operated

Type	Name	Seats	Delivered
CAT Westamaran 88	Marexpress	150	1990

NEW ENTRY

ALISCAFI SNAV SpA

Società di Navigazione Alta Velocita
Subsidiary Company of Rodriquez SpA

Via S Raineri 22, I-98100 Messina, Italy

Tel: +39 (90) 7775
Fax: +39 (90) 717358

Main Terminal: Via F Caracciolo 10, I-80122 Naples, Italy

Tel: +39 (81) 761 2348
Fax: +39 (81) 761 2141

High-speed craft operated

Type	Name	Seats	Built
HYD Rodriquez PT 20	*Freccia delle Eolie*	70	1957
HYD Rodriquez PT 20	*Freccia del Tirreno*	70	1957
HYD Rodriquez PT 50	*Freccia di Sorrento*	140	1959
HYD Rodriquez PT 50	*Freccia di Sicilia* (ex-*Condor 1*)	130	1964
HYD Rodriquez PT 50	*Sun Arrow*	140	1968
HYD Rodriquez PT 50	*Freccia Adriatica*	140	1969
HYD Rodriquez PT 50	*Freccia di Casamicciola*	140	1970
HYD Rodriquez RHS 200	*Superjumbo*	250	1981
HYD Rodriquez RHS 150	*Dynasty*	161	1984
HYD Rodriquez RHS 160	*Fast Blu*	180	1986
HYD Rodriquez RHS 160	*Sinai*	180	1986
HYD Rodriquez RHS 150	*Salina*	161	1990
HYD Rodriquez RHS 150	*Panarea*	210	1990
FAMH Rodriquez	*Procida*	180	1990
HYD Rodriquez RHS 160F	*Cittiships*	210	1990
HYD Rodriquez RHS 160F	*Moretto I*	210	1991
HYD Rodriquez RHS 160F	*Zibibbo*	210	1991
HYD Rodriquez RHS 160F	*Alijumbo Messina*	210	1992
HYD Rodriquez MEC	*MEC Ustia*	–	1992
HYD Rodriquez RHS 160F	*Alijumbo Eolie*	210	1991
CAT Fjellstrand 40.0 m	*Alcione Primo*	357	1990

Operations
Eolie to Napoli to Eolie
Lipari to Vulcano to S M Salina to Panarea to Stromboli to Napoli and back

Milazzo to Isole Eolie
Milazzo to Lipari to Vulcano to S M Salina to Rinella to Filicudi to Alicudi to Filicudi to Rinella to S M Salina to Lipari to Panarea to Stromboli to Panarea to S M Salina to Lipari to Vulcano to Milazzo to Vulcano to Lipari to Vulcano to Milazzo

Isole Eolie to Messina to Reggio C
S M Salina to Vulcano to Lipari to Messina to Reggio C to Messina to Vulcano to Lipari to S M Salina to Rinella to Lipari to Vulcano to Messina to Reggio C to Messina to Reggio C to Messina to Vulcano to Lipari to Rinella to S M Salina

Messina to Reggio C to Isole Eolie
Messina to Reggio C to Messina to Vulcano to Lipari to Milazzo to Lipari to Vulcano to Panarea to Stromboli to Messina to Reggio C to Messina to Stromboli to Panarea to S M Salina to Lipari to Vulcano to Messina to Reggio C to Messina

Messina to Isole Eolie Bis
Messina to Reggio C to Messina to Stromboli to Panarea to S M Salina to Lipari to Vulcano to Messina to Reggio C to Messina to Vulcano to Lipari to S M Salina to Rinella to Lipari to Vulcano to Panarea to Stromboli to Messina to Reggio C to Messina

Isole Eolie to Palermo
Vulcano to Lipari to S M Salina to Rinella to Filicudi to Alicudi to Palermo and back

Palermo to Cefalu' to Eolie
Palermo to Cefalu' to Alicudi to Filicudi to Rinella to S M Salina to Vulcano to Lipari to Milazzo to Vulcano to Lipari to S M Salina to Rinella to Lipari to Vulcano to S M Salina to Rinella to Filicudi to Alicudi to Cefalu' to Palermo

Messina to Reggio C
Napoli to Capri
Napoli to Procida to Casamicciola
Napoli to Sorrento to Capri
Portoferraio to Livorno to Capraia to Bastia

UPDATED

Citti Ships Rodriquez RHS 160F ***1992***

CAREMAR

Campania Regionale Marittima SpA

Molo Beverello 2, I-80133 Naples, Italy

Tel: +39 (81) 551 5384
Telex: 720054

High-speed craft operated

Type	Name	Seats	Delivered
HYD Rodriquez RHS 140	*Albireo*	140	1977
HYD Rodriquez RHS 160	*Algol*	180	1978
HYD Rodriquez RHS 160	*Alioth*	180	1979
HYD Rodriquez RHS 160F	*Anilam*	210	1986
HYD Rodriquez RHS 160F	*Aldebaran*	210	1986
CAT Rodriquez Seagull 400	*Achernar*	354	1993

Operations
Naples to Capri
Naples to Ischia Porto
Naples to Procida
Formia to Ponza/Ventotene.

VERIFIED

Campania Regionale Marittima's Algol ***1990***

ELBA FERRIES

A Member of the Tourship Group

Italy

High-speed craft operated

Type	Name	Seats	Additional Payload	Delivered
CAT Westamaran 5000 CF	*Elba Express* (ex-*Madikera*, ex-*Anne Lise*)	450	35 cars	1995

Operations
Piombino to Portoferraio (Elba).

NEW ENTRY

FODERARO NAVIGAZIONE

Italy

High-speed craft operated

Type	Name	Seats	Delivered
MH C N Foschi, Sciomachen 290	*Neocastrum*	350	1993
MH C N Foschi, Sciomachen 290	—	350	1994

Operations
Vibo Marina to Tropea to Vakano to Lipari to Stromboli to Tropea to Vibo Marina.

VERIFIED

LINEE LAURO Srl

Via Roma 1, I-80078 Pozzuoli, Naples, Italy

Tel: +39 (81) 551 3352/552 2828
Fax: +39 (81) 991889

Salvatore Lauro, *Chairman*
A M Lauro, *Managing Director*

High-speed craft operated

Type	Name	Seats	Delivered
MH Crestitalia	*Serena Lauro*	350	1988

UPDATED

MINISTERO DEI TRASPORTI

Gestione Governativa Navigazione Laghi

Via L Ariosto 21, I-20145 Milan, Italy

Tel: +39 (2) 481 2086/6230
Telex: 311294 NAVIGE I

Dott Ing Pietro Santini, *Government Manager*

The Italian Ministry of Transport has three subsidiary hydrofoil-operating companies which run services on Lake Como, Lake Garda and Lake Maggiore as detailed in other entries in this section.

VERIFIED

MISANO ALTA VELOCITA' Srl

Corso Garibaldi 96/98, I-72100 Brindisi, Italy

Tel: +39 (831) 529771
Telex: 813384
Fax: +39 (831) 527968

Anacleto Ippati - Brindisi
Fabio Fazzina - Brindisi
Nicola Bonetti - Ravenna

Misano Alta Velocita' Srl operates the SES *Santa Eleonora* as detailed below and is a branch of Misano di Navigazione and is part of Italian Ferries Srl.

High-speed craft operated

Type	Name	Seats	Delivered
SES Ulstein UT 904	*Santa Eleonora*	354	February 1992

Operations
Brindisi to Corfu
Brindisi to Paxi.

UPDATED

Santa Eleonora ***1993***

NAVIGAZIONE LAGO DI COMO

Gestione Governativa Navigazione Laghi

Via Per Cernobbio 18, 22100 Como, Italy

Tel: +39 (31) 579211
Fax: +39 (31) 570080

Dott Ing F Parigi, *Director*

High-speed craft operated

Type	Name	Seats	Delivered
Rodriquez PT 20	*Freccia delle Azalee*	80	1969
Rodriquez RHS 70	*Freccia delle Betulle*	80	1974
Rodriquez RHS 70	*Freccia delle Gardenie*	80	1976
Rodriquez RHS 150SL	*Freccia delle Valli*	180	1980
Rodriquez RHS 150SL	*Guglielmo Marconi*	180	1983
Rodriquez RHS 150SL	*Voloire*	180	1989
Rodriquez RHS 70	*Freccia dei Gerani*	80	1995

Freccia delle Valli (Aerea I Buga) *1993*

Operations
Como to Argegno to Lezzeno to Lenno to Tremezzo to Bellagio to Menaggio to Varenna to Bellano to Dongo to Gravedona to Domaso to Gera to Colico.

UPDATED

NAVIGAZIONE LIBERA DEL GOLFO SpA

Molo Beverello, I-80133 Naples, Italy

Tel: +39 (81) 552 0763/7209
Telex: 722661 NAVLIB I
Fax: +39 (81) 552 5582

High-speed craft operated

Type	Name	Seats	Delivered
MH FBM Marine 41 m	*Capri Jet*	394	26 July 1988
MH FBM Marine 41 m	*Sorrento Jet*	394	June 1990
MH Marinteknik 41 m	*Napoli Jet*	394	May 1992
MH Marinteknik 41 m	*Amalfi Jet*	350	1993
MH Marinteknik 41 m	*Ischia Jet*	350	1994

Operations
Naples to Capri, 40 minutes
Sorrento to Capri, 20 minutes.

VERIFIED

Napoli Jet *1993*

NAVIGAZIONE LAGO MAGGIORE

Gestione Governativa Navigazione Laghi

Viale F Baracca 1, I-28041 Arona, Italy

Tel: +39 (322) 46651
Fax: +39 (322) 249530

Dott Ing Piero Ferrozzi, *Director*

High-speed craft operated

Type	Name	Seats	Delivered
Rodriquez RHS 70	*Freccia delle Camelie*	80	1974
Rodriquez RHS 70	*Freccia delle Magnolie*	80	1975
Rodriquez RHS 150SL	*Freccia dei Giardini*	176 + 20	1981
Rodriquez RHS 150SL	*Enrico Fermi*	200	1984
Rodriquez RHS 150FLS	*Lord Byron*	200	1989

Rodriquez RHS 150SL Freccia dei Giardini *1994*

Operations
RHS 70: Luino to Cannero to Cannabui. RHS 150: Arona to Angera to Ispra to Belgirate to Stresa to Baveno to Isola
Madre to Intra to Pallanza to Luino to Cannobio to Brissago to Ascona to Locarno.

UPDATED

NAVIGAZIONE SUL LAGO DI GARDA

Gestione Governativa Navigazione Laghi

Piazza Matteotti 2, I-25015 Desenzano del Garda, Italy

Tel: +39 (30) 914 1321/2/3
Fax: +39 (30) 914 4640

High-speed craft operated

Type	Name	Seats	Delivered
HYD Rodriquez RHS 150SL	*Freccia delle Riviere*	200	1981
HYD Rodriquez RHS 150SL	*Galileo Galilei*	200	1982
HYD Rodriquez RHS 150FL	*Goethe*	200	1988
CAT Conavi 22 m	*Catullo*	105	1992
CAT Conavi 22 m	*Parini*	105	1993

Operations
Peschiera del Garda to Desenzano to Sirmione to Bardolino to Garda to Salò to Gardone to Torri to Maderno to Gargnano to Malcesine to Limone to Torbole to Riva del Garda.

UPDATED

Rodriquez RHS 150FL Goethe *1991*

OCEAN BRIDGE INVESTMENTS

Italy

High-speed craft operated

Type	Name	Seats	Additional Payload	Delivered
MH Fincantieri MVD 1200	—	600	170 cars	(1996)

NEW ENTRY

SAREMAR

Sardegna Regionale Marittima

Via Mameli 40, 09131 Cagliari, Italy

High-speed craft operated

Type	Name	Seats	Delivered
MH Rodriquez 47 m	Isola di S.Pietro	400	1993

Operations
Portevesme to Isola di S.Pietro and Isola di S.Antioco.

NEW ENTRY

SIREMAR

Sicilia Regionale Marittima SpA

Via Principe di Belmonte, 1/C, I-90139 Palermo, Sicily, Italy

Tel: +39 (91) 582688
Telex: 910135 SIRMAR I
Fax: +39 (91) 582267

High-speed craft operated

Type	Name	Seats	Delivered
Rodriquez PT 50	*Pisanello*	130	1961
Rodriquez RHS 140	*Duccio*	140	1977
Rodriquez RHS 160	*Donatello*	184	1980
Rodriquez RHS 160	*Botticelli*	184	1980
Rodriquez RHS 160F	*Masaccio*	210	1987
Rodriquez RHS 160F	*Mantegna*	210	1989
Rodriquez RHS 160F	*Giorgione*	210	1989
Rodriquez RHS PT50	*Giotto**	130	1992
Rodriquez Foilmaster	*Tiziano*	220	1994

**Giotto* was damaged in a storm in 1994

Operations
Milazzo to Eolie (Vulcano to Lipari to Salina to Panarea to Stromboli to Filicudi to Alicudi)
Palermo to Ustica
Trapani to Egadi (Favignana to Levanzo to Marettimo).

VERIFIED

Sicilia Regionale Marittima's Giorgione **1991**

TIRRENIA NAVIGAZIONE

Rione Sirignano 2, I-80121 Naples, Italy

High-speed craft operated

Type	Name	Seats	Additional Payload	Delivered
MH Rodriquez Aquastrada	*Guizzo*	450	126 cars	1993
MH Rodriquez Aquastrada	*Scatto*	450	126 cars	1994

Operations
Civitavecchia and La Spezia to Olbia.

VERIFIED

Tirrenia Aquastrada Guizzo **1995**

TOREMAR

Toscana Regionale Marittima SpA

Via Calatati 6, I-57123 Livorno, Italy

Tel: +39 (586) 22772
Telex: 590214 I

High-speed craft operated

Type	Name	Seats	Delivered
HYD Rodriquez RHS 160F	*Fabricia*	160	1987

Operations
Portoferraio to Cavo to Piombino (Elba to mainland).

VERIFIED

VETOR Srl

Italy

High-speed craft operated

Type	Name	Seats	Delivered
HYD Kometa	*Vetor 944*	102	1984
HYD Kometa	*Freccia Pontina*	102	1985
HYD Kolkhida	*Gabri*	120	1989
HYD Kolkhida	*Vemar*	120	1991

Operations
Anzio to Naples
Anzio to Ponza to Ventotene
Formia to Ponza to Ventotene.

VERIFIED

JAPAN

AWAJI FERRY BOAT COMPANY

4-1-1 Sotohama, Suma-Ku, Kobe 654, Japan

High-speed craft operated

Type	Name	Seats	Delivered
CAT Mitsui CP25 Supermaran	*Queen Rokko*	250	June 1988

VERIFIED

Mitsui catamaran ferry Queen Rokko *operated by Awaji Ferry Boat Company* **1989**

AWASHIMA KISEN COMPANY LTD

1-67 Iwafuneminato-machi, Murakami-shi Niiga-ken 958, Japan

High-speed craft operated

Type	Name	Speed	Seats	Delivered
MH Sumidagawa Zosen Co Ltd	*Iwayuri*	24 kts	144	May 1979
MH Sumidagawa Zosen Co Ltd	*Asuka*	24 kts	173	May 1989

Operations
Awashima to Iwafune.

VERIFIED

Asuka *operated by Awashima Kisen* **1992**

BANTAN RENRAKU KISEN

Japan

High-speed craft operated

Type	Name	Seats	Delivered
CAT Mitsui MES CP15	*Marine Bridge*	–	1995

Operations
Akashi to Iwaya.

NEW ENTRY

BIWAKO KISEN COMPANY LTD

Biwa Lake Sightseeing Company

5-1 Hamaotsu, Otsu-City 520, Shiga Prefecture, Japan

Tel: +81 (775) 245000

High-speed craft operated

Type	Name	Speed	Seats	Delivered
MH Mokubei Shipbuilding Co Ikeda 22 m	*Lansing*	27 kts	78	April 1982

Operations
Biwa Lake, sightseeing.

UPDATED

The Mokubei Shipbuilding Company water-jet-propelled Lansing **1995**

DIAMOND FERRY COMPANY

7-11 Ikushi-5-Chrome, Oita, Oita Prefecture, Japan

High-speed craft operated

Type	Name	Seats	Delivered
CAT Austal 43 m	*Speeder*	–	1995

NEW ENTRY

FUKE KAIUN COMPANY LTD

3-3-25 Hon-machi, Sumoto-City 656, Japan

High-speed craft operated

Type	Name	Seats	Delivered
MH Miho 24 m	*Hikari*	–	1978
MH Miho 24 m	*Itchigo*	–	1978
MH Miho 24 m	*Nigo*	–	1978
MH Miho 24 m	*Hirari Sango*	–	1978
CAT Sanuki 36 m	*Iris*	250	1990
CAT IHI SSTH 30	*Trident*	68	1992
F-CAT Hitachi Superjet 30	*Trident Ace*	200	1993
F-CAT Hitachi Superjet 30	*Artemis*	200	1993
F-CAT Hitachi Superjet 30	*Apollon*	200	1994

Operations
Fuke to Sumoto
Fuke to Kansai Airport.

VERIFIED

GOTO RYOKAYKUSEN COMPANY LTD

5-35 Matsugae-machi, Nagasaki-City 850, Japan

Tel: +81 (958) 251631
Fax: +81 (958) 252537

Sakichi Yasuda, *President and main stock holder*

High-speed craft operated

Type	Name	Seats	Delivered
MH Nankai	*New Gotoh*	193	June 1984

New Gotoh *operated by Goto Ryokaykusen Co Ltd* **1996**

Operations
Gonokubi to Wakamatsu, 4.5 km, 10 minutes; Wakamatsu to Kirifurusato, 5.5 km, 15 minutes; Kirifurusato to Doinoura, 8.0 km, 15 minutes; Doinoura to Naru, 14 km, 15 minutes; Naru to Fukue, 17.8 km, 30 minutes.

UPDATED

HANKYU KISEN COMPANY LTD

45 Harima-Cho, Chuo-Ku, Kobe-City 650, Japan

Tel: +81 (78) 331 5191

Asaziro Katsumata, *Maritime Director*

High-speed craft operated

Type	Name	Seats	Delivered
HYD Hitachi Zosen PT 50	*Zuiho*	123	January 1972
HYD Hitachi Zosen PT 50	*Hoo*	123	March 1972
HYD Hitachi Zosen PT 50	*Kaio*	123	February 1974
HYD Hitachi Zosen PTS 50 Mk II	*Housho*	123	January 1983

Operations
Kobe to Kameura (Naruto)
Kobe to Tokushima.

VERIFIED

HIGASHI-NIHON FERRY COMPANY

Minami 4-jo, Nishill-chome Chuo-Ku, Sapporo 064, Japan

High-speed craft operated

Type	Name	Seats	Delivered
HYD KHI Jetfoil 929-117	*Unicorn*	–	1990

Operations
Aomori to Hakodate.

VERIFIED

HIROSHIMA IMABARI KOSOKUSEN COMPANY LTD

853 Miyajima-Cho, Saeki-Gun, Hiroshima-Ken 739-05, Japan

High-speed craft operated

Type	Name	Seats	Delivered
MH Miho Zosenjyo Co Ltd	*Waka*	84	July 1984
MH Miho Zosenjyo Co Ltd	*Seto*	84	August 1984

Operations
Ujina to Imabari.

VERIFIED

IMABARI KOSOKUSEN COMPANY LTD

1-2 Katahara-Cho, Imabari-City 794, Japan

High-speed craft operated

Type	Name	Seats	Delivered
MH Miho Zosenjyo Co Ltd	*Kamome No 2*	52	November 1973
MH Miho Zosenjyo Co Ltd	*Kamome No 5*	80	May 1976
MH Miho Zosenjyo Co Ltd	*Chidori No 7*	70	January 1980
MH Miho Zosenjyo Co Ltd	*Kamome No 7*	93	April 1982

Operations
Imabari to Iguchi
Imabari to Onomichi.

VERIFIED

ISHIZAKI KISEN COMPANY LTD

1-4-9 Mitsu, Matsuyama-City 791, Ehime Prefecture, Japan

Tel: +81 (899) 510128

High-speed craft operated

Type	Name	Seats	Delivered
HYD Hitachi Zosen PT 20	*Kansei**	66	1962
HYD Hitachi Zosen PT 50	*Kosei*	125	1969
HYD Hitachi Zosen PT 50	*Saisei*	126	1974
HYD Hitachi Zosen PT 50	*Shunsei*	123	1975
HYD Hitachi Zosen PT 20	*Ryusei*	69	1981
F-Cat Hitachi Superjet 30	*Suiko*	200	1994
F-Cat Hitachi Superjet 30	*Shoko*	200	1994

*Spare craft

Operations
Matsuyama to Hiroshima (PT 50s)
Matsuyama to Onomichi (PT 20s).

VERIFIED

IWAKUNI HASHIRAJIMA KOSOKUSEN COMPANY LTD

Iwakuniko 4, Shinminato-machi, Iwakuni-City 740, Japan

High-speed craft operated

Type	Name	Seats	Delivered
MH Kiso Zosen Tekko Co Ltd	*Suisei*	96	November 1982

Operations
Iwakuni to Hashirashima.

VERIFIED

KAGOSHIMA SHOSEN COMPANY LTD

12-2 Kamoikeshinmachi, Kagoshima 890, Japan

High-speed craft operated

Type	Name	Seats	Delivered
HYD Kawasaki Jetfoil 929-117	*Toppy*	265	June 1989
HYD Kawasaki Jetfoil 929-117	*Toppy 2*	265	1992
HYD Kawasaki Jetfoil 929-117	*Toppy 3*	265	1995

Operations
Kagoshima to Nishinoomote to Miyanoura.

UPDATED

KAIJO ACCESS COMPANY

9-1 Minatojima, Chuo-Ku, Kobe 650, Japan

High-speed craft operated

Type	Name	Delivered
HYD Kawasaki Jetfoil 929-117	*Crystal Wing*	March 1994
HYD Kawasaki Jetfoil 929-117	*Emerald Wing*	March 1994
HYD Kawasaki Jetfoil 929-117	*Pearl Wing*	1994
HYD Kawasaki Jetfoil 929-117	*Sapphire Wing*	1994

Operations
Kobe to airport Kensai.

UPDATED

KATO KISEN COMPANY LTD/KANSAI KISEN COMPANY LTD JET LINE

7-15 Benten 6-Chome, Minato-Ku, Osaka 552, Japan

High-speed craft operated

Type	Name	Delivered
HYD Boeing Jetfoil 929-115	*Jet 7* (ex-*Spirit of Friendship*)	August 1980
HYD Boeing Jetfoil 929-115	*Jet 8* (ex-*Spirit of Discovery*)	April 1985

Operations
Started 1987, Seto Inland Sea.

VERIFIED

KOSHIKISHIMA SHOSEN LTD

Japan

High-speed craft operated

Type	Name	Seats	Delivered
MH Mitsubishi 48 m	*Sea Hawk*	301	1990

Operations
Kushikino to Koshikijima.

NEW ENTRY

KUMEJIMA FERRY COMPANY LTD

3-25-25 Maejima, Naha 900, Japan

High-speed craft operated

Type	Name	Seats	Delivered
CAT Mitsui CP20 Supermaran	*Blue Sky* (ex-*Blue Hawk*)	162	1987

VERIFIED

KYODO KISEN KAISHA LTD

5 Kaigan-dori, Chuo-Ku, Kobe 650, Japan

Tel: +81 (78) 391 2726
Telex: 5622665 KBKYD J
Fax: +81 (78) 391 8010

High-speed craft operated

Type	Name	Seats	Delivered
MH Miho Shipyard Co Ltd	*Seifu*	150	July 1986
CAT MES CP15	*Aquajet I*	196	March 1989
CAT MES CP15	*Aquajet II*	196	June 1989
CAT MES CP15	*Aquajet III*	190	July 1990
CAT MES CP15	*Aquajet IV*	190	October 1990
CAT Miho Shipyard Co Ltd	*Aquajet Super I*	235	March 1993
CAT Miho Shipyard Co Ltd	*Aquajet Super II*	235	May 1993
CAT Miho Shipyard Co Ltd	*Aquajet Super III*	235	July 1994

Operations
Osaka (Honshu) to Sumoto via Tsuna (Awaji Island) & Kansai Airport
Kobe (Honshu) to Sumoto via Tsuna (Awaji Island).

UPDATED

Aquajet III ***1992***

Aquajet IV ***1992***

Aquajet Super I, II *and* III ***1995***

KYUSHI FERRY BOAT COMPANY

Japan

High-speed craft operated

Type	Name	Seats	Additional Payload	Delivered
WPC Kawasaki/ AMD 1500	*Hayabusa*	460	94 cars	1995

Operations
Yawatahama to Usuki.

VERIFIED

Hayabusa *1995*

KYUSHU RAILWAY COMPANY

14-1 Okihamacho, Hakata-Ku, Fukuoka 812, Japan

High-speed craft operated

Type	Name	Seats	Delivered
HYD Kawasaki Jetfoil 929-117	*Beetle 2*	263	1991

VERIFIED

KYUSHU SHOSEN COMPANY LTD

16-12 Motofune-Cho, Nagasaki-City 850, Japan

High-speed craft operated

Type	Name	Seats	Delivered
HYD Kawasaki Jetfoil 929-117	*Pegasus*	282	March 1990
MH Mitsubishi 48.5 m	*Sea Grace*	–	March 1993

Operations
Nagasaki to Narao to Fukue
Sasebo to Narao.

VERIFIED

KYUSHU YUSEN COMPANY LTD

1-27 Kamiya, Hakata, Fukuoka 812, Japan

High-speed craft operated

Type	Name	Seats	Delivered
HYD Kawasaki Jetfoil 929-117	*Venus*	263	March 1991

Operations
Hakata to Ashibe
Gonoura to Izuhara.

VERIFIED

MARITIME SAFETY AGENCY OF JAPAN

2-1-3 Kasumigaseki, Chiyoda-ku, Tokyo, Japan

Tel: +81 (3) 3591 6361
Fax: +81 (3) 3597 9420

Hiroharu Hagihara, *Director of Ship Division, Equipment and Technology Department*

High-speed craft operated

Type	Name	Delivered
23 m patrol craft type		
MH Mitsubishi Heavy Industries Ltd	*Hayagiri*	February 1985
MH Hitachi Zosen	*Shimagiri*	February 1985
MH Hitachi Zosen	*Setogiri*	March 1985
MH Sumidagwa Zosen Co Ltd	*Natsugiri*	January 1990
MH Sumidagwa Zosen Co Ltd	*Suganami*	January 1990
180 ton patrol vessel type		
Mitsubishi Heavy Industries Ltd	*Mihashi*	September 1988
MH Hitachi Zosen	*Saroma*	November 1989
MH Mitsubishi Heavy Industries Ltd	*Inasa*	January 1990
MH Hitachi Zosen	*Kirishima*	March 1991
MH Mitsubishi Heavy Industries Ltd	*Takatsuki*	March 1992
MH Hitachi Zosen	*Nobaru*	March 1993
MH Hitachi Zosen	–	1994
MH Mitsubishi Heavy Industries Ltd	–	1994
MH Mitsubishi Heavy Industries Ltd	*Kamui*	January 1994
MH Hitachi Zosen	*Bizan*	January 1994

Only those craft with a maximum speed of over 30 knots have been listed here.

Operations
The Maritime Safety Agency of Japan (JMSA) was established in May 1948 for the protection of life and property at sea.

VERIFIED

Suganami *23 m patrol craft* *1992*

Kirishima *180 tonne patrol vessel* *1992*

MARUNAKA KISEN COMPANY LTD

Japan

High-speed craft operated

Type	Name	Seats	Delivered
CAT Miho Zosensho	–	280	1991

Operations
Onagawa to Ayukawa to Kin Kazan.

VERIFIED

MEITETSU KAIJO KANKOSEN COMPANY LTD

18-1 Sanbonmatsu-Cho, Atsuta-Ku, Nagoya-city 456, Japan

High-speed craft operated

Type	Name	Seats	Delivered
MH Suzuki Zosen Co Ltd	*Ohtoki*	97	February 1981
MH Suzuki Zosen Co Ltd	*Ohtoki 2*	97	July 1981
MH Suzuki Zosen Co Ltd	*Ohtoki 3*	97	March 1982
MH Suzuki Zosen Co Ltd	*Kaien 5*	61	March 1982
MH Suzuki Zosen Co Ltd	*Kaien 6*	79	July 1982
MH Mitsubishi 25 m	*Hiryu 1*	70	July 1988
MH Mitsubishi 25 m	*Hiryu 3*	70	July 1988
MH Mitsubishi 25 m	*Hiryu 2*	70	July 1988

Operations
Shinojima to Morozaki to Himakajima
Gamagohri to Toba
Nishiura to Higashihaza
Morozaki to Irako
Kowa to Irako.

VERIFIED

NANKAI FERRY COMPANY LTD

6-5 Chikkoh, Wakayama 640, Wakayama Prefecture, Japan

High-speed craft operated

Type	Name	Seats	Delivered
CAT Mitsui CP30 Mk 4	*Argo*	280	December 1992

Operations
Wakayama to Tokushima.

UPDATED

OITA HOVER FERRY COMPANY LTD

1-14-1 Nishi-shinchi, Oita 870, Japan

Tel: +81 (975) 58 7180
Fax: +81 (975) 56 6247

Takeshi Jimbo, *President*
Kiyoshi Iwai, *General Director*

Oita Hover Ferry Company Ltd was established in November 1970 and began operating in October 1971. Annual traffic is approximately 450,000.

High-speed craft operated

Type	Name	Seats	Delivered
HOV Mitsui MV-PP5 Mk 2	*Hakuchyo No 3*	75	June 1970
HOV Mitsui MV-PP5	*Hobby No 6* (ex-*Akatombo 51* and stretched)	75	—
HOV Mitsui MV-PP5	*Angel No 5*	75	April 1975
HOV Mitsui PP-10	*Dream No 1*	105	October 1989
HOV Mitsui PP-10	*Dream No 2*	105	Feb 1991

Operations
Oita city to Oita Airport, 15.6 n miles, 35 minutes
Oita city to Beppu city, 6.5 n miles, 13 minutes.

UPDATED

Oita Hover Ferry Mitsui PP-10 Dream No 2 ***1992***

OKI KISEN KK

Nakamachim, Saigo-cho, Okigun, Shimane Prefecture, Japan

Tel: +81 (85) 122 1122
Telex: 628966 J

High-speed craft operated

Type	Name	Seats	Delivered
F CAT Mitsubishi Super Shuttle 400	*Rainbow*	341	April 1993

Operations
Sakai to Okinoshima.

VERIFIED

RYOBI UNYU

1-1-8 Bancho, Okayama City, Japan

High-speed craft operated

Type	Name	Seats	Delivered
MH Miho Zosen	*Princess Olive*	94	July 1981
MH Miho Zosen	*Queen Olive*	94	October 1981

Operations
Okayama to Tonosho.

VERIFIED

SADO KISEN KAISHA

9-1 Bandaijima, Niigata City 950, Japan

Tel: +81 (25) 2457255
Fax: +81 (25) 2478830

S Nakamura, *Jetfoil Director*

High-speed craft operated

Type	Name	Seats	Delivered
HYD Boeing Jetfoil 929-115	*Mikado*	260	May 1979
HYD Boeing Jetfoil 929-115	*Ginga* (ex-*Cu na Mara*)	260	July 1986
HYD Kawasaki Jetfoil 929-117	*Tsubasa*	260	April 1989
HYD Kawasaki Jetfoil 929-117	*Suisei*	260	April 1991

The Boeing Jetfoil *Okesa* formerly owned by this company was sold to the Far East Hydrofoil Company Ltd of Hong Kong in November 1990.

Operations
Niigata, Honshu Island, to Ryotsu, Sado Island, 36.3 n miles, 1 hour
Naoetsu, Honshu Island to Ogi, Sado Island, 42.1 n miles, 1 hour.

The number of passengers carried in 1994 was 724,522

UPDATED

Kawasaki Jetfoil Suisei *in service with Sado Kisen Kaisha* ***1996***

SEA-COM CRUISE CORPORATION

7 Taiso Marine Building, 4-23 Kaigandouri, Naka-ku, Yokohama 231, Japan

High-speed craft operated

Type	Name	Seats	Delivered
CAT Yamaha 291	*Bay Bridge*	230	1989
CAT Yamaha 291	*Bay Dream*	178	1989
CAT Yamaha 291	*Bay Frontier*	230	1989
CAT InCat 40 m WPC	*SeaCom 1*	265	1990

Operations
Yokohama Minatomirai Pier and Hakkeijima Sea Paradise.

VERIFIED

SETONAIKAI KISEN COMPANY LTD (SETO INLAND SEA LINES)

1-12-23 Ujinakaigan, Minami-ku, Hiroshima 734, Japan

Tel: +81 (82) 255 3344
Telex: 653625 STSHRM J
Fax: +81 (82) 251 6743

Nobue Kawai, *Tour Co-ordinator of Akinada Line*

Setonaikai Kisen Company has been operating transport services linking the islands in the Inland Sea for many years. It now has a fleet of 38 vessels, operating regular services along nine routes between Hiroshima and Shikoku, including a main route between Hiroshima and Matsuyama as well as Hiroshima to Kobe and Osaka.

High-speed craft operated

Type	Name	Seats	Delivered
HYD Hitachi Supramar PT 50	*Ohtori No 2**	113	February 1970
HYD Hitachi Supramar PT 50	*Ohtori No 3**	113	October 1972
HYD Hitachi Supramar PT 50	*Hikari No 2**	123	March 1975
HYD Hitachi Supramar PT 50	*Ohtori No 5*	113	May 1973
MH Miho Zosenjo	*Marine Star 2*	103	November 1979
MH Miho Zosenjo	*Marine Star 3*	120	January 1983
Setouchi Craft MH	*Akinada*	125	May 1989
HYD Hitachi Supramar PT 50	*Ohtori**	118	June 1968
HYD Hitachi Supramar PT 50	*Condor*	32 kts	118
HYD Hitachi Supramar PT 50	*Condor 2*	118	June 1968
HYD Hitachi Supramar PT 50	*Condor 3*	32 kts	118
MH Miho 22 m	*Waka*	84	June 1984
MH Miho 22 m	*Seto*	84	July 1984
F-CAT Hitachi Superjet 30	*Dogo*	200	1993
F-CAT Hitachi Superjet 30	*Miyajima*	200	1994

*spare craft

Operations
Miyajima to Hiroshima to Omishima Island (Port of Inokuchi) to Setoda *(Akinada)*
Hiroshima to Matsuyama 1 hour (*Ohtori No 2, 3 and Ohtori No 5*), some services stopping at Kure, then 1 hour 10 minutes (*Hikari No 2*)
Mihara to Imabari 1 hour (*Marine Star 2, Marine Star 3*), some services stopping at Setoda, then 1 hour 7 minutes.

VERIFIED

Akinada, *introduced into service by Setonaik Kisen in May 1989* ***1990***

SHIKOKU FERRY COMPANY (BRIDGE LINE)

10-32 Tamamo-cho,Takamatsu City 760, Japan

High-speed craft operated

Type	Name	Delivered
CAT Sanuki Shipbuilding and Iron Works 30 m	*Sea Chateau*	1988

VERIFIED

TENMAYA MARINE COMPANY LTD

Japan

High-speed craft operated

Type	Name	Seats	Delivered
CAT Mitsui CP5 Supermaran	*Mon Cheri*	58	May 1988

VERIFIED

THIRD DISTRICT PORT CONSTRUCTION BUREAU

Japan

High-speed craft operated

Type	Name	Delivered
SWATH Mitsubishi 27.01 m	*Ohtori*	March 1981

VERIFIED

TOKAI KISEN

1-11-1 Kaigan, Minato-ku, Tokyo 105, Japan

Tel: +81 (3) 432 4551

High-speed craft operated

Type	Name	Seats	Delivered
MH Mitsubishi Heavy Industries Ltd	*Seahawk 2*	401	February 1980
SWATH Mitsui	*Seagull 2*	420	December 1989

Operations
Seagull
Atami to Ohshima
Tokyo to Ohshima*
Tokyo to Niijima*
Ohshima to Tokyo
Seahawk 2
Inatori to Ohshima
Ito to Ohshima
Atami to Ohshima*
*Summer services only

VERIFIED

TOKUSHIMA SHUTTLE LINE COMPANY LTD

3-1-3 Sannomiya-Cho, Chao-Ku, Kobe 650, Japan

Hiromu Harada, *President*

High-speed craft operated

Type	Name	Delivered
CAT MES CP30 Mk II	*Marine Shuttle*	February 1986
CAT MES CP30 Mk III	*Blue Star*	1987
CAT MES CP30 Mk III	*Sun Rise*	1987
CAT MES CP30 Mk IV	*Sun Shine*	1991
CAT MES CP30 Mk IV	*Soleil*	1991
CAT MES CP30 Mk IV	*Polar Star*	1993
CAT MES CP30 Mk IV	*Venus*	1993
CAT MES CP30 MkIV	*Neptune*	1995

Operations
Wakayama to Tokushima, Shikoku Island.

UPDATED

YAEYAMA KANKO FERRY COMPANY

1-3 Misaki-cho, Isigaki-City 907, Okinawa, Japan

Tel: +81 (98) 082 5010
Telex: 792681 K

High-speed craft operated

Type	Name	Seats	Delivered
MH Miho Zosenjyo Co Ltd	*Hayabusa*	88	December 1974
MH Sumidagawa 26 m	*Marine Star*	—	1979
MH Shinju Shipyard Co Ltd 27.3 m	*Tropical Queen*	150	July 1982
MH Suzuki 19 m	*Hirugi No 2*	—	1986
MH Toukai 15 m	*Hirugi No 3*	—	1987
MH Gouriki 17 m	*Hirugi No 5*	—	1989
MH Gouriki 16 m	*Hirugi No 7*	—	1990

Operations
Ishigaki to surrounding islands.

VERIFIED

YASUDA SANGYO KISEN COMPANY LTD (YASUDA OCEAN GROUP) AIRPORT LINE

5-35 Matsugae-machi, Nagasaki-City 850, Japan

Tel: +81 (958) 260188
Telex: 755556
Fax: +81 (958) 242182

Sakichi Yasuda, *President and main stockholder*

High-speed craft operated

Type	Name	Seats	Delivered
MH Nankai	*Erasmus*	123	October 1984
MH Nankai	*Airport Liner 7*	66	March 1986
MH Nankai	*Airport Liner 8*	66	March 1986
MH Nankai	*Airport Liner 10*	66	December 1986
MH Nankai	*Airport Liner 11*	66	February 1987
MH Nankai	*Airport Liner 13*	66	April 1987
MH Nankai	*Airport Liner 15*	66	June 1987
MH Nankai	*Airport Liner 17*	66	June 1987
MH Nankai	*Nagasaki 8*	39	June 1987
MH Nankai	*Nagasaki 10*	39	August 1987
MH Nankai	*Taiyo*	231	March 1988
MH Uehara	*Ocean Liner 1*	88	April 1988
MH Euhara	*Ocean Liner 3*	88	September 1988
MH Uehara	*Ocean Liner 5*	97	February 1989
MH Nankai	*Ocean Liner 7*	97	February 1989
MH Nankai	*Ocean Liner 8*	97	February 1989
SES Brødrene Aa CIRR 120P	*Nissho*	320	September 1990

Operations
Nagasaki Airport to Nagasaki (Togitsu), 17 km, 20 minutes
Nagasaki Airport to Ohkusa, 8.8 km, 10 minutes
Nagasaki Airport to Nagasaki Holland Village, 27 km, 40 minutes
Nagasaki Airport to Sasebo, 38 km, 50 minutes
Nagasaki Holland Village to Sasebo, 23 km, 35 minutes
Nagasaki Holland Village to Hirado, 63 km, 65 minutes
Nagasaki Holland Village to Higashisonogi, 22 km, 30 minutes
Mogi to Obama, 30 km, 40 minutes
Mogi to Tomioka, 33.7 km, high-speed passenger ship, 40 minutes, car ferry, 170 minutes
The total number of passengers per year is 600,000
Nagasaki to Kagoshima (Kushikino) began March 1991 with 320 seat Brødrene Aa 35.24 m SES. Route length 135 km, 100 minutes.

UPDATED

JORDAN

ARAB BRIDGE MARITIME CO

Aquaba, Jordan

Tel: +962 (3) 313235/37/40
Telex: +62354
Fax: +962 (3) 316313

High-speed craft operated

Type	Name	Seats	Delivered
CAT Fjellstrand 40 m	MSB Universal MK5	266	1995

Operations
Aquaba (Jordan) to Nuwaibeh (Egypt), 60 minutes.

NEW ENTRY

JORDAN PORTS CORPORATION

PO Box 115, Aquaba, Jordan

Tel: +962 (3) 314031
Fax: +962 (3) 316204

Dr Duried Mahasneh, *Director General*
Aakef Abu Tayeh, *Deputy Director General*
Samir Mustafa, *Manager, Boats and Crafts*

High-speed craft operated

Type	Name	Delivered
SES Hovermarine HM 218	*Amira Sumaiah*	1980
SES Hovermarine HM 218	*Amira Badeaah*	1980

Operations
Aquaba to Farohirland, 10 n miles, 20 minutes
(These craft were both out of service through 1995).

UPDATED

KOREA, SOUTH

DAE-A FERRY COMPANY LTD

140-6 Dongbin 2 Ga, Pohang City, Kyung buk, South Korea

Tel: +82 (562) 425111
Tel: +82 (562) 425114

C K Kim, *Technical Manager*

High-speed craft operated

Type	Name	Seats	Delivered
CAT Fjellstrand	*Dae Won Catamaran*	392	November 1988
SES Ulstein CIRR 120P	*Sea Flower*	345	August 1991
SES Ulstein UT 904	*Ocean Flower*	341	January 1992
CAT Incat K50	*Sun Flower*	835	July 1995

Operations
Mukho to Ullung Do, 86 n miles, 3 hours, US$25
Pohang to Ullung Do, 117 n miles, 3 hours, US$48
Hupo to Ullung Do, 86 n miles, 3 hours, US$25.

UPDATED

DONG YANG EXPRESS

45-1 Kwangchul Dong, Jongro Ku Seoul, South Korea

High-speed craft operated

Type	Name	Seats	Delivered
SES Samsung 37 m	*Dong Yang Gold*	352	1994

VERIFIED

GEO JE HAEWOON

5 Ga 16, Jung-Ang Dong, Jung Gu, Pusan City 600, South Korea (terminal)

Tel: +82 (51) 463 0354

K S Kim, *President*

High-speed craft operated

Type	Name	Seats	Delivered
SES KTMI 18 m	*Cosmos*	60	1980
SES KTMI 18 m	*Air Ferry*	60	1994

Operations
Masan to Geo Je Island.

UPDATED

GOVERNMENT

South Korea

High-speed craft operated

Type	Name	Delivered
HOV Korea Tacoma Industries Ltd Turt IV type, 12 m	*Eagle II*	1984

VERIFIED

JUNG AHANG EXPRESS COMPANY

South Korea

High-speed craft operated

Type	Seats	Delivered
MH Miwon Trading and Shipping Co 28 m	20	August 1986
MH Miwon Trading and Shipping Co 28 m	128	September 1986

Operations
A four-craft fleet operates on the manmade Choong Joo Dam where it is engaged in sightseeing tours.

VERIFIED

KANG WON HUNGUP

205-3 Chungpyeng Ri, Buksan Myeon, Chunsung Kun, Kangwon Do 206-875, South Korea

High-speed craft operated

Type	Name	Seats	Delivered
SES KTMI 17 m	*Que-Ryong II*	—	1988

UPDATED

KUMSAN HUNGUP

1000-16 Sinkum Ri, Bongrae Myeon, Koheng Kun, South Korea

High-speed craft operated

Type	Name	Seats	Delivered
SES KTMI 18 m	*Sun Star*	60	1990

Operations
Yeosu to various islands.

UPDATED

NAM HAE EXPRESS COMPANY

Hang-Dong 1 ka 6, Passenger Boat Terminal 201, Mokpo City, South Korea

High-speed craft operated

Type	Name	Seats	Delivered
HYD Hitachi PT50	*Nam Hae No 1*	–	1974
CAT MES CP20	*Nam Hae No 7*	–	1978
CAT Fjellstrand 38.8 m	*Nam Hae Star*	350	1989
CAT Marinteknik (S) 41 CPV	*Nam Hae Prince*	354	January 1993
CAT Fjellstrand 40 m	*Nam Hae Queen*	–	1994

Operations
Mokpo City to Hong-do Island.

VERIFIED

SEMO COMPANY LTD MARINE CRAFT

5 Ga 16-5 Jung-Ang Dong, Jung-Gu, Busan 600-015, South Korea

Yeong Rok Son, *President*
Sang Gyun Mok, *General Manager*
Jung Sik Kim, *Ferry Operating Manager*

Semo Company Ltd Marine Craft is the ferry operating division of the Semo Company. In January 1989 Semo took over operation of three of the Han Ryeo Development Company vessels, *Angel I*, *Angel III* and *Angel IX,* and on 1 March 1990 they took control of vessels previously operated by the Shin Young Shipbuilding and Engineering Company. *Angel I* was scrapped in 1995.

High-speed craft operated

Type	Name	Seats	Delivered
HYD Hitachi PT 20	*Angel III*	71	1978
HYD Hyundai PT 20	*Angel IX*	71	1985
SES Korea Tacoma	*Duridoongsil*	158	1983
SES Korea Tacoma	*Dudoongsil*	200	1983
SES Korea Tacoma	*Soonpoong*	158	1983
SES Ulstein CIRR 120P	*Perestroika*	346	1990
SES Semo 36	*Democracy*	336	1992
SES Semo 40	*Democracy II*	350	1994
SES Semo 40	*Democracy III*	400	1994
SES Semo 40	*Democracy V*	400	1995

Democracy *operating from Inchon to Bagryung Island* ***1994***

Perestroika *operated by Semo Company Ltd Marine Craft* ***1994***

Operations
Southern coast of South Korea
Busan to Yeosu
Yeosu to Gemun Island
Inchon to Bagryung Island
Busan to Geoje Island
Cheju to Mokpu
Chungmu to Cheju.

UPDATED

SEO KYUNG HAEWOON

South Korea

High-speed craft operated

Type	Name	Delivered
F-CAT Daewoo 40 m	*Royal Ferry*	1994
CAT Fjellstrand 40 m	*New Arcadia*	1995

Operations
Pusan to Geo Je.

UPDATED

WON KWANG SHIPPING

South Korea

High-speed craft operated

Type	Name	Delivered
CAT Fjellstrand 40 m	*Paradise*	1994

VERIFIED

MALAYSIA

KUALA PERLIS LANGKAWI FERRY SERVICE SDN BHD

37-39, Jalan Pandak Mayah 5, Pusat Bandar Kuah, 07000 Langkawi, Kedah Darul Aman, Malaysia

Tel: +60 (4) 9667868/9667878
Fax: +60 (4) 9667190

Ooi Cheng Choon, *Managing Director*

High-speed craft operated

Type	Name	Seats	Delivered
MH Miho 19.5 m	*Pantas Ekspres*	70	1978
MH Binan 23.5 m	*Saga Ekspres*	87	1986
MH WaveMaster 31 m	*Kita Ekspres*	152	1987
MH WaveMaster 27 m	*Suka Ekspres*	140	1988
MH WaveMaster 27 m	*Senang Ekspres*	130	1989
CAT Marinteknik 36 m	*Selesa Ekspres*	350	1990
MH WaveMaster 36 m	*Langkawi Ekspres* (ex-*Barbaros*)	248	1991
CAT K Fjellstrand (S) Flying Cat 40 m	*Perdana Ekspres*	356	March 1992
CAT Marinteknik 30 m	*Mustika Ekspres*	188	1993
MH Wavemaster 33 m	*Langawi II*	200	1994
MH Wavemaster 33 m	*Langawi III*	200	1994

Operations
Langkawi Island to Kuala Kedah, Kuala Perlis, Penang and Satun (Thailand)
Penang to Medan (Indonesia), Lumut to Medan (Indonesia), Tanjung Gemuk to Tioman Island.

UPDATED

Selesa Ekspres ***1995***

LADA LANGKAWI HOLDINGS

Malaysia

High-speed craft operated

Type	Name	Seats	Delivered
CAT SBF 32 m	*Lada Satu*	250	1993
CAT SBF 32 m	*Lada Dua*	250	1993
CAT SBF 32 m	*Lada Tiga*	250	1994
CAT SBF 32 m	*Lada Empat*	250	1994
CAT SBF 20 m	*Lada Lima*	—	1994

VERIFIED

MISC

Malaysian International Shipping Corporation Berhad

2nd Floor Wisma MISC, No 2 Jalan Conlay, PO Box 10371, 50712 Kuala Lumpur, Malaysia

Tel: +60 (3) 242 8088/240 5360
Telex: 30428/31057/31058/30325 NALINE MA
Fax: +60 (3) 241 6651

Ariffin Alias, *Managing Director*
Captain Ghani Ishak, *Director Petroleum Services*

High-speed craft operated

Type	Name	Seats	Delivered
34 m FBM Marinteknik (S)	*Layar Sentosa*	70	June 1987
34 m FBM Marinteknik (S)	*Layar Sinar*	70	June 1987

*hull built in Sweden

Operations
Both of these crew boats are on time charter to a multinational oil company.

VERIFIED

MISC crew boat Layar Sentosa ***1988***

SRIWANI TOURS AND TRAVEL

Malaysia

High-speed craft operated

Type	Name	Seats	Delivered
CAT InCat/NQEA 24 m	*Payar*	210	1994

Operations
Langkawi to Pulau Payar reef.

NEW ENTRY

MALTA

GOZO CHANNEL COMPANY LTD

Hay Wharf, Sa Maison, Malta

Tel: +356 243964/5/6
Telex: 1580
Fax: +356 284007

J Engerer, *Operations Manager*

High-speed craft operated

Type	Name	Seats	Delivered
SES Hovermarine HM 218	*Gozo Express*	84	May 1988

Operations
Mgarr (Gozo) to Sliema (Malta), 25 minutes
Mgarr (Gozo) to Sa Maison (Malta), 35 minutes
Also services to Comino Island.

UPDATED

VIRTU FERRIES LTD

A subsidiary of The Virtu Steamship Company Ltd

PO Box 285, Valletta, Malta

Tel: +356 317088/071/316766
Telex: 1214/1667 SHIPAZ MW
Fax: +356 314533/4633

F A Portelli, *Director*
C A Portelli, *Director*
M A Portelli, *Director*
J M Portelli, *Director*

High-speed craft operated

Type	Name	Seats	Delivered
SES Ulstein CIRR 120P	*San Frangisk*	330	1990

Operations
Valetta, Malta to Pozzallo, Sicily, 52 n miles, 1 hour 30 minutes
Valetta, Malta to Catania, Sicily, 113 n miles, 3 hours
Valetta, Malta to Licata, Sicily, 80 n miles, 2 hour 30 minutes.

UPDATED

San Frangisk operated by Virtu Ferries ***1996***

MEXICO

CRUCEROS MARITIMOS DEL CARIBE SA DE CV

Calle 6 Nte No 14, Cozumel, Quintana Roo, Mexico

Tel: +52 (987) 21508/88
Fax: +52 (987) 21942

Venado 30, m18, SM 20, Cancún, Mexico

Tel: +52 (988) 46846/46656

Jose Trinidad Molina Caceres, *Chairman of the Board*
Mario Arturo Molina Caceres, *Chief Executive Officer*
Rogelio Molina Caceres, *Managing Director*
Captain Manuel Pirez, *Operations Manager*
Javier Guillermo Clausell, *Operative Executive Officer*
Captain Luis Claudio Fernández, *Marine Superintendent*

High-speed craft operated

Type	Name	Seats	Delivered
CAT Fjellstrand 38.8 m	*Mexico*	390	February 1986
MH Breaux's Baycraft 30 m	*Mexico II*	250	November 1988
MH Breaux's Baycraft 43 m	*Mexico III*	800	April 1993

Operations
Mexican Caribbean area tourist service
Cancún to Cozumel, 43 n miles
Cozumel to Playa del Carmen, 10 n miles.

VERIFIED

Mexico II ***1993***

PEMEX

Petroleos Mexicanos

Tampico, Mexico

High-speed craft operated

Type	Name	Seats	Delivered
CAT Harding Verft A/S 26 m	*Havstril*	200	January 1990

This vessel was purchased from Simon Møkster by the US company Daysland.

Operations
Transport of oil workers in Gulf of Mexico.

VERIFIED

NETHERLANDS

REDERIJ G DOEKSEN EN ZONEN BV

PO Box 40, 8880 AA Terschelling-West, Netherlands

Tel: +31 (5620) 2141
Fax: +31 (5620) 3241

H Oosterbeek, *Managing Director*

High-speed craft operated

Type	Name	Seats	Delivered
CAT Harding Verft 35 m	*Koegelwieck*	315	June 1992

Operations
Harlingen to Terschelling, 45 minutes
Harlingen to Vlieland, 45 minutes
Terschelling to Vlieland, 15 minutes.

UPDATED

Koegelwieck *operated by BV Rederij G Doeksen en Zonen* ***1996***

NEW ZEALAND

FIORDLAND TRAVEL LTD NZ

PO Box 1, Te Anau, New Zealand

Tel: +64 3 249 7816
Fax: +64 3 249 7817

Bryan Hutchins, *Chief Executive*

Commander Peak *operated by Fiordland Travel* ***1996***

Fiordland Flyer *operated by Fiordland Travel* ***1996***

High-speed craft operated

Type	Name	Seats	Delivered
CAT Incat 18m	*Fiordland Flyer*		90
September 1984			
CAT NQEA InCat 22 m	*Commander Peak*	140	September 1985

Operations
Lake Manapouri and Doubtful Sound.

UPDATED

FULLERS CRUISES NORTHLAND LTD

PO Box 145, Maritime Building, Paihia, Bay of Islands, New Zealand

Tel: +64 (09) 402 7421
Fax: +64 (09) 402 7831

Chris Jacobs, *Director*
Roger Dold, *Director*
Mike Simm, *Director*

The Fullers Company is privately owned. Fullers has plied the Bay of Islands since 1886 and the company presently operates a fleet of eight vessels including an 18 m 40 passenger underwater viewing craft.

High-speed craft operated

Type	Name	Seats	Delivered
CAT Wanganui Boats InCat 22 m	*Tiger III* (ex-*Tiger Lily III*)	240	1986
CAT NQEA InCat 26 m	*Tiger IV* (ex-*Taupo Cat*)	240	1993
CAT Terry Bailey 11 m	*Tutunui*	35	1993

Operations
Cape Brett 'Hole in the Rock' cruise, 4 hours, fare NZ$52.
Whale watching, swimming with dolphins, 4 hours NZ$75.

UPDATED

Tiger III *coming through the 'Hole in the Rock'* ***1991***

FULLERS GROUP LTD

9th Floor, Downtown House, 21 Queen Steet, Auckland, New Zealand

Tel: +64 (9) 367 9102
Fax: +64 (9) 379 9105

George R Hudson, *Executive Chairman*
Douglas G Hudson, *Managing Director*

High-speed craft operated

Type	Name	Seats	Delivered
CAT SBF Engineering 33.37 m	*Quickcat*	600+	March 1987
MH WaveMaster Int 37 m	*Jet Raider*	400	December 1990
CAT Fast Craft	*Seaflyte*	170	December 1993
CAT Sabre	*Quickcat II*	200	December 1993

Operations
Auckland to Waiheke Island, 30 minutes
Auckland to Great Barrier Island
plus Gulf cruises.

UPDATED

Jet Raider *operated by Fullers Group Ltd* ***1991***

INTERISLAND LINE

3rd Floor, Wellington Railway Station, Private Bag, Wellington, New Zealand

High-speed craft operated

Type	Name	Seats	Additional Payload	Delivered
WPC InCat Australia 74 m	*Condor 10**	600	80 cars	1994

* On lease from Holyman Ferries

Operations
Cook Strait (Wellington to Picton).

NEW ENTRY

STEWART ISLAND MARINE

New Zealand

High-speed craft operated

Type	Name	Seats	Delivered
CAT Sabre Catamarans	*Foveaux Express*	67	1992

Operations
Stewart Island to Bluff (Foveaux Strait).

VERIFIED

WANAKA LAKE SERVICES LTD

PO Box 20, Wanaka, New Zealand

Tel: +64 (03) 443 7495
Fax: +64 (03) 443 1323

Paul Miller, *Director*

High-speed craft operated
HOV *Riverland Surveyor 8*. Originally operated by Airborne Hovercraft Services

Operations
30 minute tourist trips over farm land and in river and lake areas of Lake Wanaka, Ram Island, Matukituki River and Glendhu Bay.

VERIFIED

NORWAY

NORTH CAPE MINERALS A/S

N-9543 Stjernsund, Norway

Tel: +47 78 434555
Fax: +47 78 436267

Sven Fagerli, *Plant Manager*
Sigbjorn Solli, *Shipping Manager*

High-speed craft operated

Type	Name	Seats	Additional payload	Delivered
MH Fjellstrand 26 m	*Nefelin IV*	84	32 m³	1980

Operations
This craft operates a 47 km route from Alta to Sjernoey three times a day with a crossing time of 70 minutes.

UPDATED

Fjellstrand Nefelin IV *operated by North Cape Nefelin* ***1986***

FINNMARK FYLKESREDERI OG RUTESELSKAP

PO Box 308, N-9601 Hammerfest, Norway

Tel: +47 (78) 411000
Telex: 64257N
Fax: +47 (78) 412773

Stig Solheim, *Managing Director*

High-speed craft operated

Type	Name	Seats	Additional payload	Delivered
CAT Westamarin W86	*Brynilen*	94	cargo	June 1975
CAT Westamarin W86	*Hørnøy*	136	—	October 1979
MH Brødrene Aa Båtbyggeri	*Tanahorn*	49	cargo	1986
CAT Brødrene Aa Båtbyggeri 25.5 m	*Ingøy*	48	4 cars	July 1987
CAT Fjellstrand 38.8 m	*Varangerfjord*	164	3 cars	June 1990
CAT Fjellstrand 40 m	*Vargøy*	—	—	1994

Operations
Masry to Hammerfest to Sørøysundbass
*Masry to Havrøysund to Hammerfest
Kirkenes to Murmansk (CIS) Summer service.

VERIFIED

FOSEN TRAFIKKLAG A/S

Pirterminalen, N-7005 Trondheim, Norway

Tel: +47 (73) 525540
Telex: 65720
Fax: +47 (73) 524133

High-speed craft operated

Type	Name	Seats	Delivered
CAT Westamarin W86	*Kongsbussen** (Yard No 27)	161	April 1973
CAT Westamarin W86	*Hertugbussen* (Yard No 28)	161	May 1973
CAT Lindstøl	*Fosningen* (Yard No 298)	118	June 1991
CAT Mjosundet	*Frøyfart*	72 + cargo	June 1991
CAT Harding 29 m	*Agdenes**	210	July 1991
CAT Fjellstrand 38.8 m	*Ternen* (Yard No 1595)	274	July 1994

*Leased to joint venture company

Ternen *operated by Fosen Trafikklag* ***1995***

Operations
Trondheim to Brekstad to Storfosna to Hestvika to Fjellvoer to Fillan to Sistranda to Mausundvøer to Vadsøysund to Bogoyvøer to Sula
Sistranda to Sula to Froan
Trondheim to Kristansund, 3.5 hours
Trondheim to Vanvikan, 25 minutes.

UPDATED

FYLKESBAATANE I SOGN OG FJORDANE

PO Box 354, N-6901 Florø, Norway

Tel: +47 (57) 746200
Telex: 40646
Fax: +47 (57) 743760

Atle Tornes, *Director*

High-speed craft operated

Type	Name	Seats	Delivered
CAT Westamarin W86 (Yard No 21)	*Fjordglytt*	140	May 1971
MH Brødrene Aa A/S	*Hyen*	156	1980
CAT Fjellstrand 38.8 m	*Fjordprins*	201	October 1987
CAT Fjellstrand 38.8 m	*Sognekongen*	201	December 1987
CAT Fjellstrand 40 m Flying Cat	*Kommandøren*	252	June 1990
CAT Brødrene Aa 20 m	*Alden*	–	1990
CAT Brødrene Aa 17 m	*Tornerose*	–	1990
MH Eikefjord 22 m	*Høydalsfjord*	–	1991
MH Båtutrustning 20 m	*Hennøy*	–	1993
CAT Fjellstrand 38.8 m	*Solundir*	–	1993

Operations
Askvoll to Bulandet, Årdalstragen to Bergen, Bergen to Flåm
Eivindvik to Nåra and Anneland, Florø to Svanøy, Flåm to Balestrand, Fjaerland and Kaupanger
Måloy to Forø
Selje to Bergen.

UPDATED

Hyen (Alan Bliault) ***1991***

Kommandøren at Bergen (Alan Bliault) ***1991***

HELGELAND TRAFIKKSELSKAP A/S

PO Box 603, N-8801 Sandnessjøen, Norway

Tel: +47 (86) 43066
Fax: +47 (86) 40256

Jarl Høberg, *Chairman of the Board*
Robert Kolvik, *Managing Director*
Roger Hansen, *General Manager*

High-speed craft operated

Type	Name	Seats	Additional payload	Delivered
CAT Fjellstrand Alumaran 165 25.6 m	*Traena*	128	6 t	1976
MH Fjellstrand 25.9 m	*Råsa*	93	4 t	1979
CAT Fjellstrand 31.5 m	*Helgeland*	160	8 t	1983
CAT Rosendal 29 m	*Thorolf Kveldulfsøn*	–	–	1995

Operations
Sandnessjøen to Herøy and Veger
Sandnessjøen to Lovund and Træna.

UPDATED

HSD

Hardanger Sunnhordlandske Dampskipsselskap

PO Box 2005, N-5024 Nordnes, Bergen, Norway

Tel: +47 (55) 238700
Telex: 42607 HSD N
Fax: +47 (55) 238701

Arne Dvergsdal, *Managing Director*

High-speed craft operated

Type	Name	Seats	Delivered
CAT Westamarin W86	*Tedno I*	140	June 1973
CAT Westamarin W95	*Sunnhordland*	180	April 1975
CAT Westamarin W86	*Teisten* (ex-*Øygar*)	140	September 1975
CAT Fjellstrand 38.8 m	*Draupner*	–	1991
CAT Fjellstrand 38.8 m	*Sleipner*	–	1991
CAT Fjellstrand 38.8 m	*Tjelden*	–	1991
CAT Harding 29 m	*Tedno*	173	December 1992
CAT Holen 24 m	*Baronen*	–	1994
CAT Holen 24 m	*Baronessa*	–	1994
CAT Oma 19.8 m	*Vøringen*	–	1995

Operations
Bergen to Austevoll to Sunnhordland approximately 80 n miles
Os to Sunnhordland approximately 50 n miles
Odda to Norheimsund approximately 45 n miles.

UPDATED

Sleipner ***1994***

L RØDNE AND SØNNER A/S

Skagenkaien 18, N-4006 Stavanger, Norway

Tel: +47 (4) 5189 5270
Fax: +47 (4) 5189 5202

High-speed craft operated

Type	Name	Seats	Delivered
MH Brødrene Aa 24.4 m	*Clipper*	120	1981
MH Batutrustning TMS 19.3 m	*Clipper Skyss*	88	1990

Operations
Stavanger to Pulpit Rock and Lysebotn.

VERIFIED

MØRE OG ROMSDAL FYLKESBÅTAR A/S

Gotfred Lies Plas 2, PO Box 216, N-6401 Molde, Norway

Tel: +47 71219500
Fax: +47 71219501

Olav Smørdal, *Managing Director*
Harald Ekker, *Assistant Director*
Anker Grøvdal, *Head of Department*
John Åage Rasmussen, *Technical Maritime Manager*
Ottar Lillevik, *Head, Quality Department*
Kåre Sandøy, *Nautical Personnel Manager*
Øivind Ohr, *Traffic Manager*
Rolf D Holten, *Economics Manager*

High-speed craft operated

Type	Name	Seats	Delivered
CAT Fjellstrand 31.5 m	*Hjørungavåg*	250	1983
CAT Brødrene Aa Båtbyggeri CIRR 265P	*Fjørtoft*	120	June 1988
MH Brødrene Aa Båtbyggeri	*Romsdalsfjord*	89	–
CAT Harding 28 m	*Lauparen** (ex-*Steufdik*)	200	April 1992
CAT Fjellstrand 38.8 m	*Ternen**	290	July 1994

*Operated in cooperation with Fosen Trafikklag

Operations
Ålesund to Valderøy to Hareid, 300,000 passengers in 1994
Molde to Helland to Vikebukt, 130,000 passengers in 1994
Ålesund to Nordøyane, 100,000 passengers in 1994
Kristiansund to Edøy to Trondheim, 330,000 passengers in 1994.

UPDATED

Hjørungavåg *(background) and* Lauparen ***1993***

Fjørtoft ***1994***

NAMSOS TRAFIKKSELSKAP A/S

PO Box 128, D-S Kaia, N-7801 Namsos, Norway

Tel: +47 742 72432
Fax: +47 742 72467

High-speed craft operated

Type	Name	Seats	Delivered
CAT Lindstøl Skip 22.5 m	*Namdalingen*	107	August 1990

Namdalingen ***1993***

Operations
Leka to Rørvik to Namsos.

UPDATED

NESODDEN-BUNDEFJORD DAMPSKIPSSELSKAP A/S

Stranden 1, N-0250 Oslo, Norway

Tel: +47 (2) 833072
Fax: +47 (2) 2483 0948

Ulf Nygaard, *Managing Director*

High-speed craft operated

Type	Name	Seats	Delivered
CAT Westamarin 28 m	*Princess*	175	November 1990

Operations
Nesoddtangen to Fornebu to Lysaker and Ildjernet
Oslo to Drøbak (May to August).

UPDATED

Princess ***1996***

ROGALAND TRAFIKKSELSKAP A/S

PO Box 7033, N-4001 Stavanger, Norway

Tel: +47 (51) 890499
Telex: 33032 N
Fax: +47 (51) 531361

Båtservice Fjordbris (Alan Bliault) ***1991***

High-speed craft operated

Type	Name	Seats	Delivered
CAT Båtservice Sea Lord 28	*Fjordbris*	150	1991
CAT Båtservice Sea Lord 28	*Fjorddrott*	150	1990
CAT Båtservice Sea Lord 28	*Fjordsol*	150	1991
MH Boghammar 26.5 m	*Fjordtind*	130	1989
CAT Westamarin W86	*Ryfylke*	186	1992

VERIFIED

SALTENS DAMPSKIPSSELSKAP A/S

A Subsidiary of Ofotens og Vesteraalens DSS A/S

PO Box 1064, N-8000 Bodø, Norway

Tel: +47 (75) 521020
Fax: +47 (75) 520835

High-speed craft operated

Type	Name	Seats	Additional payload	Delivered
MH Fjellstrand 26 m	*Rødøyløven*	–	–	1977
MH Fjellstrand 23 m	*Tysfjord*	–	–	1981
MH Fjellstrand 25.5 m	*Øykongen*	–	–	1982
MH Fjellstrand 25.5 m	*Øydronningen*	–	–	1982
CAT Westamarin 3600SC	*Salten*	186	65 m^3	1988
CAT Westamarin 3000	*Børtind*	130	30 m^3	1989
CAT Westamarin 3600SC	*Ofoten*	184	65 m^3	1991
CAT Harding Verft 29 m	*Skogoy*	130	30 m^3	1991

VERIFIED

SIMON MØKSTER SHIPPING A/S

PO Box 108, Skogstøstraen 37, N-4001 Stavanger, Norway

Tel: +47 (51) 839000
Telex: 33101 MOKS N
Fax: +47 (51) 839090

Per Haram, *Managing Director*
Atle W Holgersen, *Operations Manager*

High-speed craft operated

Type	Name	Seats	Delivered
CAT Westamarin W86	*Strilbris* (ex-*Carib Link*)	113	1975
MH Fjellstrand 26 m	*Veslestril*	94	1981

UPDATED

The 25 knot Fjellstrand Veslestril *owned by Simon Møkster Shipping A/S* ***1986***

SØRLANDS CRUISE

PO Box 135, 4401 Flekkefjord, Norway

High-speed craft operated

Type	Name	Seats	Delivered
CAT Cirrus 27 m	Sørlands Cruise (ex-*Helgelandsekspressen*)	184	1995

Operations
Oslo to Arendal

NEW ENTRY

TORGHATTEN TRAFIKKSELSKAP A/S

PO Box 103, N-8901 Brønnøysund, Norway

Tel: +47 (75) 022311
Telex: 55089 N
Fax: +47 (75) 021719

High-speed craft operated

Type	Name	Seats	Additional payload	Delivered
CAT Brødrene Aa Båtbyggeri 25 m	*Heilhorn*	48	4 cars	1987
CAT Rosendal Verft 29 m	*Vegtind*	100	–	1995

Operations
Brønnøysund to Vega to Sandnessjøen and Bindalsflorden.

UPDATED

TFDS

Troms Fylkes Dampskibsselskap A/S

PO Box 548, N-9001 Tromsø, Norway

Tel: +47 (77) 686088
Telex: 64457 TTDS N
Fax: +47 (77) 688710

Bjørn Kald , *Managing Director*
Jan M Leinebø, *Financial Manager*
Kjell Ravnbø, *Technical Manager*
Reider Klingenberg, *Marine Superintendent*

High-speed craft operated

Type	Name	Seats	Delivered
CAT Westamarin W86	*Fjorddronningen II*	174	January 1976
CAT Westamarin W86	*Fjordprinsessen*	163	March 1977
CAT Westamarin W95	*Tromsprinsen*	210	June 1981
MH Brødrene Aa Båtbyggeri	*Gapøy*	43	June 1980
MH Djupviks Varv	*Reinfjord*	49	June 1984
SES Cirrus 120P	*Fjordkongen II*	–	1990
CAT Fjellstrand 40 m	*Fjordkongen* (ex-*Fjordkongen*)	320	1994
CAT Batservice 38 m	*Fjorddronningen*	–	1995

Operations
Fjordkongen, Tromsø to Harstad
Fjorddronningen, *Fjordprinsessen* and *Gapøy* operate Harstad area, *Tromsprinsen*, Tromso area, and *Reinfjord*, Skjervøy area

UPDATED

Fjordprinsessen (Alan Bliault) ***1992***

VEST-TRAFIKK A/S

N-5353 Straume, Norway

Tel: +47 (56) 323500
Fax: +47 (56) 323560

B O Børnes, *Managing Director*

High-speed craft operated

Type	Name	Seats	Delivered
CAT Båtservice Sea Lord 32	*Beinveien*	177	December 1992

Operations
Bergen to Kleppestø, 2.8 n miles, 7 minutes.

VERIFIED

PAKISTAN

PAKISTAN WATER AND POWER DEVELOPMENT AUTHORITY

WAPDA Offices Complex, Hussainabad, Fatima Jinnah Road, Hyderabad, Pakistan

High-speed craft operated

Type	Name	Seats	Delivered
HOV Griffon Hovercraft Ltd 1000 TD (008) (GH 9456)	—	—	1987
HOV Griffon Hovercraft Ltd 1000 TD	—	—	1993

VERIFIED

Griffon Hovercraft 1000 TD (008) operated by the WAPDA of Pakistan ***1992***

PARAGUAY

ALISCAFOS ITAIPU SA

Yegros 690, Asunción, Paraguay
Main harbour: Hernandarias, Alto Panama, Paraguay

Tel: +595 063479
Telex: 264 IE PY

Darius Morgan, *President*
Erminio Gatti, *Vice President*

High-speed craft operated

Type	Name	Seats	Delivered
HYD Ludwig Honald Manfacturing Co Albatross	*Flecha Guarani**	22	June 1985
HYD Ludwig Honald Manfacturing Co	*Flecha de Itaipu*	22	June 1985

*built 1964, overhauled and re-engined in Miami

Operations
Tourist use on Itaipu Lake on the border between Brazil and Paraguay
Puerto Hernandarias to Puerto Guarani.

VERIFIED

*One of the boarding points for Aliscafos Albatross hydrofoils operating on Lake Itaipu in Paraguay (*Darius Morgan) ***1987***

PHILIPPINES

ABOITEZ SUPERCAT

Philippines

High-speed craft operated

Type	Name	Delivered
CAT Cat Craft 27 m WPC	*Supercat I*	1993

VERIFIED

GRAND SEAWAY FERRIES INC

Philippines

Grand Seaway Ferries Inc is a joint venture company formed in 1995 by the Seaway Marine Group of Norway, the Anglo-Asian Group of the Philippines and the Jaya Group of Singapore.

High-speed craft operated

Type	Name	Seats	Delivered
CAT Fjellstrand 40 m (M2)	*Flying Cat*	346	1996

Operations
Manila to Puerto Azul and Subic Freeport

NEW ENTRY

UNIVERSAL ABOITIZ

2nd Floor, 110 Legazpi Street, Legazpi Village, Makati City Metro Manilla, Philippines

High-speed craft operated

Type	Name	Seats	Delivered
CAT Marinteknik 41 m	*SuperCat I* (ex-*Oregrund*)	306	1995
CAT Marinteknik 41 m	*SuperCat II* (ex-*Camoes*)	306	1995
CAT Marinteknik 41 m	*SuperCat III* (ex-*Estrala Je Mar*)	306	—
CAT Marinteknik 41 m	*SuperCat IV* (ex-*Magellan*)	306	—
CAT FBM Tricat 35 m	*SuperCat VI* (ex-*Universal VI*)	160	—

NEW ENTRY

POLAND

ZEGLUGA GDANSKA

Ul Wartka 4, Gdansk, Poland

Tel: +48 (58) 311975

High-speed craft operated

Type	Name	Delivered
HYD Sormovo Kometa	*Poswist*	1975
HYD Sormovo Kometa	*Poryw*	1976
HYD Sormovo Kometa	*Pogwizd*	1977
HYD Sormovo Kometa	*Polot*	1977

Operations
Gdynia to Hel, 25 minutes
Gdansk to Hel, 55 minutes
Gdynia to Jastarnia, 25 minutes
Sopot to Hel, 25 minutes
Gdynia to Sopot, 10 minutes
Gdynia to Hel to Wladyslawowo.

VERIFIED

PORTUGAL

SERVICO DE TRANSPORTES MARITIMOS

Avenida Sá Carneiro, 3, 4 e 5, P-9000 Funchal, Portugal

Tel: +351 (91) 225281/7
Fax: +351 (91) 228881

J F G Marque Reis, *Director for Madeira Island Harbours*
Captain Manuel F Cruz Santos, *Co-ordinator of Maritime Transport Services*

Independencia ***1996***

Patria **1996**

High-speed craft operated

Type	Name	Seats	Delivered
CAT Westamarin W100 (Yard No 76)	*Independencia* (ex-*Gimle Bird*)	244	November 1983
SWATH FBM Marine FDC400	*Patria*	400	March 1990

Operations
Funchal to Porto Santo Island, 42 n miles, 1 hour 35 minutes

Independencia passenger traffic 1992: 33,437, 1993: 41,790, 1994: 30,775
Patria passenger traffic 1992: 63,119, 1993: 47,080 (3 months in dry dock), 1994: 73,239

UPDATED

PUERTO RICO

PUERTO RICO PORTS AUTHORITY

Apartado 2829, San Juan, Puerto Rico 00936

Edwin Rodríquez Colón, *Manager, Acuaexpreso Project*

High-speed craft operated

Type	Name	Seats	Delivered
CAT Nichols Bros InCat 22 m	*Martin Peña*	167	August 1989
CAT Nichols Bros InCat 22 m	*Amelia*	167	November 1989
CAT Nichols Bros InCat 22 m	*Covadonga*	167	December 1989
CAT Nichols Bros InCat 22 m	*San Jerónimo*	167	April 1990
CAT Nichols Bros InCat 22 m	*Viejo San Juan*	167	April 1990
CAT Nichols Bros InCat 22 m	*Cristobal Colón*	167	June 1990

VERIFIED

SAUDI ARABIA

DERY SHIPPING LINES

Saudi Arabia

High-speed craft operated

Type	Name	Delivered
CAT Westamarin W95	*Salem* (ex-*Tryving*)	1990

VERIFIED

SAUDI ARAMCO

Saudi Arabia

High-speed craft operated

Type	Name	Delivered
CAT Båtservice Sea Lord 36	*Ain Dar 7*	1992
CAT Båtservice Sea Lord 36	*Ain Dar 8*	1992

Operations
Pollution control vessels.

VERIFIED

SIERRA LEONE

SIERRA LINK

An Aliscafi SNAV Company

PO Box 73, Freetown, Sierra Leone

High-speed craft operated

Type	Name	Seats	Delivered
CAT Westamarin W95	*Nastro Azzuwo* (ex-*Martini Bianco*)	220	1991

Operations
Freetown to Conakry.

VERIFIED

SINGAPORE

AUTO BATAM FERRIES

1 Maritime Square, 02-04 World Trade Centre, Singapore 0409

High-speed craft operated

Type	Name	Seats	Delivered
MH Bintan Senpokau 26 m	*Auto Batam 2*	–	1982
MH SBF Engineering 30 m	*Auto Batam 6*	200	1990
MH SBF Engineering 30 m	*Auto Batam 7*	200	March 1991
MH SBF Engineering 30 m	*Auto Batam 1*	–	1993
CAT NQEA InCat 30 m	*Diamond 2*	–	1994
MH Greenbay 32 m	*Auto Batam 10*	–	1995
MH Greenbay 32 m	*Auto Batam 12*	–	1995
MH Greenbay 32 m	*Auto Batam 13*	–	1995
MH Greenbay 35.5 m	*Auto Batam 15*	–	(1996)

UPDATED

BINTAN RESORT FERRIES

80 Marine Parade Road, 16-01 Parkway Parade, 1544, Singapore

High-speed craft operated

Type	Name	Seats	Delivered
CAT Fjellstrand 40 m	*Indera Bupala*	–	1994
CAT Fjellstrand 40 m	*Akia Bupala*	–	1995

UPDATED

J & N CRUISE PTE LTD

1 Maritime Square, 12-04 World Trade Centre, Singapore 0409

Tel: +65 270 7100
Fax: +65 278 4367

Tokuhisa Asayama, *Chief Executive Officer*

High-speed craft operated

Type	Name	Seats	Delivered
CAT Austal Ships 38 m	*Equator Triangle*	216	May 1991

Operations (Cruises)
Singapore to Batam to Singapore
Singapore to Desaru (West Malaysia) to Singapore
Local harbour cruises.

VERIFIED

Equator Triangle **1992**

PELAYARAN BINTAN BARUNA SAKTI

1 Maritime Square, 09-01 World Trade Centre, Singapore 0409

High-speed craft operated

Type	Name	Seats	Delivered
MH SBF 31 m	*Sea Flyte*	240	1985
MH WaveMaster 32 m	*Sea Raider II*	250	1986
MH WaveMaster 32 m	*Golden Raider III* (ex-*Sea Spirit*)	250	1989
MH WaveMaster 37 m	*Jet Raider III*	330	1991
MH WaveMaster 39 m	*Ocean Raider*	339	1992

Operations
Singapore to Sekupang
Singapore to Tanjong to Pinang
Singapore to Bintan

VERIFIED

RESORT CRUISES (S) PTE LTD

337 Telok Blangah Road, 02-03 Shing Loong Building, Singapore 0409

Tel: +65 278 4677
Fax: +65 278 3301

High-speed craft operated

Type	Name	Seats	Delivered
CAT Aluminium Craft (88) 34 m	*Island Pearl*	200	1990
CAT Aluminium Craft (88) 34 m	*Sea Pearl*	211	1991
CAT NQEA InCat 30 m	*Island Jade*	–	1992

Operations
Singapore to Tioman Island and excursions.

VERIFIED

SHELL EASTERN PETROLEUM (PTE) LTD

PO Box 1908, Pulau Bukom, Singapore 9038

Tel: +65 229 4150
Telex: 21251 RS

Captain V K Nanda Kumar, *Marine Manager*

Operator: Kapal Management Pte Ltd
15 Hoe Chiang Road 10-05, Sanford Building, Singapore 0208

Tel: +65 225 9338

High-speed craft operated

Type	Name	Seats	Delivered
SES Vosper Hovermarine 218	*Bukom Deras*	90	1983
SES Vosper Hovermarine 218	*Bukom Pantas*	90	1983
SES Vosper Hovermarine 218	*Bukom Lekas*	90	1983
SES Vosper Hovermarine 218	*Bukom Maju*	90	1983
SES Vosper Hovermarine 218	*Bukom Jaya*	90	1983

Operations
Pasir Panjang to Pulau Bukom refinery.

VERIFIED

SINBA SHIPPING

Singapore

High-speed craft operated

Type	Name	Seats	Delivered
ALH Stolkraft	*Batam Express III*	45	1988

VERIFIED

TIAN SAN SHIPPING PTE LTD

Singapore

High-speed craft operated

Type	Seats	Built
MH 28 m Troika Class	150	1990
MH 28 m Troika Class	150	1990
MH 28 m Troika Class	150	1990
MH 28 m Troika Class	150	1990

VERIFIED

YANG PASSENGER FERRY SERVICE

407 Jalan Besar, Singapore 0820

Telex: 56408 YANGFE RS

Yong Kian Chin, *Director*

High-speed craft operated

Type	Name	Seats	Delivered
CAT Lloyd's Ships 36.5 m	*Auto Batam 8*	–	1989

Operations
Singapore to Batam Island (Indonesia).

VERIFIED

SLOVAKIA

SLOVENSKÁ PLAVBA DUNAJSKÁ LODNÁ OSOBNÁ DOPRAVA (PASSENGER SHIPPING)

Fajnorovo nábr. 2, 811 02 Bratislava, Slovakia

Tel: +42 (7) 363518/322280
Fax: +42 (7) 363516

Miroslav Gerhát, *Director*

High-speed craft operated

Type	Name	Seats	Delivered
HYD Meteor	*Kośice*	112	1978
HYD Voskhod	*Piestany*	71	1981
HYD Meteor	*Myjava*	112	1988
HYD Meteor	*Modra*	112	1991
HYD Meteor	*Bratislava*	112	1991

Operations
Vienna to Bratislava, 1 hour and 45 minutes
Bratislava to Vienna, 1 hour 30 minutes
Bratislava to Budapest, 4 hours
Budapest to Bratislava, 5 hours.

UPDATED

Piestany *1995*

Bratislava *1995*

SLOVENIA

KOMPAS INTERNATIONAL DD

PO Box 307/IV, Prazakova 4, 61001 Ljubljana, Slovenia

Telex: 31209 KOMPAS SI
Fax: +386 (61) 318262

Janez Urbas, *Director*

Prince of Venice *1994*

High-speed craft operated

Type	Name	Seats	Delivered
CAT Westamarin W100	*Poreč 1**	250	1982
CAT NQEA Wave piercer InCat	*Prince of Venice*	303	1989

*Currently chartered out.

Operations

Prince of Venice operates Portorož to Venice, *Poreč* to Venice, Venice to Mali Lošinj and along the Istrian Coast. Poreč 1 operates from Cyprus.
Between April and October 1993, *Prince of Venice* carried 30,000 passengers
Services are operated from April until October each year.

VERIFIED

SPAIN

COMPAÑIA TRASMEDITERRANEA SA

Plaza Manuel Gómez Moreno s/n, Edificio Bronce-Centro Azca, E-28020 Madrid, Spain

Tel: +34 (1) 455 0049/456 0009
Telex: 27666 TRASM E

High-speed craft operated

Type	Name	Seats	Additional payload	Delivered
HYD Rodriquez RHS 160F	*Pez Volador*	220	–	1988
HYD Rodriquez RHS 160F	*Barracuda*	204	–	1989
HYD Rodriquez RHS 160F	*Marrajo*	204	–	1989
HYD Rodriquez RHS 160F	*Tintorera*	204	–	1990
HYD Kawasaki Jetfoil 929-117	*Princesa Dacil*	286	–	1990
HYD Kawasaki Jetfoil 929-117	*Princesa Teguise*	286	–	1991
MH EN Bazán Mestrel 96 m	*Albayzin*	450	76 cars	1995
MH EN Bazán Mestrel 96 m	*Alcantara*	450	76 cars	1995

Operations

Las Palmas, Grand Canaria to Santa Cruz de Tenerife, 52 n miles, 1 hour 20 minutes
Las Palmas to Morro Jable, 1 hour 30 minutes
Algeciras to Ceuta, 15 n miles, 30 minutes
Cristianos to Gomera, Canary Islands, 21 n miles, 45 minutes
Valencia to Ibiza (July to September).

VERIFIED

FLEBASA LINES

Spain

High-speed craft operated

Type	Name	Delivered
HYD Rodriquez RHS 140	*Rapido de Ibiza* (ex-*Viggen*)	1988
CAT Westamarin W95	*Rapido de Formentera* (ex-*Sunnhordland*)	1991
HYD Rodriquez RHS 200	*Rapido de Mallorca*	1994

Operations

Ibiza to La Savina.

VERIFIED

Rapido de Formentera (Duncan P Trillo) **1992**

FRED OLSEN SA

Poligono Industrial Añaza, s/n, Santa Cruz de Tenerife, 38109 Canary Islands, Spain

Tel: +34 9 22 628200
Fax: +34 9 22 628201

High-speed craft operated

Type	Name	Delivered
SES Cirrus 120 P	*Bahia Express*	1994

Operations

Lanzarote to Fuerteventura.

UPDATED

Bahia Express operated by Fred Olsen S.A. **1996**

TRASMAPI

Avenida Santa Eulalia, 17-5 Bajos Edificio Cabiro, Spain

High-speed craft operated

Type	Name	Delivered
CAT Marinteknik JC-F1	*Formentera Jet*	1990
CAT Westamarin W95	*Ibiza Jet* (ex-*Tunen*)	1993
CAT Westamarin W95	*Tagomago Jet* (ex-*Tranen*)	1993

Operations

Ibiza to La Savina.

VERIFIED

ISLENA DE NAVEGACION SA

C/Teniente Maroto, 1, 1, Algeciras, Spain

Tel: +34 (56) 652000/950/561
Telex: 78132

V S Lopez, *President*

High-speed craft operated

Type	Name	Seats	Delivered
CAT Fjellstrand 38.8 m	*Sevilla 92* (ex-*Caribbean Princess*)	310	1990
CAT Fjellstrand 38.8 m	*Rapido de Algeciras* (ex-*Bahamian Prince*)	310	1990
HYD RHS 160F	*Rapido de Mallorca* (ex-*San Cristobal II* ex-*Cittiship*)	223	1993

Operations

Algeciras to Centa.

UPDATED

ST PIERRE ET MIQUELON (France)

ARMEMENT BOROTRA FRÈRES

PO Box 4218, F-97500 St Pierre et Miquelon

Tel: +508 412078
Telex: 914407
Fax: +508 414608

High-speed craft operated

Type	Name	Seats	Delivered
MH SFCN 35 m	*St Eugene 5*	200	March 1988

Operations
St Pierre to Miquelon, 55 minutes.

VERIFIED

SWEDEN

JUSTIN MANAGEMENT AB

PO Box 183, S-185 23 Vaxholm, Sweden

Tel: +46 (8) 541 33309
Fax: +46 (8) 541 32284

Captain Bjørn Justine, *Director*

High-speed craft operated

Type	Name	Seats	Delivered
MH Marinteknik 41 m	*Cinderella III*	450	1990

Operations
Stockholm to Archipelago

UPDATED

KOSTER MARINE

Sweden

High-speed craft operated

Type	Name	Seats	Delivered
CAT Westamarin W86 (Yard No 21)	*Kosterfjord* (ex-*Fjordglytt*)	140	1995

NEW ENTRY

PILEN (KÖPENHAMNSPILEN AB)

Skeppsbron 7, 5-211 20 Malmö, Sweden

Tel: +46 40 234411
Fax: +46 40 6110109

High-speed craft operated

Type	Name	Seats	Delivered
CAT Westamarin W 3700	*Pilen 3* (ex-*Vindile*)	300	1989
CAT Westamarin W88	*Delfinen*	170	1994

Operations
Malmö to Copenhagen in 45 minutes.

UPDATED

SEA CONTAINERS SWEDEN AB

Base 4040, Fishamgaten S-400 40 Gothenburg, Sweden

Tel: +46 (31) 775 4200
Fax: +46 (31) 420015

Geoffrey Ede, *Managing Director*

Sea Containers Sweden AB, a subsidiary of Sea Containers Limited, was formed in May 1993 to operate an InCat 74 m wave piercing catamaran on the cross Kattegat route between Sweden and Denmark. It has carried more than 1,000,029 passengers and 186,000 vehicles since the service started.

High-speed craft operated

Type	Name	Seats	Additional payload	Delivered
WPC InCat Australia 74 m	*SeaCatamaran Denmark*	431	80 cars	1993

Operations
Gothenburg to Frederikshavn, 105 minutes.

VERIFIED

STENA LINE

S-405 19, Gothenburg, Sweden

High-speed craft operated

Type	Name	Seats	Delivered
CAT Westamarin HSS 900	—	—	(1996)
CAT Westamarin HSS 900	—	—	(1996)

Operations
Gothenburg to Frederikshavn

NEW ENTRY

TAIWAN

TIEN PENG YANG HOVERTRAVEL CORPORATION

Koahsiung, Taiwan

High-speed craft operated

Type	Name	Seats	Delivered
HOV NQEA BHC AP1-88	*Tien peng yang*	94	May 1990

VERIFIED

TUNG HSIN STEAMSHIP COMPANY LTD

Ping Tung, Taiwan

High-speed craft operated

Type	Name	Seats	Delivered
MH SBF 26.55 m	*Tung Hsin*	193	February 1993

VERIFIED

THAILAND

FAST FERRY SIAM LTD

5/7 Chaafa Road, Tambol Vichit, Amphur Muang, Phuket 83000, Thailand

Tel: +66 076 210 769

High-speed craft operated

Type	Name	Seats	Delivered
CAT Westamarin W100	*Jet Cruise 1* (ex-*Gibline I*)	250	1991

Operations
Phuket to Phi Phi Island.

UPDATED

JET CAT TOUR COMPANY LTD

A subsidiary of Seatran Travel Company

599/1 Chua Phloeng Road, Klontoey, Bangkok 10110, Thailand

Tel: +66 (2) 240 2582
Fax: +66 (2) 249 5656

Tanan Tanphaibul, *Managing Director*
Pornrat Tanphaibul, *General Manager*

High-speed craft operated

Type	Name	Seats	Delivered
MH Mitsubishi 45 m	*Seatran Express*	N/K	1990
CAT Fjellstrand Flying Cat 40 m	*Jet Cat* (ex-*Pattaya Express*)	272	1991

Operations
Phuket to Similan, 2 hours.

VERIFIED

40 m Fjellstrand Flying Cat Jet Cat *1994*

THAI GENERAL TRANSPORT LTD

3/63-63 The Teppukdee Building, 4th Floor, Rachadabhisek Road, Hueykhwang, Bangkok, Thailand

Tel: +66 (2) 7653 1344

High-speed craft operated

Type	Seats	Delivered
HOV Griffon 3000 TD	30	1991
HOV Griffon 3000 TD	30	1991

VERIFIED

TUNISIA

SEA BUS SA

PO Box 108, 4089 el Kantaoui, Tunisia

Tel: +216 (3) 41791
Fax: +216 (3) 42663

High-speed craft operated

Type	Seats	Delivered
HOV Griffon 2000 TDX	20	March 1991
HOV Griffon 2000 TDX	20	March 1991

VERIFIED

TURKEY

ISTANBUL DENIZ OTOBÜSLERI

81110 Bostanci, Istanbul, Turkey

There were 10 Fjellstrand 38.8 m, 449 passenger catamarans purchased to provide a ferry service for commuters across the Strait of Bosphorus. Five have a 24 knot cruise speed capability and five, 32 knot. Two monohull craft were purchased from Austal in 1994.

High-speed craft operated

Type	Name	Seats	Delivered
CAT Fjellstrand 38.8 m	*Umer Bey*	449	April 1987
CAT Fjellstrand 38.8 m	*Sarica Bey*	449	August 1987
CAT Fjellstrand 38.8 m	*Uluç Ali Reis*	449	January 1988
CAT Fjellstrand 38.8 m	*Nusret Bey*	449	March 1988
CAT Fjellstrand 38.8 m	*Hezarfen Çelebi*	449	September 1988
CAT Fjellstrand 38.8 m	*Çaka Bey*	449	February 1987
CAT Fjellstrand 38.8 m	*Yeditepe I*	449	May 1987
CAT Fjellstrand 38.8 m	*Ulubatli Hasan*	449	September 1987
CAT Fjellstrand 38.8 m	*Karamürsel Bey*	449	March 1988
CAT Fjellstrand 38.8 m	*Cavli Bey*	449	September 1988
MH Austal 30 m	*Aksemseddin*	*155*	November 1994
MH Austal 30 m	*Ertugrul Gazi*	*155*	November 1994

Operations
The company operates within the Marmara Sea area covering: Bostanci to Kabatas, 8 n miles, 22 minutes
Bostanci to Karaköy, 8 n miles, 22 minutes
Bostanci to Bakirköy, 11 n miles, 27 minutes
Bostanci to Yenikapi, 7 n miles, 20 minutes
Bostanci to Yalova, 20 n miles, 45 minutes
Yalova to Kartal, 14 n miles, 30 minutes
Yalova to Kabatos, 28 n miles, 55 minutes
Kadiköy to Bakirköy, 6 n miles, 18 minutes
Kadiköy to Emenönii, 3 n miles, 10 minutes
Istanbul to Mudanya to Armuthi, 52 n miles, 115 minutes.

UPDATED

UNITED KINGDOM

CONDOR LTD

Commodore House, Bulwer Avenue, St Sampson's, PO Box 10, Guernsey, Channel Islands, UK

Tel: +44 (1481) 48771
Fax: +44 (1481) 45049

D C Butcher, *Chairman*
R N Adams, *Managing Director*
A R White, *Technical Manager*
S R Maycock, *Financial Director*
S G Spindlow, *Marketing Manager*
R W Sumner, *Operations Manager*

Condor Ltd operates a fast passenger network between St Malo in France and Jersey, Sark, Guernsey and Weymouth in the UK. In 1992, TNT, an Australian based company, became a joint partner in Condor Ltd. In 1993 Condor Ltd started a passenger/car ferry service employing its first Incat Australia 74 m WPC operating on routes between Weymouth and the Channel Islands. This had now been replaced by the larger 78 m WPC.

High-speed craft operated

Type	Name	Seats	Additional payload	Delivered
CAT Marinteknik (S)	*Condor 8*	300	–	June 1988
WPC InCat/ASL 49 m	*Condor 9*	450	–	1990
WPC Incat Australia 78 m	*Condor 11*	580	80 cars	1995

Operations
St Malo to Jersey, 38 n miles, 1 hour 10 minutes
Jersey to Sark, 27 n miles, 45 minutes
Jersey to Guernsey, 28 n miles, 1 hour
St Malo to Guernsey, 57 n miles, 1 hour 20 minutes
Guernsey to Weymouth, 70 n miles, 2 hours 15 minutes
Jersey to Weymouth, 3 hours.
Torquay to Guernsey and Jersey

UPDATED

HOVERSPEED LTD

International Hoverport, Western Docks, Dover, Kent CT17 9TG, UK

Tel: +44 (1304) 240101
Fax: +44 (1304) 240099

Geoffrey Ede, *Managing Director*
John Smith, *Marketing Director*

Hoverspeed Ltd is a subsidiary of Sea Containers Ltd and was bought in 1986. It currently operates two Mk3 Hovercraft between Dover and Calais and one SeaCat *Hoverspeed Great Britain* on the Folkestone to Boulogne route.

Hoverspeed Great Britain operated by Hoverspeed Ltd ***1996***

The Princess Anne operated by Hoverspeed Ltd ***1996***

High-speed craft operated

Type	Name	Seats	Additional payload	Delivered
HOV BHC SR. N4 Modified to Mk 3 in 1979	*The Princess Margaret* (GH 2006)	390	55 cars	1968
HOV BHC SR. N4 Mk 1 modified to Mk 3 in 1978	*The Princess Anne* (GH 2007)	390	55 cars	1969
WPC InCat Australia 74 m	*Hoverspeed Great Britain*	600	80 cars	August 1990

Note: Capacity of *Hoverspeed Great Britain* increased from 450 passengers in 1993-94 refit.

The hovercraft *Princess Anne* made a record crossing of the channel in September 1995, covering the 23 miles between Calais and Dover in 22 minutes.

Operations
Dover to Calais, 23 n miles, 35 minutes by SR. N4
Folkestone to Boulogne, 28 n miles, 55 minutes by SeaCat.

Traffic carried by SR. N4 hovercraft and SeaCats

	Passengers	Vehicles
1985	1,000,645	238,000
1986	1,000,575	257,000
1987	1,600,587	287,200
1988	1,578,738	334,096
1989	1,110,722	316,633
1990	1,514,640	277,329
1992	1,000,980	393,000
1993	2,000,100	411,000
1994	2,000,175	377,000

Up to 14 return trips daily on the Dover to Calais route.

UPDATED

HOVERTRAVEL LTD

12 Lind Street, Ryde, Isle of Wight PO33 2NR, UK

Tel: +44 (1983) 565181
Telex: 86513 HOVERWORK G
Fax: +44 (1983) 812859
WWW: Hoverwork.co.uk/

Terminal offices: Quay Road, Ryde, Isle of Wight (Tel: +44 (1983) 811000); Clarence Pier, Southsea (Tel: +44 (1705) 811000)

C D J Bland, *Chairman and Managing Director*
E W H Gifford, *Director*
J Gaggero, *Director*
R K Box, *General Manager (Solent Services)*
G M Palin, *Company Secretary*
B A Jehan, *Operations Manager*

Hovertravel Ltd, the world's longest established commercial hovercraft company, was formed in 1965 using two SR. N6 Winchester hovercraft to operate the service. Today the 98 seat AP1-88 hovercraft make the crossing between Ryde and Southsea in under 10 minutes and carry over 650,000 passengers per year. The company is also a registered carrier of Royal Mail. A high-speed freight service is provided on each crossing. By December 1995 the company had carried over 14.5 million passengers.

High-speed craft operated

Type	Name	Seats	Delivered
HOV BHC/HW AP1-88 GH 2107	*Double O Seven*	98	1989
HOV BHC/NQEA AP1-88 GH 2108	*Courier*	84	1989
HOV BHC/HW AP1-88 GH 2114	*Freedom 90*	98	1990

Courier *arriving on the beach* **1995**

AP1-88 *Perseverance* and *Resolution* were sold to Textron Marine for delivery to the US Navy for training purposes.

Operations
Ryde, Isle of Wight to Southsea, Portsmouth

UPDATED

HOVERWORK LTD

12 Lind Street, Ryde, Isle of Wight PO33 2NR, UK

Tel: +44 (1983) 565181
Telex: 86513 HOVERWORK G
Fax: +44 (1983) 812859
WWW: Hoverwork.co.uk/

C D J Bland, *Managing Director*
R H Barton, *Director*
R K Box, *Director*
E W H Gifford, *Director*
G M Palin, *Director*
B A Jehan, *Operations Manager*

Hoverwork is a wholly owned subsidiary of Hovertravel Ltd which provides a hovercraft service linking Portsmouth on the mainland to the Isle of Wight; the service operates 13 hours a day, 363 days a year.

Hoverwork has access to all the craft operated by Hovertravel, which includes 80 and 98 seat AP1-88 diesel-powered hovercraft built under licence at the company's engineering facility on the Isle of Wight.

High-speed craft operated

Type	Name	Seats	Delivered
HOV BHC/HW AP1-88 GH 2087	*Tenacity*	80	1983

Operations
The company has trained over 60 hovercraft captains and received some 40 charter contracts, including film sequences and the operation of hovercraft for mineral surveys throughout the world.

The company has undertaken operations in over 25 countries from the Arctic to the equator, which include logistics, passenger services, mineral surveys and medical evacuation duties.

UPDATED

ISLE OF MAN STEAM PACKET COMPANY

Imperial Buildings, Douglas, Isle of Man IM99 1AF

Tel: +44 1624 623344
Fax: +44 1624 672800

D Dixon, *Managing Director*
N Martin, *Finance Director*

High-speed craft operated

Type	Name	Seats	Additional payload	Delivered
WPC InCat Australia 74 m	*SeaCat Isle of Man**	546	80 cars	1994

*It is understood that the charter option for 1996 will not be taken up by IMSPC.

Operations
Douglas to Belfast, Dublin, Fleetwood and Liverpool.

UPDATED

RED FUNNEL FERRIES

12 Bugle Street, Southampton, Hampshire SO14 2JY, UK

Tel: +44 (1703) 333042
Fax: +44 (1703) 639438

Red Jet 1 **1992**

A Whyte, *Managing Director*
O H Glass, *Marketing Director*
N Palmer, *General Manager*
J Sheard, *Group Chief Accountant*
R A Marshall, *Technical Manager*

High-speed craft operated

Type	Name	Seats	Delivered
HYD Rodriquez RHS 70	*Shearwater 5*	67	1980
HYD Rodriquez RHS 70	*Shearwater 6*	67	1982
CAT FBM Marine 31.5 m	*Red Jet 1*	138	1991
CAT FBM Marine 31.5 m	*Red Jet 2*	138	1991

Operations
Southampton to West Cowes, Isle of Wight, 10.8 n miles, 20 minutes
Fares: single £5.95, return £10.60, day return £9.00 (from June 1995)

Passengers carried
In 1993 780,000 passengers were carried
In 1994 800,850 passengers were carried

UPDATED

Stena Sea Lynx **1996**

Stena Sea Lynx II **1995**

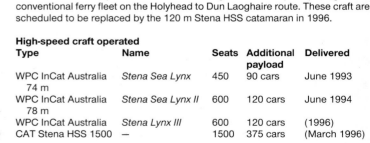

Stena HSS **1996**

SEA CONTAINERS LTD

Sea Containers House, 20 Upper Ground, London SE1, UK

Tel: +44 (171) 928 6969
Fax: +44 (171) 928 1469

Also: 41 Cedar Avenue, PO Box HM1179, Hamilton, Bermuda, HMFX

James B Sherwood, *President*
Michael Stracey, *Executive Vice President*
Daniel O'Sullivan, *Senior Vice President, Finance*
Robert Ward, *Senior Vice President, Containers*
David Benson, *Vice President, Ferries and Ports*

Sea Containers Ltd is the parent company of Hoverspeed, Sea Containers Ferries Scotland and SeaCat AB in Sweden. Between them these subsidiary companies operate three Tasmanian built InCat 74 m SeaCats and two Mk 3 Hovercraft. There are also two SeaCats currently on charter, one to the Isle of Man Steam Packet Company and the other to Ferry Lineas of Argentina. Sea Containers Ltd holds a 43 per cent share of the Isle of Man Steam Packet Company and, in addition to its status as a world leader in the design, manufacture and lease of containers, has extensive leisure industry interests which include owning and managing Orient Express Hotels and Trains. Sea Containers is the world's leading fast ferry operator. In 1994 it handled nearly eight million passengers and 1.6 million vehicles worldwide.

UPDATED

SEA CONTAINERS FERRIES SCOTLAND LTD

34 Charlotte Street, Stranraer DG9 7EF, UK

Tel: +44 (1776) 702755
Fax: +44 (1776) 705894

Hamish Ross, *Managing Director*
John Burrows, *Route General Manager*

Sea Containers Ferries Scotland Ltd is a subsidiary of Sea Containers Ltd and was formed in 1992 to operate the Irish Sea route from Stranraer to Belfast.

High-speed craft operated

Type	Name	Seats	Additional Payload	Delivered
WPC InCat Australia 74 m	*SeaCat Scotland*	450	80 cars	1992
WPC InCat Australia 74 m	*SeaCat Isle of Man**	546	80 cars	1993

*Charter arrangements to be finalised for 1996.

Operations
Belfast to Stranraer, 90 minutes.

Passengers carried
1.6 million passengers and 360,000 vehicles between June 1992 and September 1995

UPDATED

STENA LINE

Charter House, Park Street, Ashford, Kent TN24 8EX, UK

Tel: +44 (1233) 647022
Telex: 965181
Fax: +44 (1233) 620364

W G Cooper, *Managing Director*
M Storey, *Ship and Port Management Director*
J Hannah, *Communications Director*

Stena Sealink Line operates two Wave Piercing Catamarans (WPC) alongside its conventional ferry fleet on the Holyhead to Dun Laoghaire route. These craft are scheduled to be replaced by the 120 m Stena HSS catamaran in 1996.

High-speed craft operated

Type	Name	Seats	Additional payload	Delivered
WPC InCat Australia 74 m	*Stena Sea Lynx*	450	90 cars	June 1993
WPC InCat Australia 78 m	*Stena Sea Lynx II*	600	120 cars	June 1994
WPC InCat Australia	*Stena Lynx III*	600	120 cars	(1996)
CAT Stena HSS 1500	—	1500	375 cars	(March 1996)

Operations
In 1996 Stena Line will operate on the following routes:
Stena Sea Lynx: Fishguard to Rosslare
Stena Lynx IV: Newhaven to Dieppe
Stena HSS 1500: Holyhead to Dun Laoghaire
Stena Lynx III: Dover to Calais - craft due to arrive in July 1996.

UPDATED

WHITE HORSE FERRIES LTD

Stanley House, 65 Victoria Road, Swindon, Wiltshire SN1 3BB, UK

Tel: +44 (1793) 618566
Fax: +44 (1793) 488428

Harold Peter Lay, *Director*
Sidney Richard Lay, *Director*
Spencer Lloyd Lay, *Director*
Lawrence Lester Lay, *Director*

White Horse Ferries Ltd operates passenger ferry services on the River Thames and Southampton Water.

The company currently operates one medium-speed catamaran and two high-speed trimaran river taxis. A further river taxi is currently on order.

High-speed craft operated

Type	Name	Seats	Delivered
TRI Griffon Trimaran	*Ebenezer Scrooge*	12	1993
TRI Griffon Trimaran	*Martin Chuzzlewit*	60	1995

UPDATED

12 seat Fast River Taxi Ebeneezer Scrooge **1994**

Fast River Ferry Martin Chuzzlewit **1996**

WIGHTLINK LTD

70 Broad Street, Portsmouth, Hampshire PO1 2LB, UK

Tel: +44 (1705) 812011
Telex: 86440 WIGHTL G
Fax: +44 (1705) 855475

Michael Aiken, *Executive Chairman*
Michael Mulvey, *Managing Director*

Wightlink Ltd operates ferry services on three routes across the Solent to the Isle of Wight. The two vessels on the Portsmouth to Ryde route are high-speed passenger catamarans. The seven other conventional ferries on the other two routes, Portsmouth to Fishbourne and Lymington to Yarmouth, carry all sizes of vehicles as well as passengers. In 1994 Wightlink carried 4.9 million passengers and 898,000 vehicles on all its services.

High-speed craft operated

Type	Name	Seats	Delivered
CAT InCAT 30 m	*Our Lady Patricia*	452	March 1986
CAT InCat 30 m	*Our Lady Pamela*	452	July 1986

Operations
Portsmouth Harbour to Ryde Pier, Isle of Wight, 15 minutes.

UPDATED

Our Lady Pamela **1994**

UNITED STATES OF AMERICA

ALASKA TRAVEL

Alaska, USA

High-speed craft operated

Type	Name	Seats	Delivered
CAT Allen 24 m	*Golden Spirit*	–	1987

VERIFIED

ARNOLD TRANSIT COMPANY

PO Box 220, Mackinac Island, Michigan 49757, USA

Tel: +1 (906) 847 3351

Robert Brown, *General Manager*

High-speed craft operated

Type	Name	Seats	Delivered
CAT Gladding-Hearn InCat 25 m	*Mackinac Express*	350	1987
CAT Gladding-Hearn InCat 25 m	*Island Express*	300	1988
CAT Marinette 30 m	*Straits Express*	300	1995

Operations
Mackinaw City to Mackinac Island
St Ignace to Mackinac Island, 14 minutes, May to November.

UPDATED

Arnold Transit's Island Express **1991**

BAR HARBOR WHALE WATCH

29 Cottage Street, Bar Harbor, Maine 04609, USA

High-speed craft operated

Type	Name	Delivered
CAT Gladding-Hearn InCat 34 m	*Friendship V*	1995

Note: The 28 m vessel *Friendship IV* operated in 1994/95 was sold to Florida Cruises in 1995.

UPDATED

BLUE AND GOLD FLEET

Pier 39, Box Z-2, San Francisco, California, USA

High-speed craft operated

Type	Name	Delivered
CAT Nichols Bros InCat 22 m	*Olone Spirit*	1989
CAT Nichols Bros InCat 31 m	*Bay Breeze*	1994
CAT Gladding-Hearn InCat 31 m	*Jet Cat Express*	1994

VERIFIED

BOTTOM TIME ADVENTURES

PO Box 11919, Fort Lauderdale, Florida, 33339-1919, USA

Tel: +1 (305) 921 7798

A J Bland, *Director*

High-speed craft operated

Type	Name	Seats	Delivered
CAT Atlantic and Gulf Boat Building 23.8 m InCat	*Bottom Time II*	49 (14 cabins)	August 1986

Operations
Diving expeditions, dolphin research, movie support vessel and naturalist group charters (Bahamas, Florida, Gulf of Mexico and Caribbean).

VERIFIED

CATALINA CHANNEL EXPRESS LINES

Berth 95, San Pedro, California 90731, USA

Tel: +1 (310) 519 1212/7971
Fax: +1 (310) 548 7389

Doug Bombard, *Chief Executive Officer*
Greg Bombard, *President*
Audrey Bombard, *Secretary/Treasurer*
Tom Rutter, *Vice President Operations*
Elaine Vaughan, *Vice President Marketing*

High-speed craft operated

Type	Name	Seats	Delivered
MH Westport 56	*Channel Express*	60	1981
MH Westport Shipyard Inc 27.44 m 90	*Catalina Express*	149	1984
MH Westport Shipyard Inc 27.44 m 90	*Two Harbors Express*	149	1986
MH Westport 95	*Catalina Super Express*	149	1989
MH Westport 95	*Avalon Super Express*	149	June 1990
MH Westport 30.5 m	*Catalina Express*	149	1994
MH Westport 30.5 m	*Islander Express*	149	1994

Operations
San Pedro to Avalon and Two Harbors, Santa Catalina Island, 60 minutes
Long Beach to Avalon, Catalina Island, 60 minutes

UPDATED

Catalina Express ***1996***

CATALINA PASSENGER SERVICES

USA

High-speed craft operated

Type	Name	Seats	Delivered
CAT Nichols InCat 36 m	*Catalina Flyer*	500	May 1988

Operations
Newport Beach to Catalina Island, 26 n miles, 75 minutes.

VERIFIED

CLIPPER NAVIGATION INC

2701 Alaskan Way, Pier 69, Seattle, Washington 98121, USA

Tel: +1 (206) 443 2560
Fax: +1 (206) 443 2583

254 Belleville Street, Victoria, British Columbia V8V 1W9, Canada

Tel: +1 (604) 382 8100
Fax: +1 (604) 382 2152

Merideth Tall, *President*
Leonard Tall, *Executive Vice President*
Darrell E Bryan, *Vice President and General Manager*

High-speed craft operated

Type	Name	Seats	Delivered
CAT Fjellstrand 38.8 m	*Victoria Clipper*	300	April 1986
CAT Gladding-Hearn InCat 31 m	*Victoria Clipper III* (ex-*Audubon Express*)	239	1991
CAT Fjellstrand Flying Cat 40 m	*Victoria Clipper IV*	324	May 1993

Operations
Seattle to Victoria, British Columbia, Canada, 71 n miles, 2 hours 30 minutes
Fares vary by season: single US$49-55, return US$79-89.

VERIFIED

Victoria Clipper IV *departing from Seattle* ***1994***

CROSS SOUND FERRY SERVICES

Po Box 33, New London, Connecticut, USA

High-speed craft operated

Type	Name	Seats	Delivered
WPC Nichols/InCat 37 m	*Sea Jet I*	400	1995

Operations
New London to Orient Point

NEW ENTRY

EXPRESS NAVIGATION INC

Two First Avenue, Atlantic Highlands, New Jersey 07716, USA

Tel: +1 (908) 872 2628
Fax: +1 (908) 872 9691

Mark J Stanisci, *President*
Gary R Dunzelman, *Operations Manager*

High-speed craft operated

Type	Name	Seats	Delivered
MH Gladding-Hearn InCat 24 m	*Express I*	265	February 1989
MH Gladding-Hearn InCat 24 m	*Express II* (ex-*Vineyard Spray*)	296	June 1990

Operations
Monmouth County, New Jersey and Brooklyn, New York to Wall Street, 45 minutes.

VERIFIED

Express I *and* Express II ***1992***

FLORIDA CRUISE

USA

High-speed craft operated

Type	Name	Seats	Delivered
CAT InCat/Gladding Hearn 28 m	*Friendship IV*	149	1994

Operations
Key West area cruises

NEW ENTRY

GOLDEN GATE FERRY

Golden Gate Bridge, Highway and Transportation District, 101 East Sir Francis Drake Boulevard, Larkspur, California 94939, USA

Tel: +1 (415) 925 5570
Fax: +1 (415) 925 5510

Robert McDonnell, *President*
John E Fraser, *1st Vice President*
Bob Ross, *2nd Vice President*
Carney J Campion, *General Manager*
Eric A Robinson, *Division Manager*
Carl D Harrington, *Operations/Maintenance Manager*

The Ferry Division was formed in 1970 to operate water-borne mass transit on San Francisco Bay, operating between Marin County and San Francisco. In 1976, service was expanded with three semi-planing, triple gas-turbine, 25 knot, water-jet-propelled vessels. For economic reasons these three vessels have now been repowered with twin diesel engines using conventional propellers and rudders and with a resulting speed of 20.5 knots. The last of the three vessels modified was delivered in its new form in October 1985.

The Golden Gate Ferry vessel Sonoma ***1986***

High-speed craft operated

Type	Name	Seats	Delivered
MH Campbell Industries Spaulding S-165 51.2 m	*Marin*	partially open deck 118 open deck 42 enclosed decks 372	December 1976
MH Campbell Industries Spaulding S-165 51.2 m	*Sonoma*	partially open deck 118 open deck 42 enclosed decks 372	March 1977
MH Campbell Industries Spaulding S-165 51.2 m	*San Francisco*	partially open deck 118 open deck 42 enclosed decks 372	September 1977

Operations
San Francisco to Larkspur, Marin County, 45 minutes.

UPDATED

HARBOR BAY MARITIME

1141 Harbor Bay Parkway, Alameda, California 94502, USA

Tel: +1 415 247 1600
Fax: +1 415 247 1606

P Bishop, *General Manager*

High-speed craft operated

Type	Name	Seats	Delivered
MH Gulfcraft 24.5 m	*Harbor Bay Express*	278	1991
CAT USA Catamarans	*Harbor Bay Express II*	149	1994

Operations Harbor Bay in Alameda to the Ferry Building in San Francisco. Operated as a commuter service with a crossing time of 22 minutes. 100,000 passengers are carried per year.

UPDATED

Harbor Bay Express II ***1996***

HAWAIIAN CRUISES LTD

Hawaii, USA

Tel: +1 (808) 848 6360

High-speed craft operated

Type	Name	Seats	Delivered
SWATH Navatek	*Navatek 1**	430	1991
SWATH Navatek	*Navatek 2*	149	1994

*Medium speed vessel.

Operations
Daytime and evening cruises off Oahu's Gold Coast and whale watching when in season.

VERIFIED

HY-LINE CRUISES

36 Ocean Street, Hyannis, Massachusetts 02601, USA.

High-speed craft operated

Type	Name	Seats	Delivered
CAT InCat/Gladding Hearn 28 m	Grey Lady	149	(1996)

Operations
Hyannis to Nantucket Island

NEW ENTRY

KENAI FJORDS TOURS

PO Box 1889, Seward, Alaska 99664, USA.

High-speed craft operated

Type	Name	Seats	Delivered
MH Westport 90	*Kenai Explorer*	149	1993
MH Westport 95	*Alaskan Explorer*	149	1995

Operations
Tours of Kenai Fjords National Park (April to October).

UPDATED

Kenai Fjords Tours' Alaskan Explorer **1996**

NEW YORK FAST FERRY SERVICES INC

311 East Boston Post Road, Mamaroneck, New York 10543, USA

High-speed craft operated

Type	Name	Seats	Delivered
CAT Derecktor 37.7 m	Unnamed	–	(1996)
CAT Derecktor 37.7 m	Unnamed	–	(1996)

Operations
Manhattan to Staten Island (New York harbour)

NEW ENTRY

NY WATERWAY

Pershing Road, Weehawken, New Jersey 07087, USA

Tel: +1 (201) 902 8700

Arthur E Imperatore, *President*

High-speed craft operated

Type	Name	Seats	Delivered
MH Blount Marine Corporation	*Port Imperial*	149	1984
MH Blount Marine Corporation	*Port Imperial Manhattan*	149	1986
MH Gulf Craft	*New Jersey*	350	1988
MH Gulf Craft	*George Washington*	399	1989
MH Gulf Craft	*Thomas Jefferson*	399	1989
MH Gulf Craft	*Alexander Hamilton*	399	1989
MH Gulf Craft	*Abraham Lincoln*	399	1989
MH Gulf Craft	*West New York*	149	1990
MH Gladding-Hearn	*Henry Hudson*	397	1992
MH Gladding-Hearn	*Robert Fulton*	397	1993
MH Gladding-Hearn	*Empire State*	397	1994
MH Gladding-Hearn	*Garden State*	397	1994

The 350 passenger 24 knot Port Imperial Manhattan **1990**

Operations
Weehawken (New Jersey), to 38th Street and 12th Avenue Manhattan, every 15 minutes from 06.45 to midnight.
Weehawken (New Jersey), to slip 5 in Lower Manhattan during the rush hours.
Hoboken (New Jersey), to the World Financial Centre, Manhattan, every 5 minutes during peak and every 20 minutes off-peak from 0630 to 2200.
Colgate pier in Jersey City (New Jersey), to the World Financial Centre, Manhattan every 15 minutes from 0645 to 2200.
Hunters Point in Queens, New York, to East 34th Street, Manhattan, every 15 minutes during rush hours.

VERIFIED

PARTY LINE CRUISE COMPANY

905 South America Way, Miami, Florida 33132, USA

Tel: +1 (305) 381 6360
Fax: +1 (305) 381 6831

John Martin, *President*
Antoine Gurrey, *General Manager*

High-speed craft operated

Type	Name	Seats	Delivered
SWATH SI Super 4000	*Cloud Ten*	365	(1996)

Operations
Miami to Key West.

VERIFIED

PHILLIPS CRUISES & TOURS (YUKON RIVER CRUISES)

509 West Fourth Avenue, Anchorage, Alaska 99501, USA

Tel: +1 (907) 276 8023
Fax: +1 (907) 276 5315

Brad Phillips, *President/Owner*
Helen Phillips, *Executive Vice President*

High-speed craft operated

Type	Name	Seats	Delivered
CAT Nichols Brothers InCat 22 m	*Klondike*	210	1985
CAT Nichols Brothers InCat 30 m	*Klondike Express*	330	1992

Operations
Whittier, Alaska to College Fjord to Barry Arm to Harriman Glacier. 110 miles, 6 hours. Fare (1994) US$119 + tax.

VERIFIED

Klondike Express *operated by Phillips Cruises & Tours* **1995**

PUT-IN-BAY BOAT LINE

Po Box 69, South Bass Island, Lake Erie, Ohio, USA

High-speed craft operated

Type	Name	Seats	Delivered
CAT Gladding-Hearn InCat 28 m	*Jet Express I*	380	May 1989
CAT Gladding-Hearn InCat 29 m	*Jet Express II*	400	May 1992

Operations
Put-In-Bay to Port Clinton, 13 n miles, 22 minutes.

VERIFIED

RED AND WHITE FLEET

A subsidiary of Crowley Maritime Corporation

Pier 41, Fisherman's Wharf, San Francisco, California 94133, USA

Tel: +1 (415) 546 2800

Alan Zurawski, *Vice President and General Manager*
Carolyn Horgan, *Operations Manager*

High-speed craft operated

Type	Name	Seats	Delivered
CAT Nichols Brothers InCat 26 m	*Catamarin*	274	1985
CAT Nichols Brothers InCat 26 m	*Dolphin*	274	1986

Operations
Marin County area commuter and cruise services
Catamarin and *Dolphin* operating ferry services between San Francisco and Sausalito, Tiburon on San Francisco Bay.

VERIFIED

Catamarin *operated by the Red and White Fleet* **1992**

SAYVILLE FERRY SERVICE INC

41 River Road, PO Box 626, Sayville, Long Island, New York 11782, USA

Tel: +1 (516) 589 0810
Fax: +1 (516) 589 0843

Captain Kenneth Stein, *President*

Sayville Ferry Service has a total fleet of eight vessels with passenger capacities of from 88 to 350. Most of them are operated at between 15 and 20 knots but the *Fire Island Clipper* can cruise at 26 knots at full load.

High-speed craft operated

Type	Name	Seats	Delivered
MH Derecktor Shipyard	*Fire Island Clipper*	350	1979

Operations
Sayville, Long Island (South Shore) to Fire Island, 5 n miles, serving three Summer communities, stops at Cherry Grove and Fire Island Pines. The ferries also serve Sunken Forest and Sailor Haven Federal Parks.

VERIFIED

Sayville Ferry Service Fire Island Clipper **1988**

SEA PRINCESS (GUAM) CORPORATION

790 North Marine Drive, Box 432, Tamuning, Guam 96911, USA

Tel: +671 477 5680
Fax: +671 477 5666

Graham Poon, *General Manager*

The *Sea Princess* operates as a dinner cruise boat out of Guam.

High-speed craft operated

Type	Name	Seats	Delivered
CAT InCat 30 m	*Sea Princess*	230	1993

UPDATED

SHEPLER'S MACKINAC ISLAND FERRY

PO Box 250, Mackinaw City, Michigan 49701, USA

High-speed craft operated

Type	Name	Seats	Delivered
MH Camcraft Boats Inc (Hargrave) 18.3 m	*The Welcome*	120	1969
MH Camcraft Boats Inc (Hargrave) 17.1 m	*Felicity*	150	1972
MH Bergeron 19.9 m (Hargrave)	*Hope*	150	1975
MH Bergeron 23.5 m (Hargrave)	*Wyandot*	265	1979
MH Aluminium Boats Inc (Hargrave) 23.78 m	*Captain Shepler*	265	1986

Operations
St Ignace (Upper Peninsula) and Mackinaw City (Lower Peninsula) to Mackinac Island, Michigan on Lake Huron.

VERIFIED

STAR LINE

590 North State Street, St Ignace, Michigan 49781, USA

High-speed craft operated

Type	Name	Seats	Delivered
MH Gulf Craft 19.8 m	*Maquette*	150	1979
MH Gulf Craft 19.8 m	*La Salle*	150	1983
MH Gulf Craft 19.8 m	*Nicolet*	150	1985
MH Gulf Craft 25.9 m	*Radisson*	350	1988
MH Gulf Craft 19.8 m	*Cadillac*	150	1990
MH Gulf Craft 20 m	*Juliet*	150	1993

VERIFIED

MH Gulf Craft Radisson *in service with Star Line* **1994**

WASHINGTON STATE FERRIES

Seattle Ferry Terminal, 801 Alaska Way, Seattle, Washington 98104-1487, USA

Tel: +1 (206) 464 7181

David Black, *Marine Operations Manager*

High-speed craft operated

Type	Name	Seats	Delivered
CAT Nichols Bros InCat 26 m	*Tyee* (ex-*Express*)	319	October 1986
MH Equitable 34 m	*Kalama*	253	1990
MH Equitable 34 m	*Skagit*	253	1990

Operations
Seattle to Bremerton, 14 n miles
Seattle to Vashon.

UPDATED

Skagit *operated by Washington State Ferries* **1992**

URUGUAY

ALISCAFOS SA

Plaza Cagancha 1124, Montevideo, Uruguay

Tel: +598 (2) 924004
Fax: +598 (2) 922626

High-speed craft operated

Type	Name	Seats	Additional Payload	Delivered
HYD Rodriquez PT 50	*Fletcha de Buenos Aires*	–	–	1994
HYD Rodriquez PT 50	*Fletcha de Colonia*	–	–	1994
HYD Rodriquez RHS 140	*Tyrving*	145	–	1994
HYD Rodriquez RHS 140	*Colonia del Sacramento* (ex-*Condor 3*)	134	–	1994
HYD Rodriquez RHS 140	*Farallón* (ex-*Løberon* '85)	134	–	1994
CAT InCat Australia/AMD K55	*Juan Patricio*	450	63 cars	1994

Operations
Colonia to Buenos Aires and Colonia to La Plata
Montevideo to Colonia to Buenos Aires
Montevideo to Colonia to La Plata

Annual traffic
180,000 to 200,000 passengers

NEW ENTRY

BUQUEBUS

Rio Negro 1400, Montevideo, Uruguay

High-speed craft operated

Type	Name	Seats	Additional payload	Delivered
WPC InCat Australia 74 m	*Patricia Olivia*	515	90 cars	September 1992
WPC InCat Australia 74 m	*Juan L*	600	110 cars	1993

Operations
Montevideo (Punta del Este) to Buenos Aires, 100 n miles.

VERIFIED

TRANSPORTES ANFIBIOS SA

Rivera 236, Colonia, Postal 70 000, Uruguay

Tel: +598 5224978/4982
Fax: +598 5223144

Esteban Moreira Vina, *President*

High-speed craft operated

Type	Name	Seats	Delivered
HOV NQEA AP1-88/100	*Hover*	96	May 1992

Operations
Colonia to Buenos Aires.

VERIFIED

VIRGIN ISLANDS (US)

NAUTICAL TRADING LTD

Transportation Services of St John

Po Box 28, Crue Bay, St John, US Virgin Islands

High-speed craft operated

Type	Name	Seats	Delivered
MH Aluminium Boats 29 m	*Caribe Tide*	232	1995
MH Aluminium Boats 29 m	*Caribe Cay*	232	1995

Operations
St John to St Thomas Airport.

UPDATED

VIRGIN HYDROFOIL SERVICE

US Virgin Islands

High-speed craft operated

Type	Name	Seats	Delivered
HYD S.Ord Kolkida	*Katran I*	115	1995

Operations
US Virgin Islands

NEW ENTRY

ZANZIBAR

AZAM MARINE

PO Box 744, Zanzibar

High-speed craft operated

Type	Name	Seats	Delivered
CAT Westamaran 86	*Kilimanjaro*	150	1994
HYD Rodnquez RHS160F	*Condor 7*	200	1994
MH WaveMaster 32 m	*Sea Raider*	200	1995

Operations
Dar es Salaam to Zanzibar

NEW ENTRY

PRINCIPAL EQUIPMENT AND COMPONENTS FOR HIGH-SPEED CRAFT

Engines
Transmissions
Air propellers
Marine propellers
Water-jet units
Ride control systems
Air cushion skirt systems
Marine escape systems
Fast rescue tenders

ENGINES

Company Listing by Country

Canada
Pratt & Whitney Canada, Inc

Commonwealth of Independent States
A Ivchenko (AI)
Kuznetsov Design Bureau NK-12/14
Transmash Plant
Zvezda Production Association

France
Moteurs Baudouin
Semt Pielstick
Turbomeca
Wärtsilä Sacm Diesel

Germany
Deutz Motor GmbH
Deutz MWM
MAN
MTU

Italy
CRM Motori Marini SpA
Fiat Aviazione SpA
Fincantieri
Iveco Aifo SpA
Seatek SpA
Seatek Marine Power

Japan
Mitsubishi Heavy Industries Ltd
Niigata Engineering Company Ltd

Norway
Kværner Energy A/S
Ulstein Turbine A/S

Sweden
ABB STAL AB
Scania
Volvo Penta AB

United Kingdom
GEC Alsthom Paxman
GEC Alsthom Ruston Diesels Ltd
Perkins Group of Companies
Rolls-Royce Industrial and Marine Gas Turbines Ltd

United States of America
AlliedSignal Engine Division
Allison Engine Company
Caterpillar Inc
Caterpillar, Solar Turbines Inc
Cummins Engine Company Inc
Detroit Diesel Corporation
General Electric Company
United Technologies International Inc

CANADA

PRATT & WHITNEY CANADA, INC

A United Technologies Company

1000 Marie-Victorin Boulevard, Longueuil, Quebec J4G 1A1, Canada

Tel: +1 (514) 677 9411/651 3633 (Industrial and Marine Division)

L D Caplan, *President and Chief Executive Officer*
G P Ouimet, *Executive Vice President*
R F Steers, *Vice President, Finance*
C J Pascoe, *Vice President, Counsel and Corporate Secretary*
J B Haworth, *Vice President, Industrial and Marine Division*
W M Coffin, *Manager of Marketing, Industrial and Marine Division*

In addition to its wide range of small gas-turbine aero-engines, Pratt & Whitney Canada (P&WC) also manufactures industrial and marine derivatives supplied by its Industrial and Marine (I&M) Division. Engines are rated from 410 kW (550 shp) upwards (see table) and are of the simple-cycle, free turbine type. They run on Nos 1 and 2 diesel or aviation turbine fuels.

Typical marine applications are the ST6K-77 driving the auxiliary power unit on the Flagstaff 2 class hydrofoils built for the Israeli Navy, and the ST6T-76 Twin Pac powering LACV-30 hovercraft built by Bell Aerospace Textron (now Textron Marine and Land Systems) for the US Army. Including aero-engine installations, more than 38,000 of P&WC's turbines have been delivered. They have accumulated in excess of 217 million hours of operation.

Engine features: All ST6 engines have a single spool gas generator and a multistage compressor (three axial plus one centrifugal stage) driven by a single stage axial turbine. The larger models have cooled vanes. The radial diffuser incorporates P&WC patented diffuser pipes. The burner section has a reverse flow annular combustor. A single- or two-stage free turbine provides a direct high-speed output or drives through a reduction gearbox.

Air intake is located at the rear of the engine and is through a screened annular inlet.

The ST6T-76 Twin Pac is a dual version of the ST6 with two power sections mounted side by side coupled to a twinning reduction gearbox. The gearbox incorporates automatic clutches which permit emergency operation of one side independent of the other.

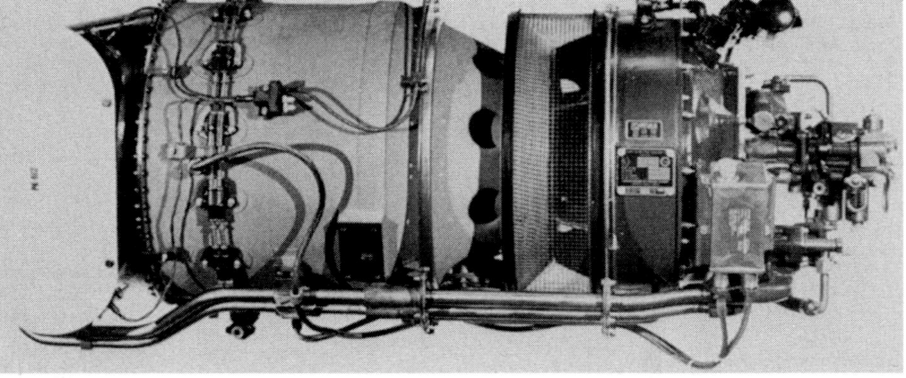

ST6 gas-turbine ***1986***

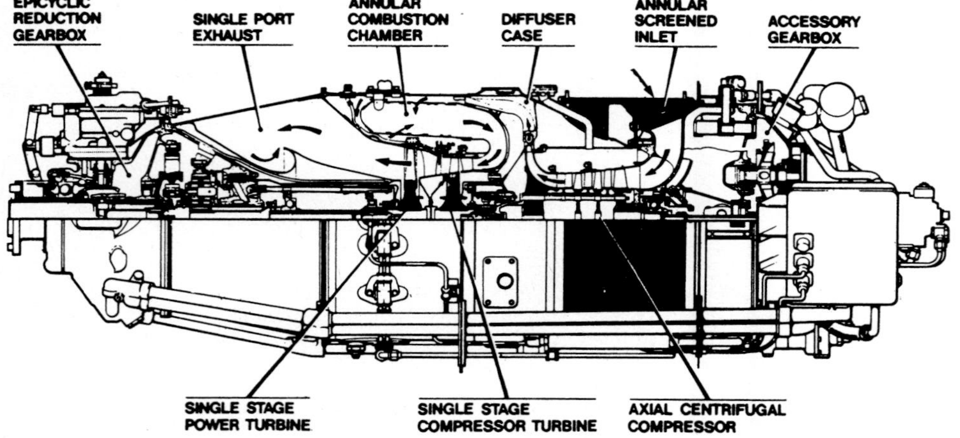

Main components of ST6 ***1986***

SPW124-2

The SPW124-2 is an industrial and marine version of the PW124 aero turboprop. This engine benefits from the experience gained by its aero counterparts with 9 million hours of operation.

Engine features: The SPW124 is a three-shaft engine. The low-pressure and high-pressure centrifugal compressors (combined pressure ratio 15:1) are each driven independently by single stage compressor turbines. This allows both compressors to operate at their optimum efficiencies without the need for complex variable geometry. Other features comprise P&WC patented pipe diffusers, reverse annular combustor, low-pressure and high-pressure stator cooling and turbine blade cooling. The two-stage power turbine retains the free turbine concept of the ST6 engine.

SPW901/1

This is a direct drive gas-turbine of rugged design intended for industrial and marine use.

Engine features: A free turbine engine incorporating a cast aluminium air intake casing, centrifugal compressor, patented P&WC pipe diffusers, reverse flow annular combustor, single stage high turbine with cooled vanes and disk. The ball and roller bearings which support the gas generator rotor assembly and power turbine shaft have under-race lubrication. Thermal insulation blankets are selectively installed on the external surfaces of the engine to maintain surface temperature below 450°F.

PW901A

The PW901A is an auxiliary power unit which is fully marinised, lightweight and compact, delivering 551 lb/min of air at 54 lb/in^2 absolute. In addition it has provision to drive two 90 kVA electrical generators.

ST6 and SPW SERIES ENGINE DATA SUMMARY (GUARANTEED PERFORMANCE)
Sea Level Standard Pressure at 15°C Inlet Temperature

Model	Max kW	Max SFC	Normal kW	Normal SFC	RPM direct drive	RPM integral gearbox	Length	Width	Height	Engine dry weight
ST6L-794	639	0.358	569	0.365	33,000	2,200 6,188 1,300	1,346 mm	559 mm	533 mm	139 kg
ST6L-812	777	0.344	674	0.357	30,000	1,700 2,000 5,700	1,447 mm	483 mm	559 mm	164 kg
ST6T-76 Twin Pac	1,380	0.374	1,076	0.395	33,000	6,600	1,676 mm	1,118 mm	838 mm	336 kg
SPW901-A	1,303	0.362	1,225	0.363	24,625	available	1,194 mm	660 mm	1,041 mm	209 kg
SPW124-2	1,843	0.294	1,585	0.307	20,000	available	1,524 mm	660 mm	838 mm	300 kg
SPW200	395	0.344	255	0.345	-	6,000	914 mm	483 mm	559 mm	111 kg

Engine data with integral gearbox available on request

Engine data shown are for direct drive

VERIFIED

COMMONWEALTH OF INDEPENDENT STATES

The following information was received on the gas-turbine engine for the Cyclone Hydrofoil.

M37 GAS-TURBINE SYSTEM

This system consists of the DO37 gas-turbine and the RO37 two-stage reduction gear with built-in supporting bearings. The M37 is used to power the Cyclone 250-passenger, 42 knot hydrofoil.

Specifications (M37)
Length: 6,350 mm
Width: 1,900 mm
Height: 2,200 mm
Shaft power, max: 5,880 kW
normal: 5,150 kW
Specific fuel consumption: 295 g/kW h
Time between overhauls: 8,000 h
Weight: 7,000 kg

Another proposed power-plant installation for hydrofoils consists of two DO37 gas-turbine units driving a common reduction gear and offering a total output of 11,760 kW.

VERIFIED

The largest Russian passenger hydrofoil which is fitted with the M37 gas-turbine system, Yalta 1990 (Antonio Scrimali) ***1992***

A IVCHENKO (AI)

This design team, which was headed by the late A Ivchenko, is based in a factory at Zaporojie in Ukraine, where all prototypes and preproduction engines bearing the 'AI' prefix are developed and built.

The first engine with which Ivchenko was associated officially was the 40 kW AI-4G piston engine used in the Kamov Ka-10 ultralight helicopter. He later progressed via the widely used AI-14 and AI-26 piston engines, to become one of the Soviet Union's leading designers of gas-turbine engines.

Two AI-20s in derated, marinised form and driving two three-stage water-jets power the Burevestnik, the first Soviet gas-turbine hydrofoil. The integrated lift and propulsion system of the Sormovich ACV was derived from the 1,894 kW gas-turbine AI-20 DK. The two AI-20s, each rated at about 2,700 kW continuous, are also thought to power the Lebed amphibious assault landing craft.

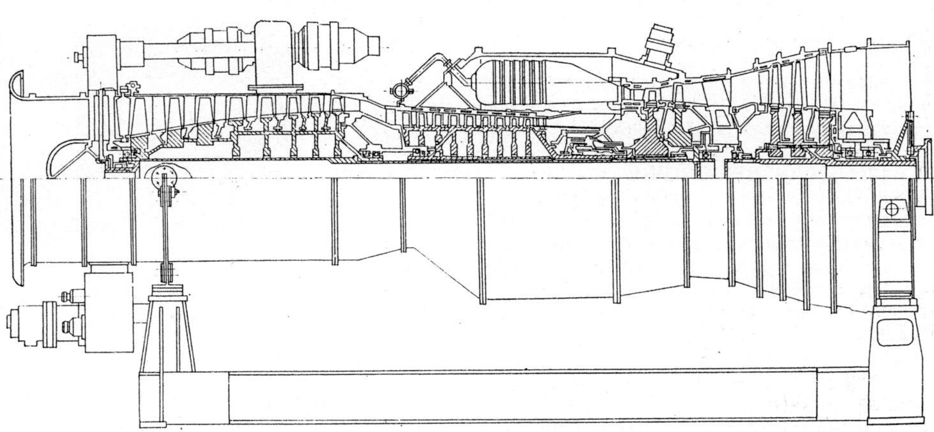

1,750 hp Ivchenko AI-23-CI marine gas-turbine ***1992***

IVCHENKO AI-20

The Ivchenko design bureau is responsible for the AI-20 turboprop engine which powers the Antonov An-10, An-12 and Ilyushin Il-18 airliners and the Beriev M-12 Tchaika amphibian.

AI-20K Rated at 3,000 kW. Used in Il-18V, An-10A and An-12.

AI-20M Uprated version with T-O rating of 3,100 kW. Used in Il-18D/E, An-10A and An-12.

Conversion of the turboprop as a marine power unit for hydrofoil water-jet propulsion (as on the Burevestnik) involved a number of changes to the engine. In particular it was necessary to hold engine rpm at a constant level during conditions of varying load from the water-jet pump. It was also necessary to be able to vary the thrust from the water-jet unit from zero to forward or rearwards thrust to facilitate engine starting and vessel manoeuvring.

The AI-20 is a single-spool turboprop, with a 10-stage axial flow compressor, cannular combustion chamber with 10 flame tubes and a three-stage turbine, of which the first two stages are cooled. Planetary reduction gearing, with a ratio of 0.08732:1, is mounted forward of the annular air intake. The fixed nozzle contains a central bullet fairing. All engine driven accessories are mounted on the forward part of the compressor casing, which is of magnesium alloy.

The AI-20 was designed to operate reliably in all temperatures from −60 to +55°C at heights up to 10,000 m. It is a constant speed engine, the rotor speed being maintained at 21,300 rpm by automatic variation of propeller pitch. Gas temperature after turbine is 560°C in both current versions. TBO of the AI-20K was 4,000 hours in Spring 1966.

Weights
Dry
AI-20K: 1,080 kg
AI-20M: 1,039 kg

Performance Ratings
Max T-O
AI-20K: 3,000 kW
AI-20M: 3,100 kW
Cruise rating at 630 km/h at 8,000 m
AI-20K: 1,700 kW
AI-20M: 2,000 kW

Specific Fuel Consumption
At cruise rating
AI-20K: 288 g/kW h
AI-20M: 264 g/kW h

Oil Consumption
Normal: 1 l/h

IVCHENKO AI-24

In general configuration this single-spool turboprop engine, which powers the An-24 transport aircraft, is very similar to the earlier and larger AI-20.

Dimensions
Length, overall: 2,435 mm

Weight
Dry: 499 kg

Performance Rating
Max power with water injection: 2,102 kW

VERIFIED

KUZNETSOV DESIGN BUREAU NK-12/14

In its original form the NK-12M developed 8,948 kW. The later NK-12MV is rated at 11,033 kW and powers the Tupolev Tu-114 transport, driving four-blade, contrarotating propellers of 5.6 m diameter. As the NK-12MA, rated at 11,185 kW, it powers the Antonov An-22 military transport, with propellers of 6.2 m diameter.

The NK-12M has a single 14-stage axial flow compressor. Compression ratio varies from 9:1 to 13:1 and variable inlet guide vanes and blow off valves are necessary. A cannular-type combustion system is used. Each flame tube is mounted centrally on a downstream injector, but all tubes merge at their maximum diameter to form an annular secondary region. The single turbine is a five-stage axial. Mass flow is 56 kg/s.

The casing is made in four portions from precision welded sheet steel. An electric control for variation of propeller pitch is incorporated to maintain constant engine speed.

The NK-14 is the modern derivative of the same engine, providing similar power outputs. The Kuznetsov design bureau is currently working on low NOx combustor designs for this engine, scheduled to be available in 1995/96.

Dimensions
Length: 6,000 mm
Diameter: 1,150 mm
Weight
Dry: 2,350 kg
Performance Ratings
Max power: 11,033 kW
Nominal power: 8,826 kW at 8,300 rpm
Idling speed: 6,600 rpm

VERIFIED

Kuznetsov NK-14E (Ken Fulton)
1995

TRANSMASH PLANT

Industrial Union, Transport Machine Building, Barnaul Plant (IU Barnaultransmash), 656037 Barnaul, Russia, CIS

Tel: +7 (095) 772013

Yuri S Cherviakov, *Chief Designer*

The Transmash Plant produces a range of high-speed diesel engines for applications in sea and river craft types including hydrofoil vessels.

Transmash 3K Δ12H-520 diesel engine ***1992***

3K Δ12H-520 DIESEL ENGINE

The 3K Δ12H-520 diesel engine is designed to be installed on sea and river ships of various applications as their main propulsion engine. The engine is a four-stroke, high-speed engine, with 12 cylinders, V-type cylinder arrangement, liquid cooling, direct fuel injection, and supercharging.

Specifications
Cylinder diameter: 150 mm
Piston stroke: 180 mm
Full power: 382 kW
Crankshaft rotation speed at full power: 1,500 rpm
Specific fuel consumption, g/kW h: 220
Dimensions
Length: 2,030 mm
Width: 1,108 mm
Height: 1,178 mm
Dry weight: 1,750 kg

3 Δ12A DIESEL ENGINE

The 3 Δ12A diesel engine is designed to be employed by sea and river ships of various applications as their main propulsion engine. The engine is a four-stroke, high-speed type, with 12 cylinders, V-type cylinder arrangement, liquid cooling and direct fuel injection.

The engine is equipped with a reversing reduction gear comprising a reduction gear and a friction clutch to couple the screw propeller with and disengage it from the crankshaft and to reverse the screw propeller sense of rotation.

Specifications
Cylinder diameter: 150 mm
Piston stroke: 180 mm
Full power at reversing reduction gear driven shaft flange, emf
at ahead running: 225 kW
at astern running, not more than: 135 kW
Crankshaft rotation speed at full power: 1,500 rpm
Gear ratio
at ahead running: 1.22 or 2.04 or 2.95
at astern running, not more than: 2.18
Dimensions
Length, with power take-off shaft: 2,464 mm
Length, without power take-off shaft: 2,390 mm
Width: 1,052 mm
Height: 1,210 mm
Dry weight: 1,814 kg

3 Δ20C2 DIESEL ENGINE

The 3 Δ20C2 diesel engine is designed to be employed by sea and river ships as their main propulsion engine and is a four-stroke, high-speed engine, with six cylinders, V-type cylinder arrangement (at an angle of 120°), liquid cooling and direct fuel injection.

The crankcase unit of the engine is of tunnel type, made integral with the cylinder jackets. The crankshaft is mounted on roller bearings. The connecting rods are of central type. The engine is provided with a first order inertial force balancing mechanism.

The engine can be equipped (on request) with an auxiliary power take-off shaft (up to 22.4 kW at 2,200 rpm). The power take-off shaft is installed coaxially with the crankshaft on the side opposite to the flywheel.

Specifications
Cylinder diameter: 150 mm
Piston stroke: 150 mm
Power: rated, 175 kW, max 194 kW
Rotational speed: corresponding to rated power 2,200 rpm, corresponding to max power 2,270 rpm
Dimensions
Length: 1,122 mm
Width: 1,140 mm
Height: 767 mm
Dry weight: 770 kg

VERIFIED

ZVEZDA PRODUCTION ASSOCIATION

123 Babuschkina Str, 193012 St Petersburg, Russia, CIS

Tel: +7 (267) 3156/(262) 1327

Zvezda produces diesels of two sizes; M500 and M400. Diesels of both families have many features in common; main housing parts are cast in aluminium alloy and highly loaded parts are made in nitrided alloy steels. These features provide for the diesels' low specific weights and high specific volumetric powers. The engines are used as main marine diesels in high-speed boats and ships where powerful,

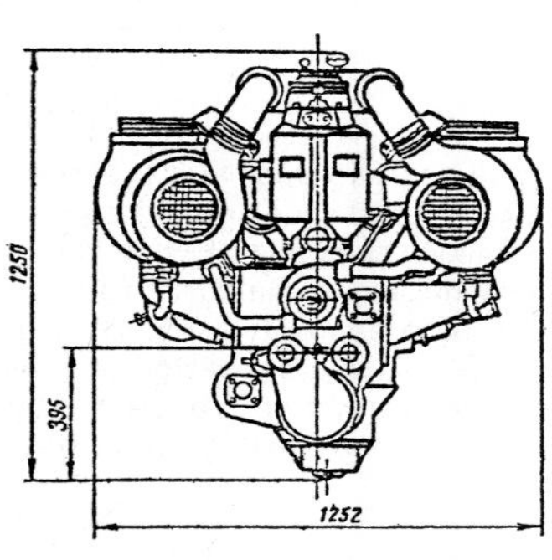

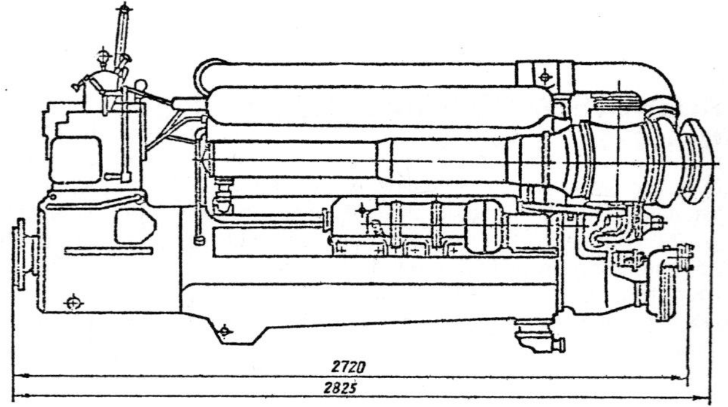

Zvezda M401A ***1986***

compact propulsion plants are required and similarly for hydrofoil vessels.

Diesels of both families have a dry crankcase lubrication system. The cooling system has a double circuit, the inner cooling circuit (of freshwater) is closed with excessive pressure at inlet of centrifugal pumps of the cooling system, which is mounted on diesel.

The seawater pump is mounted on the diesel. The water and oil coolers are installed outside the diesel and are not delivered with the engine.

At low ratings of engine and vessel reversing, the water pump provides the priming of water through water and oil coolers, as well as water supply for gas exhaust watering; at high ratings the cooling flow for the coolers is provided by the dynamic pressure of the vessel motion, but watering of gas exhaust and water priming through air-water radiators (if there are any) are carried out by the pump.

Diesel starting is by compressed air under the pressure of 15.0 to 8.0 MPa. Availability of full load of the fully warmed up diesel is possible within a short time (not over 15 seconds).

Diesels of both types are equipped and delivered with a system of emergency warning signalling and protection and a complete set of control-measuring devices, adapted for automatic remote-control.

The main technical characteristics of these diesels are given in the accompanying tables.

Both types of these diesel engines may be purchased from PO 'Zvezda', St Petersburg.

VERIFIED

Zvezda M400 ***1986***

PARAMETERS OF MAIN VARIATIONS OF MARINE DIESELS ΔH 16/17 TYPE BEING MANUFACTURED AT THE PRODUCTION ASSOCIATION "ZVEZDA" Table 1

	Unit of measurement	**Plant designation of diesels**						
		M503A	**M503B**	**M504A**	**M504B**	**M517**	**M520**	**M521**
Type of diesel		4-stroke, star-shaped with gas-turbo-compressor, connected kinematically to the crankshaft, equipped by the emergency warning signalisation and protection						
Purpose		Main marine diesel for light high-speed ships						
Nominal power	kW	2,425	1,840	3,493	3,676	3,493*	3,600	6,654*
Maximal power	kW	2,942	-	-	-	-	3,965	-
Revolutions at full (nominal) power	min^{-1}	2,000	1,780	1950	2,000	2,000	1,900	2,000
Mean effective pressure	MPa	1.01	0.86	1.12	1.15	1.09	1.16	1.04
Standard specific fuel consumption	g/kW h	211^{+11}	204^{+11}	211^{+11}	210^{+11}	211^{+11}	213^{+11}	217^{+11}*
Cooling of supercharging air	-	no	no	yes	yes	yes	yes	yes
Length	mm	3,700	3,900	4,650	4,400	4,400	4,400	7,000
Width	mm	1,555	1,555	1,676	1,676	1,676	1,676	1,820
Height	mm	1,560	1,560	1,654	1,654	1,654	1,654	2,495
Mass in full completing	kg	5,400	5,600	7,500	7,250	7,250	7,250	17100
Engine life until 1st full overhaul	h	1,000	3,500	2,500	2,500	1,600	1,500	2,500
Total engine life	h	2,500	9,000	6,500	6,500	4,500	4,500	6,500
Transmission ratio of reducer	-	0.514	0.179	0.268	0.514	0.514	0.514	0.311

* during operation in tropics

PARAMETERS OF MAIN VARIATIONS OF MARINE DIESELS 12 ΔH 18/20 TYPE BEING MANUFACTURED AT THE PRODUCTION ASSOCIATION "ZVEZDA" Table 2

	Unit of measurement	**Plant designation of diesels**				
		M400	**M401A**	**M419A**	**M417A**	**PA-210B**
Type of diesel		4-stroke, V-shaped, 12 cylinders, 18/20 dimensions with supercharging				
Purpose		Main marine engine for hydrofoils, hovercraft and so on				Main marine engine for ships with propeller of regulated- or fixed-pitch
Nominal power	kW	736	736	809	736	809
Maximal power	kW	809	809	890	809	890
Nominal revolutions	min^{-1}	1,700	1,550	1,550	1,550	1,550
Mean effective pressure	MPa	0.93	0.93	1.03	0.93	1.03
Standard specific fuel consumption	g/kW h	217^{+10}	203^{+10}	200^{+10}	205^{+10}	200^{+10}
Standard specific oil consumption	g/kW h	2.3	2.2	2.2	2.2	2.2
Cooling of supercharging air	-	no	no	yes	no	yes
Supercharging unit	-	MS	TK-18(2ps)	TK-18(2ps)	TK23	TK-18(2ps)
Length	mm	2,600	2,825	2,825	2,678	2,715
Width	mm	1,200	1,260	1,260	1,220	1,260
Height	mm	1,250	41250	1,250	1,600	1,272
Mass in full completing	kg	1,800	2,100	2,200	2,200	2,350
Engine life until 1st full overhaul	h	1,500	3,500	4,500	3,500	4,000
Total engine life	h	6,000	9,000	10,000	9,000	10,000
Reversing transmission reduction gear	-	friction cam	friction cam	friction cam	disc clutch	non-reversible planetary
Transmission ratio of reducer						
forward run		1.0	1.0	1.0	1.0	0.241
rear run		0.8	0.8	0.8	0.705	-
Power of suspended electric generator (28 V)	kW	1.0	3.0	3.0	1.0	-

FRANCE

MOTEURS BAUDOUIN

165 boulevard de Pont-de-Vivaux, BP 62, F-13362 Marseilles Cedex 10, France

Tel: +33 91 83 85 00
Telex: 410944 MOBOD F
Fax: +33 91 79 09 38

BAUDOUIN VTi SERIES

The following series of diesel engines are supplied by Baudouin. They are characterised by four-stroke, direct injection, water-cooled, 6 or 12 in 90° V cylinders and turbocharged with charge air intercooling.

V6Ti330

243 kW at 3,200 rpm, dry weight: 815 kg

V12BTi840

618 kW at 3,000 rpm, dry weight: 1,360 kg

V12BTi1200

883 kW at 2,000 rpm, dry weight: 3,002 kg

V12BTi1400

Characteristics
1,030 kW at 2,000 rpm for high-speed craft
Diesel engine, 4-stroke, direct injection turbocharged with charge air intercooling
Bore and stroke: 150 × 150 mm
Number of cylinders: 12 in 90° V
Total sweep volume: 3,181 dm^3
Compression ratio: 14/1
Number of valves per cylinder: 4
Engine rotation to ISO 1204 standard: counterclockwise
Idling speed: 700 min^{-1}
Weight without water and oil: 3,020 kg
Weight to power ratio (rating RP): 2.1 kg/HP

VERIFIED

Baudouin V12BTi1400 1,030 kW ***1990***

	A	B	C	D	E	Approx weight without water or oil
12 P 15.2 SR7						3,000 kg
12 P 15.2 SRC IRS	355 mm	1,229 mm	340 mm	1,084 mm	165 mm	3,970 kg
12 P 15.2 SRC IRX	488 mm	1,839 mm	460 mm	1,356 mm	226 mm	5,105 kg
12 P 15.2 SRC RHS	355 mm	1,611 mm	340 mm	1,084 mm	165 mm	3,965 kg
12 P 15.2 SRC RHX	488 mm	2,071 mm	460 mm	1,356 mm	226 mm	5,105 kg

SEMT PIELSTICK

2 quai de Seine, F-93202 Saint-Denis Cedex, France

Tel: +33 (1) 48 09 76 00
Telex: 233 147F
Fax: +33 (1) 48 09 78 78

SEMT Pielstick was founded in 1946. It designs and develops four-stroke high- and medium-speed diesel engines which are built under licence all over the world. The high-speed catamaran *Sun* built by Mitsui shipyard in Japan is powered by two Pielstick 16 PA4-200 VGA engines built under licence by Niigata.

The PA range of high-speed diesel engines offers four types of engines:
PA4-185 rated from 590 kW to 2,215 kW and from 1,200 to 1,500 rpm
PA4-200 rated from 1,060 kW to 2,650 kW and from 1,200 to 1,500 rpm
PA5-255 rated from 1,050 kW to 3,960 kW and from 900 to 1,000 rpm
PA6-280 rated from 1,745 to 7,920 kW and from 720 to 1,050 rpm

The PA4 types are fitted with a variable geometry combustion chamber.

The PA engines are available in a gas version with low pollutant emission versions also being available.

These engines are used in marine propulsion, railway traction, dumpers, land-based power generation and generating sets including emergency sets for nuclear power-plants.

VERIFIED

TURBOMECA

F-64511 Bordes, Cedex, France

Tel: +33 59 12 50 00
Telex: 560928 F
Fax: +33 59 53 15 12

S Meton, *President*
J L Chenard, *Director*

EURODYN

Turbomeca is involved in the development programme, Eurodyn, the aim of which is to produce a high efficiency industrial gas-turbine in the 2,500 to 3,000 kW power range.

The engine is intended for applications in the fast surface transport market such as train or boat propulsion, as well as in the more traditional market for gas-turbines of electric generation and drive of pumps or compressors.

In this Franco-Scandinavian co-operation, programme leader Turbomeca (France) holds 50 per cent, Ulstein (Norway) 30 per cent and Volvo Aero (Sweden) 20 per cent.

The Eurodyn turbine is a two-shaft engine, making extensive use of radial technology, based on an advanced and patented design.

The efficiency targets set for the Eurodyn are impressive for turbines in this power class with an efficiency of 35 per cent.

In 1992 the Eurodyn programme partners achieved a significant milestone with tests of the Eurodyn prototypes in the Turbomeca and Ulstein facilities.

The two engines underwent extensive testing during 1994, and are being further tested in a high-speed vessel in Norway and a high-speed train in France during 1995 and 1996.

MAKILA T I

Turbomeca has developed a new industrial marine gas-turbine, which the company designates Makila T I, rated 1,200 kW under ISO conditions and base load. Its modern design and the use of state-of-the-art technology have contributed to its 28 per cent efficiency; exceptionally high for this class of prime mover.

This new industrial turbine is a derivative of the Makila turboshaft model and some 1,200 units have been built for the Super Puma helicopter manufactured by Aerospatiale. Consequently the reliability of all major components has been proven in several years of service.

In 1988 the Makila T I was introduced as propulsion units on French turbotrains. At the same time

Turbomeca Makila T I industrial gas-turbine rated at 1,200 kW ***1990***

Makila T I was adapted to run on natural gas and dual fuel at 1,200 kW.

Makila T I production rate is at about three per month. Development work continues to increase engine performance.

The Makila T I gas-turbine comprises six main modules:

(1) Auxiliary drive and air intake module
(2) Three axial compressor stages with thick airfoils and fixed stators
(3) The gas generator module housing the centrifugal compressor stage, an annular combustion

chamber for homogeneous temperature distribution and the two uncooled high-pressure turbine stages with inset blades and nozzle guide vanes manufactured from refractory alloys
(4) Rear bearing casing and nozzle guide vanes of power turbine
(5) The power turbine module including the two low-pressure axial turbine stages and an integrated gearbox which reduces the power output speed from 22,000 to 800 rpm as required by the operation
(6) The dedicated electronic computer module, based on a multiprocessor and multilayered flexible card technology, performs start up, control and regulation of the engine parameters. This module includes facilities for in-line auto-test and off-line failure detection and identification.

The Makila T I is intended for generator and mechanical drive applications in land- and marine-based industries.

Main Characteristics
Length overall: 1.8 m
Width overall: 0.7 m
Weight, basic engine: 480 kg (for 6,300 rpm output version)
Power rating, ISO base load: 1,200 kW
Thermal efficiency: 28%
Specific fuel consumption: 300 g/kW h
Compressor pressure ratio: 9.6:1
Exhaust gases flow: 5.5 kg/s
Exhaust gases temperature: 505°C

UPDATED

WÄRTSILÄ SACM DIESEL

Headquarters
1 rue de la Fonderie, BP 1210, F-68054 Mulhouse Cedex, France

Tel: +33 89 66 6868
Telex: 881699 F
Fax: +33 89 66 6830

Marine Department
La Combe, BP 115, F-17700 Surgeres, France

Tel: +33 46 30 3150
Telex: 790 831 F
Fax: +33 46 30 3159

Wärtsilä Sacm Diesel designs, manufactures and markets a range of high-speed diesel engines from 300 to 4,000 kW. The company belongs to the world's largest manufacturer of medium and high-speed engines: the Wärtsilä Diesel Group. Wärtsilä-Diesel engines and related systems are used for marine propulsion and on-board generator sets. The Group has facilities in six European countries, India and the USA, supported by a worldwide network of sales and service companies. The Group employs more than 6,000 people in 60 different countries.

Wärtsilä Sacm Diesel is certified ISO 9001 by the international classification society, Det Norske Veritas.

Technical Characteristics
Compact through high integration of equipment.
Low operating costs:
easy to maintain,
low fuel consumption.
Performance range of engine adapted to particular resistance curves of various hulls.
Optimisation of propulsion line (engine reversing reducing gear-shaft line-propeller) in association with shipyards.
Calling on high-technology superchargers, a wide range of speeds and a large degree of control over mechanical stresses, give these engines an extremely wide performance range.

Type of engine	Swept vol	Bore	Stroke	RPM	kW	BHP	Length	Width	Height	Weight
Wärtsilä UD23										
UD23 12V M5D	2.6 l^3	142 mm	166 mm	1,800	735	1,000	1,975 mm	1,380 mm	1,450 mm	2,650 kg
UD23 12V M4	2.6 l/cyl	142 mm	166 mm	1,860	810	1,100	2,300 mm	1,436 mm	1,550 mm	3,150 kg
UD23 12V M5	2.6 l/cyl	142 mm	166 mm	1,860	970	1,320	2,300 mm	1,436 mm	1,550 mm	3,150 kg
Wärtsilä UD25										
UD25 6L M4	3.2 l/cyl	150 mm	180 mm	1,650	331	450	2,070 mm	1,260 mm	1,845 mm	2,850 kg
UD25 6L M5	3.2 l/cyl	150 mm	180 mm	1,650	368	500	2,070 mm	1,260 mm	1,845 mm	2,850 kg
UD25 12V M4	3.2 l/cyl	150 mm	180 mm	1,650	662	900	2,711 mm	1,624 mm	1,970 mm	4,900 kg
UD25 12V M5	3.2 l/cyl	150 mm	180 mm	1,650	736	1,000	2,711 mm	1,624 mm	1,970 mm	4,900 kg
Wärtsilä UD33										
UD33 12V M6D					1,765	2,400	2,950 mm	1,700 mm	2,280 mm	7,500 kg
UD33 12V M7D					2,020	2,745	2,950 mm	1,700 mm	2,280 mm	7,500 kg
UD33 16V M6D	5.5 l^3	195 mm	180 mm	1,600	2,355	3,200	4,030 mm	1,700 mm	2,280 mm	9,000 kg
UD33 16V M7D					2,690	3,660	4,030 mm	1,700 mm	2,280 mm	9,000 kg
Wärtsilä UD45										
UD45 12V M7D					2,850	3,875	3,800 mm	2,000 mm	2,700 mm	12,100 kg
UD45 16V M7D	10.2 l^3	240 mm	220 mm	1,350	3,800	5,170	4,400 mm	2,000 mm	2,700 mm	19,000 kg
Wärtsilä 200										
12V 200	7.5 l/cyl	200 mm	240 mm	1,500	2,400	3,260	3,640 mm	1,636 mm	2,345 mm	12,600 kg
16V 200	7.5 l/cyl	200 mm	240 mm	1,500	3,200	4,290	4,350 mm	1,636 mm	2,360 mm	16,000 kg
18V 200	7.5 l/cyl	200 mm	240 mm	1,500	3,600	4,890	4,700 mm	1,636 mm	2,360 mm	17,500 kg

Rating at engine PTO fuel stop power according to ISO 3046.1

UPDATED

Wärtsilä 12V UD23 M5, 970 kW engine ***1996***

Wärtsilä 12V 200, 2,400 kW engine ***1996***

GERMANY

DEUTZ MOTOR GmbH

Deutz-Mülheimer-Strasse 147-149, D-51057 Cologne, Germany

Tel: +49 (221) 822 2510
Telex: 88120
Fax: +49 (221) 822 2529

Group companies:
Motoren-Werke Mannheim AG and MWM Diesel und Gastechnik GmbH, Carl-Benz-Strasse 5, D-68140 Mannheim, Germany

UK subsidiary:
KHD Great Britain Ltd, 2 St Martin's Way, London SW17 0UT, UK

Tel: +44 (181) 781 7200
Telex: 8954136 KHDLON G
Fax: +44 (181) 947 6380

KHD Deutz air-cooled engines of the Type 913C and 513 family have been in large-scale production for a number of years. The BF6L 913C engine is a 141 kW engine with high power to weight ratio suitable for smaller hovercraft. For larger craft the 513 series is available as 6-, 8-, 10- and 12-cylinder V types in naturally aspirated, turbocharged and turbocharged/ charge-cooled versions. The 513 engines encompass the power range 64 to 386 kW and can be extended to 441 kW. The latest variation, the BF8L 513LC, a long-stroke cylinder version of the 513 family, meets EURO 1 exhaust emission requirements and has recently also been introduced into hovercraft applications.

Deutz BF12L 513C air-cooled diesel as fitted to BHC and NQEA AP1-88 hovercraft **1986**

Deutz-powered Griffon hovercraft, left to right: two 3000 TD (twin Deutz BF8L 513 diesels), two 2000 TDX (single Deutz BF8L 513 diesel) and one 2000 TD (single Deutz BF6L 913C diesel) **1992**

BF6/8/10/12L 513C

8-, 10- and 12-cylinder versions of this engine are installed in a variety of hovercraft.

Type: Air-cooled four-stroke diesel with direct fuel injection naturally aspirated or turbocharged; BF12L 513C with air-charge cooling system.

Cylinders: Individually removable cylinders made in grey cast-iron alloy, each with one inlet and one exhaust valve and overhead type. The valves are controlled via tappets and pushrods by a camshaft running in three metal bearings in the upper part of the crankcase. The camshaft is crankshaft driven via helical spur gears arranged at the flywheel end of the engine.

Pistons: Each is equipped with two compression rings and one oil control ring and is force oil-cooled.

Cooling system: Air-cooled, mechanically driven axial type cooling air blower with optional load-dependent, electronic control.

Lubrication: Force-fed by gear type pump. Oil is cleaned by full-flow paper filters. A centrifugal filter is installed in the fan hub as a high-efficiency secondary flow filter.

BF12L 513C

Power, max (intermittent duty): 386 kW at 2300 rpm
Number of cylinders: 12
Bore/stroke: 125/130 mm
Capacity: 19.144 l
Compression ratio: 15.8:1
Rotational speed: 2,300 rpm
Mean piston speed: 9.96 m/s
Specific fuel consumption (automotive rating flywheel net at max torque): 205 g/kW h
Shipping volume: 3.16 m^3

Dimensions
Length: 1,582 mm
Height: 1,243 mm
Width: 1,196 mm

User: British Hovercraft Corporation and NQEA Australia AP1-88

BF12L 513CP

This engine is a variant of the turbocharged and intercooled V12 which, by utilising a remotely mounted air-to-air intercooler, raises the intermittent power to 441 kW at 2,300 rpm.

This is used by BHC on its latest well-deck version of the WAP1-88 for lift and propulsion and also by Mitsui-Deutz in Japan for various other hovercraft applications.

RECENT APPLICATIONS

KHD Deutz engines are installed by the following hovercraft manufacturers:

Griffon Hovercraft Ltd	1000 TD/1500 TD/2000 TD	BF6L 913C
	2500 TD	BF6L 913C × 2
	2000 TDX/M	BF8L 513/LC
	3000 TD	BF8L 513 × 2
	4000 TD	BF10L 513 × 2
Slingsby Aviation Ltd	SAH 2200	BF6L 913C or BF8L 513
ABS Hovercraft Ltd	M10	BF12L 513C × 2
Westland Aerospace	WAP1-88	BF12L 513C × 4 or BF12L 513CP × 4

MARIC types 7210 and 716II use the BF6L 913C
Korea Tacoma Marine Industries Ltd and Mitsui-Deutz also use 913 and 513 engines for hovercraft.

BF8/10L 513

Turbocharged 8/10-cylinder engines with similar basic engine data to the BF12L 513C except that the outputs vary as follows:
BF8L 513: 235 kW (intermittent) at 2,300 rpm
211 kW (cruise) at 2,300 rpm
BF10L 513: 294 kW (intermittent) at 2,300 rpm
263 kW (cruise) at 2,300 rpm

BF8L 513LC

Turbocharged, charge-cooled eight-cylinder long stroke engine derived from the 513 engine series but giving increased power with emissions below EURO 1 levels.
Max power: 265 kW at 2,100 rpm
Bore/stroke: 125/140 mm
Capacity: 13.744 l

BF6L 913C

Built to the same specification as the 513, this six-cylinder in-line engine is also available for hovercraft applications. It is fitted with an exhaust turbocharger and charge air-cooler.
Max (intermittent duty) power: 141 kW at 2,500 rpm
Number of cylinders: 6
Bore/stroke: 102/125 mm
Capacity: 6.128 l
Compression ratio: 15.5:1
Rotational speed: 2,500 rpm
Mean piston speed: 10.4 m/s
Specific fuel consumption (automotive rating at max torque): 214 g/kW h
Shipping volume: 0.8 m^3

Dimensions
Length: 1,245 mm
Height: 991 mm
Width: 711 mm
Dry weight: 510 kg

UPDATED

DEUTZ MWM

Motoren-Werke Mannheim AG

Carl-Benz-Strasse 5, D-68140 Mannheim, Germany

Tel: +49 (621) 3840
Telex: 462341 D
Fax: +49 (621) 384328

Group companies:
Klöckner-Humboldt-Deutz AG, Deutz-Mülheimer-Strasse 147, D-51005 Cologne, Germany

UK subsidiary:
KHD Great Britain Ltd, 2 St Martin's Way, London SW17 0UT, UK

Tel: +44 (181) 781 7200
Telex: 8954136 KHDLON G
Fax: +44 (181) 947 6380

Since 1985 when Motoren-Werke Mannheim AG was taken over by Klöckner-Humboldt-Deutz AG, the company has offered a combined range of medium sized and large water-cooled engines from 100 to 7,250 kW. The principal engine ranges suitable for high-speed surface craft and hovercraft are in the table below.

Deutz MWM 616 V16 diesel engine **1994**

DEUTZ MWM TBD 616

In Spring 1993, the Deutz MWM division of the KHD Group announced the high-speed 616 engine series. It was established from the predecessor 234 series that the displacement for the engines could be enlarged by 22 per cent if the bore was enlarged from 128 to 132 mm and the stroke extended from 140 to 160 mm. It was necessary to introduce four-valve technology with a central injector arrangement in order to realise the potential for minimising exhaust emissions while maintaining a high degree of efficiency. The 616 series covers turbocharged, charge air-cooled diesel engines with 8, 12 and 16 cylinders.

DEUTZ MWM TBD 604B

The series 604B engine type is a compact high-speed diesel engine giving excellent power to weight ratios and a very favourable fuel consumption of only 190 g/kW h. The engine is four-stroke, turbocharged and intercooled, this gives a power spread of 420 kW (563 bhp) at 1,000 rpm up to 2,240 kW (3,046 bhp) at 1,860 rpm. The engine is available with an in-line six-cylinder, together with 90° V 8-, 12- and 16-cylinder variants. It is fitted with the HALLO swirl system, allowing optimum combustion even under idling and other low load conditions. This engine has been widely used for the main propulsion of high-speed ferries and patrol craft.

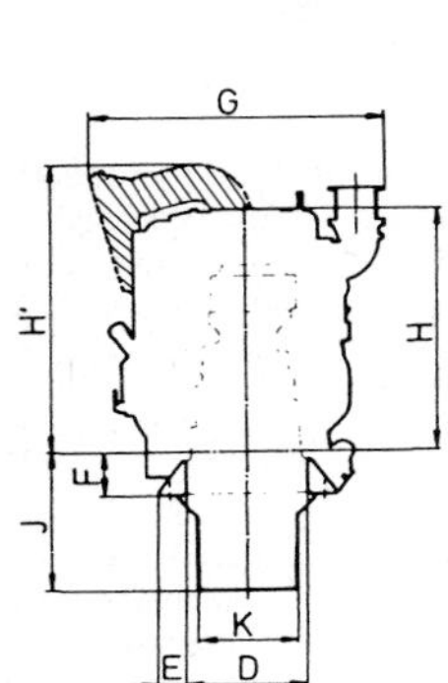

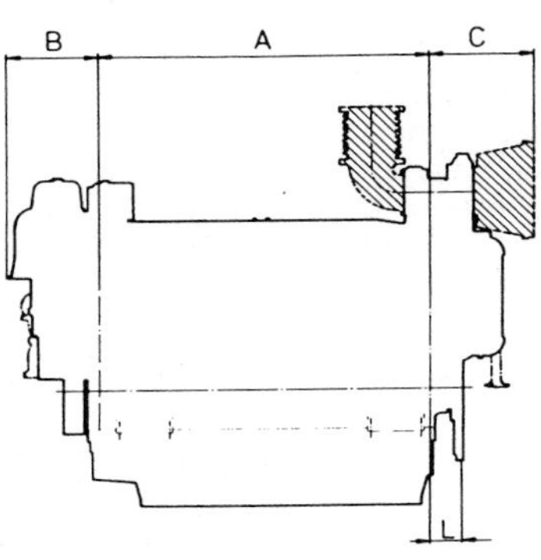

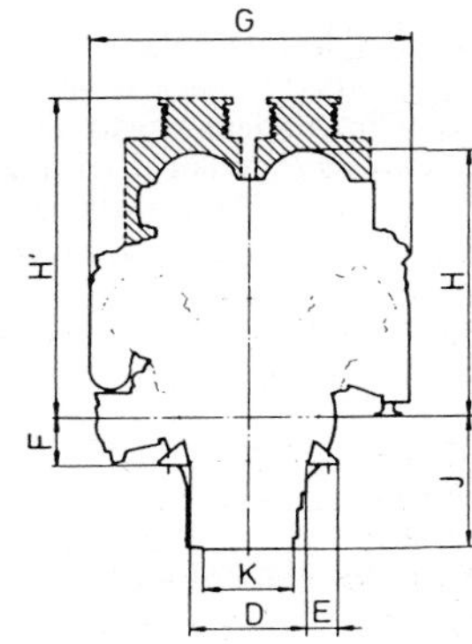

Deutz MWM TBD 604B and 620 series weights and dimensions **1993**

DEUTZ MWM series 616, 604B and 620

TYPE	kW	kg	Air intake temperature
TBD 616 V8	480	1,720	25°C
TBD 616 V12	720	2,100	25°C
TBD 616 V16	960	2,600	25°C
TBD 604B L6	640	2,115	45°C
TBD 620 V8	1,016	3,000	25°C
TBD 620 V12	1,524	4,075	25°C
TBD 620 V16	2,032	5,495	25°C

MODEL SUMMARY

Type	Number of cylinders and configuration	Power according to DIN 6271 and ISO 3046/1 Continuous net brake fuel stop power kW	Marine propulsion rpm	Length mm	Weight kg
TBD 616 V8	V8	480	2,100	1,720	1,720
TBD 616 V12	V12	720	2,100	2,100	2,100
TBD 616 V16	V16	960	2,100	2,550	2,600
TBD 604B L6	L6	640	1,800	2,194	2,115
TBD 620 V8	V8	1,016	1,800	1,913	3,000
TBD 620 V12	V12	1,524	1,800	2,629	4,075
TBD 620 V16	V16	2,032	1,800	3,129	5,495
TBD 440-6 K	L6	900	1,000	3,065	7,500
TBD 440-8 K	L8	1,200	1,000	3,675	9,000
BV 6 M 628	L6	1,350	1,000	3,537	9,500
BV 8 M 628	L8	1,800	1,000	4,233	11,500
BV 9 M 628	L9	2,025	1,000	4,544	13,400
BV 12 M 626	V12	2,700	1,000	4,343	16,300
BV 16 M 628	V16	3,600	1,000	5,126	21,200
TBD 645 L6	L6	2,550	600	5,195	25,500
TBD 645 L8	L8	3,400	600	6,235	32,500
TBD 645 L9	L9	3,825	600	7,111	37,000
BV 6 M 640	L6	2,650	650	6,348	29,000
BV 8 M 640	L8	3,530	650	7,664	37,000
BV 12 M 640	V12	5,290	650	6,641	48,000
BV 16 M 640	V16	7,060	650	7,983	60,000

DEUTZ MWM TBD 620

For the main propulsion of high-speed craft, Deutz MWM has provided cylinder powers up to 140 kW for the 620 series. There are powers from 880 to 2,240 kW (IOFN) available at speeds up to 1,860 rpm for application in yachts, catamarans, SESs and similar fast craft.

The maximum power corresponds to a net brake fuel stop power as per DIN 6271 and ISO 3046/1. It is limited to 0.5 hours within a period of six hours. The maximum continuous power (ICFN) is now 127 kW per cylinder which means a power coverage by the series from 1016 to 2,032 kW.

Specific fuel consumption of the 620 engines is as low as 195 g/kW h, related to the ICFN output and only 192 g/kW h at the optimal point of about 85 per cent output.

Considerable modifications were made to the exhaust system. Instead of the pulse charging system using several exhaust manifold pipes, Deutz MWM applied the pearl (pulse energy recovery line) exhaust system to the 620 series. In stationary duty it provides for fuel savings up to 3 g/kW h over the complete load range in comparison with conventional exhaust systems. For main propulsion and auxiliary drive, the range of the 620 series engines includes the 90° V configuration, available as 8-, 12- and 16-cylinder models. The compression ratio of the direct injection engines is 13.5.

Deutz MWM TBD 604B V12 diesel engine ***1987***

DEUTZ MWM 645

Deutz MWM presented, at Europort '91 in Amsterdam, the medium-speed diesel engines of the 645 series as an addition to its engine range in the upper power class. They are long-stroke in-line models, initially with six and eight cylinders covering a power spectrum of 2,500 to 3,740 kW and operating at a rated speed of 600 rpm. A nine-cylinder version is also planned for the near future. With an increased speed and a higher brake mean effective pressure an output of 500 kW/cylinder will be obtained at a speed of 650 rpm, thus extending the power spectrum of the series up to 4,500 kW. The engines are mainly used as marine main and auxiliary drives and prime movers for power generating and pump sets. A preproduction series became available in 1992.

VERIFIED

MAN

MAN Nutzfahrzeuge AG

Nüremberg Works, PO Box 44 01 00, D-90206 Nüremberg, Germany

Tel: +49 (911) 420 6218
Telex: 622914-0 MN D
Fax: +49 (911) 437455

MAN Marine diesels are in widespread use and have been supplied to the following shipyards: Anne Wever; BAIA; Camuffo; Canados; Eder/Knoche; Ladenstein; San Lorenzo; Lowland; Marchi; Mochi Craft; Neptunus; Posillipo; Riva; Sunseeker; Tecnomarine; Marine Projects; Gestione; Best Yachts; Rizzardi; Storeboo; Oskarshamns; Lux-Shipyard; Seggendorf Shipyard; Viking; Vosper Thornycroft; Hatteras; Bertram; Dalla Pieta; Golfo; Piantoni; Cantieri della Pasquaz; Engitalia; Fairline; Henriques and Guy Couach.

MAN marine diesel engines are blocked for different marine applications, rating 1, rating 2 and rating 3. Please see the table for rating definitions.

Model Summary

Model	No of cylinders/ configuration in mm	Bore/ stroke in litres	Displacement in kg	Dry weight in kg	Speed rpm	Heavy duty rating		Medium duty rating		Light duty rating	
						kW	ps/hp	kW	ps/hp	kW	ps/hp
D 0226 ME	6	102/116	5.69	520	2,400	79	107	83	113	-	-
					2,800	87	118	95	130	-	-
					3,000	-	-	-	-	100	136
D 0226 MTE(T)	6	102/116	5.69	530	2,600	110	150	121	170	-	-
					2,800	-	-	125	-	135	184
D 0226 MLE(L)	6	102/116	5.69	545	2,600	125	170	125	170	-	-
					2,800	-	-	147	200	154	210
D 0826 LE(L)	6	108/120	6.60	640	2,600	-	-	-	-	199	270
					1,500	125	170	132	180	-	-
					1,800	151	205	162	220	-	-
D 2866 E	6	128/155	11.97	985	2,100	165	224	178	242	-	-
					2,200	-	-	-	-	185	252
					1,800	190	258	206	280	-	-
D 2866 TE(T)	6	128/155	11.97	1,000	2,100	-	-	227	300	-	-
					2,200	-	-	-	-	235	320
					1,800	246	326	-	-	-	-
D 2866 LE(L)	6	128/155	11.97	1,035	2,100	-	-	260	354	-	-
					2,200	-	-	280	380	300	408
D 2866 LXE(LX)	6	128/155	11.97	1,045	2,200	-	-	-	-	324	440
					1,800	280	380	294	400	-	-
D 2848 LE(L)	V8	128/142	14.62	1,210	2,100	-	-	331	450	-	-
					2,300	-	-	347	472	375	510
					1,800	346	470	365	496	-	-
D 2840 LE(L)	V10	128/142	18.27	1,350	2,100	-	-	412	560	-	-
					2,300	-	-	433	590	467	635
D 2848 LXE(LX)	V8	128/142	14.62	1,200	2,100	-	-	370	500	-	-
					2,300	-	-	-	-	500	680
					1,800	420	571	441	600	-	-
D 2842 LE(L)	V12	128/142	21.93	1,550	2,100	-	-	496	675	-	-
					2,300	-	-	520	707	559	760
D 2840 LE401	V10	128/142	18.27	1,370	2,100	-	-	478	650	-	-
					2,300	-	-	-	-	603	820
D 2842 LE401	V12	128/142	21.93	1,580	2,100	-	-	-	800	735	1,000
D 2842 LE402	V12	128/142	21.93	1,600	2,300	-	-	-	-	809	1,100

T = Turbocharged model
L = Turbocharged and intercooled model

D 0826L

Type: Four-stroke diesel engine, six-cylinder vertical in-line water-cooled with turbocharger and intercooler. Direct injection system. High unit output, low noise level and quiet running with low fuel consumption. Long service life and low upkeep and all parts to be serviced are readily accessible.

Crankcase: One-piece crankcase and cylinder block. Replaceable dry cylinder liners. Seven bearing crankshaft with forged on balance weights. Induction-hardened main bearing and connecting rod bearing journals, additional hardening of journal radii. Main and connecting rod bearing journals in ready-to-install three-component bearing. Torsional vibration damper fitted at front of six-cylinder engines. Die-forged, straight split connecting rods, which are removable through top of cylinder. Three-ring pistons of special aluminium alloy with ring carrier for the top piston ring. Piston crown cooled by lubricating oil jet.

Cylinder heads and valve train: Cross-flow cylinder head for each pair of cylinders with cast swirl inlet and exhaust channels on opposite sides. Shrunk-fit inlet and outlet valve seat inserts and replaceable pressed-in valve guides. One inlet and outlet valve per cylinder arranged in overhead position. Forged camshaft with induction-hardened cams and bearing supports.

Lubrication: Force-fed lubrication with gear oil pump for crankshaft, connecting rod and camshaft bearings as well as valve train and turbocharger. Oil filter/oil cooler combination with coolant-covered, flat-tube oil cooler. Lubricant cleaned in full flow by

easy maintenance screw-on filters with fine disposable filter cartridge of paper.
Fuel system: Bosch injectors. Bosch-MW in-line injection pump. Mechanical engine speed governor and timing device. Switch-off via separate stop lever and solenoid. Fuel pre-supply pump, fuel filter with easy maintenance screw-on disposable cartridges.
Intake and exhaust system: Wet air filter, water-cooled manifold cooled by engine water.
Supercharging: Exhaust gas turbocharger, water-cooled by engine water, seawater-cooled intercooler.
Electrical system: Two-pole starter, 4 kW, 24 V and two-pole alternator 28 V, 35 A.
Applications: Workboats, customs and police patrol boats, yachts.
Technical Data for 108 mm bore
Bore/stroke: 108/120 mm
Swept volume: 6.6 l
Compression ratio: 17:1
Rotation looking on flywheel: anti-clockwise
Flywheel housing: SAE 2
Weight of engine dry, with cooling system: 640 kg
Max rating 3: 199 kW at 2,600 rpm
Mean effective pressure: 13.9 bar at 2,600 rpm
Torque: 860 n miles at 1,700 rpm.
Starter motor: Bosch solenoid-operated starter Type KB, 24 V, 5.4 kW.
Technical Data for 128 mm bore
Bore/stroke: 128/155 mm
Swept volume: 11.97 l
Compression ratio: 15.5:1
Max rating 3: 324 kW at 2,200 rpm.
Mean effective pressure: 14.8 bar at 2,200 rpm
Torque: 1,406 n miles at 2,200 rpm
Fuel consumption (+5% tolerance) at max rating 3: 215 g/kW h at 2,200 rpm.

D 2848 LX

Type: Four-stroke, direct injection.
Cylinders: Eight-cylinder, V-form, wet replaceable cylinder liners.
Aspiration: Turbocharged, intercooled.
Cooling: Water circulation by centrifugal pump fitted on engine.
Lubrication: Force-fed lubrication by gear pump, lubrication oil cooler in cooling water circuit of engine.
Injection: Bosch in-line pump with mechanical Bosch speed governor fitted.
Generator: Bosch three-phase generator with rectifier and transistorised governor Type K1, 28 V, 35 A.
Starter motor: Bosch solenoid-operated starter, Type KB, 24 V, 6.5 kW.
Technical Data
Bore/stroke: 128/142 mm
Volume: 14.62 l
Compression ratio: 13.5:1
Max rating 3: 500 kW at 2,300 rpm
Mean effective pressure: 17.8 bar at 2,300 rpm
Torque: 2,290 n miles at 1,700 rpm
Fuel consumption (+5% tolerance): 214 g/kW h at 2,300 rpm.

D 2840 HLE401

(Supersedes D 2840 LXE)
Type: Four-stroke marine diesel engine, 10-cylinder, V-form, water-cooled with turbocharger and intercooler. Direct injection system.
Crankcase: Grey cast-iron cylinder block, six-bearing crankshaft with screwed-on balance weights, three-layer type bearings, die-forged connecting rods. Replaceable wet-type cylinder liners.
Cylinder heads and valve train: Individual cylinder heads of grey cast-iron, overhead valves, one intake and one exhaust valve per cylinder, valve actuation via tappets, pushrods and rocker arms. Six-bearing camshaft, shrunk-fit valve seat inserts.
Lubrication: Force-fed lubrication by gear pump, oil-to-water oil cooler, full-flow oil filter, changeover type optional.
Fuel system: Bosch in-line injection pump with mechanical speed governor, fuel supply pump, fuel filter, changeover type optional.
Intake and exhaust system: Viscous air filter, water-cooled exhaust manifold connected in engine cooling circuit.
Supercharging: Turbochargers, water-cooled in freshwater circuit, seawater-cooled intercooler Waste Gate System.
Electrical system: Two-pole starter, 6.5 kW, 24 V, two-pole alternator 28 V, 120 A, additional alternator 28 V available with 35 A, 55 A or 120 A on request.
Applications: Yachts, customs and police patrol boats.
Technical Data
Bore/stroke: 128/142 mm
Swept volume: 18.271 l
Compression ratio: 13.5:1
Rotation looking on flywheel: anti-clockwise
Weight of engine, dry with cooling system: 1,380 kg
Speed: 2,300 rpm
Max rating 3: 603 kW/820 hp
Mean effective pressure: 17.2 bar
Fuel consumption: 215 g/kW h

D 2866 LX

Type: Four-stroke, direct injection.
Cylinders: Six-cylinder in-line, wet replaceable cylinder liners.
Aspiration: Turbocharged intercooled.
Cooling: Water circulation by centrifugal pump fitted on engine.

MAN Model D 2840 LE401 marine diesel **1988**

MAN Model D 2842 HLE402 marine diesel **1991**

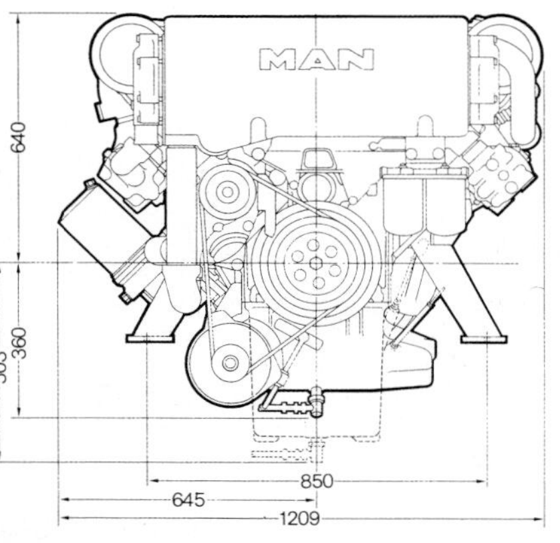

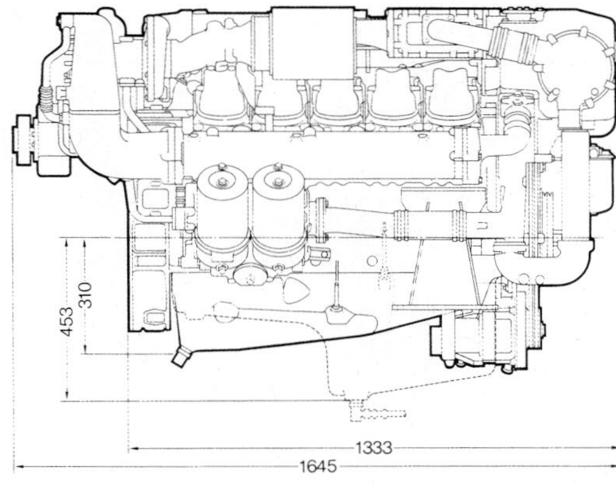

MAN Model D 2842 LZE, dimensions (mm) **1989**

Lubrication: Force-fed lubrication by gear pump, lubrication oil cooler in cooling water circuit of engine.
Generator: Bosch three-phase generator with rectifier and transistorised governor type K1, 28 V, 35 A.
Mean specific fuel consumption (+5%): 215 g/kW h.

D 2842 HLE402

(Supersedes D 2842 HLZE)
Type: Four-stroke marine diesel engine, 12-cylinder, V-form, water-cooled with turbocharger and intercooler. Direct injection system.
Crankcase: Cylinder block of grey cast-iron. Replaceable wet-type cylinder liners. Seven-bearing crankshaft with screwed-on balance weights, three-layer type bearings, die-forged connecting rods.
Cylinder heads and valve train: Individual cylinder heads of grey cast-iron, overhead valves, one intake and one exhaust valve per cylinder, valve actuation via tappets, pushrods and rocker arms. Seven-bearing camshaft, shrunk-fit valve seat inserts.
Lubrication: Force-fed lubrication by gear pump, oil-to-water oil cooler, full flow oil filter, changeover type optional.
Fuel system: Bosch in-line injection pump with mechanical speed governor, fuel supply pump, fuel filter, changeover type optional.
Intake and exhaust system: Viscous air filter, water-cooled exhaust manifold connected in engine cooling circuit.
Supercharging: Turbochargers, water-cooled in freshwater circuit, seawater-cooled intercooler Waste Gate System.
Electrical system: Two-pole starter, 6.5 kW, 24 V, two-pole alternator 28 V, 120 A, additional alternator 28 V with 35 A, 55 A or 120 A on request.
Applications: Yachts, customs and police boats.
Technical Data
Bore/stroke: 128/142 mm
Volume: 21.931 l
Compression ratio: 13.5:1
Rotation looking on flywheel: anti-clockwise
Weight of engine, dry with cooling system: approx 1,600 kg
Speed: 2,300 rpm
Max rating 3: 809 kW at 2,300 rpm
Mean effective pressure: 19.2 bar
Torque: 3,820 n miles at 1,700 rpm
Mean specific fuel consumption (+5%): 217 g/kW h

UPDATED

MTU

Motoren- und Turbinen-Union Friedrichshafen GmbH

D-88040 Friedrichshafen, Germany

Tel: +49 (7541) 900
Telex: 734280-0 mtd
Fax: +49 (7541) 905000

MTU Friedrichshafen, previously part of Deutsche Aerospace, became the Diesel Propulsion Systems division of AEG Daimler-Benz Industrie on July 1st 1994.

MTU offers diesel engines with outputs ranging from 35 to 7,400 kW (50 to 10,000 HP for marine applications, heavy vehicles, power generation installations and rail vehicles. The lower end of the power range (35 to 846 kW/50 to 1,150 HP) is covered by Mercedes-Benz industrial diesel engines for which MTU took over sales and distribution responsibility in 1987. It also supplies electronic governing, monitoring and control systems as well as

MTU diesel engines for catamaran, hydrofoil and Surface Effect Ships (SES) propulsion and similar

Engine model		Engine speed rpm	Fuel stop power kW	hp (metric)	Engine dry weight kg
6R 183 TE 72	(OM 447LA)*	1,900	305	415	1,185
8V 183 TE 72	(OM 442LA)*	2,100	405	551	1,420
12V 183 TE 72	(OM 444LA)*	2,100	610	830	1,690
8V 396 TE 74		1,900	840	1,142	2,890
12V 396 TE 74		1,900	1,260	1,714	3,900
16V 396 TE 74		1,900	1,680	2,285	5,000
8V 396 TE 74L		1,900	1,000	1,360	2,890
12V 396 TE 74L		1,900	1,500	2,040	3,900
16V 396 TE 74L		1,900	2,000	2,720	5,000
12V 595 TE 70		1,700	2,700	3,672	9,070
16V 595 TE 70		1,700	3,600	4,896	11,360
12V 595 TE 70L		1,750	2,945	4,005	9,070
16V 595 TE 70L		1,750	3,925	5,338	11,360
16V 1163 TB 73		1,200	4,800	6,528	17,550
20V 1163 TB 73		1,200	6,000	8,610	20,650
16V 1163 TB 73L		1,250	5,200	7,072	17,550
20V 1163 TB 73L		1,250	6,500	8,840	21,050

* original Mercedes-Benz designation on which types the corresponding MTU engines are based

MTU 16V 396 TE 74L **1990**

Main dimensions (mm) for series 183 engine family

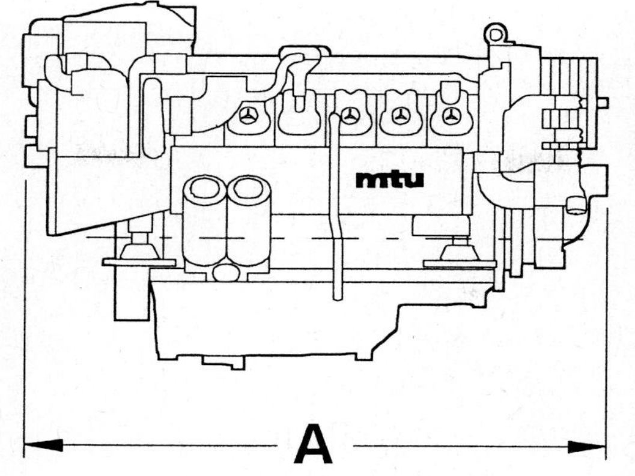

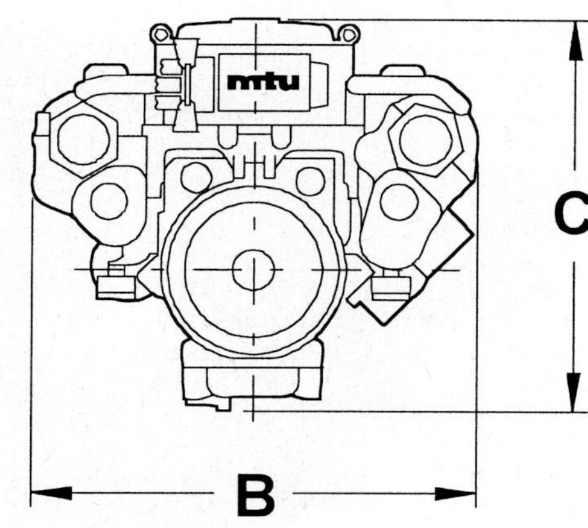

Engine model		A	B	C
6R 183 TE 72	(OM 447LA)*	1,680	885	1,175
8V 183 TE 72	(OM 442LA)*	1,530	1,315	1,245
12V 183 TE 72	(OM 444LA)*	1,845	1,315	1,260

*original Mercedes-Benz designation on which types the corresponding MTU engines are based.

1996

Main dimensions (mm) for series 396 engine family

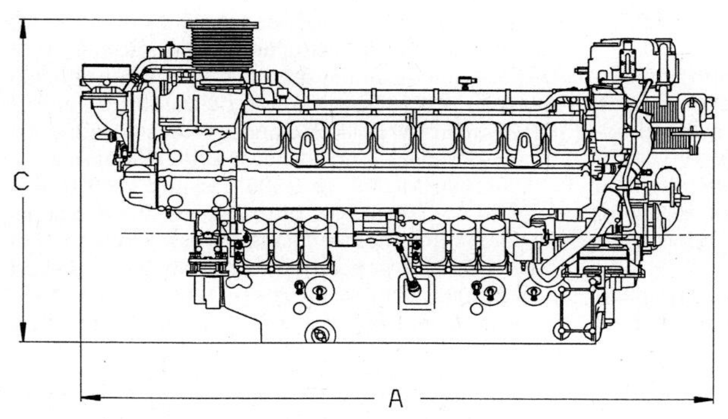

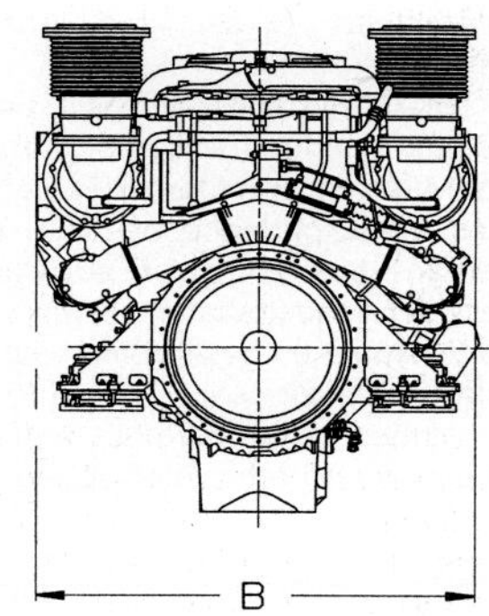

Engine model	A	B	C
8V 396 TE 74	2,300	1,540	1,520
8V 396 TE 74L	2,330	1,540	1,520
12V 396 TE 74	2,830	1,540	1,600
12V 396 TE 74L	2,870	1,540	1,600
16V 396 TE 74	3,350	1,540	1,650
16V 396 TE 74L	3,430	1,540	1,750

1996

Main dimensions (mm) for series 595 engine family

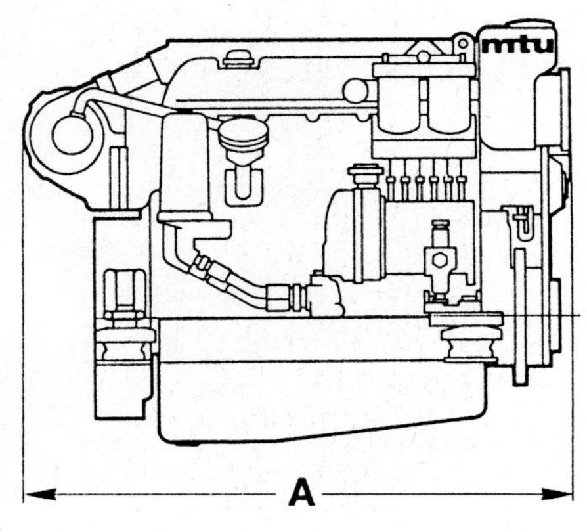

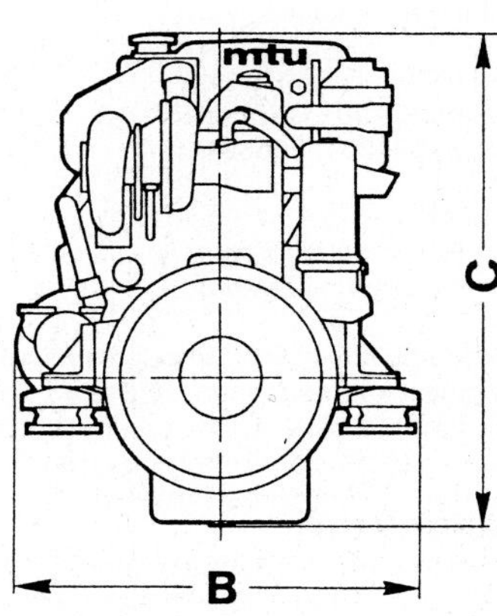

Engine model	A	B	C
12V 595 TE 70	3,390	1,500	2,570
16V 595 TE 70	3,980	1,500	2,600
12V 595 TE 70L	3,390	1,500	2,570
16V 595 TE 70L	3,980	1,500	2,600

1996

Main dimensions (mm) for series 1163 engine family

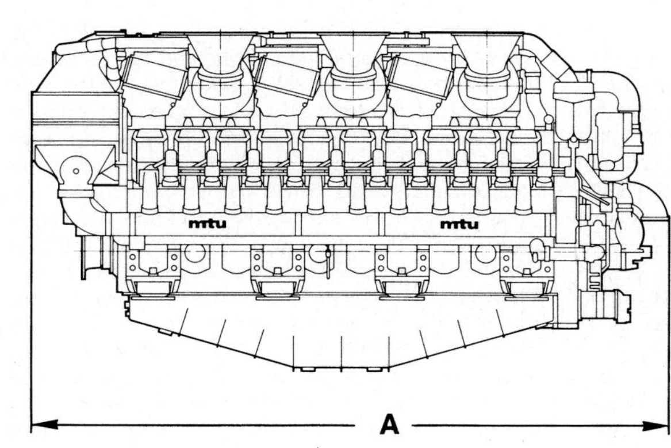

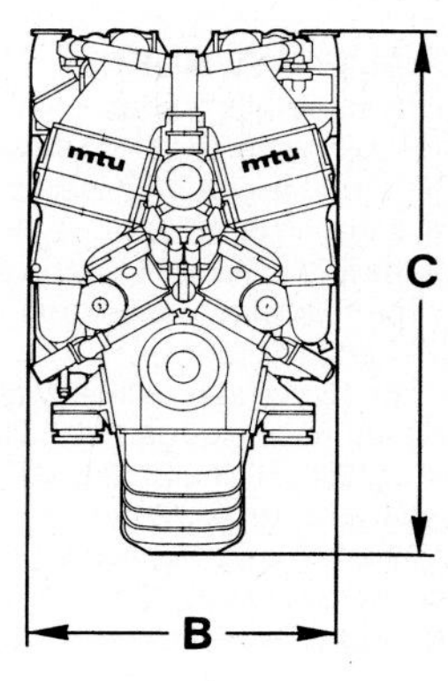

Engine model	A	B	C
16V 1163 TB 73	4,515	1,660	2,850
20V 1163 TB 73	5,415	1,660	2,940
16V 1163 TB 73L	4,515	1,660	2,850
20V 1163 TB 73L	5,415	1,660	2,940

1996

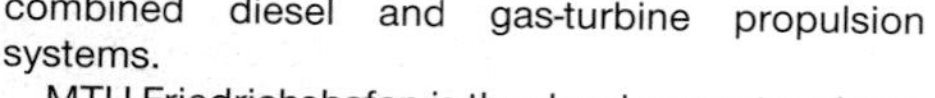

MTU 12V 183 TE 93 **1996**

MTU 20V 1163 TB74L **1996**

combined diesel and gas-turbine propulsion systems.

MTU Friedrichshafen is the development and production centre for high performance diesel engines of Maybach and Mercedes-Benz origin, and embodies the experience of these companies in diesel engine technology. In addition to diesel engines, MTU Friedrichshafen is responsible for industrial and marine gas-turbine sales and application engineering.

In the field of hydrofoils, surface-effect ships, catamarans and other high-speed craft, MTU can draw from decades of experience with nearly 2,000 engines having been supplied for the propulsion of hydrofoils and catamarans starting as early as 1955 when an MB 820 engine was delivered for the first PT 20 hydrofoil built by Cantiere Navale Rodriquez (now Rodriquez Cantieri Navali SpA) in Messina.

Currently the 099, 183, 396, 595 and 1163 engine families are offered for propulsion of these special types of craft. These engines cover a wide range of power. In the accompanying table the standard power outputs are listed; these, however, may have to be adjusted depending on the application, the power demand and the operating profile. The outputs are based on DIN/ISO 3046. By 1996, MTU has supplied over 40 units of the 20V 1163 engine for use in large fast ro-ro ferries and numerous smaller units for passenger ferries.

In addition to the delivery of the propulsion engine, MTU can lay out, design and deliver complete propulsion packages including the interface engineering and the technical assistance during installation and the start up phase.

UPDATED

ITALY

CRM MOTORI MARINI SpA

Head Office and Works: I-21053 Castellanza, Via Marnate 41, Italy

Tel: +39 (331) 501548
Telex: 334382 CREMME I
Fax: +39 (331) 505501

L Mariani, *Director*
Ing B Piccoletti, *Director*
Ing G Venturini, *Director*

CRM has specialised in building lightweight diesel engines for more than 40 years. The company's engines are used in large numbers of motor torpedo boats, coastal patrol craft and privately owned motor yachts. The engines have also been installed in hydrofoils (*Tehi*).

The range of engines comprises the 12-cylinder 12 D/S and 12 D/SS and the 18-cylinder 18 D/SS, BR-1 and BR-2. All are turbocharged with different supercharging ratios. The 12 cylinders are arranged in two banks of six and the 18 cylinders are set out in an unusual 'W' arrangement of three banks of six.

All engines are available in non-magnetic versions; the perturbation field is reduced to insignificant amounts when compensated with the anti-dipole method.

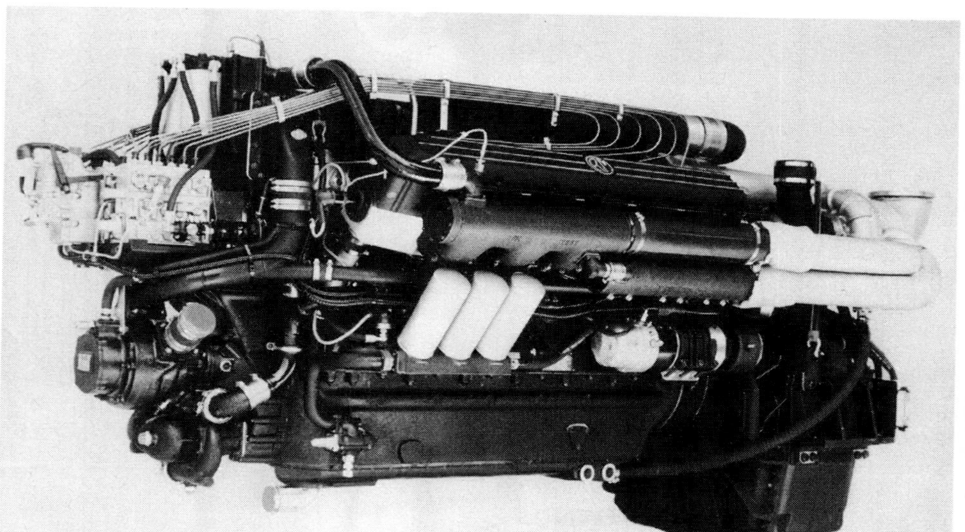

CRM 18 D/SS, BR-2 **1994**

CRM 18-CYLINDER

First in CRM's series of low weight, high-speed diesel engines, the CRM 18-cylinder is arranged in a 'W' form. Maximum power is 1,213 kW at 2,075 rpm for the 18 D/SS, 1,335 kW at 2,075 rpm for the BR-1 and 1,544 kW at 2,120 rpm for the BR-2.

The following description relates to the 18D/SS, BR-1 and BR-2:

Type: 18-cylinder in-line W-type, four-stroke, water-cooled, turbocharged with different supercharging ratios: 2.4 (18 D/SS); 2.6 (BR-1) and 3 (BR-2).

Cylinders: Bore 150 mm (5.91 in). Stroke 180 mm (7.09 in). Swept volume 3.18 l/cylinder. Total swept volume 57.3 litres. Compression ratio 14:1. Separate pressed-steel cylinder frame side members are surrounded by gas-welded sheet metal water-cooling, jacket-treated and pressure-coated internally to prevent corrosion. Lower half of cylinder is ringed by a drilled flange for bolting to crankcase. Cylinder top also houses a spherical-shaped pre-combustion chamber as well as inlet and exhaust valve seats. The precombustion chamber is in high strength, heat- and corrosion-resistant steel. A single cast light alloy head, carrying valve guides, precombustion chambers and camshaft bearings bridges each bank of cylinders. The cylinder head is attached to cylinder bank by multiple studs.

Pistons: Light alloy forgings with three rings, the top ring being chrome-plated and bottom ring acting as oil scraper. Piston crowns (hard anodised top) shaped to withstand high temperatures especially in vicinity of precombustion chamber outlet ports.

Connecting rods: Comprise main and secondary articulated rods, all being completely machined I-section steel forgings. Big end of each main rod is bolted to ribbed cap by six studs. Big end bearings are white metal lined steel shells. Each secondary rod anchored at its lower end to a pivot pin inserted in two lugs protruding from big end of main connecting rod. Both ends of all secondary rods and small ends of main rods have bronze bushes.

Crankshafts: One-piece hollow shaft in nitrided alloy steel, with six throws equally spaced at 120°. Seven main bearings with white metal lined steel shells. There are 12 balancing counterweights.

Crankcase: Cast light alloy crankcase bolted to bed plate by studs and tie bolts. Multiple integral reinforced ribs provide robust structure. Both sides of each casting braced by seven cross ribs incorporating crankshaft bearing supports. Protruding sides of crankcase ribbed throughout length.

	18 D/SS	BR-1	BR-2	12 D/S	12 D/SS
Dimensions					
Length	2,305 mm	2,305 mm	2,305 mm	1,909 mm	2,147 mm
Width	1,400 mm	1,400 mm	1,400 mm	1,210 mm	1,210 mm
Height	1,303 mm	1,303 mm	1,303 mm	1,204 mm	1,310 mm
Reverse gear	621 mm	621 mm	621 mm	621 mm	621 mm
Weights, dry					
Engine	1,950 kg	1,950 kg	1,950 kg	1,380 kg	1,560 kg
Reverse gear	340 kg	340 kg	750 kg	340 kg	340 kg
Reduction gear	150-300 kg	150-300 kg	–	150-300 kg	150-300 kg
Ratings					
Max power	1,213 kW (1,650 hp) at 2,075 rpm	1,335 kW (1,815 hp) at 2,075 rpm	1,544 kW (2,100 hp) at 2,120 rpm	687 kW at 2,075 rpm	1,010 kW at 2,075 rpm
Continuous rating	1,103 kW (1,500 hp) at 2,020 rpm	1,213 kW (1,650 hp) at 2,020 rpm	1,403 kW (1,910 hp) at 2,050 rpm	625 kW at 2,010 rpm	918 kW at 2,020 rpm
Specific fuel consumption	0.224 ±5% kg/kW h	0.230 ±5% kg/kW h	0.240 ±5% kg/kW h	0.227 ±5% kg/kW h	0.238 ±5% kg/kW h
Specific oil consumption	0.002 ±5% kg/kW h	0.002 ±5% kg/kW h	0.002 ±5% kg/kW h	0.002 kg/kW h	0.002 kg/kW h

Valve gear: Hollow sodium-cooled valves of each bank of cylinders actuated by twin camshafts and six cams on each shaft. Two inlet and two outlet valves per cylinder and one rocker for each valve. End of stem and facing of exhaust valves fitted with Stellite inserts. Valve cooling water forced through passage formed by specially shaped plate welded to top of cylinder.
Fuel injection: Pumps fitted with variable speed control and pilot injection nozzle.
Pressure charger: Two turbochargers, Brown Boveri type, on the 18 D/SS and BR-1; three turbochargers, KKK type, on the BR-2.
Accessories: Standard accessories include oil and freshwater heat exchangers with thermostats mounted on the engine; oil filters, air filters and freshwater tank with preheating system; engine room instruments panel with warning system and exhaust gas temperatures indicator; wheel room instruments panel; prelubrication electric pump; saltwater and fuel hand pumps and expansion joints for exhaust piping separate from the engine.
Cooling system: Freshwater.
Fuel: Fuel oil having specific gravity of 0.83 to 0.84.
Lubrication: Dry sump type with circulating and scavenge oil pumps.
Oil: Mineral oil to SAE 40 HD, MIL-L-2104D.
Oil cooling: Saltwater circulating through heat exchanger.
Starting: 24 V 15 kW electric motor and 85 A, 24 V alternator for battery charge, or compressed air.
Mounting: At any transverse or longitudinal angle tilt to 20°.

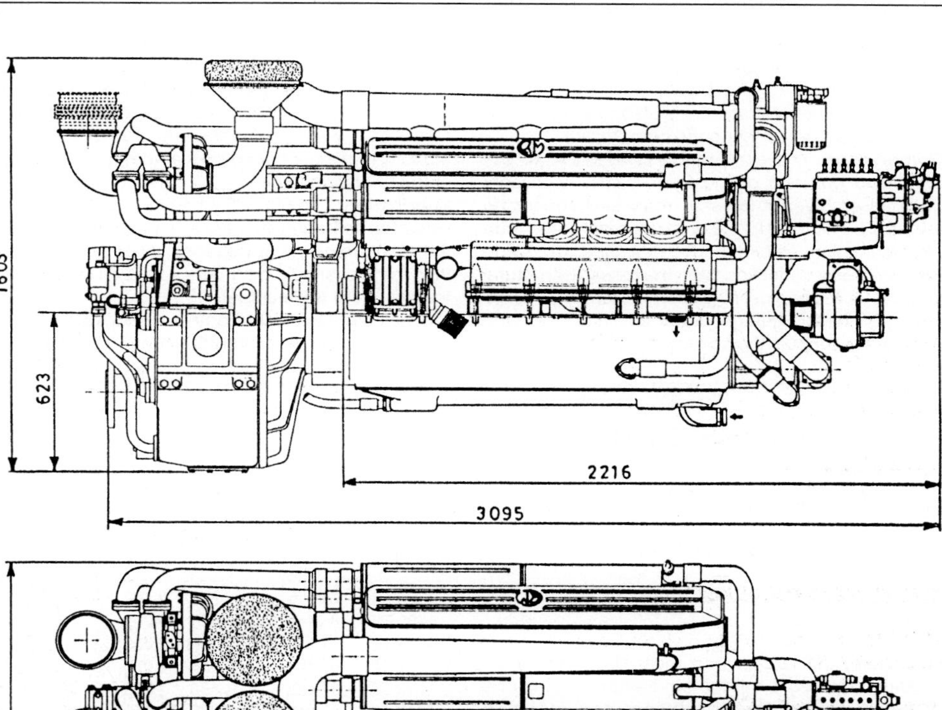

CRM 12-CYLINDER

Second in the CRM series of low-weight diesels, the CRM 12-cylinder is a unit with two blocks of six cylinders set at 60° to form a V assembly. The bore and stroke are the same as in the CRM 18 series and many of the components are interchangeable including the crankshaft, bedplate, cylinders and pistons. The crankcase and connecting rod assemblies are of a modified design; the secondary rod is anchored at its lower end to a pivot pin inserted on two lugs protruding from the big end of the main connecting rod. The fuel injection pump is modified to single block housing all 12 pumping elements located between the cylinder banks.
Type: 12-cylinder V-type, four-stroke, water-cooled, turbo-supercharged with medium supercharging ratio (2.15 for 12 D/S) and light supercharging ratio (2.85 for 12 D/SS).
Pressure charger: Two KKK type.

UPDATED

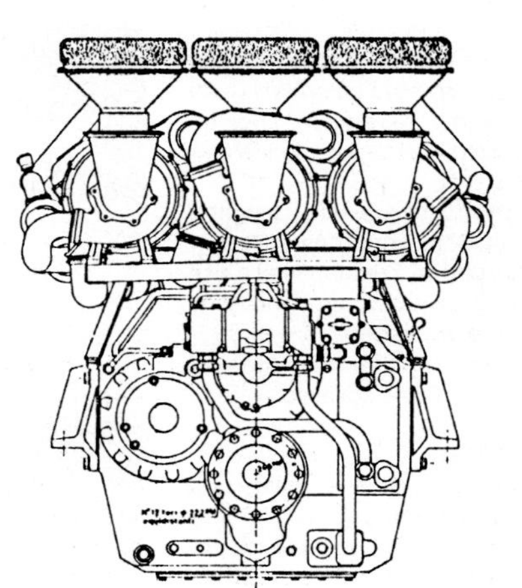

CRM 18 D/SS, BR-2
1996

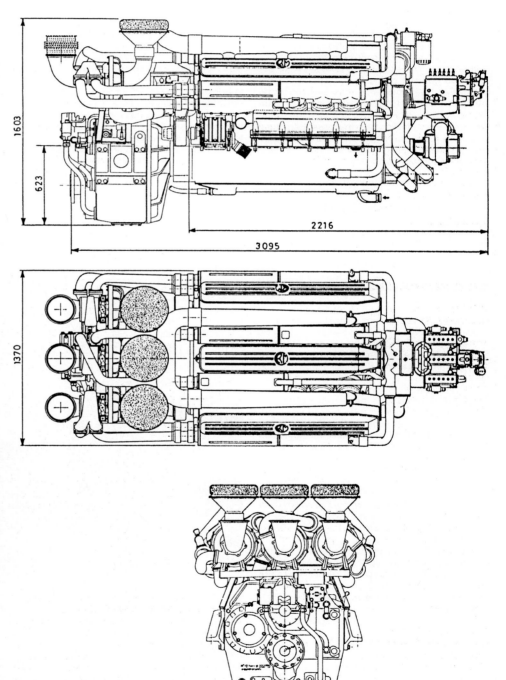

FIAT AVIAZIONE SpA

Marine and Industrial Products Department, Via Nizza 312, PO Box 1389, I-10127 Turin, Italy

Tel: +39 (11) 330 2543
Telex: 221320 FIATAV I

The LM 500 gas-turbine is a compact high-performance marine and industrial power unit in the 3,000 to 6,000 shaft horsepower class. General Electric's Marine and Industrial Engine Division and Fiat Aviazione SpA, in a co-operative undertaking, initiated the design programme in July 1978. In January 1980 the first engine began full load testing and the LM 500 went into production.

General Electric Company and Fiat Aviazione SpA have designed the LM 500 gas-turbine to produce power for marine applications requiring significant fuel economy, compactness, light weight, minimum maintenance, high tolerance to fouling/deposits and reliable operation. Such applications include military land craft, hydrofoils, air cushion vehicles, fast patrol boats, cruise power propulsion and onboard electric power generators.

LM 500

The LM 500 is a simple-cycle, two-shaft gas-turbine engine. The single shaft gas generator consists of a 14-stage high-pressure compressor with variable inlet guide vanes and variable stator vanes in the first five stages, an annular machined ring combustor with 18 externally mounted fuel injectors and an air-cooled, two-stage HP gas generator turbine. The free power turbine has four stages and the output shaft connecting flange is at the air inlet end of the engine.

Air intake: The LM 500 offers, as optional equipment, an air inlet collector to guide the inlet air from the customer's intake ducting into the engine. The inlet duct is made from aluminium and provides the structural connection for the forward engine mounts or for the reduction gearbox containing the forward mounts.

An off-engine inlet screen is also offered to prevent objects from entering the compressor.

Compressor: The compressor is identical to the TF34 and consists of the front frame, accessory drive assembly, compressor rotor and case/vane assembly. The front frame is an uncomplicated four-strut aluminium casting and is designed to provide the compressor inlet flowpath, the forward structural support for the engine, support the forward bearings and seals for the gas generator and power turbine rotors, and support the accessory gearbox.

Combustor: The LM 500 combustor is of the TF34 flight engine design. It is an annular through flow combustor using a machined ring liner construction for long life. Metered fuel is distributed and introduced through 18 central, individually replaceable injectors.

High-pressure turbine: The LM 500 high-pressure turbine is a two-stage, fully air-cooled design, identical to the TF34 turbine except for minor changes to improve performance and meet the requirements for marine and industrial applications.

Power turbine: The LM 500 power turbine is a four-stage, uncooled, high-performance design incorporating aerodynamic and mechanical features and materials identical to the TF34 low-pressure turbine. The power turbine rotor structural components are made of inconel 718 material. The four turbine discs carry tip shrouded turbine blades that are attached to the discs with single tang dovetails. The blades are made of René 77 material with the first stage Codep-coated. The durability of René 77 alleviates the need for coatings on the other stages. At operating gas temperatures 111°C less than the TF34, the LM 500 blades have virtually infinite stress rupture life. The structural integrity of the power turbine rotor has been demonstrated to a speed of 9,030 rpm, 29 per cent over the normal rated speed of the LM 500 engine.

Lubrication: The LM 500 lubricating oil system provides the following functions: lubricates and cools the gas-turbine main bearings; supplies hydraulic fluid for the variable geometry actuation system and fuel metering valve actuator.

The main engine bearings are lubricated from an accessory gearbox-driven lube pump. The scavenge circuit is based on a dry sump system and each bearing sump is scavenged by a separate pump or pump elements driven off the accessory gearbox. All scavenge oil is filtered (coarse screens) prior to entry into the pump elements.

Fuel: The LM 500 is designed to operate with marine diesel, diesel and JP fuels. The fuel system consists of on- and off-engine components. Filtered fuel is supplied by the customer to the fuel pump, which is mounted on the accessory gearbox, where the fuel pressure is increased by a centrifugal boost element and then ported externally to an on-engine last chance fuel filter. From the filter the fuel is routed to an off-engine Fuel Regulating Assembly (FRA) which meters the engine fuel flow according to signals received from the off-engine Main Electronic Control Assembly (MECA). Also included in the FRA are two fuel shut-off valves, mounted in series for redundancy, which are used to shut off the fuel to the engine during normal shut downs and automatic shut downs. Fuel is then routed to the on-engine fuel distributor which divides the fuel through separate hose assemblies to 18 fuel injectors.

Specifications

Basic engine
Length overall: 2,184 mm
Width: 864 mm
Weight: 580 kg
With optional inlet and axial exhaust duct, starter kit and output gearbox
Length overall: 3,307 mm
Width: 1,179 mm
Weight: 1,031 kg

VERIFIED

FINCANTIERI DIESEL ENGINES DIVISION

Isotta Fraschini

Bagnoli Della Rosandra 334, I-34018 Trieste, Italy

Tel: +39 (40) 3195648
Fax: +39 (40) 810246

Fincantieri, the largest and most diversified shipbuilding organisation in the Mediterranean and one of the biggest in Europe, is the company in the IRI group which unifies the capacities and facilities of the oldest and most important Italian enterprises in the sector.

The company, with continuous experience and technology acquired since the beginning of the century, is now giving new impulse to the long established Isotta Fraschini name.

The Diesel Engines Division, with its headquarters at Trieste, carries out the functions of a typical industrial enterprise for the production and sale of diesel, gas and dual-fuel engines in the marine, industrial and rail traction sectors.

Following the merging of Isotta Fraschini Motori SpA, the Diesel Engines Division of Fincantieri - with the two trademarks GMT and IF - a range of engines covering power outputs from 400 to 22,000 kW per unit is now available.

The Division has two production plants, one situated at Trieste and one at Bari. The Trieste factory extends, in the industrial zone of Trieste, over a site of 530,000 m², 150,000 m² of which are presently occupied by the offices and workshops.

The Bari factory extends on the total area of 200,000 m² of which 24,000 m² are covered.

ISOTTA FRASCHINI 1300

The 1300 family comprises a six-cylinder in-line unit and 8- and 12-cylinder 90° vee models. A 130 mm bore and a stroke of 142 mm on the in-line unit are principal features of the 1300 family. The stroke is reduced to 126 mm for the vee models. The in-line engine has a cylinder displacement of 1,885 cm³, while the Vee units have a cylinder of 1,672 cm³. The 1300 engines have an impressive power-to-weight ratio, being highly standardised and extremely reliable engines of modular type. Introduced as marine engines, these diesels will also serve the power generation and industrial market segments.

Engine model	Cylinder arrangement	Engine ratings (brake power)									
		High-performance special craft		Fast performance special craft		Commercial craft light duty		Commercial craft medium duty		Commercial craft heavy duty	
		kW	rpm	kW	rpm	kW	rpm	kW	rpm	kW	rpm
L 1306 T2	6 in line	370	2,400	350	2,400	320	2,300	280	2,200	220	1,800
L 1308 T2	8 vee	500	2,700	500	2,700	450	2,600	390	2,400	330	2,100
L 1312 T2	12 vee	780	2,700	750	2,700	675	2,600	585	2,400	495	2,100
V 1708 T2	8 vee	955	2,000	900	2,000	815	1,935	750	1,935	700	1,800
V 1712 T2	12 vee	1,680	2,000	1,540	2,000	1,400	1,940	1,260	1,935	1,050	1,800
V 1716 T2	16 vee	2,350	2,100	2,140	2,030	1,925	1,980	1,730	1,960	–	–

IF 1716 T2 16V marine engine ***1993***

The 1300 family specification may be summarised as follows:

Four-stroke diesel engines, direct injection, exhaust gas turbo-charging, supercharging air-cooling through water/air exchangers, engine double-circuit water-cooling, complete with heat exchanger, cooling system complete with centrifugal pumps, thermostats for internal circuit water and oil control, engine water-cooled exhaust manifolds, force-feed lubrication through gear pump, injection pump

IF L 1306 T2 marine engine **1993**

IF V 1308 T2 marine engine **1993**

complete with mechanical governor, fuel feed pump, oil exchanger with replaceable/cartridge oil filters, fuel oil filter, dry air filter, crankshaft vibration damper, flywheel and flywheel housing SAE standard, battery charger generator, 24 V electric starter.

ISOTTA FRASCHINI 1700

The 1700 family comprises 8 to 16 cylinder models arranged with a 90° V on a high-tensile alloy iron crankcase.

These engines feature a direct injection system with four valves per cylinder. They are built using a modular concept, with most components common to all units. A special amagnetic version is available for mine warfare vessels.

VERIFIED

IVECO AIFO SpA

Viale dell'Industria, 15/17, I-20010 Pregnana Milanese, Milan, Italy

Tel: +39 (2) 935101
Telex: 352328 AIFO I
Fax: +39 (2) 9359 0029

Pietro Bruno, *Commercial Operations Manager*
E Bettina, *Marketing Manager*

Iveco Aifo manufactures a range of marine diesel engines from 44 to 883 kW. The accompanying table details the more powerful engines.

UPDATED

Type	No of cylinders and arrangement	Displacement	Output Light duty commercial	Output Continuous duty	Length basic engine	Weight
8361 SM 21	6-cylinder/L	8.1 l	-	129 kW	1,271 mm	700 kg
8361 SRM 32	6-cylinder/L	8.1 l	236 kW	-	1,271 mm	760 kg
8361 SRM 40	6-cylinder/L	8.1 l	294 kW	-	1,275 mm	763 kg
8210 M 22	6-cylinder/L	13.8 l	-	162 kW	1,495 mm	1,130 kg
8210 SRM 36	6-cylinder/L	13.8 l	-	243 kW	1,627 mm	1,290 kg
8460 SRM 28	6-cylinder/L	9.5 l	-	206 kW	1,487 mm	1,140 kg
8460 SRM 50	6-cylinder/L	9.5 l	368 kW		1,487 mm	1,140 kg
8281 M 32	8-cylinder/V	17.2 l	-	206 kW	1,291 mm	1,455 kg
8281 SRM 44	8-cylinder/V	17.2 l	-	324 kW	1,460 mm	1,690 kg
8281 SRM 70	8-cylinder/V	17.2 l	515 kW	-	1,460 mm	1,690 kg
8291 SRM 75	12-cylinder/V	25.8 l	-	552 kW	2,362 mm	2,450 kg
8291 SRM 12	12-cylinder/V	25.8 l	883 kW	-	2,362 mm	2,450 kg

M=Naturally aspirated
SRM=Turbocharged intercooled

SEATEK SpA

Via Provinciale 71, 22040 Annone Brianza (Co), Italy

Tel: +39 (341) 579335
Fax: +39 (341) 579317

Ing P Molla, *Chairman*
Ing F Buzzi, *Managing Director*
P Fumagalli, *General Manager*
Dr A Bonomi, *Director*

Builders of high-speed marine diesel engines which are noted for their power-to-weight and power-to-size ratios as well as fuel economy and low emissions.

In 1988 a Seatek powered boat won the Italian, European and World offshore Class One Championships and since this time Seatek powered craft have continually won Class One and Two offshore races worldwide.

MODEL 6.4V.9D

Recently available as a production engine this four-cycle diesel has the following characteristics.

Specifications
Length: 1,540 mm
Width: 721 mm
Cylinder number: 6 in line
Dry weight: 800 kg
Compression ratio: 15:1
Power output: 463 kW
rpm: 3,150
Fuel consumption: 210 g/kW h

MODEL 6.4V.10D

Dry weight: 780 kg
Power output: 530 kW
rpm: 3,000

UPDATED

Seatek Model 6.4V.9D diesel with dry weight per kW of 1.66 kg **1992**

JAPAN

MITSUBISHI HEAVY INDUSTRIES LTD

5-1 Maranouchi 2-chome, Chiyoda-ku, Tokyo, Japan

Tel: +81 (3) 3212 3111
Telex: 22443 J

S16R-S

In 1992 Mitsubishi developed the S16R-S, a new high-speed diesel engine aimed at the growing market of high-performance marine vessels.

The S16R-S has been developed from the S16R series and has the following basic characteristics:

Specifications
Type: direct injection, 4-cycle, water-cooled
Turbocharger: Mitsubishi TD15
Cylinders: 16 in 60° V
Base: 170 mm
Stroke: 180 mm
Displacement: 65.4 l output, MCR: 2,100 kW at 2,000 rpm and bmep 19.3 bar
Specific fuel consumption: 218 g/kW h
Weight: 5,500 kg
Weight per kW: 2.54 kg/kW

Four of these engines power the Mitsubishi Super Shuttle 400 *Rainbow*, a 350 passenger, 40 knot catamaran.

VERIFIED

NIIGATA ENGINEERING COMPANY LTD

4-1 Kasumigaseki 1-chome, Chiuoda-ku, Tokyo 100, Japan

Tel: +81 (3) 3504 2473
Fax: +81 (3) 3591 4764

Niigata has introduced a range of high-speed marine diesel engines specifically for use in fast marine craft. The FX series, as they are known, were introduced in 1993 with the first engines being installed in the Superjet 30 craft constructed by Hitachi Zosen.

The company also builds the SEMT Pielstick PA 4 series diesels under licence.

VERIFIED

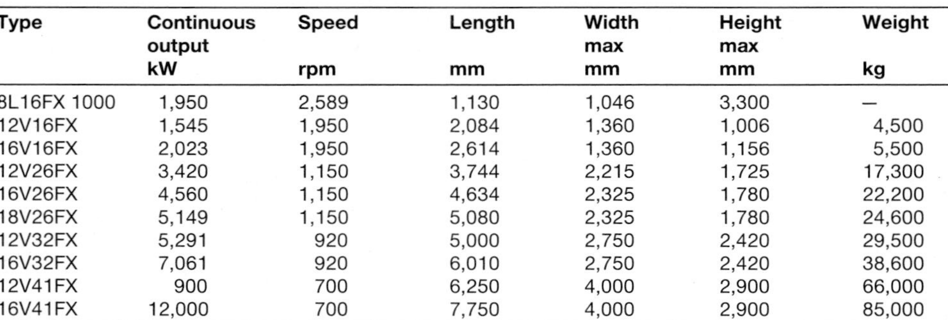

Type	Continuous output kW	Speed rpm	Length mm	Width max mm	Height max mm	Weight kg
8L16FX 1000	1,950	2,589	1,130	1,046	3,300	–
12V16FX	1,545	1,950	2,084	1,360	1,006	4,500
16V16FX	2,023	1,950	2,614	1,360	1,156	5,500
12V26FX	3,420	1,150	3,744	2,215	1,725	17,300
16V26FX	4,560	1,150	4,634	2,325	1,780	22,200
18V26FX	5,149	1,150	5,080	2,325	1,780	24,600
12V32FX	5,291	920	5,000	2,750	2,420	29,500
16V32FX	7,061	920	6,010	2,750	2,420	38,600
12V41FX	900	700	6,250	4,000	2,900	66,000
16V41FX	12,000	700	7,750	4,000	2,900	85,000

Niigata 16V26FX
1995

NORWAY

KVÆRNER ENERGY A/S

PO Box 9277, Grønland, N-0134 Oslo, Norway

Tel: +47 (22) 666666
Telex: 71650 KV N
Fax: +47 (22) 193765

Odd Sandøy, *General Manager*

Kværner Energy supplies the high-speed craft market with complete propulsion modules, including gas-turbines and water-jets.

Kværner/General Electric's marine and industrial gas-turbine modules are compact, high-performance power units. Each, from the LM 500 to the LM 6000, is a simple-cycle gas-turbine derived from highly reliable aircraft engines. In a wide range of applications they have provided years of trouble-free, unattended operation. Built incorporating the latest design technologies and corrosion resistant materials, each GE LM engine provides maximum reliability and parts life along with outstanding performance.

Kværner Energy's workshop which specialises in the overhaul, repair and testing of gas-turbines is

Kværner/GE LM 2500 gas-turbine module nearing completion ***1994***

located at Ågotnes, on the outskirts of Bergen. This workshop is one of the few of its kind worldwide with authorisation from GE to carry out maintenance and servicing on the gas-turbines at all levels.

Please see General Electric entry for technical details.

LM 500

The LM 500 is a simple-cycle, two-shaft gas-turbine, derived from GE's TF34 aircraft engine. This engine powers a Danish Navy patrol boat, a Japanese PG Class hydrofoil patrol craft and the Kværner Fjellstrand Flying Foilcat class passenger ferry.

LM 1600

The LM 1600 is a simple-cycle three-shaft gas-tubine engine, derived from GE's F404 engine. It is designed with 50 to 60 per cent fewer parts than other gas-turbines in its class. This engine has been selected as the power unit for a number of large high-speed vessels: the *Destriero* powered by three LM 1600 engines, Eco powered by one LM 1600 engine and the Danyard/NQEA Seajet 250 class of fast ferry. These engines are also used in the 'father and son' arrangement in the Stena HSS 1500 fast ferry.

The LM 1600 is a fuel efficient simple-cycle engine. Lightweight, compact and modular it combines the latest in blade-loading design, cooling technology and corrosion-resistant materials and coatings.

LM 2500

The LM 2500 is a simple-cycle two-shaft gas-turbine engine, derived from GE's military TF39 and the commercial bypass turbofan engines. Two LM 2500s in father and son configuration with two LM 1600s, power the 124 m Stena high-speed catamarans, the HSS 1500 class. Its current experience base comprises over 250 ships and 19 navies.

Compact, lightweight and powerful, the LM 2500 is adaptable to a broad range of ships. The LM 2500 has good reliability and fuel efficiency, it boasts an outstanding record for over 6 million hours of consistent, cost-effective, troublefree service for marine and industrial applications.

LM 6000

The LM 6000 is a simple-cycle, two-shaft high-performance gas-turbine engine, derived from GE's most powerful and reliable aircraft engine, the CF6-80C2. Delivering more than 40 MW at over 40 per cent thermal efficiency, the powerful LM 6000 is very fuel efficient.

All components of the LM 6000 incorporate corrosion-resistant materials and coatings to provide maximum parts life and time between overhaul, regardless of the unit's operational environment.

UPDATED

ULSTEIN TURBINE A/S

Kongsberg Næringspark, PO Box 1023, N-3601 Kongsberg, Norway

Tel: +47 (32) 737300
Fax: +47 (32) 737320

Jan Halle, *Managing Director*
Ivar Austrem, *Technical Manager*

The Ulstein Group of Norway has purchased the technology and patents related to the unique engine design of the Radial Turbine operations, which belonged to the former Kongsberg Vaapenfabrikk. Ulstein, a leading manufacturer of maritime machinery and equipment, has seen a large potential for the new, high power density turbine engine design for high-speed surface transportation in general and marine propulsion in particular.

Ulstein is implementing the Eurodyn turbine development plans through a new company, Ulstein Turbine A/S, situated in Oslo. Ulstein Turbine A/S is structured as a design and development company with some 15 turbine engine experts employed.

When the new turbine engine is in production, it will have a positive effect on more than 30 companies in the Ulstein Group, especially for Ulstein Bergen A/S, the only remaining Norwegian owned diesel engine manufacturer.

The Eurodyn gas-turbine ***1995***

EURODYN

The purpose of the Eurodyn programme, designated EU159 in the European Eureka projects frame, is to develop and produce a high-efficiency industrial gas-turbine in the 2 to 3 MW power range. The engine is intended for applications in the fast surface transport market such as train or boat propulsion, as well as in the more traditional market for gas-turbines of electric generation and drive of pumps or compressors.

In this Franco-Scandinavian co-operation Turbomeca (France) holds 50 per cent, Ulstein (Norway) 30 per cent and Volvo Aero Corporation AB (Sweden) 20 per cent.

The efficiency targets set for the Eurodyn are impressive for turbines in this power class. An efficiency of 35 per cent is the ultimate goal with an

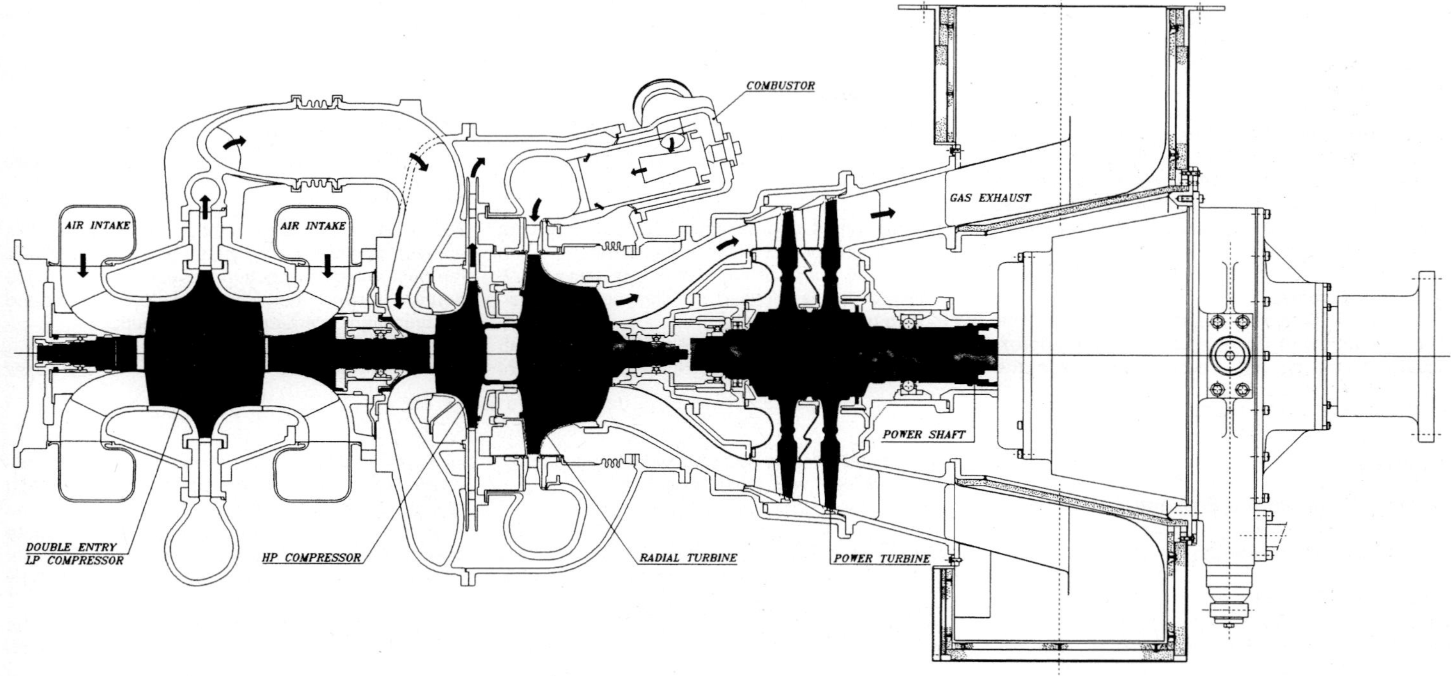

Eurodyn gas-turbine components ***1995***

interim target of 33 per cent, making the compact and lightweight Eurodyn turbine a formidable competitor for existing turbines and high-speed diesel engines.

The Eurodyn engine is particularly well suited to high-speed craft propulsion, such as catamarans and surface effect ships.

The engine provides a performance characteristic that is superior to any known, simple-cycle, gas-turbine of comparable size. It is a fully marinised industrial engine of rugged design.

A significant milestone was reached late in 1992 with the first engine test of the Eurodyn demonstrators. The first tests successfully demonstrated the high-performance characteristics of the engine. The demonstrator engines were subjected to an extensive testing programme during 1993 in France and Norway.

The first pilot applications are underway, with pre-serial engines being tested in industrial, marine and railway applications. The market launch will be in 1995.

The high-pressure ratio compressor, comprising a dual entry first stage and a single entry second stage, was developed by Turbomeca, which also supplies the auxiliary gearbox and engine accessories.

The engine hot section, featuring a multiple can low-emissions combustor with multifuel capability and a radial gas generator turbine was developed by Ulstein Turbine A/S, a company within the Ulstein Group. It also supplied the compact reduction gearbox, adaptable to both industrial and marine applications.

The inter turbine duct and free power turbine section comprising two axial stages were developed by Volvo Aero Corporation AB and its subsidiary Volvo Aero Turbines AB. They are also responsible for the engine management and fuel control system.

Each partner will manufacture its respective parts and the final engine assembly and testing will be performed in Norway and France.

The new turbine engine will have lower fuel consumption than any other turbine engine in its power range of 2 to 3 MW. The engine will be compact and will weigh significantly less than the lightweight diesels now used for high-speed surface applications. Furthermore, the engine will be largely vibration free, have a very low noise level and most importantly, will satisfy the strictest exhaust emissions regulations.

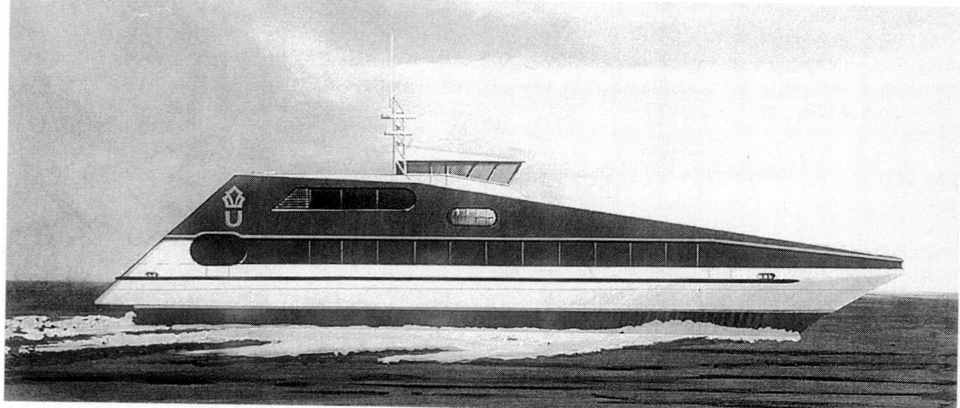

Ulstein test vessel, UT 905 catamaran **1995**

Specifications

Length overall: 3,260 mm
Height overall: 1,300 mm
Weight: 1,900-2,300 kg (inc gearbox), depending on equipment specification
Power range: 2,200-2,900 kW (ISO conditions)
Thermal efficiency: 33-35%
Airflow: 11.5 kg/s
Specific fuel consumption: 240-250 g/kW h

Ulstein has built a UT 905 catamaran containing two Eurodyn engines for propulsion. The vessel entered an extensive sea trial period in 1995. The Norwegian Navy joined the trials to verify the engine for future navy programmes.

VERIFIED

SWEDEN

ABB STAL AB

S-61282 Finspong, Sweden

Tel: +46 122 810 00
Fax: +46 122 165 80

David Nordlander, *Sales Manager*
Urban Joelsson, *Sales Manager*

On 12 June 1995, ABB STAL received an order for the supply of four GT35 gas turbines for use as the main propulsion machinery in two of Stena Line's new fast ferries, the HSS 900. The ferries can operate at a speed of 40 knots and will each be powered by two GT35 turbines. Each turbine can develop a maximum power of 17 MW.

ABB STAL is part of the Asea Brown Boveri Group, one of the world's leading technological companies within the thermal energy conversion field. The company designs, manufactures and delivers complete plants and components for power and heat production. The products include advanced steam and gas turbines for land-based offshore and marine applications for power generation, mechanical drive and propulsion systems. ABB STAL employs 2,000 people with a annual turnover in excess of 300 million US$.

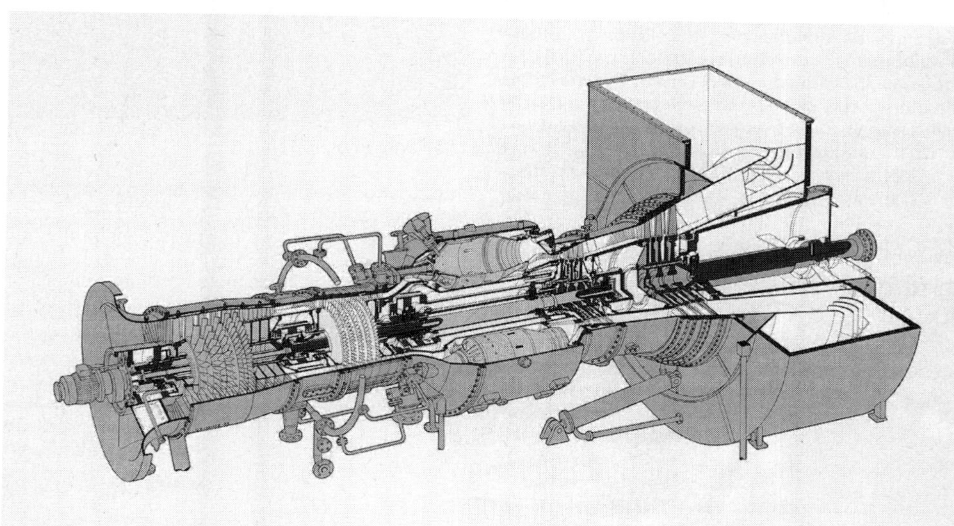

A cut-away view of the ABB STAL GT35 gas turbine **1996**

GT35 Gas Turbine

The STAL GT35 gas turbine measures 11,450 mm long by 3,220 mm diameter and weighs approximately 26 tonnes net. This turbine has a fuel consumption of approximately 0.255 kg/kW h at maximum output of 17 MW at 3,450 rpm, and can burn a wide range of fuels including heavy oil. A number of the land-based installations are understood to burn fluidised coal.

The GT35 turbine operates with a three shaft arrangement and with a low inlet temperature of 850 C, hence it does not require blade cooling. This ensures a very low maintenance requirement with the first major inspection required after 20,000 hours, a hot end refurbishment at 40,000 hours and the first major overhaul at 80,000 hours.

NEW ENTRY

SCANIA

Industrial and Marine Engines

S-151 87 Södertälje, Sweden

Tel: +46 (8553) 81000
Telex: 10200 SCANIA S
Fax: +46 (8553) 82993

Scania marine diesels cover a power output range of 153 to 497 kW with weights of 875 to 1,400 kg. Power test code ISO 3046.

Scania marine engines have recently been radically redeveloped and constitute an almost new range, still however, built for economical operation and long service life.

Scania claims that the excellent performance and low fuel consumption of its engines result from new injection equipment, carefully optimised turbochargers and a cylinder design with a top liner ring (Scania Saver Ring) which is complementary to the Keystone-type piston ring. Together they eliminate coking, keep piston ring grooves clean, prevent bore polishing and reduce lube oil consumption by more than 50 per cent.

An interesting application of Scania diesels is the use of two DSI 11 engines in the FBM Marine

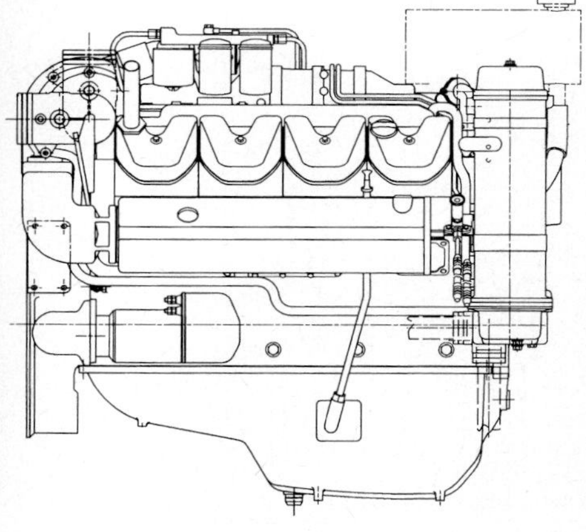

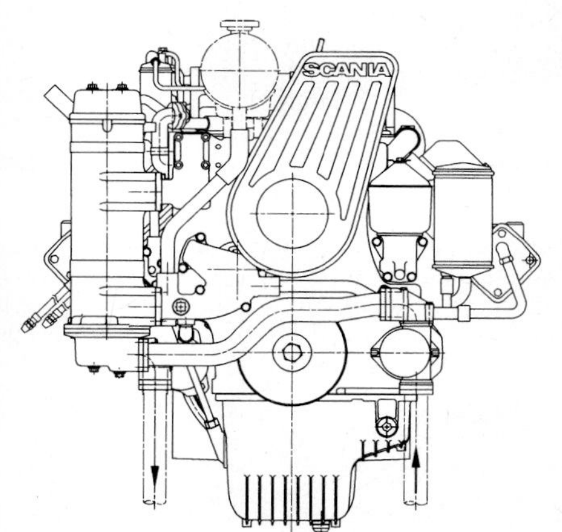

DSI 14 Marine **1995**

Thames Class RTL Hydrocat catamarans for the London City Airport service. These 62 passenger, 26 knot catamarans have extremely slender hulls to minimise wash, and high power-to-weight ratio engines are essential for the same reason.

Marine diesel engines
RATINGS

Engine type with heat exchanger	Turbo	Inter-cooled	Displacement dm³	Configuration	Propulsion High-speed workboats, patrol, and so on kW (hp) rpm	Specific fuel consumption at 1,500 rpm g/kW h
DS 9	T	-	8.5	6 L	195 (265) 2,200	208
DSI 9	T	I	8.5	6 L	258 (351) 2,200	202
DS 11	T	-	11	6 L	242 (329) 2,100	210
DSI 11	T	I	11	6 L	288 (392) 2,100	206
DSI 11	T	I	11	6 L	315 (428) 2,100	204
DSI 11	T	I	11	6 L	368 (500) 2,100	207
DSI 14	T	I	14.2	V 8	356 (484) 2,100	207
DSI 14	T	I	14.2	V 8	414 (563) 2,100	206
DSI 14	T	I	14.2	V 8	460 (625) 2,100	213
DSI 14	T	I	14.2	V 8	497 (675) 2,100	213
with keel cooling						
DS 9	T	-	8.5	6 L	165 (224) 2,200	207
DS 9	T	-	8.5	6 L	195 (265) 2,200	208
DS 11	T	-	11	6 L	242 (329) 2,100	210
DSI 11	T	I	11	6 L	286 (389) 2,100	212
DSI 14	T	-	14.2	V 8	356 (484) 2,100	207
DSI 14	T	I	14.2	V 8	414 (563) 2,100	206

WEIGHTS

Engine type	Max dimensions (mm) Length	Width	Height	Weight dry (kg)
with heat exchanger				
DS 9	1,352	786	1,093	895
DSI 9	1,413	786	1,093	900
DS 11	1,556	750	1,041	1,100
DSI 11	1,556	750	1,104	1,115
DSI 14	1,302	1,172	1,176	1,400
with keel cooling				
DS 9	1,330	754	1,084	875
DS 11	1,493	715	1,003	1,010
DSI 11	1,493	715	1,104	1,035
DSI 14	1,302	1,172	1,176	1,325

Weights and dimensions. Quoted values are only a guide; there are variations for each engine type. Weights exclude oil and water.

Turbocharged and intercooled models feature a new high-efficiency charge air-cooler, matched on marine engines to a two-compartment heat exchanger and effective gallery cooling of the piston crown. The crown is anodised for extended resistance to fatigue.

UPDATED

VOLVO PENTA AB

S-405 08 Gothenburg, Sweden

Tel: +46 (31) 235460
Telex: 20755 PENTA S
Fax: +46 (31) 510595

The Board of Volvo Penta:
Christer Zetterberg, *Chairman*
Jan Walldorf, *President*
Olle Johansson, *Director*
Anders Lindstrom, *Director*
Bo Egerdal, *Director*
Hans Eric Ovin, *Director*
Union Group: Bengt Segeheden
Gösta Gendenberg

Executive Marine Management:
Jan Walldorf, *President*
Orvar Lundberg, *Director Marine Commercial*

AB Volvo Penta designs, manufactures and markets engines, transmissions, accessories and equipment for marine and industrial use.

Part of the Volvo Group, the sales of Volvo Penta engines account for around four per cent of sales within the transport equipment sector. The engines are used in ferries, pilot vessels, fishing boats and all types of leisure craft, as well as for industrial propulsion or power generation applications.

Production facilities are in the USA and Brazil plus four locations in Sweden. Volvo Penta products are sold in 100 countries worldwide. Approximately 2,600 people are employed either directly or indirectly by Volvo Penta.

Volvo Penta TAMD 71 in-line, six turbocharged and after-cooled 7 litre engine **1988**

Volvo Penta diesels for commercial craft can provide up to 550 hp. The company has updated the entire engine range covering two-, three- and four-cylinder commercially rated diesels as well as the in-line six series.

New to the range are the heavy diesels TAMD 162, TAMD 122 and TAMD 102.

All eight units in the 31 and 41 series feature direct injection which reduces thermal stress, heat and pressure loss resulting in lower fuel consumption and longer life expectancy. Fuel consumption is around 15 per cent less than with the equivalent prechamber ignition diesels. The new turbocharger is freshwater-cooled and the pistons are oil-cooled to increase engine life.

Further up the power range are the 6 and 7 litre models TAMD 61 and TAMD 71. Both are turbocharged, after-cooled in-line, six diesels for which the latest three-dimensional computer techniques have been used as a means towards reducing engine weight and providing optimum rigidity. Interesting design features of the new 16 litre in-line six-cylinder diesel engine TAMD 162 include efficient cooling of the cylinder head with four valves per cylinder, for high efficiency. The cylinder head is bolted to the block without gaskets for increased service life and low maintenance costs. A new fast injection pump on the cold side of the engine gives good economy and environmental properties in combination with a smoke limiter.

A responsive turbo and after-cooler with low internal resistance gives efficient combustion and cleaner exhausts, as well as increasing engine service life.

The new TAMD 122 has between four and seven per cent higher power output than the previous 121 generation.

The new technical features of the engine include new cylinder head and gaskets, new cylinder linings with flame barriers and improved sealing. The engine has a new injection pump with smoke limiter and new, five-hole nozzles for better combustion and less smoke.

The new 10 litre engine for workboats has the designation TAMD 102 and will be of particular significance for sales to Japan, a market where Volvo has been active for 30 years. With its light duty configuration of 297 kW and its bore of 120 mm, the engine meets the requirements made by the authorities for power units fitted in light, fast fishing boats in Japan.

Volvo Penta TAMD 162 ***1989***

Volvo Penta TAMD 102A ***1993***

VOLVO PENTA 3 TO 12 LITRE MARINE PROPULSION ENGINES

TAMD 31	**hp**	**kW**	**rpm**
Propeller shaft output ISO 3046,			
light duty	124	91	3,800
medium duty	105	77	3,250

Weight: 385 kg including MS4 gearbox
Displacement: 2.39 l

TAMD 41	**hp**	**kW**	**rpm**
Propeller shaft output ISO 3046,			
light duty	192	141	3,800
medium duty	163	120	3,250
heavy duty	145	107	2,500

Weight: 465 kg including MS4 gearbox
Displacement: 3.59 l

TAMD 61	**hp**	**kW**	**rpm**
Flywheel output,			
light duty	306	225	2,800
medium duty	228	168	2,500

Weight: 760 kg excluding gearbox
Displacement: 5.48 l

TAMD 71	**hp**	**kW**	**rpm**
Flywheel output,			
light duty	357	263	2,500
medium duty	292	213	2,500
heavy duty	222	163	2,000

Weight: 880 kg excluding gearbox
Displacement: 6.73 l

TMD 102	**hp**	**kW**	**rpm**
Flywheel output,			
medium duty	272	200	2,000
heavy duty	238	175	1,800

Weight: 1,140 kg excluding gearbox
Displacement: 9.6 l

TAMD 102	**hp**	**kW**	**rpm**
Flywheel output,			
light duty	400	297	2,200
medium duty	360	268	2,000

Weight: 1,190 kg excluding gearbox
Displacement: 9.6 l

TAMD 122	**hp**	**kW**	**rpm**
Flywheel output,			
light duty	450	331	2,000
medium duty	400	294	1,900
heavy duty	380	279	1,800

Weight: 1,300 kg excluding gearbox
Displacement: 11.98 l

TAMD 162	**hp**	**kW**	**rpm**
Flywheel output,			
light duty	550	405	1,900
medium duty	550	405	1,900
heavy duty	510	375	1,800

Weight: 1,705 kg excluding reverse gear
Displacement: 16.12 l

The following definitions define the duty ratings given in the accompanying table.

LD: Light Duty
Engines with this power setting are for applications where rated power for rated speed is utilised for short periods only, followed by cruising at reduced speed; also when operating time is short and does not exceed 500 hours per year.
Examples: Certain patrol boats, fire boats, rescue boats and charter craft.

MD: Medium Duty
Engines with this power setting are intended for applications where rated power at rated speed is utilised during part of the operating time only (up to ⅓), followed by cruising at reduced speed. Operating time should not exceed 2,000 hours per year, or on average, one shift per working day.
Examples: Patrol boats, pilot boats, police boats and certain fishing vessels.

HD: Heavy Duty
Engines with this power setting are intended for applications where neither LD nor MD applies and rated power at rated speed could be needed continuously. No interruption or load cycling is expected other than for service and maintenance.
Examples: Tugboats, ferries, fishing boats and most commercial applications in displacement vessels.

VERIFIED

UNITED KINGDOM

GEC ALSTHOM PAXMAN DIESELS LTD

A Management Company of GEC ALSTHOM Diesels Limited

Paxman Works, Hythe Hill, Colchester, Essex CO1 2HW, UK

Tel: +44 (1206) 795151
Telex: 98151 GENERAL G
Fax: +44 (1206) 797869

T Lines, *Marketing Manager*

GEC ALSTHOM Paxman Diesels manufactures compact high-speed diesel engines suitable for high-speed marine craft propulsion duties, backed up by comprehensive worldwide product support.

The Paxman range of well proven Valenta and Vega engines was joined in 1993 by the VP 185, of which the 12-cylinder version was launched first. This new range of engines is a breakthrough in low-cost, low maintenance high-speed diesel engines in the 1,760 to 3,960 kW power range, and will eventually be available in 8-, 16- and 18-cylinder versions as well as the 12-cylinder engine shown. To support all engine and component manufacture Paxman has invested heavily in new design and manufacturing technology.

Recent customers for high-speed craft include:
Hyundai Heavy Industries
US Navy (Cyclone class PC)
Vosper Thornycroft (fast strike craft)
Batservice 49 m catamaran ferry
McTay Marine Customs Patrol Boat
HM Customs and Excise (UK)
Oceanfast 146' Superyacht

UPDATED

Paxman Valenta 18 CM **1994**

Paxman 12VP 185 **1995**

VALENTA	Max Brake power	rpm	Length	Width	Height	Dry Weight
6 CM	1,020 kW	1,600 rpm	2,673 mm	1,070 mm	1,943 mm	4,363 kg
8 CM	1,515 kW	1,600 rpm	2,133 mm	1,460 mm	2,273 mm	6,108 kg
12 CM	2,480 kW	1,640 rpm	2,497 mm	1,568 mm	2,338 mm	8,590 kg
16 CM	3,300 kW	1,640 rpm	2,953 mm	1,568 mm	2,466 mm	10,706 kg
18 CM	3,710 kW	1,640 rpm	3,245 mm	1,575 mm	2,397 mm	11,670 kg
VEGA						
12 CM	1,310 kW	1,800 rpm	2,129 mm	1,595 mm	1,738 mm	4,996 kg
16 CM	1,745 kW	1,800 rpm	2,816 mm	1,686 mm	2,092 mm	6,087 kg
12 VP 185						
12 VP 185	2,611 kW	1,950 rpm	2,646 mm	1,440 mm	2,030 mm	7,119 kg

Measurements and weights are for complete engines ready for installation. These may vary slightly depending on application.

	Valenta (60° V)	Vega (60° V)	VP 185 (90° V)
Housing	High-grade cast-iron or fabricated steel	High-grade cast-iron	High-grade cast-iron
Crankshaft and main bearings	Forged steel nitride hardened carried in tin aluminium steel-backed bearing shells	Forged steel induction hardened carried in lead bronze steel-backed bearing shells	Nitride hardened forged steel carried in tin aluminium steel-backed bearings
Connecting rods	Fork and blade rods with steel-backed aluminium tin, lined forked rod big end bearings and lead bronze lined blade rod bearings	Side by side with lead bronze steel-backed big end bearings	Side by side with tin aluminium steel-backed big end bearings
Pistons	Aluminium alloy with top compression ring fitted in an 'Alfin' bonded cast-iron insert	Aluminium alloy with top compression ring fitted in an 'Alfin' bonded bonded cast-iron insert	Cast-iron
Cylinder head	Cast-iron with four valve direct injection system	Cast-iron with four valves and unit pump injector	Cast-iron with four valves and unit pump injector
Cylinder liner	Wet type seamless steel tube, chrome-plated and honeycombed for oil retention	Wet type seamless steel tube, chrome-plated and honeycombed for oil retention	Centrifugally cast-iron
Fuel injection	Single unit pumps driven from engine via pump camshaft, multi-hole injectors retained by clamp to heads	Combined fuel pump and injector unit operated by pushrods from engine camshaft	Combined fuel pump and injector unit operated by pushrods from engine camshaft
Governor	Electronic, hydraulic or pneumatic	Electronic, hydraulic or pneumatic	Electronic or hydraulic
Pressure charging and intercooling	Single water-cooled exhaust gas turbocharger, air to water intercooler	Single air-cooled exhaust gas turbocharger mounted on each bank Intercooled using seawater or jacket water	Two stage exhaust gas turbochargers Four interchangeable low-pressure and two high-pressure turbochargers, mounted in a common water jacketed housing intercooled and after-cooled
Freshwater cooling	Single water pump driven from free end, thermostatic control	Two pumps driven from free end, thermostatically controlled	Primary and secondary freshwater cooling system each with their own water pump driven from the free end. Thermostatically controlled
Lubrication	Wet sump, single pump pressurised system with external-mounted oil coolers, full flow single or duplex oil filters	Wet sump, externally mounted oil pump pressurised system with jacket water oil cooler on each bank. Three canister oil filters to each bank	Wet sump, externally mounted oil pump, pressurised system, thermostatically controlled, with oil cooler. Canister oil filters
Exhaust	Single outlet from turbocharger, water-cooled manifolds	Dry manifold system with individual outlet from each turbocharger	Dry manifold with air/water jacket cooling
Starting	Air, electric or hydraulic starting	Air or electric starting	Electric or air starting

GEC ALSTHOM RUSTON DIESELS LTD

A Management Company of GEC ALSTHOM Diesels Limited

Vulcan Works, Newton-le-Willows, Merseyside WA12 8RU, UK

Tel: +44 (1925) 225151
Telex: 627131-2
Fax: +44 (1925) 222055

GEC ALSTHOM Ruston Diesels Ltd has built up an impressive record in fast ferry propulsion which has been achieved as a result of the relationship built up between the company, the ship builders and the operators. The company provides full support to the vessel design and construction stages.

The Ruston RK270 range of high power to weight ratio, responsive turbocharged and intercooled medium-speed diesel engines have been developed from the extensively proven RK series. The engine range was introduced in 1982 and has a proven record of service in marine propulsion, marine auxiliary, land based power generation and rail traction with major users throughout the world.

Four 16-cylinder RK270 engines were installed in the first 74m wave piercing catamaran to be built by InCat Tasmania. This was the first large passenger/car carrying high-speed ferry to enter commercial service and is the current holder of the 'Blue Riband'. Following the impressive success of the first vessel, Ruston have suppled engines for a total of 12 similar vessels. These engines have now successfully run over 350,000 hours. Three further vessels fitted with 16 RK270 engine rated at 5,500 kW at 1,000 r/min are on order.

As fast feries have developed so have the demands for more power. The first 16-cylinder engines Ruston supplied for fast ferries produced 3,650 kW at 750 r/min, the 20-cylinder engine being produced for the future will produce an MCR of 6,875 kW at 1,000 r/min.

Ruston 20RK270 engine **1996**

RK270 CONSTRUCTION FEATURES

Bedplate: The bedplate is machined from a high-grade iron casting of robust construction. Transverse diaphragms for each main bearing provide rigid support for the crankshaft, and angled joint faces ensure positive locking of the main caps in the bedplate.

Crankshaft: The crankshaft is machined from a single piece or alloy steel forging with bolted on balance weights. There is an integral forged coupling flange for the flywheel and the camshaft drive gear is split to facilitate replacement.

Bearings: The main bearings are pre-finished, steel-backed shells with bi-metal linings. The bearings are retained in their housings by caps drilled to direct oil to the bearings. These caps are located transversely in large registers in the bedplate and held in position by studs and nuts. The bearings are easily removable through the crankcase doors.

Crankcase: The crankcase housing has transverse diaphragms between each cylinder to provide water compartments around the cylinder linings. It incorporates an integral air chest is machined from a high-grade ductile S.G. iron casting. Explosion relief

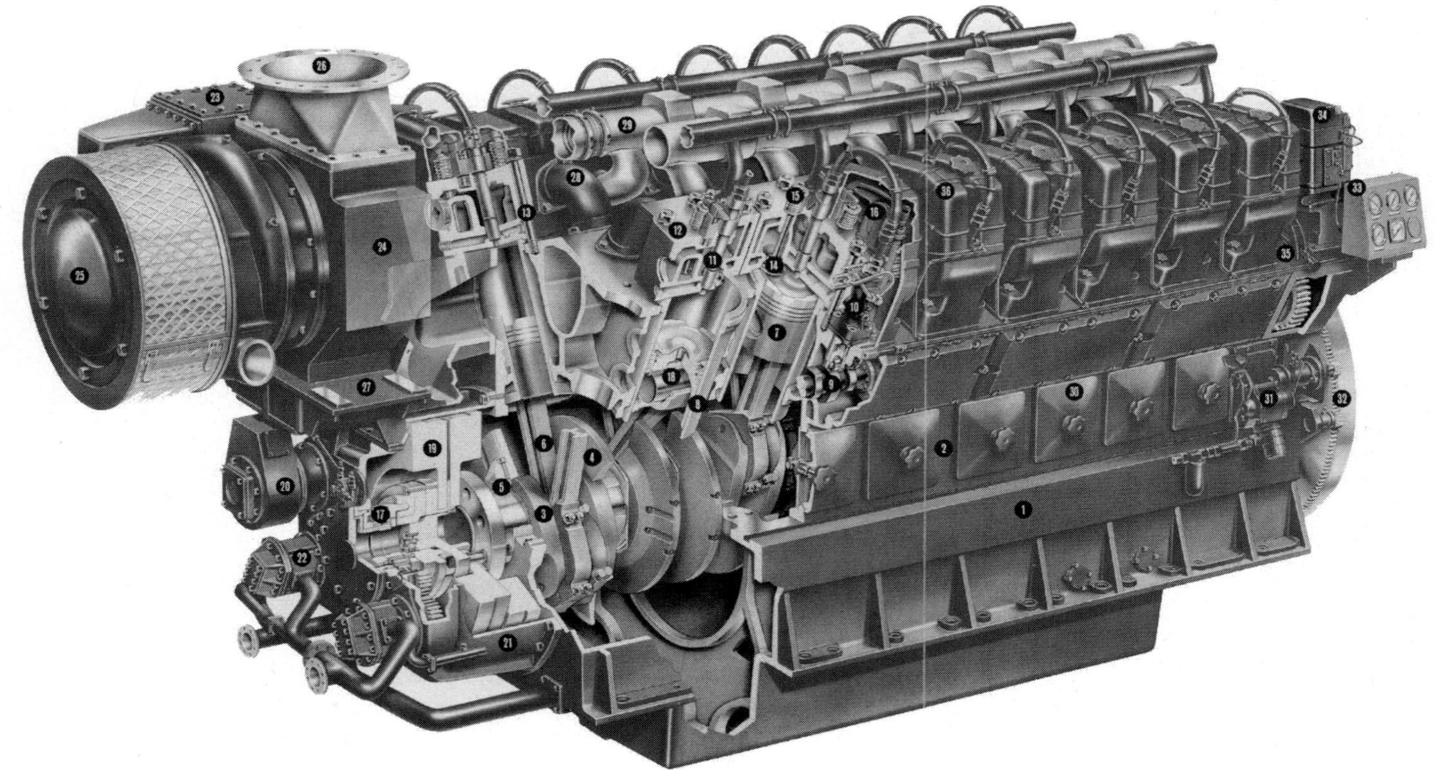

Cutaway drawing of Ruston 16 RK270

Key: **1** *Bedplate;* **2** *Crankcase;* **3** *Crankshaft web;* **4** *Crankshaft balance weight;* **5** *Main bearing cap;* **6** *Connecting rod;* **7** *Piston;* **8** *Cylinder liner;* **9** *Camshaft;* **10** *Fuel injection pump;* **11** *Injector;* **12** *Cylinder head;* **13** *Cylinder head stud;* **14** *Inlet valve;* **15** *Valve spring;* **16** *Rocker lever;* **17** *Auxiliary drive gear;* **18** *Gudgeon pin;* **19** *Viscous vibration dampers;* **20** *Seawater pump;* **21** *Pump drive casing;* **22** *Lubricating oil pump;* **23** *Charge cooler;* **24** *Turbocharger;* **25** *Air intake filter/silencer;* **26** *Exhaust uptake adaptor;* **27** *Turbocharger/charge cooler bracket;* **28** *Air inlet bend;* **29** *Exhaust manifold branch;* **30** *Crankcase door;* **31** *Starter motor;* **32** *Flywheel;* **33** *Instrument panel;* **34** *Governor;* **35** *Hand throttle lever;* **36** *Valve gear cover.* **1992**

valves are fitted to the crankcase doors which are detachable to allow easy access to the connecting rods and main bearings and to the camshaft and drive.

Liners: Separate wet type liners cast in alloy iron are flanged at their upper ends and secured by the cylinder heads. Cutting rings are fitted at the top of the liner to prevent the build up of carbon on the piston crowns. The lower ends of the liners are located in the crankcase and sealed by synthetic rubber rings. The liners are machined all over and the bore is hone finished to provide good piston/liner compatibility for long service life.

Camshaft: A single shaft for each cylinder bank is installed from the side of the engine and run in generously proportioned bearings. The camshafts are of modular construction with single cylinder sections, joined by bearing journals. Individual sections can be replaced with the camshaft in situ and the complete camshaft removed from the side. The final timing is adjustable through a slotted driven gear and hub assembly.

Camshaft drive: The camshafts on all the engines are driven by a train of hardened and ground steel spur gears from the crankshaft split gear.

Pistons: A two piece piston is standard which features a steel crown and an aluminium skirt with a combustion bowl of the Hesselman design. Cooling oil is fed from the connecting rod, through the small end of the bush and drillings in the gudgeon pin and piston body to the cooling gallery.

Connecting rods: The connecting rods are manufactured from steel forgings and the shell bearings are carried in obliquely split big ends, with the cap located by serrations on the joint face. This feature reduces the bending and shear loads across the joint. The stepped small end features a large diameter gudgeon pin with bronze bushings. A drilling through the shank of the connecting rod delivers oil for small end bearing lubrication and piston cooling.

Cylinder head: Individual cylinder heads are manufactured from iron castings. A four valve arrangement is employed with two inlet and two exhaust valves surrounding the central injector. Both the air inlet port and the exhaust port are situated on the same side of the cylinder head. The inlet port draws air from the integral air chest and the exhaust port feeds into a manifold system mounted above the air chest.

Valve gear: Each pair of valves is operated via short stiff pushrods and conventional rockers. The pushrods are driven from the side entry camshafts via roller cam followers.

Governor: A sensitive hydraulic governor is bevel driven from the camshaft. Overspeeding is prevented by a separate safety trip mechanism which returns the control shaft to the 'No-Fuel' position. A digital electronic governor is available as an option.

Auxiliary drives: Auxiliaries are driven from the free end of the engine through a spring drive and spur gears. The standard arrangement includes one water pump for the jacket water, one for the charge-air coolers and lubricating oil cooler circuits, a fuel lift pump and lubricating oil pumps. A secondary water pump may be fitted as an option. An extendion shaft may be fitted to allow power to be taken from the free end of the engine.

Turbochargers: Turbochargers and charge-air coolers are matched to optimise the engine performance. The standard location of the single turbocharger is at the free end of the engine. A flywheel end turbocharger can be provided if required.

Lubricating oil system: The system includes single or twin engine driven oil pumps, full flow filtration, thermostat and oil cooler. The oil pressure is controlled by a single or double spring loaded relief valves.

Cooling system: The jacket cooling system is thermostatically controlled and includes an engine driven water pump.

Starting system: Air motor starting is standard using one or two motors operating via spur gears onto the flywheel rim. For traction applications electric motor starting is employed.

Dimensions, weights and ratings

Engine size		6RK270	8RK270	12RK270	16RK270	20RK270
Number of cylinders		6	8	12	16	20
Cylinder configuration		In-line	In-line	Vee	Vee	Vee
Sump capacity	l	340	410	654	691	916
Dry weight less flywheel	kg	13,050	17,500	22,000	27,000	33,000
Length	mm	4,020	4,585	4,285	5,075	5,965
Width	mm	1,325	1,300	1,825	1,830	1,940
Height (overall)	mm	2,490	2,480	2,645	2,820	2,820
Speed	rpm	1,000	1,000	1,000	1,000	1,000
Rating	kW	2,065	2,750	4,125	5,500	6,875

Fuel specifications
BSMA 100 (ISO8217) Class DMA, DMB or equivalent

Marine unrestricted service power

Engine	Speed rpm	Distillate Brake power kW	bhp	Electrical kW
6 RK270	750	1,555	2,085	1,445
	900	1,875	2,515	1,655
	1,000	2,063	2,765	1,790
8 RK270	750	2,075	2,783	1,925
	900	2,500	3,350	2,210
	1,000	2,750	3,688	2,390
12 RK270	750	3,110	4,170	2,890
	900	3,750	5,030	3,310
	1,000	4,125	5,530	3,580
16 RK270	750	4,150	5,565	3,850
	900	5,000	6,700	4,420
	1,000	5,500	7,375	4,780
20 RK270	750	519	6,955	4,956
	900	6,250	8,375	5,969
	1,000	6,875	9,212	6,566

Installation examples

Name	Type	Nos of engines
Hoverspeed Great Britain	InCat 74 m	4 × 3,650 kW at 750 rpm
Atlantic II	InCat 74 m	4 × 3,650 kW at 750 rpm
Isle of Man	InCat 74 m	4 × 3,650 kW at 750 rpm
SeaCat Denark	InCat 74 m	4 × 4,050 kW at 760 rpm
SeaCat Scotland	InCat 74 m	4 × 3,650 kW at 750 rpm
Condor 10	InCat 74 m	4 × 4,050 kW at 760 rpm
Stena Sea Lynx II	InCat 78 m	4 × 4,050 kW at 760 rpm
Condor 11	InCat 78 m	4 × 4,320 kW at 782 rpm
Cat Link I	InCat 78 m	4 × 4,320 kW at 782 rpm
Super SeaCat	Austal 79 m	4 × 5,500 kW at 1,000 rpm

(Option for four more Super SeaCat craft)

Fuel injection: The fuel injection system features individual pumps, directly operated from the camshaft, and injectors for each cylinder.

Standard Equipment
Flywheel
Air filter
Air motor starting
Crankcase explosion relief valves
Water to air charge-air coolers
Jacket water cooler
Lubricating oil cooler
Speed governor
Lubricating oil pressure relief valve
Lubricating oil filter
Lubricating oil pump, engine driven
Fuel filter
Pre-start lubricating oil priming pump
Engine cooling water pump, engine driven
Electric tachometer
Engine-mounted instrument panel
Remote exhaust temperature indicator
Charge-air temperature alarm and shut down
Jacket water temperature alarm and shut down
Lubricating oil pressure alarm and shut down
Hand barring gear
Cylinder pressure relief valve
Exhaust silencer
Exhaust uptake adaptor and bellows
Tools for routine maintenance

Optional Equipment
Auto starting
Reverse direction of rotation
Alternative governor
Power take-off from free end of crankshaft
Secondary water pump
Overload switch
Fuel limiter
Flexible mountings
Centrifugal bypass lubricating oil filter
Alternative exhaust silencer
Handed engine control
Tools for engine overhaul

RK270 Technical Data
Cycle: 4-stroke
Bore × stroke: 270 × 305 mm
Mean piston speed: 10.16 m/s at 1,000 r/min
Standard rotation: Counter-clockwise looking on the drive end of the crankshaft
Aspiration: Turbocharged and chargecooled

UPDATED

PERKINS GROUP OF COMPANIES

Frank Perkins Way, Eastfield, Peterborough, Lincolnshire PE1 5NA, UK

Tel: +44 (1733) 67474
Telex: 32501 PERKEN G
Fax: +44 (1733) 582240

M Baunton, *Group Chief Executive*

The Condor family, built at the Perkins Shrewsbury plant, is the latest addition to the Perkins range of marine engines. Three ratings are available: 700 bhp (522 kW) and 800 bhp (597 kW) for pleasure pleasure applications and 600 bhp (448 kW) for light duty commercial usage.

Perkins Condor engine **1991**

CONDOR M800Ti

Type: 8 cylinders in 90 'V' form, water-cooled
Power, max: 597 kW at 2,300 rpm
Bore: 135 mm
Stroke: 152 mm
Capacity: 17.41 l
Cycle: 4-stroke
Aspiration: turbocharged, charge-cooled
Combustion system: direct injection
Rotation: anti-clockwise viewed from rear
Fuel pump: 8 element in-line with mechanical governor
Operating angle: max continuous operating angle, 20 nose up, 8 nose down, 30 thwartships
Weight, dry: 1,818 kg with ZF MPM 1RM350A and PL gearbox.

Standard Equipment
Freshwater heat exchanger cooled engine with gear driven, self-priming raw and freshwater pumps
Freshwater-cooled exhaust manifolds
Twin freshwater-cooled turbochargers
Raw water-cooled charge-air coolers
Dry type air cleaners. Closed circuit engine breather system
High inclination lube oil sump with lube oil drain facility
Freshwater-cooled lube oil system with spin-on lube oil filters
SAE 1 flywheel housing with flywheel suitable for range of marine reverse/reduction transmissions
Adjustable engine support brackets
Engine stop solenoid
Single water-injected exhaust outlet

CONDOR M700Ti

Details as for M800Ti but max power is 522 kW at 2,100 rpm.

CONDOR M600Ti

Details as for M800Ti but max power is 447 kW at 2,100 rpm.

UPDATED

ROLLS-ROYCE INDUSTRIAL AND MARINE GAS TURBINES LTD

Ansty, Coventry, West Midlands CV7 9JR, UK

Tel: +44 (1203) 624000
Telex: 37645
Fax: +44 (1203) 623250

M J Duckworth, *Marine Business Development Manager*

Rolls-Royce offers a range of aero-derived industrial and marine gas-turbines suitable for a wide variety of applications. Over 2,700 marine and industrial gas turbines have been sold or are on order for operations around the world with over 50 million operating hours' experience. Twenty-five navies and civil operators have selected Rolls-Royce engines.

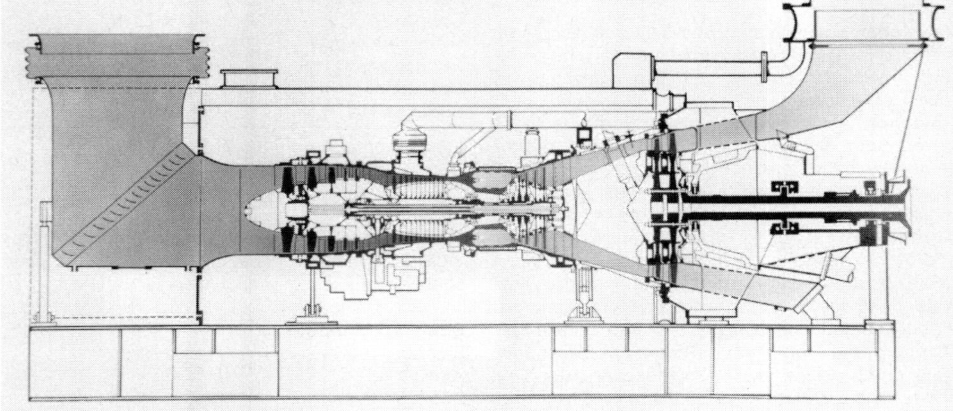

Spey SM1C module **1991**

MARINE SPEY

The Marine Spey module is a complete marine propulsion package for all types of large fast ferry and large high-speed surface transport.

It is a highly efficient fully marinised machine based on the Aero Spey and incorporating much of the state-of-the-art technology incorporated in the Aero Tay which is a development of the Spey.

There are two types available for light craft, both offering high thermal efficiency (in excess of 35 per cent). They are designed to provide the main propulsion power for all current and future large fast ferries, in addition to their existing role of providing high-speed and cruise propulsion power for all types of fast attack craft, patrol vessels, frigates and destroyers.

The Marine Spey module is a complete marine propulsion package for all types of large fast ferry and large high-speed surface transport.

The unit comprises a marinised version of the Spey aero-engine which powers the BAC 1-11 and Fokker F28. Both aircraft are used predominantly in short haul and shuttle operations which are very similar in their operating profile to any ferry operation.

The marinisation of the Aero Spey and the design and development of the complete Marine Spey module has been carried out by Rolls-Royce under contract from the British Ministry of Defence initially to provide a robust reliable naval main propulsion engine. Rolls-Royce pioneered the concept of aero-derivative marine gas-turbines over 35 years ago, current sales total over 1,000 marine engines to 25 nations, and over 4 million total operating hours. By 1993 the Marine Spey alone achieved over 1 million operating hours in service.

The Marine Spey first went to sea with the Royal Navy in 1985 and by 1993 142 units were on order or in service with three navies in six classes of warship. The latest 'C' rated version entered service in 1990 and has been formally adopted by the MoD (UK) as a standard marine propulsion engine for all future warships. It has also been selected by the Japanese Defence Agency to power a new class of DD destroyer.

Module
The module has been designed for ease of installation by the shipbuilders. It is a complete self-contained unit which incorporates as standard the gas generator, power turbine and all of the ancillary systems mounted on a common baseplate. The unit's interfaces are clearly defined and have been kept to a minimum.

Two variants of the module are available:

SM1, a fully enclosed version, which provides full acoustic and heat insulation

SM2, a lightweight version, without an acoustic enclosure.

Performance
Max shaft power: 19,500 kW at 5,650 rpm
Specific fuel consumption: 0.229 kg/kW h
Max civil marine rated shaft power: 18,000 kW at 5,000 rpm

Specific fuel consumption: 0.234 kg/kW h
at atmospheric pressure 101.3 kPa
air intake temperature 15.ldC
fuel calorific value: 42,800 kJ/kg
no inlet or exhaust losses

Weights

SM 1C module complete: 23.4 t
SM 2C module complete: 19 t
Gas generator: 1.9 t

Power Turbine

The power turbine is a long-life high-efficiency two stage design with short, rugged shrouded blades capable of withstanding significant foreign object damage. The rotor system is supported on hydrodynamic bearings housed in a rigid centrebody, and is available with either clockwise or anti-clockwise output shaft rotation.

Gas Generator

The Marine Spey gas generator is a high efficiency second-generation unit of twin spool design, providing excellent operational flexibility, rapid acceleration and good aerodynamic stability. This unit incorporates the latest technology from the Tay aero-engine. The unit operates on class 'A' diesel fuel and produces no visible exhaust smoke at any power level.

Control System

The module is designed for UMS operation and is supplied with a fully integrated electronic control system which interfaces with a ship control system and controls the engine starting, stopping, accelerating and decelerating functions.

The module mounted plant control unit cabinet, contains a full authority local control panel which enables the engine to be started, stopped and operated from the machinery space. It also contains all

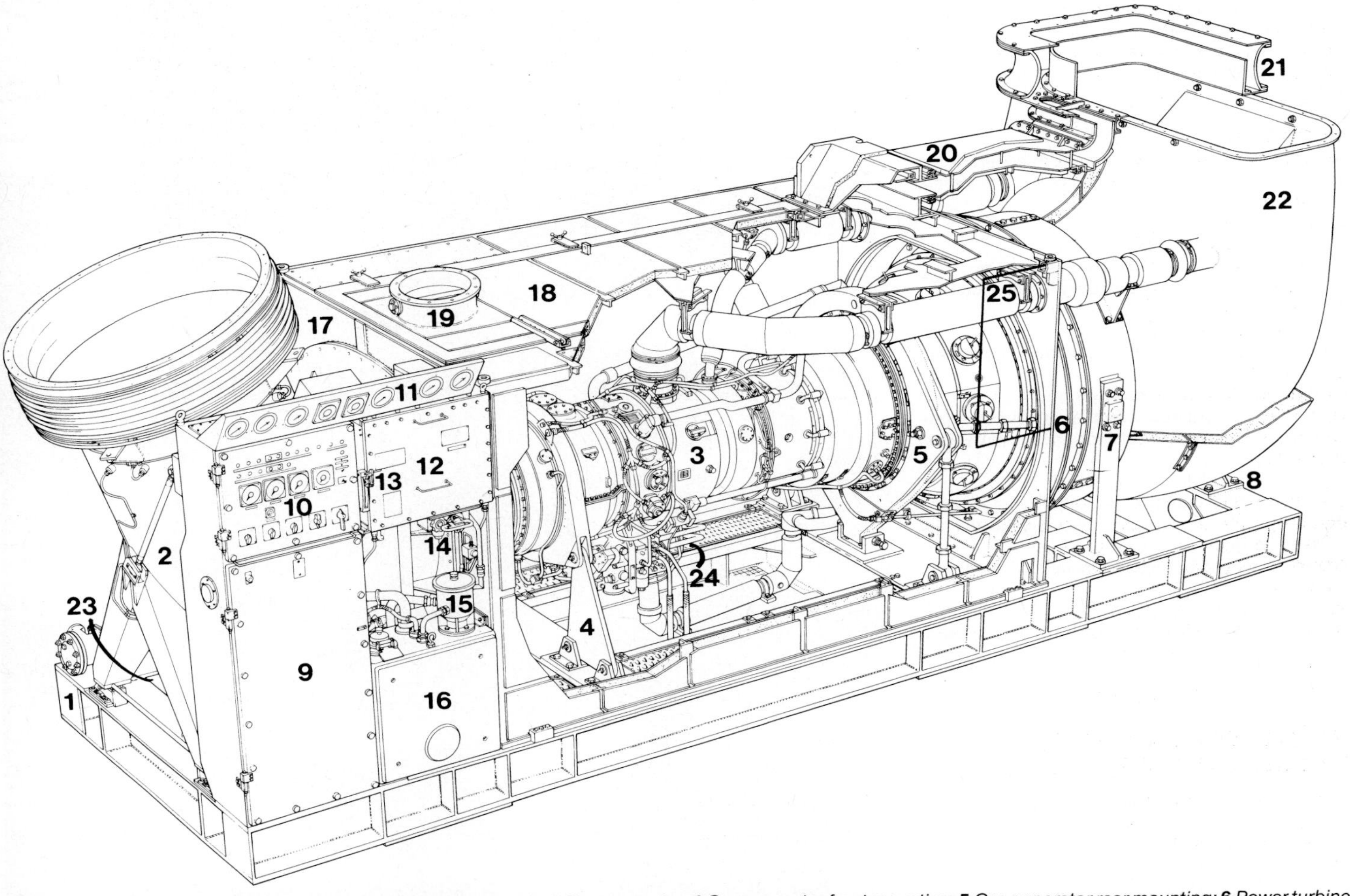

Rolls-Royce Marine Spey SM1C **1** *Baseplate;* **2** *Air intake cascade;* **3** *Gas generator;* **4** *Gas generator front mounting;* **5** *Gas generator rear mounting;* **6** *Power turbine;* **7** *Power turbine front mounting;* **8** *Power turbine rear mounting;* **9** *Plant control unit;* **10** *Local control panel;* **11** *Auxiliary gauge panel;* **12** *Fuel system enclosure;* **13** *Emergency shutdown lever;* **14** *Manual throttle control;* **15** *Air/oil separator;* **16** *Lubricating oil tank;* **17** *Enclosure;* **18** *Hinged roof panel for gas generator removal;* **19** *Enclosure ventilation inlet duct;* **20** *Enclosure ventilation exhaust duct;* **21** *Exhaust bellows assembly;* **22** *Exhaust volute;* **23** *Module's self-contained gas generator lubricating oil system, cooler and filters;* **24** *Spey engine's starter motor;* **25** *Fire extinguisher system* ***1993***

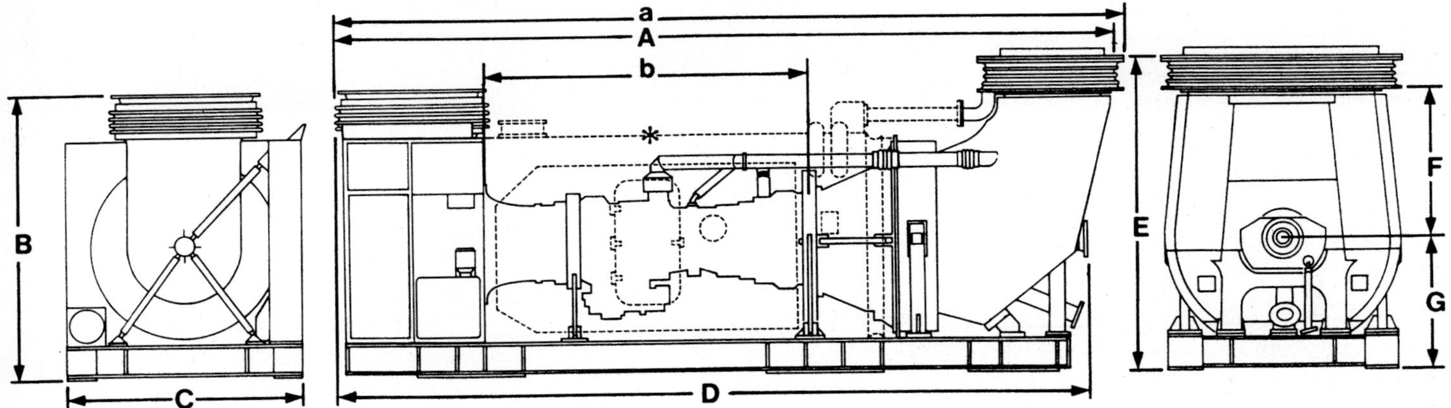

Dimensions and weights of Spey SM1C module

Notes

A = 7,500 mm
B = 2,800 mm
C = 2,285 mm
D = 7,320 mm
E = 3,090 mm
F = 1,475 mm
G = 1,300 mm

a. SM1C module complete
(dry, inclusive of gas generator): 23.4 tonnes
b. SM2C module complete
(dry, inclusive of gas generator): 19 tonnes
c. Gas generator 1.9 tonnes

1995

the instrumentation and control requirements, to permit the engine to remain fully operational including throttle control, under electrical blackout conditions.

Ancillary Systems

The module as standard is complete with the following ancillaries:

Comprehensive electronic control system and local control panel
Compressor wash system
Firefighting system with IR fire detection system
Self-powered enclosure ventilation system
Engine starter system
Air intake cascade bend and exhaust volute, complete with flexible connecting bellows
Acoustic enclosure with access door, viewing portholes, and power points and all associated pipes and fittings
Engine mounting system.

Module Options

To enable the Marine Spey module to be tailored to an individual craft design a number of equipment options is available:

With or without acoustic enclosure
Hydraulic or air engine starting
Cross-connection of engine starting systems
Solid or VLV (Very Low Vibration) module mounting in the craft
Various air intake configurations
With or without fire detection/extinguishing system (SM2C only).

Propulsion Machinery Packaging

Rolls-Royce, if required, offers a complete propulsion package tailored to suit individual craft designs comprising:

Marine Spey module
Speed reducing gearbox, designed to match the individual craft water-jet or propeller and the machinery space design
Spey module/gearbox interconnecting flexible drive coupling.

Maintenance

The Marine Spey uses the highly developed aero-practice of exchanging sections of the gas generator rather than overhauling the complete unit. The engine comprises five Maintenance Assembly Change Units (MACUs) which can be changed independently, considerably reducing the repair cost and downtime of the unit.

The Marine Spey has inherited long life and low maintenance from its Aero Spey and Tay background, coupled with the approach that scheduled maintenance should be carried out without impinging on the craft operating schedule.

WR-21 INTERCOOLED RECUPERATED MARINE GAS-TURBINE

In December 1991, the US Navy awarded an intercooled recuperated gas-turbine design and development contract to a Westinghouse-led team. The team members are: Westinghouse Marine Division as the prime contractor and system integrator; Rolls-Royce, gas-turbine design/development; AlliedSignal, recuperator and intercooler developer; and CAE Electronics, controller developer. The WR-21, as it is now known, will become the next prime mover on US Navy new construction surface combatant ships

Spey SM1C for HMS Brave *conversion* **1991**

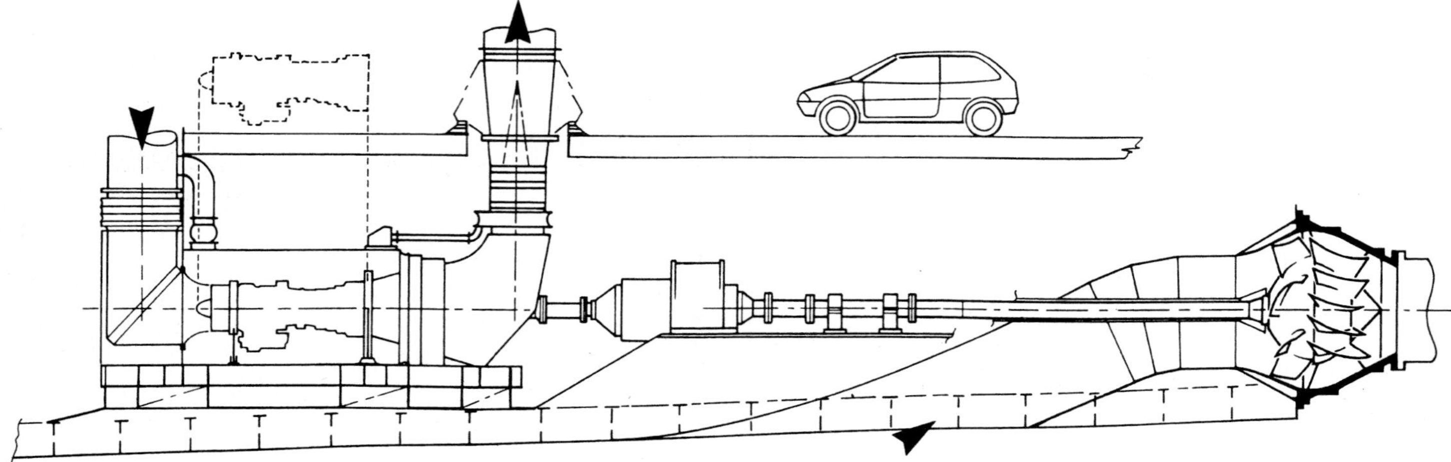

Typical engine removal route **1996**

and has been specifically designed, since its outset, to meet the USN future need for a more economical operating system than the existing simple-cycle engine. The WR-21 is derived from the Rolls-Royce family of RB211 engines. Changes to the aero components have been kept to a minimum to take advantage of the large commercial engine production base and also to profit from the aero engine technological base and accrued reliability. The WR-21 has been designed from concept through to detail design with maintainability being of prime importance.

The WR-21 programme has generated significant interest among other Navies, and became an international collaborative programme in June 1994 following the signature of a co-development Memorandum of Understanding between the British Royal Navy and the US Navy.

International collaboration was further extended in August 1995, when a similar Memorandum was signed between the French Navy and US Navy.

Between the first engine run in July 1994 and October 1995, three engine test programmes, including validation of advanced cycle performance, have been completed at the Royal Navy test facility at Pyestock, UK. A second test facility, the US Navy test site in Philadelphia, USA is nearing completion.

The prime benefit of this 25.2 MW gas turbine development will be a low specification fuel consumption of below 0.20 kg/kW h between 40 per cent and 100 per cent power, with an overall module weight of 46 tonnes.

First production orders are expected in early 1987.

UPDATED

WR-21 gas generator being installed at Pyestock test facility

1996

UNITED STATES OF AMERICA

ALLIEDSIGNAL ENGINE DIVISION

550 Main Street, Stratford, Connecticut 06497, USA

Tel: +1 (203) 385 3863
Telex: 964242
Fax: +1 (203) 385 3255

Carroll R Oates, *Group Manager for Turboshaft Sales and Marketing*

AlliedSignal manufactures a wide range of gas-turbine engines for helicopters, regional jetliners and armoured vehicles, as well as marine and industrial applications. The marine version of the turboshaft and turbofan T55 family is designated the TF40. Over 400 TF40B engines have been supplied for the US Navy LCAC programme, currently involving a fleet of 90 craft. Another 250 engines are in non-US DoD operation around the world.

With over one million hours of operational experience in the LCAC and other craft, the TF40 has passed the Navy's rigorous 1,000 hour qualification test and is the world's only 3,000 kW class marine turbine Navy certified for shipboard propulsion applications.

By January 1996, there were many new TF40 gas-turbine applications in fast ferries, megayachts and patrol boats:

Two TF40s for one 40 m Swath ferry built by Nichols Brothers of Seattle, Washington
Ten TF40s for four 40 m catamaran ferries built by Austal Ships of Fremantle, Australia, all in use in China and all operating over 3,600 hours per year
Two TF40s for lift engines on the Super-Technoliner SES ferry prototype in Japan.
Several new megayachts have been built using diesel and TF40 CODAG systems.

AlliedSignal has a joint CODAG agreement with Detroit Diesel to sell and service the TF40 worldwide. As a result, several TF40s are being placed in megayachts through the Detroit Diesel network.

The AlliedSignal TF40 marine gas turbine engine ***1996***

TF40 AND TF40B

(The 'B' designation is for military use)

The TF40, at 3,430 kW and weighing 1,325 lbs, has the highest power-to-weight ratio of any engine in its class. It is relatively small (about the size of an average office desk), and can go from 'cold' to maximum power in less than 45 seconds. The engine is modular in design with only two of its five modules containing moving parts that require maintenance; these are the combustor-power turbine and gas producer modules. The others are the inlet housing, the accessory gearbox and the oil sump (which only lubricates the bearings, meaning minimal oil consumption). Modules can be detached separately and serviced in place or easily removed through standard-size shipboard hatches.

Scheduled inspections are required after 2,000 hours. These can generally be accomplished in less than eight hours and involve disassembling the hot section of the engine to check for wear. Major maintenance intervals are at 24,000 hours. Since the TF40 is cantilevered off the gearbox, repairs do not disturb the engine's alignment, a feature which simplifies most maintenance operations.

There are plans for an upgraded version of the TF40 with a growth potential to approximately 5,300 shp to be produced by 1997.

Air intake: Side inlet casting of aluminium alloy housing internal gearing and supporting power producer section and output drive shaft. Integral or separately mounted gears are optional. Provision for intake filters and/or silencers. Integral water-wash nozzles are provided.

Compressor: Seven axial stages followed by a single centrifugal stage. Two piece aluminium alloy stator casing, with seven rows of steel stator blades bolted to steel alloy casing diffuser, to which combustion chamber casing is attached. The rotor comprises seven stainless steel discs and one titanium impeller, and is mounted on a shaft supported in a forward thrust ball-bearing and a rear roller bearing. TF40 pressure ratio is 8.4:1.

Combustion chamber: Annular reverse flow type. Steel outer shell and inner liner. Twenty-eight fuel nozzles with downstream injection.

Control system: Electronic fuel control with power and/or speed control available. All cabling and instrumentation supplied as standard. Fully automatic starting and safety systems.

Fuel grade: MIL-T-5624, JP-4, JP-5, MIL-F-16884 diesel, standard and wide-cut kerosene.

Turbine: Two mechanically independent axial flow turbines. First turbine, with two stages, drives compressor. It has cored-out cast blades and is flange-bolted to outer coaxial drive shaft. Second two stage turbine drives output shaft. It has solid blades and is mounted on inner coaxial drive shaft.

Exhaust unit: Fixed area nozzle, with inner cone, supported by six radial struts.

Accessories: Electric, air or hydraulic starter, fuel/oil heat exchanger, fuel and oil pumps and all plumbing and valves are engine-mounted.

Lubrication: Recirculating type. Integral oil tank and cooler.

Oil grade: Synthetic base oils.

Weight: 600 kg

Dimensions

Length: 1.32 m

Width: 0.88 m

Height: 1.11 m

Performance Ratings

Max intermittent (at 15°C sea level): 3,430 kW

Max continuous (at 15°C sea level): 2,983 kW

Fuel Consumption

At max continuous rating: 300 g/kW h (0.494 lb/hph)

Oil consumption: 0.24 l/h (max allowed).

UPDATED

ALLISON ENGINE COMPANY

PO Box 420 SCU5, Indianapolis, Indiana 46206, USA

Tel: +1 (317) 230 5617
Fax: +1 (317) 230 2900

H L Holzworth, *Marine Sales Manager, Industrial Gas Turbines*

Allison has been active in the development of gas-turbines for aircraft, industrial and marine use for many years. Production of the first Allison gas-turbine began in the 1940s, when the company built the power-plant for the P-39, the first jet-powered aircraft to fly in the USA.

Later, the Allison T56 turboprop aircraft engine was developed. It demonstrated outstanding reliability and the same basic design has been adapted for industrial and marine applications. In the early 1960s, the first Allison 501-K gas-turbine-powered electric power-plant went into service. Today, in excess of 1,700 501-K industrial series engines are used not only in electric power-plants but also in mechanical drive and marine applications. The two-shaft marine engine powers the Boeing/Kawasaki Jetfoil and is installed in the Israeli Shipyard Ltd M161 hydrofoil craft for primary propulsion.

By the end of September 1994, Allison had 152 Model 501-KF gas-turbines in operational use, with over one million hours of successful operation in Boeing and Kawasaki Jetfoil and military applications.

In 1995, Rolls Royce plc purchased Allison Engine Company as a strategic manufacturing base in the United States. Since the introduction of the 570/571 KF unit, there have been 23 units placed in operation with 28,000 hours of operation.

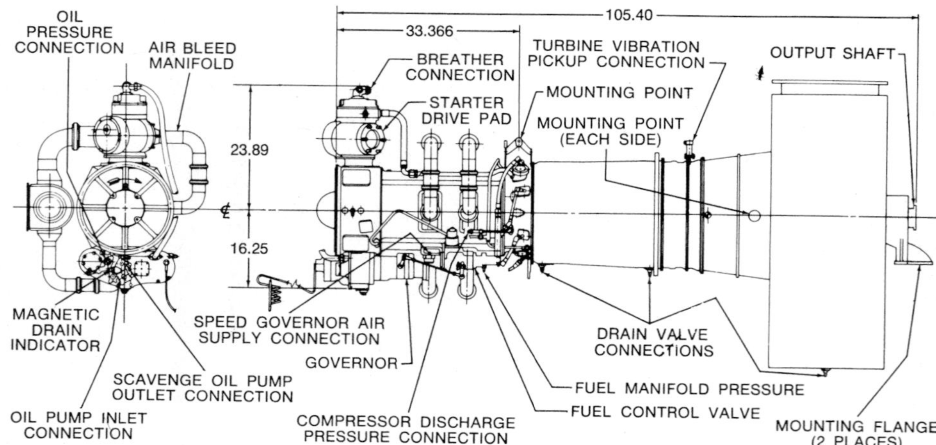

General arrangement of Allison 501-KF (dimensions in inches) **1989**

Allison markets its marine gas-turbine engines directly for commercial, US and foreign military programs. The Allison direct marketing approach includes co-operation with shipyards and local packagers.

ALLISON 501-K SERIES

The Allison 501-K series industrial gas turbine incorporates a 14 stage axial flow compressor, with bleed valves to compensate for compressor surge.

Of modular design, it comprises three main sections: the compressor, combustor and turbine. Each section can be readily separated from the other. Modular design provides ease in handling and servicing of the engine.

The first stage of the four stage turbine section is air-cooled, permitting the engine to be operated at higher than normal turbine inlet temperatures.

The combustor section of the 501-K consists of six combustion chambers of the through-flow type, assembled within a single annular chamber. This multiple provides even temperature distribution at the turbine inlet, thus eliminating the danger of hot spots.

The 501-K series engines are available in single-shaft or free turbine design.

The lightweight, compact size of the 501-K lends itself to multiple engines driving a single shaft through a common gearbox, or as a gas generator driving a customer-furnished power turbine.

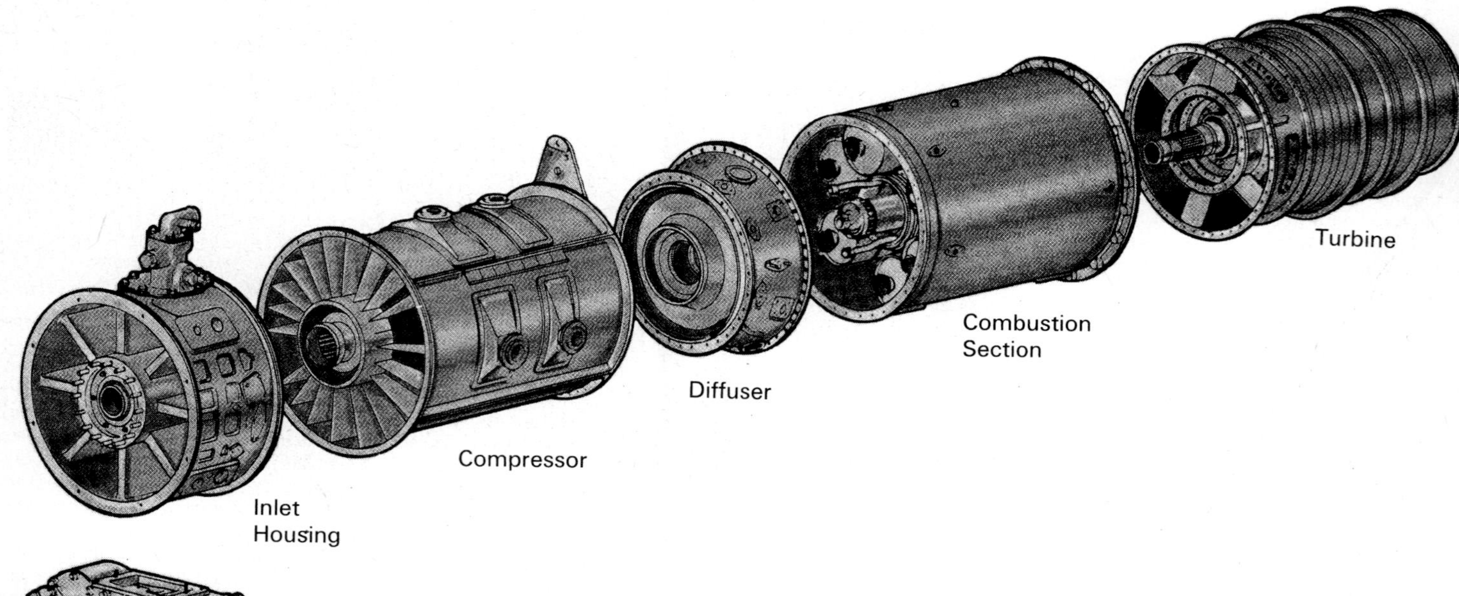

Allison 571-KF **1986**

The engine can be operated on a wide range of liquid fuels. Designation of the marine model is 501-KF5, a brief specification for which follows.

ALLISON 501-KF5
The marine version of the industrial 501-K engine at ISO, SL conditions
Specifications
Continuous power: 4,206 kW
Weight: 1,134 kg
Length: 2,667 mm
Height: 1,378 mm
Calculated temperature: 1,058°C
Exhaust gas temperature: 534°C
Power turbine rpm: 14,200
Specific fuel consumption: 305 g/kW h
Dimensions in inches are shown on the accompanying general arrangement drawing.
Inlet airflow: 26,000 ft³/min
Exhaust airflow: 81,000 ft³/min
Engine jacket heat rejection: 6,000 Btu/min
Lubricating heat rejection (Gasifier): 1,270 Btu/min
Max liquid fuel flow: 1,476 l (390 ghp)
Liquid fuel: DF-1, DF-2 per Allison EMS66
Lubricant: Synthetic oil per Allison EMS35 and 53
Required auxiliaries:
25 hp starter
20-29 V DC electrical power
Power take-off shaft and couplings
Temperature and speed controls from engine furnished signals
Oil cooler
Auxiliary lubricating pump
Compressor inlet sensor
Gauge panel, meters and associated components
Engine exhaust diffusing tail pipe

ALLISON 571-K
A 8,000 hp gas-turbine designed as a prime mover in the industrial and marine fields, the 571 series is a front drive, two-shaft gas-turbine; it entered production in 1986. The Model 571 is a derivative of the US Army's Heavy Lift Helicopter (HLH) engine.

The 571 engine uses a variable geometry, 13 stage, axial flow compressor with a compression ratio of 12.7:1; the inlet guide vanes and the first five stages of stators are variable. The compressor is directly coupled to a two stage axial flow turbine and the vanes and blades of both stages are air-cooled. A power turbine drives the output shaft at the front end of the engine through a torque sensor assembly located on the engine's centreline. The air foils of the power turbine are solid and do not require air cooling. The rear sump features a hydrodynamic, tilting pad thrust bearing.

The 571 is operated by a full authority electronic control which features automatic starting sequence, speed governing, turbine temperature limiting, vibration sensing and so on.

All production 571 engines are fully marinised using materials and coatings selected after more than ¼ million hours of marine experience with Boeing Jetfoils and DD 963 'Spruance' class destroyers.

The 571-K engine incorporates many technological advances and these have resulted in the unit having the lowest specific fuel consumption (sfc) of any turbine in its hp class. At maximum rated power of 8288 hp, the engine's sfc is 0.405 lb/hph.

The engine is installed in the Swedish Stockholm Class fast patrol boats, yachts and Canada's DDH-280 Tribal destroyer programme as the cruise engine.

571-KF three-stage gas-turbine

	Max	Continuous
Power (kW)		
15°C	6,180	5,738
26.7°C	5,669	5,151
Fuel consumption 15°C g/kW	246	249
Power turbine temperature °C	835	803
Compression ratio	12.8	12.3
Corrected airflow,kg/s	20.1	19.7
Power turbine speed (rpm)	11,500	11,500
Weight, kg	789	789
Length, m	1.87	1.87

UPDATED

CATERPILLAR INC

Lafayette Large Engine Center, 3701 State Road, 26 East Lafayette, Indiana 47905, USA

Tel: +1 (317) 448 5000
Fax: +1 (317) 448 5586

CATERPILLAR SUBSIDIARIES

Europe
Caterpillar Overseas SA, PO Box 456, CH-1211 Geneva 6, Switzerland

Tel: +41 (22) 737 4444
Fax: +41 (22) 737 4544

Far East
Caterpillar Asia Pte Ltd, 150 Beach Road, 11-00 Gateway West, Singapore 0718

Tel: +65 390 0300
Fax: +65 390 0302

Japan
Shin Caterpillar Mitsubishi Ltd, 3700 Tana, Sagamihara-shi, Kanagawa-ken 229, Japan

Tel: +81 (427) 621121
Fax: +81 (427) 628542

Australia
Caterpillar Australia Ltd, Private Mail Bag 4, Tullamarine, Victoria 3043, Australia

Tel: +61 (03) 339 9333
Fax: +61 (03) 335 3366

Mexico, the Caribbean, South America
Caterpillar Americas Company, 100 N E Adams, Peoria, Illinois 61629-6330, USA

Tel: +1 (309) 675 4774
Fax: +1 (309) 675 5364

One of four Caterpillar 3616 5420 kW (MCR) engines in the Patricia Olivia ***1993***

3500 Diesel Product Group

Over 20,000 of the 3500 Series engines have been produced, a large percentage of which are for marine applications.

The 3500 Series family consists of vee 8-, 12- and 16-cylinder versions, all with a common bore and stroke of 170 × 190 mm. For fast craft applications the 1,800 and 1,925 rpm ratings yield the highest outputs with the lowest weight to power ratios. The 3516 High-Performance version rated at 2,088 kW at 1,925 rpm for patrol craft, yachts and short trip ferries has a weight to power of 3.56 kg/kW (this a complete factory package consisting of installed fuel, air and oil filters; flywheel and flywheel housing; fuel, oil, jacket water and seawater pumps and instrument panel).

Over 50 of the 3516 High Performance propulsion engines are currently in service in such vessels as the US Coast Guard Island Class vessels, Royal Hong Kong Police patrol vessels, a Saudi Aramco oil recovery catamaran and several yachts including *The Other Woman*, *Miss Turnberry*, and a SWATH Ocean yacht. This 16-cylinder version contains the newest 3500 Series refinements to boost horsepower without penalising the weight to horsepower ratio or fuel economy. At its rated power the engine burns a modest 512.4 l/h and at 1,600 rpm the engine only consumes 286.8 l/h. The specific fuel consumption is 206 g/kW h at 1,925 rpm and 201 g/kW h at 1,600 rpm, with a tolerance of +3 per cent, with all engine driven pumps and conforms to ISO 3046/1 and SAE J1349.

The higher power density and lower fuel consumption of the High-Performance 3516 engine compared to other versions of the 3516 can be attributed to several redesigned components including an improved air intake and exhaust system, increased efficiency turbocharger, high-pressure unit injector fuel system and a two piece piston design. While several components have been changed to increase the power and reduce the weight the High-Performance 3516 shares many parts with the proven standard versions of the 3500 Series.

Like all Caterpillar Marine Engines the 3500 Series engines are expertly supported by the Caterpillar worldwide network of dealers and parts warehouses.

Caterpillar 3516 marine engine

1993

Model	Bore	Stroke	Weight	D rating	D rating	E rating	E rating
3116TA	105 mm	127 mm	681 kg	205 kW	2600 rpm	224 kW	2,800 rpm
3116TA	105 mm	127 mm	681 kg	231 kW	2,600 rpm	261 kW	2,800 rpm
3208NA	114 mm	127 mm	789 kg	157 kW	2,800 rpm	157 kW	2,800 rpm
3208T	114 mm	127 mm	816 kg	224 kW	2,800 rpm	239 kW	2,800 rpm
3208TA	114 mm	127 mm	853 kg	254 kW	2,800 rpm	280 kW	2,800 rpm
3208TA	114 mm	127 mm	943 kg	–	–	325 kW	2,800 rpm
3304BTA	121 mm	152 mm	832 kg	134 kW	2,200 rpm	142 kW	2,200 rpm
3306BTA	121 mm	152 mm	1,120 kg	250 kW	2,200 rpm	265 kW	2,200 rpm
3406BTA	137 mm	165 mm	1,470 kg	365 kW	2,100 rpm	403 kW	2,100 rpm
3408BTA	137 mm	152 mm	1,681 kg	399 kW	2,100 rpm	436 kW	2,100 rpm
3408BTA	137 mm	152 mm	1,814 kg	–	–	597 kW	2,300 rpm
3412TA	137 mm	152 mm	2,459 kg	641 kW	2,100 rpm	641 kW	2,100 rpm
3412TA	137 mm	152 mm	2,313 kg	–	–	895 kW	2,300 rpm
3508TA	170 mm	190 mm	5,216 kg	858 kW	1,800 rpm	–	–
3512TA	170 mm	190 mm	6,532 kg	1,305 kW	1,800 rpm	–	–
3516TA	170 mm	190 mm	8,029 kg	1,641 kW	1,800 rpm	–	–
3516TA	170 mm	190 mm	7,840 kg	2,088 kW	1,880 rpm	2,237 kW	1,925 rpm

Rating Guidelines:
D - for use in patrol, customs, police and some fire boats **E** - for use in pleasure craft with planing hulls, as well as for patrol, pilot and harbour master boats (Some fish boats may operate on duty cycles where **D** or **E** engine ratings apply.)

3600 Diesel Product Group

Production of the Caterpillar 3600 Series in-line engine commenced in 1985, with vee engine production following in 1986. By early 1993, over 550 had been produced, approximately 250 of which were marine engines. The longest running marine engine had 50,000 hours. Caterpillar 3600 marine engines evolved from the heavy fuel (up to 700 cSt), 750 rpm robust version. To meet the needs of fast, weight-sensitive vessels Caterpillar offers a distinct high-performance distillate version. This high-performance design is significantly lighter, offers more power and has a longer Time Between Overhauls (TBO) than the basic HFO engine. To do this, the high-performance design incorporates numerous changes, including reduced mass and special alloy components, lube and air systems optimised for use with distillate fuels, while not affecting the fundamental reliability of the basic engine.

September 1992 saw the first installation of 3600s in fast ferry operation, with four 3616s being installed in the *Patricia Olivia* operated by Buquebus Lines between Buenos Aires and Montevideo, a 74 m wave piercer built by International Catamarans Tasmania Pty Ltd. Rated at 4,020 kW at 765 rpm, they propel the 780 dwt vessel up to a light ship top speed of 42 knots and a loaded cruising speed of 38 knots.

Since that time Caterpillar 3616 engines have been specified for other large Incat catamarans, the wave piercing catamaran 'Hayabusa' and the Bazan Kawasaki monohull ferries of the Mestral and Alhambra class.

The 3,600 engine family includes in-line 6- and 8-cylinders and vee 12- and 16-cylinders, all versions turbocharged and aftercooled. Displacement is 18.5 l/cylinder, with 280 × 300 mm bore and stroke. At rated speeds of 720 to 1,000 rpm, piston speeds average 7.2 to 10.0 m/s. Peak cylinder pressure is 162 bar and BMEP ranges from 22.0 to 23.7 bar at maximum continuous ratings. Specific fuel consumption with all pumps is 188 to 197 g/kW h, based on ISO 3046/1 with +5 per cent tolerance for fuel having an LHV of 42, 780 kJ/kg and weighing 838.9 g/l.

The advantage of the Caterpillar 3600 family is high power to weight ratio combined with long Time Between Overhauls (TBO) and low maintenance costs. At Continuous Service Ratings (CSR) 40,000 hours of operation before the first major overhaul can be expected, with most major components such as pistons and liners being reusable.

Model	CSR (kW) 750 rpm	800 rpm	900 rpm	1,000 rpm	MCR 1,000 rpm	Weight (kg)
3616	3,960	4,160	4,600	4,920	5,420	28,500
3612	2,980	3,120	3,460	3,700	4,060	23,250
3608	1,980	2,080	2,300	2,460	2,710	17,950
3608	1,490	1,560	1,730	1,850	2,030	14,600

The maximum continuous rating, or 'MCR @ 1000' is the maximum rating at which the engine can be continuously applied. Engine ratings between CSR and MCR for specific applications can be matched to owners' specific requirements of TBO, based on their load profile. MCR ratings are also available at the lower engine speeds.

Weights shown include dry engine with all pumps, filters, flywheel, torsional damper, air starter, manifold shields, flexible plate coupling and resilient mounts.

In contrast to many other makes, Caterpillar 3600 engines include integral lube oil and cooling pumps, providing ease of installation and a clean engine room.

UPDATED

CATERPILLAR, SOLAR TURBINES INC

2200 Pacific Highway, PO Box 85376, San Diego, California 92186-5376, USA

Tel: +1 (619) 544 5000
Telex: 695045
Fax: +1 (619) 544 2633

Solar Turbines has designed and manufactured marine gas-turbines since the mid-1940s. In 1950, it became the first company to provide an acceptable gas-turbine of original design for the US Navy's Bureau of Ships. The Solar gas-turbine was a 335 kW (450 hp) axial flow unit which the Navy later procured for main propulsion, generating power for launching shipboard missiles and for driving pulse generators on minesweepers. In a subsequent programme for the US Navy, Solar designed the 1 MW class Saturn gas-turbine engine which has subsequently become the world's most widely used industrial gas-turbine with nearly 5,000 units sold. Today, the company produces industrial and marine gas-turbines in the 1,000 to 11,000 kW range, and more than 9,200 of Solar's Saturn, Centaur and Mars gas-turbines installed offshore and onshore in some 80 nations, have logged more than 450 million operating hours, including over 1,500 units with some 95 million hours in this marine environment.

The most recent marine application order has been for a total of twenty Taurus 60M gas turbines, each rated at 5,200 kW, for a series of ten 45 m Tricat catamarans built by FBM Marine, UK.

TAURUS MARINE GAS-TURBINE

The Taurus marine gas-turbine is a robust, modularly constructed, proven industrial powerplant that includes selected design features adapted from aero-derivative engines such as cooled first stage turbine nozzles and turbine blades for high performance and long life. The Taurus gas-turbine is a simple-cycle, two-shaft machine with a free power turbine assembly for high efficiency and power extraction. It is made with

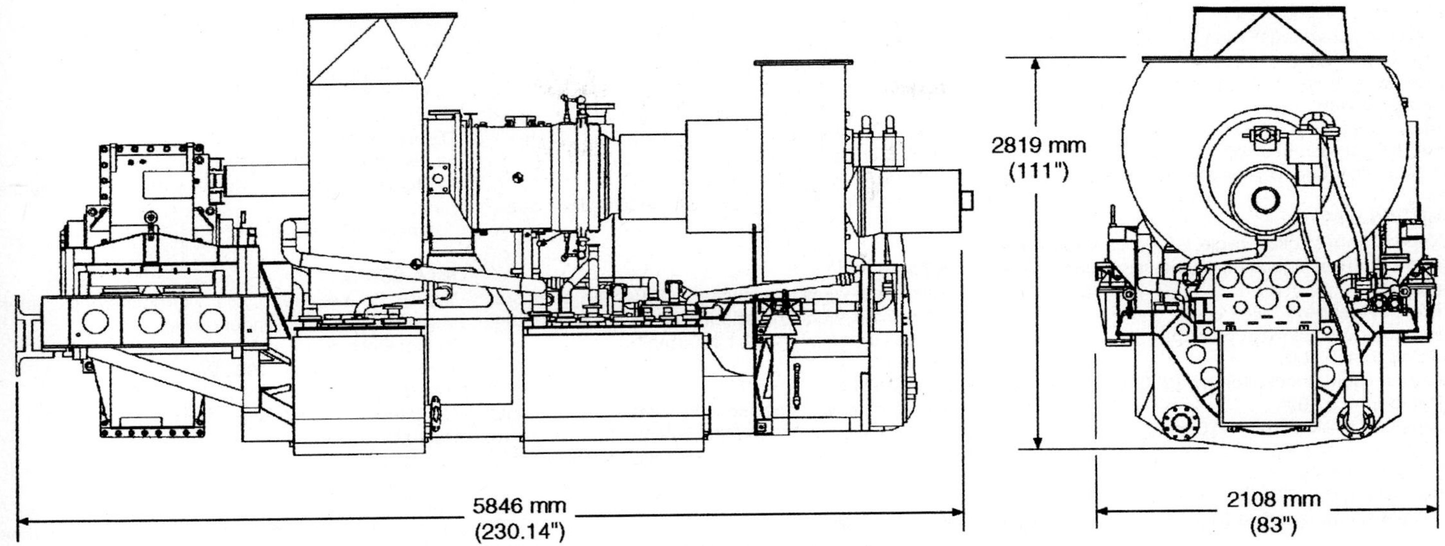

Taurus 60M Gas Turbine Propulsion Module

1996

materials selected for outstanding durability in a marine environment.

Air compressor: The Taurus gas-turbine's air compressor has 12 axial flow stages providing an 11.2:1 compression ratio. The first four stages have variable geometry stators and inlet guide vanes to facilitate smooth and reliable starting. All compressor stages have factory applied corrosion-resistant coatings.

Combustor assembly: The engine has a single annular-type combustor equipped with 12 high-precision vortex-stabilised fuel injectors for highly efficient operation, low nitrous oxide emissions, a uniform temperature profile and extremely stable combustion over a broad range of operating loads and conditions. The combustor liner's advanced alloys and film-air cooling technology contribute to a long and troublefree life.

Gas generator turbine assembly: The first two stages in the Taurus gas-turbine drive its air compressor. The advanced alloy materials, corrosion-resistant coatings and state-of-the-art cooling technology maximise turbine reliability and efficiencies.

Power turbine assembly: The Taurus marine gas-turbine's two stage free power turbine assembly provides a broad range of output speeds for propulsion applications. Power output is delivered from its hot (rear) end through speed-reduction gearing to the driven equipment such as a water-jet propulsion system or propeller.

Fuel system: The fuel system for the Taurus gas-turbine is designed for use with No 1 and No 2 fuel oil and No 1 and No 2 diesel fuel, with an option for kerosenes (JP-4, JP-5, or Commercial Grade). Its major components include a high-pressure fuel pump, boost pump and strainer, main fuel control valve, filters and pressure valve.

Lubrication: The Taurus engine is lubricated by an integral, closed-loop scavenging system that uses synthesised hydrocarbon oils.

Control system: Solar's microprocessor-based Turbotronic™ control system monitors and regulates the static and dynamic parameters of the gas-turbine system and auxiliary devices. The Turbotronic™ control system is available with serial link interfaces for connection to other control systems.

Starting system: The Taurus marine gas-turbine is equipped with an electric start system.

PERFORMANCE, Taurus Marine Gas-turbine*

	Max continuous	Continuous service
Output Power, kW	5,250	4,890
Specific Fuel Consumption, g/kW h	263	265
Inlet Air Flow, kg/s	21.6	21
Exhaust Gas Temperature. °C	500	480
Output Speed, rpm	12,760	12,500

*ISO Conditions: SL/15°/no inlet, or gear losses/60% RH
Liquid fuel, LHV = 42,780 kJ/kg

UPDATED

CUMMINS MARINE INC

4500 Leeds Avenue (Suite 301), Charleston, SC 29405, USA

Tel: +1 (803) 745 1620
Fax: +1 (803) 745 1549

David Crompton, *Marine Marketing Manager*

Formed in 1919 in Columbus, Indiana, the Cummins Engine Company produces a wide range of marine diesel engines which are now manufactured and distributed internationally. In addition to manufacturing plants in the United States, the company also produces diesel engines in Brazil, China, India, Japan, Mexico and the United Kingdom. All these plants build engines to the same specifications thus ensuring interchangeability of parts and the same quality standards. These standards meet design approvals for worldwide agency certification.

VTA-903-M

Type: Four-stroke cycle, turbocharged, after-cooled V-8 diesel engine.

Power Ratings
High output: 336 kW
Rated rpm: 2,600
Medium continuous: 283 kW
Rated rpm: 2,600
Continuous duty: 239 kW
Rated rpm: 2,300
Bore and stroke: 140 × 121 mm

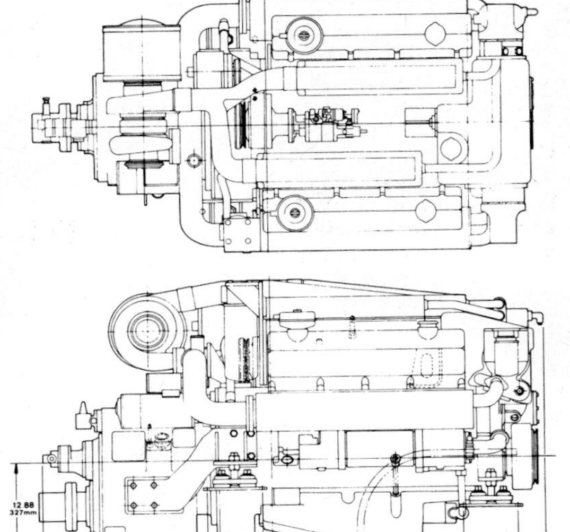

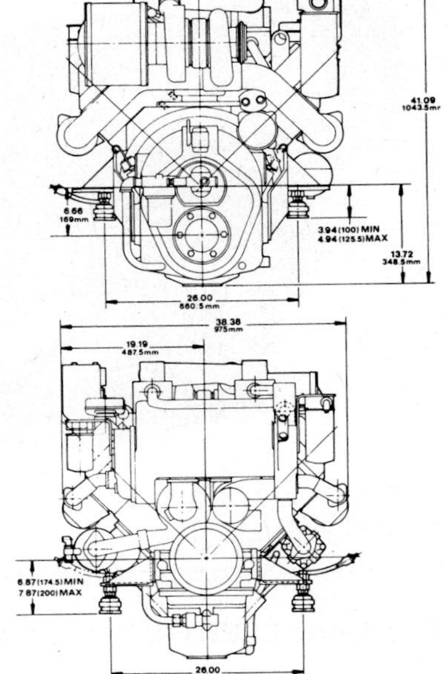

Cummins VTA-903-M turbocharged diesel engine

1986

Displacement: 14.8 l
Oil pan capacity: 19 l
Net weight, dry*: 1,660 kg
*With selected accessories and Capitol HY-22000 marine gear.

6BT5.9-M

Type: Four-stroke cycle, turbocharged, direct injection, in-line, six-cylinder diesel engine.

Power Ratings
High output: 157 kW

Rated rpm: 2,600
Medium continuous: 134 kW
Rated rpm: 2,500
Bore and stroke: 102 × 120 mm
Displacement: 5.9 l
Oil pan capacity: 14.2 l
Net weight, dry: 579 kg*
*Heat-exchanger-cooled and MG-502 marine gear.

6BTA5.9-M

Type: Four-stroke cycle, turbocharged, after-cooled, direct injection, in-line, six-cylinder diesel engine.
Power Ratings
High output: 186 kW (250 bhp)
Rated rpm: 2,600
Medium continuous: 164 kW (220 bhp)
Rated rpm: 2,500
Bore and stroke: 102 × 120 mm
Displacement: 5.9 l
Oil pan capacity: 14.2 l
Net weight, dry: 613 kg*
*Heat-exchanger-cooled and MG-506A marine gear.

KTA19-M

Type: Four-stroke cycle, turbocharged, after-cooled diesel.
Power Ratings
Continuous duty: 373 and 432 kW
Rated rpm: 1,800
Intermittent duty: 507.3 kW** and 410 kW
Rated rpm: 2,100
Bore and stroke: 159 × 159 mm
Displacement: 19 l
Oil pan capacity: 38 l
Net weight, dry: 3,084 kg*
*Heat-exchanger-cooled and MG-502 marine gear.
**Limited production.

KTA38-M

This engine was introduced in 1994 with a 38 litre, 12-cylinder V configuration, producing 780 kW continuous brake power at 1,950 rpm.

KTA50-M2

This engine was introduced in 1996 and is available in ratings from 1,340 kW at 1,900 rpm for medium to light duty to 1,030 kW at 1,600 rpm for heavy duty operations.

6CTA8.3-M

Type: Four-stroke cycle, turbocharged, aftercooled in-line, six-cylinder diesel.
Power Ratings
High output: 302 kW**
Rated rpm: 2,600
Medium continuous: 223 kW
Rated rpm: 2,500
Continuous: 209 kW
Rated rpm: 2,200
Bore and stroke: 114 × 135 mm
Displacement: 8.3 l
Net weight, dry: 824 kg*
*With heat exchanger cooling and MG-507A marine gear.
**Limited production.

NTA-855-M

Type: Four-stroke cycle, turbocharged, after-cooled, in-line, six-cylinder diesel.
Power Ratings
Medium continuous: 298 kW
Rated rpm: 2,100
Continuous: 261 kW
Rated rpm: 1,800
Bore and stroke: 140 × 152 mm
Displacement: 14 l
Net weight, dry: 205.5 kg*
*With selected accessories and MG-514 marine gear.

UPDATED

DETROIT DIESEL CORPORATION

13400 Outer Drive West, Detroit, Michigan 48239-4001, USA

Tel: +1 (313) 592 5000
Telex: 4320091
Fax: +1 (313) 592 7288

A A Kozel, *Vice President, Marine Sales*

Detroit Diesel Corporation has its headquarters in Detroit, Michigan and has the design, manufacturing and sales responsibilities for a complete line of heavy-duty diesel engines, supported by a worldwide distributor/dealer network.

A range of marine diesel engines is available with maximum power levels between 187 and 1,790 kW. The table on the right gives the maximum marine ratings for these engines.

Model	Max hp	rpm	Cyl	Displacement	Weight
DD500 T	187 kW	3,200	8	8.2 l	639 kg
DD500 TI	224 kW	3,200	8	8.2 l	655 kg
4-71	242 kW	2,600	4	4.7 l	817 kg
6V-53TI	298 kW	2,800	6	5.22 l	898 kg
6-71TI	362 kW	2,500	6	6.9 l	1,170 kg
6V-92TA	410 kW	2,300	6	9.0 l	1,223 kg
6V-92TA (DDEC)	421 kW	2,300	6	9.0 l	1,239 kg
8V-92TA	548 kW	2,300	8	12.1 l	1,570 kg
8V-92TA (DDEC)	567 kW	2,300	8	12.1 l	1,577 kg
12V-71TA	671 kW	2,300	12	13.9 l	1,793 kg
12V-71TA (DDEC)	671 kW	2,300	12	13.9 l	1,807 kg
12V-92TA	805 kW	2,300	12	18.1 l	2,225 kg
12V-92TA (DDEC)	828 kW	2,300	12	18.1 l	2,239 kg
16V-92TA	1,044 kW	2,300	16	24.1 l	2,714 kg
16V-92TA (DDEC)	1,082 kW	2,300	16	24.1 l	2,727 kg
12V-149TI (DDEC)	1,343 kW	2,100	12	29.3 l	5,063 kg
16V-149TI (DDEC)	1,790 kW	2,100	16	39.1 l	6,114 kg

VERIFIED

DDC 12V-92TA **1994**

DDC 16V-149TI **1993**

GENERAL ELECTRIC COMPANY

GE Aircraft Engines

1 Neumann Way, Mail Drop N109, Cincinnati (Evendale), Ohio 45215-6301, USA

Tel: +1 (513) 243 6136

Eugene F Murphy, *President and Chief Executive Officer*
Dennis R Little, *Vice President and General Manager, GE Marine and Industrial Engines Division*
Robert R Bass, *Manager, Marketing Communications*

General Electric Company's Dr Sanford A Moss operated the first gas-turbine in the USA in 1903 and produced the aircraft turbo-supercharger, first flown in 1919 and mass produced in the Second World War for US fighters and bombers.

The company built its first aircraft gas-turbine in 1941, when it began development of a Whittle-type turbo-jet, under an arrangement between the British and American governments.

Since then General Electric has produced over 82,000 aircraft gas-turbines for military and commercial aircraft, as well as aircraft derivative gas-turbines for marine and industrial uses.

General Electric offers three gas-turbines for marine service: the LM 2500, the LM 500 and the LM 1600.

LM 2500

The LM 2500 marine gas-turbine is a two-shaft, simple-cycle, high-efficiency engine derived from the General Electric military TF39 and the commercial CF6 high bypass turbofan engines for the US Air Force C-5 Galaxy transport and DC-10, 747 and A300 commercial jets. The compressor, combustor and turbine are designed to give maximum progression in reliability, parts life and time between overhauls. The engine has a simple-cycle efficiency of more than 37 per cent, which is due to advanced cycle pressures, temperatures and component efficiencies.

Two GE LM 2500s power the Rodriquez 101 m high-speed monohull passenger/car ferries designated Aquastrada. Two LM 2500s have been chosen to power the Stena High-Speed Service (HSS) ferry, the world's largest car/passenger ferry.

The LM 2500 marine gas-turbine provides foilborne power for the US Navy PHM hydrofoils. The six PHM Pegasus class vessels were built by the Boeing Company, Seattle, Washington. In addition to the Pegasus hydrofoils, GE LM 2500 marine gas-turbines propel over 310 ships. These ships include the 'Perry' class FFG-7 frigates, 'Spruance' class DD-963 destroyers, 'Kidd' class DDG-993 destroyers, 'Ticonderoga' class Aegis CG-47 cruisers, 'Burke' class DDG-51 Aegis destroyers and the supply class AOE-6 auxiliary ships of the US Navy.

In combination with diesels the LM 2500 powers several classes of high-speed patrol boats with top speeds of more than 40 knots. LM 2500 gas-turbines and diesel combinations also provide propulsive power for a broad cross-section of 37 ship programmes for 24 navies throughout the world, including aircraft carriers, cruisers, destroyers, frigates and corvettes.

Total operating time of LM 2500 engines in all marine service is more than four million hours.

Type: Two-shaft, axial flow, simple-cycle.
Air intake: Axial, inlet bellmouth or duct can be customised to installation.
Combustion chamber: Annular.
Fuel grade: Kerosene, JP4, JP5, diesel, distillate fuels and natural gas.
Turbine: Two stage gas generator, six stage power turbine.
Jet pipe: Vertical or customised to fit installation.
Oil specification: Synthetic turbine oil (MIL-L-23699) or equal.
Mounting: At power turbine and compressor front frame.
Starting: Pneumatic, hydraulic.
Dimensions
Length: 6,630 mm
Width: 2,100 mm
Performance rating: 24,310 kW (32,600 shp) at 15°C at sea level.
Specific fuel consumption: 0.226 g/kW h.

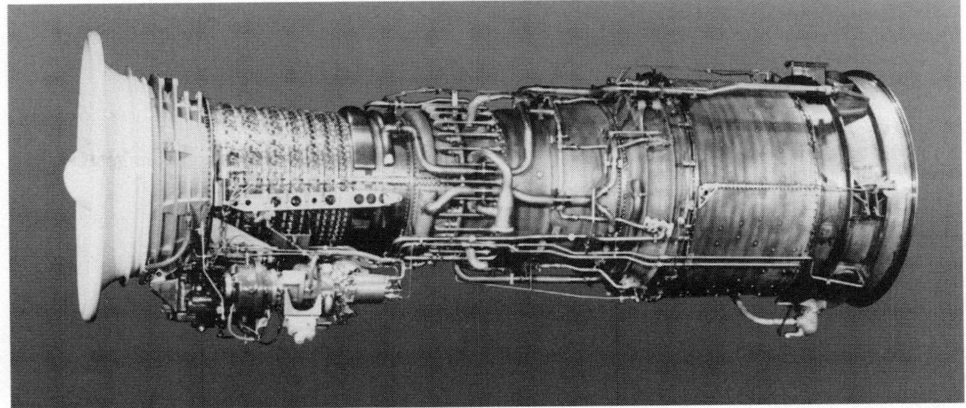

LM 2500 **1990**

LM 500 **1991**

LM 1600

The LM 1600 is derived from GE's F404 engine, which powers the F/A-18 Hornet and F-117 Stealth Fighter. A simple-cycle, three-shaft gas-turbine engine, the LM 1600 has been selected as the power-plant for a number of large high-speed vessels. The *Destriero*, which set the speed record for a transatlantic crossing without refuelling, is powered by three LM 1600 engines developing up to a total 44,740 kW (60,000 bhp). Another vessel, designed by Martin Francis and built by the Blohm+Voss shipyard, named *Eco*, is powered by one LM 1600 engine in a CODOG configuration. Additionally the two Danyard/NQEA Seajet 250 high-speed ferries are powered by two LM 1600 gas turbines each.

MTU (Motoren- und Turbinen-Union) of Germany and GE Aircraft Engines have entered into an arrangement whereby MTU will package the LM 1600 gas-turbine in marine modules for all types of naval applications.

Type: Three-shaft, axial flow, simple-cycle.
Air intake: Axial, inlet bellmouth or duct can be customised to installation.
Combustion chamber: Annular.
Fuel grade: Kerosene, JP4, JP5, diesel, distillate fuels and natural gas.
Turbine: Two stage gas generator, two stage power turbine.
Jet pipe: Vertical or customised to fit installation.

LM 1600 **1991**

Oil specification: Synthetic turbine oil (MIL-L-23699) or equivalent.
Mounting: At turbine frame and front frame.
Starting: Pneumatic, hydraulic.
Dimensions
Length: 4,890 mm
Width: 2,032 mm
Performance rating: 14,913 kW (20,000 shp) at 15°C at sea level.
Specific fuel consumption: 226 g/kW h.

LM 500

The LM 500, derived from GE's TF34 high bypass aircraft engine, is a simple-cycle, two-shaft gas-turbine engine that powers the Danish Navy's Flyvefisken (Stanflex 300) patrol boat, a Japanese PG class hydrofoil patrol craft, and the Kværner Fjellstrand Flying FoilCat class passenger ferry. Throughout its operating range, the LM 500 is characterised by outstanding efficiency, which is attributable to the high pressure ratio of the

compressor, high turbine inlet temperature, improved component efficiency and conservation of cooling airflow.
Type: Two-shaft, axial flow, simple-cycle.
Air intake: Axial; vertical inlet duct can be customised to installation.
Combustion chamber: Annular.
Fuel grade: Kerosene, JP4, JP5, diesel, distillate fuels, and natural gas.
Turbine: Two stage gas generator, four stage power turbine.
Jet pipe: Vertical or axial or customised to fit installation.
Oil specification: Synthetic turbine oil (MIL-L-23699) or equivalent.
Mounting: At turbine frame and front frame.
Dimensions
Length: 2,187 mm
Width: 864 mm
Performance rating: 4,474 kW (6,000 shp) at 15°C at sea level.
Specific fuel consumption: 270 g/kW h.

UPDATED

UNITED TECHNOLOGIES INTERNATIONAL INC

Turbo Power and Marine Systems Inc

Aircraft Road, PO Box 611, Middletown, Connecticut 06457, USA

Tel: +1 (203) 343 2000
Telex: 221432 TPM UTC
Fax: +1 (203) 343 2266

M A Cvercko, *Director, Marketing and Sales*

MFT8 gas-turbine ***1995***

Turbo Power and Marine Systems Inc (TPM) designs, builds and markets industrial and marine gas-turbine power plants and related systems throughout the world. It also provides a systems support for its installations. The current gas-turbine product line includes the 25 MW class FT8, and a 50 MW class FT8 Twin Pac (electric power generation only). Support of the existing fleet of FT4 gas-turbines is also continued.

Canadian sales of the TPM produced line are handled by Pratt & Whitney Canada which also manufactures and sells the 1.0 MW ST6 and 1.8 MW ST18 marine gas-turbines.

The FT8 is also marketed by Turbo Power's licensee/engine packaging partner MAN Gutehoffnungshutte GmbH (MAN GHH). The unit is marketed in the People's Republic of China by Turbo Power's licensee China National Aero-Technology Import and Export Corporation (CATIC).

A modified version of the FT8 called the MFT8, which consists of the GG8 gas generator and a lightweight power turbine designed and manufactured by Mitsubishi Heavy Industries, is marketed for marine and other applications by MHI and TPM.

MARINE GAS-TURBINES

TPM's FT4 marine gas-turbines were first used for boost power in military vessels, including two Royal Danish Navy frigates, 12 US Coast Guard Hamilton class high endurance cutters and four Canadian Forces DDH-280 'Iroquois' class destroyers. Another boost power application of the FT4 is in the Fast Escort and ASW vessel *Bras d'Or* also built for the Canadian Armed Forces. Another application is in two 12 000 tonne Arctic icebreakers for the US Coast Guard. With three FT4 marine gas-turbines, these vessels are capable of maintaining a continuous speed of 3 knots through ice 1.8 m thick, and are able to ram through ice 6.4 m thick. One of these vessels actually cut through the polar ice cap to reach the North Pole.

TPM's marine gas-turbines were used for both the main and boost propulsion in the four Canadian DDH-280 destroyers. These are the first military combatant vessels to be designed for complete reliance on gas-turbine power.

Twin FT4 gas-turbines were also used in the *Finnjet,* a high-speed Finnlines passenger liner which cut the Baltic crossing time in half, routinely maintaining 30 knots, with an engine availability of over 99 per cent. The record time for an engine replacement is 1 hour 20 minutes; two hours being the normal time.

FT8 MARINE GAS-TURBINE

TPM introduced the FT8 marine gas-turbine based on the Pratt & Whitney JT8D aircraft engine, which incorporates advanced technology from Pratt & Whitney PW4000 and PW2000 series commercial aircraft gas-turbine engines. Thirty FT8 units are already in commercial operation in seven countries. The FT8's continuous rating at 25,204 kW or maximum rating of 27,500 kW size is ideal for many marine applications.

FT8 marine gas-turbine ***1993***

Three MFT8 gas-turbine engines have been supplied to Mitsubishi Heavy Industries for the Techno-Superliner demonstration programme in Japan. This vessel achieved 55 knots on sea trials in 1994. The full-scale vessel is to be propelled by four MFT8's (plus one spare) at speeds of over 50 knots.

The FT8 aero-derivative marine gas-turbine is of a modular design with major components designed to be easily removed for servicing. With a spare gas generator to replace the one removed, the ship's power-plant can be changed in a matter of hours. Borescope inspection features allow internal inspection without disassembly.

GAS GENERATOR

Type: Simple-cycle two-spool gas generator. A low-pressure compressor is driven by a two stage turbine and a high-pressure compressor is driven by a single stage turbine. The burner section has nine burner cans each equipped with one fuel nozzle.
Air intake: Steel casing with radial struts supporting the front compressor bearing.
Low-pressure compressor: Eight stage axial flow on inner of two concentric shafts driven by two stage turbine and supported on ball and roller bearings. Variable geometry inlet guide vanes and the first two stages of vanes improve part power efficiencies and reduce the start up power requirements.
High-pressure compressor: Seven stage axial flow on outer hollow shaft driven by single stage turbine and running on ball and roller bearings.
Combustion chamber: Nine burner cans located in an annular arrangement and enclosed in a one piece steel casing. Each burner has one fuel nozzle.
Turbines: Steel casing with hollow guide vanes. Turbine wheels are bolted to the compressor shafts and are supported on ball and roller bearings. A single stage turbine drives the high-pressure compressor and a two stage turbine drives the low-pressure compressor.

POWER TURBINE

Power turbine (MFT8): The MFT8 power turbine was developed by Mitsubishi Takasago Works as a lightweight substitute for those FT8 power turbines directed to land-based applications. The weight of the three stage 5,000 rpm MFT8 power turbine is 2,600 kg. The MFT8 employs a cantilevered rotor design as opposed to the straddle arrangement used on the FT8.

Control system: The control system is a digital system based on the Woodward Governor Company's Netcon 5000 controller. All software is developed by TPM, and can be integrated with ship systems.

Accessory drive: Starter, fluid power pump, tachometer drives for the low-pressure compressor shaft and the high-pressure compressor shaft.

Lubrication: Scavenge pump return system and supply system pumps.

Oil specifications: Synthetic lubricating oil, PWA-521.

Starting: Pneumatic, hydraulic or electric.

Dimensions

Length: 6,373 mm
Width: 1,962 mm
Height: 2,440 mm

Fuel Specifications

Marine diesel, Aviation grade kerosene, light distillate (naptha) TPM-FR-1.
Treated crude and residual oil, refer to manufacturer.

MFT8 DESIGN PARAMETERS
59°F, Sea Level, No Losses, 43 MJ/kg
Shaft Output (kW): 25200
Heat rate (kg/kW h): 0.218
Airflow: 83.9 kg/s
Pressure ratio: 19.8:1
Combustor exit temperature: 1,190°C
Power turbine exhaust temperature: 459°C

UPDATED

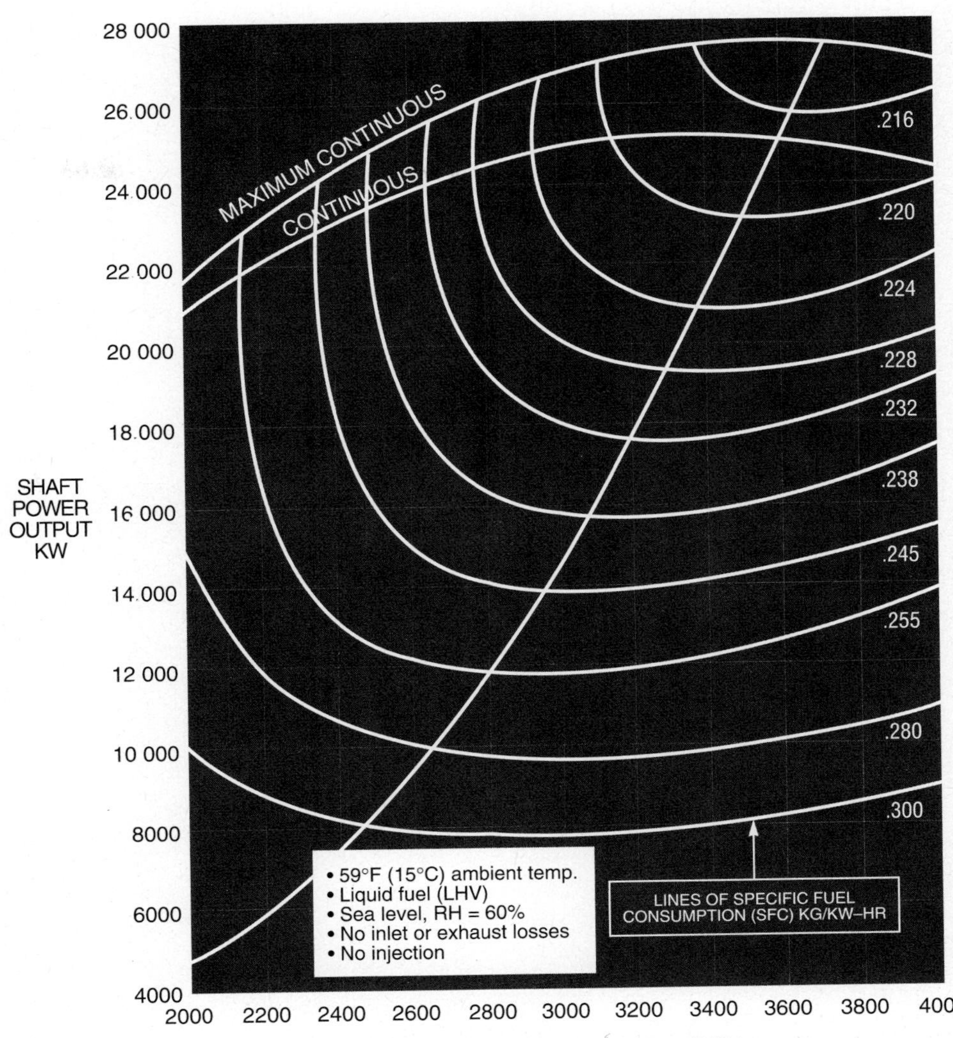

MFT8 marine gas-turbine performance
1993

TRANSMISSIONS

Company Listing by Country

Germany
Lohmann + Stolterfoht GmbH
Reintjes GmbH
Renk AG
ZF Marine

Italy
FB Design Srl
Rexroth SpA

Japan
Niigata Converter Co Ltd

Norway
Servogear A/S
Ulstein Propeller A/S

Switzerland
Maag Gear Company Ltd

United Kingdom
Allen Gears

United States of America
The Cincinnati Gear Company
Detroit Diesel Corporation
Twin Disc Inc

GERMANY

LOHMANN + STOLTERFOHT GmbH

PO Box 1860, D-58408 Witten, Germany

Tel: +49 (2302) 8770
Telex: 8229005
Fax: +49 (2302) 877400

Type	Torque	Reduction ratios available
Navilus GUU	5.0 to 16 kNm	1.5 to 6.5:1.0
Navilus GWC	15.5 to 190 kNm	2.0 to 6.0:1.0
Navilus GCS/GUC	39.0 to 2,200 kNm	1.5 to 6.0:1.0
Navilus GUT	570.0 to 3,580 kNm	1.5 to 12.0:1.0
Navilus GVA/GVE	50.0 to 1,620 kNm	2.0 to 6.0:1.0
Navilus GVG	690 to 3,580 kNm	2.0 to 6.0:1.0

Lohmann and Stolterfoht manufactures a range of gearboxes, reduction gearboxes, reverse reduction gearboxes, twin output/single output gearboxes, clutches and couplings for torques ranging from 5 kNm to 3,580 kNm for marine propeller transmissions.

VERIFIED

REINTJES GmbH

PO Box 101344, D-31784 Hameln, Germany

Tel: +49 (5151) 1040
Fax: +49 (5151) 104300

UK representative: European Marine and Machine Agencies, 22-26 Gore Road, New Milton, Hampshire BH25 6RX, UK

Tel: +44 (1425) 618704
Fax: +44 (1425) 617424

Reintjes has specialised in the manufacture of marine gearboxes for harbour craft and sea-going vessels for more than 65 years. The company has produced over 70,000 gearboxes.

Reintjes manufactures gearboxes ranging from 800 to 5000 kW for fast vessels with marine propeller transmissions, and up to approximately 6,000 kW for water-jet drives.

GEARBOXES FOR FAST VESSELS

The gearboxes of the Types WVS/WLS and VLJ have been designed specially for fast vessels and for vessels with water-jet drive, such as marine craft, patrol boats or yachts, as well as all types of vessels with similar exacting requirements.

Owing to their specific design for these fields of application, the hydraulically operated reverse reduction gearbox of Type WVS and the hydraulically operated reduction gearboxes of Types WLS and VLJ have special advantages to offer, which are: high efficiency, low weight per horsepower due to light metal housing and light construction, small size, excellently synchronised engagement and optimum smooth running.

For application in fast vessels with water-jet propulsion Reintjes has developed reduction gearboxes with and without clutches. By using various distances and arrangements of output and input the most favourable arrangement of engine and water-jet can be selected for hulls, each with either one or two engines. Requested reduction ratios are tailor-made enabling the water-jet to operate with the best possible efficiency.

Built-in disc clutches enable a diesel engine start-up with water-jet being disengaged. The

Reintjes WVS 2232 (2.025:1) gearbox ***1992***

Type	Reduction ratios	N/n1 kW/rpm	Max input speed (rpm)
WVS/WLS 234	1.179-2.542	0.385	2,400
	2.958	0.248	2,400
	3.571	0.213	2,400
	4.053	0.180	2,400
WVS/WLS 334	1.122-2.538	0.470	2,400
	2.956	0.400	2,400
	3.521	0.320	2,400
WVS/WLS 430 L	1.184-3.550	0.365	2,300
WVS/WLS 430	1.184-2.458	0.600	2,300
	2.904	0.520	2,300
	3.315	0.450	2,300
	3.550	0.420	2,300
WVS/WLS 730 L	1.414-3.047	0.700	2,100
	3.541	0.670	2,100
	3.954	0.600	2,100
WVS/WLS 730	1.414-3.047	0.950	2,100
	3.541	0.670	2,100
	3.954	0.600	2,100
WVS/WLS 930 L	1.348-3.043	1.000	2,100
	3.541	0.930	2,100
	3.958	0.830	2,100
	4.409	0.720	2,100
WVS/WLS 930	1.348-3.043	1.340	2,100
	3.541	0.930	2,100
	3.958	0.830	2,100
	4.409	0.720	2,100
WVS/WLS 2232	1.725-3.037	2.280	1,700/2,100
	3.451	2.080	1,700/2,100
	3.954	1.900	1,700/2,100
	4.590	1.600	1,700/2,100

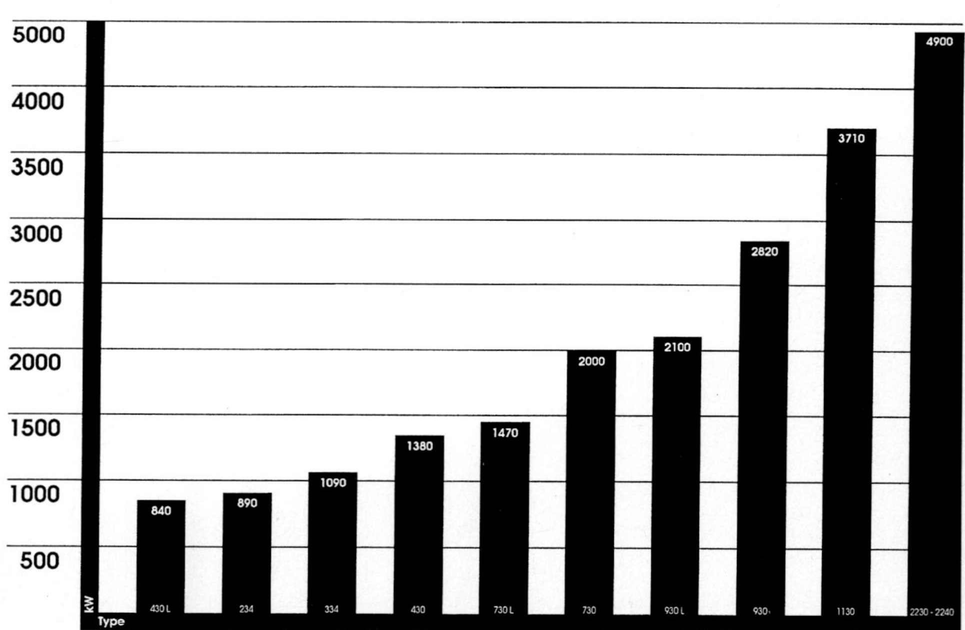

Power range of Reintjes gearboxes for fast vessels ***1995***

gearboxes are provided with connection facilities for hydraulic pumps required for water-jet control. The projected gearboxes are available for engine ratings to approximately 6,000 kW and in numerous configurations. Standard type is VLJ 930.

US NAVY PATROL BOAT GEARBOXES

WVS 2232/2.025:1 Installed in US Navy Patrol Boats. Each vessel incorporates four Paxman engines rated individually at 2,500 kW at 1,500 rpm. Thus, 10,000 kW is available in total, enough to give a top speed exceeding 30 knots. Each engine is mated to a series WVS 2232 hydraulically operated reverse reduction gearbox with vertically offset shafts and a 2.025:1 reduction ratio. The gearboxes are fitted with built-in thrust bearing, seawater-resistant oil cooler, oil pump, duplex filter and electrically actuated control and trolling valve facility. This allows operation at low propeller speeds with slipping clutch and can be used in ahead and astern running and for manoeuvring. The gear's spur wheels are helically toothed, case-hardened and tooth flank ground.

WAVE PIERCER CATAMARAN
Condor 9

The power input is from four MWM diesel engines, Type 16 V 604 B, having an output of 1.690 kW each. The diesel engines run in connection with a Reintjes reduction gear equipped with a hydraulically operated clutch, especially developed for operation in fast vessels with water-jet propulsion Type VLJ 930 HL/HR, having a reduction ratio of 1.8056:1.0. The installed water-jet is MJP Type J 650 R-DD.

Due to the built-in disc clutch the diesel engine can be started with the water-jet disengaged.

The gears of the Reintjes gearbox are horizontally offset, that is, they are equipped with horizontally left and horizontally right output shafts. The gear mounting is rigid on the foundation. Gear brackets are seated on Chock-Fast. The horizontal gear design for *Condor 9* allows an optimum arrangement of diesel engines and water-jets in the individual hulls. As *Condor 9* would operate as a ferry, there was a demand for fitting a complete spare propulsion plant at short notice. Due to the variable gear design it is possible for the first time to have a suitable replacement with only one gearbox for all four propulsion plants. Slight modification work only is required. The gears are supplied with connections for hydraulic pumps for the water-jet control system.

The gears can also be delivered vertically offset. Either a rigid or resilient gear mounting can be provided.

VERIFIED

RENK AG

Augsburg Works, Gögginger Strasse 73, D-86159 Augsburg 1, Germany

Tel: +49 (821) 57000
Telex: 53781
Fax: +49 (821) 570 0460

Rheine Works, Rodder Damm 170, D-48432 Rheine, Germany

Tel: +49 (5971) 7900
Telex: 981637
Fax: +49 (5971) 790208

PLS AND PWS GEARBOXES

Renk marine planetary gear units (PLS and PWS series) have been specifically developed for use in fast ships such as corvettes, speedboats, minesweepers, minelayers, OPVs and IPVs. Designed for a performance range between 800 and 10,000 kW, they cover a very wide range of applications. The specific characteristics and advantages of disconnectable planetary gear units (PLS) and planetary reversing gear units (PWS) are:

- ratios 1.5 to 4.8
- PWS series efficiencies 97.5 to 98 per cent
- PLS series efficiencies 98.5 to 99 per cent
- compact design, permitting favourable engine room concepts
- low power-to-weight ratio of less than 0.5 kg/kW
- coaxial input and output shafts for optimum power plant layouts
- high shock resistance due to planetary design
- insensitivity of transmission elements to hull distortion, providing high operational reliability even under extreme service conditions
- high efficiency due to epicyclic concept
- starboard and port gear units offer identical connection interfaces and with PWS units this means completely identical starboard and port gear units, even for multipropeller ships
- forward and reverse gears of PWS units are both designed for 100 per cent loads, engines can therefore operate with the same direction of rotation without affecting the gear unit
- on request, these gear units can be built under the supervision of any classification society. Antimagnetic versions are available
- high reliability
- suitable for use with gas-turbines
- if required, low-speed gear can be provided
- special design with vertically offset shafts for V drives.

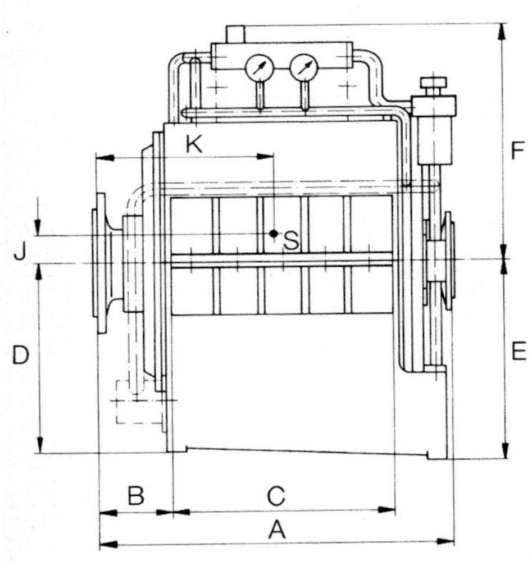

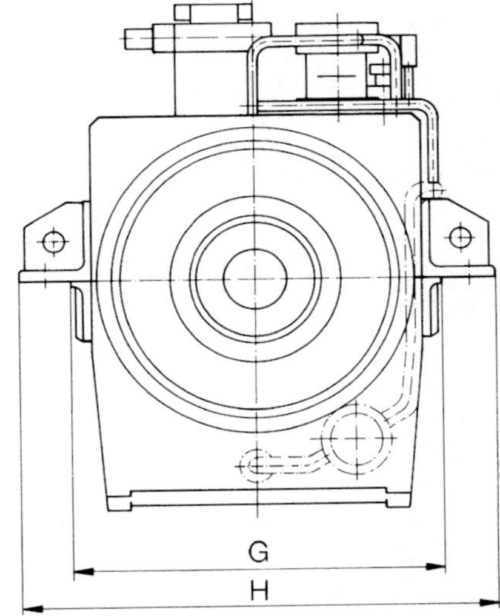
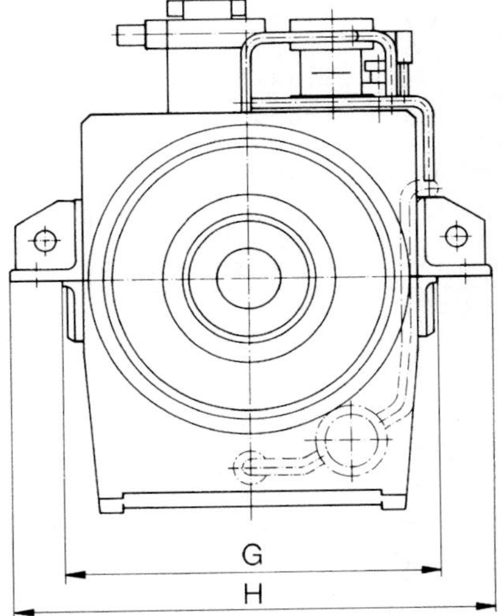

Renk PLS and PWS series gearboxes (see table for dimensions) ***1995***

PWS gearbox ***1995***

Gear unit Type Size	Dimensions A i<2.8 i>5 mm	A i>2.8 i<5 mm	B mm	C mm	D mm	E mm	F mm	G mm	H mm	J mm	K mm	Weight, dry i<2.8 i>5 kg	Weight, dry i>2.8 i<5 kg	Thrust kN	Oil content litres
PLS															
18	900	800	200	480	530	560	710	850	1,120	80	400	1,350	1,200	130	90
25	1,000	900	225	530	600	630	800	950	1,250	90	450	1,750	1,550	160	110
35.5	1,120	1,000	250	600	670	710	900	1,060	1,400	100	500	2,350	2,050	200	130
50	1,250	1,120	280	670	750	800	1,000	1,180	1,600	115	560	3,000	2,650	250	150
71	1,400	1,250	315	750	850	900	1,120	1,320	1,800	125	630	3,800	3,450	320	185
100	1,600	1,400	355	850	950	1,000	1,250	1,500	2,000	140	710	4,800	4,300	400	230
PWS															
18	1,060	950	200	600	530	560	710	850	1,120	80	480	1,600	1,450	130	120
25	1,180	1,060	225	670	600	630	800	950	1,250	90	530	2,150	1,950	160	145
35.5	1,320	1,180	250	750	670	710	900	1,060	1,400	100	600	3,000	2,800	200	170
50	1,500	1,320	280	850	750	800	1,000	1,180	1,600	112	670	4,200	3,900	250	200
71	1,700	1,500	315	950	850	900	1,120	1,320	1,800	125	750	5,750	5,300	320	235
100	1,900	1,700	355	1,060	950	1,000	1,250	1,500	2,000	140	850	8,100	7,300	400	280

UPDATED

ZF MARINE

A Division of ZF Friedrichshafen AG

D-88038 Friedrichshafen, Germany

Tel: +49 (7541) 770
Telex: 734207-17 ZF D
Fax: +49 (7541) 774000

F Petilli, *Managing Director and General Manager*
R Mosbacher, *Marine Department Manager*

ZF produces marine transmission systems in its four plants in Friedrichshafen (Germany), Padua, and Arco (Italy) and São Paulo (Brazil). ZF marine reduction and reversing gearboxes range from 3 to 5400 kW for high-speed craft application and up to 3,500 kW for workboats. Special designs are also available for powers up to 7,400 kW. All gears can be supplied with classification approval.

ZF marine transmission systems are fitted in a large number of high performance, naval, commercial and pleasure craft throughout the world.

In January 1995, ZF took over Hurth Marine Gear Co whose range of mechanically and hydraulically activated transmissions extends the ZF range at the lower end.

The addresses of the three other ZF plants are:

ZF Padova SpA, Via Penghe, 48, I-35030 Caselle di Selvazzano, Padova, Italy
Tel: +39 (49) 829 9311
Fax: +39 (49) 829 9550

ZF Hurth Marine SpA, Via S.Andrea, 16, I-38062 Arco (TN), Italy
Tel: +39 (464) 580 555
Fax: +39 (464) 580 544

ZF do Brasil SA, Rua Senador Vergueiro, 428, Cep. 09 521-901, São Caetano, Brazil
Tel: +55 (11) 744 9160
Fax: +55 (11) 744 9396

ZF MARINE GEARS WITH PARALLEL OFFSET INPUT AND OUTPUT SHAFTS

Type	Possible ratios	Max input torqued Nm* Continuous	Intermittent	Max input speed rpm	Length between flange faces mm	Centre distance mm	Weight kg
HBW 35	1.9-2.7	–	40	5,000	230	62	8
HBW 50	1.0-2.7	50	63	5,000	230	62	8
HBW 100	1.5-2.7	85	103	5,000	255	62	9.5
HBW 125	2.0-2.6	100	125	5,000	267	72	13
HBW 150	1.6-2.0	120	145	5,000	267	72	13
HBW 250	1.5-2.7	180	250	5,000	300	85	18
HBW 360H	2.1-2.9	250	360	5,000	350	105	28
IRM 50PL ⅔	1.57-3.12	464	658	5,000	492	110	30
HSW 630H1	1.5-2.8	477	682	5,000	338	127	46
IRM 220PL	1.00-3.00	711	941	5,500	380	135	63
IRM 280PL	0.81-3.00	806	1,151	3,200	371	143	73
IRM 311PL	0.80-3.45	1,444	2,063	3,000	451	30	149
IRM 320PL1	1.03-2.48	1,269	2,010	3,000	526	170	165
IRM 320-1	2.96-4.95	1,653	–	2,400	526	245	282
IRM 350PL	1.03-2.86	2,034	2,633	3,000	502	175	256
IRM 350	3.97-6.45	1,863	–	2,400	450	335	457
BW 61	2.62-4.64	647	890	3,200	396	210	105
BW 160	1.11-3.04	2,460	3,100	3,000	485	200	263
BW 161-1	3.61-6.42	2,460	–	2,600	490	365	560
BW 161	3.61-6.42	1,980	2,275	2,600	489	365	560
BW 165	1.11-3.00	–	3,880	3,000	485	200	265
BW 190	1.09-3.00	3,300	4,120	3,000	577	220	333
BW 191-1	3.50-6.46	2,690	–	2,600	567	390	680
BW 195	1.09-2.57	–	5,000	3,000	577	220	335
BW 196	2.92-4.04	–	5,000	2,500	612	310	415
BW 250	1.04-3.45	3,800	4,820	2,500	716	235	459
BW 251	2.87-5.90	3,800	4,820	2,500	776	360	852
BW 255	1.04-3.45	4,900	5,450	2,500	716	235	462
BW 256	2.86-5.90	4,900	5,450	2,500	776	360	666
BW 450-1	1.18-3.48	5,230	6,095	2,300	727	310	737
BW 451-1	2.37-5.63	5,230	–	2,300	882	460	1,372
BW 452-1	2.37-7.62	5,230	–	2,300	1,041	150	1,542
BW 456-1	2.37-5.63	5,230	6,095	2,300	822	460	1,019
BW 457-1	2.37-7.62	7,420	–	2,300	1,041	150	1,160
BW 460	1.18-3.48	6,370	7,465	2,300	727	310	741
BW 461	2.37-5.63	6,635	–	2,300	882	460	1,394
BW 465	1.18-3.23	8,085	8,820	2,300	727	310	747
BW 466	2.27-5.63	8,085	8,745	2,300	822	460	1,049
BW 487	2.76-4.45	14,860	17,310	1,820	1,041	150	1,165
BW 750	1.16-3.23	8,555	10,300	2,300	746	340	895
BW 751	4.0-6.8	10,780	–	2,300	920	600	2,300
BW 755	1.16-3.23	10,780	–	2,300	746	340	950
BW 1200	1.10-2.22	16,100	17,200	–	1,085	320	1,340
BW 1201	1.70-3.59	16,100	17,200	2,000	1,055	450	1,550
BW 1202	1.70-3.50	16,100	17,200	2,000	1,350	130	1,870
BW 1500	1.10-1.84	-	21,730	2,000	1,085	320	1,350
BW 1501	1.70-3.03	-	21,730	2,000	1,055	450	1,560
BW 1502	1.70-3.03	-	21,730	2,000	1,350	130	1,880
BW 1555	1.10-2.22	-	22,920	2,000	1,105	320	1,370
BW 1556	1.70-3.59	-	23,000	2,000	1,055	450	1,570
BW 1557	1.40-2.90	-	23,000	1,665	1,350	130	1,895
BW 2002	1.48-2.53	-	28,590	1,665	1,350	130	1,880
BW 2057	1.42-2.99	-	27,610	1,665	1,350	130	1,895
BW 2356	1.42-3.58	17,000	25,440	2,000	1,165	440	2,450

*The stated max torque ratings and speeds do not apply to all gear ratios. Actual ratings depend on duty

ZF MARINE GEARS WITH COAXIAL INPUT AND OUTPUT SHAFTS

Type	Possible ratios	Max input torqued Nm* Continuous	Intermittent	Max input speed rpm	Length between flange faces mm	Centre distance mm	Weight kg
IRM 41I	1.00	314	440	5,000	280	0	30
HSW 450 D	1.00	–	530	5,000	327	0	31
HSW 630 D	1.00	–	680	5,000	327	0	31
IRM 50I	1.00	464	785	5,000	285	0	50
IRM 301 PL2	1.00-2.69	1,022	1,381	3,000	433	0	87
IRM 310 PL	1.08-2.56	1,180	1,729	3,000	451	0	135
BWK 450-1	1.18-4.71	5,230	6,095	2,300	946	0	902
BWK 455-1	1.18-4.71	6,370	7,460	2,300	946	0	907
BWK 485	1.19-2.75	7,415	8,640	2,100	946	0	907
BWK 750	1.16-4.62	8,555	10,300	2,300	915	0	1,135
BWK 755	1.16-4.62	10,780	12,190	2,300	915	0	1,140
BWK 785	0.95-2.64	13,180	14,905	1,880	915	0	1,140
BWK 1200	1.10-2.22	16,100	17,200	2,000	1,380	0	1,640
BWK 1,500	1.10-1.84	-	21,730	2,000	1,400	0	1,650
BWK 1555	1.10-2.22	-	22,920	2,000	1,400	0	1,675

ZF MARINE GEARS WITH COAXIAL INPUT AND OUTPUT SHAFTS continued							
Type	**Possible ratios**	**Max input torqued Nm***		**Max input speed rpm**	**Length between flange faces mm**	**Centre distance mm**	**Weight kg**
		Continuous	**Intermittent**				
BWK 2000	1.15-1.53	-	28,590	1,665	1,400	0	1,650
BWK 2356	1.42-5.12	17,000	25,440	2,000	1,154	0	2,450
BWK 2386	1.12-1.76	34,550	51,700	1,000	1,154	0	2,450

*The stated max torque ratings and speeds do not apply to all gear ratios. Actual ratings depend on duty

ZF MARINE GEARS WITH DOWN ANGLED OUTPUT SHAFTS							
Type	**Possible ratios**	**Max input torqued Nm***		**Max input speed rpm**	**Length between flange faces mm**	**Centre distance mm**	**Weight kg**
		Continuous	**Intermittent**				
HSW 150A	1.9-2.6	110	145	5,000	280	96	13,3
HSW 150V	2.1-3.0	110	145	5,000	340	147	20,2
IRM 41A ⅔	1.03-2.47	314	440	5,000	440	122	30
IRM 50A ⅔	1.03-2.47	464	658	4,000	492	122	32
HSW 450A2	1.3-2.4	324	443	5,500	293	126	35
HSW 630A1	1.2-2.5	450	680	5,500	330	144	44
HSW 630V1	1.3-2.5	450	680	5,500	390	219	62
HSW 800A2	1.2-2.9	602	904	4,200	367	160	62
HSW 800V1	1.2-2.5	602	904	3,200	451	260	93
IRM 220A-1	1.24-2.45	711	890	4,500	286	145	60
IRM 220V-2	1.24-2.45	711	890	4,500	*357	145	59
IRM 220VLD	1.21-2.49	711	890	4,500	*480	247	90
IRM 225A	1.23-2.45	520	818	4,500	292	137	132
IRM 280A	1.15-2.47	806	1,151	3,200	351	147	68
IRM 301A-2	1.19-2.90	870	1,227	3,000	415	56	89
IRM 302VLD	1.30-3.16	701	1,381	3,000	*539	270	127
IRM 310A	1.08-2.56	1,036	1,381	3,000	435	37	140
IRM 311A	1.09-2.49	1,150	1,950	3,000	431	37	139
IRM 320A-1	1.55-2.52	1,596	2,009	3,000	499	212	165
IRM 350A	1.29-2.95	2,034	2,633	3,000	501	196	219
IRM 350VLD	1.32-2.03	1,455	2,639	3,000	*486	450	274
BW 160A	1.53-2.96	2,460	3,100	3,000	549	276	286
BW 160V	1.53-2.96	1,980	3,440	3,000	*680	276	286
BW 165A	1.53-2.96	-	3,880	3,000	549	276	288
BW 165V	1.53-2.96	-	3,440	3,000	*680	276	288
BW 190A	1.27-2.92	2,930	4,120	2,600	552	296	351
BW 190V	1.27-2.92	2,930	4,120	2,600	628	296	340
BW 195A	1.27-2.45	-	4,500	3,000	552	296	353
BW 195V	1.27-2.45	-	4,500	3,000	628	296	342
BW 255A	1.57-2.96	4,900	6,000	2,500	660	294	450
BW 255V	1.57-2.96	4,900	6,000	2,500	*771	294	450

*The stated max torque ratings and speeds do not apply to all gear ratios. Actual ratings depend on duty

UPDATED

ITALY

FB DESIGN Srl

Via Provinciale 73, I-22040 Annone Brianza (Co), Italy

Tel: +39 (341) 260105
Fax: +39 (341) 260108

Ing Fabio Buzzi, *Director and Administrator*

TRIMAX SURFACE DRIVE

FB Design produces the TRIMAX range of surface drive systems using Rolla surface-piercing propellers. The most popular model is the TR2100 which has been responsible for many offshore race wins over the last 15 years. This is a self-aligning system built entirely in stainless steel. The largest unit available is the TR4000 which was used in the offshore power boat *Super Hawaii*. This craft is fitted with two TR4000s and a FB/ZF splitting gearbox and is powered by one Lycoming TF40 gas-turbine with one Seatek diesel (for low-speed operation). Propulsion is by means of opposite-rotation surface-piercing

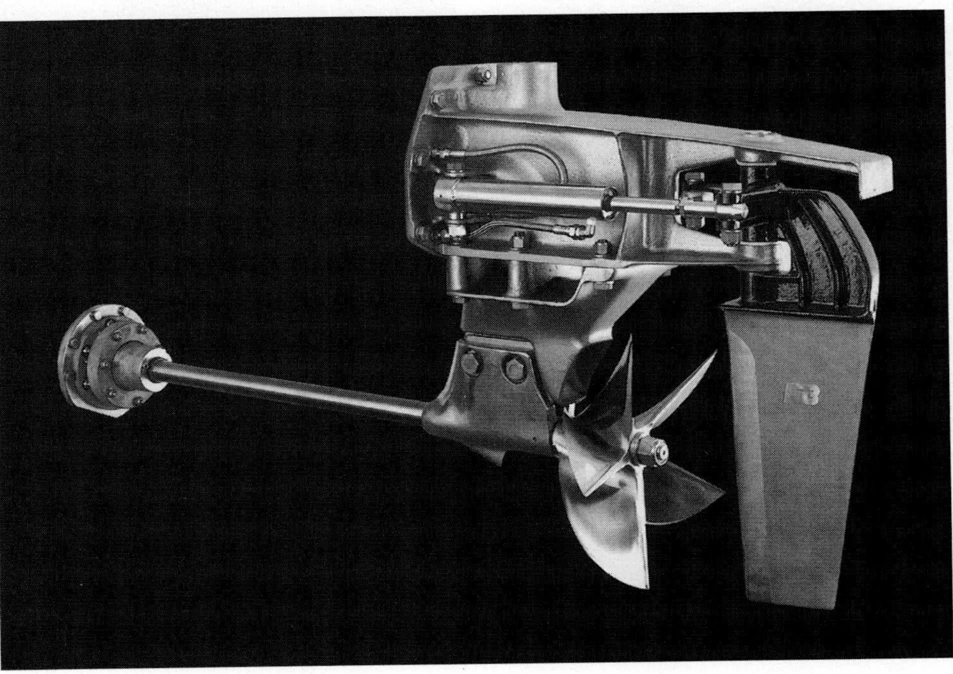

Trimax 2100 installation
1996

Super Hawaii *fitted with two FB Design TR4000 transmission systems* **1996**

propellers. In 1991, the 19.2 m *Super Hawaii* won the P3 class in the Venice to Monte Carlo 1,500 mile endurance race at an average speed of 52 knots (96 km/h).

FB Design is also involved in various high-speed patrol boats, its "FB 46 " being adopted by the Italian Guardia di Finanza for patrolling against smugglers. This type also came first overall in the Venice to Monaco, Monaco to Porto Cervo to Monaco and Round Sicillian Island races winning the Martini endurance trophy in 1992.

The smallest but latest model, the RIB 36 is a 65 knot patrol craft based on their very successful Techno 40 race boat.

UPDATED

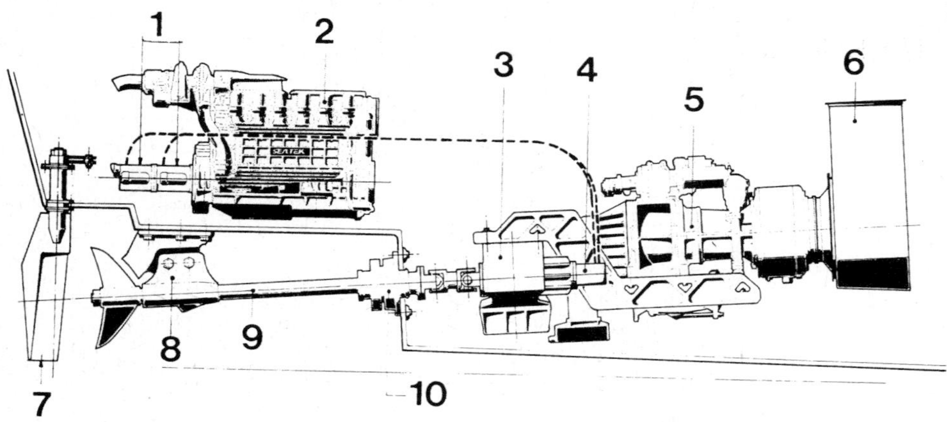

TRIMAX drive for a single gas-turbine installation with opposite-rotation surface-piercing propellers.
Key: **1** *Hydraulic pumps;* **2** *Seatek engine;* **3** *FB/ZF gearbox;* **4** *Hydraulic engines;* **5** *Lycoming TF40 gas-turbine;* **6** *Turbine exhaust;* **7** *Rudders;* **8** *Self-aligning supports;* **9** *4 in propeller shafts;* **10** *Spherical thrust sets* **1992**

REXROTH SpA

Subsidiary of Mannesmann Rexroth GmbH

Via Di Vittorio 1, I-20063 Cernusco S Naviglio, Milan, Italy

Tel: +39 (2) 923 651/924 9706
Telex: 331695 REXRTH I
Fax: +39 (2) 923 65237/924 8840

Dr Ing Hanno Speich, *Managing Director*

POWER SHAFT HS-5000 HYDROSTATIC PROPULSION SYSTEM

Using Rexroth hydraulic components the Hydromarine system is being marketed by the Hydromarine company in Italy. The development of propellers for the system has been undertaken by Marintek in Trondheim, Norway, achieving an efficiency of 85 per cent for the propeller component of the system.

The concept now developed is called Power Shaft HS-5000 and designs for units of four power levels are presently available from 350 to 2,000 kW.

Design Particulars

Incorporation of the power shaft into the design of a high-speed craft leads to the following advantages over conventional propulsion systems, it is claimed:

reduction in installed power
increased carrying capacity
lower fuel consumption
higher average speeds in transit
greater passenger comfort gained through drastic reduction in noise levels and improved sea-keeping
longer life of drive unit and longer servicing intervals
flexibility of application and ease of installation given by mutual independence in positioning power shaft and diesel engine
general improvements in structural design of craft, from the functional standpoint
availability of spare parts worldwide.

Horizontal Fixed-Pitch Tractor Propeller

Propulsion is obtained using a tractor propeller, with correct alignment to the water flow. The propeller is driven by a high-efficiency hydraulic motor installed within the power shaft, on which the rudder is also mounted.

Propeller cavitation problems are very greatly reduced by virtue of the fact that the propulsion stream is absolutely uniform and symmetrical about the rotation axis. In this way, the propeller enjoys

Test installation on a PT 20 hydrofoil **1991**

Tractor propeller power shaft installations on Baglietto motor yacht **1991**

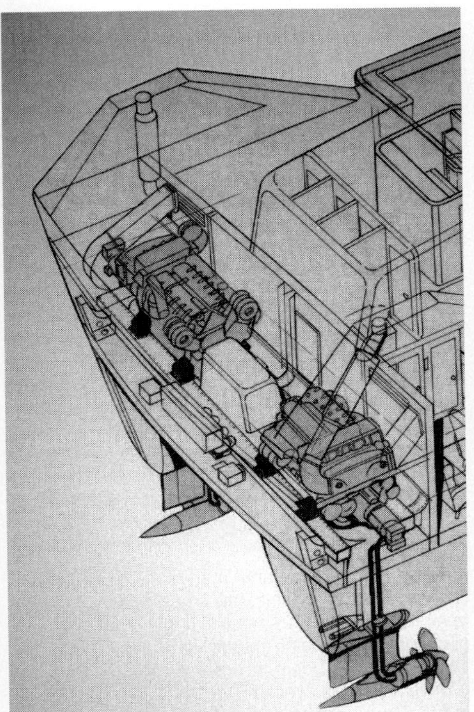

Simplified illustration of hydrostatic propulsion for a high-speed craft ***1991***

MEC 1 ***1993***

ideal operating conditions, giving high efficiency and generating no vibration or noise through the vessel. The power shaft and its propellers have been optimised to give speeds up to 50 knots.

The power shaft is flange-mounted to the bottom of the hull, selecting the most advantageous position in terms of hydrodynamics and propulsion.

Overall Efficiency and Power Range

Overall efficiency ratings of the power shaft system are higher than of the water-jet and conventional mechanical drives with inclined axis and pusher propeller. Adopting tractor-type propulsion in the power shaft signifies that the propeller operates in ideal hydrodynamic conditions; in addition, the pod-and-strut structure (which also carries the rudder and its actuator system) has been designed to recover a high percentage of the rotary kinetic energy generated by the propeller, in the form of thrust.

According to the applications, overall efficiency ratings including ratings of hydraulic transmission, propeller, power shaft (due to the water friction on its external surfaces) amounts to about 60 per cent.

The power shaft also includes the rudder and its drive, and can be supplied for nominal powers from 350 to 2,000 kW (under development).

Power Shaft as Torque Converter

The combination of variable displacement pump and fixed displacement motor provides a speed/torque converter.

Accordingly, the possibility exists of installing diesel engines with reduced power, size and weight specifications. With torque and speed thus variable the craft is able to accelerate and reach its cruising speed earlier, requiring significantly less time to plane, or to lift onto its foils than in the case of a hydrofoil. The power shaft's fixed-pitch propeller therefore functions substantially as a variable-pitch one. The transmission's flexibility in operation means that full power can also be extracted from the engine in taking craft to higher cruising speeds.

Propeller and Engine Speed Balance

With mechanical transmission eliminated, the speed reduction from engine to propeller is no longer tied to fixed ratios specified by reduction gear manufacturers, but simply a matter of choice. There is also the facility to adjust the transmission ratio during operation to suit conditions of loading, or of the sea state.

Absence of Mechanical Transmission Components

The fluid connection between hydraulic pump and motor eliminates a complete mechanical driveline incorporating speed reducing gears, shafting, bevel gears, reversing gears and clutches. Nor are there any problems arising from the close fit tolerances prescribed for mechanical components and their mounting to marine structures of limited rigidity.

Propeller Control

The operation of docking becomes especially swift and accurate because of the speed and precision with which the propeller can be controlled, reversing included; engine speed remains constant throughout all such manoeuvres.

Lightweight, Compact Drive

The power shaft brings advantages of weight and dimensions, especially when compared to water-jet propulsion, as there is no heavy mass of water drawn into the craft through jet ducts.

Approval of Maritime Insurance Agencies

The following agencies have expressed their approval of Hydromarine's power shaft propulsion system: Germanischer Lloyd, Det Norske Veritas, Bureau Veritas, Lloyd's Register of Shipping, American Bureau of Shipping and Registro Italiano Navale.

VERIFIED

JAPAN

NIIGATA CONVERTER CO LTD

27-9, Sendagaya 5-chome, Shibuya-ku, Tokyo 151, Japan

Tel: +81 (3) 3354 6931
Telex: 2323105 NICOTO J
Fax: +81 (3) 3341 5365

Works: Kamo, Niigata Prefecture and Omiya, Saitama Prefecture

Kyugo Kobayashi, *Managing Director*

Niigata Converter Company Ltd is licensed by Twin Disc Inc of Racine, Wisconsin, USA for the production and marketing of marine reverse and reduction gears for high-speed engines.

Niigata Converter Company Ltd (NICO), well-known

MARINE GEAR CAPACITIES FOR HIGH-SPEED MARINE CRAFT
(Parallel shaft models)

Model	SAE Hsg.	Standard ratios	kW/rpm PC	Max speed (rpm)	Dry weight (kg)
MGN 123	2, 1	1.52, 1.97, 2.57	0.134	3,300	190
		3.08	0.126		
		3.46	0.118		
MGN 133	2, 1, 0	1.65, 2.00, 2.48	0.178	2,800	235
		2.92	0.173		
		3.25	0.168		
		3.43	0.164		
MGN 153	2, 1, 0	1.65, 2.00, 2.48	0.221	2,800	250
		2.92	0.215		
		3.25, 3.43	0.203		
MGN 173	1, 0	1.53, 1.97	0.248	2,600	345
		2.44	0.243		
		2.93	0.233		

ZF MARINE GEARS WITH PARALLEL OFFSET INPUT AND OUTPUT SHAFTS continued

Type	Possible ratios	Max input torqued Nm* Continuous	Intermittent	Max input speed rpm	Length between flange faces mm	Centre distance mm	Weight kg
MGN 232E	1, 0		1.29, 1.50, 1.76, 1.96 2.48		0.389 0.303	2,600	370
MGN 233E	1, 0		2.52 2.96 3.52		0.389 0.336 0.283	2,600	410
MGN 272	1, 0		1.18, 1.50, 1.74, 2.04		0.479	2,500	470
MGN 273E	1, 0		2.55 3.12		0.479 0.414	2,500	525
MGN 332G	1, 0		1.00, 1.45, 1.71, 2.04 2.36		0.622 0.567	2,500	600
MGN 433E	0		1.18, 1.53, 1.71, 2.06		0.774	2,500	870
MGN 433G	0		2.52		0.780	2,500	980
MGN 472	0		1.53, 2.11 2.52		0.998 0.987	2,150	1,200
MGN 473	0		2.48, 3.03, 3.31, 3.48		0.998	2,150	1,270

(Down angle and U-drive models)

Model	SAE Hsg.	Standard ratios	kW/rpm PC	Max speed (rpm)	Dry weight (kg)
MGNV 172 MGNV 172-C	1, 0	1.55, 2.03 2.34	0.232 0.220	2,600	350
MGNV 232E MGNV 232E-C	1, 0	1.54, 1.73, 1.96 2.43	0.389 0.281	2,600	460
MGNV 271E MGNV 271E-C	1, 0	1.18 1.44 1.86	0.479 0.415 0.349	2,500	470
MGNV 272E MGNV 272E-C	1, 0	1.66, 2.06 2.46	0.479 0.437	2,500	530
MGNV 332G MGNV 332G-C	1, 0	1.53, 1.72, 1.93 2.43	0.622 0.567	2,500	630
MGNV 432 MGNV 432-C	0	1.52, 2.03 2.53	0.781 0.628	2,500	1,000
MGNV 472 MGNV 472-C	0	1.52, 1.95 2.46	0.997 0.864	2,100	1,300

Niigata gearbox configuration **1990**

for the manufacture and marketing of diversified lines of marine products, has a new series of marine reverse and reduction gears in lightweight and compact design utilising aluminium alloy housings. There are 16 models in both of the standard and U-drive versions available in the 224 to 2,145 kW range. These marine gears are ideal for such vessels as pleasure craft, passenger ferries, patrol boats and crew boats for which the essential requirement is high speed.

Built-in hydraulic clutches, cooled by the same type of oil used in the engines, give the marine gears smooth and instantaneous shifting from ahead to astern and vice versa.

Standard equipment on all models includes filters, pump(s), temperature gauges, heat exchangers for salt or freshwater cooling, output companion flanges and manually actuated range selectors and control valves.

Optional equipment such as X-control or trailing pump is available on request.

VERIFIED

NORWAY

SERVOGEAR A/S

N-5420 Rubbestadneset, Norway

Tel: +47 53 427380
Fax: +47 53 427783

S Jørgensen, *Naval Architect*

Servogear, established in 1973, produces lightweight gears to its own design with in-built servo systems for controllable-pitch propellers and hydraulic shaft clutches. Servogear gearboxes are specifically designed for high-speed craft where low weight and small size are particularly important.

Since Servogear started production in 1975 over 900 gearboxes and propeller systems have been delivered, of which more than 500 have been delivered for high-speed craft with engines from 300 to 3,300 kW and speeds from 20 to 40 knots.

Servogear's latest gearboxes, the HD250 and 295, are designed specifically for high-speed craft and are available in normal vertical offset configuration, U-drive configuration and also as a twin input single output arrangement.

The gearboxes are all type approved by DnV.

UPDATED

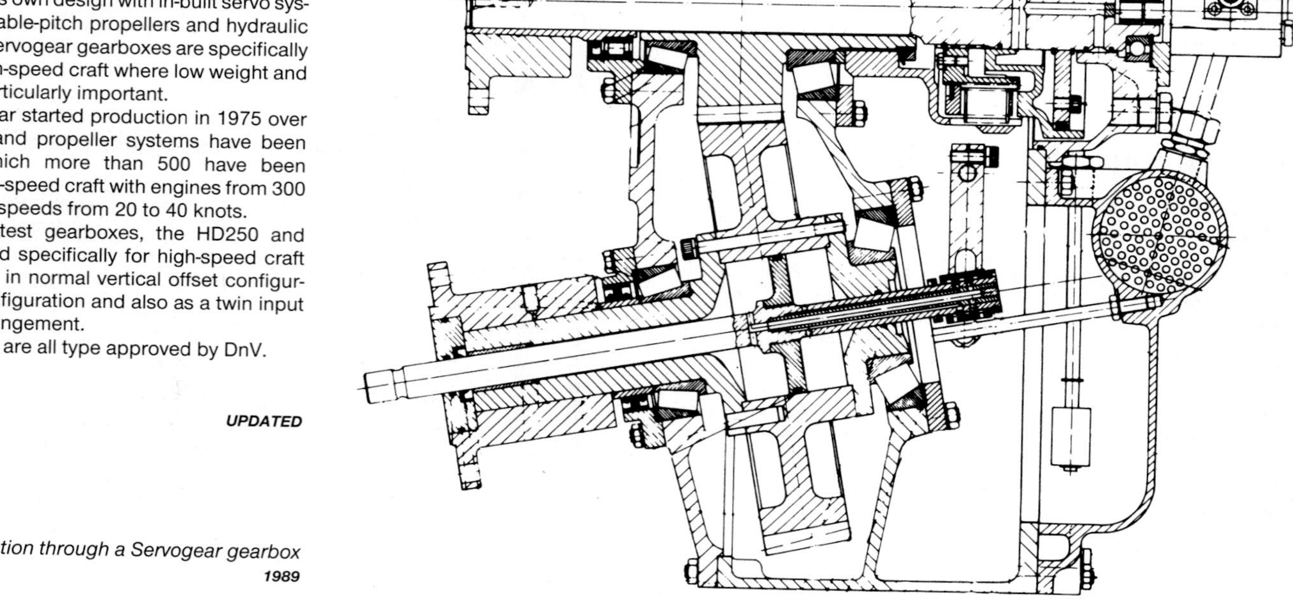

Section through a Servogear gearbox
1989

ULSTEIN PROPELLER A/S

N-6065 Ulsteinvik, Norway

Tel: +47 (700) 14000
Telex: 42848 UP N
Fax: +47 (700) 14017

Stig Ulstein, *Managing Director*
Jarle Hessen, *Sales Manager*

Ulstein Propeller A/S manufactures marine propeller and water-jet transmissions in addition to the Speed-Z system. Please see the *Marine Propellers* section for details of the Ulstein propeller systems and the *Water-jet Units* section for details of Ulstein developments in this area.

VERIFIED

Ulstein Speed-Z drive system
1991

SWITZERLAND

MAAG GEAR COMPANY LTD

Hardstrasse 219, Postfach, CH-8023 Zurich, Switzerland

Tel: +41 (1) 278 7878
Telex: 822 704 MZZ CH
Fax: +41 (1) 278 7880

The Maag Gear Company Ltd designs and manufactures a wide range of marine gears and synchronous clutch couplings.

Recent applications include:
Stena HSS catamarans, the largest high-speed vessels ordered to date, fitted with two HPG-185/C gearboxes, each taking an input from a GT LM 2500/LM 1600 combination. Each gearbox outputs to two water-jets. Total power transmission is 80,000 kW.

Kværner Fjellstrand Flying Cat now in series production, fitted with two MPU-24/G-50 gearboxes, each taking an input of 4,500 kW at 7,000 rpm from a GE LM 500 gas-turbine. Output is at 900 rpm to a water-jet propulsor.

Austal Ships series of gas-turbine powered craft. Each craft is fitted with two MPG-80 gearboxes, each taking an input of 3,088 kW from an AlliedSignal TF-40 gas-turbine with a reduction from 16,400 rpm to 920 rpm.

VERIFIED

MAAG HPG-185/C gearbox for the Stena HSS ***1995***

UNITED KINGDOM

ALLEN GEARS

Allen Power Engineering Ltd

Atlas Works, Pershore, Worcestershire WR10 2BZ, UK

Tel: +44 (1386) 552211
Fax: +44 (1386) 554491

D J Taft, *General Manager*
D E Yates, *Technical Manager*
P M Johnson, *Sales Manager*
C F W Brimmell, *Marketing Manager*

Allen Gears first became associated with high-speed surface craft in the early 1950s when the Royal Navy commissioned two Vosper prototype aluminium hull vessels. Each triple-screw craft was powered by three Rolls-Royce Proteus gas-turbines driving fixed-pitch propellers. The turbines had a rating of 3,500 hp at a speed of 11,600 rpm, and an Allen epicyclic gear was incorporated to reduce engine speed to 5,000 rpm. The secondary reduction Allen gearbox consisted of bevel gears for a shaft angle of 15°, driving into a double-train epicyclic reversing section. Since their introduction and subsequent uprating to 4,250 hp, over 260 primary gear sets have

The Allen five-shaft C form 12,000 to 681 rpm reduction gearbox as fitted to an Fr Lürssen Werft luxury yacht, two 5,406 kW (7,250 hp) gas-turbines ***1988***

Port and starboard multistage hovercraft propulsion gearboxes **1990**

been supplied by Allen Gears to many of the world's navies.

C FORM GEARBOX

In 1978 Allen Gears fitted its C form gearboxes in a Don Shead-designed 29 m, 45 knot luxury yacht. The yacht cruises on two wing, diesel engine driven jets, and a gas-turbine provides power for maximum speed. The turbine is a Textron Lycoming Super TF40 which produces 4,600 hp at 15,400 rpm and drives a Rocketdyne jet pump running at 1,664 rpm. The gearbox has a C drive configuration, both input and output shafts are at the aft end, and consists of a primary epicyclic train with a single helical parallel shaft secondary train. An idler is required to cover the necessary centre distance from the gas-turbine to the Rocketdyne jet pump and also matches their standard rotations. The jet pump houses the main thrust bearing, therefore secondary gearbox bearings need only accommodate the thrust imposed by single helical gearing. A caliper disc brake is fitted to the free end of the secondary pinion enabling the main jet pump to be held stationary when using wing engine propulsion.

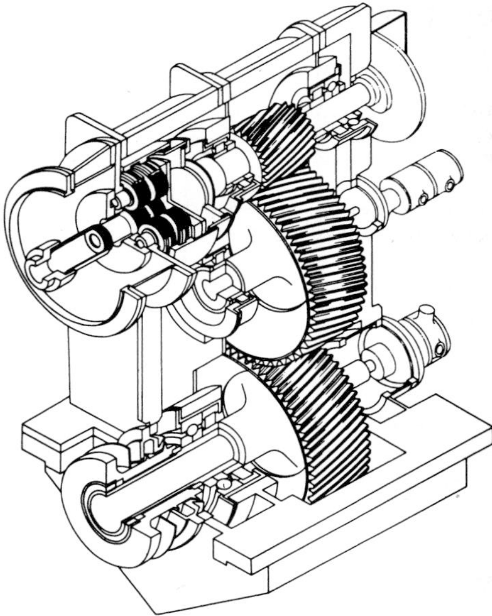

A section view of the Allen C form drive gearbox showing first and second stage reduction gears **1988**

FIVE-SHAFT C FORM DRIVE GEARBOX

As a follow-on from uprated gears for the Royal Navy, Allen Gears constructed a combined epicyclic and parallel-shaft C drive gearbox for a 46 m, 45 knot luxury yacht built by Fr Lürssen Werft of Germany. The yacht was powered by two Allison 570 gas-turbines driving Kamewa water-jets. In addition there were two wing engines driving small water-jets of 1,500 hp. Total available power was 17,500 hp. The gas-turbines were positioned aft, driving forward into the gearbox. Each of the turbines has a maximum input of 7,250 hp at 12,000 rpm giving an output speed, to the water-jet unit from gearbox, of 681 rpm. A five-shaft configuration gearbox was adopted to accommodate the centre distance between the gas-turbines and the output shaft. The input is taken from the primary epicyclic train through quill-shafts, within the secondary pinion, to SSS self-synchronising clutches at the forward end of the gear case. This arrangement permits the

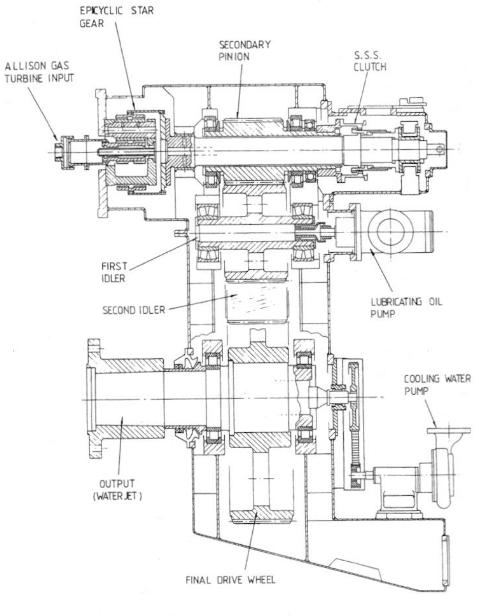

Sectioned view of one drive line of the five-shaft C form reduction gearbox **1990**

Gas-turbine boost and diesel engine cruise gearboxes for 'Standard Flex 300' **1990**

second gas-turbine to be introduced to the drive line or to be disconnected without interruption of power.

HOVERCRAFT TRANSMISSIONS

Allen Gears' association with the Spanish Company CHACONSA and its VCA-36 craft has moved on to future developments with an overseas navy for a similar sized craft. This prototype vessel which more than surpassed expectation on trials utilises Pratt & Whitney gas-turbines for the lift system and Allied-Signal gas-turbines for the propulsion system. In both cases the reduction gears are of Allen Gears' lightweight construction using the very latest gear technology. In order to achieve the best machinery layout and to meet the necessary weight targets Allen provided multistage parallel shaft gears in aluminium gear cases using gear components constructed according to proven aircraft methods. All techniques were fully tested with careful stress analysis in all areas prior to manufacture.

CODAG PROPULSION SYSTEM

The first seven ships of the Royal Danish Navy 'Standard Flex 300' multirole vessel programme use a 'CODAG' propulsion plant powered by MTU 16V 396 TB 94 diesels for cruise and a GE LM 500 gas-turbine for boost. The engines drive through Allen vertically offset custom-engineered lightweight parallel shaft gearboxes with integral lubricating system. Each gearbox is equipped with a hydraulic motor which forms part of a hydraulic system (powered by a General Motors diesel) to meet the requirements of auxiliary propulsion during silent minehunting and economic loitering at nearly stationary patrols.

UPDATED

UNITED STATES OF AMERICA

THE CINCINNATI GEAR COMPANY

5657 Wooster Pike, Cincinnati, Ohio 45227, USA

Tel: +1 (513) 271 7700
Fax: +1 (513) 271 0049

Steven J Crowell, *Marketing Manager*
Rob W Rye, *Marine Sales Manager*
Ken M Kiehl, *Advanced Programs Sales Manager*

The Cincinnati Gear Company, founded in 1907, specialises in high-performance parallel shaft and epicyclic marine drives. Successful installations include the Jetfoil passenger ferry, the LCAC air cushion landing craft, the T-AO 187 class oiler, and the AOE 6 class support ship.

A leader in the design and manufacture of high-power density gearing for gas-turbine and diesel applications, Cincinnati Gear offers a wide variety of gearbox and propulsion system designs. These include parallel shaft units ideal for offset installations and epicyclic units, featuring coaxial input and output shafts, for in-line arrangements.

Cincinnati Gear has utilised its extensive experience with military and commercial high-speed craft to develop the MA and MD series of standard marine reduction gearboxes. The MA and MD series offer the advantages of quicker delivery and lower cost than custom designs.

A CINTI MA-107 reduction gear with close coupled TF40 gas-turbine. This 3,400 kW reduction gear is one of the MA series gearboxes being produced for vessels such as high-speed ferries and megayachts ***1994***

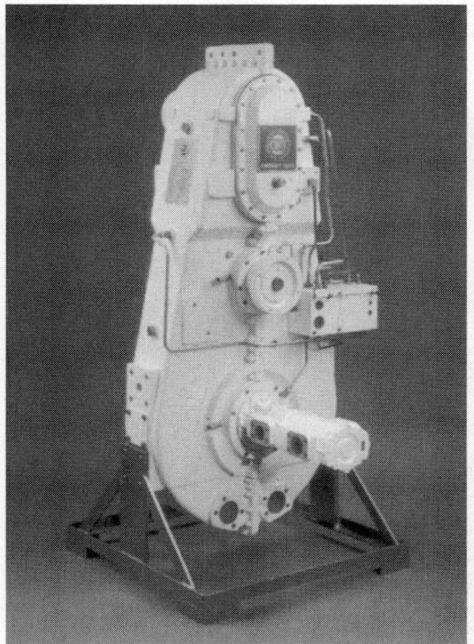

Two CINTI parallel shaft gearboxes are used on each Kawasaki hydrofoil passenger ferry. Each gearbox transmits power from a 501-KF gas-turbine to a water-jet ***1994***

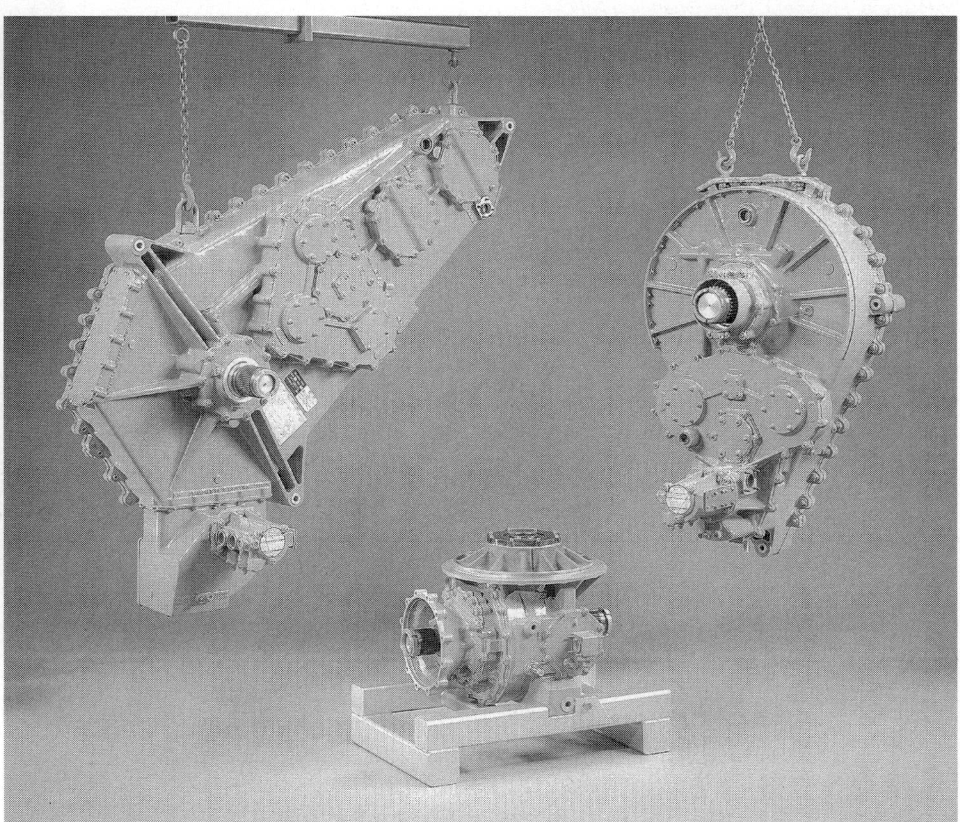

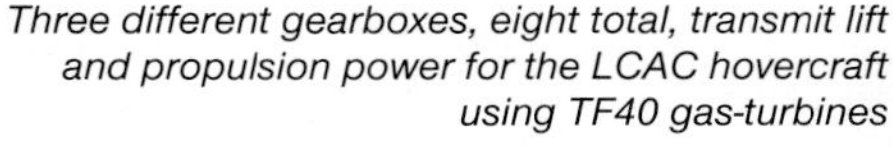

Three different gearboxes, eight total, transmit lift and propulsion power for the LCAC hovercraft using TF40 gas-turbines ***1995***

The MA series features highly versatile modular gearbox designs for gas-turbine-powered vessels such as megayachts, high-speed ferries and fast patrol boats. Standard MA gearboxes are available for a variety of gas-turbines, ranging from 800 to 25,000 kW. Available designs include epicyclic and single and dual input parallel shaft units in C- or Z-drive configurations as well as CODOG or CODAG arrangements.

The MD series was developed for marine applications using medium-speed diesels in the 3,000 to 15,000 kW range, such as tankers and container ships. Standard MD designs are available for single and dual input applications, each with a number of clutch, thrust bearing and lube system options to suit most craft requirements.

VERIFIED

DETROIT DIESEL CORPORATION

13400 Outer Drive West, Detroit, Michigan 48239-4001, USA

Tel: +1 (313) 592 5000
Telex: 4320091
Fax: +1 (313) 592 7288

Detroit Diesel Corporation provides a full range of transmissions to give an optimum match for each DDC engine. These transmissions are manufactured by Twin Disc Inc.

DDC gearbox installation **1990**

DETROIT DIESEL MARINE TRANSMISSIONS

Engine model	Configuration	Gear ratios
8.2L	10° Down Angle	1.54, 2.00
6V-53	Inline & 7° Down Angle	1.10, 1.51, 1.77, 1.98
6-71	Inline & 7° Down Angle	1.10, 1.51, 1.77, 1.98
	Vertical Offset	1.45, 1.71, 2.04
6V-92	Vertical Offset	1.45, 1.71, 2.00, 2.04
	7° Down Angle	1.45, 1.73, 1.96
8V-92	Vertical Offset	1.50, 1.74, 2.04
	7° Down Angle	1.48, 1.92
12V-71	Vertical Offset	1.29, 1.50, 1.76, 1.96, 2.48
	10° Down Angle	1.52, 1.77, 1.97
12V-92	Vertical Offset	1.29, 1.50, 1.64, 1.76, 1.83, 1.96, 2.03, 2.48,2.55
	10° Down Angle	1.52, 1.66, 1.77, 1.97, 2.06, 2.48
16V-92	Vertical Offset	1.00, 1.45, 1.74, 2.04, 2.55
	10° Down Angle	1.53, 1.71, 1.92, 2.38
16V-149	Vertical Offset	2.52

VERIFIED

TWIN DISC INC

1328 Racine Street, Racine, Wisconsin 53403, USA

Tel: +1 (414) 638 4000
Telex: 170336
Fax: +1 (414) 638 4480

M E Batten, *Chairman, Chief Executive Officer*
M H Joyce, *President, Chief Operating Officer*
L J Melik, *Vice President, Marketing*
J McIndoe, *Vice President, International Marketing*

IN-LINE ARNESON SURFACE DRIVE
WITH STANDARD TRANSMISSION.

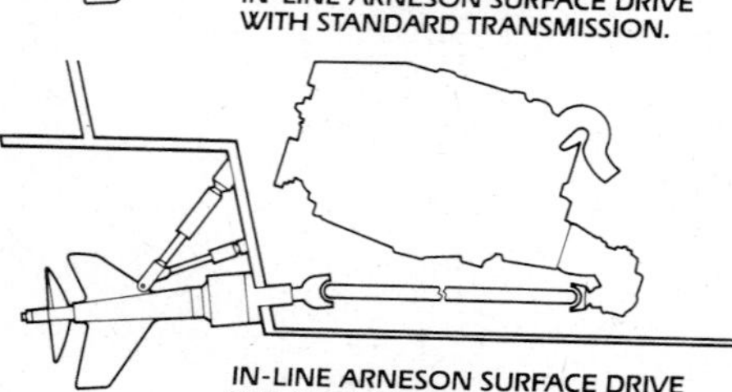

DROP-CENTER ARNESON SURFACE
DRIVE WITH STANDARD TRANSMISSION.

Three possible layouts for Twin Disc Arneson Surface Drives **1993**

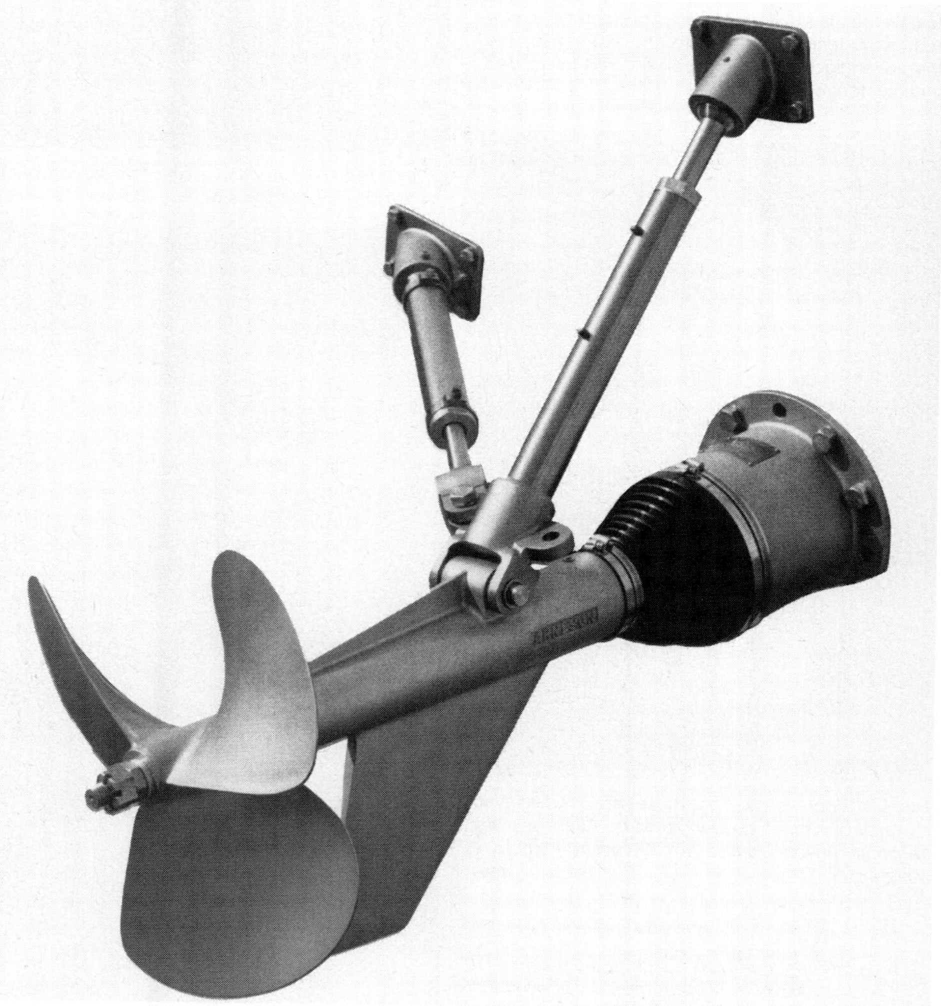

Twin Disc Arneson ASD 10 in-line unit **1993**

Twin Disc MG-5202 SC marine transmission ***1996***

Twin Disc MG-5062V, V-drive marine transmission ***1994***

Twin Disc Incorporated manufactures marine propulsion systems including marine transmissions, electronic propulsion controls and Arneson Surface Drives. Quality Assurance ISO 9001 certification for the design and manufacture of their products was awarded to Twin Disc in 1995.

Twin Disc marine transmissions feature helical gearing in most models for quieter operation; hydraulic-controlled and oil-cooled clutches for smooth, fast shifting; identical ratios in forward and reverse with full power in forward and reverse in most cases and minimal external plumbing. Down angle output configurations provide for near level engine installation and space saving remote and direct mounted V-drive models are also available.

Operational trolling valves are available for most Twin Disc models. This feature provides the ability to obtain lower propeller speeds than would be possible at engine idle with the clutch fully engaged. Omega Power Control, available on the MG-514M and MG-530M, is similar to the trolling valve except that it allows clutch modulation at higher engine speeds and provides an internal governor.

Optional torsional input couplings are available for most models and a number of power take-off options exists for many Twin Disc marine transmissions.

Twin Disc 'Power Commander' marine electronic propulsion controls feature precise, single lever control of clutch and throttle functions.

Twin Disc Arneson Surface Drives combine surface-piercing propeller technology with hydraulically actuated steering and trim control through angular displacement of the propeller shaft, providing greater propulsion and manoeuvring effectiveness. In most applications, elimination of underwater shafts, struts and rudders results in marked improvement in vessel performance and efficiency.

This concept allows complete flexibility of engine location, weight placement and effective reduction of noise and vibration. Hydraulic steering and propeller depth control provide outstanding manoeuvrability and shallow draft capability limited only by the draft of the vessel itself.

Twin Disc Arneson Surface Drives serve the commercial, military and pleasure craft markets. Differentiated by torque capacity, these drives are available for use with gasoline, diesel and gas-turbine engines up to approximately 5,000 horsepower.

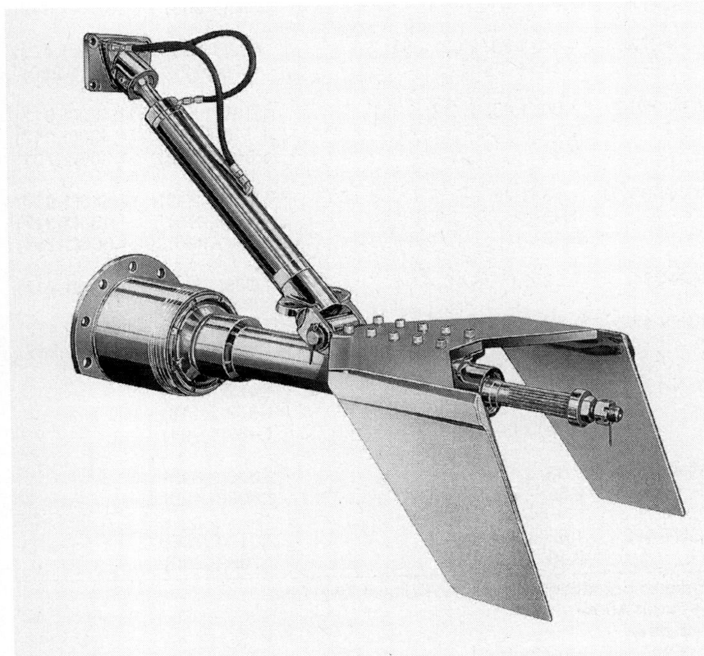

Twin Disc Arneson ASD-8 Dual Fin ***1996***

Twin Disc MGNV-232E marine transmission ***1994***

TWIN DISC MARINE TRANSMISSION

Model	Reduction Ratio (:1)	Power - kW (hp) Intermediate @2,100 rpm	Power - kW (hp) Pleasurecraft @2,300 rpm
MG-5,010	1.11, 1.50, 2.00	90(121)	122(164)
	2.39	76(102)	122(164)
MG-5010A	1.44, 1.90	90(121)	122(164)
	2.39	76(102)	122(164)
MG-5010V	1.14, 1.54, 2.06	90(121)	122(164)
	2.46	76(102)	122(164)
MG-502-1	1.54, 2.00	100(140)	165(221)
MG-502	2.47	88(118)	138(185)
MG-5050	1.23, 1.53, 1.71, 2.04	139(186)	224(300)
	2.45, 3.00	139(186)	196(263)
MG-5050A & MG-5050V	1.12, 1.26, 1.50, 1.80	139(186)	224(300)
	2.04, 2.50	139(186)	196(263)
MG-506-1 & MG-506A	1.09, 1.50, 1.97	121(162)	194(260)
	2.50, 2.96	121(162)	172(230)
MG-506	3.79, 4.48	119(159)	—
MG-5061	1.15, 1.48, 1.77, 2.00, 2.43	187(250)	275(369)
	3.00	187(250)	245(329)
MG-5061A & MG-5061V	1.13, 1.54, 1.75, 2.00, 2.47	187(250)	275(369)
MG-5062V	1.19, 1.53, 1.83, 2.07, 2.51	187(250)	263(353)
MG-507-1 & MG-507A-1	0.75, 0.81, 0.92	254(340)	313(420)
	1.10, 1.51, 1.77, 1.98	235(315)	298(400)
	2.54	201(207)	239(320)
	2.99	179(240)	213(285)
MG-507-2 & MG-507A-2	1.10, 1.51, 1.77	—	373(500)
	1.98	—	336(450)
MG-5081 & MG-5081A	1.12, 1.51, 1.97	298(400)	433(580)
	2.48	242(325)	343(460)
MG-509	1.45, 2.00	235(315)	291(390)
	2.48	235(315)	275(370)
	2.95	216(290)	242(325)
	3.39	165(220)	195(260)
	3.83, 4.50	235(315)	—
	4.95	180(242)	—
MG-5091	1.17, 1.45, 1.71, 2.04	343(460)	503(675)
	2.45	321(430)	474(635)
	2.95	321(430)	418(560)
	3.38	(205(275)@1,800)	
	3.82	321(430)	—
	4.50	298(400)	—
	5.10	(205(275)@1,800)	
MG-5090A	1.45, 1.73, 1.96	343(460)	503(675)
	2.43	321(430)	418(560)
MG-5111	1.12, 1.50, 1.74, 2.04	429(575)	597(800)
	2.54	358(480)	548(735)
	3.10	321(430)	418(560)
	3.28, 3.92	380(510)	574(770)
	4.43	373(500)	—
	4.95	(283(380)@1,800)	
MG-5111A & MG-5111V	1.20, 1.48, 1.75, 1.92	395(530)	597(800)
	2.44	358(480)	548(735)
MG-5112V	1.06, 1.23, 1.52, 1.80, 1.98	429(575)	597(800)
	2.51	358(480)	548(735)
MG-5113	5.50, 6.05, 6.48	(291(390)@1,800)	
MG-5114A	1.03, 1.20, 1.48, 1.75, 1.92	485(650)	652(875)
	2.50	467(620)	604(810)
MG-514C & MG-514M*	1.51, 2.00, 2.50, 3.00	380(510)	485(650)
	3.50	336(450)	418(560)
	4.13, 4.50, 5.16	380(510)	—
	6.00	(283(380)@1,800)	
MG-5141	1.17, 1.53, 1.71, 1.96	559(750)	746(1,000)
	2.50	522(700)	671(900)
MG-516	3.07, 3.50, 4.40, 4.52, 5.50,		
	6.00	(405(543)@1,800)	
MG-5161	5.86, 6.53, 7.00	(405(543)@1,800)	

TWIN DISC MARINE TRANSMISSION

Model	Reduction Ratio (:1)	Power - kW (hp) Intermediate @2,100 rpm	Power - kW (hp) Pleasurecraft @2,300 rpm
MG-518-1	1.48, 2.00, 2.47, 2.94, 4.06,		
	4.48,	(447(600)@1,800)	
	5.07, 5.92		
	6.48	(410(550)@1,800)	
MG-520-1	2.02, 2.51, 2.97, 3.44, 4.03,		
	4.49,	(552(740)@1800)	
	5.00, 6.11		
	7.00	(477(640)@1,800)	
MG-5202	1.17, 1.53, 1.76, 2.03, 2.48,		
	2.92	671(900)	947(1,270)
	3.48	641(860)	746(1,000)
MG-5202DC	4.03, 4.59, 5.04, 6.10, 6.55	671(900)	-
	6.59	650(872)	-
MG-530	1.59	947(1,270)	—
	1.95	895(1,200)	—
	2.34	846(1,135)	—
	3.13	794(1,065)	—
	4.04	753(1,010)	—
	4.94	899(1,205)	—
	6.06	(701(940)@1,800)	
	7.27	(637(855)@1,800)	
MG-530M*	1.59, 1.95, 2.34	832(1,115)	—
	3.13	794(1,065)	—
	4.04	753(1,010)	—
	4.94	832(1,115)	—
	6.06	(701(940)@1,800)	
	7.27	(637(855)@1,800)	
MG-540	1.92, 2.58, 2.90	(940(1,260)@1,800)	
	3.26	1,156(1,550)	—
	3.91	1,037(1,390)	—
	4.60	(925(1,240)@1,800)	
	5.17	1,115(1,495)	—
	6.18	(802(1,075)@1,800)	
	7.00	(746(1,000)@1,800)	
	7.47	(701(940)@1,800)	
MGN-80E	1.55, 1.97, 2.59, 3.04	632(845)	692(930)
	3.41	598(803)	655(880)
MGNV-232E	1.54, 1.73, 1.96	600(805)	895(1,200)
	2.43	544(729)	746(866)
MGN-232E	1.29, 1.50, 1.76, 1.96	724(971)	895(1,200)
	2.48	565(757)	699(937)
MGN-233E	1.57, 1.79, 1.97, 2.52	761(1,020)	895(1,200)
	2.96	663(890)	774(1,038)
	3.52	558(749)	652(874)
MGN-272	1.18, 1.50, 1.74	868(1,164)	1,103(1,479)
	2.04	819(1,099)	1,103(1,479)
MGNV-272E	1.66, 1.81, 2.07	868(1,164)	1,103(1,479)
	2.46	793(1,063)	1,006(1,349)
MGN-273E	1.64, 1.83, 2.03, 2.55	862(1,156)	1,103(1,479)
	3.12	725(972)	955(1,280)
MGN-332G	1.00, 1.45, 1.71	1,166(1,563)	1,430(1,917)
	2.04	1,118(1,499)	1,430(1,917)
	2.36	1,006(1,349)	1,306(1,751)
MGNV-332G	1.53, 1.72	1,004(1,346)	1,430(1,917)
	1.93	954(1,279)	1,430(1,917)
	2.43	780(1,046)	1,306(1,751)
MGN-334	2.52, 3.00, 3.46, 4.04	1,089(1,461)	1,430(1,917)
MGNV-432	1.52, 2.03	1,450(1,945)	1,798(2,412)
	2.53	1,164(1,561)	1,455(1,937)
MGN-433G	1.18	1,472(1,974)	—
	1.53, 1.71, 2.06	1,579(2,118)	—
	2.52, 3.00	1,487(1,994)	—
MGN-472	1.53, 2.11	2,008(2,693)	—
	2.52	1,809(2,426)	—
MGNV-472	1.52, 1.95	2,017(2,705)	—
	2.46	1,708(2,290)	—

* Special operating limits apply. Consult Twin Disc.
A = Down Angle
V = V-drive
M = Omega Power Control
The V in Twin Disc MGN Series transmission designations indicates 10° down angle output. C-drive and V-drive configurations are also available

Model	ASD 6	ASD 8	ASD 10	ASD 12	ASD 14	ASD 16	ASD 18
Horsepower acceptance							
petrol at 5,200 rpm	to 550	to 990	to 1,485	contact twin disc			
diesel at 2,400 rpm	to 290			to 5,000 (subject to application)			
Unit weight, dry, with							
hydraulic cylinders (in-line):	61 kg	129 kg	189 kg			900 kg A	1,769 kg A
(drop centre):	72 kg	220 kg	272 kg	352 kg	515 kg	1,150 kg B	2,268 kg B
Overall external length:	914-991 mm	1,067 mm	1,270 mm	1,638 mm	1,805 mm	2,184 mm	2,896 mm
Steering angle:	40°	40°	40°	40°	40°	36°	36°
Trim angle (max travel inclusive):	15°	15°	15°	15°	15°	15°	13°
Materials							
socket:	A or B	B	B	B	B	A or B	A or B
thrust tube:	A or B	B	B	B	B	A or B	A or B
ball:	B	B	B	B	A or B	A or B	
propeller shaft:	C	C	C	C	C	C	C

A - aluminium alloy
B - manganese bronze
C - 17.4 PH Stainless Steel

UPDATED

AIR PROPELLERS

Company Listing by Country

Germany
Hoffmann Propeller GmbH & Company KG
MT-Propeller Entwicklung GmbH & Company KG

United Kingdom
Air Vehicles Ltd
Dowty Aerospace Propellers

United States of America
Ardco
Pacific Propeller Inc

GERMANY

HOFFMANN PROPELLER GmbH & COMPANY KG

PO Box 100339, Küpferlingstrasse 9, D-83022 Rosenheim, Germany

Tel: +49 (8031) 32011
Fax: +49 (8031) 15832

Richard Wurm, *Proprietor*
Johann Sterr, *Managing Director*

Hoffmann Propeller GmbH and Company KG was founded in 1955 by Ing Richard Wurm, starting with six employees. Now Hoffmann has 70 employees and the company is not only involved in the field of general aviation propellers but also in that of hovercraft. Propellers absorbing an input power up to 2,000 kW are designed and manufactured for these craft. Besides this, blades for wind energy converters, blowers and large fan blades for wind tunnel application in the automotive industry are in current production. Propeller overhaul and service is provided for all types of Hoffmann propellers and also for other manufacturers' propellers.

The company covers the following certifications: LBA EC-2 for design and development of aircraft propellers; LBA I-C 14 for production of aircraft propellers and equipment; LBA II-A 35 for repair of aircraft propellers and governors of all types; FAA BV5Y-767M for repair and overhaul of aircraft propellers and accessories; CAA Hovercraft Approval for design and production of hovercraft propellers.

Hovercraft propellers manufactured by Hoffmann incorporate various special features. The excellent erosion resistance of the composite materials used is far superior to that of aluminium alloy. The wood laminations are reinforced with carbon or glassfibre which adds torsional strength and offers resistance to impact of particles entering the propeller disc.

For improved erosion protection the blades optionally have a special Irathane coating. The leading edge protection is made of stainless steel totally integrated into the airfoil profile. Additional protection against erosion is guaranteed by different kinds of erosion strip.

Since 1960 fixed-pitch, ground-adjustable and either hydraulically or mechanically controlled variable and reverse pitch propellers have been continuously built for air propeller driven boats, snow sledges and hovercraft.

Chaconsa, VCA-2/3; two two-blade ground-adjustable propellers, free, driven by about 150 kW, 2 m diameter.

Wärtsilä Larus; four four-blade hydraulically controlled propellers, forward and reverse pitch, driven by about 550 kW, 3 m diameter.

BHC AP1-88; two four-blade ground-adjustable propellers per craft, ducted, driven by approximately 370 kW, 2.75 m diameter.

Chaconsa VCA-36; two five-blade hydraulically controlled, forward and reverse pitch propellers (one left-hand, one right-hand rotation), free, driven by 1,000 kW, 4 m diameter.

Slingsby, Tropimere 6; two three-blade ground-adjustable propellers, 1.10 m diameter.

Slingsby SAH 2200 (ex-1500); one three-blade reversible-pitch propeller, ducted, 1.40 diameter.

Marineswift Thunderbolt 30; one five-blade ground-adjustable propeller, driven by approximately 200 kW, 1.12 m diameter.

CIS; two hydraulically controlled propellers, ducted, driven by 257 kW, 3 m diameter and for a 25 m Hovercraft a five-blade hydraulically controlled propeller, ducted, driven by 1,800 kW, 3.6 m diameter.

Griffon 2000 TDXs for the Swedish Coast Guard; two four-blade variable-pitch propellers, mechanically controlled, 1.80 m diameter, driven by 239 kW Deutz V8 diesel engines.

Several new Hovercraft propellers are in development. By the enlargement of the factory, Hoffmann Propeller is now in a position to fully engage in new projects and to explore new paths of technology.

UPDATED

Hoffmann 3.6 m diameter five-blade propeller ***1990***

Canadian Coast Guard BHC AP1-88 hovercraft propelled by Hoffmann ducted propellers HO-V254 ***1990***

MT-PROPELLER ENTWICKLUNG GmbH & COMPANY KG

PO Box 0720, Airport D-94307 Straubing, Germany

Tel: +49 (9429) 8433
Fax: +49 (9429) 8432

Gerd Mühlbauer, *President*

This company was formed in 1982 and is involved mainly in the production of propellers for aircraft. It has developed a range of electric variable-pitch propellers and hydraulic constant speed propellers. Some of the propellers are LBA approved. The largest diameter propeller built by the end of 1986 was 2.9 m for 800 shp, but designs can be undertaken up to 3.5 m 2,000 shp and above.

VERIFIED

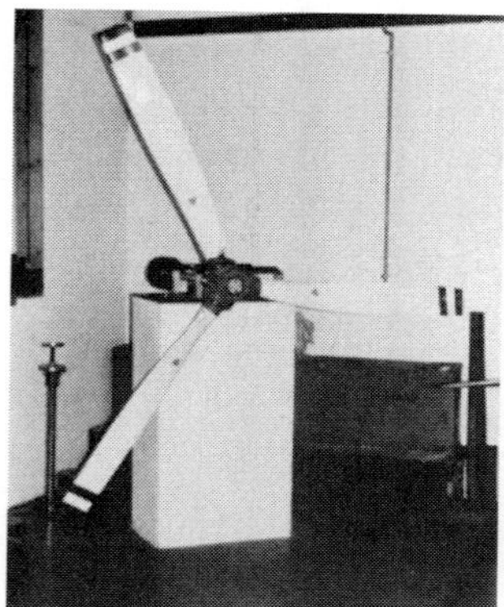

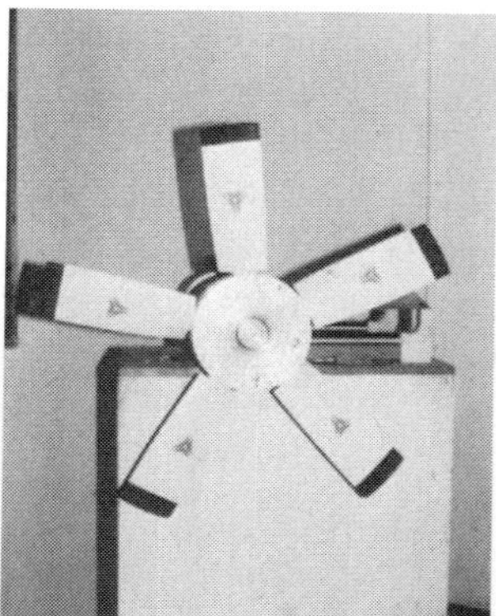

Examples of recent MT-Propeller Entwicklung propellers ***1987***

UNITED KINGDOM

AIR VEHICLES LTD

Head Office and Factory: Unit 4, Three Gates Road, Cowes, Isle of Wight, UK

Tel: +44 (1983) 293194
Telex: 86513 HVWORK G
Fax: +44 (1983) 291987

C B Eden, *Director*

Air Vehicles Limited has been involved in hovercraft since 1968 and manufactures specialist components for fully amphibious hovercraft, SES and other types of fast ferries.
Air propellers: Propellers are normally custom-designed to suit the application. Sizes up to 2.2 m diameter of fixed- and variable-pitch types have been produced. Larger sizes are available.
Propeller ducts: Associated propeller ducts are designed and manufactured up to propeller diameter of 3.6 m and absorbing 2,900 hp.
Fans: Axial, mixed flow and centrifugal fans are produced for hovercraft and SES vessels. They are usually manufactured in marine aluminium alloy giving a robust fan with good fatigue life. Systems requiring high flow and pressure such as SES are often supplied complete with lightweight volute and transmission system. As the main supplier of fans to the UK hovercraft industry, all fans are designed and manufactured to comply with the British Hovercraft Safety Requirements. This will usually ensure compliance with all other classification societies.
Skirt systems: The design and manufacture of SES and amphibious hovercraft skirt systems.
Bulkheads and doors: Design and manufacturer of lightweight bulkheads and partitioning systems for fast ferry interiors. Lightweight, easy fit door and surround assemblies.
Seating: Air Vehicles Limited designs and manufactures seating systems under the name of Advanced Seating Technology (AST) for hovercraft, SES and fast ferries. The AST range is a family of lightweight high performance fast ferry seating which complies with the latest IMO 12g dynamic test requirements and provides for tourist, club and VIP seating areas.

UPDATED

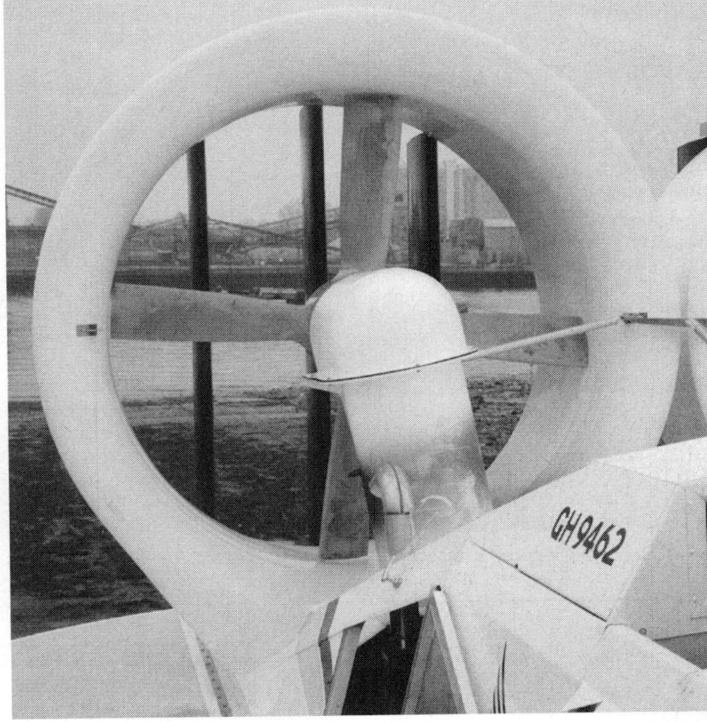

Typical centrifugal fans and propeller manufactured by Air Vehicles ***1993***

DOWTY AEROSPACE PROPELLERS

Anson Business Park, Cheltenham Road East, Gloucester GL2 9QN, UK

Tel: +44 (1452) 714888
Telex: 43246
Fax: +44 (1452) 711333

D G M Davis, *Managing Director*
R G Nailer, *Sales and Product Support Director*
M H Burden, *Engineering Director*
A R Cooper, *Marketing Manager*
G C Hanson, *Marketing Manager*

Dowty Aerospace Propellers, an operating business of Dowty Aerospace Gloucester Limited and a member of the TI Group, has been designing and manufacturing propellers for aircraft since 1937 when the company was originally formed as Rotol Airscrews Ltd. For over 30 years the company has been actively engaged in propulsion systems for air cushion vehicles.

The company is at present working on the production of propellers for the Textron Marine LCAC vehicles, together with its more recent C-7 air cushion vehicle project.

In support of Dowty Aerospace products worldwide, a network of repair and overhaul facilities are available. These facilities are strategically placed in the USA, Europe and South-east Asia.

Dowty Aerospace Aviation Services
Cheltenham Road, Gloucester GL2 9QH, UK

Tel: +44 (1452) 713111
Telex: 43246
Fax: +44 (1452) 711954

Dowty Aerospace Aviation Services
21 Loyang Crescent, Loyang Industrial Estate, 1750 Singapore

Tel: +65 545 9455
Telex: 21447
Fax: +65 542 3936

Dowty Aerospace Aviation Services
PO Box 5000, Sully Road, Sterling, Virginia 22170, USA

Tel: +1 (703) 450 8200
Telex: 824459
Fax: +1 (703) 430 9060

Hovercraft installations (Air cushion vehicles)
British Hovercraft Corporation SR. N5, SR. N6, 2.744 m diameter, four-blade hydraulic pitch control with reversing, single propeller installation, produced in aluminium alloy and composite material construction
British Hovercraft Corporation SR. N6 Mk 6, 3.049 m diameter, four-blade, hydraulic pitch control with reversing, two-propeller installation, aluminium alloy blades

Dowty ducted propeller installation on the Textron Marine LCAC ***1990***

Dowty all-composite propeller for the Textron Marine LCAC 1986

Mitsui PP15 3.201 m diameter, four-blade, hydraulic pitch control with reversing, single propeller installation, aluminium alloy blades

Vosper Thornycroft VT2 4.116 m diameter, seven-blade, two-propeller installation (ducted), composite material blades

Textron Marine LCAC 3.582 m diameter, four-blade, two-propeller installation (ducted) composite material blades

Textron Marine C-7 2.438 m diameter, four-blade, two-propeller installation (ducted), composite material blades

The extensive corrosion and erosion problems associated with air cushion vehicles led Dowty to develop composite blades with all-over erosion protection. These blades, the latest of which incorporate advanced technology aerofoil sections unique to Dowty, offer the following advantages: low weight combined with high strength, internal carbon fibre spars for high integrity, freedom from corrosion and they are easily repairable.

Dowty propellers for air cushion vehicles are designed to combine simple construction with safe operation. Techniques proven on ACVs have in turn been applied to and certificated on new generation general aviation, executive and commuter aircraft.

UPDATED

UNITED STATES OF AMERICA

ARDCO

Advance Ratio Design Company Inc

2540 Green Street, JEN Industrial Campus, Chester, Pennsylvania 19013, USA

Tel: +1 (215) 494 3200
Fax: +1 (215) 494 5079

Carl L Aley, *President*
David F Thompson, *Technical Director*
Craig D Thompson, *Vice President*

ARDCO specialises in composite airfoil blading and structures. The ARDCO team has designed and produced blades for turboprops, ducted propulsion fans, hovercraft compressors and helicopter main and tail rotors, also model blades for advanced unducted fan testing. Over the past few years ARDCO has done extensive design work on large ducted props for the Westinghouse naval airship programme. Materials include glassfibre, graphite and/or Kevlar/epoxy, oriented linear-filament reinforced materials, compression moulded with low density cores of honeycomb or foam plastic and flush co-bonded metal leading edge erosion strips. ARDCO produces blades to fit existing hubs or complete rotor assemblies, as required. The company also uses Resin Transfer Moulding (RTM) techniques where unusually massive (some hollow-ribbed) composite structures of hundreds of pounds weight are required, such as for marine propellers. Complete vehicle airframe structures are also custom-designed and fabricated.

HIGH-PERFORMANCE SURFACE-CRAFT PROPELLER

ARDCO is in the process of developing a specialised fan/propeller series useful for a variety of high-performance surface craft which utilises ducted propulsion, such as hovercraft and airboats. The family of fan/propellers to be made available will offer a spread of characteristics as follows:

Diameters: 914-1321 mm
Number of blades: 2,3,4,6,12 with equi-spaced patterns
Pitch angle: ground-adjustable pitch
Power input: approx 134 kW
Rotational tip speeds: 122-167 m/s

The objective for this propeller series is quiet operation while giving efficient performance and hence, operating at moderate tip speeds, these propellers require large blade area and/or a larger number of blades.

The blades with relatively thin aerofoils are solid glass-filament epoxy, pressure-moulded and featuring integrally bonded stainless steel leading-edge abrasion caps to protect against water spray environments.

The hub is pressure moulded in glassfibre-reinforced composite material and features ground-adjustable blade pitch, allowing power absorption versus rpm to be fine tuned.

The propeller is designed for long life and minimal maintenance in a marine environment and towards this end total elimination of metal-to-metal contact is embodied as well as minimisation of exposed metal surfaces.

ARDCO all-composite surface-craft propeller 1990

VERIFIED

PACIFIC PROPELLER INC

5802 South 228th Street, Kent, Washington 98032-1187, USA

Tel: +1 (206) 872 7767
Telex: 32-0368
Fax: +1 (206) 872 7221

Dennis Patrick, *President*
Gary Bottoms, *Director of Business Development*

Pacific Propeller manufactures, overhauls and sells propeller systems for aircraft and hovercraft use, having been in this business since 1946. PPI has manufactured over 10,000 metal propeller blades for single and multi-engine installations and is the current supplier of propellers for the Canadian Coast Guard SR. N5, SR. N6 and Voyageur hovercraft. In addition, PPI-designed and -manufactured propeller blades are the only current production units approved for installation on the US Army LACV-30 hovercraft. By Autumn 1991 over 500 AG200-1S blades had been supplied to the US Army for use on the LACV-30.

HC200-1S PROPELLER BLADE

This is a hard alloy derivative of the AG-series blades manufactured for aircraft use. It is designed to be tougher and more erosion-resistant to the effects of salt and sand spray. Typical hovercraft installations use the three-bladed HSP 43D50 hub coupled to the Pratt & Whitney ST6 TwinPac or the Rolls-Royce Gnome turbine engines. Propeller diameter is 2.72 m. This configuration has been tested in excess of 1,600 hp and is safe for operation up to 2,300 rpm. Each blade weighs 22.22 kg and can be overhauled using standard propeller overhaul facilities.

VERIFIED

MARINE PROPELLERS

Company Listing by Country

Australia
Veem Engineering Group

Denmark
Hundested Motor and Propeller Fabrik A/S

Germany
Schottel-Werft
Sulzer Hydro GmbH

Italy
Eliche Radice SpA
LA. ME Srl

Japan
Kamome Propeller Company Ltd

Netherlands
Lips BV

Norway
Servogear A/S
Ulstein Propeller A/S

Sweden
Berg Propulsion AB
Kamewa AB

Switzerland
Rolla SP Propellers SA
Rolla (USA)

United Kingdom
Brunton's Propellers Ltd
Stone Manganese Marine Ltd
Teignbridge Propellers Ltd

United States of America
Bird-Johnson Company
Michigan Wheel Corporation
T-Torque Drive System Inc

AUSTRALIA

VEEM ENGINEERING GROUP

10 Ballantyne Road, Kewdale 6105, Western Australia, Australia

Tel: +61 (9) 351 8388
Fax: +61 (9) 350 5302

M Miocevich, *Manager*

Manufacturer of propellers from 250 to 2,550 mm in diameter in three-, four- or five-blade designs. Materials include 88/10/2 gun metal, CX3 manganese bronze, AB2 aluminium bronze or CMAI bronze.

The company works to quality assurance standard ISO 9002 and provides propellers for a wide variety of craft in Australia and New Zealand including many fast commercial craft.

Propellers can be supplied with up to five, six or seven blades and finished to ISO 484/2-1981 (E) to Class 2, 1 or S standards as required.

VERIFIED

DENMARK

HUNDESTED MOTOR AND PROPELLER FABRIK A/S

Skansevej 1, DK-3390 Hundested, Denmark

Tel: +45 0233 7117
Telex: 40245 HMF DK
Fax: +45 0233 9902

Designers and manufacturers of controllable-pitch propellers since 1929. The 20 knot RMI SD-60 *Halcyon* Swath vessel is fitted with Hundested 1,143 mm diameter fully reversible (Type FR-H) propellers.

VERIFIED

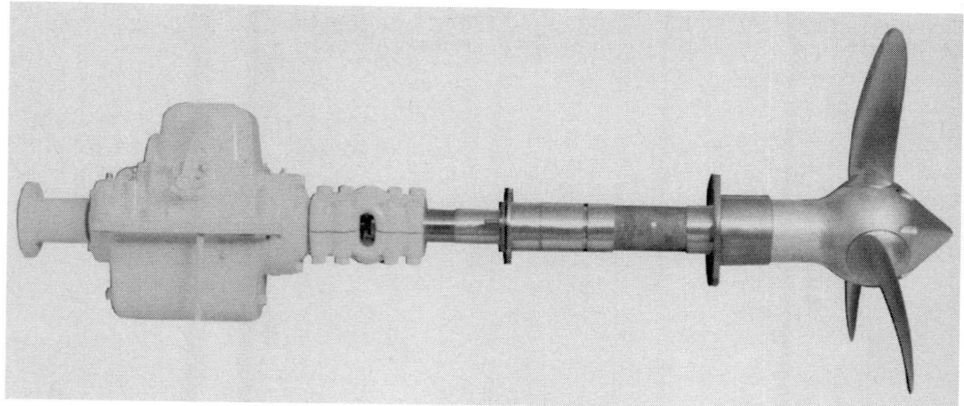

Hundested Type FR-H controllable-pitch propeller system as fitted to the RMI Halcyon **1993**

GERMANY

SCHOTTEL-WERFT

Josef Becker GmbH & Co KG

Mainzer Strasse 99, D-56322 Spay/Rhein, Germany

Tel: +49 (2628) 610
Fax: +49 (2628) 61300

Uwe Gragen, *Director, Sales and Marketing*

SCHOTTEL manufactures and supplies marine propulsion systems. The company also provides consultancy services using experience gained from the engineering and installation of more than 20,000 Rudderpropellers and pump jets.

The first two (of a planned series of 10) passenger catamarans for Sydney Harbour, Australia, have gone into operation. Both vessels are fitted with SCHOTTEL SRP 132/131 Rudderpropellers and control systems. The vessels, named *Dawn Frazer* and *Betty Cuthbert*, were built by NQEA and are operated by the State Transit Authority of New South Wales on a regular service on the Parramatta River.

VERIFIED

Dawn Frazer *and* Betty Cuthbert *fitted with SCHOTTEL Rudderpropellers* **1993**

SULZER HYDRO GmbH

PO Box 1380, D-88183 Ravensburg, Germany

Tel: +49 (751) 8300
Telex: 732901
Fax: +49 (751) 833274

Sulzer Hydro has considerable experience in the design and production of controllable pitch propellers, known as Escher Wyss CPP's, many supplied for frigates, corvettes, patrol boats, mine countermeasure vessels and special purpose vessels. Over 140 propellers have been supplied with an air ejection system to reduce noise consequences of cavitation. Designs with seven-bladed propellers developed in 1986/87 are in service successfully. Particular interest is paid to the propeller blade design with regard to hydroacoustic and hydrodynamic performance whereby five-axis CNC-machining of the complete blade is a standard procedure. Experience from the many designs made and employment of the most modern computer programs and techniques secure a continuous development in this important field of high-performance propulsion systems.

A seven-blade controllable-pitch propeller design

was supplied for the Blohm+Voss Corsair SES. The semi-submerged propellers for this vessel have the following characteristics:
Diameter: 1,200 mm
Hub ratio: 0.32
Design pitch ratio: 1.75
Max shaft power: 2,560 kW
Rotational speed: 940 rpm

UPDATED

One of the two Escher Wyss 1.2 m diameter controllable-pitch propellers fitted to the Blohm+Voss 52 knot Corsair SES
1992

ITALY

ELICHE RADICE SpA

Via Valtellina 45, I-20092 Cinisello Balsamo, Milan, Italy

Tel: +39 (2) 6604 9348
Telex: 332352 RADPRO I
Fax: +39 (2) 6612 7688

Alfredo Radice, *Proprietor*
Carlo Radice, *Proprietor*

Manufacture of fixed-pitch propellers for high-speed craft. Early Hovermarine HM2 craft were fitted with Radice propellers in stainless steel. Bronze propellers with two to five blades and diameters up to 3.5 m can be supplied.

VERIFIED

LA. ME Srl

Via Della Fornace 4, Dosso Cavalino, I-20090 Opera, Milan, Italy

Tel: +39 (2) 5760 2441
Telex: 3802831 I
Fax: +39 (2) 5760 3549

Marco Lazzati, *Managing Director*
Ing Giovanni Patrone Raggi, *Sales and Marketing Manager*

LDU

LDU is an evolution of the 'Step Drive' offering the advantages of the conventional 'Z' drive with the increased performance of surface propulsion; it is claimed to maintain all the advantages of the surface propeller and eliminates completely the negative

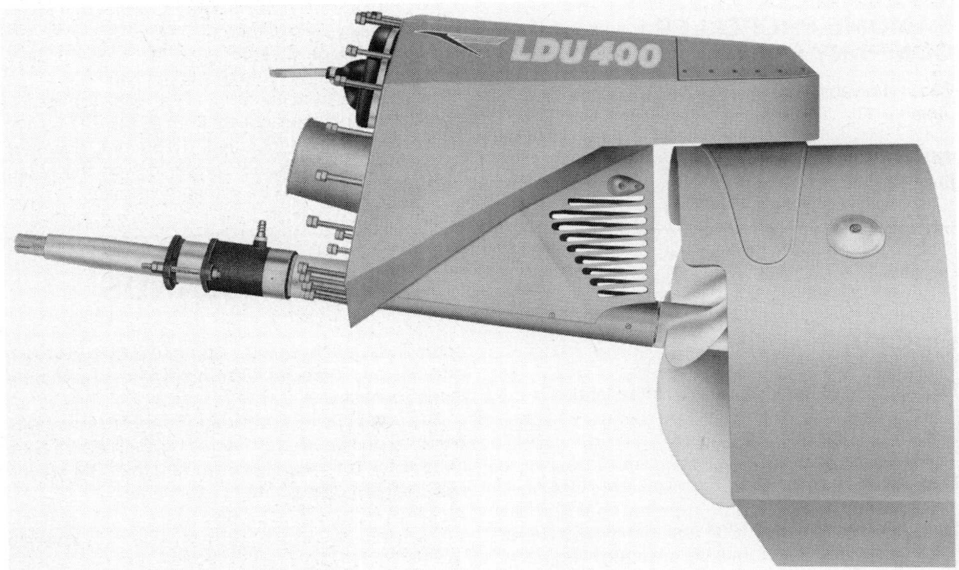

LDU, Model 400
1992

LDU Model data

Model	LDU100	200PL	300	400	600	1,000PL	2,400PL	3000PL
Max torque, shaft, kg/m	45	105	175	205	270	470	850	1,500
rpm/hp indicative limits	120 hp at 1,950 rpm to 292 hp at 4,760 rpm	280 hp at 1,920 rpm to 380 hp at 2,600 rpm	380 hp at 1,554 rpm to 600 hp at 2,460 rpm	438 hp at 1,540 rpm to 700 hp at 1,850 rpm	500 hp at 1,460 rpm to 800 hp at 2,130 rpm	700 hp at 1,070 rpm to 1,200 hp at 1,850 rpm	1,200 hp at 1,010 rpm to 2,200 hp at 1,650 rpm	2,200 hp at 1,050 rpm to 3,500 hp —
Max torque, rudder stock, kg/m	30	75	125	150	150	250	500	800
Exhaust, outside diameter mm	120	130	168	168	168	200	300	460
Fitting to transom (studs)	22	22	22	22	22	22	22	24
Lubrication, linkage	molybdenum grease	molybdenum grease	molybdenum grease	molybdenum grease	molybdenum grease	molybdenum grease	molybdenum grease	molybdenum grease
Lubrication, shaft	water	water	water	water	water	water	water	water
Dimensions: A, mm	806	878	1,030	1,117	1,117	1,356	1,596	1,995
Dimensions: B, mm	670	805	961	1,019	1,019	1,231	1,450	1,845
Dimensions: C, mm	526	635	735	798	798	952	1,120	1,400
Weight, excluding propeller, kg	85	140	240	265	600	1,100	2,200	

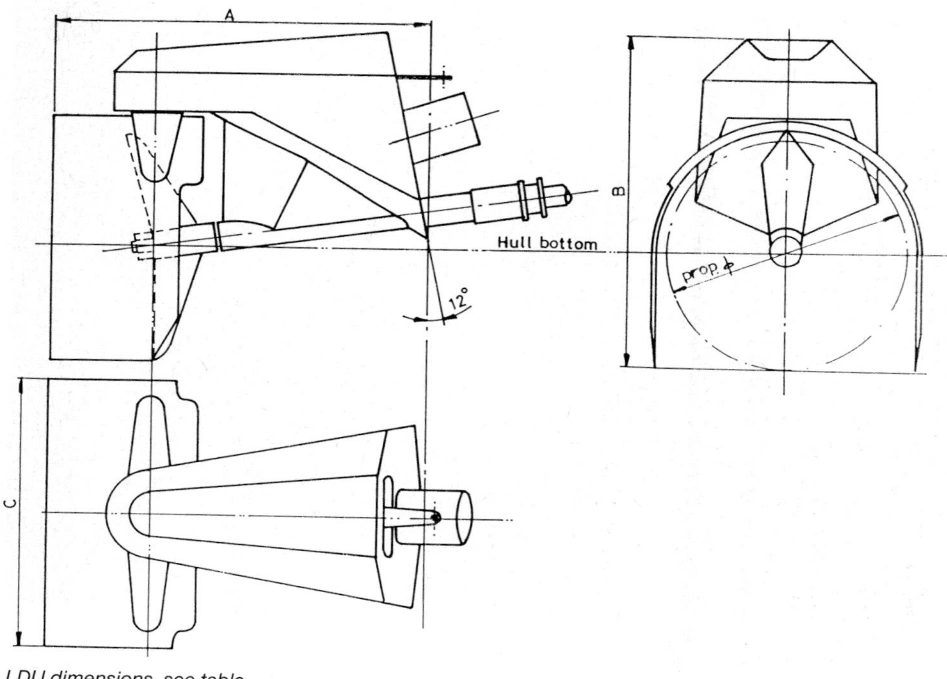

LDU dimensions, see table

1988

aspects which have plagued and prevented the acceptance of this excellent system of propulsion for many years.

During its short life the LDU has been successfully fitted on hundreds of craft in pleasure, workboat and military categories.

The engine may be fitted amidships or right aft without the added complication of a costly V-drive and transmission shaft. The tunnel rudders over the top half of the propellers have been employed to overcome some of the disadvantages of conventional rudders or propeller power steering. The two vertical rudder blades which are a continuation of the shroud act as sidewalls and, operating below the hull, give positive control as required as well as protecting the propeller in shallow water.

To enhance the reverse thrust capabilities of a fixed-pitch propeller a new blade section profile has been devised giving, on the back of the blade, a concave area towards the trailing edge, producing improved section lift coefficient and hence thrust when in reverse rotation.

The propeller incorporating this profile is called the Diamond Back surface propeller and overcomes the poor astern thrust associated with surface propellers.

The present range of LDU units extends from 37 to 2,980 kW (indicative power limits).

Principal Features

Body of LDU: monocoque structure in 316L stainless steel, welded and heat-treated
Rudder: of semi-circular design together with reinforcing plate and stock of 316L stainless steel plate and bar respectively
Rudder linkage: consisting of yoke, dummy tiller and tie rod terminals in cast 316L stainless steel, or Nickel-Aluminium-Bronze
Propeller shaft: Armco Aquamet 17-18-22 or monel k 500
Surface propeller: four-blade with Diamond Back sections cast in Nickel-Aluminium-Bronze (NAB). For the Model 2400PL and above propellers are five- and seven-blade
Shaft bearings: Water-lubricated in synthetic fibre

Recent Applications

LA. ME Srl propellers have recently been fitted to a number of larger high-speed marine craft: the Brooke Marine 33 m, 50 knot pleasure boat *G-Whiz*; the Brooke Marine 50 knot *Virgin Atlantic Challenger II*, Italian custom patrol boat 16.5 m, 49 knots, 14 other custom boats and three patrol craft for the UAE.

VERIFIED

JAPAN

KAMOME PROPELLER COMPANY LTD

690 Kamiyabe-cho, Totsuka-ku, Yokohama 245, Japan

Tel: +81 (45) 811 2461
Fax: +81 (45) 811 9444

Hiroshi Itazawa, *President*
Masayoshi Ishige, *Director*

Design and manufacture of a wide range of controllable-pitch propellers from 224 to 12,000 kW. Installations have included 1,750 mm diameter, 1,400 mm pitch CPC-53F propellers on the Mitsui 20.5 knot *Kotozaki*, a 27 m Swath vessel.

UPDATED

NETHERLANDS

LIPS BV

PO Box 6, NL-5150 BB Drunen, Netherlands

Tel: +31 (4163) 88115
Telex: 35185 LIPS NL
Fax: +31 (4163) 73162

Lips was established in 1934 and is the world leader in the field of marine propellers, covering fixed-pitch, controllable-pitch, side-thruster and systems to their own design. There are 500 employees in the Netherlands company.

The company has provided propellers for a number of high-speed craft including Fjellstrand catamarans for Turkey and Norway and the FBM Marine FDC 400 fast displacement catamaran.

VERIFIED

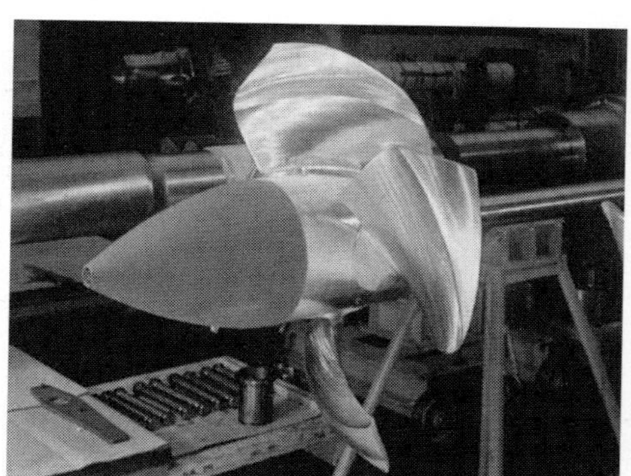
Lips transcavitating CP propeller that was designed for the US Navy SES Sea Viking

1988

NORWAY

SERVOGEAR A/S

N-5420 Rubbestadneset, Norway

Tel: +47 (53) 427380
Fax: +47 (53) 427783

S Jørgensen, *Naval Architect*

Established in 1973, Servogear produced lightweight propulsion systems for high-speed craft. The systems are supplied as complete units comprising controllable pitch propellers, shafting, gearboxes and rudders and also specifications for hull shape in way of the underwater part of the system.

Since Servogear started production in 1975, over 900 gearboxes and propeller systems have been delivered, of which more 500 have been for high-speed craft. This range has covered engine powers from 300 to 3,000 kW and ship speeds up to 50 knots.

The latest applications have been for seven triple engine 45 knot patrol craft and six twin engine 40 knot patrol craft, all for the Taiwanese Police. Fast ferry applications include the Holen and Lindstøl Skips catamarans all constructed in Norway in 1995/6.

UPDATED

Servogear propulsion system with 'Power Rudder'

1990

ULSTEIN PROPELLER A/S

N-6065 Ulsteinvik, Norway

Tel: +47 (700) 14000
Telex: 42 848 UP N
Fax: +47 (700) 14017

Stig Ulstein, *Managing Director*
Jarle Hessen, *Sales Manager*

Designers and manufacturers of controllable-pitch propellers, tunnel thrusters, compass thrusters and the Speed-Z Propulsion System. The Speed-Z system is marketed in the output range of 700 to 2,800 kW with controllable- and fixed-pitch propellers. Orders for the Speed-Z system have been received from the following shipyards: Westamarin A/S, Fjellstrand A/S, Broward Marine Inc and Baglietto Shipyard. High-speed applications have included a controllable-pitch installation on the Fjellstrand high-speed catamaran, *Asie III* and two Speed-Z four-blade propulsion units, Type CPZ, for the Westamarin W5000 *Anne Lise*, 49.5 m high-speed thermo-cargo catamaran, delivered June/July 1987. These units each absorb 2,040 kW and position the propellers in undisturbed free-stream flow. In comparison with conventional propeller systems an efficiency gain of 10 per cent is claimed. The system combines propulsion and steering functions. Other advantages of the Speed-Z propulsion system are reduced vibration and noise onboard, a cost-efficient compact installation, effective load control for protection of the drive motors and good manoeuvring capability.

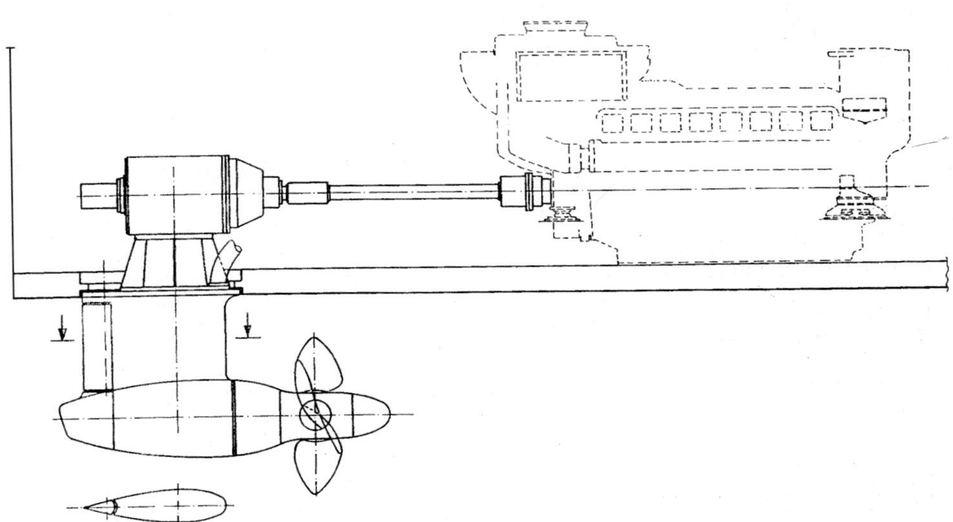

Layout of the Speed-Z Propulsion System Type CPZ

1988

Since Speed-Z is a traction (pulling) propeller there are no appendages in front of it and therefore the propeller acts in a homogeneous velocity field. These are ideal conditions for efficiency and avoidance of damaging cavitation. This has been substantiated by cavitation tests and prototypes in operation which produce no noticeable noise or vibration in the hull.

Another major advantage is the right angle drive which allows the propeller to be installed in line with the water flow. A conventional propeller installation is always a compromise between keeping the shaft angle low to avoid harmful root cavitation and ensuring sufficient clearance between the propeller and the hull to avoid noise and vibration from the high-pressure pulses created by the propeller. The Speed-Z unit has, as mentioned, the best possible conditions of flow to the propeller giving

Ulstein Speed-Z Propulsion Systems Type CPZ 60/40-125 fitted to the Westamarin 5000 Anne Lise*, 28 knot thermo-cargo catamaran. More recently Ulstein controllable-pitch propellers have been fitted to the Swath vessel* Navatek 1

1988

stable cavitation conditions and minimal fluctuating forces.

A comparison has been made, based on model test tank results with the Speed-Z unit, with a conventional installation with sloping shaft, brackets and rudder. The propeller on the conventional installation had a diameter of 1.6 m with a maximum speed of 525 rpm, while the Speed-Z unit has a diameter of 1.25 m at 769 rpm. Even though the Speed-Z unit is higher loaded, that is, the power per unit area is greater, the propeller efficiency is 76 per cent at an engine output of 2,040 kW and ship speed of 28 knots. The corresponding efficiency of a conventional installation is about 72 per cent. When the resistance of the appendages was taken into account the improvement in efficiency was even more significant. The result of the model tests showed that the overall propulsive efficiency of the model fitted with the Speed-Z was 66 per cent at 28 knots which compared with 58 per cent for the conventional system as described previously. In this case the new Speed-Z gave an improvement in efficiency of eight per cent, that is to say a saving in installed power of 13.8 per cent to achieve the same speed.

Ulstein Speed-Z Propulsion Unit showing the top reduction gear with clutch and the lower 90° reduction gear with rudder flap and propeller mounting
1988

VERIFIED

SWEDEN

BERG PROPULSION AB

S-430 90 Öckerö, Gothenburg, Sweden

Tel: +46 (31) 969020
Telex: 2401 8206027
Fax: +46 (31) 969456

Berg Propulsion AB is one of the world's leading companies in the design, development and manufacture of controllable-pitch propellers. Since 1928 Berg has manufactured and delivered more than 5,000 propulsion systems.

Berg Propulsion AB are developing a new line of propellers manufactured in composite materials. The materials are cheap and easily available and very simple production techniques have been developed. The main idea behind the concept of the FLEXPROP, as these new propellers are known, is to make use of the elastic properties of the blades in reducing load variations when they are operating in irregular flow at the stern of a vessel.

VERIFIED

KAMEWA AB

PO Box 1010, S-681 29 Kristinehamn, Sweden

Tel: +46 (550) 84000
Telex: 66050 KAMEWA S
Fax: +46 (550) 84778

Ingar Jensen, *Managing Director*
Claes Rudling, *Sales Director*
Olof Malmquist, *Public Relations Manager*

Kamewa has accumulated experience from over 50 years of activity in the marine field. The company is also the only manufacturer of propellers to possess a cavitation laboratory with comprehensive facilities for advanced testing of various forms of marine propulsion device.

The Kamewa design and manufacture of propellers for high-speed craft covers super-cavitating designs, which are modified to meet quiet and high-efficiency cruising conditions, wide-blade design for these conditions, skewed wide-blade propellers for extremely quiet cruising and the same design for ventilated blades. These propellers are manufactured in either stainless steel or nickel-aluminium-bronze. Propellers for patrol boats have been supplied over many years. Some of the most recent installations are for patrol boats and corvettes for Finland, Greece, Italy, South Korea, Malaysia, Morocco, Spain and Thailand.

Finnish Navy's Turku *equipped with three Kamewa featherable controllable-pitch propellers, 3,000 kW per shaft*
1993

The water-jet unit is becoming an ever increasing alternative for high-speed craft propulsion. Kamewa is leading in this field (please see the Kamewa entry in the *Water-jet units* section).

VERIFIED

SWITZERLAND

ROLLA SP PROPELLERS SA

Via Silva 5, PO Box 251, CH-6828 Balerna, Switzerland

Tel: +41 (91) 695 2000
Fax: +41 (91) 695 2001

Remo Cattaneo, *President*
Philip Rolla, *Managing Director*
Mark Wilson, *Director of Production*
Marzio Porro, *Research and Development*
Franco Gotta, *Applications Engineer*
John Rose, *Director of Rolla USA*

ROLLA (USA)

4030 Mustang Road, Melbourne, Florida 32934, USA

Tel: +1 (407) 242 7552
Fax: +1 (407) 242 7771

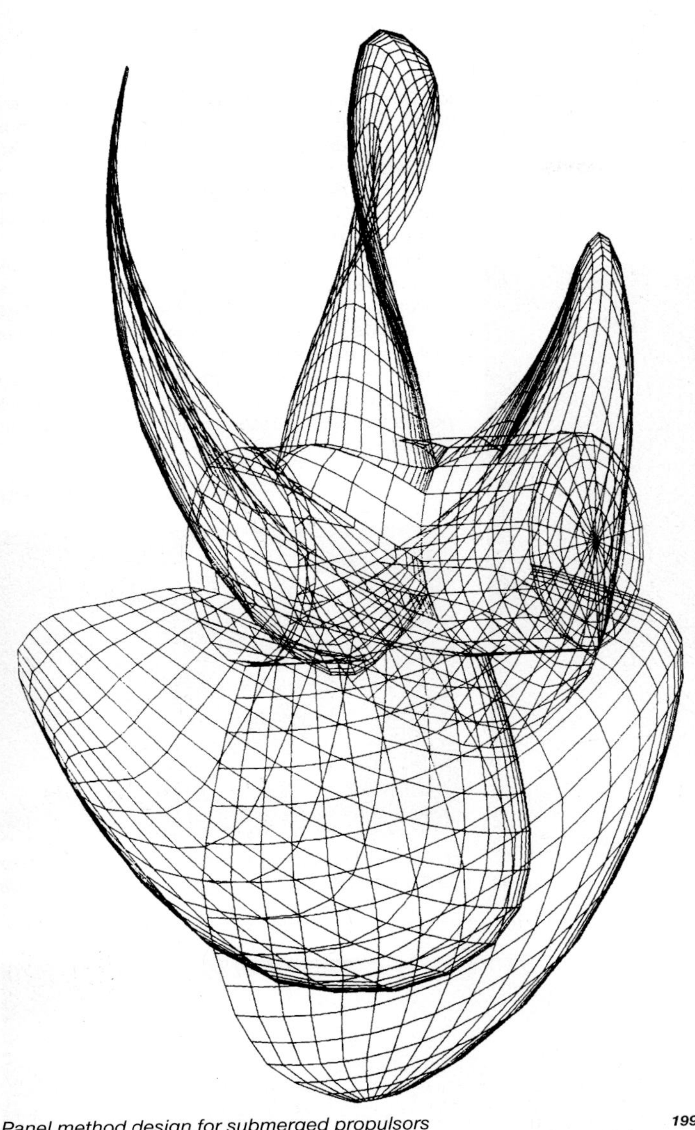

Panel method design for submerged propulsors **1996**

Rolla 7 bladed propeller **1996**

The company was founded in 1963 by Philip Rolla. The services, consultation and designs include: performance and power prediction for displacement and planing craft; propeller design; one-off propeller design; estimation of complete hydrodynamic characteristics of the propeller geometry, and propeller cavitation characteristics through exclusive lifting surface and panel method programmes; manufacturing of propeller models; model basin tests in the Berlin University cavitation tunnel and at the IMHEF cavitation tunnel at Lausanne; full-scale tests; propeller re-calculation and redesign for existing vessels; designing and manufacturing of propeller prototypes and pre-series; designing of conventional and unconventional propulsion systems; and consultation on propulsion problems.

Propellers are specially designed to be dedicated to the craft's projected operational profile by using the Rolla proprietary lifting surface and panel method programmes and manufactured using CAD/CAM 'CATIA' programme from Dassault aerospace. A Rolla associated manufacturing facility is able to mill propellers up to a 3 m diameter with a 5 axes 'MECOF' M 1000 milling machine.

Rolla also offers a complete design service for those interested in the application of surface propellers, not wanting to use a commercially available drive, but wanting to realise their own proprietary system. Rolla will collaborate with constructors in the design of their own system and make available over 30 years of experience in surface propellers and installation.

Surface-piercing, super-cavitating, transcavitating and sub-cavitating propellers are designed and produced to any required geometry and with up to eight blades.

As part of its dedication to research in 1993, Rolla became a member of the MIT/Navy/Industry Consortium on Cavitation Performance of High-Speed Propulsors. One of the principal objectives was to develop efficient computational optimisation techniques for the automated design, in the presence of cavitation, of innovative high-speed propulsive configurations. In 1994 Rolla became a member of Lausanne University consortium for testing.

In general, propellers are produced in high-tensile stainless steel (using investment casting and forging) for very high-speed craft and traditional casting in steel or Nibral for commercial, military, workboats, luxury boats and pleasure boats up to 80 knots. The Rolla families of stainless steel and Nibral surface-piercing propellers include lines specifically designed for Arneson Drives, Levi Drive Units, T-Torque Drive System, Mondrive System and Trimax. Also interesting is the recent design and production of Rolla forged steel blades for controllable-pitch surface propellers. The Rolla results obtained at the Technische Universitat Berlin constitute the first systematic series of surface propellers available in the world and permit Rolla to supply the torque and thrust coefficients and efficiency, horizontal and vertical force figures for different shaft inclinations and propeller immersions. The Rolla stainless steel propellers for stern drives include lines specifically designed for ZF-MPM, Volvo Penta, MerCruiser, Kiekhaefer, Yamaha and OMC.

Constant engagement in advanced research has allowed the company to acquire the trust of major yacht builders. The penetration of the large and fast motor yacht market has dramatically increased in the past years and now beside the traditional customers such as Hatteras and Magnum, other famous yards including Azimut, Ferretti and Sea Ray are enjoying the benefits of the Rolla expertise.

Concerning the latest technology and the production, Rolla has recently introduced three new special models, known as Super-Propellers. They are investment cast in 17-4-PH and ERO, available in five, six and seven blades, have an extremely high performance, and a maximum diameter of 870 mm. They are the largest investment cast steel propellers in the world.

It is worth noting that the Swiss company is presently custom designing and manufacturing surface-piercing propellers for military projects worldwide. The listed vessels are produced in series, confirming Rolla's past and continuing research and dedication to surface propellers. Rolla has also intensified the design and construction of special propellers for all applications, submerged as well as surface.

Recent applications of Rolla propellers to military vessels

IAI-RAMTA, Israel
Super-Dvora Mk II 2 × MTU 8V/Arneson ASD-14 & 2 × MTU 12V/ASD-16

TRINITY, USA
for US Navy and Mexico *XFPB* 3 × GM 16V/ASD-14

PETERSON BUILDERS, USA
US Navy Mk V 2 × MTU 16V 396 TB 94 21 m Cougar Cat/Fixed Surface Drives

ASTAFERSA, Spain
Spanish Customs 2 × MTU 16V 396 TB 94 21 m Cougar Cat/Fixed Surface Drives

FB MARINE, Italy
Italian Customs 3 × 600 hp Seatek/Trimax Drives

UK MoD
3 × 600 hp Seatek/Trimax Drives

SWEDE SHIPS, Sweden
Swedish Customs 3 × 600 hp Seatek/Mercury No 7 Drives

McDONNELL DOUGLAS, USA
Magnum 40 2 × CAT 600 hp/ASD-10

SIMONNEAU, France
Star Naja 2 × Cat 425 hp/Trimax Drives

SILKINE, Thailand
18 m Foil-assisted Catamaran 2 × MAN 820 hp/ASD-12

COUGAR, UK
38' Kuwait 2 × 375 hp/ASD-8

US NAVY, USA
HSAC 2 × 550 hp/Speedmaster III A Drives

JAPANESE COAST GUARD, Japan
12 m PBs 3 × 340 hp/ASD-8

UPDATED

UNITED KINGDOM

BRUNTON'S PROPELLERS LTD

Station Road, Sudbury, Suffolk CO10 6ST, UK

Tel: +44 (1787) 373611
Telex: 98400 PROPS G
Fax: +44 (1787) 881019

Brunton's Propellers Ltd is a specialist company in the design and manufacture of propellers for high-performance craft such as patrol boats, surface effect ships, hydrofoils, catamarans and so on, where the propellers have to work in very exacting conditions. The design requirements in such cases can be extremely critical and manufacturing to very close tolerances is required: ISO 484 Class 'S' and better. Brunton's parent company is Stone Manganese Ltd, designers and manufacturers of ship propellers.

As well as meeting commercial requirements, Brunton's Propellers Ltd supplies the British MoD and navies around the world.

Propellers may be manufactured in high-tensile manganese bronze, nickel-aluminium-bronze, Novostron (a manganese-aluminium-bronze alloy), Superstron 70 and gun metal, though this last material is now seldom used.

Brunton's associated company, Stone Propellers Ltd, manufactures extremely accurate model propellers for test and research work in test tanks and cavitation tunnels.

VERIFIED

1 m diameter propellers (Dr Kruppa design) for HM527 surface effect ship **1988**

Brunton five-blade propeller for twin-propeller 33.5 m patrol boat **1986**

STONE MANGANESE MARINE LTD

A member of the Langham Industries Group

Dock Road, Birkenhead, Merseyside L41 1DT, UK

Tel: +44 (151) 652 2372
Fax: +44 (151) 652 2377

J M Langham, *Chairman*
J R Wilson, *Deputy Chairman*
G Patience, *Managing Director*
B N Preston, *Director*

Stone Manganese Marine has been manufacturing propellers for more than 100 years. The company and its associates operate 10 manufacturing units throughout the world and the product range covers all sizes of fixed-pitch marine propellers for all types of ships, including high-speed marine craft.

The main factory is at Birkenhead, which includes the technical department, offering a comprehensive technical service to customers and the preparation of the company's proprietary Meridian design.

The company has a long established connection with the University of Newcastle upon Tyne, collaborating in the operation of the cavitation tunnel where the KCA design, specifically to suit high-speed craft, was developed and tested. The KCA design has been adopted for high-speed marine applications worldwide.

VERIFIED

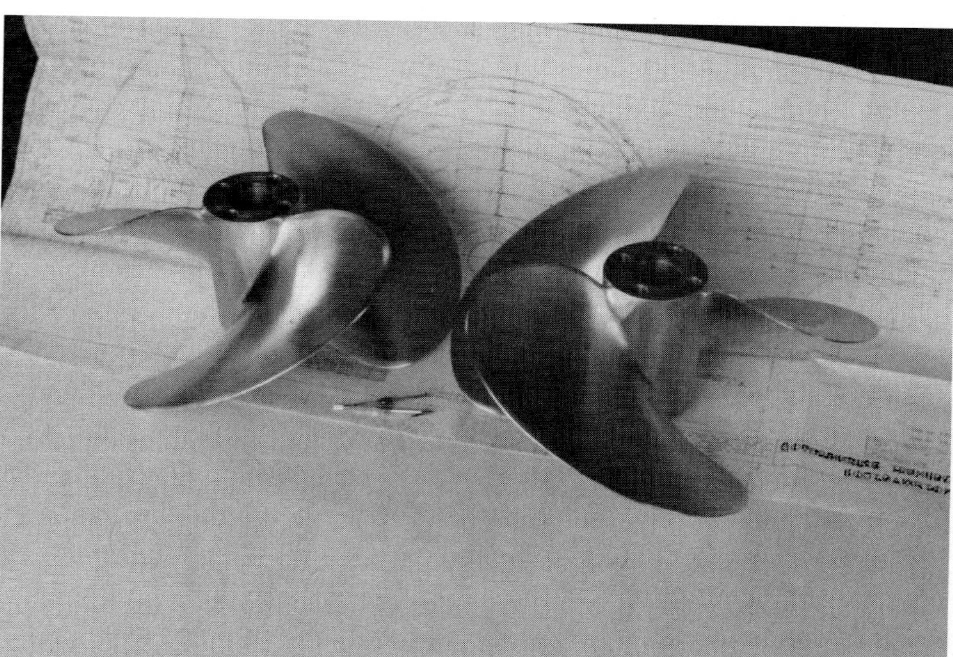

Stone Manganese Marine Ltd KCA design propellers for high-speed craft **1986**

TEIGNBRIDGE PROPELLERS LTD

Forde Road, Brunel Industrial Estate, Newton Abbot, Devon TQ12 4AD, UK

Tel: +44 (1626) 333377
Fax: +44 (1626) 60783

D A Duncan, *Chairman*
D A Hunt, *Managing Director*
T Hughes, *Sales Director*
R P Madle, *Engineering Director*
A P Bonnell, *Company Secretary*
M Izzo, *Designer, High-Speed Applications*

Operating out of three separate manufacturing facilities in the UK, Teignbridge offers a complete design and manufacturing service to naval architects, operators and builders of all types of vessels, from high-speed craft such as fast ferries, hydrofoils, patrol boats and superyachts to fishing vessels, tugs and inland vessels.

For the manufacture of high-definition propellers to ISO Class I and Class S tolerances, the most up to date CAD/CAM technology is employed.

Teignbridge also produces a range of standard and custom designed sterngear, rudders, shaft brackets and associated equipment. All products can be designed and manufactured to comply with the rules of any classification society.

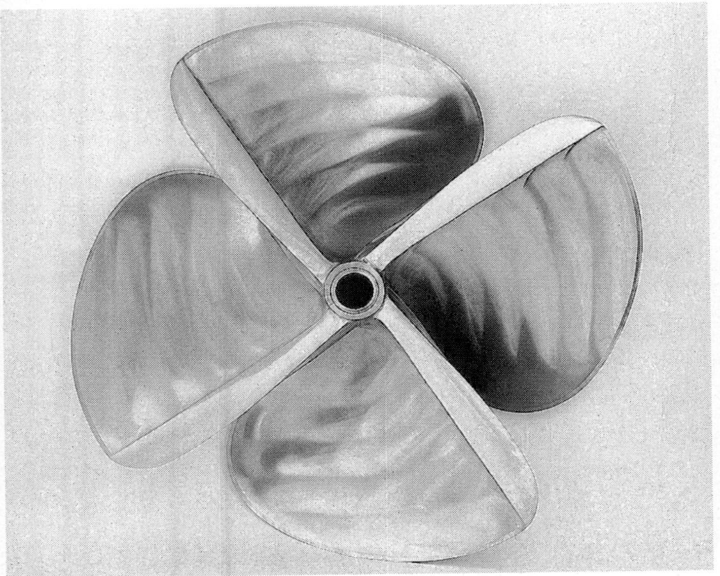
Aquaquad four-bladed surface-piercing high-speed propeller ***1996***

Aquaquin five-bladed standard high-speed propeller ***1996***

Complete sterngear systems are produced up to 300 mm shaft diameter. Shaft materials used are Temet 25 duplex stainless steel, conventional stainless steels AISI316 and 304, mild steel and Temet 17, a high-strength stainless steel. Sterntubes are manufactured to suit GRP, aluminium, steel and wooden vessels and supplied with bearings and shaft seals for water or oil lubrication.

Shaft brackets and rudder systems are supplied either cast in nickel-aluminium bronze or fabricated in carbon or stainless steels. Sterngear components are produced in purpose built machine shops on modern CNC machinery.

STANDARD RANGE PROPELLERS

For fast vessels Teignbridge produces a standard series of 'sub-cavitating' propellers manufactured in nickel-aluminium bronze and manganese bronze. This range of propellers is manufactured as standard from 305 mm diameter to 1,020 mm diameter covering all common P/D ratios.

For non-planing applications propellers are generally manufactured to ISO Class 2 tolerances. For faster vessels Class 1 tolerances are applied.

CUSTOM DESIGNED PROPELLERS

These are specified for applications where standard series propellers cannot be used. Teignbridge custom designed propellers fall into three categories: highly skewed; propellers for optimum performance in terms of speed, noise and vibration; and propellers for surface-piercing applications.

High-speed propellers are manufactured to Class S tolerances and are designed using the 'lifting surface' theory to optimise propeller geometry to suit each vessel's particular application.

Teignbridge's surface-piercing propellers are the result of many years of experience in designing partially submerged super-cavitating propellers. This has culminated in the design of a series of four- and five-blade propellers using the revolutionary 'cascade theory' for section design. This has allowed the design of very efficient, thin sections using nickel-aluminium bronze and Temet 25 duplex stainless steel. This propeller series has been optimised for use on high-speed, diesel powered ferries and military vessels between 30 and 55 knots. The four-blade series is used on highly loaded, high-speed applications.

UPDATED

UNITED STATES OF AMERICA

BIRD-JOHNSON COMPANY

Pascagoula Operations
3719 Industrial Road, Pascagoula, Mississippi 39567, USA

Tel: +1 (601) 762 0728
Telex: 589938
Fax: +1 (601) 769 7048

Peter J Lapp, *Manager*

110 Norfolk Street, Walpole, Massachusetts 02081, USA

Tel: +1 (617) 668 9610
Telex: 6817294
Fax: +1 (617) 668 5638

Peter J Gwyn, *Chief Executive Officer and President*
Joseph J Riley, *Chief Financial Officer and Vice President, Finance and Accounting*
Gary W Dayton, *Director, Marine Marketing and Services*

Bird-Johnson Company is a leading supplier of fixed- and controllable-pitch propeller systems for naval application. In-house capabilities include design, foundry, hand and NC finishing, assembly, test and repair. All products are backed by logistic support including a 24 hour emergency service network.

VERIFIED

MICHIGAN WHEEL CORPORATION

1501 Buchanan Avenue SW, Grand Rapids, Michigan 49507, USA

Tel: +1 (616) 452 6941
Fax: +1 (616) 247 0227

John Panarites, *President*
Martin Ronis, *Vice President Marketing*
Thomas Siler, *Vice President Finance*
Gary Palmowski, *Vice President Manufacturing*
William Herrick, *Director/Marketing Services*

Established in 1903, Michigan Wheel produces a wide range of fixed-pitch propellers, including the Machined-Pitch type, with a diameter up to 2.44 m, and the Dyna-foil type, diameter up to 2.44 m. These propellers can be made in manganese bronze alloy, nickel-bronze, aluminium-bronze and stainless steel.

UPDATED

T-TORQUE DRIVE SYSTEM INC

3333 NE 188th Street, North Miami Beach, Florida 33180, USA

Tel: +1 (305) 937 5064
Fax: +1 (305) 937 5071

Adam Erdberg, *President*

T-TORQUE DRIVE SYSTEM

The T-Torque Drive System (US Patent No 4 919 630) is an advanced heavy-duty marine propulsion system based on surface-piercing operation of super-cavitating propellers. The system provides the recreational, commerical or military diesel-powered craft operator with high manoeuvrability, high-speed and shallow water operation capability. The system is highly reliable due to its construction in the highest marine grade polished stainless steel (316L) and simplistic concept. The shafts connect directly to the engine transmissions and pass through the transom supported by heavy-duty struts which are mounted above the bottom of the boat. Since the propeller shafts directly penetrate the transom, the shaft angle is far less than conventional inboard systems, thereby providing greatly reduced appendage drag and increased efficiency. Shaft centres are at normal separations depending upon the particular vessel and engines. This configuration allows the

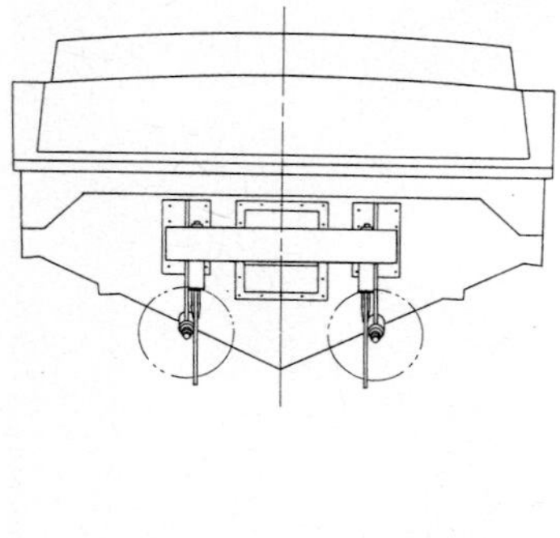

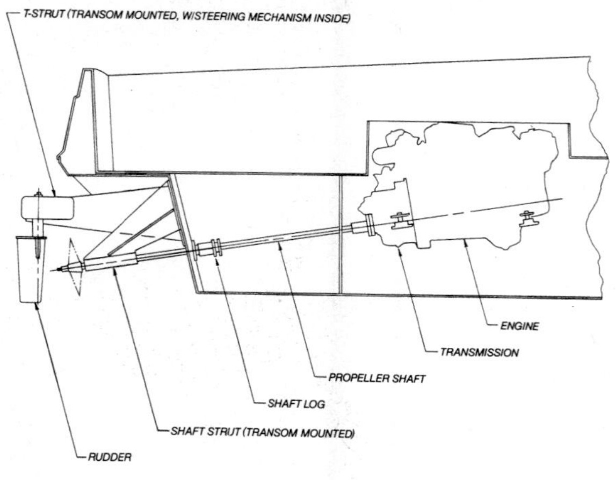

Main features of T-Torque drive system

vessel to have the low-speed dockside precision manoeuvrability of a conventional inboard-powered vessel. The T-Torque rudder system is supported by a polished stainless steel T-Strut securing the rudders behind the propellers. The rudders turn via a hydraulic power steering system with hydraulic lines built into the T-Strut (see illustration).

The system has been in service since 1984 on various recreational, commercial and military vessels up to 26 m (85 ft) in length.

VERIFIED

1992

WATER-JET UNITS

Company Listing by Country

Finland
FF Jet Ltd AB

Italy
Castoldi SpA

Japan
Kawasaki Heavy Industries Ltd (Prime Mover Division)
Mitsubishi Heavy Industries Ltd
Niigata Engineering Company Ltd

Netherlands
Lips Jets BV

New Zealand
C W F Hamilton & Company Ltd (Hamiltonjet)

Norway
Kværner Energy A/S
Ulstein Propeller A/S

Sweden
Kamewa AB
MJP

United Kingdom
PP Jets
Ultra Hydraulics Ltd

United States of America
Amjet
North American Marine Jet Inc

FINLAND

FF JET LTD AB

PO Box 79, SF-67101 Kokkola, Finland

Tel: +358 (68) 822 1505
Fax: +358 (68) 822 1435

In 1994 Kamewa of Sweden acquired FF Jet Ltd AB which has consolidated its position as the leading supplier of water-jets to this industry. The Kamewa/FF Jet product range, manufactured by FF Jet Ltd AB in Kokkola, Finland, is marketed through the Kamewa sales network (see Kamewa entry under Sweden).

FF-JET 240

Designed for planing craft up to 4 tonnes and displacement craft up to 7 tonnes. Power range 40 to 230 kW. Max 4,000 rpm. Dry weight 100 kg.

FF-JET 310

Designed for planing boats up to 7 tonnes and displacement boats up to 12 tonnes. Power range 40 to 300 kW. Max 3,000 rpm. Dry weight 190 kg.

FF-JET 375

Designed for planing boats up to 11 tonnes and displacement boats up to 22 tonnes. Power range 80 to 450 kW. Max 2,500 rpm. Dry weight 290 kg.

FF-JET 410

Designed for planing craft up to 15 tonnes and displacement craft up to 28 tonnes. Power range 200 to 1,000 kW. Max 2,300 rpm. Dry weight 380 kg.

FF-JET 450

Designed for planing boats up to 18 tonnes and displacement boats up to 35 tonnes. Power range 200 to 1,000 kW. Max 2,100 rpm. Dry weight 370 kg.

Application of FF-Jet 410 units **1994**

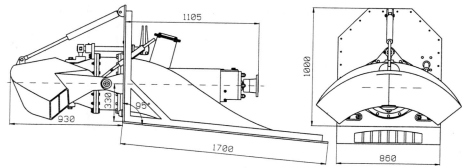

Arrangement of FF-Jet 410 unit **1994**

FF-JET 550

Designed for planing craft up to 35 tonnes. Power range 300 to 1,500 kW. Max 1,600 rpm. Dry weight 780 kg.

VERIFIED

ITALY

CASTOLDI SpA

Viale Mazzini 161, I-20081 Abbiategrasso, Milan, Italy

Tel: +39 (2) 94821
Telex: 330236CAST I
Fax: +39 (2) 9496 0800

Dr Franco Castoldi, *Managing Director*

Castoldi SpA is associated with BCS SpA, the leading European manufacturer of self-propelled agricultural machines, and MOSA SpA, manufacturer of mobile electric welding machines. The development of Castoldi water-jet units began in 1958 and they are now available for fast craft in the range of 4 to 28 m.

Castoldi manufactures a range of axial flow water-jet units, the JET 03 for powers up to 40.5 kW, the JET 05 for up to 150 kW, the Turbodrive 238 for up to 220 kW, the JET 06 for 330 kW, Turbodrive 337 for 480 kW, the JET 07 for up to 883 kW and the Turbodrive 490 for up to 1,100 kW. All the Castoldi units feature a single stage axial flow impeller; the casings are built in lightweight aluminium alloy which is very durable being hard anodised up to 80 microns. The impeller, the impeller shaft and many other parts are made in stainless steel.

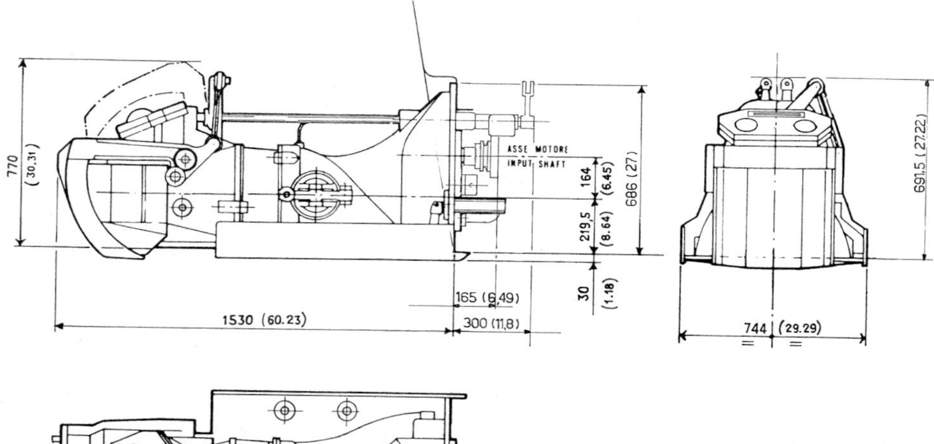

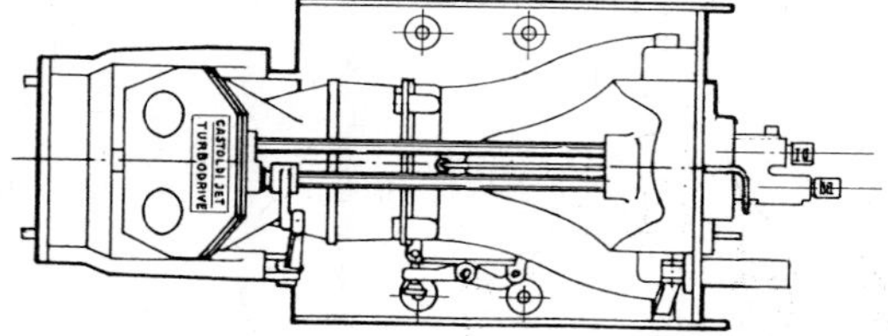

Castoldi Turbodrive 337 water-jet capable of absorbing up to 480 kW **1990**

See our editorial entry on page 395 and 396

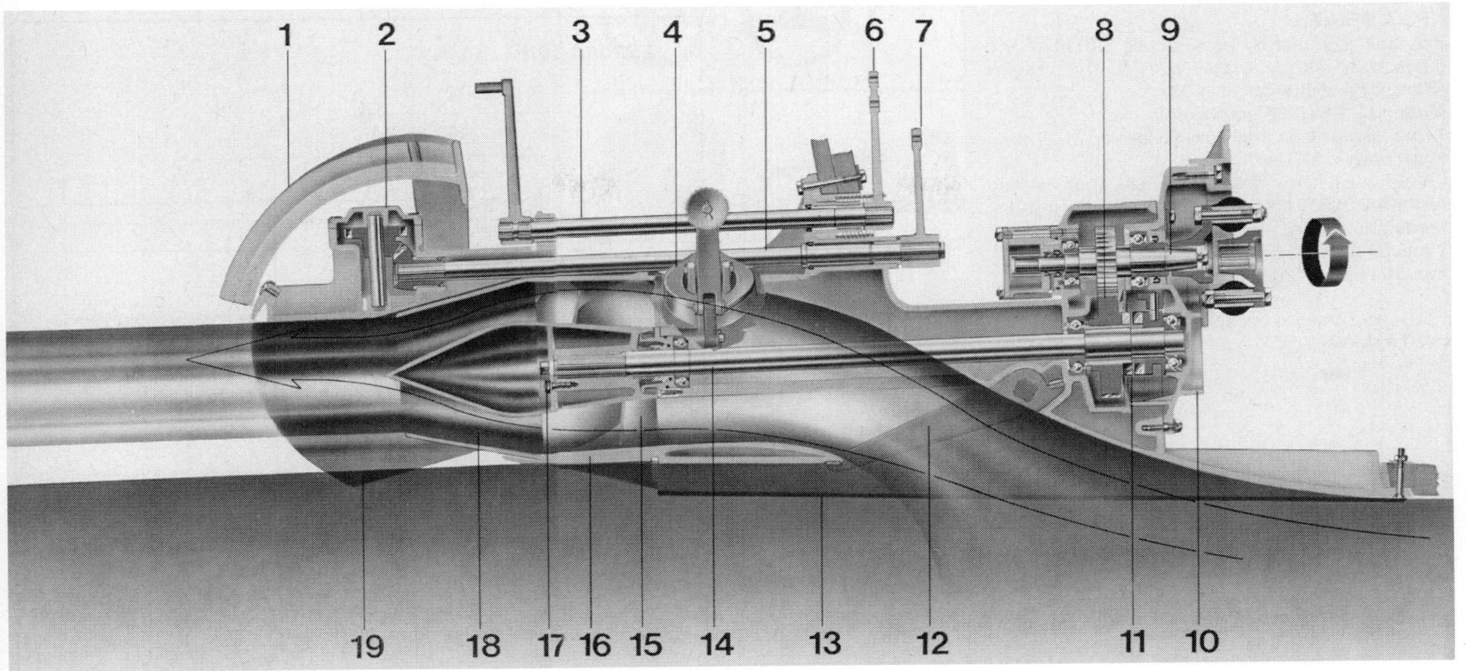

Components of a Castoldi JET 05 water-jet unit **1** *Reversing deflector;* **2** *Rudder control gears;* **3** *Reversing deflector control shaft;* **4** *Inspection port;* **5** *Steering deflectors control shaft;* **6** *Reversing deflector control lever;* **7** *Steering deflectors control lever;* **8** *Gear coupling;* **9** *Primary shaft;* **10** *Gearbox flange;* **11** *Disconnecting clutch;* **12** *Movable debris screen rake;* **13** *Body of unit;* **14** *Impeller shaft;* **15** *Impeller;* **16** *Impeller housing;* **17** *Impeller retaining bolt;* **18** *Nozzle;* **19** *Steering deflectors* ***1987***

The Castoldi drives (except for the JET 03) have several features that make them stand out from other water-jet units: a built-in gearbox with 25 gear wheel ratios for adapting the power and rpm characteristics of the engine to the jet drive; an integral disconnecting clutch allowing a true neutral condition; a remotely operated movable debris screen rake for cleaning the water intake; all oil lubricated bearings; and other refinements. The Castoldi water-jet units are equipped with especially designed mechanical/electronic/hydraulic controls which make them extremely easy to operate.

UPDATED

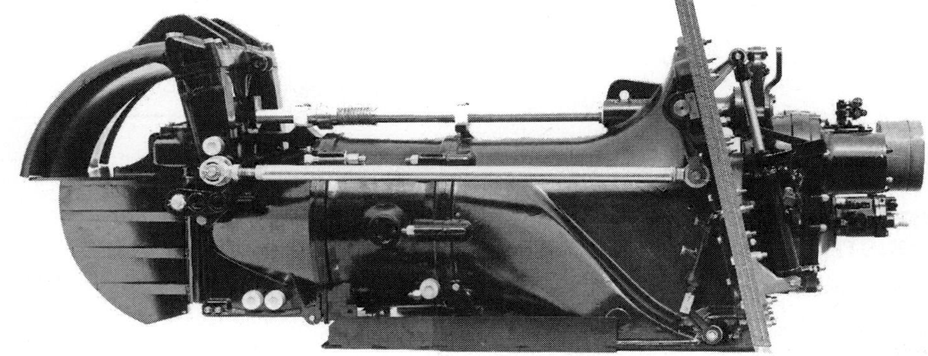

Castoldi JET 07 ***1986***

JAPAN

KAWASAKI HEAVY INDUSTRIES LTD (PRIME MOVER DIVISION)

1-1 Higashi Kawasaki-cho 3-chome, Chuo-ku, Kobe 650-91, Japan

Tel: +81 (78) 682 5355
Telex: 5623931 KHIKOB J
Fax: +81 (78) 682 5528

H Shida, *Director, General Manager*
H Kitaura, *Senior Manager, Hydraulic Machinery Department*

Kawasaki has been manufacturing PJ-20 Water-jet Propulsors for Jetfoil since 1989 and has developed a KPJ-A series of water-jet propulsors for high-speed displacement vessels. The first KPJ-A unit was delivered in 1993 and four KPJ-169A units were delivered in 1994.

PJ-20

This unit was designed to match the Rockwell International Corporation units supplied for hydrofoils such as the Jetfoil, and this business was transferred to Kawasaki in 1987.

Maximum continuous input power for these units is 2,795 kW at 2,060 rpm.

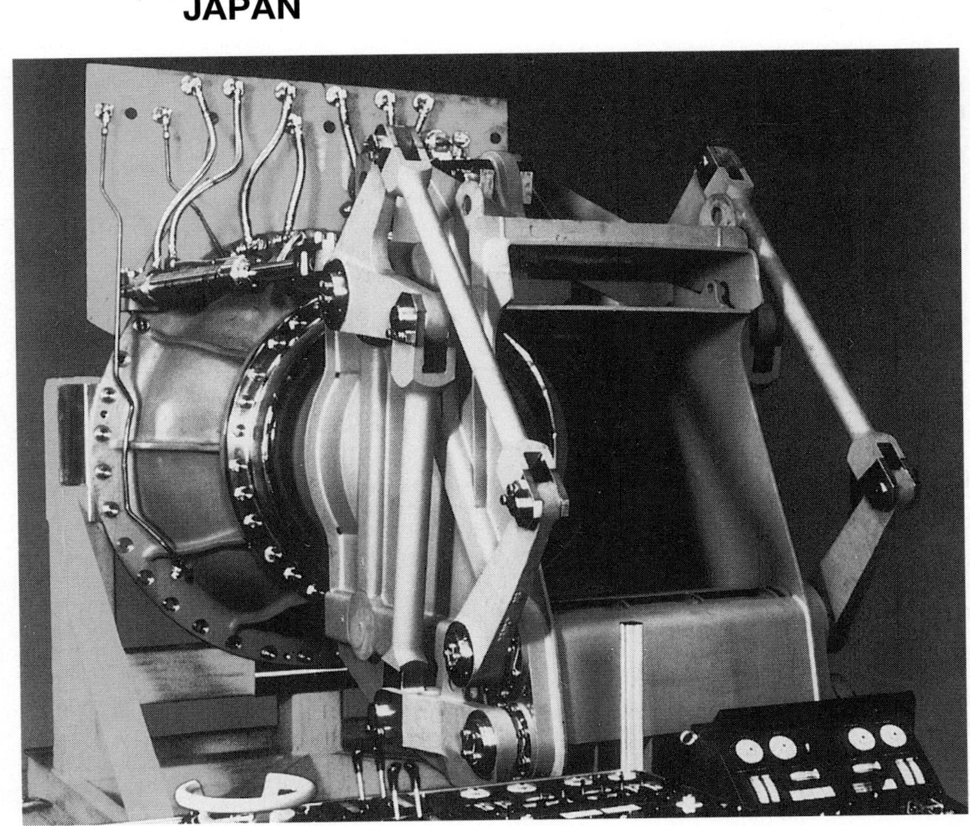

Kawasaki KPJ-169A water-jet unit ***1996***

KPJ-A SERIES

Kawasaki completed the first unit (KPJ-1A) and made a load test in Kawasaki's dry dock to prove its efficiency and strength in 1993.
Model: KPJ-1A (43A equivalent).
Type: Single stage axial flow, flush inlet.
Input power: 515 kW.

Four much larger units (KPJ-169A) were installed on the AMD1500 Mk II Kawasaki Jet Piercer in 1994:
Model: KPJ-169A.
Type: Single stage axial flow, flush inlet.
Input power: 5,420 kW.

The KPJ-A series accepts power inputs from 200 to 20,000 kW.

UPDATED

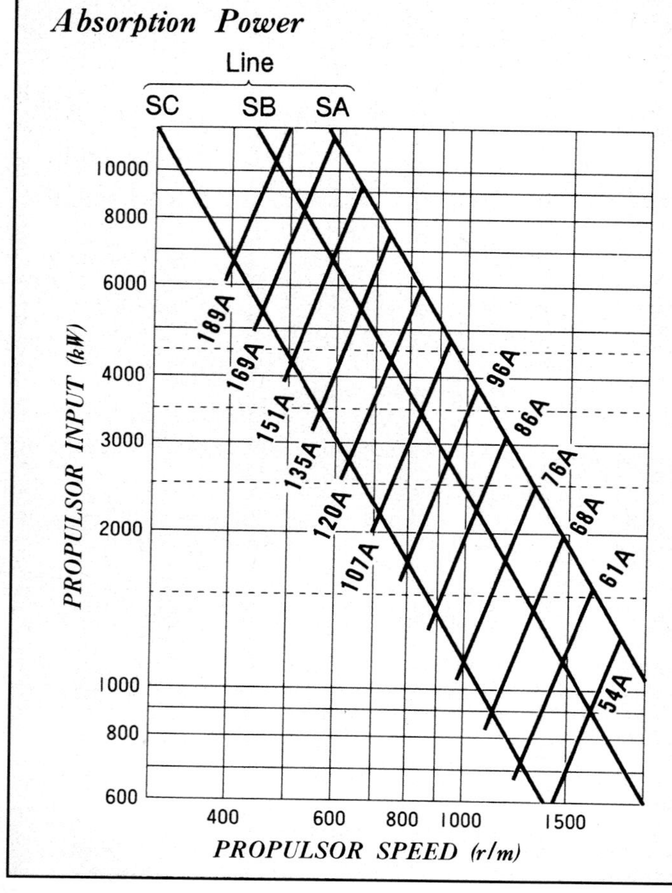

Absorption power graph
1996

MITSUBISHI HEAVY INDUSTRIES LTD

5-1 Marunouchi 2-chome, Chiyoda-ku, Tokyo, Japan

Tel: +81 (3) 3212 9414
Fax: +81 (3) 3212 9777

The Mitsubishi company has produced water-jet units for Japanese monohull fast ferries and for the Mitsubishi Super Shuttle 400 diesel driven hydrofoil catamaran. These latter units are designated MWJ-5000A and have a shaft input of 2,125 kW each. A novel feature of the units is the use of a double-cascade type of impeller and a vane cascade arrangement for reverse thrust.

VERIFIED

NIIGATA ENGINEERING COMPANY LTD

4-1 Kasumigaseki 1-chome, Chiuoda-ku, Tokyo 100, Japan

Tel: +81 (3) 3504 2473
Fax: +81 (3) 3595 2645

NIIGATA-MJP

Licensed by MJP Marine Jet Power AB of Sweden in 1991, Niigata Engineering markets the range of water-jet units as specified in the MJP Marine Jet Power AB entry and in the accompanying table.

Niigata has an extensive marine engineering business base and a broad range of engineering support divisions and subsidiaries worldwide.

Water-jet type	Max input power kW	Max input power hp	Max input speed rpm	Weight kg
J550R	1,500	2,039	1,290	1,180
J650R	2,100	2,855	1,100	1,600
J750R	2,800	3,807	950	2,100
J850R	3,700	5,031	845	3,300
J950R	4,600	6,254	750	4,200
J1100R	6,500	8,887	670	6,100
J1250R	8,900	12,100	600	7,400
J1500R	12,000	16,315	480	11,500

VERIFIED

NETHERLANDS

LIPS JETS BV

Lipsstraat 52, 5150 BB Drunen, Netherlands

Tel: +31 416 388208
Telex: 35185 lips nl
Fax: +31 416 376549

Sytze Voulon, *Sales Manager*

Lips Jets BV was established at Drunen in June 1993 as a wholly owned subsidiary of Lips BV, the only major propeller manufacturer in the world to produce fixed pitch propellers, controllable pitch propellers, side thrusters, steerable thrusters, water-jets and control systems to its own design. Lips Jets BV is a continuation of the former Riva Lips Srl, which was a joint venture between Riva Calzoni and Lips.

Under the roof of the marine oriented Lips organisation with its large group of marine specialists, Lips Jets will optimise each water-jet propulsion system for the specific requirement of the particular application.

Main features of the Lips water-jet

Each unit is fabricated in welded stainless steel. Stainless steel in a welded construction has a high resistance against corrosion and fatigue and provides good flexibility for design optimisation.

For each specific application the optimum inlet is designed to match the required flow at the craft design speed and power with the optimum inlet velocity ratio to ensure a high-efficiency in a cavitation free condition.

The axial bearing is located inside the craft which makes it easily accessible for inspection or maintenance without dry-docking and bowl dismantling, eliminates the risk of water penetration into the lubricating oil and eliminates the risk of water pollution by lubricating oil.

The mixed flow pump design has a high pump

Wing control panel of LIPSTRONIC/w control system **1995**

Four steerable water-jets type LJ-115-DL for Stena Sea Lynx II **1995**

efficiency, optimum hydraulic balancing to reduce the axial loading of the bearing, excellent cavitation characteristics and is cast in Duplex type stainless steel.

Inside the hub the shaft/impeller is supported by a water lubricated radial bearing. A very high reliability is hereby achieved by avoiding complex mechanical components outside the craft which require critical sealing in order to safeguard oil lubrication. The bearing can be inspected without dry docking, is not subject to sudden failure and has proven to be a reliable long life component.

The hydraulically operated steering and reversing jetavator has been designed such that it executes it's task in an efficient way while achieving a high reliability by limiting the number of moving parts.

Water-jet control systems

Under the name LIPSTRONIC/w an extensive range of integrated propulsion and navigation control systems is available. These systems are specially designed for the control of fast water-jet propelled craft. As this system is of modular design, for each specific propulsion configuration and craft requirement the optimum control system can be designed.

The main features of the LIPSTRONIC/w controls are:

(1) User friendly
(2) The LIPSTRONIC/w is based on micro-controller technology. In conjunction with optional fieldbus technology this allows for weight savings
(3) Integrated propulsion and navigation control
(4) High redundancy with a high degree of safety as designs are based on Failure Mode Effect Analysis
(5) Lips Jets designed it's own AUTO-PILOT specially for fast water-jet propulsed craft
(6) Combined follow-up control of bucket and impeller speed as well as steering angle
(7) The highest possible degree of manoeuvrability by use of fully co-ordinated control by means of the three axis joy-stick. This allows for short turnaround times
(8) The LIPSTRONIC/w control system can be easily extended with fully integrated diesel or gasturbine control of remote starting, local control, electronic governing, monitoring and alarming.

UPDATED

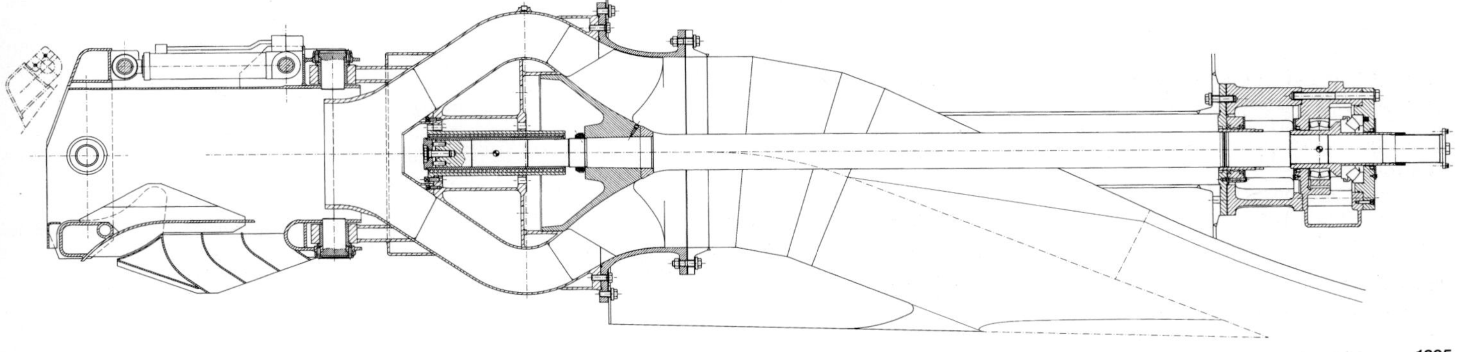
Typical cross-section of Lips water-jet unit **1995**

NEW ZEALAND

C W F HAMILTON & COMPANY LTD (HAMILTON JET)

Lunns Road, PO Box 709, Christchurch, New Zealand

Tel: +64 (3) 348 4179
Fax: +64 (3) 348 6969
Telex: NZ2938 SYNET (Attn: HamJet)

Designers and manufacturers of water-jets since the mid-1950s, HamiltonJet now offers models capable of absorbing power inputs up to 3,000 kW. With in excess of 20,000 units installed worldwide in many types of craft such as fast ferries, police patrol craft, naval troop carriers, fishing boats, crew boats, rescue craft, pleasure cruisers and fire boats, HamiltonJet will liaise with designers, builders and operators from conceptual design stages through to final commissioning. Computer speed predictions, detailed installation advice, commissioning assistance and training programmes are available to support each project. Full logistic support for all installations is provided by HamiltonJet's extensive worldwide network of factory trained distributors, who are supported by a factory-based Ready Reaction Force on permanent stand-by to fly anywhere at short notice.

The current HamiltonJet product range includes the HJ Series, HM Series and HS Series jets.

Design Features

All HamiltonJet models are designed and manufactured to meet the standards of the world's leading certifying authorities, primarily Lloyd's Register or American Bureau of Shipping. Robustly constructed from corrosion-resistant materials, each model incorporates matched intake transition duct with protection screen, high-efficiency mixed flow style pump, optimised tailpipe and discharge nozzle and integral steering and split duct astern thrust deflectors.

Intake Transition/Intake

Configured to mount inboard at the stern, Hamilton water-jets draw water through a factory-supplied intake transition which is manufactured to suit the hull. Damage to internal components is eliminated by incorporating a highly developed intake screen and, unlike some water-jets, this screen is engineered into the total package so that operational parameters such as thrust generation and cavitation resistance are unaffected by its presence. At planing speeds, this screen is largely self-cleaning.

The HamiltonJet design is such that the force of

HamiltonJet Model 321 water-jet

the generated thrust is transmitted to the hull bottom through this transition, eliminating the fore and aft propulsor loads from the transom structure and engine.

The main thrust bearing is incorporated in the intake, which is a one piece casting unaffected by the hull structure and movement, providing the bearing with a rigid housing to ensure life long alignment.

Pump

Mounted on a precision stainless steel mainshaft, the mixed flow style impeller is designed to pump large volumes of water at relatively low pressures. The impeller in each application is rated to absorb full engine power at full shaft rpm and this power is constantly absorbed regardless of boat speed, eliminating the possibility of overloading the engine. Good cavitation resistance is exhibited throughout a wide speed range, allowing full engine power to be applied at low boat speeds for quick acceleration.

While optimised for fast vessel speeds, the flexibility of the HamiltonJet design is evidenced in its ability to operate effectively in off-design conditions, such as those experienced below the planing threshold, in adverse sea conditions or when the hull is fouled.

Stator and Nozzle

Water flow exiting the pump unit passes through the stator vanes where the rotation velocity components are removed to ensure a straight uniform flow is presented to the discharge nozzle. Nozzle size is a key component in achieving maximum propulsive coefficients and the nozzle sizes of Hamilton water-jets are optimised for each application.

Control Functions

Steering in response to helm commands with a Hamilton water-jet is affected by the deflection of the jetstream to port or starboard by the integral balanced steering deflector. The steering deflector is designed to maximise lateral thrust with minimum loss of forward thrust while maintaining lightest operating loads.

Ahead/astern function is achieved with the integral split duct astern deflector, designed to provide maximum astern thrust under all conditions of boat speed, water depth and throttle opening. The split duct design angles the astern jetstream down to clear the transom and to the sides to retain a steering thrust component, an arrangement which vectors the jetstream away from the jet intake, avoiding recycling and resulting in astern thrust generation up to 60 per cent of ahead thrust which can be maintained up to high throttle settings.

On Hamilton water-jets these steering and astern functions are separate and have independent effects, but, when used in conjunction with each other, can affect complex vessel manoeuvres.

With the astern deflector fully raised, full forward thrust is available. With the deflector in the lowered position, full astern thrust is generated. In both positions, full independent steering effect is available for rotating the craft. By setting the deflector in the intermediate 'zero-speed' position; the ahead and astern thrusts are equalised for holding the craft on station but, with full steering effect still available for rotational control. Infinitely variable adjustment either side of the 'zero-speed' position enables the craft to be crept ahead or astern and, in multiple jet installations, true sideways movement can be induced.

Control Systems

A number of HamiltonJet packaged control systems to interface between the helm station and the jet is available to maximise the inherent manoeuvring capabilities of the design.

Depending on the jet model, options available include simple manual cable, hydraulic, electric or electronic systems. The latter options can be interfaced with other vessel systems. All systems are designed to be fully proportional, where the appropriate deflector movement follows that initiated by the controller at the helm station.

HJ SERIES

These are high-efficiency single stage units, typically for work and patrol boats, fast ferries and pleasure cruisers of up to 20 m. A large number of models and impeller rating combinations mean these jets can be directly driven by many common gasolene and diesel engines.

MODEL 211

Max power input: 260 kW.
Impeller diameter: 215 mm (8 rating options).
Typical 211 Jet application (single)
Vessel: 7.62 m fire/rescue craft
Displacement: 2.20 t
Speed: 29 kts
Engine: Single Volvo TAMD 41A diesel, 149 kW at 2,800 rpm
Drive: Direct
Operator: Verplanck Fire Dept, New York, USA.

MODEL 273

Max power input: 225 kW.
Impeller diameter: 270 mm (11 rating options).
Typical 273 Jet application (twin)
Vessel: 10.6 m riverine assault craft
Displacement: 7.5 t
Speed: 38 kts
Engines: Twin Cummins 6BTA5.9M2 diesels, 224 kW at 2,800 rpm each
Drive: Direct
Operator: US Marine Corps.

MODEL 291

Max power input: 375 kW.
Impeller diameter: 290 mm (11 rating options).
Typical 291 Jet application (twin)
Vessel: 11.65 m police patrol craft
Displacement: 11 t
Speed: 29 kts
Engines: Twin Volvo TAMD 71A diesels, 262 kW at 2,500 rpm each
Drive: Direct
Operator: Swedish Marine Police.

MODEL 321

Max power input: 480 kW.
Impeller diameter: 320 mm (12 rating options).
Typical 321 Jet application (single)
Vessel: 10.6 m fishing boat
Displacement: 6.4 t
Speed: 32 kts
Engine: Single Volvo TAMD 72WJ diesel, 328 kW at 2,600 rpm
Drive: Via reduction/reversing gearbox.

MODEL 362

Max power input: 580 kW.
Impeller diameter: 360 mm (9 rating options).
Typical 362 Jet application (twin)
Vessel: 14.6 m fast rescue craft
Displacement: 11.5 t
Speed: 34 kts
Engines: Twin Volvo TAMD 122D diesels, 336 kW at 2,000 rpm each
Drive: Direct
Operator: Spanish Rescue Authority.

HM SERIES

This is an extension to the HJ range and comprises a number of units suitable for power inputs ranging from 1,200 kW to 3,000 kW.

Models included in this range are:

HM422, HM521, HM571, HM651, HM721 and HM811.

These models would normally be driven via a reduction gearbox. As with all the models in the HamiltonJet range, vital control components are mounted inboard where they are protected from the elements and impact damage. All HM Series jets feature integral hydraulic power packs driven off the jet mainshaft and they are designed for the efficient propulsion of fast ferries, work and patrol boats typically in the 20 to 60 m range.

Typical twin HM Series application
Vessel: 22 m customs patrol craft
Displacement: 56 t
Speed: 32 kts
Jets: Twin HamiltonJet HM571s
Engines: Twin MTU 396 12V TE 84 diesels, 1,270 kW at 1,940 rpm each
Operator: Royal Malaysian Customs & Excise.

Typical triple HM Series application
Vessel: 28.5 m crew boat
Displacement: 63 t
Speed: 25 kts
Jets: Triple HamiltonJet HM521s

30.5 m Alaskan passenger ferry with quadruple HM422 jets

Engines: Triple MAN D2848 LE diesels, 520 kW at 2,300 rpm each
Operator: Syarikat Borcos Shipping, Malaysia.

Typical quadruple HM Series application
Vessel: 30.5 m catamaran passenger ferry
Displacement: 62 t
Speed: 33 kts
Jets: Quadruple HamiltonJet HM422s
Engines: Quadruple Caterpillar 3412 V12 diesels, 560 kW at 2,100 rpm each
Operator: Alaska Catamaran Inc, Alaska, USA.

Hamilton HM Series water-jets are also widely used in loiter/boost applications in conjunction with other propulsors.

HS SERIES

The models in this range are optimised specifically for craft operating in the 45 to 65 knot speed range. Featuring multistage pump units which allow high-power inputs to be applied to a relatively small jet, they exhibit outstanding cavitation resistance and hydrodynamic efficiencies. Suitable for powering by high-speed diesel or gas-turbine engines in high-performance pursuit or assault craft.

Typical HS Series Jet application
Vessel: 13.4 m prototype pursuit craft
Displacement: 6.6 t
Speed: 60 kts
Jets: Single HamiltonJet HS363
Engines: Twin Allison C30 gas-turbines, 485 kW each, driving the single jet through a combining gearbox.

VERIFIED

NORWAY

KVÆRNER ENERGY A/S

PO Box 9277, Grønland, N-0134 Oslo, Norway

Tel: +47 (22) 666666
Telex: 71650 KV N
Fax: +47 (22) 193765

Odd Sandøy, *General Manager, Marketing*

Kværner Energy supplies the high-speed craft market with complete propulsion modules including gas-turbines and water-jets.

Kværner Energy has developed a new range of water-jets for the high-speed craft market.

The new Kværner water-jet has been designed to provide a propulsion system for all kinds of vessels. Kværner Energy's experience and long traditions with hydrodynamic equipment, turbines and pump design has resulted in an advanced water-jet that is optimised with respect to simplicity, low weight and high efficiency. The present Kværner water-jet programme covers output between 50 kN of thrust to 400 kN of thrust, corresponding to prime mover needs of 1,500 to 23,000 kW.

The company has supplied water-jets to Kværner Fjellstrand for the 40 m Flying Cat *Vargøy* and to Kværner Mandal for the nine mine countermeasure vessels for the Norwegian Navy.

Water-jet description: The water-jet pump is optimised with respect to high efficiency, simplicity, low weight and low suction pressure requirement.

A six-blade impeller is mounted on the impeller shaft tube. The shaft sleeve is supported by a conical roller bearing at the front end, and a spherical axial bearing at the rear end.

The static bearing holder is firmly bolted on to the hub of the pump bowl which is bolted to the pump house. This ensures that the impeller is in a fixed position in relation to the pump walls. This type of design allows the pump to operate with a very small clearance between the impeller and the pump house, thus increasing the efficiency and reducing the risk of cavitation.

Pump bearings are oil lubricated. The oil system is under permanent pressure in order to avoid water leakage into the lubricating system in case of a mechanical seal failure. When the unit is not operating this pressure is maintained by the oil accumulator.

A nozzle ring is separately mounted and can be changed to alter the discharge area.

The primary shaft is connected to the impeller through a spline coupling. This gives the shaft a certain degree of freedom in relation to the location of the pump. A mechanical seal is provided where the shaft penetrates the water intake duct. The shaft runs free through the water intake duct.

Steering and reversing are provided for by a hydraulically operated steering nozzle and reversing bucket. When activated the steering nozzle is lifted out of the water-jet allowing the water to impinge on the reversing mechanism, bending the jet downwards. Further activating of the reversing mechanism will move a lower flap up and into the water-jet, forcing the jet to complete a 145° turn.

When not activated the lower flap on the reversing mechanism rests in a horizontal position below the jet, ensuring minimum resistance in the water.

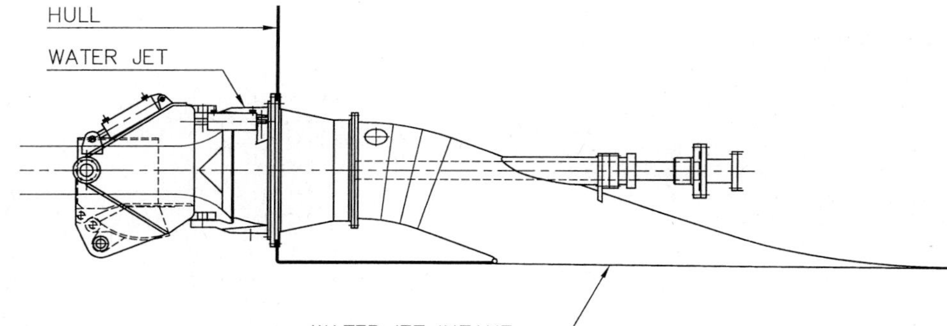

Kværner water-jet features ***1994***

Kværner Energy supplies drawings specifying the inner contour and location of the inlet duct. The purchaser designs and builds the mechanical structure of the inlet duct, and, where the shaft penetrates the water intake duct, prepares a foundation for the mechanical seal.

The hydraulic system consists of the following main parts:

Main hydraulic pump
Stand-by hydraulic pump with electrical motor
Proportion valves
Instrumentation (local and transmitter)
Piping, tubes and fittings
Oil tank
Oil accumulator pressure compensation
Filters.

Both main and stand-by hydraulic pumps are of the variable displacement variable pressure type. The main pump is mechanically driven from gearbox or engine, while the stand-by pump is driven from a standard electric motor. Oil is then delivered through a filter to the two proportional valves. From the steering proportional valves, oil is transferred through the stern to the two hydraulic cylinders mounted on the water-jet. From both steering and reversing cylinders, oil is returned through the proportion valve back to the pump suction side. An accumulator assures a pump suction pressure of approximately 3 bar.

The lubricating oil system is pressure compensated, with a constant overpressure on the return side. This prevents water leakage into the oil.

An electronic control and manoeuvring system is provided to take advantage of the flexible manoeuvring capabilities of water-jet propulsion systems.

VERIFIED

Example of Kværner integrated propulsion system ***1994***

ULSTEIN PROPELLER A/S

N-6065 Ulsteinvik, Norway

Tel: +47 (700) 14000
Telex: 42 848 UP N
Fax: +47 (700) 14017

Stig Ulstein, *Managing Director*
Jarle Hessen, *Sales Manager*

The Ulstein Group acquired the Liaaen propeller company in 1989 and has since significantly expanded its operations, now on a centralised site in Ulsteinvik.

Ulstein Propeller A/S manufactures water-jets in the power range 300 to 5,000 kW covered by four units: WJ450, WJ560, WJ630 and WJ710. Trials on the first water-jet model, the WJ630, were undertaken on the Ulstein UT 904 SES.

The prototype unit WJ630 is designed to absorb 2,400 kW at 40 knots and at an impeller speed of 1,025 rpm. Several options of intake design were analysed in two and three dimensions by solving the Navier-Stokes equations at the Norwegian Institute of Technology. This enabled the details affecting the noise and vibration characteristics as well as the propulsive efficiency to be studied.

UPDATED

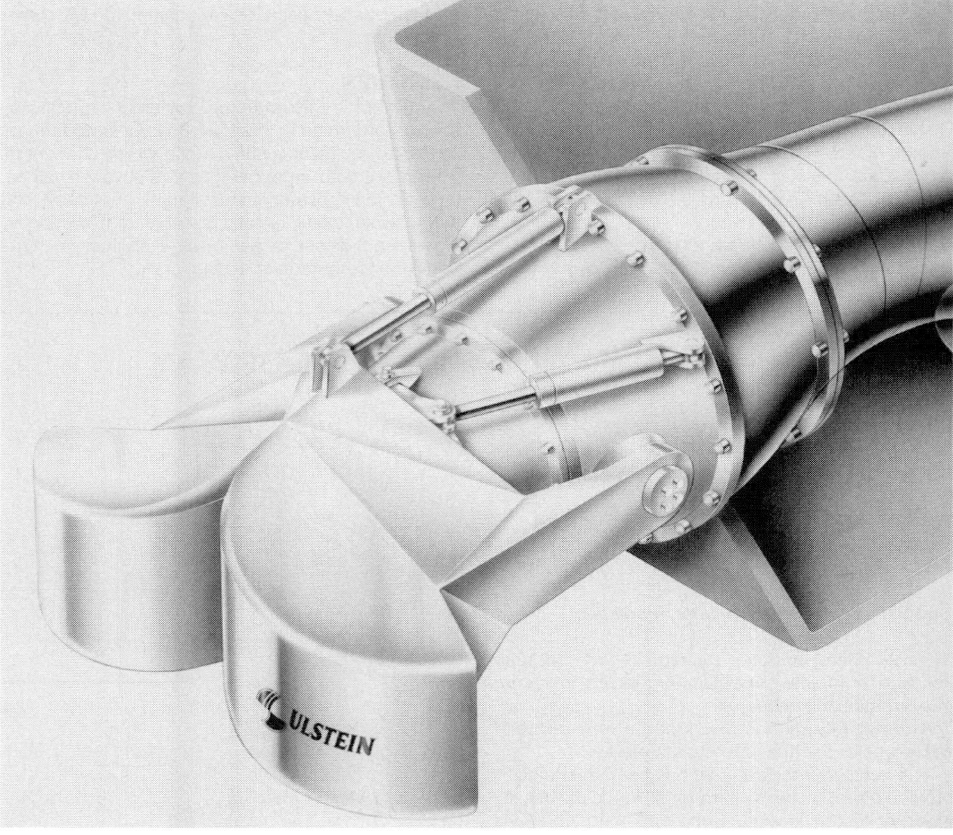

External features of the Ulstein water-jet unit
1991

SWEDEN

KAMEWA AB

A Vickers plc company

PO Box 1010, S-681 29 Kristinehamn, Sweden

Tel: +46 (550) 84000
Telex: 66050 KAMEWA S
Fax: +46 (550) 18190

Sven-Erik Pettersson, *President Water-Jet Propulsion Systems*
Björn H Svensson, *Sales Director, Water-Jet Propulsion Systems*

Since the beginning of this century Kamewa in Sweden has designed and manufactured hydroturbines and large pumps of various types. In the 1930s the first Kamewa propeller of controllable-pitch type was delivered. A vast amount of experience in the marine propulsion field has since then been collected at Kamewa. In the last two decades Kamewa has been a major supplier of controllable-pitch propellers and thrusters.

In the mid-1960s Kamewa built two prototype jet propulsion systems for small craft. The first larger units, however, were delivered in 1980 and since then Kamewa has systematically established itself as the dominant producer of larger systems for water-jet propulsion.

Kamewa's position was further strengthened in 1995, when the Finnish-based azimuth thruster and deck machinery company Aquamaster-Rauma was acquired and the Kamewa Group was formed. The Kamewa Group is today the world's leading supplier of marine propulsion systems.

An appreciable amount of research and development in hydrodynamics, mechanics and electronics constitutes the basis for the Kamewa jet propulsion system. Significant benefits for vessels with this system are high propulsive efficiency, even at part load; insensitivity to floating debris; suitability for shallow draught operation; good manoeuvrability; low hydro-acoustic and vibration levels and low magnetic signature.

These features make water-jet propulsion suitable for example in medium and high-speed vessels such as corvettes, patrol boats, landing craft, passenger ferries, motor yachts and workboats.

Design: Principally, the water-jet consists of an inlet duct leading the water to the impeller, a pump casing and an outlet nozzle, forming the jet. Steering is accomplished by a steering nozzle, directing the jet ±30° which redirects the jet of water issuing from the nozzle. Astern thrust is achieved by a reversing bucket incorporated in the steering nozzle.

The most effective propulsion will be with the jet just above the dynamic waterline. However, to secure priming of the pump at start up, the pump shaft centre must not be higher than the waterline at rest.

Inlet duct: In order to improve efficiency and to avoid excessive cavitation in the pump (the impeller and its casing), the velocity head of the inlet flow must be used to the largest possible extent. Thus, the inlet channel should lead the water to the pump with only small losses. Unsuitable inlet shapes not only cause losses but also result in choking, which can disturb the pump.

To be able to meet these demands, tests at correct cavitation numbers have been made in the Kamewa Marine Laboratory with models of various inlet designs. Based upon these model tests the inlet duct can be given an efficiency of about 75 to 80 per cent in relation to the inlet velocity head.

The inlet duct is preferably integrated into the hull and normally built by the shipyard according to Kamewa drawings. The inlet at the hull surface is well rounded to avoid vortices entering the pump at low speeds. Debris is prevented from entering the inlet by a grid. Should the pump get clogged it can be cleaned through the inspection openings in front of the impeller. The inlet duct ends at the transom with a connecting flange for the pump.

Pump: The pump is of the mixed flow type and the six-blade impeller is bolted to a stub shaft carried in

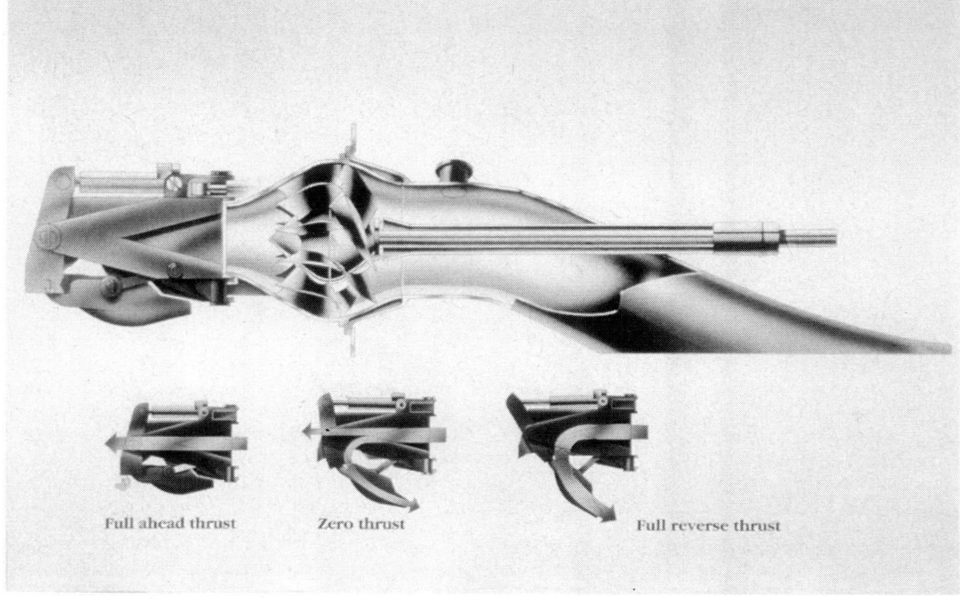

Kamewa water-jet system, basic form ***1994***

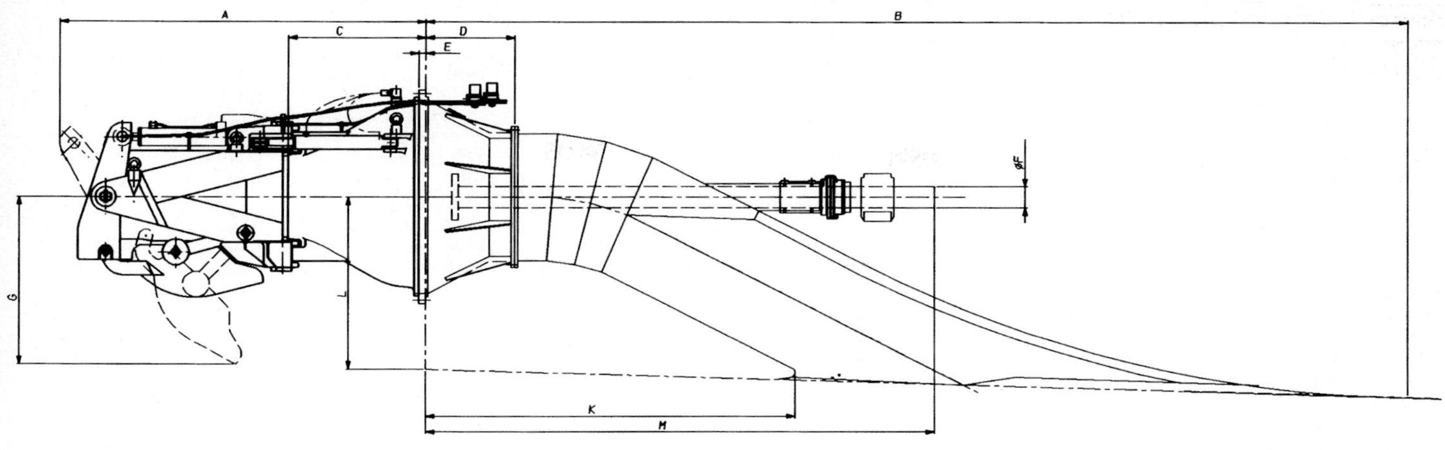

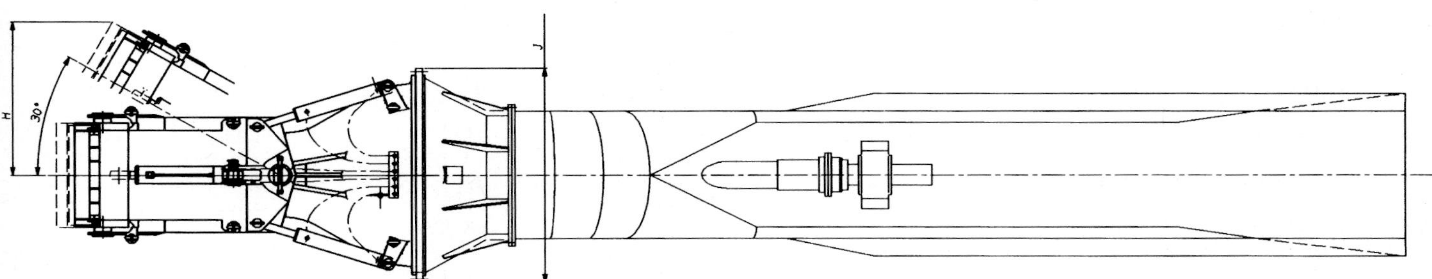

Profile of typical Kamewa Type 62 water-jet unit ***1995***

the stator hub by one radial and one axial roller bearing. The bearings are spherical with the same centre of sphere, so that they are unaffected by minor deviations from the theoretically correct centreline of the pump shaft. Movements of a semi-elastically mounted gearbox will thus not affect the bearings.

The pump unit also contains the stationary guide vanes and the outlet nozzle forming the jet.

The thrust of the pump unit is taken up and transferred to the transom of the vessel.

The impeller hub is filled with oil to lubricate and cool the bearings. The thrust bearing also acts as a centrifugal pump circulating the oil within the hub. The temperature of the oil is thus kept within about 20°C above the water temperature without any extra oil cooler. To minimise the risk of water leakage into the hub, the oil pressure is kept above the water pressure by a circulating pump and a gravity tank.

The pump unit as well as the pump shaft and the steering/reversing gear are made of acid-proof steel. Sacrificial zinc anodes are fitted within the space between the impeller chamber and the conical aft part of the inlet duct to protect the hull and inlet.

One of four Kamewa size 160 water-jet units installed in Stena's High Speed Sea Service Ferry. With an output of 16,354 kW each, these units are the most powerful water-jets with steering and reversing gear built in the world to date ***1995***

Steering and reversing gear: Steering forces are achieved by deflecting the jet sideways turning the steering nozzle 30° port or starboard. The steering nozzle also incorporates the reversing device. Jet reversal is obtained by turning the bucket under the nozzle, where it gradually enters the jet from below and finally gives full reverse thrust. By setting the bucket in intermediate positions the thrust can be continuously and smoothly varied from zero to maximum ahead and astern.

The fact that the bucket is coming from under the jet means that a very low vibration level is achieved on the gear since only that part of the jet which needs to be deflected is affected while the remaining part of the jet is undisturbed.

The bearings for the steering as well as for the reversing bucket are of the self-lubricating type. On top of the steering nozzle are two supports for the pivoted hydraulic cylinders for steering. The reversing bucket consists of upper and lower parts linked together by bearings at the aft end. The movement of the two parts is controlled by a yoke welded to the upper part and journalled in the steering nozzle. The lower part is coupled to the steering nozzle by one link on each side of the nozzle. The yoke is connected to the pivoted hydraulic cylinder for reversing positioned on top of the steering nozzle. When reversing, the upper part closes the steering nozzle and deflects the jet down to the lower part which further changes the jet direction to forward/down, resulting in astern thrust.

For feedback and position indication, there are cables connected to the steering nozzle and to the reversing bucket. The cables are drawn through the transom and connected to potentiometers.

Hydraulic and lubricating system: A separate hydraulic power pack for each unit is used for manoeuvring. Normally the load-compensated main pump is PTO-driven and for start and stand-by a small electric motor driven pump is used. The control valves are mounted on top of the power pack.

The power pack also contains the lubricating system. A small pump is used for circulating the oil as well as to maintain a pressure higher than the waterhead outside the seal. The pack should be positioned above the waterline in order to keep a static head at standstill.

Electronic remote-control system: The positions of the steering nozzle and the reversing bucket as well as engine speed are set by the electronic remote-control system. Usually the reversing bucket and the engine speed are controlled by a common combinator lever. When in transit all jet units are normally controlled simultaneously regarding steering

Kamewa water-jet unit deliveries 1994 onwards
Kamewa delivered over 600 units between 1989 and 1994

Delivery	Name of Ship	Type of Ship	Owner	Shipyard	Yard No	Number of units	kW/ shaft	Size of unit
1994	—	Catamaran	Stena Rederi AB,	Finnyards OY.	404	4	17,035	160S
1994	*Mark V*	—	—	Trinity Marine, New Orleans, USA	1393	2	1,680	50S
1994	*A. Super III*	Catamaran	—	MIHO, Japan	338	2	1,980	63S
1994	—	Tricat	CTS Parkveiw	FBM Marine Ltd,	1407	2	4,200	90S
1994	—	Tricat	CTS Parkview	FBM Marine Ltd,	1408	2	4,200	90S
1994	—	Tricat	CTS Parkveiw	FBM Marine Ltd,	1409	2	4,200	90S
1994	—	Tricat	CTS Parkveiw	FBM Marine Ltd,	1410	2	4,200	90S
1994	—	Tricat	CTS Parkview	FBM Marine Ltd,	1411	2	4,200	90S
1995	—	Catamaran	Stena Rederi AB,	Finnyards OY,	405	4	17,035	160S
1994	*Ono Ono*	Monohull	SPI Maritime, Tahiti	Austal Ships Pty Ltd, Henderson, Australia	35	2 1	2×1,960+ 1×1,960	63S 63B
1994	*Ariake*	Monohull	—	Hitachi, Japan	7313	2	1,745	56S
1994	*A Shitaka*	—	MSA, Japan	Mitsui, Japan	—	1	1,820	80S
1994	*Sifka Viking*	Catamaran	—	Kværner Fjellstrand, Omastrand, Norway	1621	2	2,000	63S
1994	*Alacantra*	Monohull fast ferry	Transmediterraneo, Spain	Empresa Nacional Bazan, San Fernando, Spain	316	2 2	2×5,000+ 2×5,000	100S 100B
1994	*Nan Sha 28*	Catamaran	—	Wavemaster International Pty Ltd, Henderson, Australia	69	4	1,960	63S
1994	*Akiyda*	Motoryacht	His Highness The Aga Khan, CH	Hakvoort Shipyard Holland	213	2	809	40S
1995	*Neptune*	Catamaran	Kyasho Kisen	Mitsui, Japan	TH1625	2	2,647	71 S11
1994	*Paradise*	Catamaran	—	Kvaerner Fjellstrand (S) Singapore	012	2	2,000	63 S11
1994	*Xin He Shan*	Catamaran	Yuet Hing, HK	Austral Ships Pty Ltd Australia	111	2	1,960	71 S11
1994	*Juan L*	Catamaran	Buquebus, Argentina	Incat, Tasmain Australia	36	2 2	5,400 5,400	80 S11 80 B11
1994	*Lada Empat*	Catamaran	Lada-Langkawi developm.MY	SBF Shipbuilders Australia	LK 32/4	2	1,450	56S
1994	*AMD 350*	Catamaran	—	AMD, Australia	Astra Bay	2	1,960	71 S11
1994	*HKF 3*	Catamaran	HK Ferry	Kvaerner Fjellstrand (S) Singapore	014	2	2,000	63 S11
1994	—	Wave piercer	Quicksilver Australia	NQEA, Australia	192	4	1,343	56 S
1994	*Speeder*	Catamaran	Diamond Ferry, Japan	Austral Ships Pty Ltd Australia	39	4	1,960	63 S11
1994	*Kattegat*	Monohull	European Ferries Denmark	Mjellern & Karlsen Verft Norway	151	4	5,800	112 S11
1994	*Aremiti*	Catamaran	—	Kvaerner Fjellstrand (S) Singapore	016	2	2,000	63 S11
1994	—	Catamaran	—	Kvaerner Fjellstrand (S) Singapore	017	2	2,000	63 S11
1994	—	—	—	Kvaerner Fjellstrand Norway	1626	2	2,000	63 S11
1994	*Foilcat 1*	Foilcat	Far East Hydrofóil Co Ltd, HK	Kvaerner Fjellstrand Norway	1624	2	4,474	80 S11
1995	*Foilcat 2*	Foilcat	Far East Hydrofoil Co Ltd, HK	Kvaerner Fjellstrand Norway	1625	2	4,474	80 S11
1994	*Nan Sha 38*	Catamaran	Fok, HK	Alufast, Hongkong	1	4	2,000	63 S11
1994	*Nan Sha 68*	Catamaran	Fok, HK	Alufast, Hongkong	2	4	2,000	63 S11
1994	—	Catamaran	Sea Container, UK	Austal Ships Pty Ltd Australia	37	4	4,950	100 S11
1995	*Corsair*	Monohull	SNCM, France	Leroux et Lotz France	11000	2 2	6,000 6,000	112 S11 112 B11
1995	—	Monohull	Corferry, Corsica	Rodriquez, Italy	257	2 1	6,000 12,000	112 S11 160 B11
1994	*Zhing Shan*	Catamaran	Yuet Hing, HK	Austral Ships Pty Ltd Australia	115	2	3,130	71 S11
1995	—	Patrol boat	MSA, Japan	MHI Shimonoseki, Japan	1006	1	1,820	80 S11
1995	—	Catamaran	Stena Rederi AB	Finnyards Oy, Finland	407	4	17,035	160 S11
1995	—	Catamaran	Dae-A Ferry Co Korea	Incat, Tasmania Australia	37	2 2	5,300 5,300	80 S11 80 B11
1994-95	—	Catamaran	—	Kvaerner Fjellstrand (S) Singapore	019	2	2,000	63 S11
1994-95	—	Catamaran	—	Kvaerner Fjellstrand (S) Singapore	021	2	2,000	63 S11
1994-95	—	Catamaran	—	Kvaerner Fjellstrand (S) Singapore	022	2	2,000	63 S11
1995	*New Arcadia*	Catamaran	Seo Kyung Shipping Korea	Kvaerner Fjellstrand Norway	1628	2	1,985	63 S11
1995	—	Monohull	Trasmediterranea Spain	Empr.Nacional Bazan Spain	325	2 2	5,000 5,000	100 S11 100 B11
1995	—	Catamaran	SURF, Guadalope	Marinteknik Shipbuilders (S) Singapore	H140	4	1,477	63 S11
1995	—	SES-Catamaran	Tahiti	Int. Shipyards, Australia	15	2	1,960	63 S11
1995	—	Catamaran	Mols-Linjen Denmark	Danyard A/S, Denmark	740	4	6,200	112 S11
1995	—	Catamaran	Mois-Linjen Denmark	Danyard A/S, Denmark	741	4	6,200	112 S11

Kamewa water-jet unit deliveries 1994 onwards (continued)
Kamewa delivered over 600 units between 1989 and 1994

Delivery	Name of Ship	Type of Ship	Owner	Shipyard	Yard No	Number of units	kW/ shaft	Size of unit
1995	–	Catamaran	–	Kvaerner Fjellstrand Norway	1629	2	2,000	63 S11
1995	–	Catamaran	–	Kvaerner Fjellstrand Norway	1631	2	2,000	63 S11
1995	–	Catamaran	–	Wavemaster Australia	126	4	1,960	63 S11
1995	*Seajet 1*	Catamaran	Sea Jet Shipping Greece	Oskarhamns Varv AB Sweden	535	4	1,485	56 S
1995	–	Catamaran	Catamaran Lines Greece	Royal Schelde Netherland	00379	4	5,700	112 S11
1996	*Alhambra*	Monohull	Buquebus, Argentina	Empr. Nacional Bazan Spain	327	4 1	5,650 11300	112 S11 140 B11
1995	–	Monohull	Corsica Ferry France	INMA, Italy	4248	2 1	6,000 13,800	112 S11 160 B11
1995	–	Catamaran	Yuet Hing, HK	Austral Ships Pty Ltd Australia	116	2	3,130	71 S11
1996	–	Motoryacht	Samsung	Samsung Korea	H4005	2 1	2,483 3,327	80 S11 80 B11
1995	–	Monohull	Ocean Bridges Greece	Fincantieri, Italy	5965	2	6,000	112 S11
1995	–	Monohull	European Ferrier Denmark	Mjellem & Karlsen Norway	158	4	5,800	112 S11
1995	–	Catamaran	Hayman Island	NQE, Australia	195	2	1,222	56 S
1995	–	Catamaran	Yuet Hing	Austal Ships Pty Ltd Australia	118	2	1,960	71 S11
1996	–	Catamaran	Emeraude Lines	Kvaerner Fjellstrand Norway	1630	2	5,400	100 S11
1995	–	Monohull	Corsica Ferry France	INMA, Italy	4249	2 1	6,000 13,800	112 S11 160 B11
1995	–	Catamaran	–	Kvaerner Fjellstrand (S) Singapore	023	2	1,415	63 S11
1995	–	Catamaran	TT Lines	Austal Ships Pty Ltd Australia	46	4	6,000	112 S11
1996	–	Monohull	SNCM, France	Leroux et Lotz France	623	2 2	6,500 6,500	112 S11 112 B11
1996	–	Catamaran	Stena Rederi AB Sweden	Westamarin AS Norway	238	2	17,730	160 S11
1996	–	Catamaran	Stena Rederi AB Sweden	Westamarin AS Norway	239	2	17,730	160 S11
1996	–	Catamarn	–	Austal Ships Pty Ltd Australia	52	4	6,000	112 S11
1993	–	Catamaran	–	S.A. Ships, Australia	56	4	2,009	63 S11
1995	–	Catamaran	–	Kvaerner Fjellstrand (S) Singapore	024	2	2,000	63 S11
1995	–	Catamaran	D.S.L. India	SBF Shipbuilders 953 Australia	2	1,107	50 S11	
1994-97	*Fearless Class*	Patriot vessel	Singapore Navy	SSE Singapore	–	12 × 2	3,145	100 S11
1996	–	Motoryacht	–	Heesen Shipyard Netherlands	10235	2	2,560	112 S11
1996	–	Catamaran	B C Ferry Corp Canada	B C Ferry Corp Canada	1	4	6,500	112 S11
1997	–	Catamaran	B C Ferry Corp Canada	B C Ferry Corp Canada	2	4	6,500	112 S11
1997	–	Catamaran	B C Ferry Corp Canada	B C Ferry Corp Canada	3	4	6,500	71 S11
1996	–	Motoryacht	–	Cantieri Navali D Adriactico Italy	Pershing 90	2	1,323	50 S11
1996	*Tricat 6*	Tricat	HK Park View	FBM Marine Ltd England	–	2	4,200	90 S11
1996	*Tricat 7*	Tricat	HK Park View	FBM Marine Ltd England	–	2	4,200	90 S11
1996	*Tricat 8*	Tricat	HK Park View	FBM Marine Ltd England	–	2	4,200	90 S11
1996	–	Motoryacht	–	Groupe Rodriquez Italy	Mangusta 100' Sport	2 1	1,078 2,942	63 S11 50 B
1996	–	Catamaran	Yuet Hing, HK	Austal Ships Pty Ltd Australia	119	2	1,980	71 S11

angle, reversing and shaft rpm. To achieve optimum manoeuvrability during docking, station keeping and under low-speed manoeuvring the different water-jet units are individually controlled. After some practice an operator can select steering angle, reverse flap position and shaft rpm of each individual unit to achieve the desired manoeuvre. However, Kamewa has also developed a computerised system that calculates and orders the optimum combination of settings of the water-jets and side thrusters. By means of an azimuth lever the operator selects a desired force and its direction in relation to the vessel. With a special knob the turning moment on the vessel can be controlled.

The Kamewa water-jet units have the following advantages and characteristics:

(1) They are designed to give high performance at high ship speeds as well as at low cruising speed. The efficiency has been verified in a number of full-scale installations; please see accompanying graph
(2) For medium-speed vessels with a top speed of 20 to 25 knots, the fuel economy is in general competitive with that achieved with propellers
(3) For fast patrol boats fuel economy may be improved compared with fixed-pitch propeller installation from top speed down to the 10 to 15 knots region
(4) The water inlets have a very low drag when idling during cruising which makes the Kamewa water-jet units attractive as booster units, also in combination with propellers
(5) The thrust/weight ratios of the Kamewa water-jet units are optimised for most common hull forms, that is, planing and semi-planing hulls, catamarans and sidewall hovercraft (SES)

Destriero, *the Atlantic Blue Riband holder* **1994**

Guizzo, *the Tirrenia Aquastrada* **1994**

(6) Kamewa's modern marine laboratory provides the testing facility required for inlet design, cavitation and performance studies

(7) Fixed geometry inlets can be designed to operate satisfactorily at full engine load from low cruising speeds (when running on a reduced number of shafts) up to the top speed of the vessel

(8) The pump shaft speed is practically independent of ship speed at constant power output. This means that the water-jet unit will never overload a diesel engine as the power absorption is always approximately proportional to rpm^3. Reduced maintenance costs due to prolonged MTBO for the diesels may be achieved in certain installations

(9) Due to the absence of appendages and the rugged design of the Kamewa water-jet units the costs for maintenance and off-hire time due to damages from floating debris can be reduced

(10) In multishaft installations CODAG/CODAD propulsion is possible without complex gearing and control systems. Full diesel power is always available irrespective of increased ship resistance due to bad weather and fouling or at extreme light displacements. This means an increased top speed for the vessel

(11) The Kamewa water-jet units are designed to simplify maintenance and overhaul. The units can be mounted and dismounted from outside the ship

(12) The Kamewa water-jet installations are characterised by low noise and vibration levels

(13) Excellent manoeuvrability over the whole speed range of the vessel. Full engine torque is always available for manoeuvring and acceleration

(14) Years of operating in the debris-laden waters of the Hong Kong area have proved that the units are very reliable and insensitive to sand and floating debris in the water.

Very low hydro-acoustic noise combined with high efficiency make the Kamewa water-jets attractive for navy craft. Two 63S units capable of absorbing 2,040 kW each are used for the propulsion of the Swedish Navy SES stealth craft.

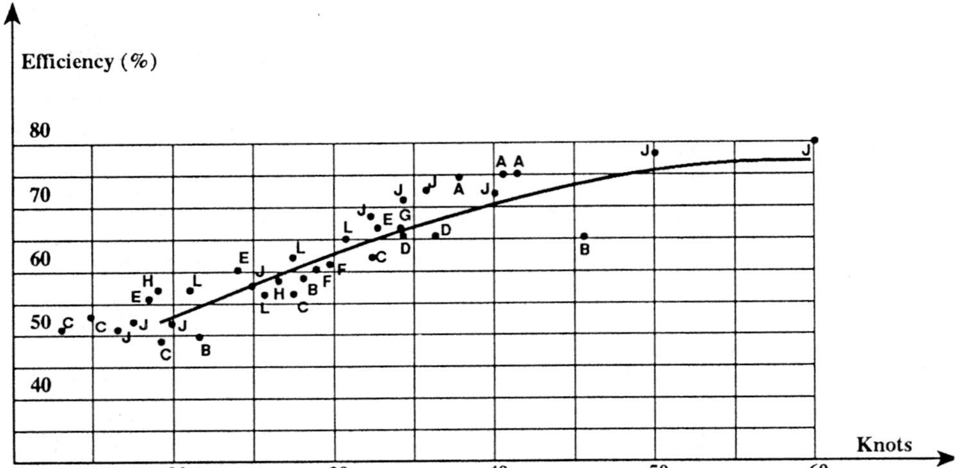

Typical efficiency results for Kamewa water-jet propulsion systems

Key:

A	100 t	catamaran,	full-scale tests, resistance tested, torque measurements
B	240 t	monohull,	full-scale tests, resistance tested, torque measurements
C	130 t	monohull,	full-scale tests, resistance tested, fuel rack
D	85 t	monohull,	full-scale tests, resistance tested, torque measurements
E	230 t	monohull,	full-scale tests, resistance tested, torque measurements
F	135 t	catamaran,	full-scale tests, resistance tested, torque measurements
G	100 t	SES,	full-scale tests, R from trials with propellers
H	360 t	monohull,	model tests in towing basin and cavitation tunnel
J	930 t	monohull,	model tests in towing basin and cavitation tunnel
K	1,000 t	monohull,	model tests in towing basin and cavitation tunnel
L	400 t	monohull,	full-scale tests, resistance tested, fuel rack

1992

Destriero

On the 9 August 1992 this vessel completed the 3,106 n miles from New York to Bishop Rock (the Scilly Isles), off the west coast of England, in 58 hours and 34 minutes, winning the coveted Atlantic Blue Riband. The vessel maintained an average speed of 53.09 knots with maximum speed intervals of more than 65 knots.

The *Destriero* has a fuel capacity of 750 tonnes. It is equipped with three Kamewa size 125 water-jet units powered by gas-turbines with a total rating of 60,000 bhp.

Aquastrada

The Rodriquez Aquastrada monohull's three engines deliver a total output of about 38,000 bhp. In the centre, a gas-turbine transmits 27,880 bhp to a Kamewa 180 water-jet that acts as a booster for high-speed operation. On each side a high-speed diesel engine rated at 4,850 bhp drives a Kamewa 100 wing water-jet. This arrangement ensures high manoeuvrability, short stopping distance and a cruising speed of 20 knots.

Stena HSS

The Finnyards Stena HSS catamarans are the largest high-speed water-jet-propelled catamarans built to date and are propelled by four Kamewa 160 water-jet units. With an output of 16,354 kW each, these units are the most powerful water-jets with steering and reversing gear in the world.

The new ferries have a service speed in the region of 40 knots and accommodation for 1,500 passengers and 375 cars.

UPDATED

MJP

Marine Jet Power AB

S-740 63 Österbybruk, Sweden

Tel: +46 (295) 20785
Fax: +46 (295) 21383

Torbjörn Ahlbäck, *Managing Director*
Gerard Törneman, *Managing Director and General Manager*
Björn Hanberg, *Sales Manager*
Michael Näsström, *Service Manager*

MJP Marine Jet Power AB is a Swedish company developing and designing advanced propulsion systems for high-performance vessels in commercial operations. MJP is also a division of Österby Gjuteri AB, responsible for the marketing and production of the MJP water-jets for the European, Asian, Australian and American markets. The MJP water-jet units are also marketed and produced by Niigata Engineering in Japan under licence from MJP Marine Jet Power AB. MJP is developing water-jets to absorb up to 10,000 kW and the range covers jet propulsion systems for double, triple and quadruple drive installation between 600 kW and 10,000 kW. The new models are named S92 and they include all design developments and experience gained from over 150,000 operating hours in various types of vessels and environments.

Manoeuvring capability: The system includes jet propulsors, steering/reversing units, electro-hydraulic controls and a computerised Remote Manoeuvre Controller (RMC), which is claimed to be the first digital control system in this field. With the computerised RMC the crew's learning period for

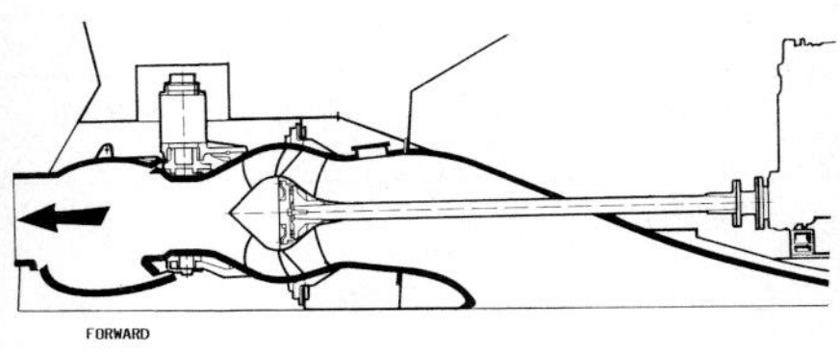

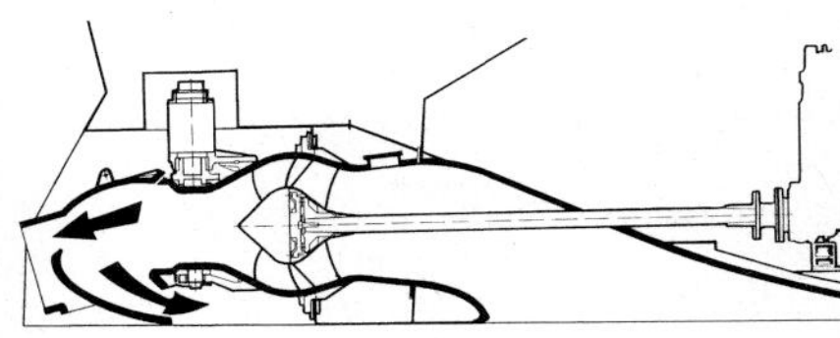

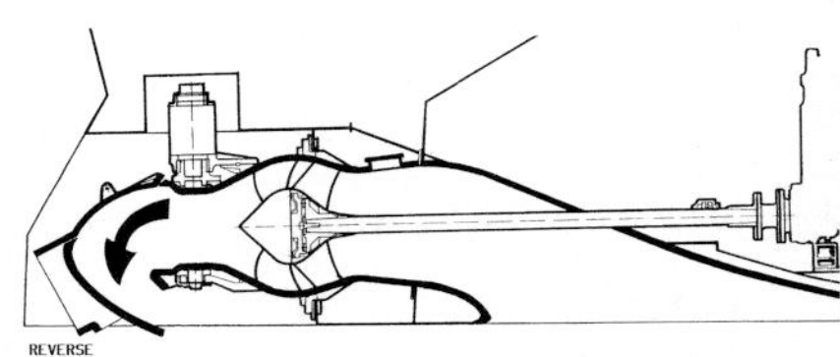

Mechanism of flow redirection on MJP water-jet units **1988**

MJP water-jet unit mounted on the 41 m Marinteknik monohull ferry Rosaria Lauro **1989**

advanced water-jet operation has been reduced to a minimum and the risk for mistakes in critical situations has been minimised. The RMC includes control levers for steering, speed/forward/reverse and a single combinator for cruising/harbour mode. Normally a twin installation of water-jets requires two combinators, one for each unit, but with the digital control system advanced manoeuvres are made with one single combinator. The combinator can be used in two ways: in cruising mode for different speed setting on each unit, and in harbour mode for lateral movement of the vessel without the need of bow thrusters and rotation around the vessel's centre of flotation.

The different settings of the water-jets, that is forward/neutral/reverse, outward/inward inclination and speed are controlled by the computer and can be adjusted for different vessels and loading conditions by the crew.

For steering purposes hydraulic rotary actuators are used which allow full nozzle turning from one side to the other within 2.5 seconds. The feedback to the electrohydraulic controls and the inclination to the mimic panel in the wheelhouse are done through double built-in electrical transmitters in the hydraulic actuators.

The complete steering and reversing unit is made of stainless steel castings and the reverser is positively balanced, this allows a stepless redirection of the jetflow from full speed ahead to full speed astern.

Efficiency: To achieve predicted efficiency and speed a new type of mixed-flow pump was developed. The blade-to-blade flow analysis was carried out on a computer together with the finite element strength analysis of the impeller. This design technique is ensuring low drag and high freedom from cavitation.

To further increase the efficiency a new type of impeller bearing was designed including a continuous bearing monitoring system. This careful design also increases vessel comfort due to freedom from vibration of impeller and shaft.

Operating reliability: Many of today's high-speed surface craft are constructed in light alloy plate, and therefore a new type of intake including plastic parts has been designed to avoid corrosion problems by insulating the stainless steel pump unit from the hull. All other components and materials are also chosen to avoid corrosion and mechanical wear in the demanding marine environment.

The monitoring system for the RMC has built-in measuring points which give fast fault indication and considerably shorten the servicing time.

RMC-DD
Advanced manoeuvring system for water-jets

Background: During the last five years, MPJ has delivered over 35 advanced manoeuvring systems installed in high-speed catamarans and monohull ferries, in the range of 33 to 42 m length and with speeds between 20 and 40 knots.

This system, the 'Remote Manoeuvre Controller—Dual Drive' (RMC-DD) is unique on the market, with two preselectable modes of 'cruise' and 'harbour' for open sea and confined harbour operations respectively.

New generation: The two separate combinator levers for direction and thrust control in the older system are now combined in one two-axis single combinator of joystick type with some special mechanical tracking control facilities to give the operator an improved sense of direction control during cruise as well as in confined harbour manoeuvres.

This leaves the other hand free for steering control or to switch over to the autopilot.

The autopilot makes the harbour manoeuvres

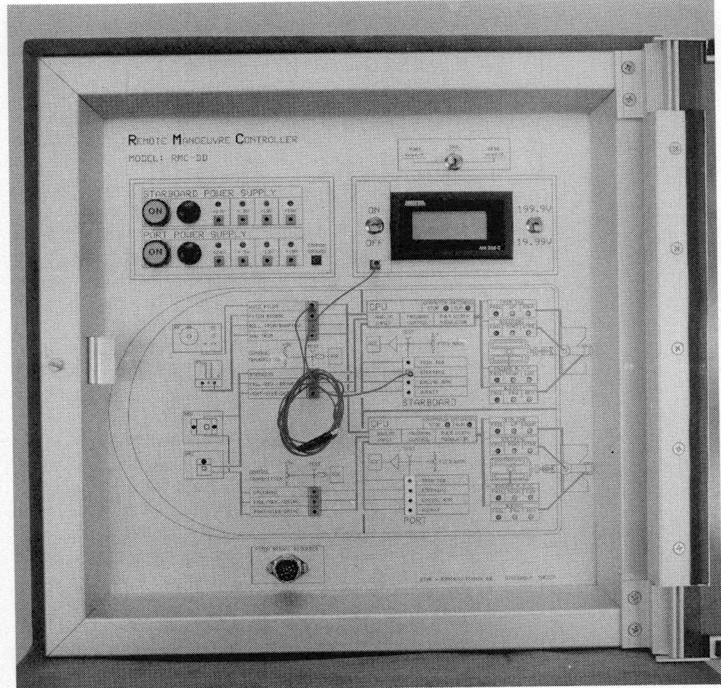

Computerised MJP Remote Control System **1988**

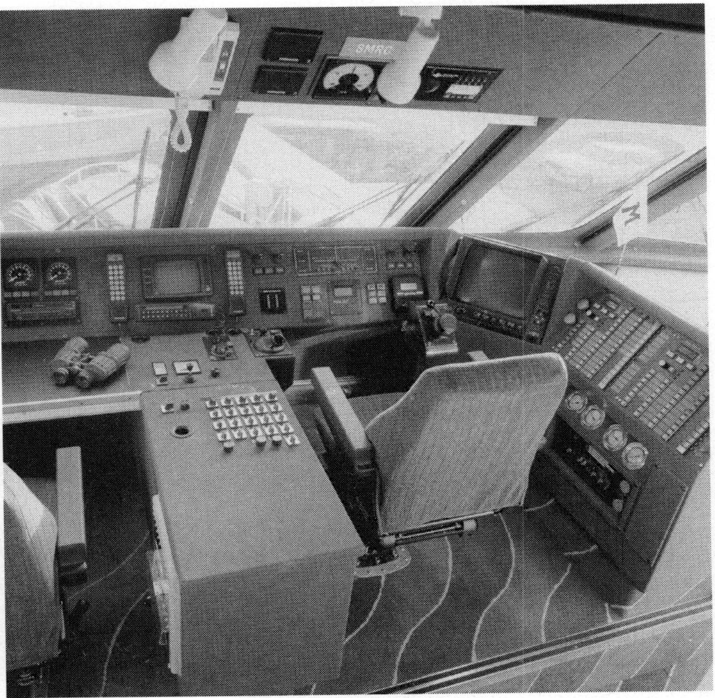

Bridge installation of Remote Control System **1990**

MJP Marine Jet Power AB deliveries 1994 onwards (MJP delivered over 120 water-jets prior to 1994)

No	Water-jet model	Output kW	Engine make	Shipowner	Area of operation	Yard/Hull	Name of vessel	Classi-fication	Hull type	LOA (m)	Speed (kts)	Delivery
50	J650R-DD	2 × 1,839	Niigata	Seto Inland Sea Lins	Japan	Hitachi Zosen C	—	JG	Catamaran	31.5	38	Jan 1994
51	J650R-DD	2 × 1,839	Niigata	Fuke Kaiun	Japan	Hitachi Zosen C	—	JG	Catamaran	31.5	38	Feb 1994
52	J500S-DD	2 × 735	MTU	Swedish Coast Guard	Swedish Coast	Karlskronavarvet	*KBV 302*	DnV	Monohull	20	33	1994
53	J500s-DD	2 × 735	MTU	Swedish Coast Guard	Swedish Coast	Karlskronavarvet	*KBV 303*	DnV	Monohull	20	33	1994
54	J500S-DD	2 × 735	MTU	Swedish Coast Guard	Swedish Coast	Karlskronavarvet	*KBV 304*	DnV	Monohull	20	33	1994
55	J500S-DD	2 × 735	MTU	Swedish Coast Guard	Swedish Coast	Karlskronavarvet	*KBV 305*	DnV	Monohull	20	33	1995
56	J500S-DD	2 × 735	MTU	Swedish Coast Guard	Swedish Coast	Karlskronavarvet	*KBV 306*	DnV	Monohull	20	33	1995
57	J500S-DD	2 × 735	MTU	Swedish Coast Guard	Swedish Coast	Karlskronavarvet	*KBV 307*	DnV	Monohull	20	33	1995
58	J500X-DD	2 × 735	MTU	Swedish Coast Guard	Swedish Coast	Karlskronavarvet	*KBV 308*	DnV	Monohull	20	33	1995
59	J500S-DD	2 × 735	MTU	Swedish Coast Guard	Swedish Coast	Karlskronavarvet	*KBV 309*	DnV	Monohull	20	33	1995
60	J500S-DD	2 × 735	MTU	Swedish Coast Guard	Swedish Coast	Karlskronavarvet	*KBV 310*	DnV	Monohull	20	33	1995
61	J500S-DD	2 × 735	MTU	Swedish Coast Guard	Swedish Coast	Karlskronavarvet	*KBV 311*	DnV	Monohull	20	33	1995
62	J650R	4 × 1,415	MTU	Surf	Caribbean	Marinteknik Singapore	*H 130*	DnV	Catamaran	41	42	1994
63	J650R-DD	2 × 1,970	MTU	Cheerful Prospects Ltd	Hong Kong	Marinteknik Singapore	*H 118*	DnV	Catamaran	34	39	1994
64	J650R-DD	2 × 1,920	MTU	Bintan Resort	Singapore	Kværner Fjellstrand	*H 017*	DnV	Catamaran	40	37	1994
65	J650R-DD	2 × 1,935	MWM	Hong Kong Resort Co Ltd	Hong Kong	Marinteknik Singapore	*H 137*	DnV	Catamaran	42	34	1994
66	J650R-DD	2 × 1,935	MWM	Hong Kong Resort Co Ltd	Hong Kong	Marinteknik Singapore	*H 138*	DnV	Catamaran	42	34	1995
67	J650R-DD	2 × 1,935	MWM	Hong Kong Resort Co Ltd	Hong Kong	Marinteknik Singapore	*H 139*	DnV	Catamaran	42	34	1995
68	J650R-DD	2 × 2,000	MTU		India	Kværner Fjellstrand	*H 016*	DnV	Catamaran	40	37	1994
69	J650-DD	2 × 1,720	MTU	Daikyo	Australia	Lloyd's Ship Yard	*Reef Prince*	DnV	Catamaran	36	30	1994
70	J650R-DD	2 × 2,000	MTU			Kværner Fjellstrand	*H 019*	DnV	Catamaran	40	37	1994
71	J650R-DD	2 × 2,000	MTU			Kværner Fjellstrand	*H 020*	DnV	Catamaran	40	37	1994
72	J750-DD	2 × 2,400	Niigata	Semo	Korea	Semo	—	KR	Catamaran	41	35	1995
73	J650-DD	2 × 2,000	Niigata	Semo	Korea	Semo	—	KR	Catamaran	41	35	1995
74	J650-DD	2 × 2,000	Niigata	Semo	Korea	Semo	—	KR	Catamaran	41	35	1995
75	J500S-DD	2 × 850	—	Hy-Line Ferry	USA	Gladding Hearn	—	ABS	Catamaran	25	31	1995
76	J650-QD	4 × 1,960	MTU	—	India	International Shipyard	—	DnV	Catamaran	42	38	1995
77	J650-DD	2 × 1,960	MTU	NYFF	USA	Derecktor	—	DnV	Catamaran	35	35	1996
78	J650-DD	2 × 1,960	MTU	NYFF	USA	Derecktor	—	DnV	Catamaran	35	35	1996
79	J750-DD	2 × 1,960	MTU	City of Valledo	USA	Dakota Creek	—	ABS	Catamaran	36	32	1996
80	J750-DD	2 × 1,960	MTU	City of Valledo	USA	Dakota Creek	—	ABS	Catamaran	36	32	1996

MJP J500R-DD water-jets for the Swedish Coastguard ***1995***

easier; by switching it to control the steering in harbour mode during lateral (sideway) movement, the helmsman can leave the parallel steering control to the autopilot. In this case, the autopilot will provide automatic parallel steering when leaving or approaching a pier in transversal direction. By setting the autopilot course parallel to the pier and activating it, the helmsman needs only to concentrate his attention on controlling the sideway propulsive thrust and make required adjustment of the forward/reverse power that may be needed depending on current and wind affecting the movement, or when moving in diagonal fashion, still under 'parallelism' with the preset course. All these thrust control adjustments can now be done with the single hand combinator lever.

If the helmsman wants to take over the steering for a short adjustment or turning during the transversal movement, without switching the autopilot control off, he can override the autopilot by turning the lever in the desired direction. Retransmitting the control to the autopilot is done by setting the steering lever in neutral position (electrical autopilot interface) or by letting go of the lever, if the autopilot interface is driven by a friction coupled DC motor directly on the steering lever shaft. (Alternative optional AP-interface.)

Upgrading of the first-generation of RMC-DD: A

retrofit kit, for upgrading the earlier deliveries of RMC-DD equipped with the older manoeuvring lever system, is available on request.

Remote Manoeuvre Station (RMS)
The RMS can be easily moved to different positions such as the bridge wing, the fly bridge or the aft deck if required. The possibility to operate more than one RMS with an advanced and safe 'takeover' routine is incorporated in this development.

The RMS will be accumulator powered, and communicate with the main RMC-DD system by a non-galvanic ('contactless') adaptor to a simple communication net.

When not in use, the RMS unit(s) is connected to a charger, preferably placed on the main manoeuvre bridge. A highly sophisticated internal self-check and communication protocol and a very safe 'takeover routine' assure safe handling and operation of the overall system.

Even the first generation of RMC-DD can be modified and upgraded with RMS units since it is pre-adapted with input/output channels for that use.

MJP J450R, J550R, J650R and J750R
Four types of complete propulsion systems, single or double, including water-jets, hydraulics and computerised remote-control system.
Output: 200-3,500 kW per unit
Speed range: 18-60 knots
Material: stainless steel in water-jets
Weight: 600-2,000 kg
Manoeuvring: electrohydraulic servo system
Remote-control: computerised control including combinator for lateral movement and rotation

VERIFIED

Size	*Nom kW	Max kW	A	B	∅C	∅D	E	F	G	H	Weight per unit kg** Steerable	Booster
500	1200	1800	510	1290	855	500	2050	3400	575	460	815	575
550	1500	2250	560	1412	940	550	2250	3790	630	505	1090	710
650	2100	3150	665	1680	1120	650	2675	4510	750	600	1560	1035
750	2800	4200	765	1900	1255	750	3075	5180	860	690	2105	1460
850	3700	5550	880	2100	1440	850	3540	5890	990	795	3145	2125
950	4900	7350	1010	2460	1610	950	4070	6590	1100	915	4330	3000
1100	6950	9750	1200	2845	1890	1100	4820	7630	1350	1090	6040	4080
1350	9200	13800	1355	3490	2110	1350	5560	9370	1555	1250	8450	5830
1550												
1750												
2050												

* Above figures are nominal, final data in accordance to technical specification.
** Weight figures incl hydraulics, excl shafting & intake.

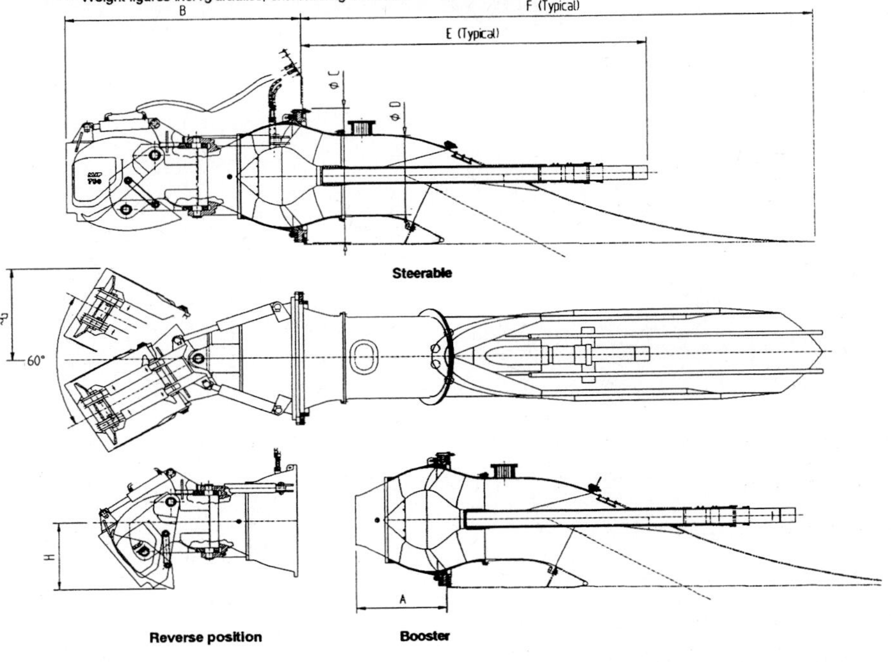

Dimensions of MJP water-jet units
1995

UNITED KINGDOM

VOSPOWER WATER JETS

Vosper Thornycroft (UK) Ltd, Hydraulic Power Division

Northarbour Road, Cosham, Portsmouth, Hampshire PO6 3TL, UK

Tel: +44 (1705) 383311
Telex: 86860 VTHYPO G
Fax: +44 (1705) 325133

W Dormer, *Sales and Marketing Manager*
R G Parker, *Technical Consultant*
D King, *Sales Manager (Water-jets)*

VOSPOWER Water Jets is owned by the Hydraulic Power Division, part of the international shipbuilding and engineering group Vosper Thornycroft (UK) Ltd. They manufacture a range of marine equipment comprising bow thrusters, stabilizers, steering gear and waterjets which are fitted to a wide range of vessels in the naval, commercial and leisure market sectors.

VOSPOWER type number	**65**	**90**	**100 90G**	**115**	**140**	**170**	**210**	**250**	**300**
Engine size (hp)									
petrol	40-200	60-350	—	—	—	—	—	—	—
diesel	10-50	40-250	60-350	70-400	100-600	200-900	400-3,000	600-2,000	1,500-4,000
Impeller diameter at inlet	165	229	254	292	356	431	533	635	762
Materials									
Jet unit body	aluminium LM25 hard anodised (VOSPOWER 90G-GRP)	composites	composites	composites	composites	composites	composites	composites	composites
Impeller	Aluminium bronze	Aluminium bronze	Aluminium bronze	Superston 70	Superston 70	Superston 70	Superston 70	Superston 70	Superston 70
Weight (kg)	30	60 (VOSPOWER 90G-70)	100	125	200	350	600	900	1,500

VOSPOWER 140
PERFORMANCE EXAMPLES
At max quoted power levels:
Thrust at 10 knots, 400 shp, 1,650 kg
Thrust at 20 knots, 400 shp, 1,320 kg
Thrust at 40 knots, 400 shp, 770 kg

Cutaway version of VOSPOWER 115 water-jet **1992**

The company offers a range of jet units up to its Model VOSPOWER 300 of 762 mm impeller diameter suitable for powers up to 3,000 kW (4,000 hp).

VOSPOWER Water Jets have for a number of years successfully used GRP for the major fixed components of their water-jet units. The range of jet units from Model PP 115 upwards is now being built with a mixture of glassfibre, Kevlar and carbon fibre reinforcement. These materials are totally corrosion resistant and give excellent structural properties. All metal parts exposed to the water can be made in stainless steel or, for special applications, in more exotic materials eliminating problems associated with dissimilar metals in contact with saltwater.

The method of construction allows the form of the jet to be made to match the hull contour with comparatively simple additions to the mould. Further, the moulded surface presents a highly polished finish for the water flow.

An adjustable trim facility is available on most models giving up and down nozzle movement of ±10°.

Model VOSPOWER 140 water-jet unit
1986

ULTRA HYDRAULICS LTD

An Ultra Group Company

Anson Business Park, Cheltenham Road East, Staverton, Gloucester GL2 9QN, UK

Tel: +44 (1452) 857711
Telex: 437452 G
Fax: +44 (1452) 858222

D Burton, *Managing Director*
R J Scarborough, *Director*
M J Lane, *Engineering Manager, Marine Products*
C R G Ellis, *Sales Manager*

Ultra Hydraulics, an Ultra Group company, is a high-technology engineering company based in the UK with overseas representation in many countries including Canada, Germany and the USA.

The product range of Ultra Hydraulics includes water-jets, developed over a 30 year involvement in the marine field, starting with the Dowty Turbocraft jet boats of the 1950s. Ultra water-jets are now among the most numerous water-jet units in the world.

Water-jets have been produced for defence markets and are principally designed to produce very high thrust at relatively low speed, without suffering from cavitation.

The basic component of the water-jet is an axial flow impeller (single or two stage) made of stainless steel, set within a stainless steel reaction casing. The intake and outlet ducts are of cast aluminium.

The control mechanisms are simple and are designed to be robust and reliable. Both the steering and reversing actuator arms penetrate the transom plate and are readily adapted to match the boat's control systems. The zero thrust condition is achieved by the downward vectoring of the jet.

The control of the unit is identical to conventional rudder practice, requiring no retraining of crew. The jet can be directed 33° either side of the central position and the pivot arrangement ensures a high level of flow efficiency, in all conditions.

The components are all made from high-quality materials and require minimal maintenance. Ingested debris can be cleared from within the boat by means of an access hatch, or simply discharged by back-flushing the unit.

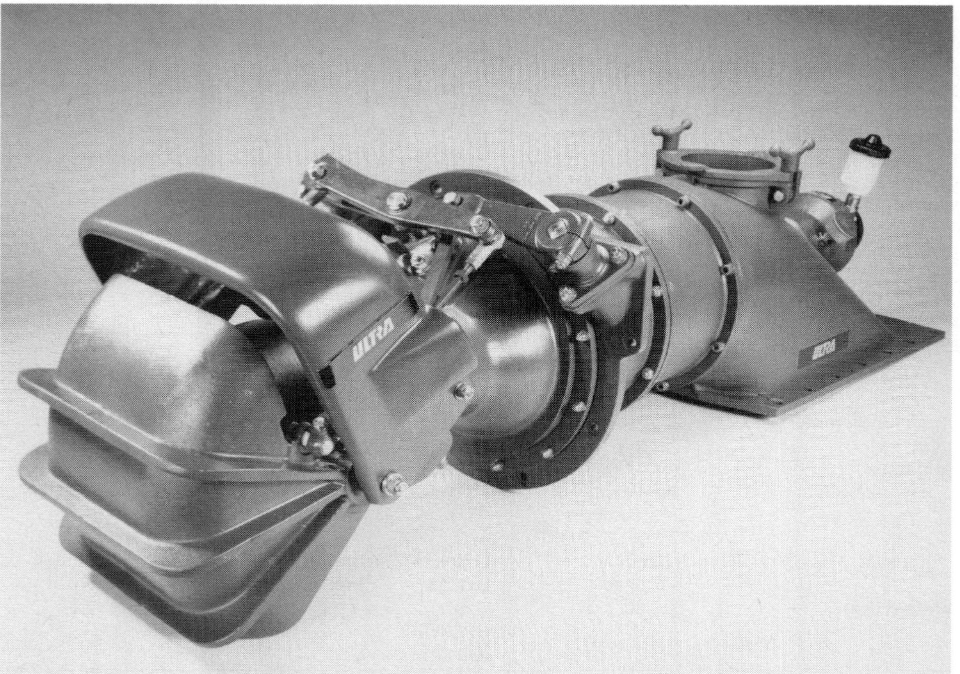

Dia 300 two stage water-jet for marine craft applications **1991**

Typical high-speed craft utilising Ultra water-jets include combat support boats (bridge erection boats).

The Water-jet 300 is installed in over 500 craft, including combat support boats for the Far Eastern, Greek, NATO, UK and US armies. Versions of the basic unit have also been installed in army amphibious vehicles, where space constraints have dictated changes to the unit's layout.

There are also applications in the field of auxiliary or loitering propulsion for larger craft, such as patrol boats, where good manoeuvrability and slow speed economy are required.

A recent development is the rotating nozzle jet which is capable of being directed through 360°. Another development utilises a high-solidity stainless steel impeller which results in a craft speed increase combined with smaller unit size and hence weight reduction.

Water-jets are purpose-built to meet customer requirements. Production has included units from 250 to 450 mm, capable of absorbing up to 1,300 bhp and the company is prepared to investigate other sizes and powers to suit special applications. Development is proceeding on higher thrust water-jets.

VERIFIED

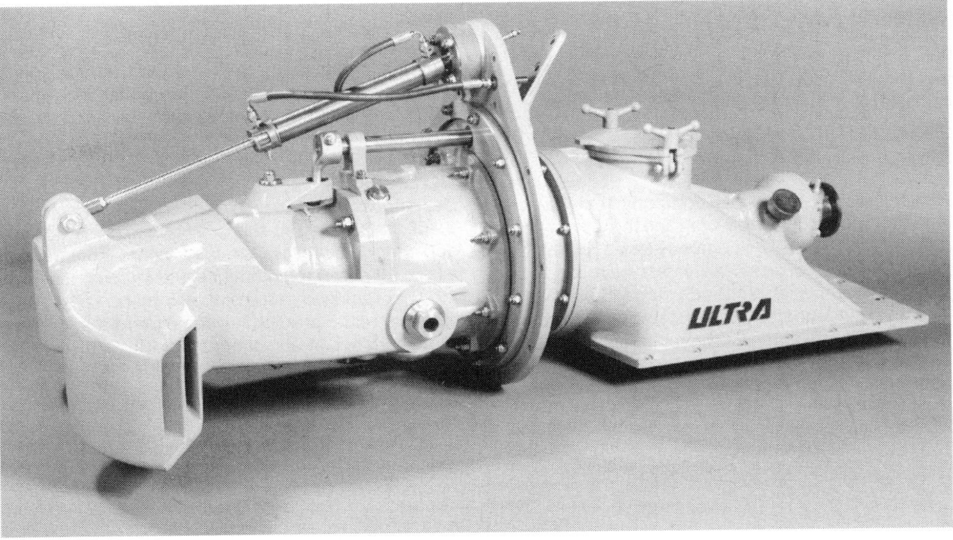

The Ultrajet 300 mm water-jet unit
1994

UNITED STATES OF AMERICA

AMJET

American Hydro Jet Corporation

2033-F West McNab Road, Pompano Beach, Florida 33069, USA

Tel: +1 (305) 978 8996
Fax: +1 (305) 978 6597

P W Roos, *President*
R Filippino, *Vice President, Manufacturing*
A L Cohen, *Marketing Manager*

American Hydro Jet Corporation began the design and manufacture of water-jet units in 1988.

AMJET presently supplies water-jets in six ranges to absorb power levels up to 3,750 kW. The six ranges are designated J-1200, J-1400, J-1700, J-2200, J-2700 and J-3500.

AMJET J-3500 SERIES HYDRO JET DRIVE

The AMJET J-3500 series jet drive is designed for power inputs of 1,120 kW (displacement hulls) to 5,250 kW (high-speed planing hulls). The impeller diameter can be selected from 71 to 88 cm. The maximum shaft speed is 1,200 rpm and the weight range is up to 2,000 kg. The power steering and reverse systems provide for efficient steering, especially at high speeds, as well as conventional reverse direction steering with excellent manoeuvrability.

The complete water-jet propulsion system is modular in concept and designed with flexibility, allowing many applications from displacement speed to very fast planing hulls, each with highest efficiency possible. The use of the reduction gear as the forward pump shaft support eliminates the need for a double universal drive line and allows the engine to be placed further aft. It makes possible the prefabrication of modules, and customer fabrication of the intake duct as an integral part of the hull. All modules (except intake duct) are pre-assembled, tested and all controls adjusted at the factory so that reassembly in the field requires no further adjustment. It allows for effective cost control during manufacture and installation in the field. All hydraulic controls are placed inside the vessel and the lubrication oil, void space and water pressure ducting are internal to the pump, eliminating all external hose and tubing connections.

VERIFIED

AMJET J-3580 ***1992***

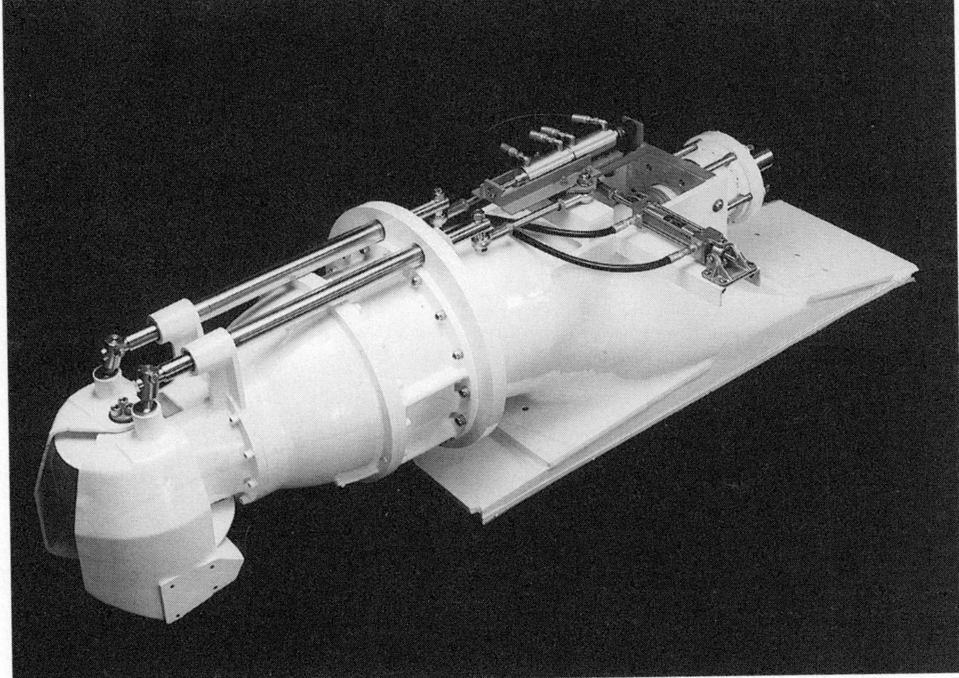

AMJET 1700 ***1995***

NORTH AMERICAN MARINE JET INC

PO Box 1232, Benton, Arkansas 72018, USA

Tel: +1 (501) 778 4151
Fax: +1 (501) 778 6381

Established in 1980, this company manufactures water-jets for high-speed craft for the power range 110 kW to 560 kW. The company also supplies high-thrust, low-speed units. Water-jets have been supplied to a variety of craft including US Navy patrol boats, fishing boats, workboats, dive boats, crew boats, fire boats and excursion boats.

The company has in-house facilities for the fabrication of steel, stainless steel and aluminium, backed up by analytical design software, and a CAD system.

The Nomera range is offered to the high-speed craft market, and a new 300 kW unit for high-speed craft of 30 to 60 knot speeds is soon to be introduced.

NOMERA 14

Designed to operate with diesel or petrol engines at 2,400 to 3,000 rpm, this unit provides high thrust and manoeuvrability. Straightforward construction allows for easier maintenance and increased reliability. There are two models, the Nomera 14A and the Nomera 14-OB offering the same performance but a slight variance in unit dimensions.

Specifications
Dry weight: 180 kg
Length: 1.56 m (Nomera 14A); 1.57 m (Nomera 14-OB)
Power: 120-224 kW
Shaft speed: 2,400-3,000 rpm
Impeller diameter: 0.29 m

NOMERA 20

Specifications
Dry weight: 500 kg
Length: 2.19 m
Power: 186-560 kW
Shaft speed: 1,800-2,400 rpm
Impeller diameter: 0.40 m

VERIFIED

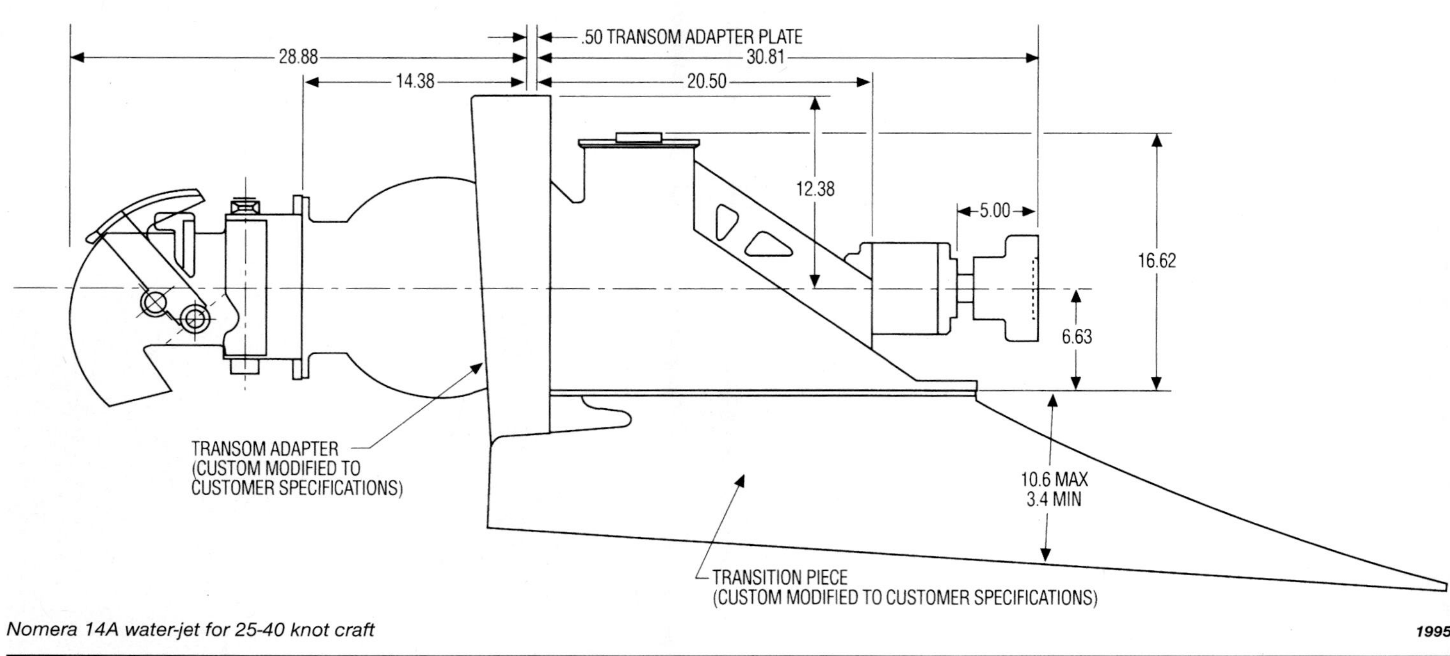

Nomera 14A water-jet for 25-40 knot craft ***1995***

RIDE CONTROL SYSTEMS

Company Listing by Country

Japan
Hitachi Zosen Corporation

Norway
Kværner Fjellstrand A/S
Ulstein Marine Electronics A/S

United Kingdom
Brown Brothers and Company Ltd

United States of America
MDI
SES Ride Controls Inc

JAPAN

HITACHI ZOSEN CORPORATION

Head Office: 3-28 Nishikujo 5-chome, Konhana-ku, Osaka, 554 Japan

Tel: +81 (6) 466 7546
Telex: 63376 J
Fax: +81 (6) 466 7578

Hitachi Zosen developed a ride control system with Supramar for the PTS 50 type hydrofoil, *Housho,* a PTS 50 Mk II which was delivered to Hankyu Kisen KK on 19 January 1983.

The underside of the bow foil is fitted with two flapped fins to improve ride comfort. Operated by automatic sensors, the fins augment stability and provide side forces to dampen rolling and transverse motions.

VERIFIED

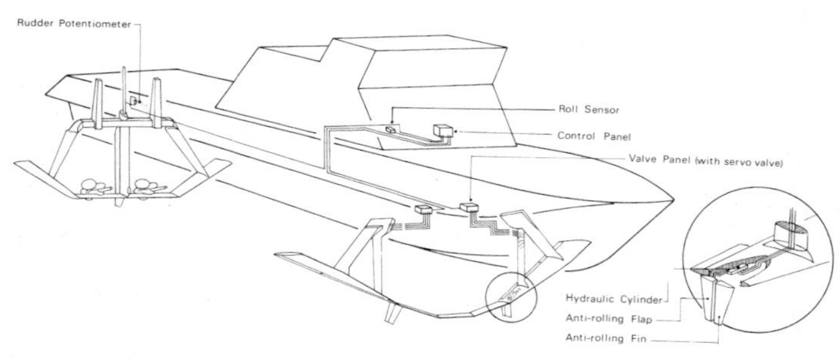

PTS 50 Mk II roll-stabilising system as fitted to Housho **1992**

Flapped roll-stabilisation fin on Housho **1992**

NORWAY

KVÆRNER FJELLSTRAND A/S

N-5632 Omastrand, Norway

Tel: +47 (5) 554100
Telex: 42148 FBOAT N
Fax: +47 (5) 554244/4268

Erling Berge, *Vice President, Business Development*
Knut Eide, *Marketing Manager*
Alf Steine, *Financial Manager*

KVÆRNER MOTION DAMPENING SYSTEM (MDS)

Kværner Fjellstrand developed the Kværner Motion Dampening System (MDS) in order to improve the sea-keeping characteristics of their high-speed catamarans in rough seas. By counteracting the impact of the waves on the hull, Kværner MDS minimises slamming, pitching and rolling.

The Kværner MDS comprises a strut carrying the controlling fins, a hydraulic transmission system, a control system and sensors.

Struts on which the controlling fins are mounted are installed at the forward end of each hull at the point where they can provide maximum dampening effect. An adjustable fin with a surface area corresponding to 2 m^2 is mounted on each strut. Vessel motion data are acquired by sensors and then passed to a computer which in turn continuously adjusts the angle of the fins to counteract the motion of the vessel.

The system can be installed on Kværner Fjellstrand's 38.8 m Advanced Slender Catamarans and 40 m Flying Cats. Retrofitting is also possible on existing models.

The first Kværner MDS was mounted on *Victoria Clipper*, operated by Clipper Navigation Inc of Seattle, USA.

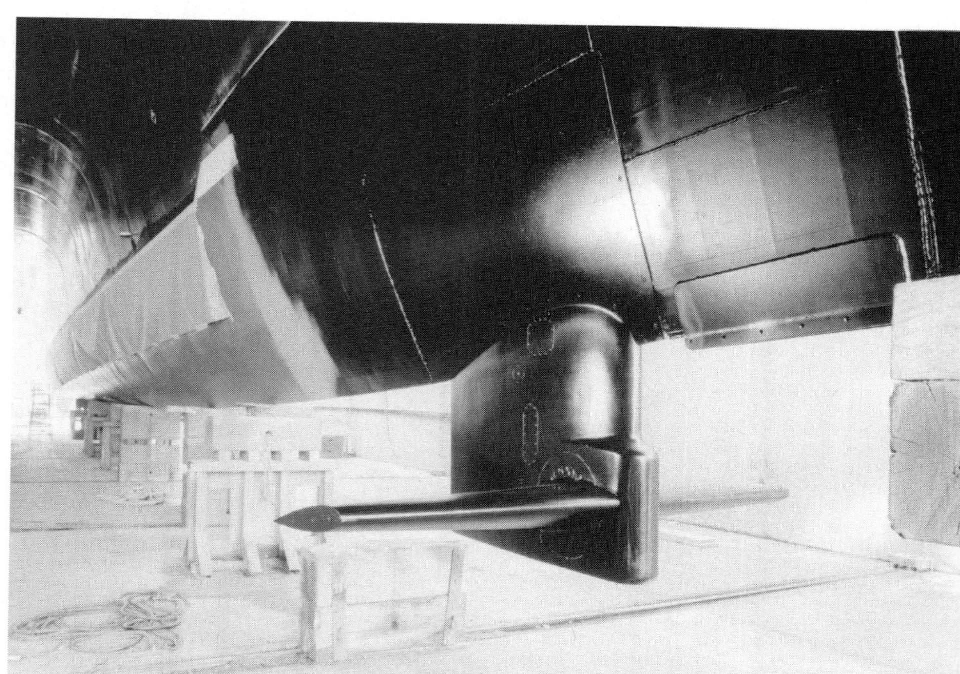

One of the hull installations of Kværner Fjellstrand's first Motion Dampening System mounted on Victoria Clipper **1994**

Experience with the 38.8 m *Victoria Clipper* and other craft has shown that bow accelerations in 1.5 to 2 m significant wave heights are reduced by 36 per cent and with the Kværner MDS in use in lower wave heights of 0.5 to 1 m the reduction is as much as 46 per cent. The operator has found that the Kværner MDS dramatically reduces motion discomfort in 2.4 m seas (6.2 per cent of craft length) and that in following seas it is possible for the first time to continue on autopilot.

UPDATED

ULSTEIN MARINE ELECTRONICS A/S

Kjopmannsgt. 23, N-6025 Alesund, Norway

Tel: +47 (71) 29929
Fax: +47 (71) 21225

Stig Ulstein, *Managing Director*

The company is the result of a merger between the two Ulstein companies Ulstein Marine Electronics A/S and Peilo Teknik A/S. Manufacture of electronic equipment for the marine industry is the main activity. In addition to the well-known remote-control systems for ship manoeuvring, propulsion control systems, tank measuring systems and alarm systems, Ulstein Marine Electronics is also involved in cockpit design for high-speed craft and is developing a ride control system for these craft.

VERIFIED

UNITED KINGDOM

BROWN BROTHERS AND COMPANY LTD

Broughton Road, Edinburgh EH7 4LF, UK

Tel: +44 (131) 556 2440
Telex: 72151
Fax: +44 (131) 556 3253

D J McNeill, *Sales and Marketing Director*
R J McFarlane, *Sales and Marketing Manager*

Brown Brothers offers a range of ride control systems for high-speed vessels, including: non-retractable fin stabilisers and trim tabs, controlling pitch and roll for monohulls and Swath motion control equipment comprising non-retractable fin stabilisers with a multivariable gain control for independent or simultaneous control of pitch, roll and heave.

Both systems permit roll stabilisation of up to 90 per cent.

UPDATED

UNITED STATES OF AMERICA

MARITIME DYNAMICS, INC

424X Great Mills Road, Lexington Park, Maryland 20653, USA

Tel: +1 (301) 863 5499
Fax: +1 (301) 863 0254

Clarence A Lysdale, *President*
John D Adams, *Vice President*
Mark E Lindler, *Director of Operations*
Charlotte R Sebra, *Sales and Marketing*
Robert L Chandler, *Service Manager*

For over 15 years, Maritime Dynamics, Inc (MDI) has designed, developed and manufactured ride control systems for advanced marine vehicles. MDI's capability includes the analysis and simulation of ship motions, control system design, software development, hardware fabrication, installation and crew training. MDI control systems are in operation on Surface Effect Ships (SES), Air Cushion Vehicles (ACV), Catamarans (CAT), Small-Waterplane-Area Twin-Hull (SWATH) ships and monohulls. See table of MDI Ride Control System Installations.

Surface Effect Ships

MDI ride control systems for SES provide motion control and real-time data for optimisation of overall craft performance. In 1980, MDI designed and

Maritime Dynamics cushion vent valve assembly for use in SES ride control systems ***1991***

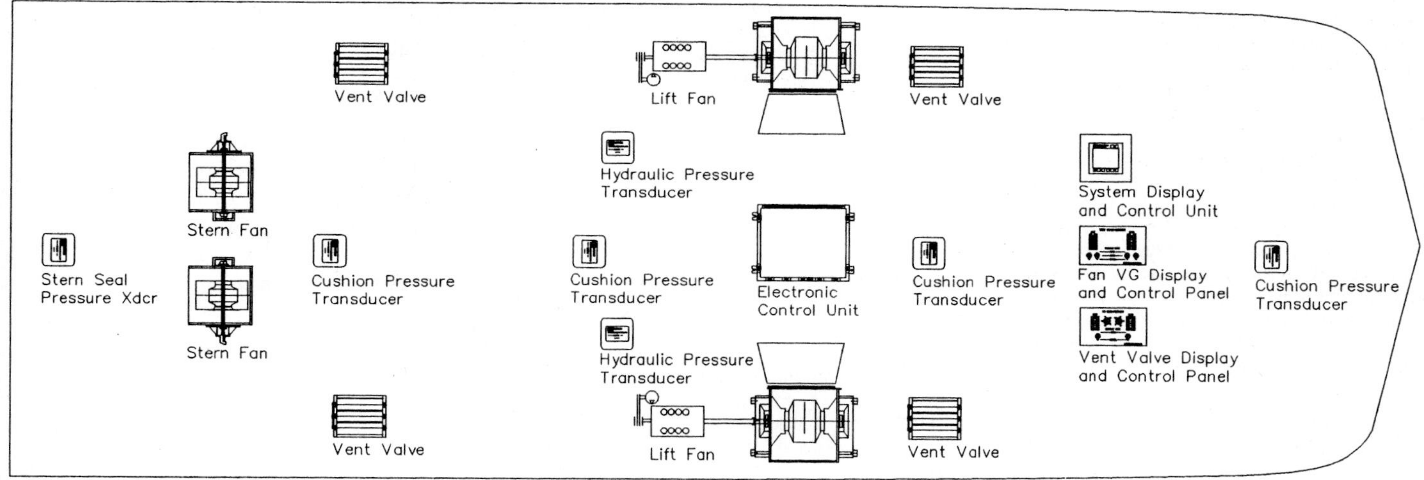

Major components of a typical Maritime Dynamics ride control system for an SES ***1991***

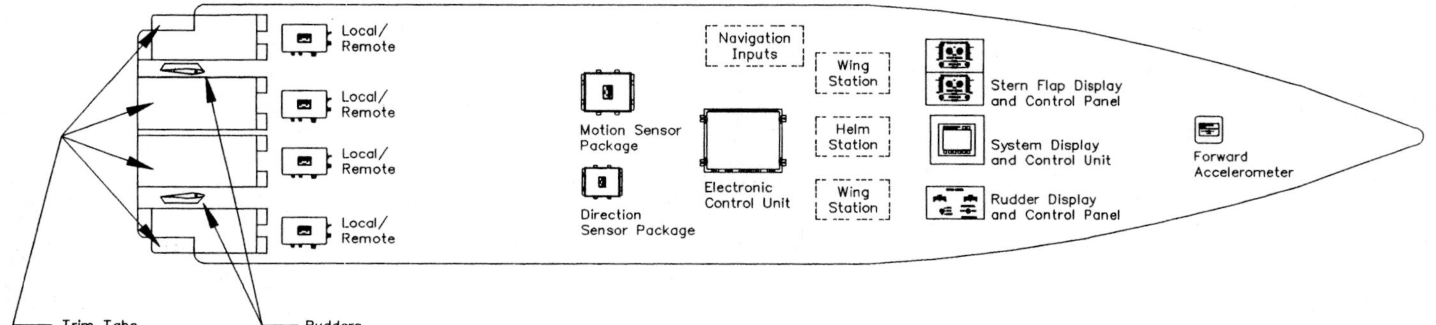

Major components of a typical Maritime Dynamics ride control system for a monohull ***1994***

supplied a ride control system for the USN XR-1D SES. This was the first active ride control system to demonstrate significant improvements in SES ride quality under rough sea conditions. MDI has continued the development of SES ride control systems and currently manufactures microprocessor-based systems for both military and civilian craft.

The ride control system minimises wave-induced pressure changes in the air cushion, to reduce the craft motions and vertical accelerations caused by 'wave pumping' of the cushion volume. The resulting attenuation of the vertical accelerations can significantly reduce fatigue and discomfort during moderate and high-speed cushionborne operations. Control is provided by an Electronic Control Unit (ECU) which controls hydraulically driven cushion vent valves and/or variable flow fans dynamically regulating the net cushion airflow to maintain a constant pressure.

Components for a typical SES ride control system installation consist of pressure, attitude, and acceleration sensors; a microprocessor-based ECU with applicable control algorithms; a hydraulic system; and a set of vent valves that are connected to the ship's air cushion. Each vent valve assembly consists of aerodynamically shaped louvres driven by a servo-controlled hydraulic cylinder.

The ECU uses a 16 bit microprocessor to implement sampled data control algorithms using cushion pressure and ship motion feedback signals, and to output servo control signals to each vent valve or fan inlet guide vane selected for active control. Fault monitoring of the system's electronic, hydraulic and mechanical components is performed between each control algorithm computation. MDI ride control systems installed on SESs operating from 35 to 45 knots consistently achieve a 50 per cent reduction in heave accelerations and have demonstrated reductions as high as 70 per cent.

The ride control display also provides a menu-driven real-time display of measured craft parameters relating to air cushion and craft operating conditions (for example, means and standard deviations of trim, roll, cushion pressure, vent valve position and vertical acceleration). These data have proven to be extremely valuable to the vessel operator for optimising overall performance in different sea conditions.

The ECU can be used on any SES or Air Cushion Vehicle (ACV) equipped with either vent valves or variable flow fans by programming it with appropriate control algorithms. MDI has developed a systematic technique for deriving these control algorithms which is based on classical and optimal control theory as well as extensive experimental testing.

Ride control systems have been installed on over 30 SES craft, including the following vessels: USN *SES-200,* USCG WSES *Sea Hawk*, the CIRR 120P class of passenger ferries, Royal Schelde's 23 m SES, the Blohm+Voss SES *Corsair*, SEMO's 37 m *Democracy*, the Swedish Navy's *Smyge*, Beliard Polyship's 30 m *Manto* and the Norwegian Navy's Mine Countermeasures Vessel.

Future systems are expected to utilise actively controlled bow T-foils to further improve motion reduction and enhance ride quality.

Catamarans

In 1991, MDI introduced the first ride control system to improve passenger comfort on catamarans. The system consists of a microcomputer-based controller that measures the vessel's motions and commands hydraulically actuated fins to reduce wave-induced pitch, roll and heave motion. MDI's first installation was on Condor 9, an Incat Design 49 m wave piercing catamaran built by Aluminum Shipbuilders Ltd. This 450 passenger vessel is operated on the western end of the English Channel by Condor Ltd between Weymouth, UK and St Malo, France. The vessel has bow fins mounted inboard and outboard on each hull and a stern fin that is mounted inboard on each hull.

During tests in February 1992, in measured seas of 2.4 m significant wave height, the ride control system installed on Condor 9 consistently reduced the vessel's pitch and roll motions by 50 per cent relative to the uncontrolled case. In head seas, the vertical accelerations at the forward, mid and aft passenger seats were reduced by 45 per cent, 35 per cent and 20 per cent respectively.

Ride Control System Installations

Type	Builder	Hull no	Length	Commission date	Vessel name
SES	Bell Halter, Inc	—	50 m	1982	*SES-200*
SES	Bell Halter, Inc	—	33 m	1982	*Sea Hawk*
SES	Brødrene Aa	170	32 m	1984	*Ulstein Surfer* (ex-*Fjordkongen* ex-*Norcat*)
SES	Brødrene Aa	184	35 m	1986	*Santa Lucia* (ex-*Ekwata*)
SES	Bell Halter, Inc	—	50 m	1986	*SES-200* (with additional lift fans)
SES	Brødrene Aa	190	35 m	1988	*Talieh* (ex-*Wight Queen,* ex-*Virgin Butterfly* ex-*Ekwata II*)
SES	Brødrene Aa	199	35 m	1988	*Express La Paz* (ex-*Santa Maria*)
SES	Brødrene Aa	201	35 m	1989	*Wight King* (ex-*Sant' Agata*)
SES	Eikefjord Marine	202	35 m	1989	*San Pietro*
SES	Blohm+Voss	—	37 m	1989	*Corsair*
SES	Royal Schelde	—	23 m	1989	*Wight Prince* (ex-*Seaswift 23*)
SES	Brødrene Aa	210	35 m	1989	*San Frangisk*
SES	Eikefjord Marine	200	35 m	1989	*San Pawl*
SES	Eikefjord Marine	219	35 m	1990	*Fjordkongen I*
SES	Eikefjord Marine	211	35 m	1990	*Catamaran II* (ex-*Golden Olympics,* ex-*Supercat One*)
SES	Brødrene Aa	218	35 m	1990	*Yasuda Ocean Liner*
SES	Eikefjord Marine	213	35 m	1990	*Perestroika*
SES	Brødrene Aa	212	35 m	1990	*La Vikinga*
SES	Brødrene Aa	204	35 m	1991	*Sea Flower*
SES	Karlskronavarvet	—	30 m	1991	*Smyge*
SES	Ulstein	208	38 m	1991	*Ocean Flower*
SES	Brødrene Aa	226	35 m	1991	*Catamaran I*
SES	Semo Co Ltd		35 m	1992	*Democracy*
SES	Ulstein	205	38 m	1992	*Santa Eleonora*
SES	Karlskronavarvet	—	30 m	1993	*Smyge*
SES	Beliard Polyship	—	30 m	1993	*Manto*
SES	Kværner Mandal	—	55 m	1993	*MCMV*
SES	Kværner Mandal	—	55 m	1994	*MCMV*
SES	Samsung Heavy Industries	—	37 m	1994	*Dong Yang Gold*
SES	Semo Co Ltd	PMS-02	40 m	1994	*Democracy II*
SES	Semo Co Ltd	PMS-03	40 m	1994	*Democracy III*
SES	Semo Co Ltd	PMS-04	40 m	1994	*Democracy V*
SES	B. Polyship	—	33 m	1994	*Alescandros*
SES	ISY	14	38 m	1995	*Altantica*
SES	Kværner Mandal	—	55 m	1994	*MCMV*
SES	Kværner Mandal	—	55 m	1995	*MCMV*
SES	Kværner Mandal	—	55 m	1995	*MCMV*
SES	ISY	15	38 m	1995	*Tamahine Moorea*
CAT	International Catamarans, Tasmania	023	74 m	1990	*Seacat Calais* (ex-*Seacat Tasmania*)
CAT	Aluminium Shipbuilding, Ltd		49 m	1990	*Condor 9*
CAT	International Catamarans, Tasmania	025	74 m	1990	*Hoverspeed Great Britain*
CAT	International Catamarans, Tasmania	026	74 m	1990	*Seacat Boulogne* (ex-*Sardegna Express,* ex-*Hoverspeed France*)
CAT	International Catamarans, Tasmania	027	74 m	1991	*Hoverspeed Boulogne*
CAT	International Catamarans, Tasmania	028	74 m	1992	*Seacat Scotland*
CAT	International Catamarans, Tasmania	024	74 m	1992	*Patricia Olivia*
CAT	Nichols Brothers		37 m	1992	*SeaJet I* (ex-*Nantucket Spray,* ex-*Metro Atlantic*)
CAT	International Catamarans, Tasmania	030	74 m	1993	*Condor 10*
CAT	International Catamarans, Tasmania	031	74 m	1993	*Stena Sea Lynx*
CAT	International Catamarans, Tasmania	032	74 m	1993	*Juan L*
CAT	Hyundai Heavy Industries	—	45.5 m	1993	—
CAT	WaveMaster International	048	45 m	1994	*Fei Long*
CAT	International Catamarans, Tasmania	033	78 m	1994	*Stena Sea Lynx II*
CAT	InCat Australia	034	78 m	1995	*Condor 11*
CAT	InCat Australia	035	78 m	1995	*Catlink*
CAT	InCat Australia	036	78 m	1995	*Juan Patricia*
CAT	AMD	—	—	1995	*AMD 350*
CAT	FBM Marine	1407	45 m	1994	*Universal Mk 2001*
CAT	FBM Marine	1408	45 m	1994	*Universal Mk 2002*
CAT	FBM Marine	1409	45 m	1995	*Universal Mk 2003*
CAT	Båtservice	—	38 m	1995	*Fjorddroningen*
CAT	Semo	—	40 m	1995	Pegasus
CAT	WaveMaster	—	42 m	1995	—
CAT	InCat Australia	037	79 m	1995	*Sunflower*
CAT	Oskorshams	—	42 m	1995	*Seajet I*
Swath	Hyundai Heavy Industries	—	37 m	1993	
Swath	Swath Ocean Systems	—	20 m	1993	*Houston*
Swath	Swath Ocean Systems	—	27 m	1993	*Chubasco*
Swath	USCG Yard - Curtis Bay, Maryland	—	27 m	1994	*Kaimalino*
Swath	SOS	—	36 m	1995	*Western Flyer*
Monohull	WaveMaster International	034	45 m	1993	*Super Flyte*
Monohull	Westport Shipyard	8,501	30 m	1994	*Catalina Express*
Monohull	Westport Shipyard	8,502	30 m	1994	*Islander Express*
Monohull	Bazan	—	84 m	1995	*Alcantara*
Monohull	Leroux and Lotz	—	—	1994	*Corsaire 6000*

In co-operation with Vosper Thornycroft (UK) Ltd, MDI has provided a similar system for *SeaJet I*, a 37 m wave piercing catamaran built by Nichols Brothers. This vessel has operated successfully in Hawaii and is currently operating between San Diego, California and Catalina Island.

MDI ride control systems have been installed on nine 74 m wave piercing catamarans built by International Catamarans Tasmania. The controller commands two very large hydraulically actuated stern flaps (such as trim tabs) mounted on the transom of each hull. The hydrodynamic, mechanical and hydraulic design of these flaps has been jointly developed by International Catamarans and MDI. Without increasing the vessel's resistance, these flap systems substantially reduce the pitch and roll accelerations that cause motion sickness.

The ride control system installed on the 74 m wave piercing catamaran *Condor 10* utilises both stern flaps and bow T-foils. The bow T-foil design was designed jointly by MDI and Condor Ltd and produced by MDI. This system provides *Condor 10* with satisfactory ride quality to operate all year round on the western end of the English Channel.

Swath

MDI ride control systems for Swath provide trim and list stabilisation (such as mean attitude control) and pitch, roll and relative bow motion control.

Components for a typical Swath installation consist of ship motion sensors; a microprocessor-based ECU with applicable control algorithms; a fin control panel; a hydraulic system; a pair of forward fins or canards; and a pair of aft fins or stabilisers. Control of rudders for manoeuvring is provided if desired.

The Swath ECU and control panels provide automatic and manual control of the fins; real-time display of vessel pitch, heave, roll and fin motions; and display of mean values for trim and list.

MDI ride control systems are currently installed on the *Houston*, a 65 ft pilot vessel, and *Chubasco*, a 90 ft high-performance yacht, both built by Swath Ocean Systems of San Diego. A third system is installed on a 37 m Swath vessel built by Hyundai Heavy Industries for the Korean Agency for Defence Development and a fourth system was delivered to the USN for installation on the test ship *Kaimalino* in 1994.

Monohulls

In early 1993 MDI introduced a ride control system for high-speed monohulls. The monohull system integrates steering, trim and list stabilisation and pitch, roll and yaw motion damping to provide superior control of craft motions during high-speed operation in calm and rough water. This is possible through integrated control of the craft's rudders and

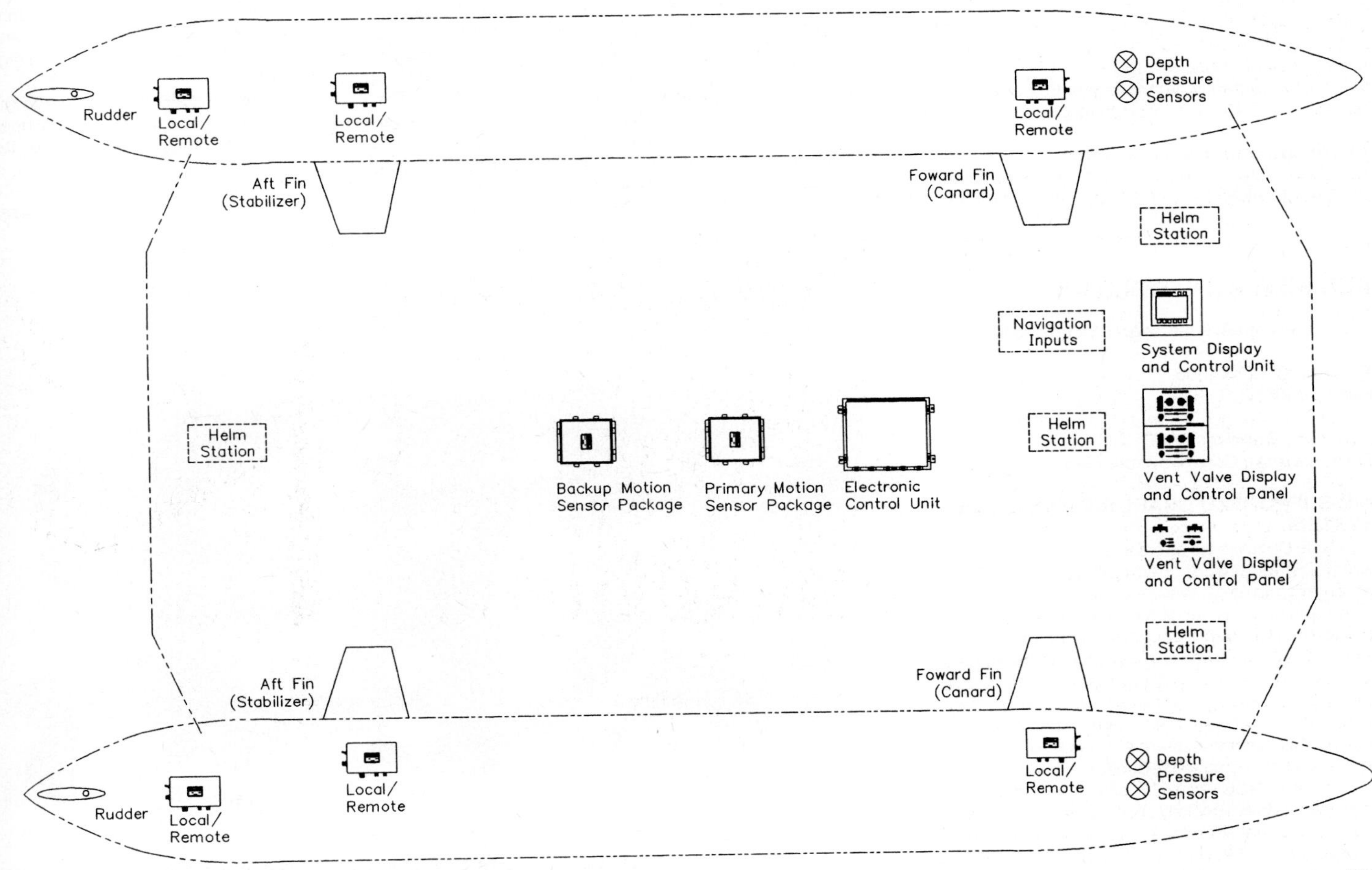

Major components of a typical Maritime Dynamics ride control system for a Swath **1992**

Stern Flap Assembly
Local/ Remote
Port Accelerometer
Local/ Remote
Bow T-Foil Assembly
System Display and Control Unit
Aft Accelerometer
Motion Sensor Package
Electronic Control Unit
Stern Flap Display and Control Panel
Forward Accelerometer
T-Foil Display and Control Panel
Stern Flap Assembly
Local/ Remote
Stbd Accelerometer
Local/ Remote
Bow T-Foil Assembly

Major components of a typical Maritime Dynamics ride control system for a catamaran **1992**

Typical installation arrangement for Maritime Dynamics Alarm and Monitoring System (AMS)

1992

active stern-mounted flaps in response to ship motions and helm commands. MDI's first monohull installation is on WaveMaster International's 40 m monohull *Super Flyte*. In 1 to 2 m bow seas, the system has consistently demonstrated 60 per cent roll reduction and 40 per cent pitch motion reduction.

Alarm and monitoring systems

MDI manufactures a machinery Alarm and Monitoring System (AMS) for mid-size vessels designed for flexibility in installation, software programming and operation. It consists of up to 12 Remote Transmitter Unit (RTU) modules on a multiplexed databus which is controlled by a bridge-mounted Data Processing/display Unit (DPU). Dual DPUs may be installed in separate locations and operated in parallel for full time on-line redundancy. Alternatively, since the system is designed to utilise standard PC compatible computers, one redundant (backup) DPU can run commercial software for electronic charts, voyage accounting, fax reception and so on. The system is capable of monitoring 192 analogue channels and 192 discrete channels, and can also control 180 digital outputs.

The AMS is installed on SES and catamaran ferries and high-speed monohull yachts. It has been approved by both Det Norske Veritas and the Korean Register of Shipping.

UPDATED

SES RIDE CONTROLS INC

15840 S W 84th Avenue, Miami, Florida 33157, USA

Tel: +1 (305) 233 4306
Fax: +1 (305) 233 1339

Don Burg, *President*
Steve Zarzecki, *Control Systems Design*

AIR-SUPPORTED CRAFT RIDE CONTROL SYSTEM

SES Ride Controls Inc offers a new Ride Control System (RCS) for air-supported craft such as the SES, hovercraft and GEM. Wave-induced pressure pulses in the air cushions supporting such craft can produce an uncomfortable bouncy or 'cobblestone' ride effect. This bouncy ride can be reduced by decrease in power to the powered fan that supplies the air cushion, however, a significant reduction in vessel speed results. It has been demonstrated that an active RCS results in dramatic reductions in craft motions with little speed reduction.

This new RCS uses brushless electric servo motors that drive specially constructed vanes at very high operational speeds. These vanes are mounted in valve assemblies that vent the pressure peaks as they occur and/or occlude airflow into the fan inlet to avoid formation of pressure peaks.

Vent valve operation is directed by a pilot-house-mounted microprocessor-based controller that processes dynamic changes in air cushion conditions and other parameters. There is a fully automatic mode setting and there are operator-selectable input parameters for fine tuning. Data presented on a high-resolution display screen include cushion pressure, hull roll and pitch, and *g* forces (accelerations). This information is invaluable to the operator for monitoring ride and trim control and for other operational purposes.

Particular attention has been given in the design to ensure maximum reliability and simplicity of operation, as is evident by the use of brushless electric motors and the elimination of linkages and hydraulics. There is an individual servo motor for each vane, thus eliminating high wear linkages. The only movable contacting components are the vane support and motor bearings. All bearings are sealed and self-lubricated, they are also fully rotated several times at each start up to insure a random change of bearing and race contact points and good distribution of bearing lubrication. The vanes are made of Type 316 stainless steel and the valve housings of Type I5086 marine aluminium to ensure maximum life in a salt spray environment.

A pneumatically energised vane-locking system is included which automatically locks the vanes in a

Components for a typical SES Ride Controls Inc RCS for an air cushion vehicle installation

1991

Controller (right-hand side) for SES Ride Controls Inc RCS

1992

closed position in the event of power failure. This ensures the craft can operate without the RCS, if such an unlikely power failure occurs.

The smaller component is the pilot-house control and high-resolution display module while the larger electronic module houses servo motor control and drive components. The larger flanged units are two identical vane assemblies with one showing two vane drive motors and their driven vanes, and the other showing the pneumatic vane locking components. It can be seen from these vane assemblies that simple flange mounting is provided for in-craft vent ducts. An entire vane can be easily removed from a vane assembly with no requirement to remove the vane assembly from the craft vent duct.

This new patent-pending RCS concept offered by SES Ride Controls Inc has application to all types of air cushion craft. It has been designed for easy installation, low power consumption, maximum life and reliability and ease of maintenance. Power requirements are only 5 to 8 kW for a typical 35 m SES.

The new Air Ride 'Dual-Air' SES (see the *Air Cushion Vehicles* section under USA) with fore-and-aft air cushions used in each side hull will enable trim and pitching control to be obtained by varying fore-and-aft air cushion pressures. Control will be achieved using an SES Ride Controls Inc ride control system similar to that presented here.

VERIFIED

AIR CUSHION SKIRT SYSTEMS

Company Listing by Country

France
Aerazur SA
Pennel & Flipo

Spain
Neumar SA

United Kingdom
Air Cushion Ltd
Avon Technical Products
British Hovercraft Corporation Ltd
Greengate Polymer Coatings Ltd
Northern Rubber Company Ltd

United States of America
Bell Avon Inc

FRANCE

AERAZUR SA

Division Applications des Elastomères, 58 boulevard Gallieni, F-92137 Issy-Les-Moulineaux Cedex, France

Tel: +33 (1) 41 23 23 23
Telex: 631891 F
Fax: +33 (1) 46 48 74 85

F Menard, *Department Manager*

In January 1990, Aerazur (the aerospace subsidiary of the Zodiac group, active in flexible material technologies and a world leader in inflatable boats) purchased the Coated Fabric Division of Kléber Industrie (part of the Michelin Group). The activities of this division and the corresponding division of Aerazur have been merged into a new 'Division Applications des Elastomères'.

The synergy between Aerazur (in charge of air cushion seal design on various French SES programmes since 1980, including Molenes and Agnes 200), and the extensive coated fabrics development and manufacturing capabilities of the former Coated Fabric Division of Kléber, resulted in the creation of a significant industrial base in the design and manufacturing of SES seals.

Design expertise is available within the company for various SES and hovercraft seal designs (loop and segments and full height segments or innovative designs such as a proprietary self-adjusting front-seal design used on Agnes 200). Various simulation software and computer-assisted design systems have been developed and are used for preliminary design, full-scale development or test data analysis. Installation services and full-scale test and maintenance support are available.

The division is one of the world's major producers of coated fabrics, specialising in high quality products, conforming to the rigorous standards and specifications prevailing in the aerospace and marine (notably liferafts and military inflatables) fields.

For hovercraft and SES seals, a range of fabrics has been specially developed, using advanced base fabrics and rubber compounds (based on Hypalon, neoprene or natural rubber, according to the projected use). These products are tested and qualified on specially designed test rigs, reproducing the conditions encountered in real use. Various materials are available in surface weights ranging from 170 to 4,000 g/m^2.

These materials are used on the seals designed and manufactured by Aerazur or are sold to other skirt manufacturers like Griffon Hovercraft Ltd and Air Vehicles Ltd in the UK. Recently, Aerazur has designed, manufactured and installed the seal system for the French SES Agnes 200 and a new aft seal design for the Blohm+Voss Corsair SES.

During Summer 1992, Agnes 200 was used commercially for a scheduled trans-Channel service between Brighton and Dieppe, a 770 n miles crossing in often difficult sea conditions (diagonal or transverse seas, waves over 2 m height being encountered 17 per cent of the time). Normal service and full operational speed (35 knots) were maintained up to Sea State 5, with several crossings in Sea State 6. More than 500 hours of cushionborne service were logged, with negligible wear on the aft seal and very little on the front seal. The side fingers were replaced for inspection, as a precautionary measure, every 200 hours and returned to service within a week; the central fingers remained on the ship and showed no wear after 500 hours. All the inspection and replacement was conducted without dry-docking; due to the modular design the side fingers were replaced in less than four hours, between two trips. Of particular interest is the fact that the good performance of the seal system resulted in a stable and comfortable ride, confirming the design option that no ride control system is needed with these seals (Agnes 200 has no RCS installed), and the good pressure retention characteristics allowed frequent operation on a single supply fan. Subsequent design activity has resulted in an improved design with more than 500 hours of service life possible without maintenance.

The Division is also one of the world leaders in flexible fuel cells and fuel systems for aerospace and armoured vehicles and this technology has been applied to various high-speed marine vehicles. An example of this is that Aerazur has designed, manufactured and installed the complete fuel system of the French Blue Ribbon challenger *Jet Ruban Bleu* and supplied the fuel cells for the Spanish Chaconsa hovercraft.

VERIFIED

Agnes 200 at high speed, fitted with Aerazur skirt systems (French Navy)
1992

PENNEL & FLIPO

384 rue d'Alger, F-59052 Roubaix Cedex 1, France

Tel: +33 20 36 92 60
Telex: 820373F
Fax: +33 20 24 55 10

Philippe Lemyze, *Export Manager*

Pennel & Flipo, a subsidiary of Vev Prouvost, employs 600 people. This 60 year old company has concentrated its considerable experience in developing a diverse range of products, and coatings based on the calendering and laminating of rubber, PVC and polyurethane.

Hypalon rubber-coated fabrics are produced for inflatable boats, either on a polyamide-base enka nylon or on a high-tenacity polyester trevira. A whole range of neoprene-coated fabrics has been produced for general use including hovercraft skirt applications. Finished weights for the various materials are in the range of 950 to 2,500 g/m^2.

Polyurethane-coated fabrics are available from 145 to 1,500 g/m^2.

VERIFIED

SPAIN

NEUMAR SA

La Rinconada, B-6, E-28023 Madrid, Spain

Tel: +34 (1) 548 2071
Fax: +34 (1) 547 4696

M de la Cruz, *Technical Director*
J A Barbeta, *Manufacturing Manager*

Neumar SA specialises in the research, development and design of air cushion lift systems, and in the manufacture of flexible structures for hovercraft.

The company was formed to bring together a group of engineers and technicians all of whom had previous experience in hovercraft technology. Of this previous experience it is worth mentioning the research and development, design and manufacture of the hovercraft lift system and skirt for the

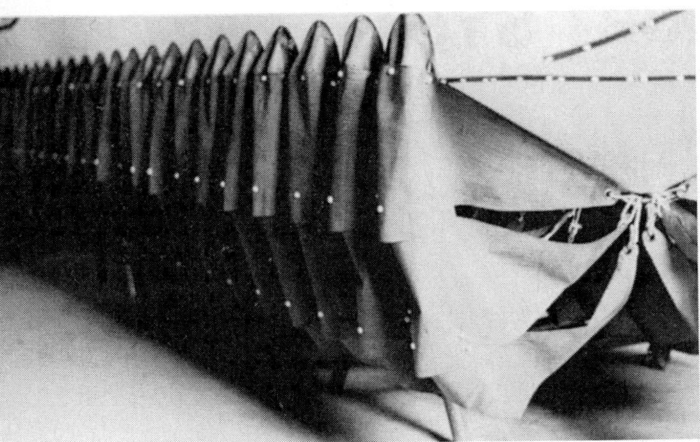
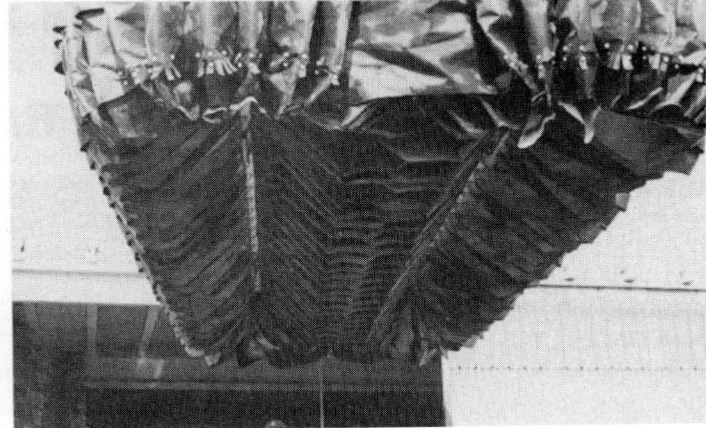

Two views of the Neumar skirt system developed to secure high stability with low power requirements ***1986***

company Chaconsa under a contract for the Spanish Ministry of Defence.

Neumar has developed a hovercraft lift system offering very high stability with low power requirements and reduced manufacturing and maintenance costs. It has been called an Automatic Transversal Air Distribution or ATAD lift system because of the main function it performs. Several two-dimensional models and two prototypes have been built and tested, with which the viability of this new lift system has already been demonstrated. The ATAD lift system is described in detail in the *Air Cushion Vehicles* section under the Neumar SA entry.

VERIFIED

UNITED KINGDOM

AIR CUSHION LTD

Unit 4SW, Marchwood Industrial Park, Marchwood, Southampton, Hampshire SO40 4PB, UK

Tel: +44 (1703) 870077
Fax: +44 (1703) 870044

J D Hake, *Chairman (USA)*
P Auston, *Director*
D Gosden, *Operations Director*

Air Cushion Limited (ACL) specialises in the manufacture of flexible structures, mainly for the hovercraft industry. The company produces skirts for hovercraft manufacturers all over the world, for craft ranging from small two-seaters to large hoverbarges.

As hovercraft skirts are an integral part of a system, the ACL design contribution varies from skirt design to full-scale development of the craft manufacturer's own design. In all cases, templates are produced and held by ACL. As a result of the company's long period of involvement with the hovercraft industry, it is able to advise on material suitability, manufacturing techniques and assembly methods.

The new ACL factory in Southampton has equipment capable of making hot bonded (vulcanised) seams up to 5.18 m long and bonding areas up to 2.44 × 1.22 m in one operation. The workshops are fitted with an extraction system which allows large areas to be safely coated with adhesives associated with cold bonding. The company also possesses long-arm sewing machines and HF welding equipment which is in continuous use for the manufacture of flexible tanks and inflatables for use in boats and other applications. These are marketed under the trade name 'Stowaway'.

A wide range of material is stocked coated with neoprene, natural rubber, hypalon, nitrile, polyurethanes, PVC and others. Material weights range from 170 to 3,500 g/m^2.

UPDATED

AVON TECHNICAL PRODUCTS

Melksham, Wiltshire SN12 8AA, UK

Tel: +44 (1225) 791823
Telex: 44142 AVOMEL G
Fax: +44 (1225) 705585

P D Miller, *Managing Director*
J E Fitzgerald, *General Manager*
P S Smart, *Sales Manager, ACV*
M E Prentice, *Design Engineer, ACV*

Avon Technical Products Division has facilities to provide the comprehensive design, development, manufacture and material supply services to craft manufacturers and operators. Present development programmes include investigations relating to the design of seals for SES vehicle ferries and fast cargo craft.

The majority of Avon air cushion skirt materials are coated with natural synthetic rubber blends, or neoprene rubber calendered on to specially selected base fabrics. Avon can also provide plied materials from their range, with two or more layers of base fabrics to increase the mechanical properties to satisfy the requirements of certain components within the structure of the skirts.

Avon can offer special experience in the design of the attachments of skirts to craft and attachments between flexible components. Mechanical fastenings for these purposes are stocked and can be offered when these form part of a seal. In the design of skirt components Avon provides for the rapid attachment and removal of all parts during maintenance periods.

Applications of Avon skirt materials include the following:

SR. N4 Mk 2 and Mk 3 (BHC)

Avon has been sole supplier of fingers (segments) for all of the SR. N4 Mk 2 and Mk 3 craft, operated by Hoverspeed, having first supplied to Hoverspeed's predecessors (Hoverlloyd and Seaspeed) in 1972. Avon also supplied and developed fingers for Hoverlloyd and Seaspeed SR. N4 Mk 1 craft dating back to 1969. Avon's involvement over the years has led to major increases in finger life, and has provided a high throughput testbed for the development of improved coated fabric materials and bonding systems.

LCAC (Textron Marine Systems)

Involvement with this programme started in 1980. Avon is an approved supplier of materials for the skirt system on this craft and, in conjunction with Bell Avon, has been heavily involved in the development and manufacture of components for all ship sets to date.

HM5/HM2 (Hovermarine International)

Avon developed the new bow and stern seals for the four HM5 SES craft which operate on the route between Hong Kong and Macau and has supplied materials and components.

BH 110 SES-Bell Halter (now Textron Marine Systems)

Avon has been sole supplier of bow and stern seals for Bell Halter's BH 110 craft since development craft were produced. It has also been manufacturing and developing components for the prototype since 1979, until the establishment of Bell Avon in the USA.

CIRR 105 (Brødrene Aa A/S)

The detailed design of seals for the *Norcat* fast ferry air cushion catamaran (SES) was undertaken in 1984 and included the geometric and structural design of the flexible components and their attachments to the craft. Since then Avon has manufactured seals for all successive craft of this type and supplied seals to their customers for operation in various parts of the world.

UT904 (Ulstein International A/S)

Supplier of bow and stern seals for the UT904 vessels (first delivered in 1991), using novel materials to improve stability of the stern seal.

Karlskronavarvet AB

Avon was awarded a contract in 1987 for the design and supply of the seal system for the two Jet Rider 3400 craft, followed by contracts for the SES 4000 vessels built by Westmarin A/S.

AP1-88 (Westland and licensees)

Avon has supplied all types of material for this craft since its inception, and now manufactures skirts under contract to Westland Aerostructures.

SES SEASWIFT 23 (Royal Schelde)

Design and supply of seals in 1988-89.

CORSAIR (Blohm+Voss AG)

Design and supply of seals for the Corsair SES test craft.

SMYGE (Karlskronavarvet/Kockoms AB)

Development of materials with special underwater signature properties and the manufacture of seals for the SMYGE Test Craft 1990-91, plus spares and replacements.

MCMV (Royal Norwegian Navy)

Supply of bow and stern seals plus spares and replacements.

Samsung Heavy Industries

Supply of bow and stern seals plus spares for 37 m SES.

UT 928 (Oceanfast Ferries Pty Ltd)

Supply of bow and stern seals.

UPDATED

BRITISH HOVERCRAFT CORPORATION LTD

Division of GKN Westland Aerospace

East Cowes, Isle of Wight PO32 6RH, UK

Tel: +44 (1983) 294101
Telex: 86781 WAD G
Fax: +44 (1983) 298872

C C Gustar, *Managing Director, GKN Westland Aerospace*
J M George, *Commercial Director*

BHC has been producing hovercraft for over 35 years, which has involved a great deal of research, particularly in the design and manufacture of flexible skirts. BHC has also designed skirt systems for other builders and, most notably, was responsible for the design of the skirts for the LACV-30 and LCAC.

BHC continues to design flexible skirt systems and conduct hydrodynamic testing. The manufacturing of the company's skirts is now subcontracted, under strict BHC quality control, to specialist rubber fabricators, principally SMR Technologies Inc and Avon Industrial Polymers.

VERIFIED

GREENGATE POLYMER COATINGS LTD

Greengate Works, Greengate, Manchester M3 7WS, UK

Tel: +44 (161) 834 5652
Fax: +44 (161) 834 1497

E J Thomas, *Sales and Marketing Director*
R W Collier, *Technical Manager*
P Keast, *Business Manager*

GPC manufactures many high-performance fabrics for hovercraft uses including buoyancy tubes, skirt, finger (segment) and ancillary applications.

UPDATED

Example materials:

GPC quality	Composition	Total weight (g/m²)	Breaking strength (kg/50 mm width)	Tear strength (kg)
1,188	Neoprene/Nylon	375	100	57.5
6,816	Natural rubber/Nylon	620	250	20
2,026	Neoprene/Nylon	1,040	275	20
3,144	Neoprene/Nylon	1,200	450	35
3,504	Hypalon/Nylon	1,300	300	25

Tiger 4 hovercraft with GPC skirt ***1986***

NORTHERN RUBBER COMPANY LTD

A Member of the Tomkins plc Group

Retford, Nottinghamshire DN22 6HH, UK

Tel: +44 (1777) 706731
Fax: +44 (1777) 709739

D E P Owen, *Managing Director*
W J Newbold, *Technical Director*
M Thompson, *Sales and Marketing Director*
K D Bacon, *Assistant Director Sales*
J Stanfield, *Sales*

The Northern Rubber Company has worked in co-operation with many major constructors of hovercraft around the world, supplying skirt materials, components and complete fabrications for lightweight sport vehicles to some of the largest craft currently in service.

Experience gained during initial development of skirt fabrics in the UK, together with continuing development closely matched to the requirements of constructors and operators, has led to an established range of materials used for the complete requirements of skirt structures. This includes fingers (segments), cones, loops, doublers, spray suppressors, anti-bounce webs and so on.

Recent applications for Northern Rubber's materials include:

Seaswift 23 SES fitted with Northern Rubber natural rubber/polybutadiene coated nylon skirt ***1992***

Royal Schelde Seaswift 23 SES

Northern Rubber has supplied the skirt bow segments for this SES. The material used is a multilayer construction of natural rubber/polybutadiene, sandwiched with a specially designed nylon fabric producing a tough semi-flexible material 3 mm thick.

SR. N4 Series British Hovercraft Corporation (BHC)

Northern Rubber supplies materials used extensively on the above series, having been closely involved with BHC during the development of the skirt system for the SR. N4 Mk 1 which came into service in 1969. Hoverspeed as operators continue to use Northern Rubber materials in the maintenance of these skirts.

SR. N6 Series (BHC)

Both civil and military variants of this series have incorporated skirt materials from the Northern Rubber range. The abilities of the materials to withstand the most rigorous operating conditions has contributed to the development of the SR. N6 Mk 6 which features significantly enhanced all-weather performance and improved manoeuvrability partly due to skirt construction in which Northern Rubber materials feature.

AP1-88 (BHC)

Northern Rubber currently supplies skirt component materials to the UK and overseas constructors and operators of the AP1-88.

HM5/HM2 Series (Hovermarine International)
Many of these craft are in service in the Far East with the Hong Kong and Yaumati Ferry Company on routes to Macao and China, where Northern Rubber skirt fabrics perform under conditions of high utilisation.

PUC 22 C (*Larus*) (*Wärtsilä*)
The complete skirt system for *Larus* was fabricated by Northern Rubber, and completed in a restricted period to schedule. On transfer to Canada, the craft underwent modification to allow operation in temperatures as low as −50°C, temperatures which caused no detrimental effects on the skirt or the flexibility and integrity of its materials.

Materials: The range of composite flexible materials is manufactured in combinations of natural rubber or neoprene polymer and nylon substrates. All materials are tested in accordance with the highest standards covered by BS 4F100, but to properly demonstrate the adhesive properties of the hovercraft materials, Northern Rubber has developed a system of testing the materials which gives results related to closely monitored representative conditions.

Neoprene composite materials have outstanding oil and ozone resistance, and good low temperature flexibility down to −30°C. Natural rubber composite materials combine excellent abrasion resistance and lower temperature flexibility to −51°C.

VERIFIED

Properties of Northern Rubber Skirt Materials

	Breaking Strength	Tear Strength Across	Adhesion Peel	Total Weight	Width
NR-11 520-12 ozs (410 g/m²) Neoprene					
Use: Skirt and finger segments for use on two- and four-seated Hovercraft					
Warp	1,200 N/25 mm	225 N	44 N/25 mm	410 g/m²	1,370 mm
Weft	1,200 N/25 mm	225 N	44 N/25 mm	410 g/m²	1,370 mm
NR-11 323-28 ozs (950 g/m²) Neoprene					
Use: Segment fabric for hover trailers and also inflatable craft					
Warp	1,780 N/25 mm	310 N	66 N/25 mm	950 g/m²	1,370 mm
Weft	1,780 N/25 mm	310 N	66 N/25 mm	950 g/m²	1,370 mm
NR-11 111-40 ozs (1,360 g/m²) Neoprene					
Use: Finger segments for use on sidewall hovercraft					
Warp	2,200 N/25 mm	880 N	110 N/25 mm	1,360 g/m²	1,270 mm
Weft	2,000 N/25 mm	830 N	110 N/25 mm	1,360 g/m²	1,270 mm
NR-C11 569-40 ozs (1,360 g/m²) Neoprene					
Use : Skirt segments for hovercraft. Water skates and heavy load trailers					
Warp	2,200 N/25 mm	620 N	110 N/25 mm	1,360 g/m²	1,370 mm
Weft	2,000 N/25 mm	570 N	110 N/25 mm	1,360 g/m²	1,370 mm
NR-C11 533-60 ozs (2,040 g/m²) Neoprene					
Use: Finger segments for sidewall hovercraft, also segments for water skates					
Warp	2,200 N/25 mm	800 N	110 N/25 mm	2,040 g/m²	1,320 mm
Weft	2,000 N/25 mm	800 N	110 N/25 mm	2,040 g/m²	1,320 mm
NR-C10 863-74 ozs (2,515 g/m²) Neoprene					
Use: Skirt and finger fabric for commercial passenger-carrying vehicles					
Warp	2,450 N/25 mm	800 N/25 mm	130 N/25 mm	2,515 g/m²	1,270 mm
Weft	2,200 N/25 mm	800 N/25 mm	130 N/25 mm	2,515 g/m²	1,270 mm
NR-C11 843-83 ozs (2,800 g/m²) Natural Rubber					
Use: Skirt and finger fabric for commercial passenger-carrying vehicles					
Warp	3,800 N/25 mm	800 N/25 mm	200 N/25 mm	2,800 g/m²	1,270 mm
Weft	2,200 N/25 mm	800 N/25 mm	200 N/25 mm	2,800 g/m²	1,270 mm
NR-C11 184-85 ozs (2,890 g/m²) Neoprene					
Use: Skirt and finger fabric for commercial passenger-carrying vehicles					
Warp	4,000 N/25 mm	2,200 N	222 N/25 mm	2,890 g/m²	1,270 mm
Weft	3,800 N/25 mm	2,000 N	222 N/25 mm	2,890 g/m²	1,270 mm
NR-C11 828-90 ozs (3,000 g/m²) Natural Rubber					
Use: Skirt and segment fabric for heavy load transporters and passenger-carrying vehicles					
Warp	3,800 N/25 mm	2,200 N	200 N/25 mm	3,000 g/mW	1,270 mm
Weft	3,550 N/25 mm	2,200 N	200 N/25 mm	3,000 g/mW	1,270 mm
NR-C11 748-95 ozs (3,220 g/m²) Neoprene					
Use: Segments for heavy load transporters and passenger-carrying vehicles					
Warp	4,000 N/25 mm	2,200 N	222 N/25 mm	3,220 g/m²	1,270 mm
Weft	3,800 N/25 mm	2,000 N	222 N/25 mm	3,220 g/m²	1,270 mm
NR-C11 549-100 ozs (3,400 g/m²) Natural Rubber					
Use: Segments for heavy load transporters and passenger-carrying vehicles					
Warp	5,300 N/25 mm	3,100 N	222 N/25 mm	3,400 g/m²	1,270 mm
Weft	5,300 N/25 mm	3,100 N	222 N/25 mm	3,400 g/m²	1,270 mm
NR-C11 580-110 ozs (3,740 g/m²) Natural Rubber					
Use: Segments for heavy load transporters and passenger-carrying vehicles					
Warp	6,000 N/25 mm	4,000 N	222 N/25 mm	3,740 g/m²	1,270 mm
Weft	6,000 N/23 mm	4,000 N	222 N/25 mm	3,740 g/m²	1,270 mm

UNITED STATES OF AMERICA

BELL AVON INC

1200 Martin Luther King Jr Blvd, Picayune, Mississippi 39466-5427, USA

Tel: +1 (601) 799 1217
Fax: +1 (601) 799 1360

L Sipe, *President*
P Gene Smith, *Plant Superintendent*
P Inch, *Technical Manager*
M Toler, *Sales Office Manager*
K Stockstill, *Sales Administrator*

Bell Avon Inc is a joint venture between Avon Rubber Company Ltd and Textron Marine and Land Systems. As a subsidiary of Avon, Bell Avon has full access to the resources of the world's largest and most experienced manufacturer of hovercraft skirt materials. Avon has been producing coated fabrics since the 1920s and has been developing materials for hovercraft systems and other sophisticated applications since the 1960s.

In April of 1985, Bell Avon opened its facility in Picayune, Mississippi, as the only specialised manufacturer of hovercraft skirt systems in North America.

Textron Marine Systems LACV-30 for which Bell Avon has manufactured a new stern seal skirt configuration ***1987***

Bell Avon's facility in South Mississippi currently occupies over 50,000 ft² of manufacturing space. Specific manufacturing equipment includes:
High-precision hydraulic presses
Large beam presses
A range of 'C' frame presses
Thermoplastic welding machines
Dialectic welding equipment
Surface preparation machines
Die cutting presses
Specialised mixing equipment.

Manufacture and assembly is carried out at this purpose-built plant. Bell Avon utilises state-of-the-art bonding processes to produce an extremely well

Textron Marine Systems Landing Craft, Air Cushion (LCAC) for which Bell Avon has now become a major supplier of skirt systems and components **1995**

integrated composite structure. The proprietary thin adhesive layer provides considerably better flexural fatigue properties than bonding tapes.

Bell Avon, and its parent, Avon, offer full skirt design, including stress analysis, design appraisal, finite element analysis and reduced or full scale model testing.

Bell Avon is able to offer customers many refurbishment options for prolonging the life of skirt components, often at a fraction of the cost of a new component.

LCAC: The LCAC skirt comprises more than 80 different components, and is supplied to craft manufacturers as assembled segments for ease of installation. The skirt is developed from the conventional bag and finger design, utilising lock bolts to facilitate the changing of worn or damaged components. The skirt design embraces many differing weights of coated fabric and calendered sheet to arrive at the optimum combination of weight, flexibility and operational life. Coated fabric weights vary between 1,390 g/m^2 and 3,050g/m^2, and both natural and synthetic rubbers are used.

Bell Avon has rapidly become a major supplier of original equipment and spares for this programme. Since its inception, Bell Avon has produced, or has orders in hand to produce, over 72 of the original skirt sets used on the 91 LCACs currently operated or scheduled for construction.

Surface Effect Ships (SES): Bow fingers and stern seal components manufactured and assembled by Bell Avon have been installed on Bell Halter commercial craft operated in Egypt and South America, on US Coast Guard craft formerly based in Key West, Florida, on the US Navy's SES 200 and on the US Army corps of Engineers survey boat, *Rodolf.*

In 1990, the US Navy's SES 200 was upgraded by Textron Marine and Land Systems to include water-jet propulsion and a new three-lobe stern seal. The seal was designed utilising the vast experience gained from supplying the European SES market and in conjunction with Avon a new seal was fabricated. This seal has consistently exceeded all specification and craft requirements.

Commercial hovercraft: Bell Avon regularly works with customers on skirt design for both military and commercial ACVs. Skirt systems, utilising the vast range of coated fabrics available, have been produced for the Utility Air Cushion Vehicle (UACV) and the C7/FR7 craft designed and produced by Textron Marine and Land Systems. The C7 hovercraft is a commercial craft operating in Asia as a passenger craft for Freeport McMoran and the FR7 is used as a fire/rescue craft by the Singapore Aviation Authority.

UPDATED

MARINE ESCAPE SYSTEMS

Company Listing by Country

Australia
Liferaft Systems Australia Pty Ltd

Denmark
Viking Lifesaving Equipment

Norway
Selantic Industrier A/S

United Kingdom
ML Lifeguard Equipment Ltd
RFD Ltd

AUSTRALIA

LIFERAFT SYSTEMS AUSTRALIA PTY LTD (LSA)

5 Sunmont Street, Derwent Park, Tasmania 7009, Australia

Tel: +61 02 739277
Fax: +61 02 739281

Liferaft Systems Australia (LSA) manufacture inflatable marine escape systems specifically for use on high-speed ferries, covering a range of drop heights from 5 to 10 m.

The LSA MES deploys perpendicular to the ship side and an integral liferaft is arranged so that passengers can proceed down the slide and directly into the raft without transferring from a conventional platform. The liferaft can accommodate 100 passengers. A second independent liferaft can be deployed for evacuation of more than 100 people.

LIFERAFT

The 100 man liferaft is packed in a container 1.9 m by 0.9 m diameter and weighs 420 kg. Inflated, it has a length of 12.1 m, a width of 5.7 m and a height of 2.65 m. The raft contains a SOLAS B survival pack.

LSA inflatable marine escape system arrangement **1996**

SLIDE

The slide length supplied depends on the drop height required but the standard slide lengths are 10, 12, 14, 16, 18 and 20 m. The stowage for the 14 m slide and one integral liferaft has a length of 2.0 m, a depth of 1.2 m and a height of 1.8 m and weighs 680 kg.

NEW ENTRY

DENMARK

VIKING LIFESAVING EQUIPMENT A/S

PO Box 3060, 6710 Esbjerg V, Denmark

Tel: +45 76118100
Telex: 54114 VIKNGDK
Fax: +45 76118101

Viking supply two main inflatable marine escape systems: the MES ED 50 EP which is a single track slide for use with drop heights from 2.5 to 9 m, and the MES DD 100 EP which is a twin slide for drop heights of between 7 and 15 m. Both systems feature an inflatable slide which has at its base a circular inflatable platform. Passengers slide into this platform from where they then board the conventional liferafts.

LIFERAFT

The Viking inflatable liferafts each have a capacity of 50 persons. The rafts are housed as single units or as pairs (100 person capacity) in fibreglass containers mounted on stowage racks on deck.

SLIDE

The single track MES ED 50 EP slide is fabricated from 6 independent inflatable components and is supplied in lengths from 5 to 17 m. The evacuation platform at the base of the slide has a capacity for 50 people and may serve as an open liferaft when evacuation has been completed and the connections to the slide cut. The capacity of the slide is tailored to the specific requirements but this slide has been tested with 200 to 250 passengers being evacuated in under 30 minutes.

The twin track MES DD 100 EP slide is fabricated from 8 independent inflatable components and is supplied in lengths from 12 to 28 m. The evacuation platform at the base of the slide has a capacity for 100 people and may serve as an open liferaft when evacuation has been completed and the connections to the slide cut. The capacity of the slide is tailored to the specific requirements but this slide has been tested with 400 to 450 passengers being evacuated in under 30 minutes.

Both slides are supplied in a stowage box designed for simple access, installation and maintenance.

NEW ENTRY

Viking MES DD 100 EP twin track marine escape system **1996**

NORWAY

SELANTIC INDUSTRIER AS

Selje, N-6740, Norway

Tel: +47 57856350
Fax: +47 57856515

Selantic supply a vertical descent MES known as the SES-3 (Selantic Evacuation System) based on the patented Selantic chute. The system has no height limitation and the single stowage contains all required chutes, platforms and liferafts.

The chute is constructed from a netting material and is deployed vertically downwards which provides for a lightweight system and a simple physical arrangement. The SES-3 stowage has a height of 2.2 m, a length of 2.6 m and a depth of 1.32 m. The weight of the complete single chute system is approximately 2,000 kg. This system can evacuate 350 passenger in under 30 minutes. A twin chute system can evacuate 400 passengers in under 20 minutes.

NEW ENTRY

Selantic SES-3 vertical descent MES
1996

UNITED KINGDOM

ML LIFEGUARD EQUIPMENT LTD

292 Leigh Road, Trading Estate, Slough, Berkshire, SL1 4BD, UK

Tel: +44 1753 523838
Fax: +44 1753 532444

Nigel Evans, *Sales and Marketing Director*

ML Lifeguard are well known for their range of defence, marine and aerospace safety equipment. In 1994 the company was awarded the contract to develop, approve and supply a new inflatable MES for the Stena HSS 1500 class of fast ferries.

Whilst few details have been released, the system comprises a twin track 25 m slide at the base of which are attached two integral 135 man liferafts. Two further rafts are deployed bringing the total evacuation capacity of one slide to over 500 passengers.

The ML MES underwent sea trials in early 1996 and is due to be fitted to the Stena HSS prior to arrival in UK waters.

NEW ENTRY

RFD LTD

Kingsway, Dunmurry, Belfast, Northern Ireland, BT17 9AF, UK

Tel: +44 1232 301531
Telex: 747264 RFDBFS
Fax: +44 1232 621765

RFD Ltd manufacture and supply a range of marine and aviation survival systems and was the first company worldwide to supply inflatable marine escape systems (MES). For fast craft, the company supply both single and twin track inflatable MES. The single track slide is for use where drop heights are less than 6 m and the twin track slides have a maximum drop height of 16.5 m.

The RFD MES is supplied in a self-contained steel or aluminium container which can be bolted to the ship structure with minimal installation time.

LIFERAFT

The liferafts are independent to the slide and consist of two 50 man rafts joined to form a 100 man raft and stowed in a single container. This 100 man liferaft pack is 2.0 m long, 1.0 m diameter and weighs 575 kg. Inflated the liferaft is 6.6 m long, 5.3 m wide and 2.6 m high.

SLIDE

The slide is deployed at an angle of approximately 30° to the ship side. The passengers slide down into a 7.5 m, self-draining circular platform at its base from where they can board RFD 100 man liferafts. The platform can also be used to provide secondary capacity for up to 104 passengers.

NEW ENTRY

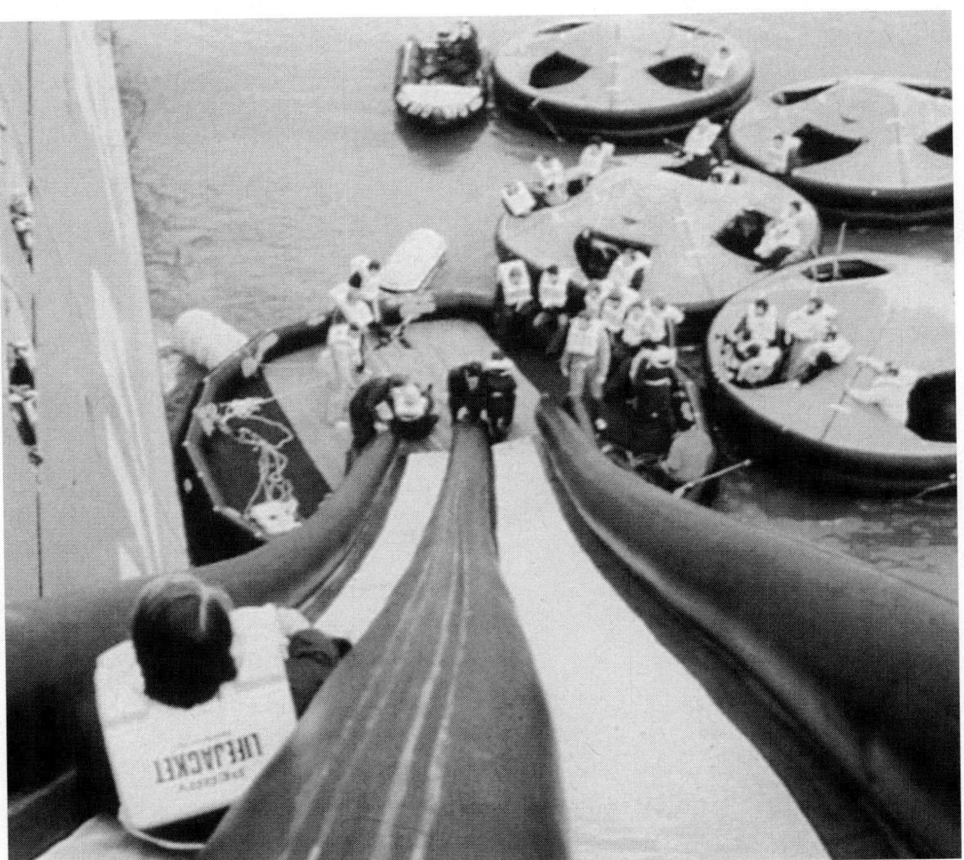

RFD inflatable twin track marine escape system
1996

FAST RESCUE TENDERS

Company Listing by Country

Australia
KBM
NAiAD Rigid Inflatables

Chile
Asmar

France
Zodiac International

Germany
DSB (Deutsche Schlauchboot)

Italy
Novurania SpA

New Zealand
Lancer Industries Ltd

Spain
Duarry

United Kingdom
Avon Inflatables Ltd
Dunlop Marine Safety Ltd
Halmatic Ltd
ML Lifeguard Ltd
Ribtec Ltd
RTK Marine

United States of America
Ambar Marine Inc
Boston Whaler Inc

AUSTRALIA

KBM PTY LTD

Unit 4, 14 Anella Avenue, Castel Hill, NSW 2154, Australia

Tel: +61 2 899 7011
Fax: +61 2 899 7025

David Sheil, *Sales Manager*

KBM Pty Ltd supply a range of unflatable products including a 9.0 m fast rescue craft, a version of which is in service with the Australian armed forces.

KBM Raider
1996

Craft supplied

Model	Length Overall (m)	Beam Overall (m)	Tube Dia (mm)	No of Compart-ments	Boat Weight (kg)	Capacity (weight) (kg)	Capacity (persons)	Maximum Engine Power (kW)	Approx Speed (knots)
Raider	9.0 m	3.0 m	575	—	3,900	1,600	15	—	38

NEW ENTRY

NAiAD RIGID INFLATABLES

147 Randall Road, Wynnum, Queensland 4178, Australia

Tel: +61 7 3893 1445
Fax: +61 7 3893 2852

J Ferguson, *Director Marketing*
E Boast, *Director Production*

NAiAD produce aluminium hulled inflatable rescue craft for diving and rescue operations. SOLAS approval has been applied for.

NAiAD 5.8 XL
1996

Craft supplied

Model	Length Overall (m)	Beam Overall (m)	Tube Dia (mm)	No of Compart-ments	Boat Weight (kg)	Capacity (weight) (kg)	Capacity (persons)	Maximum Engine Power (kW)	Approx Speed (knots)
NAiAD 4.3 XL	4.30	1.90	440	3	135	—	9	30	—
NAiAD 4.8	4.8	2.15	440	3	255	—	13	70	—
NAiAD 5.0 XL	5.0	2.15	440	3	265	—	13	70	—
NAiAD 5.3 XL	5.3	2.15	440	3	280	—	14	75	—
NAiAD 5.8 XL	5.8	2.15	440	3	310	1,100	10	90	—
NAiAD 6.8	6.8	2.6	550	5	700	1,700	—	220	—
NAiAD 8.0	8.0	2.6	550	5	825	2,000	—	220	—

NEW ENTRY

CHILE

ASMAR

PO Box 150-V, Avenida Altamirano 1015, Valparaiso, Chile

Tel: +56 32 259427
Telex: 230527 CL
Fax: +56 32 214032

Claudio Pelaez, *Sales Manager*

ASMAR Shipbuilding and Docking Company manufactures a range of fast rescue craft constructed from GRP with a flexible, inflatable collar. The company is currently developing a 5.8 m and 9.00 m version for rescue purposes.

PUMAR 540 R
1996

Craft supplied

Model	Length Overall (m)	Beam Overall (m)	Tube Dia (mm)	No of Compart-ments	Boat Weight (kg)	Capacity (weight) (kg)	Capacity (persons)	Maximum Engine Power (kW)	Approx Speed (knots)
PUMAR 420 W	4.20	1.73	450	3	110	595	7	30	32
PUMAR 540 W/R	5.40	1.96	500	5	300	1,100	11	56	35
ASMAR 1160	12.66	10.78	—	—	7,200	—	36	—	25

NEW ENTRY

FRANCE

ZODIAC INTERNATIONAL

58 Boulevard Gallieni, 92137, Issy-Les-Moulineaux Cedex, France

Tel: +33 1 45 54 92 80
Fax: +33 1 45 57 96 72

Mark Hart, *Sales Manager*

Zodiac International supply a very wide range of industrial inflatable products including a range of SOLAS approved fast rescue craft.

Zodiac RIBI 6 (SOLAS)
1996

Craft supplied

Model	Length Overall (m)	Beam Overall (m)	Tube Dia (mm)	No of Compart-ments	Boat Weight (kg)	Capacity (weight) (kg)	Capacity (persons)	Maximum Engine Power (kW)	Approx Speed (knots)
RB 4	3.80	1.75	455	5	100	540	4	7.5	–
RB 6	4.70	1.90	500	5	150	1,000	6	29	–
RIBO 6	4.70	2.08	500	5	240	1,000	6	29	–
RIBI 6	4.70	2.08	500	5	400	1,000	6	22	–
RIBO 9	5.30	2.34	520	5	310	1,250	9	59	–
RIBI 9	5.30	2.34	520	5	600	1,300	9	55	–

NEW ENTRY

GERMANY

DSB (DEUTSCHE SCHLAUCHBOOT)

A member of the Contitech Group

PO Box 1169, Angerweg 5, D-37628 Eschershausen, Germany

Tel: +49 5534 3010
Telex: 965 331

The DSB rescue boats have been developed in accordance with the SOLAS/IMO regulations and are approved by a number of shipping authorities for use as ships rescue boats.

DSB Zephyr 5.1SR
1996

Craft supplied

Model	Length Overall (m)	Beam Overall (m)	Tube Dia (mm)	No of Compart-ments	Boat Weight (kg)	Capacity (weight) (kg)	Capacity (persons)	Maximum Engine Power (kW)	Approx Speed (knots)
DSB 420 IRB	4.20	1.80	460	5	110	600	6	30	–
DSB 470 IRB	4.70	1.98	500	5	145	700	7	37	–
Zephyr 5.1SR	5.10	2.05	450	5		1,300	10	62	–

NEW ENTRY

ITALY

NOVURANIA SpA

Via Circonvallazione 3, I-38079, Tione Di Trento, Italy

Tel: +39 465 321162
Fax: +39 465 321551

Novurania supply a range of inflatable rescue and workboat craft. The rescue craft are SOLAS approved (whitecap range and MOB SOLAS). The MOB 570 SOLAS are powered by inboard engines and water-jets.

Novurania MOB 570 SOLAS
1996

Craft supplied

Model	Length Overall (m)	Beam Overall (m)	Tube Dia (mm)	No of Compart-ments	Boat Weight (kg)	Capacity (weight) (kg)	Capacity (persons)	Maximum Engine Power (kW)	Approx Speed (knots)
Whitecap 330	3.30	1.58	420	3	70	–	4	20	–
Whitecap 360	3.60	1.63	430	3	78	–	5	20	–
Whitecap 390	3.90	1.75	450	3	85	–	6	30	–
MOB 500	5.05	2.07	500	5	220	1,100	8	50	–
MOB 570	5.70	2.30	540	5	351	1,500	8	100	–
MOB 650	6.50	2.76	580	5	583	2,050	12	170	–
MOB 500 SOLAS	5.02	2.10	500	5	560	–	6	50	25
MOB 570 SOLAS	5.70	2.30	540	5	1,335	–	6	85	28

NEW ENTRY

NEW ZEALAND

LANCER INDUSTRIES LTD

PO Box 83136, Edmonton, Auchland, New Zealand

Tel: +64 9 8371206
Fax: +64 9 8371208

R Winstone, *Technical Director*

Lancer Industries manufactures inflatable products for the defence and commercial industry sectors including SOLAS and USCG approved rescue craft.

Lancer R750
1996

Craft supplied

Model	Length Overall (m)	Beam Overall (m)	Tube Dia (mm)	No of Compart-ments	Boat Weight (kg)	Capacity (weight) (kg)	Capacity (persons)	Maximum Engine Power (kW)	Approx Speed (knots)
R470	4.70	–	–	–	–	–	–	–	–
R750	7.50	–	–	–	–	–	–	–	–

NEW ENTRY

SPAIN

DUARRY

Astilleros Neumaticos Duarry SA

Pasaje Rosers, S/N-08940, Curnellà de Llobregat, Barcelona, Spain

Tel: +34 375 65 05
Telex: 57408
Fax: +34 375 76 03

Juan Forgas Duarry, *Director*

Duarry manufacture a range of fast rescue craft and liferafts approved for SOLAS use.

Duarry Cormoran 730
1996

Craft supplied

Model	Length Overall (m)	Beam Overall (m)	Tube Dia (mm)	No of Compart-ments	Boat Weight (kg)	Capacity (weight) (kg)	Capacity (persons)	Maximum Engine Power (kW)	Approx Speed (knots)
Brio 520 MFB	5.15	2.17	500	5	135	–	6	50	40
Cormoran 730	7.30	2.75	550	7	1,400	–	18	150	35

NEW ENTRY

UNITED KINGDOM

AVON INFLATABLES LIMITED

Dafen, Llanelli, Dyfed, SA14 8NA, UK

Tel: +44 1554 74115
Fax: +44 1554 741500

Geoffrey Tetley, *Military and Commerical Sales Manager*

Avon pioneered the development of inflatable craft for military and commercial applications and are in service worldwide with navies, coastguards, rescue organisations and as ships boats.

Avon SR7.4M in use with the US Navy
1996

Craft supplied

Model	Length Overall (m)	Beam Overall (m)	Tube Dia (mm)	No of Compart-ments	Boat Weight (kg)	Capacity (weight) (kg)	Capacity (persons)	Maximum Engine Power (kW)	Approx Speed (knots)
SR4M	4.05	1.80	430	3	159	650	6	40	30
SR4.7M	4.70	2.03	600	4	250	700	8	50	36
SR5.4M	5.43	2.03	500	5	320	750	10	70	38
SR6M	6.05	2.34	510	7	680	1,125	15	135	40
SR6.4M	6.40	2.39	500	7	1,272	1,275	17	165	36
SR6.4MD	6.40	2.39	500	7	1,361	1,275	17	150	30
SR7.4M	7.47	2.62	560	7	1,710	1,500	20	210	50
SR7.4MD	7.47	2.62	560	7	2,000	1,500	20	180	34
SR8.4M	8.38	2.84	560	7	2,350	1,650	24	335	50
SR8.4MD	8.38	2.84	560	7	3,690	1,000	24	315	38

NEW ENTRY

DUNLOP MARINE SAFETY LTD

A member of Dunlop-Beaufort Ltd

Beaufort Road, Birkenhead, Merseyside, L41 1HQ, UK

Tel: +44 151 653 6464
Telex: 629478
Fax: +44 151 652 8276

David Price, *Sales Manager*

Dunlop-Beaufort have been a leading manufacturers of inflatable rescue boats for over 40 years and supply a range of SOLAS approved craft.

Dunlop-Beaufort RB6RC craft
1996

Craft supplied

Model	Length Overall (m)	Beam Overall (m)	Tube Dia (mm)	No of Compart-ments	Boat Weight (kg)	Capacity (weight) (kg)	Capacity (persons)	Maximum Engine Power (kW)	Approx Speed (knots)
RB6	4.50	2.07	500	5	190	–	6	15	–
RB6R	4.50	2.07	500	5	240	–	6	20	–
RB6RC	4.50	2.07	500	5	250	–	6	30	–

NEW ENTRY

HALMATIC LTD

A member of Hunting Plc

Saxon Wharf, Lower York Street, Northam, Southampton, SO14 5QF,UK

Tel: +44 1703 337477
Fax: +44 1703 337478

Mike Burnham, *Sales Director*

Halmatic are another well-known supplier of high-quality fast rescue craft to the military and commercial marine industry sector. They supply a wide range of approved rescue craft. The Arctic and Atlantic range of craft are for use with outboard motors and the Pacific range for use with inboard diesel engines.

Halmatic fast rescue craft from their Arctic range
1996

Craft supplied

Model	Length Overall (m)	Beam Overall (m)	Tube Dia (mm)	No of Compart-ments	Boat Weight (kg)	Capacity (weight) (kg)	Capacity (persons)	Maximum Engine Power (kW)	Approx Speed (knots)
Arctic 18/20	5.50	2.24	–	–	725	–	10	90	37
Atlantic 21	6.48	2.60	–	–	1,100	–	15	90	30
Arctic 22	6.75	2.64	–	–	1,100	–	15	90	45
Arctic 24	7.32	2.64	–	–	1,500	–	20	150	40+
Arctic 28/30	9.15	2.44	–	–	1,850	–	20	300	40+
Pacific 22/24	7.32	2.59	–	–	1,800	–	10	220	35
Pacific 23/25	7.74	2.64	–	–	1,900	–	15	220	35
Pacific 28/30	9.15	2.97	–	–	2,200	–		375	40
Pacific 32	9.75	3.2	–	–	4,000	–	–	375	35
Pacific 36/38	11.6	3.73	–	–	7,600	–	–	410	30

NEW ENTRY

ML LIFEGUARD LTD

292 Leigh Road, Trading Estate, Slough, Berkshire, SL1 4BD, UK

Tel: +44 1753 523838
Fax: +44 1753 532444

Nigel Evans, *Sales and Marketing Director*

ML Lifeguard Equipment Ltd supplies safety and survival equipment and protective clothing for marine, defence and aerospace markets worldwide. The company's inflatable rescue boats are all SOLAS approved.

ML Lifeguard IR455
1996

Craft supplied

Model	Length Overall (m)	Beam Overall (m)	Tube Dia (mm)	No of Compartments	Boat Weight (kg)	Capacity (weight) (kg)	Capacity (persons)	Maximum Engine Power (kW)	Approx Speed (knots)
IB 395	3.95	1.73	460	5	127	740	4	7	17
IB 455	4.55	1.88	480	5	150	970	8	7	15
IR 455	4.55	1.88	480	5	180	935	6	20	20

NEW ENTRY

RIBTEC LTD

Hambleside, Shore Road, Swanwick, Southampton, SO31 7EF, UK

Tel: +44 1489 885773
Fax: +44 1489 885845

T J Wilks, *Managing Director*

Ribtec Ltd supplied fast semi-rigid inflatable craft for both military and commercial use.

Ribtec
1996

Craft supplied

Model	Length Overall (m)	Beam Overall (m)	Tube Dia (mm)	No of Compartments	Boat Weight (kg)	Capacity (weight) (kg)	Capacity (persons)	Maximum Engine Power (kW)	Approx Speed (knots)
Ribtec 455	4.55	2.05	440	5	210	–	–	50	–
Ribtec 535	5.37	2.05	440	5	275	–	–	70	–
Ribtec 585	5.90	2.28	485	5	310	–	–	95	–
Ribtec 600	6.10	2.28	485	5	400	–	–	110	–
Ribtec 645	6.50	2.30	485	5	445	–	–	150	–
Ribtec 700	7.35	2.55	495	5	490	–	–	225	–

NEW ENTRY

RTK MARINE

446 Blandford Road, Hamworthy, Poole, Dorset, BH16 5BL, UK

Tel: +44 1202 685581
Fax: +44 1202 683347

J E Pratchett, *Marketing Manager*

RTK Marine is well-known for its rugged series of workboats in service with a number of military and commercial organisations. In their wide range of craft, a SOLAS approved fast rescue craft is also available.

RTK FRC 606 outboard version
1996

Craft supplied

Model	Length Overall (m)	Beam Overall (m)	Tube Dia (mm)	No of Compart-ments	Boat Weight (kg)	Capacity (weight) (kg)	Capacity (persons)	Maximum Engine Power (kW)	Approx Speed (knots)
FRC 606 (inboard)	7.15	2.52	–	–	2,150	1,150	15	150	27
FRC 606 (outboard)	7.15	2.52	–	–	1,450	1,150	15	–	25

NEW ENTRY

UNITED STATES OF AMERICA

AMBAR MARINE INC

221 Rue de Jean, Suite 301, PO Box 51271 Lafayette, Louisiana 70505, USA

Tel: +1 318 237 5300
Fax: +1 318 232 9696

Peter Reeves, *Programme Director*

Ambar Inc produce a range of fast rescue tenders approved by SOLAS and manufactured by Bollinger Machine Shop and Shipyard Inc in aluminium. The ALsafe AM 900 is a 9 m, water-jet propelled craft powered by an inboard diesel engine. The ALsafe AM 700 and 550 craft can be configured with inboard or outboard engines.

The Ambar ALsafe AM 900 fast rescue craft
1996

Craft supplied

Model	Length Overall (m)	Beam Overall (m)	Tube Dia (mm)	No of Compart-ments	Boat Weight (kg)	Capacity (weight) (kg)	Capacity (persons)	Maximum Engine Power (kW)	Approx Speed (knots)
ALsafe AM 900	8.90	3.30	–	–	2,700	2,750	10	225	33
ALsafe AM 700	6.50	2.90	–	–	2,000	2,275	10	185	35
ALsafe AM 550	6.50	2.30	–	–	1,125	–	10	112	32

NEW ENTRY

BOSTON WHALER INC

Commerical Products Division, 4121 South US Highway One, Edgewater, Florida 32141-7221, USA

Tel: +1 904 4280057
Fax: +1 904 4287310

Terry Dunagin, *Sales Manager*

Boston Whaler supply a very wide range of small to large fast boats for military and commerical use, all built in GRP foam sandwich materials which render the craft unsinkable. Only the 'soft-sided' range of craft is described below.

Boston Whaler Impact 21
1996

Craft supplied

Model	Length Overall (m)	Beam Overall (m)	Tube Dia (mm)	No of Compart-ments	Boat Weight (kg)	Capacity (weight) (kg)	Capacity (persons)	Maximum Engine Power (kW)	Approx Speed (knots)
Impact 21	6.4	2.5	–	–	816	2,300	11	150	–

NEW ENTRY

SERVICES

Marine Craft Regulatory Authorities
Consultants and Designers
Societies involved with High-Speed Craft

MARINE CRAFT REGULATORY AUTHORITIES

ARGENTINA
Prefectura Naval Argentina
Avenida Madero 235
1106 Buenos Aires
Argentina

Tel: +54 (1) 318 7400/7500/7600
Fax: +54 (1) 314 0317/4913

Prefecto General Jorge Humberto Maggi, *Argentine Coast Guard Commandant*
Prefecto General Jorge Arnoldo Gentiluomo, *Deputy Commandant*

AUSTRALIA
ACVs and Hydrofoils
Covers interstate and international voyages. Smaller craft come under jurisdiction of state or local authorities.

Australian Maritime Safety Authority
Ship and Personnel Safety Services
PO Box 1108
Belconnen ACT 2616
Australia

Tel: +61 (62) 279 5048
Fax: +61 (62) 279 5966

T Rose, *Chief Marine Surveyor, Survey Operations*

New South Wales
Sydney Ports Corporation
Level 12
207 Kent Street
Sydney
New South Wales 2000
Australia
or
PO Box 25
Millers Point
Sydney
New South Wales 2000
Australia

Tel: +61 (2) 364 2999
Fax: +61 (2) 364 2742

Reg McGee, *Marine Operations Manager*

Northern Territory
Department of Transport and Works
Marine Branch
PO Box 2520
Darwin
Northern Territory 0801
Australia

Tel: +61 (89) 995285
Fax: +61 (89) 995300

Chris Bigg, *Director*

Queensland
Department of Primary Industries
PO Box 2454
Mineral House
George Street (Cnr Margaret Street)
Brisbane
Queensland 4001
Australia

Tel +61 (7) 3224 2279
Fax: +61 (7) 3229 6079

T Finn, *Manager*

South Australia
South Australian Ports Corporation
PO Box 19
Port Adelaide
South Australia 5015
Australia

Tel: +61 (8) 470611
Telex: 82525 AA
Fax: +61 (8) 470605

Tasmania
Navigation and Survey Authority of Tasmania
1 Franklin Wharf
PO Box 202B
Hobart
Tasmania 7001
Australia

Tel: +61 (02) 347122
Fax: +61 (02) 341329

Captain J W Lewis, *Superintendent*

Victoria
The Port of Melbourne Authority
PO Box 4721
Melbourne Victoria 3001
Australia

Tel: +61 (3) 611 1777
Telex: 34211 AA
Fax: +61 (3) 611 1905

Kingsley Culley, *Chairman*
John King, *Chairman/Chief Executive*
Peter Olszak, *General Manager Port Operations*
Mike McCarthy, *General Manager Finance and Admin*
Anthony Honeyborne, *Manager Port Operations*

BELGIUM
Ministere des Communications et de l'Infrastructure
Administration des Affaires Maritimes et de la Navigation
rue d'Arlon 104
B-1040 Brussels
Belgium

Tel: +32 (2) 233 1211
Telex: 61880 VERTRA B
Fax: +32 (2) 230 3002

CANADA
Transport Canada
Director General
Maritime Regulation Branch
Canadian Coast Guard
Canada Building
344 Slater Street
Ottawa
Ontario K1A 0N7
Canada

Tel: +1 (613) 998 0660
Fax: +1 (613) 991 5670

K Tue-Fee, *Senior Surveyor Hulls*
M Andrades, *Senior Surveyor Machinery*

Design approval and safety certification of all craft and operators complying with the IMO High-Speed Craft Code, and certification of personnel.

DENMARK
Danish Maritime Authority
Vermundsgade 38C
DK-2100 Copenhagen Ø
Denmark

Tel: +45 (39) 271515
Telex: 31141 SOFART DK
Fax: +45 (39) 271516

EGYPT
Egyptair
Cairo International Airport
Heliopolis
Cairo
Egypt

Fax: +20 (2) 245 3861

FIJI
Director of Marine
Marine Department
PO Box 326
Suva
Fiji

Tel: +679 315266
Fax: +679 303251

W Salu, *Director*
A Vata, *Assistant Director*

FINLAND
Board of Navigation
Vuorimiehenkatu 1
PO Box 158
SF-00141 Helsinki
Finland

Telex: 12-1471

FRANCE
Ministère de L'Equipment des Transports et Tourisme
3 Place de Fontenoy
F-75700 Paris 07SP
France

Tel: +33 (1) 44 49 80 00
Telex: 250 823 (Mimer Paris) F
Fax: +33 (1) 44 49 80 52 (général du Ministère)
Fax: +33 (1) 44 49 83 47 (Bureau de la Documentation et de l'Information)

GAMBIA
Gambia Ports Authority
Wellington Street
PO Box 617
Banjul
The Gambia

GERMANY
See-Berufsgenossenschaft
Ships Safety Department
Reimerstwiete 2
D-20457 Hamburg
Germany

Tel: +49 (40) 361370

GHANA
Shipping Commissioners
Division of Shipping and Navigation
Ministry of Transport and Communications
PO Box M38
Accra
Ghana

GREECE
Ministry of Mercantile Marine
Merchant Ships Inspectorate
Palaiologou 1 str
GR-18535 Piraeus
Greece

Tel: +30 (411) 1214
Telex: 212581 GR

V Stauropoulos, *Commodore*

HONG KONG
Director of Marine
Marine Department
Harbour Building
38 Pier Road
PO Box 4155
Hong Kong

Tel: +852 852 4512
Telex: 64553 MARHQ HX
Fax: +852 545 0556

HUNGARY
General Inspection for Transport
PO Box 102
H-1389 Budapest 62
Hungary

Tel: +36 (1) 22800/24290

István Tóth, *General Director*

ICELAND
Directorate of Shipping
PO Box 7200
Hringbraut 121
IS-127 Reykjavik
Iceland

Tel: +354 552 5844
Fax: +354 552 9835

INDIA
Directorate General of Shipping
Jahaz Bhavan
Walchand Hirchand Marg
Ballard Estate
Bombay 400 038
India

INDONESIA
Department of Transport, Communications and Tourism
8 Medan Merdelka Barat
Jakarta-Pusat
Indonesia

IRELAND
Department of the Marine
Leeson Lane
Dublin 2
Ireland

Tel: +353 (1) 785444
Telex: 618214

Thomas Wickham, *Maritime Safety Division*

ISRAEL
Ministry of Transport
Administration of Shipping and Ports
PO Box 33993
102 Ha'atzmauth Road
Haifa 33411
Israel

Tel: +972 (4) 520241
Telex: 46632
Fax: +972 (4) 511161

J Lapidas, *Chief Naval Architect*

ITALY
Ministero della Marina Mercantile
Ispettorato Tecnico
Viale Asia
I-00100 Rome
Italy

IVORY COAST
Ministère des Travaux Publics et des Transports
BP V6
Abidjan
Ivory Coast

JAMAICA
The Marine Board
c/o The Port Authority
15-17 Duke Street
Kingston
Jamaica

Tel: +1809 922 0290/8

Carrol Pickersgill, *Secretary Marine Board*

JAPAN
Japanese Ministry of Transportation
2-1-3 Kasumigaseki
Chiyoda-ku
Tokyo
Japan

KOREA, SOUTH
Bureau of Marine Transportation
Ministry of Transportation
1-3 Do Dong
Choong-ka
Seoul
South Korea

KUWAIT
Department of Customs and Ports
PO Box 9
Kuwait

Tel: +965 481 4371/2
Telex: US PTT 22197 KT

LEBANON
Ministère des Travaux Publics
Direction des Transports
Beirut
Lebanon

LUXEMBOURG
Ministère des Transports
19-21 boulevard Royal
L-2938 Luxembourg

Tel: +352 478-1
Telex: 1465 CIVAIR LU
Fax: +352 467790

Commissariat aux Affaires Maritimes
19-21 boulevard Royal
L-2938 Luxembourg

Tel: +352 479 4521
Fax: +352 465753

Service de la Navigation
36 route de la Machtum
L-6753 Grevenmacher
Luxembourg

Tel: +352 75048
Fax: +352 758822

MADAGASCAR
Direction des Transports Maritimes
101 Tananarive
BP 581
Madagascar

Tel: +261 25860
Telex: 22301 MTMT MG
Fax: +261 24001

MALAWI
Ministry of Transport and Communications
Chief Surveyor of Vessels
Private Bag 322
Lilongwe 3
Malawi

Tel: +265 730122 (Marine Department)
Fax: +265 733826

MALAYSIA
The Ministry of Transport
Wisma Perdana
Jalan Dungun
Damansara Heights
50616 Kuala Lumpur
Malaysia

Tel: +60 (3) 254 8122
Cables: MINCOM, KL
Telex: 30999 MA
Fax: +60 (3) 255 7041

MEXICO
Departamento de Licencias
Direction de Marina Mercante
SCT
Luerpo A
2 Piso
Mexico 12
Mexico

MOROCCO
Ministère de l'Equipement
Direction des Affaires Techniques
Rabat-Chellah
Morocco

NETHERLANDS
Ministry of Transport, Public Works and Water Management
Directorate General of Shipping and Maritime Affairs
PO Box 5817
2280 HV Rijswijk
Netherlands

Tel: +31 (70) 395 5555
Fax: +31 (70) 399 6274

NEW ZEALAND
Maritime Safety Authority of N.Z.
Level 8, AMP House
109 Featherstone Street
PO Box 27006
Wellington
New Zealand

Tel: +64 (4) 473 0111
Fax: +64 (4) 473 6699

High speed craft are subject to the ship construction and safety equipment (code of practice for new high-speed craft) notice, 1994.

NORWAY
Sjøfartsdirektoratet
Norwegian Maritime Directorate
Holbergs Terrasse
Stensberggt. 27
Oslo
Norway

Tel: +47 (22) 454500
Telex: 21557 SDIR N
Fax: +47 (22) 568780

SOUTH AFRICA
The Director General
Department of Transport
Chief Directorate Shipping
Private Bag X193
Pretoria 0001
South Africa

Tel: +27 (12) 290 9111
Fax: +27 (12) 323 7009

SPAIN
Dirección General de la Marina Mercante
C/ Ruiz de Alacrón, num 1
E-28014 Madrid
Spain

Tel: +34 (1) 580 1400
Telex: 43579 MAMER E
Fax: +34 (1) 522 2752

D Rafael Lobeto Lobo, *Director General*

SWEDEN
The National Maritime Administration
Sjofartsverket
S-601 78 Norrkoping
Sweden

Tel: +46 (11) 191000
Telex: 64380 SHIPADM S
Fax: +46 (11) 191049

K Janerus, *Director*

SWITZERLAND
Lake Constance
Kantonspolizei Thurgau Seepolizei
Bleichestrasse 42
PO Box 660
CH-8280 Kreuzlingen
Switzerland

Tel: +41 (72) 752222
Fax: +41 (72) 752284

Strassenverkehrs und Schiffahrtsamt des Kantons St Gallen
Abr. Schiffahrt
CH-9400 Rorschach
Switzerland

Tel: +41 (71) 411474

Kantonale Schiffahrtskontrolle
Rosengasse 8
CH-8200 Schaffhausen
Switzerland

Tel: +41 (53) 827604

Lake Geneva
République et Canton de Genève Service de la Navigation
Route de Veyrier 86
CH-1227 Carouge
Switzerland

Tel: +41 (22) 319 2754

Lake Lucerne
Strassenverkehrsamt des Kantons Luzern
Schiffsinspektorat
Obergrund
CH-6000 Luzern 4
Switzerland

Tel: +41 (41) 228 6111

Lake Lugano and Lake Locarno
Sezione della Circolazione
Ufficio amministrativo
Capo Servizio Navigazione
CH-6528 Camorino
Switzerland

E Regazzi, *Director*

Lake Neuchatel
Departement de Police
CH-2000 Neuchatel
Switzerland

Lake Thoune, Lake Brienz and Lake Biel
Strassenverkehrs-und Schiffahrtsamt des Kantons Bern
Schermenweg 5
PO Box
3001 Bern
Switzerland

Tel: +41 (31) 634 2111
Telex: 911520 sabe CH
Fax: +41 (31) 634 2680

Dr R Netzer, *Director*

Lake Zürich
Kantonspolizei Zürich
Seepolizei/Schiffahrtskontrolle
Seestrasse 87
CH-8942 Oberrieden
Switzerland

Tel: +41 (1) 720 7021

Oblt R Hotz, *Chief*

TURKEY
T C Denizcilik Müsteşarliği
Undersecretariat for Maritime Affairs
General Directorate for Maritime Transport
Anit Caddesi
No 8 Safak Apt
Tandogan
Ankara
Turkey

Tel: +90 312 212 8061
Fax: +90 312 212 8453

UNITED KINGDOM
UK Civil Aviation Authority
Hovercraft Certification, Issue of Type, Safety, Experimental and Export Certificates. Approval of persons or organisations from whom the CAA may accept reports on the design, construction, maintenance or repair of hovercraft or elements thereof. Approval of hovercraft items and equipment.
Publication of 'British Hovercraft Safety Requirements'
Technical enquiries to:

A C G Seal
Design Liaison Surveyor
Rotorcraft & Hovercraft Section
CAA Safety Regulation Group
Aviation House
Gatwick South
Gatwick
West Sussex RH6 OYR
UK

Tel: +44 (1293) 573294
Telex: 878753
Fax: +44 (1293) 573976

Publications:

Civil Aviation Authority
Printing and Publication Services
Greville House
37 Gratton Road
Cheltenham
Gloucestershire GL50 2BN
UK

Tel: +44 (1242) 235151
Fax: +44 (1242) 584139

UK Marine Safety Agency
Hovercraft Operating Permits and Registration
High-Speed Marine Craft

Marine Safety Agency
Spring Place
105 Commercial Road
Southampton
Hampshire SO15 1EG
UK

Tel: +44 (1703) 329140
Fax: +44 (1703) 329161

Capt A Esmiley, *Principal Marine Surveyor*

UNITED STATES OF AMERICA
Department of Transportation
Commandant (G-MMS-1)
US Coast Guard
Washington DC 20593-0001
USA

Tel +1 (202) 267 2997
Fax: +1 (202) 267 4816

VENEZUELA
Ministerio de Transporte y Comunicaciones
Dirección General Sectorial de Transporte Acuatico Dirreccion de Navegacion Acuatico
Caracas
Venezuela

YUGOSLAVIA (Serbia and Montenegro)
Federal Economic Secretariat
Transport Department
Bulevar AVNOJ-a 104
Belgrade
Serbia

CONSULTANTS AND DESIGNERS

Company Listing by Country

Australia
Advanced Multihull Designs Pty Ltd
Australian Maritime Engineering CRC Ltd
Crowther Multihulls Pty Ltd
International Catamaran Designs Pty Ltd (InCat)
Kamira Holdings Pty Ltd
Laubreaux Marine Design
Mark Ellis Design
Phil Curran Design
Stolkraft Pty Ltd

Belgium
Eurosense Hoversounding NV

Canada
D F Dickins Associates Ltd
Fleet Technology Ltd
Promaxis Systems Inc
Robert Allen Ltd
The Mariport Group Ltd

Commonwealth of Independent States
Forma Ltd
Kort
Sudoexport
Transal-Aks Engineering Co

Croatia
Brodoprojekt

Denmark
Jan Kjærulff Yacht Design

France
Bertin & Cie
Ifremer
Techni Carène

Germany
MTG Marinetechnik GmbH

Greece
National Technical University of Athens

Italy
Sciomachen

Japan
Masaru Ikeda Ship Consulting Office

Korea, South
Korea Research Institute of Ships and Ocean Engineering

Netherlands
Nevesbu

New Zealand
Malcolm Tennant Multihull Design

Norway
Amble & Stokke A/S
Camo
Cirrus Ship Design A/S
Ola Lilloe-Olsen
Paradis Nautica

Singapore
Swan Hunter Singapore Pte Ltd

Spain
Neumar SA
Ur Tekniks S.L.

Sweden
Marinteknik Design (E) AB
Pelmatic AB
SSPA Maritime Consulting AB

Switzerland
Dr Ing E G Faber Marine Engineering Consultant
Dipl Ing E Schatté
Supramar Ag

United Kingdom
Air Cushion Ltd
Air Vehicles Ltd
Associated & Marine Technology Ltd
Blyth Bridges Marine Consultants Ltd
BMT Group Ltd
Lorne Campbell
Maritime Services Ltd
Nigel Gee and Associates
Hovercraft Consultants Ltd
Hovercraft Development Ltd
Hovercraft Sales and Marketing
Hoverwork Ltd
Independent Maritime Assessment Associates Ltd
JCL High Speed Marine Craft Consultancy
John McNeece Ltd
Ray Harvey Design
Seaspeed Technology Ltd
Robert L Trillo
Wolfson Unit for Marine Technology and Industrial Aerodynamics, University of Southampton
W S Atkins Marine & Structural Technology

United States of America
Aero-Marine Engineering
Air Craft Corporation
Air Ride Craft Inc
Aquamarine, Inc
Band, Lavis & Associates Inc
Donald L Blount & Associates Inc
CGZ Design Inc
Davidson Laboratory Stevens Institute of Technology
Elliott Bay Design Group Ltd
Fast Hulls International Inc
Fryco Inc
Gibbs & Cox Inc
The Harbor Consultancy International
J B Hargrave Naval Architects Inc
J W Johnson Naval Architects
Raymond Hunt Associates Inc
MDI
Payne Associates
Quadrimaran International
M Rosenblatt & Son Inc
SSSCO
SWATH International Ltd
George C Sharp Inc
TGMD Inc

AUSTRALIA

ADVANCED MULTIHULL DESIGNS PTY LTD

55 Grandview Street, Pymble, Sydney, New South Wales 2073, Australia

Tel: +61 (2) 488 9877
Fax: +61 (2) 488 8144 (Administration)
Fax: +61 (2) 488 8466 (Technical)

John Szeto, *Managing Director*
Allan Soars, *Technical Director*
Bahram Ossivand, *Financial Controller*

Advanced Multihull Designs Pty Ltd was formed in late 1989 to specialise in the design of conventional fast catamarans, wave piercing catamarans and foil-assisted multihull craft.

The company has licensed eight builders in seven countries to build their designs, they are: Kawasaki Heavy Industries Ltd (Japan), Van der Giessen-de Noord NV (Netherlands), Constructions Mecaniques de Normandie (France), A Fai Engineers and Shiprepairers (Hong Kong), InCat (Australia), Dakota Creek Industries (USA), Freeport Shipbuilding (USA) and Hang Tong High-Speed Ship Development Co (China).

As of early 1996 the company had seven catamarans operating to its designs with a further two either under construction or on trials.

The largest wave piercing catamaran built to date, the AMD/Kawasaki Jet Piercer, was launched by Kawasaki in late 1994. The fastest car-carrying catamaran to date, the K55 ferry built by InCat Australia in Hobart, was also launched in late 1994.

A larger vessel of a similar design to the K55, code-named the K50, has also been designed by AMD for InCat Australia, and was delivered to Dae A Gosh Ferry Company of South Korea in 1995.

An AMD350 passenger-only wave piercing catamaran was recently completed at Astra Bay Enterprises in Fremantle, Australia. This is a 42.5 m vessel capable of carrying 350 passengers at speeds of up to 36 knots.

An AMD150 has recently been built by the Chinese licensee as has an AMD80 by A Fai in Hong Kong.

The company has a number of other designs available including the AMD2000, a 97 m wave piercing catamaran and the K40, a 58 m, 43 knot car-carrying design.

Details of AMD craft can be found under the headings of their builders/licensees.

K40 CAR/PASSENGER FERRY (DESIGN)

In January 1994 Incat Australia commissioned Advanced Multihull Designs Pty Ltd to design a budget car ferry design which would be suitable for short routes (10 to 30 n miles), where there is a volume of light vehicle and passenger traffic.

Specifications

Length overall	58 m
Beam	14.5 m
Draught	2.5 m
Passengers	351
Vehicles	42 cars
Max speed	43 kts
Operational speed	36 kts

Classification: +1A1 HSLC R3 Car Ferry 'B' EO.

Propulsion: The vessel will be powered by two medium-speed diesel engines, which will directly drive water-jet propulsors.

AMD2000 WAVE PIERCING CATAMARAN FERRY (DESIGN)

The AMD2000 is the largest of the AMD designs with a capacity for 900 passengers and 200 cars.

Specifications

Length overall	96.75 m
Length waterline	86 m
Beam	29.6 m
Draught	2.5 m (normal)
	3.3 m (max)
Crew	24
Passengers	874
Vehicles	196 cars or
	10 buses and 149 cars
Fuel capacity	240,000
Water capacity	20,000
Propulsive power	2 × 16,850 kW
Max speed	45 kts
Operational speed	40 kts

Classification: Lloyd's Register + 100 A1 HSC WPC Group 3.

Propulsion: Engines: two Rolls-Royce Spey SM1C gas-turbines, 16,850 kW each.
Thrust devices: four Kamewa 125 SII water-jets.

UPDATED

The new AMD350 vessel built by Astra Bay Enterprises (Australia) ***1996***

AUSTRALIAN MARITIME ENGINEERING CRC LTD

PO Box 986, Launceston, Tasmania 7250, Australia

Tel: +61 (03) 354875
Fax: +61 (03) 266261
E-mail: s.clark@crc.amd.edu.av

Don Lennard, *Executive Director*

The Australian Maritime Engineering Cooperative Research Centre (AMECRC) was established in July 1992 with the support of the Australian Government, Australian maritime engineering industries and a number of academic institutions. The centre provides a scientific and technological base for research and development in maritime engineering. It combines the specialist skills and resources of its participants and its work covers a wide range of Australia's maritime engineering services.

Recent export successes by Australia's burgeoning high-speed craft industry require stepped up research and development to underpin further advances into the large replacement market for world ferry fleets.

Present areas of research include:

Calm water performance of marine vehicles: Research in this field covers the hydrodynamic performance of marine vehicles and devices. This includes investigation of innovative high-speed craft forms, propellers and water-jets.

Ocean influence on ships and maritime structures: Research here includes dynamic loading, seakeeping, motion sickness and survivability.

Structural design and fabrication of ships and maritime structures: Included in this research topic are problems of lightweight maritime structures, the durability of these structures and new approaches to design and fabrication.

Ongoing research work includes the testing of a series of high-speed displacement ship hull forms and the prediction of wave making resistance of a catamaran in restricted water. AMECRC also carries out contract research: one major contract involved the design and installation of a ride control system for high-speed vessels including catamarans and monohulls in the Asia Pacific region.

Research Facilities

Cavitation Tunnel: working section 0.6 × 0.6 m, maximum speed 12 m/s.

Towing tank: 60 × 3.5 × 1.5 m (Australian Maritime College), maximum speed 4.5 m/s. Full-scale prediction can be carried out for powering in calm water and in waves, for seakeeping ability and for squat and bank interaction in shallow water.

Full scale trials: motions data acquisition system; ocean wave recorders; shaft power measurement; stabilised accelerometer platform; strain gauge suite.

UPDATED

CROWTHER MULTIHULLS PTY LTD

PO Box 204, Newport, Sydney, NSW 2106, Australia

Tel: +61 (2) 9970 8300
Fax: +61 (2) 9970 8023

Brett Crowther, *Director*

Crowther Multihulls has vast experience in all aspects of multihull design from efficient, high-performance catamaran ferries and large, luxurious power and sailing yachts through to smaller cruising craft and high-performance racing sailboats.

The company is an Australian Government approved research organisation and clients can be eligible for government grants (in Australia) on research and development work carried out by the office.

Designs completed in recent years include:

DMB, 22.4 m ketch-rigged pearling/diving catamaran (design no 73) of exceptional performance under sail and power;
Tafua, four 18 m luxury charter motor sailers (design no 58);
Southern Spirit, 29.9 m luxury motor sailer/yacht (design no 96 Mk II);
Ocean Spirit, 32 m tourist motor sailer yacht (design no 126);
Sunbird, Sunseeker and *Quickcat*, three 34 m high-speed passenger ferries (design nos 109, 117 and 132);
Kimberley Explorer, 34 m mini passenger liner catamaran (design no 120);
Xin Ning and *Shun Feng*, (lines, powering and developmental design for Precision Marine Holdings) two 39.7 m 36 knot water-jet passenger ferries (design no 155) for China;
Melanesian Discoverer, 35 m mini passenger liner catamaran for Papua New Guinea;
Reef Adventurer II, 33 m high-speed ferry (design no 136);
Capricorn Reefseeker, 35 m high-speed passenger ferry (design no142);
Majistic, 25 m 28 knot water-jet luxury motor sailer (design no 161 Mk II);
Equator Dream, 35.6 m 25 knot luxury cruise catamaran (design no 160) for Singapore;
Princess of Rhodes, 35.6 m 33 knot high-speed ferry (design no 157) for Greece;
Micronesian Dream, 33.5 m cruise catamaran (design no 153/3);
Island Pearl, 34.2 m high-speed ferry (design no 192);
Peisunna, 16.8 m motor catamaran yacht;
Aussie One, 30 m ketch-rigged day-charter catamaran (design no 167);
Blade Runner, 43 m 29 knot 400 passenger ferry (design no 201);
Tai An, 35 m 33 knot 250 passenger *Blade Runner* style high-speed ferry for Hong Kong;
Reef Queen, design by Lock Crowther Designs, superstructure styling by Hydronautics Australia and Lloyd's Ships. A 38 m 31 knot 380 passenger water-jet fast tourist ferry (design no 218);
On The Edge, a 20 m 60 passenger sloop rigged fast day charter catamaran (design no 223);
Aussie Magic, a 26 m 150 passenger day charter (or 110 passenger formal dining sloop rig catamaran (design no 213);
Tara Vana, a 50 m sail/game fishing charter catamaran for Bora Bora, French Polynesia (design no 222);
Reef Prince, a 38 m 31 knot 380 passenger water-jet fast tourist ferry (design no 250). Hull and structural design are by Lock Crowther Designs, superstructure styling, general arrangement and systems engineering by Lloyd's Ships Australia;
Qu Er Hao, a 35 m 33 knot, 250 passenger *Blade Runner* style high-speed ferry for Hong Kong.

UPDATED

Lloyd's Ship Reef Queen ***1994***

Tai An ***1995***

INTERNATIONAL CATAMARAN DESIGNS PTY LTD (InCat)

1 Mafeking Avenue, Lane Cove, Sydney, NSW, Australia 2066

Tel: +61 (2) 427 2822
Fax: +61 (2) 427 7238

Philip Hercus, *Director*

International Catamaran Designs Pty Ltd, better known as InCat Designs, was formed in 1988 as a result of the restructuring of International Catamarans Pty Ltd. Even prior to that time International Catamarans, which was formed in 1977, was one of the world's leading catamaran designers and builders. In 1996 InCat Designs is still the world's leading catamaran design company, having designed over 140 catamaran craft which are operating in over 15 countries. The company is possibly best known as the designer of the wave piercing catamaran, the 30 m prototype of which was launched in 1985 as *Spirit of Victoria*.

A turning point for InCat Designs, and as a consequence for the fast ferry industry, was the delivery of *Hoverspeed Great Britain* in 1990. This was at that time by far the largest and fastest catamaran to have been designed and built, and was ordered by Sea Containers for operation across the English Channel. Subsequently eight further 74 m wave piercing

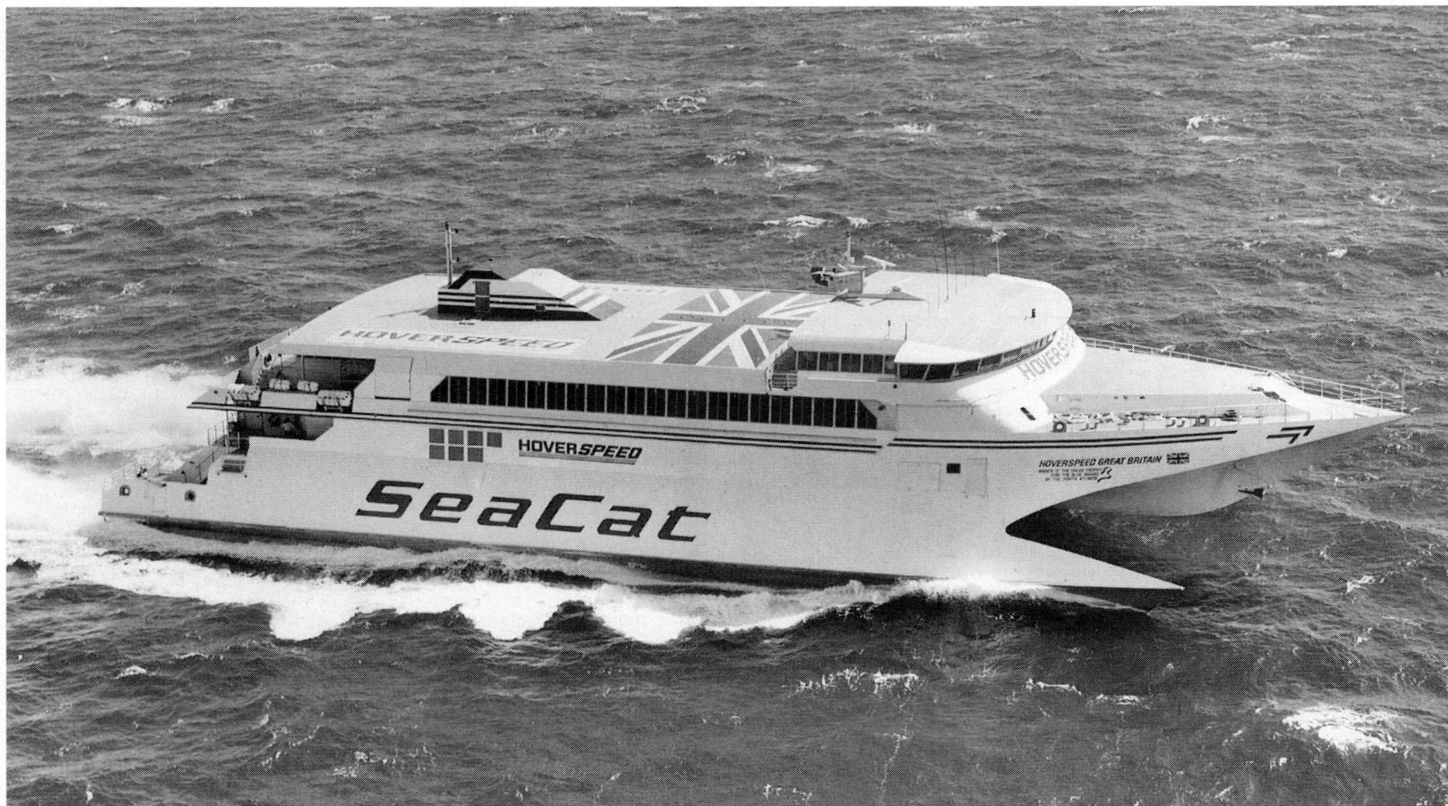

The InCat 74 m Hoverspeed Great Britain, *the first of the world's large fast ferries (*Hoverspeed) **1993**

catamarans were built with a further six 78 m and 81 m versions built to date.

A noticeable achievement of the 74 m *Hoverspeed Great Britain* was a crossing of the Atlantic in June 1990 during its delivery voyage, at an average speed of 36.6 knots, hence qualifying for the Blue Riband award.

To date, over 28 wave piercing catamarans have been constructed. The company is currently designing their largest craft which will be built in Vancouver for operation by British Columbia Ferries.

The ship designs from InCat Designs are largely marketed and built by licensees around the world. A notable development in 1994 was the formation of South Australia Ships Pty Ltd, the most recent licensee which has been specifically organised to build the large freight catamarans. Such designs at present cover vessels carrying 1,000 tonnes deadweight at speeds of up to 50 knots.

InCat Designs is also a vital associate of Nichols International, a new company formed in 1995 to market large car carrying passenger vessels on the InCat design. This company is currently marketing the most recent InCat design, a 93 m wave piercing catamaran carrying 800 passengers and 193 cars at speeds of up to 40 knots.

Licensees of InCat Designs Pty Ltd:
Aluminium Shipbuilders Ltd, UK
Gladding Hearn Inc, USA
InCat Australia Pty Ltd, Australia
Nichols Brothers Inc, USA
South Australia Ships Pty Ltd, Australia

UPDATED

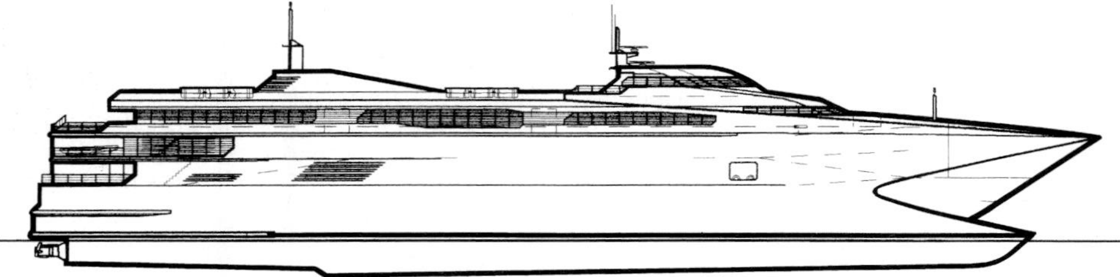

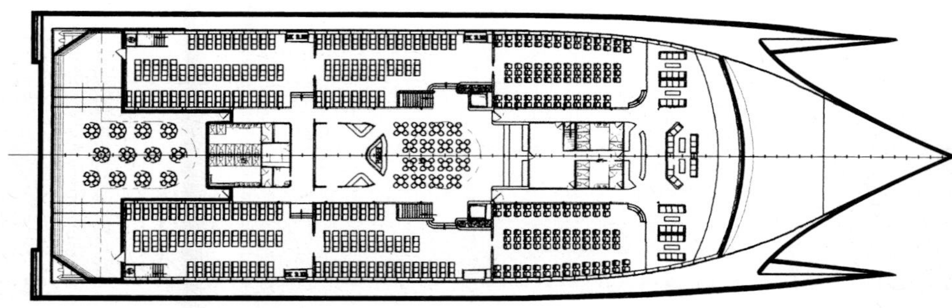

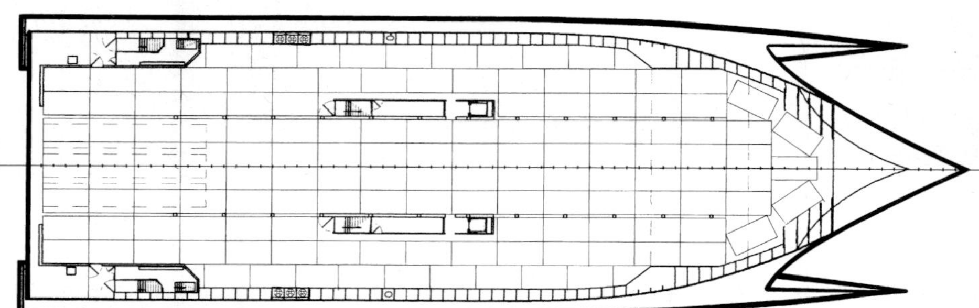

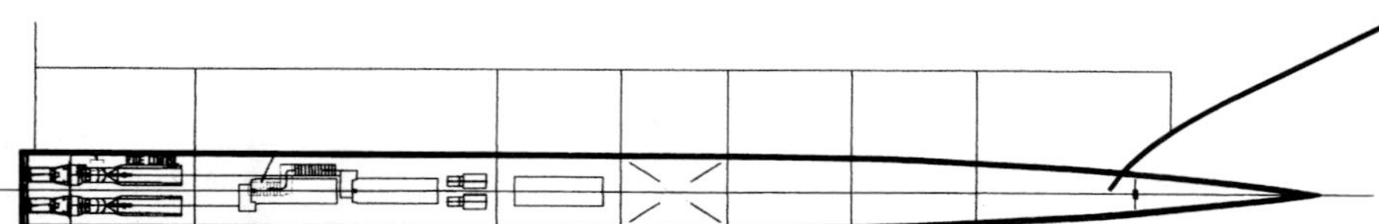

General arrangement of InCat 93 m wave piercing catamaran (design)
1996

KAMIRA HOLDINGS PTY LTD

PO Box 118, Stockton, NSW 2295, Australia

Tel: +61 (49) 201344
Fax: +61 (49) 201344

Greg Cox, *Managing Director and Naval Architect*

Kamira Holdings is a firm of naval architects and engineers specialising in the custom design of high-speed monohull craft in the 12 to 30 m range. The company has a building partner, Macquarie International Motor Yachts, which has a range of Greg Cox-designed craft under construction.

VERIFIED

LAUBREAUX MARINE DESIGN

PO Box 637, Spit Junction NSW 2088, Australia

Tel: +61 (612) 968 4177
Fax: +61 (612) 960 1499

Tony Laubreaux, *Director, Naval Architect*
David Lyons, *Director*

Laubreaux undertakes complete design and project management for high-speed passenger vessels and other commercial and paramilitary craft. It also acts as a consultant on the structural design of high-speed marine vehicles in aluminium and advanced composites.

Recent designs have included the *Seaflyer 750*, a 7.5 m, 40 knot catamaran fisheries vessel built in aluminium and a multipurpose catamaran, an 8 m, 20 knot craft, built in fibreglassed plywood for a Pacific Island.

Current projects include:
A 72 passenger, 25 knot, 17 m aluminium catamaran; a 110 passenger, 30 knot, 21 m aluminium catamaran; a 250 passenger, 30 knot, 38 m aluminium catamaran; and work on a new high-speed river catamaran for Sydney harbour, which will be launched shortly.

VERIFIED

MARK ELLIS DESIGN

11 Mews Road, Fremantle, Western Australia 6160, Australia

Tel: +61 (9) 430 5270
Fax: +61 (9) 430 5601

Mark Ellis, *Naval Architect*

Designers of high-speed catamaran and monohull craft. Recently built designs include the Fremantle Volunteer sea rescue catamaran, a 20 m oil spill response catamaran, a 15 m Pilot catamaran for Burrap, *GAC Shamal*, a 23 m monohull offshore supply vessel and a 23 m monohull passenger ferry.

VERIFIED

Oil spill response catamaran
1994

PHIL CURRAN DESIGN

Lot 300 Sparks Road, Henderson, Western Australia 6166, Australia

Tel: +61 (09) 410 2988
Fax: +61 (09) 410 2553

Phil Curran, *Director, Naval Architect*
Steve Bruyn, *Design Manager, Naval Architect*

Phil Curran designs range from 6 m vessels to high-speed private luxury yachts over 65 m. Phil Curran Design has produced nearly 500 designs since first commencing business some 16 years ago.

Commercial and pleasure craft are designed in all forms of construction, specialising in modern high-technology construction materials such as aluminium, composites, foam sandwich, carbon fibre and Kevlar.

Phil Curran Design has now developed a range of computer cut designs, up to 45 m high-speed catamarans (*Moecca*). This process offered by its subsidiary CDM, provides boat builders with a cost-effective package.

Designs have included the following craft:

Customised, 21 m, 38 knot, 15 tonne planing vessel with water-jet propulsion.

PM 17, built by Precision Marine Holdings Pty Ltd. This 17 m power boat design has received numerous orders and won the 1986 and 1988 Power Boat of the Year awards and the Australian Design Award. With a 24 tonne displacement the boat is capable of 40 knots.

PM 40, Precision Marine 40' sports fisherman. This production vessel is capable of 35 knots and has proved a very successful design with 37' and 43' vessels added to the range.

Numerous high-speed fishing vessels with speeds ranging from 20 to 50 knots built of aluminium and composites.

Oceanfast 2800 *Mercedes*, 27 m, 30 knot luxury motor yacht with twin water-jets, operating out of Florida waters.

Oceanfast 3000 *Never Say Never*, 33.3 m, 30 knot luxury charter vessel operating in the Caribbean.

Oceanfast 3000/2 *Antipodean*, sister ship to Oceanfast 3000, *Never Say Never*.

Oceanfast 4000 *Parts VI*, 46.69 m, 30 knot, 150 tonne (light ship) luxury motor yacht used by the Royal Perth Yacht Club as their flagship during the 1986-87 America's Cup Regatta in Fremantle, Western Australia.

Oceanfast 5000 *Mystique*, 49.5 m, 34 knot, 180 tonne, planing vessel with water-jet propulsion operating out of New York waters.

Wilderness Seeker, 100 seat, 19.95 m, 30 knot ferry with water-jet propulsion, built for Gordon River operations in Tasmania.

Moecca, 44.5 m, 29 knot, 270 tonne (lightship) pleasure catamaran with water-jet propulsion for worldwide cruising.

VERIFIED

STOLKRAFT INTERNATIONAL PTY LTD

Suite 1, Level 10, Seabank, 12 Marine Parade, Southport, Queensland 4215, Australia

Tel: +61 (7) 55270159
Fax: +61 (7) 55327466

J D Aitkenhead, *Managing Director*

Stolkraft is the registered trademark for an innovative hull form, conceived by the late Mr Leo Stolk and subsequently developed in Australia for high-speed applications. The hull form makes use of both hydrodynamic and aerodynamic lift at high speeds achieved solely by the forward speed of the craft.

Performance has been proven by a number of model and prototype tests. Commercial applications to date include a 13 m pilot boat for the Port of Auckland and a series of water taxis for river use.

UPDATED

BELGIUM

EUROSENSE HOVERSOUNDING NV

Main office: Nerviërslaan 54, B-1780 Wemmel, Belgium

Tel: +32 (2) 460 7000
Telex: 26687B
Fax: +32 (2) 460 4958

E Maes, *Managing Director*
J Van Sieleghem, *Project Leader*

BEASAC (Belfotop Eurosense Acoustic Sounding Air Cushion platform)

Since 1983 Eurosense has been under contract with the Belgian Ministry of Public Works, Coastal Services, for the constant monitoring of the access channels to the major Belgian seaports, and for the study of the coastal morphology. For this purpose, Eurosense has used a hydrographic survey technique based on the use of a fully amphibious hovercraft.

Nearshore bathymetric surveys by hovercraft ensure an overlap with beach observations (executed by aerial or terrestrial survey), thus enabling a complete coverage of the coast and nearshore sea bottom to be achieved. Furthermore, the manoeuvrability of the hovercraft and the high survey speed (up to 55 km/h, or 30 knots) result in measurements being obtained up to four times faster than those with classic hydrographic vessels.

This new concept in the field of hydrography was developed by Eurosense and called BEASAC (Belfotop Eurosense Acoustic Sounding Air Cushion platform). The first BEASAC was developed using the SR. N6 Mk 1S hovercraft. A second version, the twin-propeller SR. N6 Mk 6, was named BEASAC III.

The Eurosense SR. N6 Mk 6, BEASAC III **1991**

BEASAC

The first BEASAC hovercraft is a modified SR. N6 Mk 1S.

There are two hydraulically operated arms mounted on each side deck to bring acoustic transducers in and out of the water. Eurosense has developed an automatic retraction and deployment system allowing the measurements to be performed up to the last available metre of water depth.

In front of the pilot, a navigation screen shows the predefined tracks and harbour planimetry. This screen is continuously updated with the position of the craft, its speed, direction and the distance off track.

BEASAC III

The BEASAC III is based on the twinpropeller SR. N6 Mk 6. In the centre of the craft a hydraulically operated arm lowers the acoustic transducers into the water through a moon pool in the floor of the craft. The longitudinal and transverse cushion dividers of the skirt are modified to allow for this movement. As for BEASAC, a mechanical weak link construction and an automatic retraction and deployment system are installed.

Operations equipment: The data are acquired by a computer system extended with interfacing networks to gather all sensor registration. Graphical navigation screens inform the pilot and surveyor of track, planimetry and quality control of the data. Computer hardware and software, developed by Eurosense, enable continuous chart production to be achieved, as well as further data processing, for example Digital Terrain Modelling, differential map production, volume computation and refraction calculation.

VERIFIED

CANADA

D F DICKINS ASSOCIATES LTD

4-124 Valhalla Road, Salt Spring Island, British Columbia V8K 2V1, Canada

Tel: +1 (604) 537 4492
Fax: +1 (604) 537 2310

David Dickins, *President*

D F Dickins Associates Ltd is actively involved in marine transportation studies. The company provides a variety of services including route evaluation, conceptual design and testing, technical and economic feasibility studies and environmental impact studies.

A project for Gulf Canada Resources in 1986 involved the conceptual design of large self-propelled hovercraft up to 845 tonnes gross weight. During the same year, Dickins Associates worked with the Canadian Coast Guard Hovercraft Base in Vancouver to test an SR. N6 as a potential platform for spraying dispersants on oil slicks at sea.

A number of studies has examined the feasibility of using hovercraft in resupply and emergency response roles. In 1989, Dickins assisted Cominco Metals in an environmental, technical and economic evaluation of hovercraft servicing their Snip gold mine in northern British Columbia.

A 1990 project for the Municipality of Anchorage examined the technical feasibility and demand for a hovercraft operating as an emergency response vessel in Cook Inlet. This study concluded that the AP1-88 would satisfy the mission requirements.

Recently the company assisted Lynden Transport (Alaska Hovercraft) with environmental noise impact issues surrounding their proposed new services in Alaska using ex-US Army LACV-30's and ex-US Navy AP.1-88's. A further project in 1995 involved participating in the production of a video to defend claims of minimal environmental impact from long-term hovercraft operations in a sensitive wilderness area.

Recent publications are included in the bibliography section of this edition.

UPDATED

FLEET TECHNOLOGY LIMITED

311 Legget Drive, Kanata, Ontario K2K 1Z8, Canada

Tel: +1 (613) 592 2830
Fax: +1 (613) 592 4950

I Glen P.Eng, RCNC, *President*

Established in 1973, Fleet Technology Limited of Kanata, Ontario, provides design and construction support for marine vehicles including advanced marine vehicles. FTL carries our performance prediction, concept development, vessel fitness for purpose, seakeeping analysis, structural analysis, model testing and full scale trials on advanced marine vehicles. In addition FTL can support operator and business decisions through economic analysis, route analysis and Failure Mode and Effects Analysis.

With a staff of about 20, FTL operates laboratories and workshops for prototype/model development, which include a unique materials and welding laboratory which develops production and repair procedures, carries out materials and fracture testing, fatigue analysis and materials and fabrication consulting in steels, aluminium and composites. An inventory of trials and data acquisition equipment is also maintained.

FTL's advanced craft experience includes involvement in ACV mine countermeasures concepts, concept studies for an SES Sovereignty vessel, catamaran manoeuvring and seakeeping predictions, full scale manoeuvring and seakeeping trials on various small high-speed craft and SAR cutters, and FE analysis of multihulls. Current work includes a route and economic evaluation study for fast ferries for the Canadian Government.

NEW ENTRY

PROMAXIS SYSTEMS INC

2385 St Laurent Boulevard, Ottawa, Ontario K1G 4J3, Canada

Tel: +1 (613) 737 2112
Fax: +1 (613) 737 0229

James D Beer, *President*

SWATH CPV (DESIGN)
Promaxis has developed a design for a Swath coastal patrol vessel for use in search and rescue, fisheries patrol, defence surveillance, MCM and other related missions in rough seas such as those that exist off the east and west coasts of Canada.

This 360 tonne all-aluminium vessel is arranged to facilitate handling and treatment of survivors by providing dedicated rescue zones, recessed into the port and starboard sides of the upper hulls. At each zone 15 m^2 of deck space is provided leading to a triage area and treatment room amidships. Within the accommodation, seating and bunks are provided for up to 25 survivors. A helicopter landing pad is designed to enable landing and take-off of a Jet-Ranger helicopter in up to Sea State 5 conditions. For ship external firefighting two monitors are located between the funnels.

The vessel will be driven at 15 knots in Sea State 5 head seas by two medium-speed diesels, developing a total of 3,600 hp. The main engines are located within the main deck structure with a mechanical transfer of drive to controllable-pitch propellers.

Accommodation, all above main deck level, provides for a mixed 14 person crew with officers forward and ratings aft. Stores, fuel and water requirements are designed for 15 days' endurance at economical speed.

The design minimises development risks by employing standard, proven systems technology. The vessel will be built to Transport Canada regulations and classed with an international classification society.

VERIFIED

ROBERT ALLAN LTD

1690 West Second Avenue, Vancouver, British Columbia V6J 1H4, Canada

Tel: +1 (604) 736 9466
Fax: +1 (604) 736 9483

Robert Allan, *Director*

Well known for the company's tug designs, Robert Allan Ltd has also been closely involved in the development of high-speed craft in Canada.

The company has specialist experience in the use of CAD and CAM technology to assist shipyards in the planning and construction process and in particular is the leading consultant for the construction of the new fast catamaran ro-ro vessels for BC Ferries.

UPDATED

THE MARIPORT GROUP LTD

PO Box 1758, Cambridge, Ontario N1R 7G8, Canada

Tel: +1 (905) 333 8171
Fax: +1 (905) 333 1162

Christopher Wright, *President*

The Mariport Group Ltd conducts marine systems analysis and work has included projects for: Toronto Waterbus, Busan-Yeosu Ferry (South Korea), High-Speed Ferry (S E Alaska), Mine Supply and Personnel Vessel (Alaska, Newfoundland and China).

UPDATED

CHINA, PEOPLE'S REPUBLIC

CACTEC

China Air Cushion Technology Development Corporation

41 Changdi Road, Tianjin, People's Republic of China

Tel: +86 (22) 311984/313544
Fax: +86 (22) 3333

Hu Wenliang, *Manager*

Branch office: 132 Jichang Road, Shanghai, People's Republic of China

Zhu Bi Yu, *General Manager*

Tel: +86 (21) 377 0539
Telex: 33157 CSQXS CN

(DESIGN, RESEARCH, DEVELOPMENT AND PRODUCTION ASSISTANCE ORGANISATION)

Formed in 1984, CACTEC is a subsidiary of the China State Shipbuilding Corporation (CSSC). It is a specialised business corporation, working jointly with MARIC on a wide variety of applications of the air cushion principle with emphasis on the research, development, design and production of amphibious and sidewall (SES) hovercraft. Craft operated by CACTEC are given in the *Civil Operators* section of this edition.

VERIFIED

COMMONWEALTH OF INDEPENDENT STATES

FORMA LTD

15 Lakhtinskaya Street, 197136 St Petersburg, Russia, CIS

Tel: +7 (812) 230 2672/3905
Fax: +7 (812) 230 8112

Igor Mizin, *President*

Incorporated in 1991 in St Petersburg, Forma Ltd is one of the first Russian private companies specialising in the research and design of high-speed vessels. The firm unifies about fifteen specialists who for many years had worked in leading research and design centres, and have experience in the design of practically all fast craft built in the former USSR, including a 500 t hydrofoil with fully submerged foil system and foilborne speed of 50 knots in Sea State 5; 750 t SES with speed of 40 knots in Sea State 4; 400 t ACV with speed of 55 knots. At present Forma provides support to the Russian design bureaus.

The company develops and uses calculation methods and software for hydrodynamic predictions of foil systems, lift systems, high-pressure head water-jets, resistance and performance, mathematical modeling of 3D motion, automatic control system algorithms, ship surface description and optimisation. Model testing services are also offered.

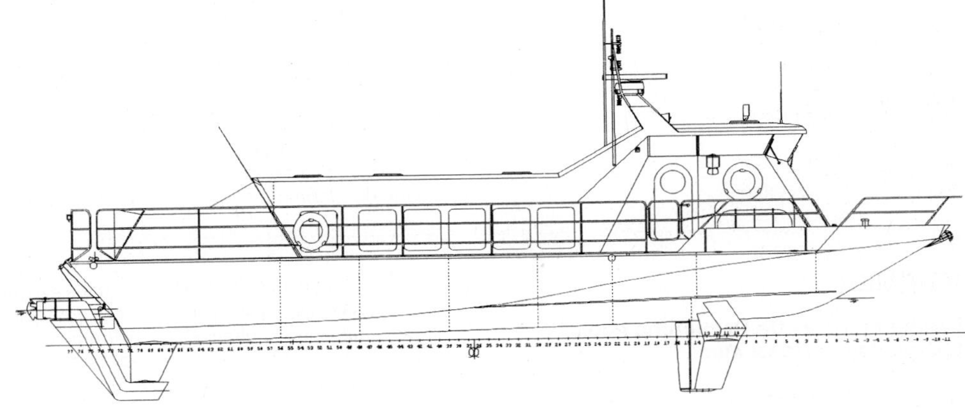

'Nevka-3F hydrofoil'

Specialists of the company have obtained several author patents for inventions concerned with high-speed craft. They have presented over thirty technical reports at international conferences and symposiums.

The company is currently looking for collaboration in the implementation of a production programme for its Nevka-3F hydrofoil design for patrol or passenger ferry duties. The vessel has an overall length of 18 m, a carrying capacity of 22 persons, a range of 200 n miles and a speed of 32 knots when propelled by two 310 kW diesels. The hull is constructed of aluminium with a composite superstructure.

UPDATED

KORT

Moscow, Russia, CIS

Tel: +7 (095) 153 1477
Fax: +7 (095) 153 1477

V G Moulev, *Chairman*
S A Yendrikhovsky, *General Director*

The key task of Kort is the integration of CIS high-speed ship manufacture into the world market. This process has already involved enterprises such as the Central Hydrofoil Ship Design Office (Nizhny Novgorod), Poti Shipyard and other businesses. Companies in Cyprus, Germany and Greece have indicated interest in this integration programme.

VERIFIED

SUDOEXPORT

11 Sadovaja-Kudrinskaja St, 123231 Moscow, Russia, CIS

Tel: +7 (095) 252 4491
Telex: 411116
Fax: +7 (095) 200 2250

Vladimir A Chnyr, *General Director*
Vjacheslav V Yanchenko, *Director of Imports*
Yuri I Fomichev, *Export Director*

Sudoexport is a Russian organisation engaged in the export and import of all kinds of sea-going and riverine ships and ship's equipment, and the export and import of technological equipment for shipbuilding and associated engineering activities.

Sudoexport offers skilled services in shiprepair including repair for the naval-defence fleet. The company is also an investor in various joint ventures and has a worldwide agent network.

VERIFIED

TRANSAL-AKS ENGINEERING CO

3 Sovetskaya Pl, Nizhny Novgorod, 603106 Russia, CIS

Tel: +7 (831) 268 4989
Fax: +7 (831) 268 0574

TRANSAL-AKS is a research, design and consultancy company specialising in the field of high-performance marine and amphibious craft. Only limited information concerning its military and commercial designs is currently available, although it is clear that fast passenger transportation is one of the main markets being considered. One craft being discussed has a speed of over 300 knots with a passenger capacity of 50. The range is 250 n miles with a payload of 5 tonnes. Fuel consumption is predicted to be 0.054 kg/seat.n miles.

VERIFIED

CROATIA

BRODOPROJEKT

Ship Design & Marine Engineering

Ciottina 17a, 51000 Rijeka, Croatia

Tel: +385 51 211078
Telex: 24335 BROPRO
Fax: +385 51 211318

Sinisa Reljic, *Naval Architect, Marketing Manager*

This organisation is developing a number of high-speed catamaran designs. However political unrest in this country continues to inhibit commercialisation of their technology.

UPDATED

DENMARK

JAN KJÆRULFF YACHT DESIGN

Engvej 9, DK-2960 Rungsted Kyst, Denmark

Tel: +45 (42) 867215
Fax: +45 (42) 867215

Jan Kjærulff, *Naval Architect*

Jan Kjærulff Yacht Design is a firm of consulting naval architects and marine engineers involved in the design and surveying of fast craft. Recent projects have included two 16 m craft, a fast catamaran ferry and a 16 m fast crew boat. The company has also completed a 70 m fast ferry design for Danish State Railways. The company works closely with Temex, the owner of the specialist marine craft operator Supply-Trans.

Current designs include a 13 m, 12 passenger ACV, with a speed of up to 60 knots. Trials for this craft took place during November 1994.

A 16 m fast car and passenger catamaran ferry has also been designed for services to Danish islands.

VERIFIED

FRANCE

BERTIN & CIE

PO Box 3, F-78373 Plaisir Cedex, France

Tel: +33 (1) 34 81 85 00
Telex: 696231 F
Fax: +33 (1) 30 54 04 14

Hervé Hamon, *Chairman*
Alain Pirovano, *Secretary*

Bertin has been engaged in developing the Bertin principle of separately fed multiple plenum chambers surrounded by flexible skirts since 1956. A research and design organisation, the company employs a staff of more than 500, mainly scientists and design engineers who are involved in many areas of industrial research, including air cushion techniques and applications.

The Bertin principle of multiple air cushions has led to the development of the Aérotrain high-speed tracked transport system and to numerous applications in the area of industrial handling and aeronautics. These applications, developed by Bertin, are described in the sections devoted to Air Cushion Applicators, Conveyors and Pallets and Air Cushion Landing Systems in *Jane's Surface Skimmers 1980* and earlier editions.

VERIFIED

IFREMER

Institut Français De Recherche Pour L'Exploitation De La Mer

Centre de Brest, PO Box 70, F-29280 Plouzané, France

Tel: +33 98 22 40 40
Telex: 940627 OCEAN F
Fax: +33 98 22 41 35

Philippe Marchand, *Director*

IFREMER was formed in 1984 from the merger between CNEXO (National Centre for Sea Development) and ISTPM, Scientific and Technical Institute for Sea Fisheries. IFREMER is commissioned by the French Government to conduct studies for the evaluation of unconventional ships, for example amphibious hovercraft, surface effect ships, hydrofoil craft, catamarans and Swath vessels and may participate in any development of these concepts. Test facilities are located at Brest in Brittany. The largest part of the unconventional ship research programme of IFREMER is concerned with air cushion technology and the relevant patents have been acquired from the former SEDAM company. Since 1985 IFREMER has been mainly involved in the design of the ADOC 12 hovercraft and the NES 24 surface effect ship. Since December 1991 IFREMER has been involved in a national programme called MENTOR.

MENTOR

The objective of the MENTOR (Modele Explorative de Navire de Transport Oceanique Rapide) national programme is to study three types of high-speed ferries with the following characteristics; a payload of 250 tonnes (including 500 passengers and 100 cars), a speed of 50 knots on Sea State 5 and a range of 300 miles. There are three types of ferries under evaluation, SES, Swath and slender monohull with stabilisation.

ADOC 12

In 1986 IFREMER conducted complete performance tests on the ADOC 12 craft from its establishment at Brest. In 1988 the craft was improved with diesel engines and a new propulsion system for better manoeuvrability.

VERIFIED

TECHNI CARÈNE

6 Route de Bû, Les Christophes, F-28260 Sorel Moussel, France

Tel: +33 16 37 41 80 38
Fax: +33 37 41 73 81

Philippe Nineuil, *Director*

Techni Carène is a naval architecture and engineering office established in 1979 by Philippe Nineuil, naval architect and a member of the Institut Français des Architectes Navals (IFAN).

The company is involved in the design of all types of ships from 15 m up to 60 m in length, in all materials and adopted to a wide range of operation programmes such as: passenger transport, hydrographic, diving support, fishing, patrol, and offshore supply.

It has also developed a range of displacement and medium-speed catamarans named CATATRANS, which include fishing, hydrographic and passenger units.

Two examples of high-speed craft built to Techni Carène designs are: *Azenor*, a 25 m, 200 passenger aluminium catamaran operated in Brittany, France, delivered in 1992; and *Dravanteg*, a 27 m mixed cargo and passenger catamaran, powered by 2 × 895 kW diesels driving Kamewa water-jets, operated in Brittany, France. Both of these vessels were built by the shipyard Navale Aluminium Atlantique, Saint-Nazaire.

VERIFIED

GERMANY

MTG MARINETECHNIK GmbH

Wandsbeker Königstrasse 62, PO Box 701249, D-2000 Hamburg 70, Germany

Tel: +49 (40) 65830
Telex: 215200
Fax: +49 (40) 658 3392

Franz-Josef Görgen, *Managing Director*
Werner Kurz, *Commercial Director*

MTG Marinetechnik GmbH was founded in 1966 at the instigation of the Federal German MoD as a central planning and design office for naval systems, especially naval surface craft and general naval technology. MTG shareholders are major shipyards and electronics companies. MTG designs naval systems, prepares tender documents for naval projects and is involved in all project development phases with particular emphasis on the early planning stages. The company is staffed by some 120 employees, the majority of whom are technical/scientific engineering graduates. MTG is renowned for its competence and impartial consulting services.

For several years now MTG has been working on the design of unconventional marine platforms. Initial basic studies have led to the design of the Fast Test Craft SES 700 and a Swath design for a research vessel.

In the years 1984 to 1988 a design study for naval fast test craft was worked on in the Federal Republic of Germany. The selected vessel is a large steel-hulled surface effect ship, with a full load displacement of 720 tonnes and a maximum speed in excess of 50 knots. The design study was managed by MTG Marinetechnik GmbH in Hamburg, on behalf of the German MoD in close co-operation with the US Naval Sea System Command under a Data Exchange Agreement. Extensive model tests were performed at the David Taylor Model Basin (DTRC), leading to the development of manned model, MOSES. MTG integrated into the overall design, contributions from Maritime Dynamics Inc for a seal and lift system design and a ride control system.

During the last few years extensive investigations have been performed by MTG on Swath technology leading to the design of a naval research vessel. This design is intended to replace the 2,000 tonne conventional monohull, *Planet,* which is currently in operation for the German Navy. The Swath 3,200 tonne, 13 to 15 knot vessel has been designed to meet the operational requirements of the German MoD for the tasks which are anticipated in the field of naval research in the year 2000. The basic missions and tasks are related to: underwater acoustics, maritime geology and geophysics, and meteorology and aerology.

MTG has developed a high standard of expertise in the design of unconventional craft which can be readily exploited for a wide range of naval and commercial applications.

VERIFIED

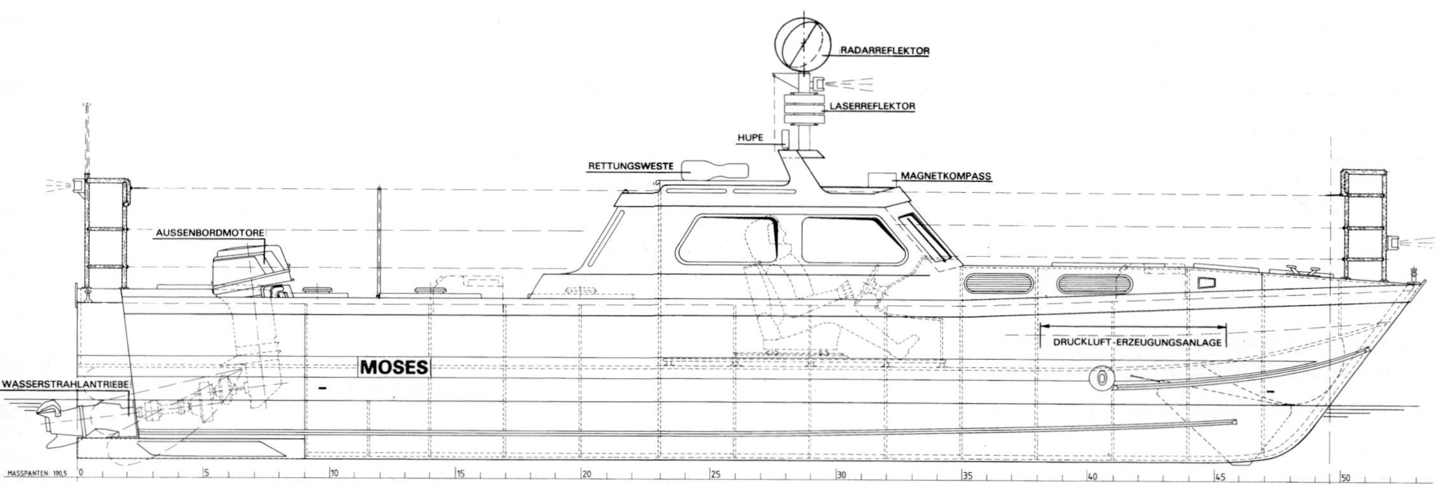

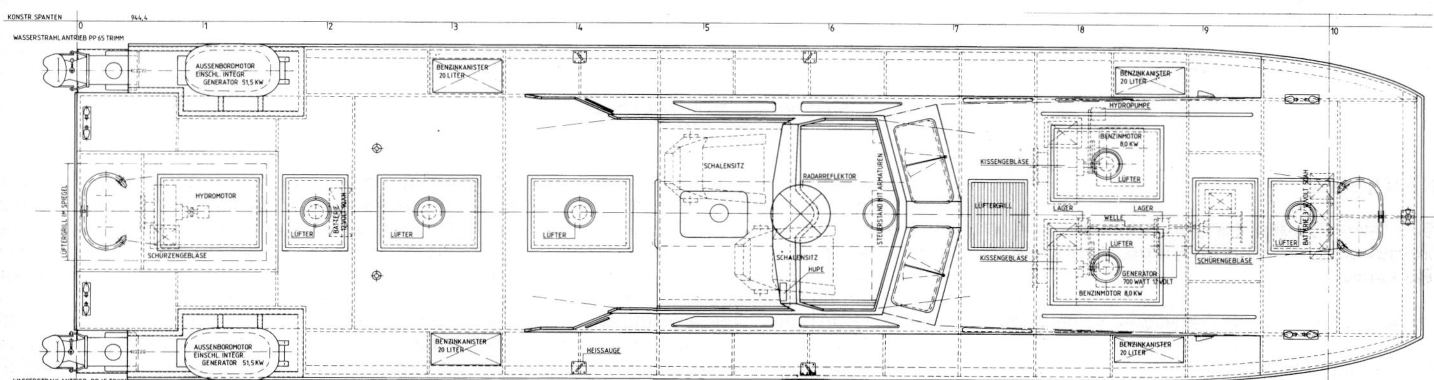

MTG Marintechnik MOSES manned test craft

GREECE

NATIONAL TECHNICAL UNIVERSITY OF ATHENS

Laboratory Of Ship Design

9 Heroon Polytechniou Str, GR-15773 Athens, Greece

Tel: +30 (1) 772 1416
Telex: 221682 NTUA GR
Fax: +30 (1) 772 1408
E-mail: papa@hermes.deslab.naval.ntua.gr

Apostolos Papanikolaou, *Professor, Director*

AEGEAN QUEEN (DESIGN)
This 1,000 tonne displacement Swath passenger/car ferry design, able to carry approximately 750 passengers and 88 cars at a speed of 30 knots, was announced in 1989 and has been designed by the Laboratory of Ship Design at the National Technical University of Athens, Department of Naval Architecture and Marine Engineering. Resistance and seakeeping model testing has been performed at the Towing Tank of NTUA, Laboratory of Naval and Marine Hydrodynamics.

The concept of Aegean Queen is to develop a rapid, safe and comfortable marine transportation system for connecting the Greek mainland with the surrounding and even more distant islands in the Aegean and Ionian Sea.

Recently completed designs include a 600 tonne displacement Swath multipurpose research vessel (so called SMURV) for the Mediterranean area and a 60 TEU high-speed Swath multipurpose container carrier (so called SMUCC) for short sea shipping operations in Europe.

UPDATED

ITALY

SCIOMACHEN NAVAL ARCHITECTS

Via Massarenti 410, I-40138 Bologna, Italy

Tel: +39 (51) 533043
Fax: +39 (51) 531304

Franco Sciomachen, *Director*
Ernesto Sciomachen, *Director*
Aldo Sciomachen, *Director*

The Sciomachen name has been associated with yachts and boats since 1951. After being devoted to mainly sailing craft in the early years, the company's projects today encompass a full range of marine designs from high-speed power yachts to fast ferries, excursion vessels, fishing vessels and displacement yachts, as well as racing and cruising sailboats. Construction materials include fibreglass, steel, aluminium and wood, with sizes from about 7 m to over 45 m.

The company's yacht design experience is reflected in the design of its commercial vessels, where functionality is always matched with aesthetically pleasing lines.

Sciomachen's European headquarters are in Bologna, Italy, with an office in San Diego, California, serving the Pacific Rim.

VERIFIED

JAPAN

MASARU IKEDA SHIP CONSULTING OFFICE

2-1-8-907 Benten, Minato-ku, Osaka, Japan

Tel: +81 (6) 574 1658
Fax: +81 (6) 574 1658

Masaru Ikeda, *Surveyor and Consulting Engineer*

Masaru Ikeda is a representative surveyor, registered consulting engineer for the Scientific Technology Department, Reg No 8533. Projects have included a catamaran research boat, a high-speed fishery patrol boat and a high-speed passenger vessel. Many of the craft designed by this company are built by Mokubei Shipbuilding of Japan.

UPDATED

KOREA, SOUTH

KOREA RESEARCH INSTITUTE OF SHIPS AND OCEAN ENGINEERING

Yusong PO Box 101, Taejon 305-600, South Korea

Tel: +82 (42) 8617401
Fax: +82 (42) 8687711

This company was founded in 1989 and is supported by the South Korean government, but has been affiliated with companies working in the shipbuilding industry since 1973.

KRISO is a research institute specialised in high-performance ships, offshore structures, deep sea submersibles and underwater robots.

A towing tank (216 m × 16 m × 7 m) is used for evaluation of hull and propulsor technology, seakeeping and manoeuvring, and other purposes; for high-speed craft such as SESs, catamarans, hydrofoil catamarans and hybrid ships. Computational fluid dynamics are also widely used.

Other areas of interest being researched include advanced ship design technology, strength and vibration technology, and marine machinery performance evaluation using physical testing and theoretical computer techniques.

UPDATED

NETHERLANDS

NEVESBU

B.V. Nederlandse Verenigde Scheepsbouw Bureaus, (Netherlands United Shipbuilding Bureaus)

PO Box 16350, 2500 BJ The Hague, Netherlands

Tel: +31 (70) 3497979
Fax: +31 (70) 3854460

This marine engineering company was founded in 1935, and concentrates on ship design, maritime technology and marine engineering. It is a private company, with an average (last four years) net turnover of DFl 15 million. Its shareholders are: Royal Schelde Group of Vlissingen, Rotterdam Dockyard, Wilton-Fijenoord of Schiedam, Stork of Naarden and Signaal of Hengelo. Nevesbu provides research, design and engineering services to customers all over the world. Among these customers are several navies, including the Royal Netherlands Navy, shipowners, shipyards, dredging companies, offshore industry, petro/chemical industry and government organisations. Consultancy activities include feasibility and reliability studies, engineering software development and probabilistic risk analyses.

Nevesbu employs approximately 85 dedicated people of which more than 30 are highly qualified specialists holding MSc and BSc degrees in various fields of engineering such as naval architecture, marine engineering and information technology. Nevesbu also counts many experienced design engineers and draftsmen. In addition, the close co-operation with technical universities, research institutes and industry is a valuable asset.

Two examples of high-speed craft designed by Nevesbu are a 46 m coastguard vessel (design), of 22 knots speed; and a 66 m customs patrol boat of 30 knots speed, delivered in 1988.

VERIFIED

NEW ZEALAND

MALCOLM TENNANT MULTIHULL DESIGN

PO Box 21-857 Henderson, Auckland 8, New Zealand

Tel: +64 9 838 6593
Fax: +64 9 836 6749

M Tennant, *Director*

Known for their sailing and powered catamaran designs, Malcolm Tennant Multihull Design currently have a number of craft to their design under construction. The most recent design is a 20 m fast dive boat, carrying 18 divers plus diving gear, at speeds of up to 23 knots and designed with a significant endurance.

NEW ENTRY

NORWAY

AMBLE & STOKKE A/S

PO Box 1616, Valhalla, N-4602 Kristiansand, Norway
Office: Kongsgaard Alle 53, N-4632 Kristiansand S, Norway

Tel: +47 (380) 95803
Fax: +47 (380) 95871

Eivind Amble, *Naval Architect*
Tor Stokke, *Naval Architect*

Specialists in the design of high-speed marine craft and related research and development. With 20 years' experience as naval architects, their reference list ranges from luxury Mega motor yachts to small dinghies, from offshore racing power boats to military craft and to high-speed commercial vessels.

During recent years Amble & Stokke A/S has been involved in a variety of design tasks. In 1991 the company received an award for 'The Best Engineered Motoryacht 1991' as the naval architects of the 76 m motor yacht *Golden Odyssey*, teamed with Platou Ship Design and Veritas Marine Services and builders Blohm+Voss. They designed the latest generation of high-speed rescue craft for the Norwegian Society for Sea Rescue, and the latest pilot cutter for the Norwegian Coastal Directorate.

Amble & Stokke has been involved in the design of the Sea Lord high-speed passenger catamarans built by the Båtservice Group, and in some of the SES projects undertaken by the Kværner Mandal yard. During the last few years, Amble & Stokke has been involved in the high-speed craft research and development programme initiated by the Royal Norwegian Council for Scientific and Industrial Research, both as naval architects and through its sister company CETEC (Consultancy - Engineering - Technology) in structural design and studies on the application of advanced composites. On specific projects, the firm works in association with IMAA (Independent Maritime Assessment Associates) of Romsey, UK.

VERIFIED

CAMO

Computer-aided Modelling A/S

Jarlev 4, N-7041 Trondheim, Norway

Tel: +47 (7) 514966
Fax: +47 (7) 514257

CAMO was established in 1984 by a group of leading experts in the control engineering field and early in 1993 12 people were employed.

FoilCat 2900 is a Norwegian high-speed foilborne catamaran. At normal cruising speed the foils of the Westamarin FoilCat 2900 will lift both hulls above the water surface. The vessel is stabilised in flight condition by a control system that ensures extremely good passenger comfort even in 3 to 4 m waves. The control system is developed by CAMO.

By dynamic simulation of the vessel, expensive prototype development and the overall time for system development can be significantly reduced.

FoilCat 2900 is a 29 m catamaran with fully submerged foils fore and aft. In flight condition at 50 knots, the system is unstable and has to be stabilised by a control system.

A mathematical model of the hydrodynamic properties of the vessel was developed in close co-operation with Marintek, Trondheim. The model was programmed in the Cypros simulation programme ESIM.

A control system was developed based on the simulation model. Its purpose is to stabilise the vessel in three degrees of freedom: heave, roll and pitch. The control system is based on modern theories for non-linear and multivariable control. All failure modes were tested against the simulator, and a comprehensive Failure Mode Effect Analysis was worked through before going on sea. The control system handles all sensor and servo errors by detecting and isolating any erroneous device.

The simulation system was used to verify vessel design details; specify sensors; develop the control system; perform failure mode effect analysis; specify sea trial test programme and prepare documentation for the shipyard and the authorities.

VERIFIED

CIRRUS SHIP DESIGN A/S

Våkleiva 133, PO Box 130, N-5062 Bønes, Bergen, Norway

Tel: +47 (5) 513 5400
Telex: 40422 CIRR N
Fax: +47 (5) 513 5411

Dick Vinkler, *President*
Atle Ulvesæter, *Vice President*

Cirrus Ship Design A/S is the leading designer of air cushion catamarans (SES).

There are 15 Cirrus air cushion catamarans in operation worldwide. These are CIRR 105 and 120P designs with a capacity up to 330 passengers and a top speed of approximately 50 knots.

The range of Cirrus air cushion catamarans also includes both naval vessels such as minehunters and patrol craft, as well as large ferries with capacity for cars and buses.

The Royal Norwegian Navy is currently building nine 56 m minehunters based upon the Cirrus air cushion catamaran design. This is the largest SES project in the world. For this project Cirrus Ship Design A/S also supplies all cushion-related hardware, computers, skirts and so on.

Cirrus Ship Design A/S has provided Blohm+ Voss AG with the CIRR 200PO air cushion design as a basis for the Corsair 600 car ferry. This vessel, which has a capacity for 400 passengers and 56 cars (or eventually a combination of buses and cars), will have a top speed of about 47 knots.

Cirrus Ship Design A/S is also co-operating with the Tencara yard of the Montedison Group, Italy, for building of the CIRR 120P type passenger vessels under licence. Through the introduction of advanced FRP production technology the performance of this vessel has now been further improved.

The latest design from Cirrus Ship Design A/S is the CIRR HSPC 42. This is an advanced patrol craft based upon the proven technology of the CIRR 120P and designed to meet NATO requirements. The vessel incorporates stealth design and the Cirrus patented missile silent launch system. Top speed is in the range of 65 knots.

VERIFIED

OLA LILLOE-OLSEN

N-6780 Hyen, Norway

Tel: +47 (578) 69805
Fax: +47 (578) 69925

Ola Lilloe-Olsen, *Director*

A well established Naval Architect in the development and design of high-speed monohulls and catamarans in Norway. Designer of a large number of

Ola Fox, *a 16 m fast ferry*
1996

passenger and ambulance-vessels in operation, as well as the Norwegian Skomvaer-Class of rescue vessels. Development work includes 60 knot patrol monohulls, catamarans for passenger/car transportation, catamaran purse seiners and long-liner fishing vessels, high-speed yachts and a series of work and passenger vessels.

Long experience, a well-established network and a large computer database of designs enables the company to rapidly produce well documented solutions to customer requirements.

UPDATED

PARADIS NAUTICA

PO Box 171, N-5040 Paradis, Bergen, Norway

Tel: +47 (55) 910010
Fax: +47 (55) 910009

Asbjørn Tolo, *Partner*
Hans J Runshaug, *Partner*
Eirik Neverdal, *Partner*
Kåre Angell Hamnes, *Partner*
Eilev Instanes, *Partner*

Paradis Nautica is a marine consultancy based in Bergen, Norway. The partners have a total of 80 years of experience in various aspects of the the fast ferry industry, and offer services to ship owners, operators, investors, yards and government agencies.

Some examples of the services offered by Paradis Nautica include: craft feasibility studies, evaluation of contracts and companies, market studies, charter assistance, new building tenders, ship concept development, design, technical support, and engineering design, sales and purchases.

UPDATED

SPAIN

NEUMAR SA

La Rinconada B-6, E-28023 Madrid, Spain

Tel: +34 (1) 548 2071
Fax: +34 (1) 547 4696

J Peire, *General Manager*
M de la Cruz, *Technical Director*
J A Barbeta, *Manufacturing Manager*

Neumar SA was founded in 1983 as a consulting engineers and designers company for air cushion technology. The services it offers include research and development with an emphasis on lift systems; hovercraft design; project management, which can comprise construction subcontracting with collaborating shipyards; hovercraft skirt design; and manufacturing, technical and economic feasibility studies.

The company offers a range of hovercraft designs which are based on a new lift system that it has recently developed and patented. This has been called an Automatic Transversal Air Distribution (ATAD) lift system because of the main function it performs in providing very high stability with low power requirements and reduced manufacturing and maintenance costs. To prove the viability of this lift system, several two-dimensional models and two prototypes have been built and tested.

Please see the 1992-93 edition of this book for details of the Neumaran NM-6 three- to four-seat hovercraft.

VERIFIED

UR TEKNIKS S.L.

Amézqueta 10, Entlo E, 20010 San Sebastián, Spain

Tel: +34 (43) 472396/472144
Fax: +34 (43) 472271

Xavier Urkiola, *Director*

UR Techniks is a firm of naval architects specialising in construction projects for fast catamaran vessels. The company has already had 15 and 20 m catamarans built for the tourist trade in Spain and has designs for cargo, fishing, oceanographic survey craft and pollution control catamarans.

UPDATED

SWEDEN

MARINTEKNIK DESIGN (E) AB

Varvsvägen 6, S-740 71 Öregrund, Sweden

Tel: +46 173 313 15
Fax: +46 173 313 65

Marinteknik Design have offices in Sweden and Singapore and undertake research and development projects, not only for the Marinteknik Group but also for shipbuilders worldwide. The company offers a comprehensive project capability covering design consultancy, construction support, crew training, transfer of technology and production under licence.

NEW ENTRY

PELMATIC AB

Drottninggatan 65, S-371 33 Karlskrona, Sweden

Tel: +46 455 191 25
Fax: +46 455 31 15 91

Gert-Ove Lind, *Managing Director*

Pelmatic AB is a firm of consulting engineers specialising in product development and design projects for the shipbuilding, offshore, aircraft and vehicle manufacturing industries. The company has offices in Sweden, Denmark and Singapore which together employ 150 engineers.

Pelmatic has been involved in the design of high-speed military and commercial vessels, notably the structural design of the 95 m fast ferry Kattegat and the Stockholm, Göteborg and Smyge classes of fast patrol craft.

NEW ENTRY

SSPA MARITIME CONSULTING AB

PO Box 24001, S-400 22 Gothenburg, Sweden

Tel: +46 (31) 639500
Telex: 20863 SSPAGBGS
Fax: +46 (31) 639624

Hans Broberg, *Managing Director*
Claes Källström, *Technical Director*
Bo Jansson, *Chief Naval Architect*

SSPA has been involved in the testing of high-speed craft designs and their associated equipment for many years. Noted for their contribution to the success of the Royal Swedish Navy's high-speed vessels, the company has also been closely involved in the testing and development of commercial high-speed craft, notably the Italian *Destriero*, the Stena HSS catamaran, and the Fast Ship project for transatlantic freight shipping.

The main areas of consulting expertise offered by the company are engineering design, fluid mechanics, naval system design and ship and control system simulation for fast commercial and military vessels.

VERIFIED

SWITZERLAND

DR ING E G FABER MARINE ENGINEERING CONSULTANT

Gratstrasse 20, CH-8472 Seuzach, Switzerland

Tel: +41 (52) 533040
Fax: +41 (52) 533040

Consultant in application engineering with special emphasis on the field of interaction between hull, propulsor and engine. A writer of engine matching software.

VERIFIED

DIPL ING E SCHATTÉ

Amlehnstrasse 33, CH-6010 Kriens (Lucerne), Switzerland

Tel: +41 (41) 412794

Consultant in hydrodynamics, aerodynamics, marine technology, and high-speed craft.

VERIFIED

SUPRAMAR AG

Seestrasse 78, CH-8703, Erlenbach, Switzerland

Tel: +41 (1) 912 1808
Fax: +41 (1) 912 1809

Dipl Ing Volker Jost, *President*
Dipl Ing Harry Trevisani, *General Manager*
Dr Ing Herrmann de Witt, *Hydrodynamics*
Dr Ing Otto Münch, *Stabilisation and Control*

(PATENT HOLDERS AND DESIGNERS)

Since its foundation in 1952, Supramar has provided a worldwide consultancy service, covering not only its hydrofoil vessels but also other aspects of fast marine transport. Its scientists have delivered papers to most of the world's leading professional bodies.

The company has been under contract to many governments and military services.

Supramar developed on a commercial basis the hydrofoil system introduced by the Schertel-Sachsenberg Hydrofoil syndicate and its licensee, the Gebrüder Sachsenberg Shipyard. The development started in the 1930s and led to the realisation of a number of military hydrofoils of up to 80 tonnes displacement and 41 knots in speed.

The inherently stable, rigid surface-piercing V-foil system which is typical for the Supramar type craft was developed by the late Baron Hanns von Schertel.

In May 1953 the world's first passenger hydrofoil service started on Lake Maggiore in Italy with a Supramar type PT 10 craft *Freccia d'Oro*. She was later transferred to Lake Lucerne. A larger craft, the PT 20, was built by Lürssen Shipyard in 1953 and named *Bremen Pioneer*. Since then many Supramar-type hydrofoils have been built under licence from Supramar, mainly by Rodriquez, Hitachi and Westermoen. Full details of all Supramar designs are given in *Jane's Surface Skimmers 1985* and earlier editions. Many Supramar PT 20 and PT 50 hydrofoil vessels are still in service.

Supramar Ltd is also engaged in new designs of high-speed craft such as fast monohulls and catamarans as well as general engineering services. The company has been involved in re-equipping Kometa-type hydrofoils with MTU high-speed diesel engines.

UPDATED

UNITED KINGDOM

AIR CUSHION LTD

Unit 4SW, Marchwood Industrial Park, Southampton, Hampshire SO40 4PB, UK

Tel: +44 (1703) 870077
Fax: +44 (1703) 870044

J D Hake, *Chairman (USA)*
P Auston, *Director*
D Gosden, *Operations Director*

Air Cushion Ltd is the largest supplier of skirts for medium size passenger hovercraft in the world and has been in business for 25 years. ACL can offer experience on designing skirts and associated parts for a variety of air-propelled passenger craft, from two-seat leisure craft to large passenger craft.

ACL has also designed many industrial and non-passenger carrying applications of the fluid cushion principle. These include water skate heavy load moving system, tank moving equipment and heavy lift platforms and trailers.

The firm can provide a complete consultancy design and manufacturing service on all aspects of ACV design and performance, as well as inflatable or flexible structures.

Skirts manufactured include those for all Griffon hovercraft.

UPDATED

AIR VEHICLES LTD

Head Office and Factory: Unit 4, Three Gates Road, Cowes, Isle of Wight, UK

Tel: +44 (1983) 293193
Telex: 86513 HVWORK G
Fax: +44 (1983) 291987

C B Eden, *Director*

Air Vehicles Ltd, formed in 1968, has a wide experience of all types of hovercraft and hovercraft operations and can offer a full range of services as consultants. Particular fields in which it has specialised knowledge are the design of hovercraft up to 20 tonnes payload, the design and manufacture of ducted propeller systems for installations up to 3.6 m in diameter and the design and manufacture of lift fans for amphibious hovercraft and SES vessels.

Approved by the Civil Aviation Authority, the company can design and undertake modifications to existing craft. Typical examples are the conversion of SR. N5 and SR. N6 to flat deck layout for logistic operations, the addition of high-speed, dunking hydrographic equipment to SR. N6 and Tiger 12 craft and various modifications for seismic surveying operations. The company also has hovercraft available for charter.

Air Vehicles Ltd also undertakes feasibility studies and was responsible for an original design concept leading to the AP1-88 80 passenger diesel craft operated by Hovertravel Ltd.

VERIFIED

BLYTH BRIDGES MARINE CONSULTANTS LTD

8 Manor Court, Barnes Wallis Road, Fareham, Hampshire PO15 5TH, UK

Tel: +44 (1489) 574432
Fax: +44 (1489) 578862

Andrew G Blyth, *Director*
David C Bridges, *Director*

Independent naval architecture and marine engineering services for high-speed conventional and unconventional surface craft. The company was formed in 1990 by the joining of two established independent consultants.

The directors between them have 50 years' experience in the research, design and construction of advanced monohulls and multihulls, including Surface Effect Ships (SES) and Small-Waterplane-Area Twin-Hull (SWATH) ships. Both are graduates and Chartered Engineers and spent a significant part of their careers working for warship builders, Vosper Thornycroft.

Andrew Blyth is a naval architect whose clients include SSPA Maritime Consulting AB in Sweden, for the design and testing of SES for a wide international clientele; Swath International Ltd, on the design of a range of Swath ships; the International Standards Organisation, as convenor of a working group writing criteria for stability of all types of small craft; the Civil Aviation Authority, for work on SES stability criteria and Westland Aerostructures Test Facilities; for technical direction of a research programme into SES stability for the UK Department of Transport and US Coast Guard.

David Bridges is a marine engineer with particular experience in the conceptual and detailed design and commissioning of gas-turbine and high-speed diesel machinery installations for fast patrol boats, SES, Swath ships and large monohulls, for military, recreational and commercial applications. His clients include well-known shipyards all over the world.

The company offers clients an objective, independent marine consultancy service, from the conceptual stage, through model testing to detail design of arrangement, structure and machinery, oversight of construction and conduct of performance trials.

The company was formed in order to provide specialist expertise to Societa Esercizio Cantieri

SpA in Viareggio, Italy, in connection with the design and construction of large (over 1,000 tonnes) SES passenger/vehicle ferries in high-tensile steel and propelled by gas-turbines and water-jets.

A number of other studies and concept designs have been undertaken for large monohull and SES passenger and passenger/vehicle ferries.

HM Customs and Excise (UK Marine Branch) has selected the Company several times to assist in the procurement of new high-speed monohull surveillance cutters. These projects have included technical and commercial evaluation of competing design and build proposals for 34 m and 26 m cutters, and 15 m and 12 m regional boats, and oversight of the construction of the prototype regional boat.

Trans-Atlantic Freighter: the Company has also undertaken model testing and machinery and systems design for a large, high-speed monohull container ship being designed for trans-Atlantic service. This design is propelled by multiple gas turbines and water-jets.

Other recent projects include naval architecture and marine engineering design in connection with a 28 m aluminium luxury motor yacht under construction in Singapore and an FRP 18 m amphibious hovercraft.

UPDATED

BMT GROUP LTD

Orlando House, 1 Waldegrave Road, Teddington, Middlesex TW11 8LZ, UK

Tel: +44 (181) 943 5544
Telex: 263118 MARFEL G
Fax: +44 (181) 943 5347/977 3622

Dr I Dand, *Manager*

The vessel hydrodynamics section of BMT Group offers extensive services in consultancy, centred mainly on its capabilities in the fields of physical and mathematical modelling.

The company manages the hydrodynamic facilities at Haslar which are one of the largest in Europe. Hydrodynamic and aerodynamic studies are undertaken for clients in the field of high-speed craft, ferries, small craft and ships.

Major tank testing studies have been undertaken for the Department of Transport Marine Directorate into ship safety (notably that of ro-ro passenger ferries) and the RNLI for the design of new high-speed lifeboats. Resistance, propulsion, sea-keeping and manoeuvring experiments are offered as a standard service and the company has a long history of such work for high-speed planing and semi-displacement craft. The well-known NPL Round-Bilge Displacement craft series stems from a forerunner of the company.

Work has been carried out for sailing yachts, mainly in connection with the America's Cup and this, in common with many studies carried out by the company, has been accomplished with a blend of physical and mathematical modelling, allied to design expertise.

Mathematical models relating to resistance, seakeeping, propeller design and manoeuvring simulation are available to clients, supported by CAD systems which are compatible with those used in the high-speed and small boat industry.

As part of the BMT Group, the company can help clients by access to its wider expertise, ranging from environmental studies in the sea and air to CAD/CAM, available throughout the Group.

VERIFIED

CETEC CONSULTANCY LTD

Six Oaks House, Rudd Lane, Upper Timsbury, Romsey, Hampshire SO51 0NU, UK

Tel: +44 (1794) 368988
Fax: +44 (1794) 368967

Eur Ing Anthony Marchant, *Director*
David Kendall, *Director*

CETEC is a recognised authority on the structural design and analysis of all types of high speed marine transportation. The company also provides project management for any project from conception to completion, together with structural integrity surveys and expert witness services.

Over the years, CETEC's personnel have been involved in the development of structures for hovercraft, surface effect ships, catamarans, monohulls, SWATHs and foil assisted vessels, in all materials including fibre-reinforced polymers, aluminium alloys and steel.

Recent work has been in large fast displacement ships, where a direct calculation approach has been used to provide minimum weight structures. This approach establishes the global loads by computational analysis which are then fed into an overall finite element (FE) analysis model to establish the buckling and fatigue characteristics within a defined operational envelope. Full structural optimisation is undertaken computationally with detailed FE analysis in critical areas.

CETEC has also extensive expertise in the design and application of fibre-reinforced polymers for the primary structure of specialised vessels, such as hovercraft, surface effect ships and fast monohulls.

Projects in hand and recently completed include a 35,000 tonne, 40 knot trans-Atlantic container vessel; a 220 m, 30 knot container vessel and the structural optimisation of 120 m car carrying vessels. Other projects completed include the ABS M-10 hovercraft FRP structure and involvement in the ABS P89 hovercraft. CETEC have been employed to check the structure of a 44 m sailing ketch constructed entirely in carbon fibre and to develop FRP structures for high-speed ferries which could meet the requirements of the 1996 IMO High Speed Craft Code with respect to fire.

Project management work includes the organisation of a 28 m luxury yacht constructed in the Far East for Greek clients. Surveys have included surface effect ships and high-speed luxury yachts.

Anthony Marchant served as a specialist panel member for the 1994 International Ship and Offshore Structures Congress (ISSC), concerned with the particular aspect of SES structures. He is currently a specialist panel member for structures of high-speed vessels on the 1997 ISSC Committee.

UPDATED

LORNE CAMPBELL DESIGN

13A Moor Road, Broadstone, Dorset BH18 8AZ, UK

Tel: +44 (1202) 657466
Fax: +44 (1202) 657466

Lorne F Campbell, *Principal*

Design, naval architecture and consultancy in the area of high-speed power craft.

The principal, Lorne Campbell, has been working in the area of high-speed marine craft for nearly 30 years.

Much experience has been gained in the design of high-speed offshore racing powercraft and numerous successes have been gained over the years with monohull, hydroplane, catamaran and trimaran configurations, including six offshore world championships and three world speed records, an interesting one being the current world speed record for electrically powered craft at 52.82 mph.

Much has been learned about the complicated aerodynamic and hydrodynamic interaction affecting high-speed craft working close to the air/water interface, and the design and handling of craft which have to maintain high speeds in rough water.

The company can offer a unique blend of practical and theoretical experience in the design, performance and naval architecture of high-speed craft for both calm and rough conditions. Both wind tunnel and free running scale models are used during the design of craft which have no previous 'parent' form to work from. Considerable experience has been gained in the area of propulsion systems in general and surface propellers in particular. Propellers have been designed in-house when nothing suitable has been available.

A service is offered ranging from concept design and preliminary investigation through general arrangement, layout and styling, resistance, propulsion and stability, up to project management.

UPDATED

NIGEL GEE AND ASSOCIATES

9 Mitchell Point, Ensign Way, Hamble, Southampton, Hampshire SO31 4RF, UK

Tel: +44 (1703) 456433
Fax: +44 (1703) 456438

Nigel Gee, *Managing Director*
John Bonafoux, *Tecnical Director*

Nigel Gee and Associates offers a comprehensive service for all aspects of high-speed marine craft technology. A staff of 12 engineers and naval architects specialise in the complete range of high-speed craft design and consultancy activities. Over the last 10 years the company has designed in excess of 150 high-speed vessels, of which over 80 are either built or currently being built.

The company has experience across the whole spectrum of high-speed craft types and has design and build experience concerning monohulls, catamarans, surface effect ships, hovercraft, foil assisted craft, SWATH and semi-SWATH hulls, trimarans and other combinations of hulls, air and foil assistance.

Recent design and consultancy activities carried out by the company include:

Samsung Heavy Industries, South Korea - Concept, preliminary and detailed design for a 50 knot, 37 m surface effect ship passenger vessel now in service based in Pusan.

AlliedSignal Gas Turbines, USA - Market research and continuing consultancy for applications of marine gas turbines to high-speed ferries and other vessels.

British Columbia Ferry Corporation (BCFC) - Consultancy for the selection of high-speed car and passenger ferry designs for BCFC's routes in British Columbia.

National Marine Services, Abu Dhabi - Design of a fleet of high-speed water taxis, the first two of which are now operating in the Gulf.

Leeward Island Ferry Transport Project - Concept and detailed design for a high-speed monohull for operating in the Leeward Islands.

Derecktor Shipyards/New York Fast Ferries -

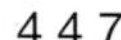

Beliard Polyship 30 m SES 1994

Samsung 37 m SES 1995

Concept, preliminary and detailed design for a fleet of 350 passenger, 35 knot catamarans to operate on commuter routes in New York harbour.
Pacific Marine, Hawaii - Hull design and stability work on novel multihulled vessels.
European Ship Owner - Parametric studies, preliminary design and tank testing for a fast freight carrier of novel hull form.

The package of services offered to the high-speed marine industry include:
Market research, initial concept design and production of specifications for quotation purposes, preliminary design and naval architecture, design of tank test models and tank test supervision, structural design from first principles or to classification society rules, engineering design - machinery, systems and electrics, detailed fitout design, presentation drawings, artist's impressions, interior artwork.

The NGA directors, Nigel Gee and John Bonafoux, have in excess of 40 years' experience in the high-speed marine craft field and, in particular, have recent experience relevant to the new markets for large high-speed car and freight carriers and in applications of gas turbine technology to these and similar vessels.

UPDATED

HART FENTON AND CO LTD

70 Broad Street, Old Portsmouth, Hampshire PO1 2LB, UK

Tel: +44 1705 875277
Fax: +44 1705 875280

J Pawsey, *Managing Director*
M Simpson, *Deputy Managing Director*
R Bryce, *Business Development Manager*

Hart Fenton & Co Ltd provide consultancy services covering structural analysis, hydrodynamic analysis, project technical assessment, FMEA and condition surveys.

Hart Fenton are the consultancy arm of Sea Containers Ltd and consequently have been closely involved in the High-Speed Ferry industry for over 10 years and brings to bear broad expertise in the sector. In particular the company has overseen the build of the Sea Containers Seacats and Super Seacat.

NEW ENTRY

HOVERCRAFT CONSULTANTS LTD

22 Nash Road, Dibden Purlieu, Hythe, Hampshire SO4 5RS, UK

Tel: +44 (1703) 843178
Fax: +44 (1703) 814292

M J Cox, *Managing Director*
J F Cox, *Secretary*
J E Rapson, *Associate*

Hovercraft Consultants Ltd (HCL) was founded in 1981 by members of the air cushion research company, Hovercraft Development Ltd, to provide commercial design and advisory services to the hovercraft and related industries.

HCL specialises in providing design expertise in those areas of air cushion technology which are not covered by conventional naval architecture. HCL is often involved at the start of new hovercraft projects, providing performance, weight, cost and general arrangement projections. Skirt and seals, lift systems and air propulsors form the main part of HCL's detailed design work.

Skirt systems have been designed for a great variety of craft, both amphibious and SES, with design speeds from the lowest to over 70 knots. Design payloads have ranged from two people to 300 tonnes and climatic conditions from the tropics to the Arctic. Much of the design process is now computer-based which has eliminated the need for three-dimensional skirt models and full-scale manual lofting. This has reduced design time and has made possible the direct, computer-controlled laser cutting of full-scale components. Computer programs developed in-house are also used for craft performance prediction, thrust estimation and fan performance.

HCL is currently developing a new type of lift fan which is intended to provide characteristics better suited to air cushion devices than the more conventional backward curved foil blade type in common use. The new fan is designed to provide substantially more airflow per intake while maintaining the high efficiency levels of traditional designs.

Many design projects undertaken by HCL have involved the use of scale models to predict behaviour and performance. Such models have varied from simple static skirt inflation rigs to fully dynamic models for use on towing tanks, in wind tunnels and for free-flight radio control tests.

Since HCL has no affiliation with any manufacturer or operator, it is able to provide unbiased appraisals of existing and projected craft. The suitability of such craft for particular routes and duties is assessed both technically and economically. The company keeps records of both technical and commercial aspects of high-speed waterborne transport.

VERIFIED

HOVERCRAFT DEVELOPMENT LTD

101 Newington Causeway, London SE1 6BU, UK

Tel: +44 (171) 403 6666
Telex: 894397 G
Fax: +44 (171) 703 7586

M L Martin, *Chairman*
D J Veasey, *Director*
J Williams, *Secretary*

(PATENT HOLDING AND LICENSING ORGANISATION)

Hovercraft Development Ltd (HDL) was formed in January 1959 by the National Research Development Corporation (NRDC), the assets of which are now owned by the British Technology Group Ltd. The company uses its portfolio of patents as the basis of licensing agreements with hovercraft manufacturers to manufacture and sell in Canada.

HDL's patents concern the HDL skirt shift system. Licences are available to all companies in the industry.

VERIFIED

HOVERCRAFT SALES AND MARKETING

PO Box 7, Sarisbury Green, Southampton, Hampshire SO31 8YS, UK

Tel: +44 (1703) 403547
Fax: +44 (1703) 406747

Graham A Gifford, *Managing Director*

Hovercraft Sales and Marketing (HOVSAM) undertakes general hovercraft consultancy work, specialising in the recommendation of various amphibious and non-amphibious hovercraft for particular routes and applications. In the 0.5 to 7 tonne payload range of amphibious hovercraft, HOVSAM acts as consultant to Griffon Hovercraft Ltd; for the Surface Effect Ship (SES) range of craft, HOVSAM is consultant to Hovermarine International Ltd. Graham Gifford has placed many hovercraft and SES into various countries around the world and will advise on route feasibility and economics, and the suitability of both commercial and military hovercraft for particular areas and applications.

VERIFIED

HOVERWORK LTD

12 Lind Street, Ryde, Isle of Wight PO33 2NR, UK

Tel: +44 (1983) 565181
Telex: 86513
Fax: +44 (1983) 812859
WWW: hoverwork.co.uk

C D J Bland, *Managing Director*
E W H Gifford, *Director*
R H Barton, *Director*
R K Box, *Director*
G M Palin, *Director*
B A Jehan, *Operations Manager*

Hoverwork Ltd was formed in 1966 to provide support to the high-speed marine industry. The services offered include route analysis and feasibility studies, the charter of hovercraft and crews, logistic duties, crew changes and many types of survey work in shallow water areas often difficult for other forms of transport. Full maintenance and spare parts can be provided to support services worldwide. Within the company there is a recognised training school which offers comprehensive courses to operational crews and the training of engineering personnel for other operators.

UPDATED

INDEPENDENT MARITIME ASSESSMENT ASSOCIATES LTD

35 Knights Bank Road, Hill Head, Fareham, Hampshire PO14 3HX, UK

Tel: +44 (1329) 663202
Fax: +44 (1329) 668176

John Lewthwaite, *Naval Architecture*
Anthony Marchant, *Structural Design Engineering*
David Bridges, *Marine Engineering*
Darrol Stinton, *Aero-marine Engineering*
Klaus Suhrbier, *Hydrodynamics*
Anthony Wardle, *Electrical Engineering*

IMAA is an amalgamation of advanced design and commercial talents drawn together from the marine engineering industry. Its purpose is to offer a completely integrated independent consultancy service to designers, builders, operators and owners of marine craft.

The consultancy offers expertise in all aspects of naval architecture, marine engineering, advanced structural design, aero-marine engineering, risk analysis, operational analysis, turnkey project management and commercial marketing disciplines.

IMAA's collective experience covers all configurations from conventional monohulls and fast planing hulls, to catamarans, Surface Effect Ships (SES), Swath vessels and surface effect aircraft (WIG) forms. IMAA's offices are fully equipped to offer an integrated advisory service on all aspects of craft design and performance, to technical audits on route analysis, operational assessments, procurement and cost/risk evaluations.

UPDATED

JCL HIGH SPEED MARINE CRAFT CONSULTANCY

35 Knights Bank Road, Hill Head, Fareham, Hampshire PO14 3HX, UK

Tel: +44 (1329) 663202
Fax: +44 (1329) 668176

John C Lewthwaite, *General Manager*

The JCL consultancy offers concept design, and research and development skills based on over thirty years of experience in the fast craft business. A wide range of activities is covered and includes SES, fast monohull, catamaran and hovercraft types. Work is carried out on both commercial and military applications and the consultancy advises companies in several European countries.

VERIFIED

JOHN McNEECE LTD

2 Holford Yard, Cruikshank Street, London WC1X 9HD, UK

Tel: +44 (171) 837 1225
Fax: +44 (171) 837 1233

John McNeece, *Chairman*
Mark T Hilferty, *Design Director*
Erol Aziz, *Planning Director*
Gordon Craigmyle, *General Manager*

McNeece was formed in 1963 and is an acknowledged leader in the design of ferry and cruise ship interiors, with three UK national design awards. It has extensive experience covering monohulls, catamarans and Swath vessels.

The most recently completed contracts include work on two 400 seat high-speed catamarans for Wightlink Ferries and a 1,400 passenger cruise ship, the *MV Zenith*, for Chandris Celebrity Cruises. McNeece is interior design consultant for Swath International Ltd for its Super Regency and Swath Ocean 4000 vessels.

McNeece design is targeted to the end user; the passenger. At the outset, it establishes a clear understanding, with the co-operation of the owners, of the passenger profile and their aspirations. This strategic guidance enables the firm to focus on the marketing aspects of the design. An important factor, essential for the success of the interior design as a motivational tool in the process of earning revenue and adding value to the product.

CAD facilities are available, as are layering and three-dimensional modelling capabilities. Services include the production of general arrangements; full colour artist's impressions; working drawings; interior fit-out specifications; schedules of fixtures and finishes; weight calculations and budgeted fit out costs.

VERIFIED

MARITIME SERVICES LTD

Stone Lane, Gosport, Hampshire PO12 1SS, UK

Tel: +44 (1705) 524490
Fax: +44 (1705) 524498
E-mail: 70630.2067@compuserve.com

Ian C Biles, *Managing Director*
Duncan Saunders, *Operations Manager*

Vessel refit, repair, new building and refit supervision, feasibility studies, route evaluation and vessel management.

Maritime Services International Ltd was set up seven years ago to provide an expert technical service to owners and operators of fast craft worldwide.

Recent projects have included a hull damage repair supervision and full refit of two Cirrus 120P SES catamarans, proposal of a fast patrol boat conversion for an oil company operating on the west coast of Africa and feasibility study into the repair of the badly damaged *Catamaran 1*. In addition to the technical side of their work the company has carried our economic evaluations of possible fast ferry routes in the Persian Gulf and South America, either using existing vessels or recommending new vessels.

Current work includes a full economic and technical feasibility study into a long distance route in the Indian Ocean, a proposal for a full management structure for a new fast cross channel passenger service and multiple surveys on private superyachts.

UPDATED

RAY HARVEY DESIGN

12 Pamplyn Close, Lymington, Hampshire SO41 9LD, UK

Tel: +44 (1590) 675242
Fax: +44 (1590) 675243

Ray Harvey, *Director*

Ray Harvey design was formed in 1991 to offer technical and design services for sail and powered craft covering pleasure, commercial and military vessels. Mr Ray Harvey has 25 years' experience of the marine industry and is a qualified naval architect, marine engineer, stylist and artist. Recent projects have included a 15 m high-speed patrol craft design for anti-smuggling and other Coastguard duties.

NEW ENTRY

SEASPEED TECHNOLOGY LTD

The Old Mill, Botley, Southampton, Hampshire SO30 2GB, UK

Tel: +44 (1489) 795222
Fax: +44 (1489) 795333

S J Phillips, *Director*

Seaspeed Technology Ltd is an independent company specialising in the technology of high-speed marine craft. A worldwide multidisciplinary marine consultancy and design support service is provided in both the commercial and military industry sectors. The company offers a high level of academic, professional and practical experience over the complete range of design, build and operational technologies.

The main activities of the company include:
High-speed craft preliminary and detail design
Speed, manoeuvring and sea-keeping predictions
Structural design and materials selection
Computer simulations of multihull manoeuvring and seakeeping
Model construction, testing and data analysis
Ship sea trials and instrumentation
Risk and FMEA analysis for ship systems and equipment
Design assessments
Market analysis.

Seaspeed Technology has provided consultancy services to major companies around the world, generally in the field of high-speed craft design, production and operation.

Recent contracts have included:
Military patrol craft and commercial fast ferry designs
Fast catamaran research for the UK Defence Research Agency
Stability of workboat research for the UK Marine Safety Agency
Risk analysis for the Department of Transport and industrial companies
Market research for the UK-based Marine Technology Directorate
Radio controlled model construction and testing
Shallow water testing of fast multihull vessels
Fast craft manoeuvring and sea-keeping simulations
Advanced material developments
Marine escape system design, simulation and trials
Design and technology assessments and patent developments.

UPDATED

ROBERT L TRILLO

Broadlands, Brockenhurst, Hampshire SO42 7SX, UK

Tel: +44 (1590) 622220
Fax: +44 (1590) 622220

Eur Ing Robert L Trillo, *Principal*

An independent consultancy formed in 1969, since when work has been undertaken in many countries throughout the world, principally concerned with the introduction of new concepts and innovation in advanced forms of marine transport.

Capabilities:
Consultancy and design work on all forms of high-speed waterborne transport (urban transport and sea-going) including catamarans, hovercraft and Surface Effect Ships (SES). Feasibility studies and appraisal of projects for development financing and supervision of programmes from preliminary design through to production.

High-speed ferry evaluation:
Engineering capabilities of specific relevance to high-speed waterborne urban transport systems including the design of quiet air propulsion systems (designs of Robert Trillo ducted propellers are now employed on over a dozen types of hovercraft), and the development of techniques for the avoidance or minimisation of vessel wash.

An extensive database of statistics and information on all types of high-speed ferries is available to assist in feasibility studies concerned with the choice of vessels and power-plants.

The principal has been engaged as an expert witness on arbitration cases and is the author of the book *Marine Hovercraft Technology*.

Projects:
High-speed river craft innovation and development for minimum wash and minimum noise in relatively calm and sheltered waters. A catamaran concept with extremely slender hulls and introduced as the RTL Hydrocat, is now patented and has been actively taken up by FBM Marine Ltd, Isle of Wight, UK, as their Thames Class catamaran.

Further work has continued on the development of propulsion systems for amphibious vehicles for use in swamps and canal restoration work and the development of quiet amphibious hovercraft.

A particularly interesting low-speed project has been the preliminary design and project management for an Italian air cushion vehicle for rice cultivation work, two prototypes having been built by Griffon Hovercraft Ltd.

VERIFIED

WOLFSON UNIT FOR MARINE TECHNOLOGY AND INDUSTRIAL AERODYNAMICS

University of Southampton, Southampton, Hampshire SO17 1BJ, UK

Tel: +44 (1703) 585044
Fax: +44 (1703) 671532
E-mail: jlr@soton.ac.uk

Ian Campbell, *Senior Trials Engineer*
Andrew Claughton, *Senior Naval Architect*
John Robinson, *Software Sales Manager*

The Wolfson Unit is a commercial consultancy within the Department of Ship Science at the University of Southampton. The Unit was established in 1967 to provide a comprehensive advisory service in marine technology and industrial aerodynamics. It is staffed by full-time qualified consulting engineers, with a wide range of academic and industrial experience. It is also able to draw on the experience of academic staff and other consulting engineers throughout the university to broaden the scope of the services offered.

The unit has always specialised in small fast vessels, with towing tank testing of high-speed motor yachts, patrol craft and pilot boats forming a significant proportion of the work in its early years. Test techniques have developed to keep pace with the demands of industry, and specialised equipment has been designed to address the particular requirements of catamarans, SWATHS and dynamically supported craft.

With the importance of sea-keeping in high-speed craft design, much of the Unit's work now includes assessment of motions and accelerations. These can be predicted using the Wolfson Unit's own computer software or measured in the towing tank. The Unit has considerable experience in the measurement of motions at full scale, and has developed an acceleration meter for permanent installation on high-speed craft to monitor motions with regard to passenger comfort, crew performance, or structural limitations. For trial measurements the Wolfson Unit has a range of portable PC-based trials data acquisition systems tailored for routine acceptance trials, and instrumentation packages to cater for specialised requirements.

In the field of model testing the Unit has access to high-speed towing tanks, with carriage speeds of up to 15 m/s, for resistance, sea-keeping and related testing, and two large aeronautical wind tunnels for measurement of aerodynamic forces and flow studies for funnel and superstructure designs. Radio-controlled models may be used in the study of manoeuvring or sea-keeping, and a variety of sheltered inland and coastal sites are available locally, in addition to controlled sea-keeping basins. The same facilities and expertise are employed by sailing yacht designers, and the Wolfson Unit's capabilities were demonstrated in 1995 when the yacht 'Black Magic', which was tested in an extensive towing tank and wind tunnel programme at the Wolfson Unit, won the America's Cup.

All computer software developed by the Unit is offered for sale and by bureau service. Programs include a comprehensive suite of design software for hydrostatics, stability and damage, a power prediction and propeller design suite, lines generation and fairing, sea-keeping, manoeuvring, and trials data acquisition. A recent addition to the range is an onboard loading program approved for use on passenger vessels by the U.K. Marine Safety Agency. The wide experience of the engineers makes them invaluable in troubleshooting problems with propulsion, vibration, sea-keeping, structures, stability and aerodynamics.

UPDATED

W S ATKINS MARINE & STRUCTURAL TECHNOLOGY

Division of WS Atkins Consultants Ltd

Woodcote Grove, Ashley Road, Epsom, Surrey KT18 5BW, UK

Tel: +44 (1372) 726140
Telex: 266701 ATKINS G
Fax: +44 (1372) 740055

W S Atkins is a large, international, multidisciplinary consultancy offering a wide range of services useful to designers, builders and operators of fast craft. Although a relatively recent entrant into the fast craft arena, the company has been established for many years in the offshore industry.

Structural and naval architectural work is carried out by the Marine and Structural Technology division which specialises in engineering analysis, using software which has been developed in-house. The main areas of work are analysis of hydrodynamic loads and motions in regular and irregular waves; linear and non-linear structural analysis, including fracture mechanics; fatigue analysis.

There have been two major software packages developed; AQWA deals with hydrodynamic analysis whilst ASAS is a finite element package. Both have been widely used by the company and others for analysis of fixed and floating marine structures, including offshore platforms, VLCCs and fast catamarans.

The Marine and Structural Technology division is supported by the other divisions in the group which offer a range of relevant skills, including computational fluid dynamics; noise and vibration; design of port and harbour facilities; safety and reliability; planning of transport systems and cargo management systems.

Recent experience has included work on large wave piercing catamarans, in which hydrodynamic analyses were performed with waves from various directions to compare sea-keeping and loads on different vessels. This was followed by extensive structural analysis involving global stress distribution, design of fatigue-resistant details and investigation of superstructure mounting systems.

VERIFIED

UNITED STATES OF AMERICA

AERO-MARINE ENGINEERING

9727 Hagel Circle, Lorton, Virginia 22079, USA

Tel: +1 (703) 550 1236
Fax: +1 (703) 550 1236

Harold Ginsberg, *President*

Mr Harold Ginsberg founded Aero-Marine Engineering in 1994. Aero-Marine Engineering is a technical consulting firm for the aerospace and marine industry and performs project management, design, development and engineering support of advanced marine vehicles. It specialises in hovercraft, surface effect ships, hydrofoils, wing-in-ground-effect craft and high-speed catamarans.

Prior to starting this firm Mr Ginsberg was a project engineer at the US Army's Belvoir RD&E centre's Marine Division and designed, developed and provided engineering support to the US Army's hovercraft programmes.

VERIFIED

AIR CRAFT CORPORATION

4112 Victoria Blvd, Hampton, Virginia 23669, USA

Tel: +1 (804) 722 6994

Ronald Gorton, *President*
Simon T Gorton, *Vice President*
Steven G Doleac, *Project Manager*

Air Craft Corporation is a consulting, manufacturing and marketing company that was formed to fill a need in the industry for affordable air cushion vehicles. Air Craft is involved in the development of ACV design and analysis software, the development of light hovercraft, and the fabrication of lightweight marine structures made of composite materials and corrosion resistant metals. In addition, the company develops and fabricates tooling for composite parts.

Using moulded fibreglass construction techniques, Air Craft has developed a hovercraft, called Ranger, which is capable of carrying a 545 kg payload, or up to six passengers. Uses for this craft include cargo and passenger transport, and recreation. The craft is designed for use in saltwater, has 0.6 m freeboard, is propelled by two ducted fans, and is supported on-cushion by a single independently controlled lift fan. Ranger is available as a low-cost kit product as well as a fully assembled turnkey product.

Air Craft has developed a variety of low-cost fabrication techniques for constructing lightweight composite structures that have foam core and/or blade stiffened geometries. Composite fabrication techniques include hand lay-up, spray up, vacuum bagging and adhesive bonding. Fabrication techniques used to construct lightweight metal structures include SMAW, GTAW and adhesive bonding. Air Craft also has expertise in the fabrication of master and production tooling. The materials used to construct the tooling include composites and industrial plasters. Production tooling structures, measuring up to 9 by 23 ft, have been built.

VERIFIED

AIR RIDE CRAFT INC

15840 SW 84th Avenue, Miami, Florida 33157, USA

Tel: +1 (305) 233 4306
Telex: 6974096 LARAMIE
Fax: +1 (305) 233 1339

Don Burg, *President*

(PATENT HOLDERS, DESIGNERS AND DEVELOPERS)

The Air Ride concept, designed and patented by Don Burg, has been configured in a number of ways on mono- and multihull designs. The concept is based on supporting a percentage of the craft weight on a cushion of air thereby reducing frictional resistance. In the catamaran designs it is reported that 85 per cent of the weight of the craft would be supported by the air cushion.

A number of models, prototypes and operational craft have been built using Air Ride designs, the first test craft having been built in 1978 with a 12.8 m demonstration craft built in 1980. A 19.8 m crew/supply craft was launched in 1983 and by 1991 two other Air Ride craft for passenger transportation had been built by Avondale.

There is a number of associated patents held by Don Burg, possibly the most interesting of which is a locking docking system, which uses the variation in height of the vessel in the water produced by variation in air cushion pressure.

General arrangement of the 49 m SeaCoaster 50 knot ferry **1994**

Air Ride is currently marketing a number of designs including a 26 m, 40 knot ferry; a 26 m, 55 knot private yacht; a 49 m, 50 knot, 500 passenger ferry; a 100 m car and vehicle ferry; and a 215 m, 44 knot freighter.

VERIFIED

AQUAMARINE, INC

33 Sharon Avenue, Piedmont, California 94611-3511, USA

Tel: +1 (510) 654 4448
Fax: +1 (510) 654 2650

P Michael Watson, *President*

Aquamarine provides management services and consultation to passenger vessel operators, for ferry, tourist and dining yacht businesses. The company specialises in financial evaluations, operations and services analysis and standards, guest services organisation and vessel design and construction.

Recent work includes the management of dining cruise and tourist sightseeing operations in San Diego, Newport Beach, Long Beach, Los Angeles, San Francisco and Hawaii; contract and construction management of numerous passenger vessels; analysis and planning for high-speed ferry services in San Francisco Bay and between San Diego and Mexico; and analysis for cruise-ferry operations in California and from Seattle to Canada.

VERIFIED

BAND, LAVIS & ASSOCIATES INC

Corporate Office: Ritchie Highway, Severna Park, Maryland 21146, USA

Tel: +1 (410) 544 2800, +1 (301) 261 1030
Fax: +1 (410) 647 3411
E-mail: bla@access.digex.net

David R Lavis, *President and Chief Executive Officer*
Shirley A Wilson, *Vice President, Finance*
Brian G Forstell, *Vice President, Systems Analysis*
Daniel L Wilkins, *Vice President, Engineering*
John L Allison, *Chief Engineer*
Daniel G Bagnell, *Chief Naval Architect*
Philippe Goubault, *Special Projects*

Band, Lavis & Associates Inc is an independent engineering firm offering a comprehensive range of advanced and conventional marine engineering and naval architectural services. Since 1977, the company has pioneered advanced marine vehicle design and technology development, principally for US military applications. The company provides considerable technical support to the US Navy's ACV and SES programmes, including ship and subsystem design, engineering, analysis, model testing, full-scale tests and trials, computerised performance and motion simulation, and finite element static and dynamic structural analysis. Similar work is performed for the US Army's ACV programmes and for the US Coast Guard's patrol boat and cutter programmes. The staff has made significant contributions to all major ACV and SES programmes in the USA and a large number of earlier programmes in the UK.

The company's dedication to quality was recognised in 1991 with the presentation of two US Small Business Administration (SBA) awards for excellence in contributing to the SBA goal of building America's future.

The company offers particular expertise in the design of high-speed marine craft. Since 1977, the company has been developing a comprehensive range of unique computer software to support this capability, including procedures for the design of hull structure, propulsion systems and the analysis of craft resistance, stability, sea-keeping, manoeuvrability, structural loads and structural design.

The company now has six AutoCAD stations, a fully catalogued product library to support high-speed vessel detail design, a prototype fabrication shop, an expanded experience in conducting ship surveys and ship checks for the US Navy, US Army and USCG, and an expanded experience base in the detail design, manufacturing and testing for the US Navy, Army and commercial clients.

BLA has considerable experience in virtually all areas of ship propulsion including resistance and powering calculations; propeller design and performance for subcavitating, transcavitating, supercavitating and fully ventilated propellers; fully and partially-submerged propellers; propeller testing at model and full-scale, including installation effects, wakes, pressure pulses on hull, noise and miscellaneous cavitation effects; design and performance of thrusters with free and ducted propellers; tow tank self-propulsion tests and cavitation tunnel propeller tests, open water and behind condition; water-jet and water-jet inlet design, model testing, full scale testing and performance; water-jet (and propeller) selection, matching to hull and power plant characteristics and whole-ship design synthesis optimisation; water-jets and propellers for low-speed and conventional ships and craft as well as for high-performance advanced high-speed ships and craft.

BLA also has experience in virtually all areas of ship hydrodynamics including resistance, ship motions, accelerations and human tolerance using SMP and BLA-developed programs; prediction of still water and seaway induced structural loads, slamming and rudder forces; ship manoeuvring, and all other features affecting ship performance.

The company has performed Computational Fluid Dynamic (CFD) analyses for the prediction of surface wave elimination and wake contours of ACV's at various speeds and displacements. In conjunction with a company in Alabama, BLA has performed CFD analysis of water-jet inlets and impellers for several commercial and military clients.

The company has also developed four extensive computer-aided design-synthesis models, one each for SES, ACVs, catamarans and monohulls, all of which permit whole-ship design trade-offs to be examined with respect to cost and craft performance. The software has been extensively validated and has, to date, been used to support 36 separate design projects. Ship designs and detailed hardware designs are developed on the company's CAD system.

Recent Projects:
The company has developed, through full-scale fabrication and operation, vehicles and systems for the US Army aimed at improving the Army's capability to off-load vehicles and cargo over undeveloped shorelines during amphibious operations.

The Pontoon Air Cushion Kit (PACK) was developed to be installed on existing platforms formed of standard 40 × 8 ft pontoons. The prototype PACK ACV system was designed for an 80 × 32 ft platform and provides the platform with an amphibious capability. The company was responsible for the concept, design, fabrication, field assembly and operation of this ACV.

The High-Seastate Container Transfer System (HISEACOTS) was developed to facilitate the off-loading of containers from container ships to LACV-30 ACV lighters. The HISEACOTS was subject to subsystem tests in 1989 and two series of full-scale trials in 1991 and 1992.

In 1991, the company was awarded a US Navy Small Business Innovative Research (SBIR) contract to develop the design of an improved Combat Rubber Raiding Craft (CRRC) with enhanced performance, increased survivability and reduced detectability for US Navy SEALs.

Also in 1991, the company began the design of a unique planing craft referred to as the Advanced Materiel Transporter (AMT) for the Naval Surface Warfare Center (NSWC). In early 1992, the design of a one-third scale GRP model, 44 ft long, was completed and constructed by Seemann's Composites in Gulfport, Mississippi.

In addition to work for the US Department of Defense and the Department of Transportation, the company has become increasingly involved in fast ferry projects in France, Germany, Italy, Japan, South Korea, Norway, Singapore, Sweden and the UK.

UPDATED

DONALD L BLOUNT & ASSOCIATES INC

2550 Ellsmere Avenue, Suite K, Norfolk, Virginia 23513, USA

Tel: +1 (804) 857 1943
Fax: +1 (804) 857 4160

Donald L Blount was design manager for *Destriero*, the 67.7 m vessel which succeeded in achieving the Blue Riband prize for the fastest Atlantic crossing at an average speed of 53.09 knots. Details of *Destriero* are given in the *High-speed Monohull Craft* section of the book.

VERIFIED

Destriero (Will Cofnuk) BRI *1994*

CGZ DESIGN INC

201D Eastbrook, Greenville, North Carolina 27858, USA

Tel: +1 (919) 768 8000

Jim Caldwell, *Chief Designer*
Dr Andrew Zborowski, *President*

ECLIPSE PROJECT (DESIGN)
Designers of monohull and catamaran craft employing a patented 'Constant Lift Hull Configuration,' Jim Caldwell and Andrew Zborowski have established design and model test facilities concentrating on the development of highly efficient hull forms over very wide speed ranges: 20 to 100 knots. Caldwell designed and developed the first true offshore Tunnel Boat in 1979 and holds a patent for the constant lift bottom concept. Zborowski has degrees in naval architecture from The Technical University of Gdansk and has also studied experimental naval architecture at The Hydro and Aerodynamic Laboratory at Lyngby, Denmark. Their latest projects include the Eclipse 140 CAT megayacht and the Fluid Travel 146 CAT high-speed ferry.

VERIFIED

DAVIDSON LABORATORY STEVENS INSTITUTE OF TECHNOLOGY

711 Hudson Street, Hoboken, New Jersey 07030, USA

Tel: +1 (201) 216 5345
Fax: +1 (201) 216 8214

Dr Michael S Bruno, *Director*

Organised in 1935 as the Experimental Towing Tank, the Laboratory is active in basic and applied hydrodynamic research, including smooth water performance and manoeuvrability, sea-keeping, propulsion and control of marine vehicles including ACV, SES, hydrofoil craft, planing craft and so on. Special model test facilities are available to investigate the dynamic behaviour of all types of vessels and platforms in smooth water and waves.

Projects have included:
Towing tank studies of various seaplane model configurations for the analysis of bow spray, porpoising, high-speed resistance and impact loads.
An experimental investigation into the stability, course-keeping and manoeuvring characteristics of planing hulls, performed primarily in the Laboratory's rotating arm facility.

VERIFIED

ELLIOTT BAY DESIGN GROUP LTD

5301 Shilshole Avenue, NW Suite 200, Seattle, Washington 98107, USA

Tel: +1 (206) 782 3082
Fax: +1 (206) 782 3449
E-mail: ebdg@w/n.com

John Waterhouse, *President*
Kenneth Lane, *Vice President*
Douglas Wolff, *Chief Naval Architect*
Brian King, *Chief Marine Engineer*
Annette Grimm, *Finance Manager*
James Cole, *Business Development Manager*

Elliott Bay Design Group is a firm dedicated to providing naval architecture, marine engineering and shipyard support services. Using microcomputer technology and an extensive reference library, the company offers a wide range of services. The firm handles projects ranging from concept design of high-speed hulls to numerical lofting of structure. The full time staff of 22 includes six naval architects, three marine engineers and one electrical engineer.

Elliot Bay Design Group's design experience is focused on commercial workboats and passenger boats. High-speed vessel designs up to 45 m and 50 knots have been created using both high-speed diesels and gas-turbines. The firm has completed work on hydrofoils, catamarans, planing hulls and Swaths. The staff are knowledgeable about the requirements of various regulatory bodies including USCG, ABS, IMO and DnV.

Projects undertaken within the past several years include: the design of an 18.6 m aluminium pilot boat, performance analysis of a 12.8 m high-speed survey boat, design of a harbour service craft with firefighting and oil spill recovery capabilities, a ferry transportation study for Cook Inlet, Alaska, contract design of a 20 m aluminium fireboat and the structural design and lofting of a 7 m rigid inflatable boat. The company has also lofted a variety of hulls from other designers.

UPDATED

FAST HULLS INTERNATIONAL INC

3020 Daurine Court, Gilroy, California 95020, USA

Tel: +1 (408) 842 8913

Bryan Duffty, *President*
Raymond Villareal, *Vice President, Marketing*
Christopher Barry, *Vice President, Engineering*

Fast Hulls International, Inc (FHI) was formed to further develop an advanced hybrid hydrofoil system for general maritime use. The concept was originally developed at FMC Corporation for the US Marine Corps Advanced Amphibian Assault Vehicle (AAAV) programme. FMC has sublicensed the original inventors to use their patents for non-amphibious vehicles.

The basic concept uses one or more stepped planing hulls forward and a fully submerged hydrofoil aft. The planing hull provides the surface reference for the hydrofoil and the hydrofoil provides lift at high efficiency for a portion of the vessel weight. The vessel centre of gravity is well forward of the hydrofoil so that it provides substantial pitch damping. This eliminates the pitch instability common in many hybrid hydrofoil designs, improving sea-keeping without compromising efficiency. The vehicle design can be optimised for efficiency, speed, load carrying and sea-keeping by suitable proportions and design of the planing components and foils and the lift contributed by each.

In late 1992 FHI was testing a subscale manned testbed and smaller self-propelled free models to investigate six degree of freedom dynamic behaviour. FHI is also developing a generalised computer simulation of vehicle dynamics and sea-keeping to evaluate ride quality, structural loads and economics for various services.

Current design projects include a recreational version in the 7 m size range, a human-powered demonstrator to attempt the 20 knot Du Pont prize and a conceptual design for a 149 passenger catamaran ferry.

FHI intends to license their technology to US and international builders when it is fully developed and proven.

VERIFIED

FRYCO INC

7107 Silver Leaf Lane, Houston, Texas 77088, USA

Tel: +1 (713) 820 6617
Fax: +1 (713) 931 5168

Edward D Fry, *President*

Edward Fry established FRYCO in 1978 after 22 years of building experience. He has supervised the design and construction of over 700 commercial, military and pleasure craft including: US Navy high-speed combatants for Navy SEAL Teams, catamarans for commercial and US Army use, monohull yachts up to 50 knots and rig service vessels up to 30 knot speed. He has also conducted scale model tests at various institutions and has data available for design study, designed equipment and written training manuals for oil pollution recovery equipment at five major ports and supervised Middle East licensee shipyard for US builder for four years.

FRYCO designs vessels up to 50 m and specialises in high-speed craft. The company is experienced in gas-turbine engine packaging and installation as well as diesel and petrol engines. Computer models are used for speed prediction and hydrostatics. Hulls are created with computer graphics making fully developed offsets available to the builder for automatic CAD/CAM cutting. Fry's building background assures practical, economic designs with emphasis placed on reliability and serviceability.

Fryco currently has more than a dozen building projects in five countries ranging from fibreglass yachts of 18 m up to aluminium and steel passenger vessels of 70 m. The newest project under development is a 70 m Swath fast ferry vessel. The design is for 1,000 passengers, at 35 knots, and will be model tested by Stevens Institute, Hoboken, New Jersey.

UPDATED

GIBBS & COX INC

50 West 23rd Street, New York, New York 10010, USA

Tel: +1 (212) 366 3900
Fax: +1 (212) 366 3916

Anthony P Romano, *Chairman of the Board*
Henry E Buttelmann, *President*

Arlington Office: 1235 Jefferson Davis Highway, Arlington, Virginia 22202, USA

Tel: +1 (703) 979 1240

Bath Office: 46 Church Road, Brunswick, Maine 04011, USA

Tel: +1 (207) 721 8200

Project management, co-ordination and consultation on conceptual and preliminary designs, contract drawings and specifications and construction drawings for commercial or naval ships of the SES/ACV or submerged hydrofoil systems, destroyers, escorts, frigates, corvettes and VTOL/Helo carriers.

VERIFIED

THE HARBOR CONSULTANCY INTERNATIONAL

34 Otis Hill Road, Hingham, Massachusetts 02043, USA

Tel: +1 (617) 749 0078
Fax: +1 (617) 749 0078

Martha A Reardon, *Managing Director*

The Harbor Consultancy International, founded by Martha A Reardon in 1987, provides ferry transit system consultancy to public agencies and private businesses and individuals. Services range from the initial development of ferry concepts, public participation programmes (including the establishment and management of Water Transportation Task Forces and Ferry Conferences), use of ferries for the relief of traffic congestion, investigation of environmental considerations and constraints, historic research, slide presentations of existing international ferry systems, government liaison, troubleshooting, the development of marketing proposals and project management. THCI provides liaison services between technical specialists and local government planners and redevelopment authorities. THCI works with consultant teams of transportation planners, naval architects and mechanical engineers. THCI associates have extensive experience in fast ferry system management and operations. Recent projects have included the Water-Transportation Programme for the Commonwealth of Massachusetts, Newport Marine Facilities Study, Rhode Island Water-Transportation Master Plan for the Year 2000, as well as the San Francisco Bay Area Ferry Study and the Massachusetts Water Resources Authority Water-Transportation Programme.

Recent presentations have included: 'Ferries of the United States', International Union of Public Transportation (UITP), Lisbon, September 1995; 'Landside/Waterside Issues in Ferry System Development', Boston Society of Civil Engineers, September 1995; organization of the programme 'Ferries of New England' for the summer meeting of the Transportation Research Board, Boston, June 1995; 'Initiatives and Opportunities in Water Transportation', American Planning Association, Newport, October 1994; 'Fast Ferries: Some Environmental Considerations', 4th International Conference on High Speed Marine Craft, Kristiansand, September 1994; 'Water Transportation and the Urban Environment', Citta d'Acqua, Venice, March 1993 (published in the volume: Cities on the Water and Transport, published by Citta d'Acqua in April 1995).

The Harbor Consultancy International provides the secretariat for the members of the International Marine Transit Association.

UPDATED

J B HARGRAVE NAVAL ARCHITECTS INC

205½ Sixth Street, West Palm Beach, Florida 33401, USA

Tel: +1 (407) 833 8567
Fax: +1 (407) 833 7791

J B Hargrave, *President*

Designers of a wide range of medium to high-speed monohull craft. A 36.5 m fibreglass yacht is presently under construction and is scheduled for completion in January 1996.

Preliminary designs include several 39 m fibreglass motor yachts. In addition design work for production vessels is still continuing.

The company has over 35 years of experience in the design of passenger ferries, commercial vessels and custom motor yachts. These designs range in size from 5.5 m runabouts to 190.5 m chemical tankers.

VERIFIED

J W JOHNSON NAVAL ARCHITECTS

2135 Whispering Sands Lane, Virginia Beach, Virginia 23455, USA

Tel: +1 804 460 0971

FAST-1

The FAST-1 (Fast Air Supported Trimaran) was designed by J W Johnson for Todd Marine in Norfolk Virginia. The prototype, *Wild Thing* was designed to carry 150 passengers as a high-speed thrill ride operating in the Atlantic off Virginia Beach during summer and in the US Virgin Islands during winter.

The vessel is easy to build and maintain. The hull is constructed of Airex composite fibreglass and the engines are Caterpillar diesels driving fixed surface drives with conventional rudders. The prototype is currently in operation and has proved to be fast, reliable and economical.

Currently Josh Johnson is working with three fast ferry operators for commuter ferries built on this same hull platform. Bollinger Shipyard has signed a non-exclusive builder's agreement to market and build this design.

Wild Thing *at speed* ***1996***

The designer specialises in high-speed vessel design and production management in fibreglass, steel and aluminium.

Specifications

Length overall	30 m
Beam	11 m
Draught	1.2 m
Displacement, max	80 t
Crew	3
Passengers	149
Fuel capacity	4500 l
Propulsive power	3 × 750 kW
Max speed	45 kts

Propulsion: The main engines are 3 × Caterpillar 3512 rated at 750 kW; driving J W Johnson designed JSD-1 surface drives, via ZF 195A 2:1 gearboxes.

UPDATED

RAYMOND HUNT ASSOCIATES INC

69 Long Wharf, Boston, Massachusetts 02110, USA

Tel: +1 (617) 742 5669
Fax: +1 (617) 742 6354

John H Deknatel, *President*
Winn Willard, *Manager Commercial and Military Projects*

C Raymond Hunt Associates created the deep-V hull design in 1959 and has been refining the concept since. Specialising in the design of deep-V fast yachts and commercial and military craft, the company's in-house capabilities include the full range of design and engineering services. The present staff of seven includes naval architects and engineers with expertise in all construction materials and methods of propulsion.

Other commercial applications of the Hunt deep-V concept have included:

Sandy Hook, a 20 m, 24 knot, aluminium pilot boat for Port of New York and New Jersey, built by Gladding-Hearn Shipbuilding Corporation
P-150, a 24 m, 27 knot FRP patrol vessel for Western Australia syndicate, now a fisheries patrol vessel in the Solomon Islands
TPB-86, a 26 m, 30 knot FRP water-jet patrol vessel built in Thailand by Technautic Company Ltd
1988, study for Massachusetts Port Authority concerning water transportation in Boston Harbor and Logan Airport focusing on high-speed ferries
1990, design of 22 and 30 knot 18.3 m FRP patrol boats for India
1990 design of 18 m very fast patrol and pursuit craft for Boston Whaler Commercial Products Division.

Recent projects include the 20 m, 25 knot *Golden Gate* pilot boat for San Francisco, and the 29 m, 32 knot FRP sportsfishing yacht *Golden Odyssey II*.

VERIFIED

MARITIME DYNAMICS INC

424X Great Mills Road, Lexington Park, Maryland 20653, USA

Tel: +1 (301) 863 5499
Fax: +1 (301) 863 0254

Clarence A Lysdale, *President*
John D Adams, *Vice President*
Mark E Lindler, *Director of Operations*
Charlotte R Sebra, *Sales and Marketing*
Robert L Chandler, *Service Manager*

Maritime Dynamics Inc (MDI) was founded in 1972 to provide engineering services for the design, development and testing of advanced ships and their subsystems, including: Surface Effect Ships (SESs), Air Cushion Vehicles (ACVs), hydrofoils, catamarans and Small-Waterplane-Area Twin-Hull (SWATH) vessels.

During its 23 year history, MDI has developed simulations to predict the motions of the following types of craft, operating in random seas, with and without active ride control:

Surface Effect Ships
Air Cushion Vehicles
Catamarans
Hydrofoil Catamarans
Monohulls.

MDI offers engineering services in support of conceptual, preliminary, contract and detail design of high-speed craft and related systems in the following areas:

Sea-keeping predictions with and without ride control
Control surface design and hull integration
Lift system design for SES, ACV and foil-supported craft

Structural design and stress analysis
Electronics design of machinery, monitoring and craft control systems
Vibration analysis
Instrumentation systems
Model fabrication, testing, analysis and full-scale prediction
Full-scale testing and analysis.

MDI's engineering capabilities are backed by direct participation in military and commercial high-speed craft that are in operation in various parts of the world. Many of these vessels are fitted with MDI ride control systems, see the *Ride Control Systems* section of this book. This participation provides continuous feedback to improve design methods and simulation programmes.

VERIFIED

PAYNE ASSOCIATES

300 Park Drive, Severna Park, Maryland 21146, USA

Tel: +1 (410) 647 4943
Fax: +1 (410) 647 0954

Mr Payne is an authority on the biodynamics of ride comfort and a US member of the International Standards Organization committees responsible for standards in this field.

Payne designed and launched two experimental Swath vessels (FICATs I and II) in 1964-65, the first supercritical planing hulls (GAYLE Boats) in 1968, the first Seaknife in 1971 and the first foil-supported catamaran (the Wavestrider) in 1983. Modern Swath designs have tended to follow Dr Tom Lang's configuration, but all these boats have had an impact on the more advanced designs recently appearing around the world. Because foil supported craft occasionally 'plough-in', no matter how active their control systems, and are not considered smooth riding enough for speeds above 40 knots, Payne started developing an improved configuration in 1989. A 3 tonne prototype was launched in Spring 1994, and preliminary trials have been conducted successfully in 1995.

In 1990, Payne Associates introduced the first time-domain personal computer programme for high-speed boats. BOAT3D replicates all the capabilities of a sophisticated towing tank for calm water or any kind of random seaway. Estimates of ride comfort and probability of kinetosis are part of the programme's printed output. BOAT3D can also calculate the pressure distribution and peak plating stress throughout the hull, once typical scantlings are defined. The programme has a number of internal hull algorithms which can replicate the vast majority of lines by adjusting a few coefficients. User-supplied lines which are incompatible with these internal algorithms can be inserted via a user-written subroutine, such as a list of offsets.

The programme can also utilise 'external forces' not generated by the hull in the main programme. It has been used in this way to add the aerodynamic forces and moment of a wingship, in the study of take off, landing and occasional wave impacts while cruising over a seaway. The forces and moments from the hydrofoils of Payne Associates' Dynafoil prototype were also coupled to BOAT3D for an extensive optimisation and evaluation of the boat in a seaway prior to commencing construction.

Dynafoil prototype at speed ***1996***

UPDATED

QUADRIMARAN INTERNATIONAL

c/o Baltimore Steam Packet Company Inc, PO Box 1959, Williamsburg, Virginia 23185, USA

Tel: +1 (804) 220 2355
Fax: +1 (804) 253 8110

Trond Conradi, *President*

The Quadrimaran, a four-hulled fast multihull craft, was designed by Daniel Tollet of France, and developed using a large-scale prototype craft. An 18.5 m vessel was constructed in France in 1991 and has since then been operational in the Mediterranean. Two 27 m, 28 knot vessels were delivered in 1994 and a 60 knot prototype is currently under construction in Portsmouth, Virginia, USA.

The benefits of the craft are reported to be related to low fuel and running costs and a high level of stability and sea-keeping ability.

Designs are offered from 22.5 m to 175 m with payloads ranging from 5 to 3,000 tonnes.

VERIFIED

M ROSENBLATT & SON INC

350 Broadway, New York, New York 10013, USA

Tel: +1 (212) 431 6900
Fax: +1 (212) 334 0837

Lester Rosenblatt, *Chairman and Chief Executive Officer*
P W Nelson, *President and Director*
A M Stein, *Vice President, Operations and Director*
B Rosenblatt, *Vice President and Director*
S Halpern, *Vice President and Manager, Western Division*
N M Maniar, *Vice President and Technical Director*
D M Krepchin, *Vice President and Manager, San Diego Branch*
A Baki, *Vice President and Manager, Washington DC Area Branch*
C Laviola, *Vice President and Design Manager, Eastern Division*
P B Kimball, *Vice President*

M Rosenblatt & Son Inc is an established naval architectural and marine engineering firm with nearly 50 years of proven experience in all phases of ship and marine vehicle design.

With offices in nine US cities and abroad, the firm is close to the entire shipbuilding community and has a thorough understanding of its problems and needs. Its experience covers programme management, inspection of construction and integrated logistics support, as well as design.

A major portion of the company's design activities has been and is for the US Navy. Completed assignments are of the broadest possible variety, covering research and development, feasibility studies, preliminary, contract and detail design for all classes of major combatants, auxiliaries and high-performance craft. In addition, the company has provided extensive design services for the conversion, overhaul and repair of naval combatants, auxiliaries, submarines, amphibious warfare supply and landing craft.

The service to the maritime industry includes a wide variety of tasks covering the new and modification design of oceanographic ships, container ships, tankers, general cargo ships, dredgers, bulk carriers, drilling platforms and ships, survey vessels, pipe-laying barges and a great variety of supporting craft.

Typical high-speed marine craft and ACV assignments have included:
Concept designs of a 20 tonne wheeled ACV and a 60 tonne wheeled hydrofoil for the US Army
Preliminary and detail design of a 30 m combat hydrofoil for a foreign army
Steering and manoeuvring system design for a tracked ACV for Bell Textron
Surface Effect Ship Advanced Design and Technology handbook for US Navy
PHM design producibility and cost reduction review for US Navy
Development of Advanced Marine Vehicle (AMV) bibliography for US Navy.

ARPA Advanced Surface Effect Vehicles

Conceptual studies, parametric studies and propulsion machinery analysis for phase 'O' studies of Advanced Surface Effect Vehicles for Advanced Research Project Agency. Work performed for American Machine and Foundry Company.

JSESPO Surface Effect Ship Test Craft

Conceptual and feasibility design studies of candidate SES vehicles for the JSESPO sizing study for second-generation SES test craft in the 1,000 to 3,000 tonne range. The work included studies of various candidate versions of SES to identify and evaluate their unique operational and design capabilities; technological assessment of various structural materials and systems; and preparation of a proposed development programme with required supporting research and development. Work performed for Joint Surface Effect Ship Program office.

AAV(P) Advanced Assault Amphibious Vehicle Personnel

Assistance to FMC Corporation with development of alternative concepts for proposal to the US Navy.

VERIFIED

SSSCO

Semi-submerged Ship Corporation

417 Loma Larga Drive, Solana Beach, California 92075, USA

Tel: +1 (619) 481 6417
Fax: +1 (619) 481 7282

Dr Thomas G Lang, *President*

SSSCO was founded by Dr Thomas G Lang, the inventor of the Semi-Submerged Ship (S^3). The S^3 consists of two parallel torpedo-like hulls attached to which are two or more streamlined struts which pierce the water surface and support an above-water platform. Stabilising fins are attached near the aft end of each hull and a pair of smaller fins are optionally located near their forward ends.

Semi-submerged ship technology (also known as Swath) has been proven over the past 20 years by the 190 ton SSP *Kaimalino*, a US Navy-developed range-support vessel which has been operating in the rough seas off the Hawaiian islands since 1975. Following private development, Dr Lang introduced the concept into the US Navy. He led the Navy's first research work and initiated and developed the hydrodynamic design for the SSP *Kaimalino*, the world's first high-performance, open-ocean Swath ship.

The performance features that distinguish S^3s from conventional vessels are greatly reduced motions with sustained speed even in heavy seas, lower hydrodynamic drag and reduced power requirements at moderate to high speeds, and superior course-keeping characteristics at all sea headings.

SSP Kaimalino (US Navy) **1986**

Kaimalino

Operated by the Naval Command Control and Ocean Surveillance Centre at San Diego, California, the SSP *Kaimalino* has operated from near calm conditions to beyond Sea State 6 at speeds up to 25 knots. Its motion is small relative to a conventional monohull of similar payload capacity, either when at rest or underway. The SSP has made smooth transits in 4.57 m swells without any impacts; however, in short, steep 3.7 m waves occasional bow impacts have occurred. No structural damage has occurred, even during storm conditions when 7.6 to 9.2 m high waves were encountered.

In February 1985 ten Woods Hole Oceanographic Institution scientists participated in a series of two- and three-day cruises off Hawaii on the Swath vessel *Kaimalino* over a two week period; as a result they highly recommended the Swath design for oceanographic research. In 1993 the two gas-turbines used for propulsion were replaced by two 671 TA Detroit Diesel engines to provide greater economy but lower speeds as indicated below.

Specifications

Length	27 m
Beam	14 m
Height	9.7 m
Displacement	217 t
Payload	50 t
Max speed	15 kts
Operational speed	13 kts
Range	400 n miles

UPDATED

GEORGE G SHARP, INC

100 Church Street, New York, New York 10007, USA.

Tel: +1 212 732 2800
Fax: +1 212 732 2809

I Hilary Rolih, *Chairman*
A Chin, *President*

This company provides consulting services for the marine transportation and business development industries. In particular the expertise is based around marine engineering, marine surveying and naval architecture.

NEW ENTRY

SWATH INTERNATIONAL LTD

4061 Powder Mill Road, Calverton, Maryland 20705, USA

Tel: +1 (301) 595 9850
Fax: +1 (301) 595 9854

Captain C W Hayes, *Managing Director*

Swath International Ltd is a ship design company specialising in the technology of Swath craft, particularly those with a fast operational speed. A wide range of designs is marketed by the company which also has agreements with shipyards worldwide including Bollinger Shipyard in the USA, Greenbay Marine in Singapore and Rodman Polyships in Spain, to build their vessels. Nichols Brothers of Seattle, USA, commenced construction of a Super 4000 Class high-speed passenger Swath in 1993 which was completed in 1995.

The range of designs covers passenger and ro-ro ferries, cruise ships, supply ships, hydrographic survey vessels and pilot/patrol craft ranging in size from 18 to 100 m

The baseline designs cover: the 80 m Super Regency Class carrying 876 passengers and 258 cars at 37 knots; and the 37 m Super 4000 Class which can be configured as a ro-ro or passenger only ferry. The vessel of this class currently under construction at Nichols Brothers is designed as a casino ferry carrying 384 passengers at 27 knots; the 33 m Euro 4000 has been configured in a number of arrangements such as a cruise vessel, supply vessel and passenger ferry. The smallest design offered is the 18.7 m Channel Class craft carrying 100 passengers at a speed of 25 knots.

The design of these craft offers extremely low ship motions and minimal degradation in speed performance in rough weather compared to all other multihull craft, these aspects being clear advantages of the Swath concept.

80 m SUPER REGENCY CLASS (DESIGN)

Ro-ro passenger ferry.

Specifications

Length overall	80 m
Beam	33.2 m
Draught	7.1 m
Passengers	1,400
Vehicles	365 cars or 10 coaches + 265 cars
Max speed	40 kts
Operational speed	40 kts

UPDATED

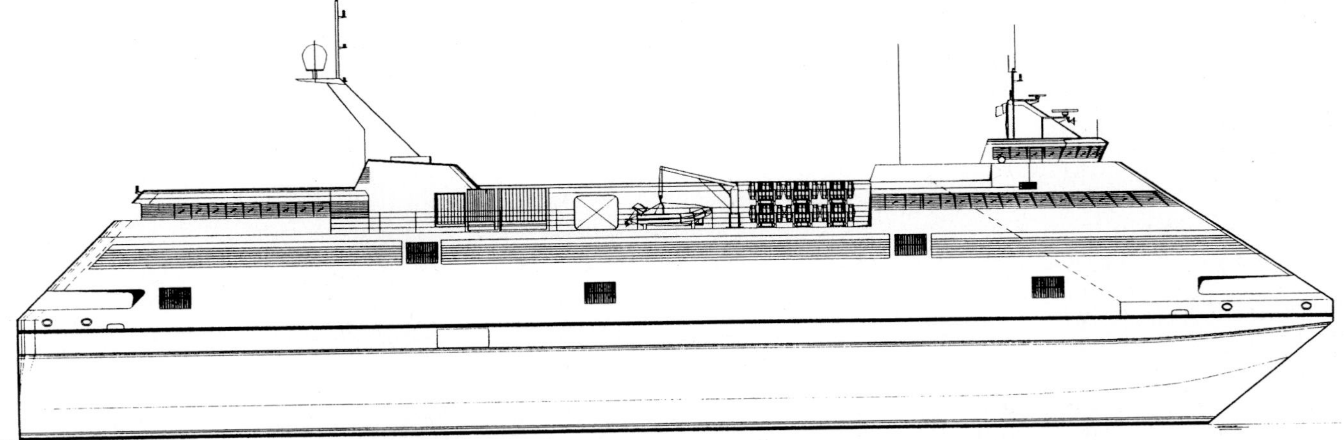

General arrangement of Super Regency Class Design **1995**

TGMD INC

211 North Third Avenue, PO Box 290, Sturgeon Bay, Wisconsin 54235, USA

Tel: +1 (414) 743 5092
Fax: +1 (414) 743 7936

Timothy Graul, *Principal*

TGMD Inc, was incorporated in 1994, continuing the naval architecture, marine engineering, design and consulting practice begun when the firm was established in 1981 as Timothy Graul Marine Design. A separate branch, Timothy Graul Marine Surveys, offers surveys and appraisals. Graul is a non-exclusive surveyor for DnV.

The design of patrol boats, ferries, pilot boats, tugs, fire boats, military vessels, research boats, passenger craft and river tow boats and barges remain specialities of TGMD, particularly those less than 61 m (200 ft) in length. As a result, the staff are especially skilled in design techniques and applications of rules and regulations applicable to small ships. All staff have hands on experience in vessel construction and operation.

TGMD uses computer programs for stability, powering and performance analyses; for structural design optimisation and for configuration control. Computer-aided drafting is employed whenever it is appropriate.

Major projects completed by TGMD in 1994 include a 600 passenger dinner/excursion boat, a 300 passenger transfer boat, an aluminium catamaran, several dinner/cruise boats, a crew/supply boat and a ferry barge/tug combination. In addition, the firm assisted builders of many other craft with engineering services, regulatory body approval assistance and working plans.

Timothy Graul, president of TGMD Inc, is a graduate of the University of Michigan and a registered Professional Engineer. He is a member of SNAME and its small craft committee and is Chairman of panel SC-5 (small passenger vessels). He is assisted by a staff of five designers and engineers.

VERIFIED

SOCIETIES INVOLVED WITH HIGH-SPEED CRAFT

Company Listing by Country

Canada
Canadian Air Cushion Technology Society
International Marine Transit Association

United Kingdom
The Hovercraft Society
Rapid Marine Transport Group

United States of America
The International Hydrofoil Society

CANADA

CANADIAN AIR CUSHION TECHNOLOGY SOCIETY

130 Slater St, 818 Ottawa, Ontario K1P 6E2, Canada

Tel: +1 (613) 234 0191
Fax: +1 (613) 234 9039

Capt D L'Heureux, *Chairman*

The Canadian Air Cushion Technology Society (CACTS) is a constituent society of the Canadian Aeronautics and Space Institute (CASI). It is devoted to the development and application of air cushion technology, principally with regard to the transportation domain, but also in industry and in other fields where this technology may be of benefit. The goal of the society is to keep its members abreast of developments in the field through information dissemination and exchange. This is done through periodic conferences to which participants from various countries involved in air cushion technology and hovercraft are invited.

UPDATED

INTERNATIONAL MARINE TRANSIT ASSOCIATION

34 Otis Hill Road, Hingham, Massachusetts 02043, USA

Tel: +1 604 381 1401
Fax: +1 604 381 7238

Frank A Rhodes, *President*
Martha A Reardon, *Secretary, Treasurer*

Tel/Fax: +1 (617) 749 0078

IMTA was formed in 1977 'to research and collect information on developments within and affecting the ferry service industry; to exchange information and technical data through an international network of members; and to stimulate industry co-operation and advancement by providing a forum for people to share experiences and learn from others'. Annual conferences have been held in Europe, Asia and North America. The agenda includes subjects of interest to large and small ferry operators of conventional and high-speed craft, passenger-only, ro-ro ferry systems and public and private agencies.

Conferences during the last three years were held in San Francisco, Bergen and Sydney, and were managed by the IMTA President in the host city.

The membership of IMTA includes ferry operators, naval architects, shipbuilders and equipment manufacturers, government agencies, support service companies, marine engineering and planning consultants, academia and specialists in maritime training.

Future conference venues include: Vancouver, Canada in 1996 and Helsingborg, Sweden in 1997.

UPDATED

UNITED KINGDOM

THE HOVERCRAFT SOCIETY

15 St Mark's Road, Gosport, Hampshire PO12 2DA, UK

Tel: +44 (1705) 601310

Lord Romsey, *Patron*
Sir Christopher Cockerell, *President*
R L Wheeler, *Vice President*
J E Rapson, *Vice President*
E G Tattersall, *Vice President*
M A Pinder, *Vice President*
N MacDonald, *Chairman*
W Jacobs, *Hon. Secretary*

Formed in 1971, The Hovercraft Society (THS) was the UK constituent of the 'International Air Cushion Engineering Society'. Membership is open to persons engaged in hovercraft related fields and to those having a *bona fide* interest in hovercraft in the UK and overseas. Current membership is drawn from ACV manufacturers, ferry operators, design groups, government departments and agencies, financial and insurance organisations, consultants, journalists and universities.

THS organises regular meetings at which talks are given on technical, commercial and military design and operation of amphibious craft, SES and other air cushion devices. It also produces a monthly Hovercraft Bulletin available to all members, containing information and news on air cushion related topics.

A collection of references on the subject of hovercraft has been accumulated by the Society. Access to these documents is by prior arrangement with the Secretary.

THS has introduced an annual student award (presently up to £500). This will be granted to a chosen applicant proposing to carry out a project or thesis in the UK on a subject connected with the design, construction or operation of a hovercraft, SES or some other air cushion device (details from the Secretary).

Details of the Hovercraft Museum Trust, now housing a wide range of hovercraft and associated equipment, can be obtained from THS.

VERIFIED

RAPID MARINE TRANSPORT GROUP

c/o RINA, 10 Upper Belgrave Street, London SW1X 8BQ, UK

Tel: +44 (171) 235 4622
Fax: +44 (171) 245 6959

S J Phillips, *Chairman*
M Porter, *Secretary*

The Rapid Marine Transport Group was founded in 1995 as a special interest group of the Royal Institution of Naval Architects (RINA). The objective of the group is the promotion of the fast ferry industry within the context of intermodal transportation and in particular the cross-fertilisation of ideas and views between the marine sector and the equivalent road, rail and air transport sectors. In 1995 the UK Department of Trade and Industry provided funding to promote the activities of the Group, aimed at increasing the UK's contribution to the rapid marine transport industry worldwide.

The steering committee of the Group consists of twelve individuals representing a broad spectrum of relevant industries. The much larger general membership of the Group also represents a wide range of government, academic, manufacturing and service industries within the UK.

NEW ENTRY

UNITED STATES OF AMERICA

THE INTERNATIONAL HYDROFOIL SOCIETY

PO Box 51, Cabin John, Maryland 20818, USA

John R Meyer, *President*
Mark R Bebar, *Vice President*
Capt John W King, *Secretary, Treasurer*
Patsy N Jackson, *Recording Secretary*

A quarterly newsletter is published by the International Hydrofoil Society and is available from Captain John King, USN (Ret), 4313 Granada Street, Alexandria, Virginia 22309, USA

The membership fee for this society is US$ 20.00.

IHS Board of Directors

1991-94
Mark R Bebar
George Jenkins
Capt John W King
Wade Webster

1992-95
John R Meyer
John Monk
Dr James R Wilkins Jnr
Phillip Yarnall

1993-1996
Barney C Black
James H King
Mark Rice
Kenneth B Spaulding Jr

VERIFIED

ADDENDA

AUSTRALIA

INCAT DESIGNS PTY LTD

1 Mafeking Avenue, Lane Cove, Sydney, NSW 2066, Australia

Tel: +61 (2) 427 2822
Fax: +61 (2) 427 7238

Philip Hercus, *Director*

General arrangement details of the 122 m fast passenger/car ferries being designed for BC Ferries of Canada were recently released.

NEW ENTRY

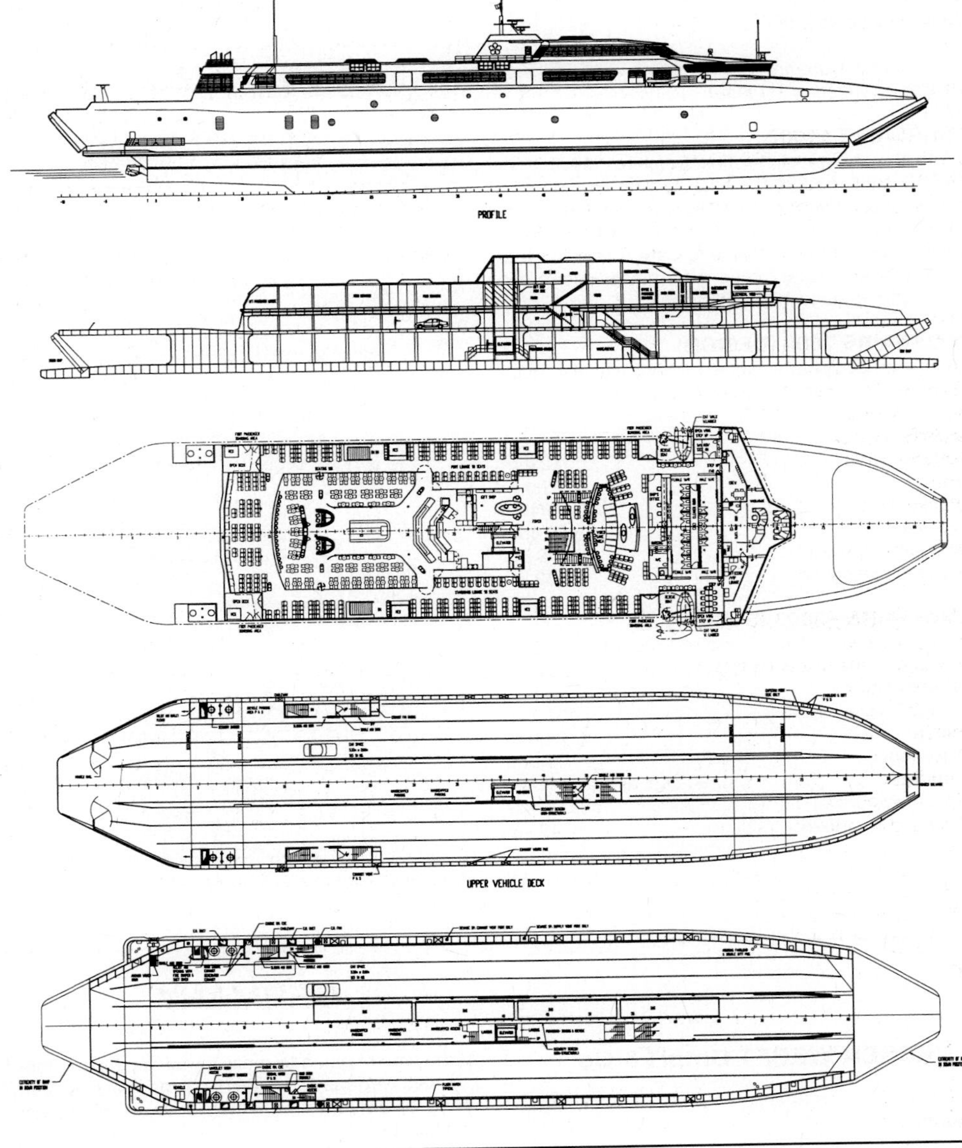

General arrangement of InCat Designs' 122 m catamaran for BC Ferries ***1996***

CHINA, PEOPLE'S REPUBLIC OF

AFAI

Nam Fai High-Speed Craft Manufacturing Ltd

Panyu, Guangdon Province, China

A Fai High-Performance Ships Ltd of Hong Kong (see page 121 of this book) have opened an additional shipyard in the Guangdon Province of China.

The new yard is specifically designed for the building of high-speed craft and is situated on a 50,000 m² site with two 100×48×25 m covered building sheds. The yard has produced a number of small fast vessels and is currently building a 25 m AMD – designed catamaran, the AQUAN 2400. Contacts with this new yard are currently made via the Hong Kong office.

NEW ENTRY

COMMONWEALTH OF INDEPENDENT STATES

ALMAZ SHIPBUILDING COMPANY LTD

26 Petrovsky Prospect, St Petersburg, 197042, Russia, CIS

Tel: +7 (812) 350 1164
Fax: +7 (812) 235 7069

Kizhevich Lisa, *Marketing*

Almaz Shipbuilding Company Ltd have two main high-speed craft projects currently under construction. The 32 m fast passenger ferry swath craft described on page 168 in this book and a 30 m fast workboat described as a Nature Protection Vessel and code named ECOPATROL-1. The passenger ferry was designed by JSC (Joint Stock Company) Marine Systems of Sukhoi and the ECOPATROL Vessel by JSC Association of Marine Instruments Manufacture.

ECOPATROL-1

This is a specialised ecological monitoring catamaran built in aluminium and fitted with over 60 different ecological sensors.

Specifications

Length overall	30.2 m
Beam	6.6 m
Draught	0.8 m
Crew	6
Speed	22 kts
Range	150 n miles

Propulsion: The vessel is conventionally propelled with two ducted fixed pitch propellers each driven by a 590 kW diesel engine.

NEW ENTRY

FRANCE

LEROUX AND LOTZ

10 Rue des Usines, F-44100 Nantes, France

Tel: +33 40 959697
Fax: +33 40 465206

M Breheret, *Commercial Director*
J Ninet, *Marketing Manager*

CORSAIRE 11000

With the launch of the first Corsaire 11000 NGV ASCO early in 1996 the final general arrangement drawing has become available as presented below. The first and second vessels of this class are scheduled to operate on the Nice to Calvi (Corsica) route later this year. Specifications for these vessels can be found on page 192 of this book.

CORSAIRE 7000 (DESIGN)

A smaller design, the Corsaire 7000 has also been introduced based on the first Leroux and Lotz fast ferry *Emeraude*.

Specifications

Length overall	72.4 m
Beam	11.1 m
Passengers	450
Vehicles	50 cars
Propulsive power	10,440 kW
Operational speed	32 kts

CORSAIRE 13000 (DESIGN)

A still larger vessel, the Corsaire 13000 is being marketed with the following specification:

Specifications

Length overall	137.0 m
Beam	21.0 m
Passengers	1,000
Vehicles	290 cars and 6 coaches
Propulsive power	58,000 kW
Operational speed	42 kts

NEW ENTRY

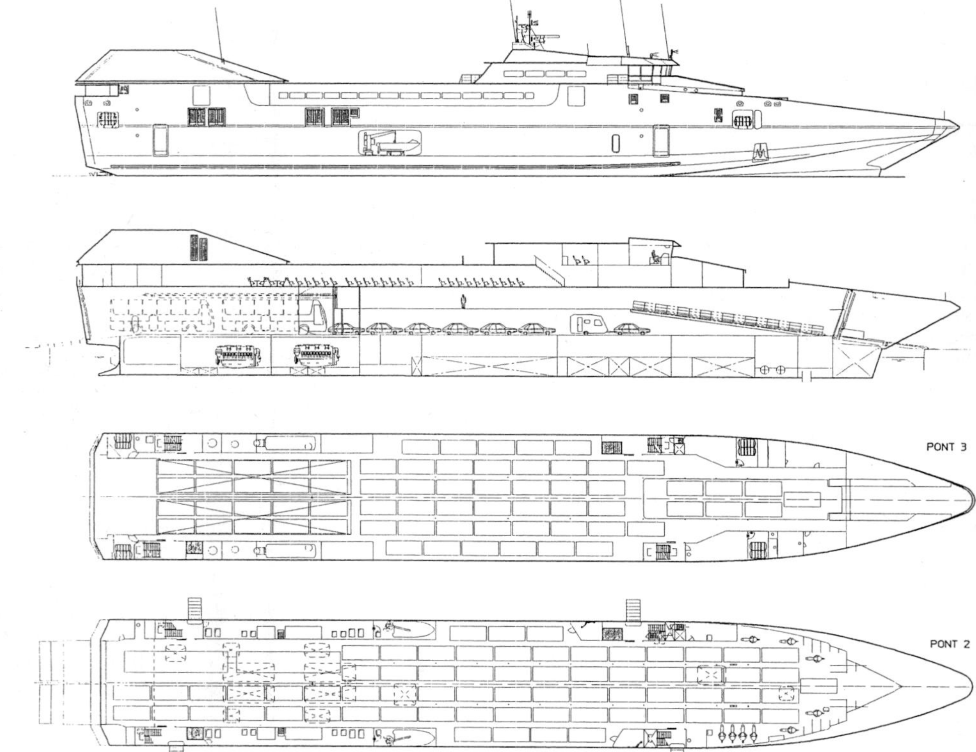

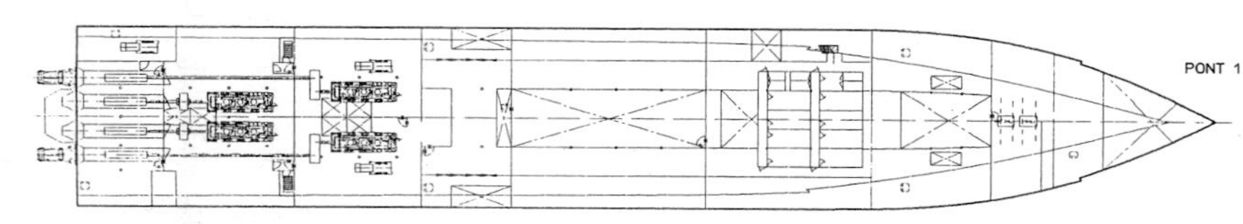

General arrangement of Corsaire 11000

1996

GERMANY

LÜRSSEN WERFT GmbH & Co

Friedrich-Kuppert-Strasse 1, D-28759, Bremen, Germany

Tel: +49 421 66040
Fax: +49 421 4443

At the time of going to press it was announced that Lürssen Werft had received an order for five 70 m monohull fast ferries from the Indonesian Ministry of Transport.

The vessels are understood to have been specified in aluminium and powered by four MTU diesels giving a total power output of 16,000 kW for speeds of up to 38 knots. Powered by water-jets, the vessels have a range of over 500 n miles, carrying 900 passengers. The first two vessels are scheduled for delivery in 1997 with the other three being delivered in 1998.

NEW ENTRY

INDONESIA

PT PAL INDONESIA

Head Office: BPP Teknologi Building 1, Floor 17, JL, Mh Thamrin No 8, Jakarta 10340, Indonesia

Tel: +62 (21) 3156860
Telex: 61725 PAL JKT 1A
Fax: +62 (21) 3156866

Shipyard: Ujung, PO Box 1134, Surabaya, Indonesia

Tel: +62 (31) 3292275
Fax: +62 31 3292516

B J Habbie, *Chairman, President and CEO*
Suleman Wiriadidjaja, *Senior Executive Vice President*
Suhadi, *Executive Vice President, Technology*
Arief Aini, *Executive Vice President, Production*
Wulang Widada, *Executive Vice President, Maintenance*
Bambang Arjunadi, *Vice President Commercial*
Budi Wahono, *Vice President Naval Vessels*
Muhammad Munir, *Vice President Merchant Vessels*

In January 1996 PT PAL Indonesia changed address and contact numbers to those given above. The company is one of the largest and most modern shipbuilding industries in South-east Asia, employing a 6,000 strong workforce. The shipyard offers a wide range of capabilities including construction of naval vessels up to 2,500 tonnes, merchant vessels up to 50,000 DWT, offshore rigs, diesel engines, power generation facilities and chemical plants. The company has recently fitted out two Jetfoil 929-119 troop transports and two Jetfoil 929-120 patrol craft.

NEW ENTRY

ITALY

FINCANTIERI CANTIERI NAVALI ITALIANI SpA

Via Genova 1, I-34121 Trieste, Italy

Tel: +39 (10) 59951
Fax: +39 (10) 5272

Mario De Negri, *General Manager, Naval Shipbuilding Division*

With Fincantieri having accumulated nine orders for 95 m to 100 m monohull fast ferries all within 1995, activity at the company's shipyards is brisk. However with such a large and available shipyard capacity, further ferry orders are being negotiated with Tirrenia, the country's main ferry operator, for two much larger ferries, the 146 m MDV 3000 Jupiter Class.

100 m MDV 1200 PEGASUS

Six of these craft have been ordered by Sea Containers, the first of which is due for delivery in March 1997. These craft are slightly larger than the three MDV 1200 Pegasus designs ordered by Ocean Bridge Investments which are described on page 203. The new order is for a series of all aluminium vessels with the following specifications:

Specifications

Length overall	100 m
Length waterline	88 m
Beam	17.1 m
Passengers	800
Vehicles	175
Propulsive Power	27,500 kW
Operational Speed	38 kts

Structure: All aluminium construction with vehicles entering and leaving by the rear doors. There will be no bow doors fitted to these craft.

Propulsion: Four Ruston 20 RK 270 diesel engines each rated at 875 kW and each driving a Kamewa 112S steerable water-jet via a Renk reduction gearbox.

MDV 3000 JUPITER (DESIGN)

The specification for these craft has changed slightly since they were first released. The current specification is understood to be:

Specifications

Hull of high-tensile steel with aluminium alloy superstructure.

Propulsion: The proposed propulsion arrangement consists of two pairs of diesel engines each pair driving a single steerable water-jet and two gas turbine engines each driving a booster water-jet.

NEW ENTRY

Model of the MDV 3000 Jupiter (design) proposed for Tirrenia ***1996***

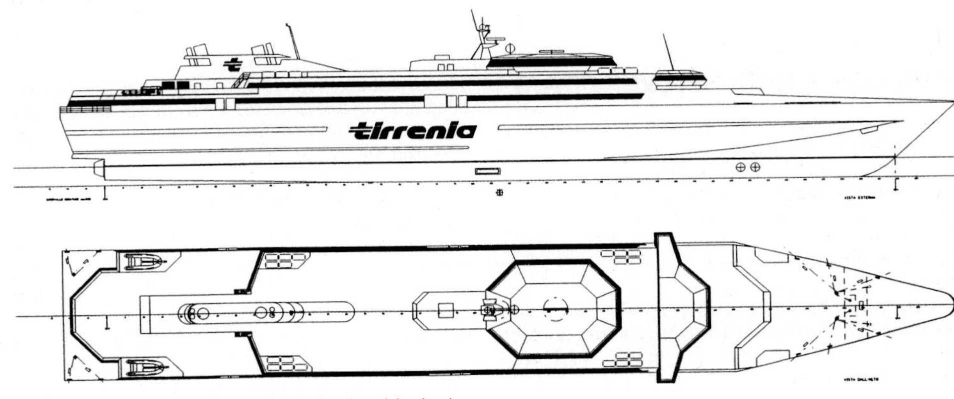

Profile and plan of the MDV 3000 Jupiter (design) ***1996***

KOREA, SOUTH

HYUNDAI HEAVY INDUSTRIES COMPANY LTD

1 Cheonha-Dong, Dong-Ku, Ulsan, South Korea

Tel: +82 (522) 302841
Fax: +82 (522) 330491

In March 1996 it was announced that Hyundai was to build a 35 m fast ferry catamaran for delivery in late 1996. The vessel is understood to be fitted out for 250 passengers and able to operate at speeds of up to 45 knots. This is also the first fast ferry to be powered by Paxman 12VP185 diesel engines. These engines are each rated at 2,185 kW at 1,835 rpm and have been proven in a number of applications. Twelve of these engines are currently being fitted in six 28 m Taiwanese fast patrol craft.

NEW ENTRY

NETHERLANDS

SCHELDE SHIPBUILDING

PO Box 16, 165 Glacisstraat, 4380 AA, Vlissingen, Netherlands

Tel: +31 (118) 482118
Fax: +31 (118) 485010

A Van der Knapp, *Marketing and Sales*

On 17 February 1996 the CAT70HL fast passenger/car catamaran was named *Captain George*. The vessel is due to start service in June 1996 between Italy and Greece for its owner Catamaran Lines Maritime Company of Piraeus.

NEW ENTRY

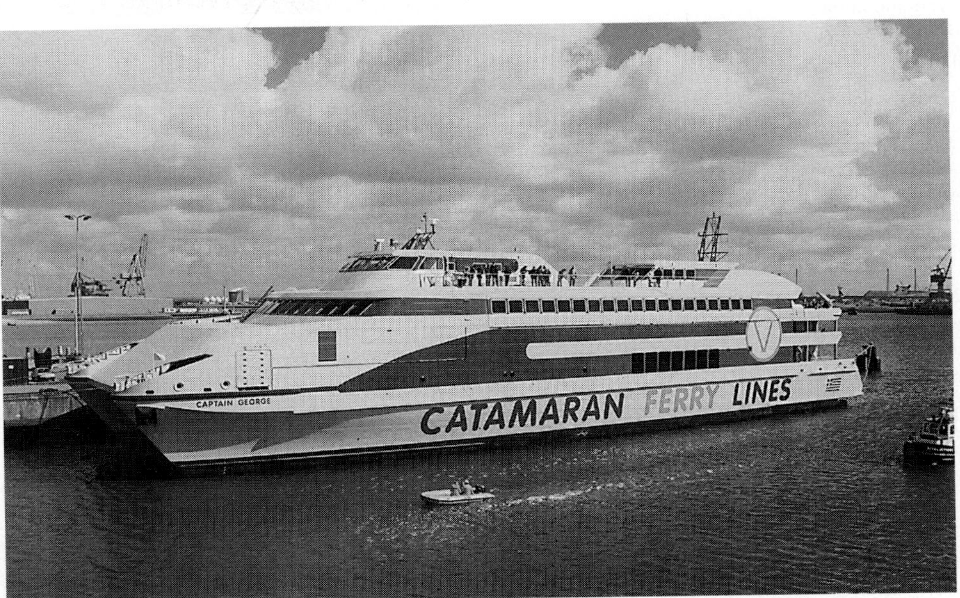

Schelde Shipbuilding CAT70HL Captain George *prior to trials* ***1996***

NORWAY

COLOR SEACAT KS

Sea Containers Ltd announced that it has formed a joint venture company with Norway's leading ferry operator Color Line AS, to launch a new fast ferry service in Scandinavia.

The current 74 m wave piercing catamaran *SeaCat Isle of Man* will be renamed *SeaCat Norge* and will partner with *SeaCat Danmark* to be repainted in the Color SeaCat livery. The new route will involve an operation between Langesund, Grenland in Norway to Frederikshavn in Denmark. The service is due to start in May 1996 with a journey time of 3 hours 15 minutes. Staff currently employed by SeaCat AB in Gothenburg will have their employment contracts transferred to a new company Color SeaCat AB, a subsidiary company of Color SeaCat KS. The Danish employees will be taken on by Color Line Denmark AS

NEW ENTRY

The new Color SeaCat livery
1996

MJELLEM & KARLSEN VERFT A/S

Thormøhlensgt 35/51, PO Box 2713, Møhlenpris, N-5026 Bergen, Norway

Tel: +47 (55) 542200
Fax: +47 (55) 542201

Paul Martens, *Vice President*

In early 1996 Mjellem & Karlsen announced a new 123 m design of a monohull fast ferry based on their successful 95 m vessels. The vessel is constructed of aluminium and powered by six diesel engines giving a total output of over 36,000 kW and a speed of approximately 40 knots.

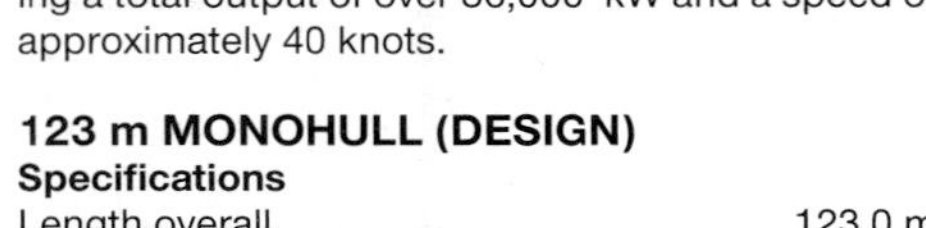

123 m MONOHULL (DESIGN)

Specifications

Length overall	123.0 m
Beam	20.0 m
Draught	4.0 m
Passengers	1,000
Vehicles	254 cars or 4 buses and 218 cars
Propulsive power	36,000 kW
Operational speed	39 kts

Classification: DnV +1A1 HSLC R2 Car Ferry A M CDK EO

Propulsion: Six MTU 20V 1163TB73 diesel engines arranged such that the aft two engines drive individual waterjets via reduction gearboxes and the forward four engines are arranged in pairs, each pair driving through a twin input, single output reduction gearbox to an individual water-jet.

NEW ENTRY

WESTAMARIN A/S

Andøyvein 23, PO Box 8114, Vågsbygd, N-4602 Kristiansand, Norway

Tel: +47 (38) 088200
Fax: +47 (38) 085012

In March 1996 Westmarin A/S announced a series of new fast ferry designs. Further details of the HSS 900 vessels under construction for Stena were also released. It is understood that the original W-12000 and W-9600 designs are still being marketed but the W-8700 and W-7800 designs have been superseded

W-80 (DESIGN)

This design supersedes the W-7100 design and is the largest craft that can be offered with diesel engines only.

Specifications

Length overall	81.1 m
Beam	27.0 m
Draught	3.7 m
Passengers	700
Vehicles	200 cars or 10 buses and 155 cars
Fuel capacity	60,000 l
Propulsive power	34,000 kW
Operational speed	40 kts
Range	450 n miles

Propulsion: Four diesel engines of 5,000 to 6,000 kW each or two gas turbines of 17,000 kW each.

W-90 (DESIGN)

This is a new design although effectively it replaces the W-8700 designs.

Specifications

Length overall	91.3 m
Beam	32.0 m
Draught	4.0 m
Passengers	1,000
Vehicles	270 cars or 12 buses and 220 cars
Fuel capacity	140,000 l
Propulsive power	52,000 kW
Operational speed	45 kts
Range	500 n miles

Model of Stena HSS 900 vessel, two of which are currently under construction ***1996***

Propulsion: Two gas turbines for lower speeds and a CODAG arrangement for higher speeds.

W-100 (DESIGN)

This design supersedes the W-9500 design which itself was used as the basis for the Stena HSS 900 design.

Specifications

Length overall	103.3 m
Beam	32.0 m
Draught	4.5 m
Passengers	1,200
Vehicles	310 cars or 14 buses and 240 cars
Fuel capacity	140,000 l
Propulsive power	52,000 kW
Operational speed	45 kts
Range	500 n miles

Propulsion: Two gas turbines for lower speeds and a CODAG arrangement for the higher speeds.

Stena HSS 900

Two of these vessels have been ordered for Stena Line and are currently under construction. As with other Westmarin craft the hulls are of a semi-swath type giving a high level of seakeeping and speed performance. Vehicle loading arrangements are based on entry and exit over the stern; the vessel can transport buses in the outer lanes and cars, vans and caravans on the two central decks.

Specifications

Length overall	88.0 m
Beam	30.0 m
Draught	3.7 m
Crew	50
Passengers	900
Vehicles	212 cars or 10 buses and 154 cars
Fuel capacity	104,000 l
Propulsive power	34,000 kW
Operational speed	40 kts
Range	400 n miles

Classification: DnV +1A1 HSLC R1 Car Ferry A EO ICS Naut.

Structure: All welded aluminium

Propulsion: The vessel is powered by two ABB Stal G35 gas turbines, one in each hull and each driving via an epicyclic reduction gear to a KMW 160 S11 water-jet unit.

NEW ENTRY

WESTAMARIN WEST A/S

PO Box 143, 4501 Mandal, Norway

Tel: +47 (38) 262222
Fax: +47 (38) 262302

Svein Berntsen, *Technical Manager*

In January 1996 it was announced that after 35 years of high-speed craft construction a decision had been taken to stop all future craft building activities at Westmarin West.

NEW ENTRY

SINGAPORE

KVÆRNER FJELLSTRAND (S) PTE LTD

29 Tuas Crescent, Singapore 2263

Tel: +65 861 4180
Fax: +65 861 4181

Are D Dahl, *President*
P P Wee, *Senior Marketing Manager*
Aage Christensen, *Senior Operations Manager*

Kværner Fjellstrand (S) Pte Ltd was awarded a twin vessel contract by Jindo Transportation of South Korea in 1996 to supply a 40 m and new 34 m Flying Cat fast passenger catamaran. Brief specifications of the vessels were released as follows:

40 m FLYING CAT

In addition to the passenger saloon, this vessel incorporates a cargo section containing two freezer rooms, cargo handling facilities and a reinforced deck section for cargo loads.

Specifications

Length overall	39.9 m
Beam	10.0 m
Passengers	333
Speed	35 kts

Propulsion: Two MTU 16V396 TE74L diesel engines each driving a Kamewa water-jet via a reduction gearbox.

34 m FLYING CAT

Specifications

Length overall	34.0 m
Beam	10.0 m
Passengers	250
Speed	35 kts

Propulsion: Two MTU 12V396 TE74L diesel engines each driving a Kamewa water-jet via a reduction gearbox.

NEW ENTRY

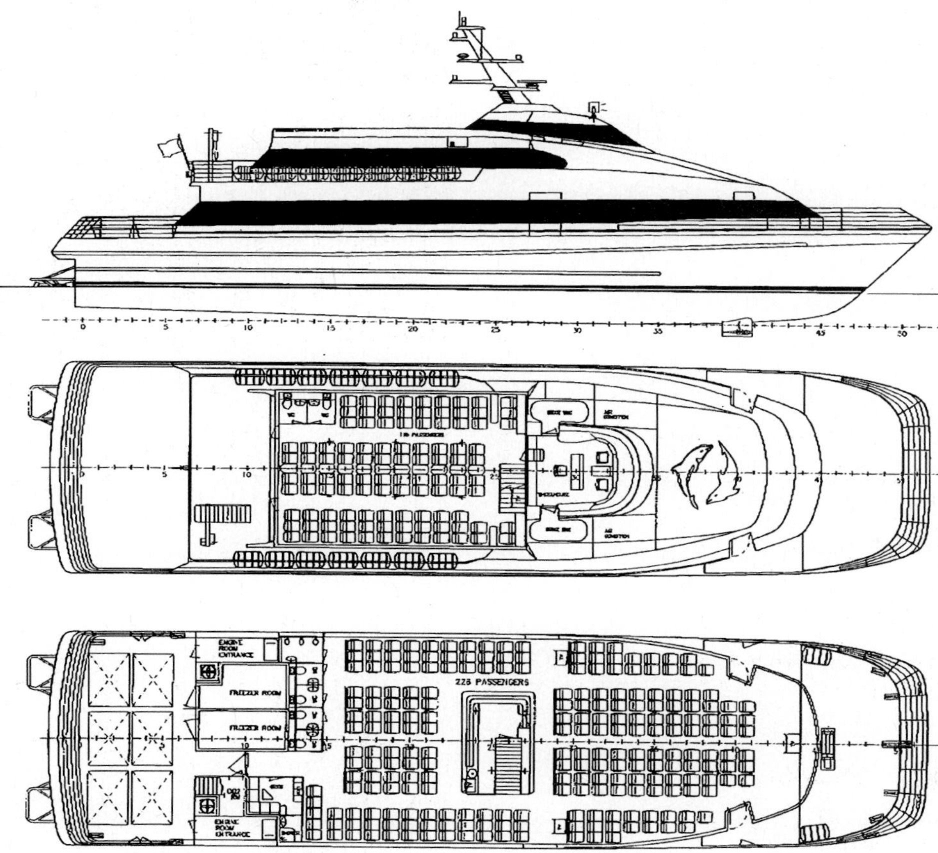

40 m Flying Cat arrangement for Jindo Transportation

1996

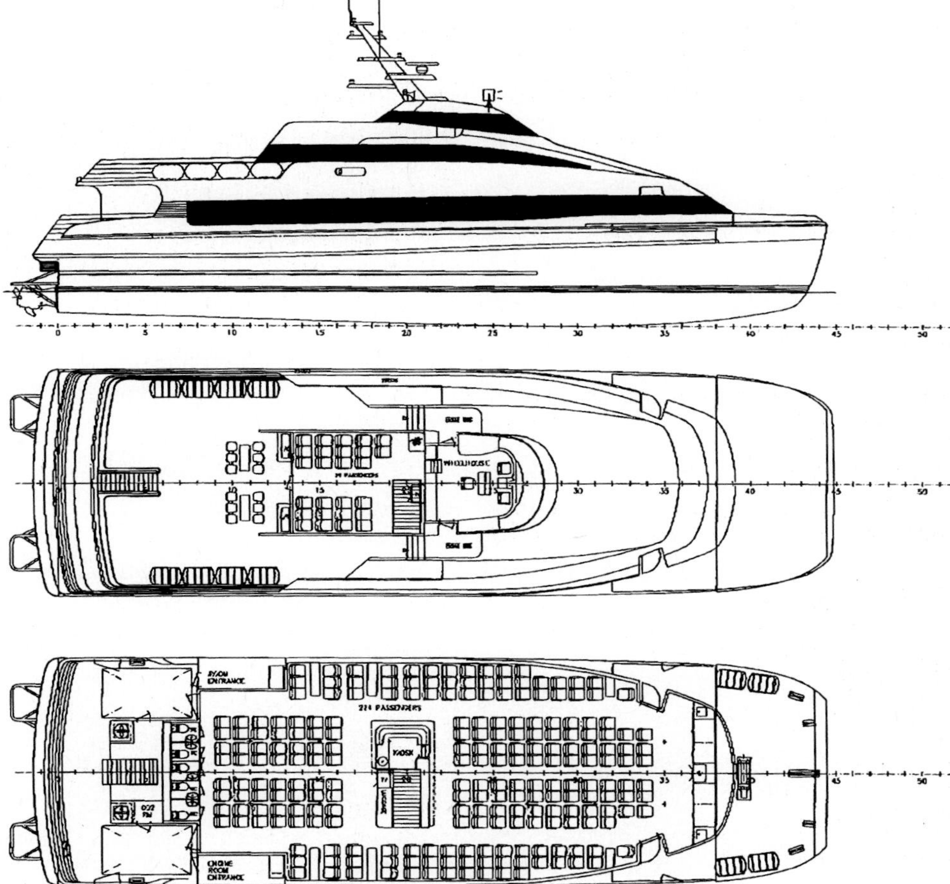

34 m Flying Cat arrangement for Jindo Transportation

1996

UNITED KINGDOM

DUNLOP-BEAUFORT LTD

Beaufort Road, Berkenhead, Merseyside L41 1HQ, UK.

Tel: +44 (151) 652 9151
Fax: +44 (151) 653 6639

Dunlope-Beaufort have developed and tested a new vertical descent Rapid Evacuation System (RES) for deployment from fast passenger craft. The system has been approved by the US and Canadian Coast Guards to IMO Resolution A.689 standards.

NEW ENTRY

BIBLIOGRAPHY

In general only papers specifically concerned with high-speed marine craft are included in this bibliography. In a few instances some of the papers listed may not be available in published form.

CONFERENCE PROCEEDINGS 1991-1996

See previous editions of this book for coverage of earlier papers.

Papers Presented at Cruise + Ferry 91 Conference, London, UK, 29-31 May 1991.

Car Ferries - Looking to the Future, B Langford (P & O European Ferries Ltd, Dover, UK).

Ferry Routes, Ship Motions and Passenger Comfort - Analysing the Relationship, J R MacGregor, G R Lamb, T D Kelley (SWATH Ocean International, USA).

Human Comfort Onboard Fast Passenger Ferries, E Brubakk, F Tellsgaard (Det Norske Veritas Classification, Norway).

Fast Craft and the Competition on the London to Paris and London to Brussels Routes. Time and Cost Comparisons City-to-City, J Charlier (Institute of Geography UCL, Belgium).

A 50 knot Gas Turbine Powered Foilcat for 300-400 Passengers, E Instanes (Kværner Fjellstrand A/S, Norway).

The DB Catafoil - A New Foil-Assisted Catamaran Passenger Ferry. Breaking the 40 knot Barrier at Minimum Cost, N Gee (Nigel Gee & Associates, Southampton, UK).

Application of Light Alloy on Passenger Vessels, G Bacicchi, A Maccari (Fincantieri, Trieste, Italy).

Regulatory Considerations for SWATH Ships, A P Ritola (American Bureau of Shipping, USA).

Service Experience of the Seamaster Fast Displacement Catamaran (SWATH) Ferry, R Milner (FBM Marine Ltd, Isle of Wight, UK).

Compact Diesel Engines for Fast Ferries, G Haussmann (MTU, Friedrichshafen, Germany).

The Impact of New High Performance Fast Ferries on Port Facilities - the Design Process, D Byrne (Transmarine Ltd, UK).

Port Opportunities for Maximising the Use of High-Speed Catamaran Ferries, J Rose (Marine Development Ltd, Scotland).

Papers presented at the Fast '91, First International Conference on Fast Sea Transportation, The Norwegian Institute of Technology, Trondheim, Norway, 17-21 June 1991.

High-Speed over Water, Ideas from the Past, the Present and for the Future, R L Trillo (Robert Trillo Limited, UK).

Waves and Wave Resistance of a High-Speed River Catamaran, L J Doctors (University of New South Wales, Australia).

A Fundamental Study on a Flow Field around a Submerged Body of Revolution with Surface-Piercing Struts, T Fuwa, N Hirata, T Hino (Ship Research Institute, Japan).

Computational Fluid Dynamics Applied to High-Speed Crafts with Special Attention to Water Intake for Water-Jets and Super Structure Aerodynamics, M Førde, H Norstrud, N Kubberud (Norwegian Institute of Technology, Norway).

Concept of a Large Surface Effect Ship for Fast Ocean Transport, D W Czimmek, B H Schaub (Newport News Shipbuilding, USA).

A Review of Current Fast Wave-Piercing Car Ferries, P C Hercus (INCAT Designs, Australia).

The Catafoil - a Foil-Assisted Catamaran for Fast Ferry and Yacht Applications, N Gee (Nigel Gee and Associates, UK).

The Effect of an Advanced Spray Rail System on Resistance and Development of Spray of Semi-Displacement Round Bilge Hulls, B Müller-Graf (Berlin Model Basin, Germany).

Aspects of Hydrofoil Design; with Emphasis on Hydrofoil Interaction in Calm Water, H J B Mørch, K J Minsaas (Marintek, Norway).

A Submerged Hull and Foil Hybrid Super-High-Speed Liner, N Yamanaka, O Yamamoto, R Satoh, T Nagatsuka, T Arii, T Fuwa (Kawasaki Heavy Industries Ltd, Japan).

SES 500 - Fincantieri - Design Criteria, L De Martini (Fincantieri, Italy).

Development and Trials of Experimental Craft SES 'Corsair', N Schlichthorst, J Wessel (Blohm+Voss AG, Germany).

A Concept Design Study of 'Techno-Superliner', Y Kunitake, H Ozawa, S Morishita, R Oimatsu (Mitsui Engineering & Shipbuilding Company, Japan).

Sea-keeping of Foilcatamarans, S Falch (Kværner Båtservice, Norway).

Research on Hydrodynamic Aspects of TSL-A, M Hirano, N Toki, Y Kusaka, Y Wada (Akishima Laboratories Inc, Japan).

Experimental Investigation of Resistance and Sea-keeping Characteristics of a Catamaran Design, A Incecik, B F M Morison (The University of Glasgow, UK).

Economy and Speed in Commercial Operations, B Foss (Møre and Romsdal College, Norway).

Synthetic Aspects of Transport Economy and Transport Vehicle Performance with Reference to High-Speed Marine Vehicles, S Akagi (Osaka University, Japan).

Comparison of a Cargo Catamaran with a Container Ship and a Transport Aircraft, A Kraus, A Naujeck (Howaldtswerke-Deutsche Werft, Germany).

A State of the Art of Fast Sea Transportation in Japan, T Koyama (Tokyo University, Japan).

A Calculation of Free-Surface Flows Generated by Planing Craft, T Hino, N Hirata, T Hori (Ship Research Institute, Japan).

On Dynamic Stability of Fast Planing Craft, M Simeone (Istituto Universitario Navale, Italy).

Open Ocean Operation and Manoeuvrability at High Speed, S Hellstroem, D Blount, P Ottosson, L Codega (SSPA Maritime Consulting AB, Sweden).

Assessment of Long Term Effects of Slamming Loads on FRP Sandwich Panels, L Buene, A T Echtermeyer, O E Sund, M K Nygård, B Hayman (A S Veritas Research, Norway).

Response of Fast Craft Hull Structures to Slamming Loads, B Hayman (Veritas Marine Services, Norway).

Enhanced Shock Performance of FRP Sandwich Structures, R P Reichard (Florida Institute of Technology, USA).

Hydrodynamic Analysis and Performance of Surface Effect Ships (SES), D Nakos, A Nestegård, T Ulstein, P D Sclavounos (MIT, USA).

A New Method for Analysing the Sea-keeping of SWATH Ships, D Kring, P D Sclavounos (MIT, USA).

The Motion Response of an ACV with a Bag-Finger Skirt in Waves, G J Lee, K P Rhee (Seoul National University, South Korea).

FRP-Sandwich as Construction Material for High-Speed Craft, A Mortenson (Ulstein International A/S, Norway).

Structural Optimisation of a High Performance GRP-Sandwich Ship Hull, O Gullberg, O Romell (Karlskronavarvet AB, Sweden).

Design and Manufacturing of NES 24 Structure, J F Rolin, A Ifremer (Ifremer, France).

On the Potential of SWATH Ships for Very High-Speed Operations, R C McGregor, J R McGregor, H H Chun (The University of Glasgow, UK).

Hydrodynamic Optimisation of High-Speed SWATH, A Papanikolaou, M Androulakakis (National Technology University of Athens, Greece).

Hydrodynamic Design of Fast Ferries by the Concept of Super-Slender Twin Hull, R Sato, H Nogami, Y Shirose, A Ito, H Miyata, K Masaoka, E Kamal (Ishikawajima-Harima Heavy Industry, Japan).

The Design, Delivery, Trial and Operation of Hovercraft Ferry 'Hong Xiang', L Hu (MARIC, China).

Romanian Experimental Hovercraft 1960-1990, K Matei (ICEPRONAV-Galatz, Romania).

'DESTRIERO': The Realisation of a Technological Challenge, M Parodi, L Grossi (Fincantieri Cantieri Navali, Italy).

Experimental Investigation on Air Cushion Catamarans, Y Liang, Q S Huang (MARIC, China).

Hydrodynamic Analysis of Surface Effect Ships: Experiences with a Quasi-Linear Model, G McHenry, P Kaplan, F Korbijn, A Nestegård (DnV Classification A/S, Norway).

High-Speed Long-Range Catamaran Design, K S Min (Hyundai Heavy Industries, South Korea).

A Production Model of WIG as a High-Speed Marine Craft: 'Marine Slider µSky-2', S Kubo, T Matsubara, T Matsuoka, T Kawamura (Tottori University, Japan).

Hybrid Hydrofoil Technology - An Overview, J R Meyer (David Taylor Research Center, USA).

Basic Principles for Choosing Skirt Arrangements for Amphibious ACV's, V V Klichko (Krylov Shipbuilding Research Institute, CIS).

EKRANOPLAN - A High-Speed Marine Vehicle of New Type, B Chubikov, V Pashin, V Treshchevsky (Hydrofoils Design Bureau, CIS).

Research and Development Program of Techno-Superliner, K Sugai, M Yamaguchi (Technology Research Association Techno-Superliner, Japan).

Added Resistance in Waves of a Catamaran at High Froude Number, M Ohkusu (Kyushu University, Japan).

The Prediction of Resistance of Surface Effect Ships, H Oehimann, J C Lewthwaite (MTG Marinetechnik GmbH, Germany).

Speed Loss and Operability of Catamarans and SES in a Seaway, O Faltinsen, K Minsaas, R Zhao, J B Helmers (Norwegian Institute of Technology, Norway).

Structural Design of an Aluminium Missile Boat, P Olkinuora, E Knuuttila, M K Hakala, S Rintala, J Vuorio (Hollming Ltd, Finland).

Structural Analysis and Design of Hydrofoils and Struts, T Moan, B Skallerud, O Skjåstad (Norwegian Institute of Technology, Norway).

Methods of Avoiding Common Problems with Aluminium Structures, W J Allday (University of Southampton, UK).

Structural Loads on Advanced Marine Vehicles, including Effects of Slamming, P Kaplan (Hydromechanics Inc, USA).

Offshore Measurements of Design Loads on Large Scale Self-Propelled Model of a High-Speed Monohull SAR Vessel, J Talvia, R Wiefelspuett (RWTH, Aachen, Germany).

Prediction of Sea-keeping Performance of a SWATH Ship and Comparison with Measurements, T E Schellin, A Papanikolaou (Germanischer Lloyd, Germany).

Vertical Motions and Wave Loads of Large Sized High-Speed Ships with Hydrofoils, H Ohtsubo, A Kubota (The University of Tokyo, Japan).

A 4000 Horsepower Marine Gas Turbine, Installation and Control in High-Speed Commercial Craft, T B Lauriat, R DiGiovanni (Textron Lycoming, USA).

Engine Running Conditions During High-Speed Marine Craft Operation, B Meek-Hansen, H Engja (Marintek, Norway).

Interfacing the LM 1600 Gas Turbine Module with Advanced Marine Vessels, J M Thames (GE Marine & Industrial Engines, USA).

Prime Movers for High-Speed Vehicles, C Günther (MTU, Germany).
The German High-Speed Research Programme. Unconventional and Fast Seaborne Vehicles, H Wilckens (Forschungzentrum Schiffbaus, Germany).
Roll Damping Due to Lift Effects on High-Speed Monohulls, J J Blok, A B Aalbers (MARIN, Netherlands).
Performance and Dynamic Stability of a High-Speed Semi-Submersible Vehicle with Wings, K Mori, Y Doi (Hiroshima University, Japan).
Feasibility Study on a High-Speed Hydrofoil Catamaran of Lesser Pitching, M Nakato, O Matsumoto, Y Osawa, H J Nobukawa, M Tamashima (Hiroshima University, Japan).
The Design Process for Military Vessels, A Wangsholm (Royal Norwegian Navy Material Command, Norway).
Comparative Parametric Studies of Monohull and Surface Effect Ships, P Goubault, H Oehlmann, D R Lavis, W Goetsch (Band, Lavis & Associates Inc, USA.
AGNES 200: Description of the Development Programme and Presentation of Initial Results from Sea Trials, J P Guezou, P Letty, Y P Picart (STCAN, France).
The Development of an Automatic Control System for a Submerged Hull and Foil Hybrid Super-High-Speed Liner, T Itoko, S Hitashino, Y Yamagami, T Ikebuchi (Kawasaki Heavy Industries Ltd, Japan).
The Rough Water Capabilities of Fully Submerged Hydrofoil Craft 'Jetfoil', Y Saito, M Ika, T Ikebuchi, M Asao (Kawasaki Heavy Industries Ltd, Japan).
New Method for Improvement of Performance and Sea-keeping Characteristics of High-Speed Craft, A V Ponomarev (Krylov Shipbuilding Research Institute, CIS).
Non-linear Behaviour of Single-Skin and Sandwich Hull Panels, M Hentinen, M Hildebrand (VTT, Ship Laboratory, Finland).
Lightweight Propeller Shaft Made of FRP for High Performance Vessel, G Behrens, M Eklund (Karlskronavarvet AB, Sweden).
Fire Safety - Principles and Priorities in Future Rules and Regulations, S E Jacobsen (DnV Classification A/S, Norway).
Safety of Collision Avoidance Manoeuvre under High-Speed Navigation, K Hara (Kobe University of Mercantile Marine, Japan).
Safe and Comfortable Operation of Foil catamarans, E Instanes, P Werenskiold, J T Pedersen (Kværner Fjellstrand, Norway).
Noise and Vibration Aspects of High-Speed Passenger Vessels, K A Abrahamsen, P T Gravastrand (Det Norske Veritas, Norway).
Surface-Piercing Propellers - Methodical Propellers Series Model Test Results, J C Rose, C F L Kruppa (Rolla SP, USA).
The Effect of Water-jet-Hull Interaction on Thrust and Propulsive Efficiency, T van Terwisga (MARIN, Netherlands).
A Description of the Water-jets Selected for the 'DESTRIERO', R Svensson (Kamewa AB, Sweden).
Design Research of SES Ride Control System, T Ma, W L Zhou, Y N Xie (Marine Design & Research Institute of China, China).
Dynamic Analysis and Control of Air-Cushion and Bag Systems of SES, S Steen, A Sørensen, O Egeland, O Faltinsen (Marintek, Norway).
Full-Scale Experiments by the First Hydrofoil Catamaran WINGSTAR 12 'Exceller', H Kawaguchi, H Miyata, H Yamato, T Takai (Setouchi Craft Company Ltd, Japan).
The Maximum Attenuation of Seaway Induced Motions, within a Given Set of Constraints, Possible for Hydrofoil Supported Ships, W C O'Neill, USA.
Power Shaft Hydrostatic Transmission for Propulsion of High-Speed Craft, H Speich, A Cappiello (Rexroth SpA, Italy).
Computer Programs in the Feasibility Design of New SES Projects, P Ottosson, O Rutgersson (SSPA Maritime Consulting AB, Sweden).
The Prediction of the Hydrodynamic Performance of Hydrofoil Craft in Waves, F van Walree, C Buccini (Maritime Research Institute Netherlands, Netherlands).
The Take-Off Characteristics of Hydrofoil and its Optimum Hullform Design, B J Zhong (China Ship Scientific Research Centre, China).
Some Considerations on Rules and Regulations for Fast Sea Transportation in Japan, K Ogawa (Ministry of Transport, Japan).
Safety of Fast Sea Transport, Sandvik (Norwegian Maritime Directorate, Norway).

Papers presented at the 16th Annual Conference, International Marine Transit Association, 29 September to 3 October 1991, Estoril, Portugal.

Planning for Commuter Ferry Systems, Mark Conway (Toronto Harbour, Canada).
An Environmental Problem: Ferry Wakes in Puget Sound, Kenneth Fox (Ferry Services, Art Anderson Associates, Seattle, Washington, USA).
The New Westfoil 25 m, Randy Rust (Westport Shipyard Inc, Westport, Washington, USA).
Emissions and Alternative Fuels - Engine Design Considerations, P B Palmer (Caterpillar Overseas, Geneva, Switzerland).
Access Issues for the Handicapped, Terry Ivany (Marine Atlantic, New Brunswick, Canada).
Venice: The New Electric Ferry and Introduction to the Ferry System, Bruno della Logia (Cetena, Venice, Italy).

Papers presented at the International Symposium on Hydro- and Aerodynamics in Marine Engineering, Hadmar '91, 28 October to 1 November 1991, Varna, Bulgaria.

Hydrofoils for Stabilizing Fast Ships - A Concept with Future?, E Mohr and V Bertram (Technische Beratungen Mohr and Institut fur Schiffbau, Hamburg, Germany).
Empirical Formulae to Presume the Resistance Performance of High-Speed Craft, Y Yoshida (Japan Defence Agency, Japan).
The Method for Calculating Hovercraft Motion Characteristics Taking into Account Dynamics of the Flexible Skirt, E A Paravjan (Krylov Shipbuilding Research Institute, CIS).
Computational Investigations of Airfoils Characteristics for Wing-in-Ground-Effect Vehicles, A R Besyadovsky, N V Kornev, N B Plisov, V K Treshkov (Leningrad State Marine University, CIS).

Papers presented at IMAS 91, Sixth International Maritime and Shipping Conference, High-Speed Marine Transportation, 11-13 November 1991, at the University of New South Wales, Sydney, Australia by The Institute of Marine Engineers in association with The Institute of Marine Engineers (Sydney Branch), The Royal Institution of Naval Architects (Australian Division) and the University of New South Wales (Naval Architecture Section).

The Sea-keeping Comfort of Large Fast Catamarans, P C Hercus, N A Armstrong and B K Egan (International Catamaran Designs Pty Ltd).
Speed Loss and Operational Limits of High-Speed Marine Vehicles, O M Faltinsen (Norwegian Institute of Technology), K O Holden and K J Minsaas (Marintek).
Fast Ferry by Super-Slender Twin Hull, H Miyata (Tokyo University), H Nogami, M Shiria and Y Shirose (IHI Company Ltd).
Research and Development Programme of Techno-Superliner, M Yamaguchi (Technological Research Association of Techno-Superliner).
The Design, Development and Construction of a 35 m Low-Wash Fast Catamaran River Ferry, N Hornsby (State Transit Authority), G Parker (Grahame Parker Design Pty Ltd), L J Doctors (University of New South Wales) and M R Renilson (The Australian Maritime College).
Research and Development of Super-Conducting Magnetohydrodynamic Ship Propulsion, S Motora (University of Tokyo), S Takezawa and H Tamama (Ship & Ocean Foundation, Japan).
Development of the Surface Effect Ship 500, A Cordano and L de Martini (Fincantieri).
Agnes 200: an Outline for a Future Surface Effect Ship, J P Guezou, P Letty and Y P Picart (DGA Direction des Construction Navales).
A Concept for a Fast Ship Stabilised by Hydrofoils, V Bertram (HSVA) and E Mohr (Technische Beratungen Mohr).
The Development of a 50 knot 40 m FoilCat, J H Jorde (Kvaerner Fjellstrand).
A Three Dimensional Structural Analysis of a Large Wave-Piercing Catamaran Design, J A Morris (Lloyd's Register).
Classification of High-Speed Marine Transportation with Particular Emphasis on Structural Strength, E H Olbjorn, C T Hughes and B V Govindasamy (Det Norske Veritas Classification Sydney Plan Approval Centre).
Marine Grade Aluminium Alloys for High-Speed Craft Construction, J T Callahan (Alcan Australia Ltd).
Propulsion of Small-Waterplane-Area Twin-Hull Ships, J R MacGregor, D C Bridges and A G Blyth (Swath Ocean International).
Two-Stage Water-Jets for High-Speed Commercial Craft, K Alexander (CWF Hamilton and Company Ltd).
Water-Jet Propulsion of High-Speed Craft, R Svensson (Kamewa AB).
Engines for Fast Passenger and Utility Craft, G Haussmann (Motoren- und Turbinen-Union Friedrichafen GmBH).
Engine Parameters for High-Speed Marine Transportation, R M Halleen (Caterpillar Inc).
Medium-Speed Engine Designs Meet the Requirements of High-Speed Ships, M Whattam (Ruston Diesels Ltd).
Requirements of Diesel Engines and their Application for the Propulsion of High-Speed Craft, W A Sprogis (Motoren-Werke Mannheim AG, MWM).
Gas Turbine Propulsion for Large Fast Ferries, P Sweatman (Rolls Royce Industrial & Marine Gas Turbines Ltd).
Aeroderivative Gas Turbine Propulsion for High-Speed Craft, P A Dupuy and R E Reid (GE Marine & Industrial Engines).
Considerations in Applying Gas Turbines to High-Speed Vessels, J E Horne (Turbo Power and Marine Systems Inc) and J Taschner (MAN/GHH).
The Marine Transportation System between Kobe City and Kansai International Airport Utilising the High-Speed Passenger Ship Jetfoil, T Yagi (Kawasaki Heavy Industries).
Lessons to be Learned from the Apollo JetCat Casualty in Hong Kong, Ck A Jenman (Global Maritime (London) Ltd) and M H Rowe (Global Maritime (Sydney) Pty Ltd).
The Administration's Role in the Development and Implementation of Safety Standards for High-Speed Craft, W A Graham (Department of Transport (UK)).
Certification of a High-Speed Craft - an Administration's View, R C Gheling and I M Williams (Australian Maritime Safety Authority).
Keeping Up with High-Speed Commercial and Passenger Craft Development - Legal and Insurance Implications for Owners and Certifying Authorities, C Jenman (Global Maritime Ltd) and D Coleman (Mills Oakley McKay).
Safe and Economic Operation of High-Speed Craft with Special Attention to the Diesel Engine Running Conditions, B Meek-Hansen and P Werenskiold (Marintek A/S).
Do Fast Car Ferries Have a Profitable Future?, R M Mabbott (Ferrysystems Ltd).

Papers presented at the Eighth International High-Speed Surface Craft Conference, 21-23 January 1992, Heathrow, London, UK, published by High-Speed Surface Craft, 69 Kings Road, Kingston-upon-Thames, Surrey KT2 5JB, UK.

Fast Ferry Economy - Development of the Harding 35.5 m Catamaran, Kjartan Stensones and Emil Abry (Harding Verft and Abry & Tandberg Industrial Design).

Operational Experience with Hydrofoils on the Danube, Kiroslav Gerhat (CSPD Division of Passenger Transport).
Capacity, Speed and Economy, Bjorn Foss (More & Romsdal College, Norway).
Motion Sickness Evaluation on Ships, Allan Soars and Julius Schmidt (Advanced Multi-Hull Designs).
The Reliability of Aero-derived Marine Gas Turbines, Tim and Brian Wilkinson (Rolls-Royce Industrial & Marine Gas Turbines).
Application of the FT8 Marine Gas Turbine to Large High-Speed Surface Craft, J E Horner and T W Prete (Turbo Power & Marine Systems) and Joachim Taschner (MAN/GHH).
Cats at the Cape of Storms, Bob van Niekerk (Bobkat, Antwerp).
The Practical Application of Hybrid Design Techniques to Fast Ferries for the 1990's, Nigel Gee (Nigel Gee and Associates).
Hydrostatic Transmissions - New Proposals for the Propulsion of High-Speed Craft, Hanno Speich and Alessandro Cappiello (Mannesmann Rexroth and Hydromarine).
Some Issues in Water-jet Design and Selection, Rik Hothersall (CWF Hamilton).
Modern Manoeuvring of Ships with Water-jets, Kurt Nilsson and Henry Holmberg (Styr-Kontroll Teknik).
25 Years of SES Development and the Future, Ted Tattersall (Hovermarine International).
Is Big Beautiful?, John Lewthwaite, David Bridges and Tony Marchant (Independent Maritime Assessment Associates).
Aquastrada - A Complete Model Testing and Numerical Evaluation of a New Deep V Monohull Design, Bruno Galtier and Claudio Buccini (Bassin d'Essais des Carenes and Rodriquez Cantieri Navali).
Computer Aided Design and Development of a High-Speed Catamaran, Grant Firth (Firth Marine Design/Coastdesign UK).
The SeaCockpit Bridge Concept - A Functional Analytic Design Approach to Safe Operation, Svein Kristiansen (Norwegian Marine Technology Research Institute/Norwegian Institute of Technology - Division of Marine Systems Design) and Arild Tomter (Norsk Forsvarsteknologi).
Bridge and Systems Integration on High-Speed Ferries, Noel Hogg (Vosper Thornycroft, UK).
Trials of the New 23 m Thames Class Catamaran, Nigel Warren and Robert Milner (FBM Marine Group).
The Economics of Designing High-Speed Ferries, Max Martin (International Maritime Transportation Advisory Services) - (not presented at the Conference).

Papers presented at the Fifth International Symposium on Practical Design of Ships and Mobile Units, PRADS '92, 17-22 May 1992, the University of Newcastle upon Tyne, UK.
Motion Control and Wave Loads of High-Speed Ships with Hydrofoils, H Ohtsubo and A Kubota (University of Tokyo, Japan).
Development of a Practical Swath Ship with High Performance, H Hwan Chun and R C McGregor (Hyundai Research Institute, Korea and University of Glasgow, UK).
Structural Loading Aspects in Designing Swath Ships, H S Chan, E B Djatmiko, A F Miller and L Blyth (University of Glasgow, UK).
Global Wave Loads on High-Speed Catamarans, O Faltinsen, J R Hoff, J Kvalsvold and R Zhao (Norwegian Institute of Technology and Marintek, Norway).

Papers Presented at ATMA Conference, Navires a Grande Vitesse, 20-21 May 1992, Paris, France, by Association Technique Maritime et Aeronautique
L'ACQUASTRADA, Une Evaluation Numerique et Experimentale Complete d'un Nouveau Concept de Monocoque en V Profond, B Galtier ("Navires de Commerce", Bassin d'Essais des Carenes de Paris) and C Buccini (Rodriquez Cantieri Navali, Italy).
The Sea-keeping Comfort of Large Fast Catamarans, C Hercus, T Armstrong and B K Egan (International Catamaran Designs Pty Ltd, Sydney, Australia).
Ride Quality of Fast Ferries, B Lamb and D Holcomb (Swath Ocean International Limited, Fareham, Hampshire, UK).
Essais d'Evaluation des Performances du Navire a Effect de Surface "AGNES 200", S Skorupka, P Perdon and D Le Coz (Bassin d'Essais des Carenes de Paris).
Navire Semi-Submersible Trimaran, J-C Nahon (Bureau d'Etudes Mauric, Marseilles) and M Bourgeois-Gaffie (Direction des Recherches Etudes et Techniques, Paris).
HYDRAIR: Une Nouvelle Generation de NES, Nguyen Manh Khanh (Societe Khanh Hydrair, Garches).
Developpement de Navires Rapides en Europe, Y Rouille (Constructions Mecaniques de Normandie, Cherbourg, France).
Criteres Operationnels pour les Navires a Grande Vitesse, L De Martini and L M Martini (Departement Commercial et Marketing, Division des Navires Militaires, Fincantieri, Genes, Italy).
Navires a Grande Vitesse: Marches Potentiels et Reponses Esquissees, H Michea, (Departement Offshore, Barry Rogliano Salles, Paris).
Water-Jet Propulsion of High-Speed Passenger Vessels, R Svensson, (Kamewa AB, Sweden).
Aeroderivative Gas Turbine Propulsion for High-Speed Craft - an Update, J J Ferrera, P A Dupuy and R E Reid (General Electric, Marine and Industrial Engines, Cincinnati, Ohio, USA).
Propulsions a Hautes Performances pour Navires a Passagers Rapides, V Jost and G Haussmann (MTU-Friedrichshafen) and M Gorce (SEMT- Pielstick, Saint-Nazaire).
Transmission Electrique pour Navires Rapides du Futur, J-L Sabrie (GEC ALSTHOM Belfort), H Godfroid (CEGELEC Belfort) and P Asselin (ALCATEL ALSTHOM International Mission Marine).
Etude d'un Catamaran a Faibles Remous, M R Milner (FBM Ferries, FBM Marine Group, Isle of Wight, UK).
A Three Dimensional Structural Analysis of a Large Wave-Piercing Catamaran Design, J-A Morris (Class Computational Group - Shipdivision, Lloyd's Register of Shipping, London, UK).
Aspects Reglementaires de la Classification des Navires Rapides et Legers par le Bureau Veritas, J-N Babinet, (Division Nouvelles Constructions, Bureau Veritas, Paris La Defense).
Evaluation de la Structure d'AGNES 200 - Presentation du Programme - Premiers Resultats, Y-P Picart, (Service Technique des Constructions et Armes Navales, Groupe Materiaux Structures Navales, Paris).
Navires a Grande Vitesse. L'Aspect Reglementaire, D Allain, (Bureau de la Reglementation, Secretariat d'Etat a la Mer, Paris).

Papers presented at HPMV '92, Intersociety High Performance Marine Vehicle Conference and Exhibit, 24-27 June 1992 at Arlington, Virginia, USA, by Flagship Section American Society of Naval Engineers.
Hydrofoil Development and Applications, John R Meyer and James R Wilkins, Jr. (USA).
Hybrid Hydrofoil Technology Applications, John R Meyer (USA).
Recent PHM Operational Experience, L J Jackson (USA).
Jetfoil Operational Experience in Japan, T Yagi, Y Saito, T Ikebuchi and M Asao (Japan).
Numerical Simulation of some Manoeuvrability Characteristics for a Surface Piercing Hydrofoil Craft, Igor Prislin (former Yugoslavia).
An Estimation Method of the Motions in Waves for a Submerged Hull and Foil Hybrid High-Speed Ship, Y Yamagami, T Ikebuchi, Y Saito and T Itoko (Japan).
Hydro-Numeric HYSWAS Design, Volker Bertram and Ernst Mohr (Germany).
Offshore Minibases for Small Naval Combatants, M D Van Orden, (USN, Retd) and Roy D Gaul (USA).
Hovercraft Development, David R Lavis (USA).
Dynamic Response of an Air Cushion Lift Fan, Philip A Sullivan, F Gosselin and M J Hinchey (Canada).
The Research of Resistance and Motion Characteristics of ACV with Responsive Skirt, Zhou Weilin, Ma Tao and Zheng Nan (China).
Operational Experience with a Very High Stability Skirt System for Amphibious Hovercraft, Mariano de la Cruz (Spain).
Air Cushion Vehicle Simulation: The First Full Mission Trainer, Mark E Donner, Jeanne Class and Mary R Sabo (USA).
The Evolution of Chinese ACV/SES, Yun Liang and Peng Guihua (China).
On the Operation of an Experimental Hovercraft for the Antarctic, Rinichi Murao, Sadao Takeuchi and Minoru Inaba (Japan).
COMINCO's AP.1-88 Operation: A Successful Application of Hovercraft in the Mining Industry, David Dickins, Merlyn Royea and Paul Morrison (Canada).
LCAC: A Systems Evolution, John Auzins and U H (Jack) Rowley (USA).
Summary of Recent Developments in the Recreational and Commercial Light Hovercraft Industry, Kevin D Bedsworth (USA).
Recent Development of Air Cushion Vehicles in Japan, S Ono, S Yamashita, I Yoshino, H Ozawa and M Inaba (Japan).
The LCAC in Tests & Trials, Daniel F Bobeck (USA).
The Evolution of Crew Training in US Navy Landing Craft, Air Cushion (LCAC) Operations, David C Braa and David M Eakin (USA).
Air Cushion Vehicles and Oil Spills, Daniel L'Heureux, CCG (Canada).
Frequency Response Characteristics of an ACV Bag-Finger Skirt, Xie You Nong (China).
Model C-7: Amphibious Transportation for the 1990s, Frank P Higgins (USA).
The Evolution of the US Navy SES-200, Robert C Moore and Gregory L Bender (USA).
The BES 16 - A Spanish Surface Effect Ship, Jose A Alaez and Juan Ponce (Spain).
Cobblestone Effect on SES, Asgeir Sorensen, Sverre Steen and Odd M Faltinsen (Norway).
The SES - Optimum Hullform for Patrol Boats, Gregory L Bender (USA).
US Coast Guard WSES: Nine Years Old and Going Strong, Peter J DiNicola (USCG (USA)).
Long Range Maintenance Planning for USCG WSES, Dwight G Hutchinson, (USCG) and Mark R Schwender (USA).
The Use of Pressure Distributions to Model the Hydrodynamics of Air Cushion Vehicles and Surface Effect Ships, Lawrence J Doctors (Australia).
A Collection of Simplified Field Equations for SES Design, Chris B McKesson (USA).
Optimization of SES Designs by Use of Calculations and Model Tests, Olle Rutgersson (Sweden) and Andrew G Blyth (UK).
An Experimental Study on Air Drawing of a Water-jet Inlet for Surface Effect Ships, Shigenori Mishima (Japan).
Seal System of a Large Surface Effect Ship (Japan), Yasumi Toyama, Shirou Ono and Seichiro Nishihara (Japan).
Buoyantly Supported Multi-Hull Vessels, B-O Jansson (Sweden) and G Robert Lamb (USA).
Design and Comparison of Long Hull SWATHs and Overhanging Strut SWATHs for Oceanographic Survey Missions, Jeffery A Peters (USA).
Wave Cancellation Multihull Ship Concept, Michael B Wilson and Chun Che Hsu (USA).
An Experimental Study of Automatic Pitch Control on a SWATH Model, Edward M Lewandowski and James A White (USA).
Full-Scale Experiment and Advanced Design of SSTH Fast Ferries, A Abe, Y Shirose, A Ito, H Nogami, R Michida, H Miyata and T Ohmori (Japan).

Main Hydrodynamic Features and Performance Characteristics of SWATH Ships, V A Dubrovsky (Russia).
Design of a Tandem Canted Strut Commercial SWATH, Jonathan M Ross and Manfred J Zapka (USA).
The "Surfing TRIS" Concept, Design and Performances, Alfredo Magazzu (Italy).
Design & Operation of the 400-Passenger SWATH Ship NAVATEK I, Ludwig H Seidl, William F Clifford and James P Cummins (USA).
Three-Hulled Ships; Distinctive Features and Applications, Victor A Dubrovsky (Russia).
Hydroaviation, Stephan F Hooker and Michael R Terry (USA).
Power Augmentation of Wing-in-Ground-Effect Craft, Roger W Gallington (USA).
Matched Asymptotics in Aerodynamics of WIG Vehicles, K V Rozhdestvensky (Russia).
Numerical Simulation of Wingships, J M Elzebda (UAE), D T Mook and A H Nayfeh (USA).
Numerical Investigation of Non-linear Unsteady Aerodynamics of the WIG Vehicle, N V Kornev and V K Treshkov (Russia).
Modelling of Smart Structures for Wingships, P F Pai, A H Nayfeh and D T Mook (USA).
USSR Research & Design Efforts in the Development Marine Ekranoplans and their Transportation Capability in Various Water Areas, L D Volkov, V M Pashin, A V Ponomarev, D N Sinitsin and B V Chubikov (Russia).
Amphibian "A-40" - A Step in the Future of Hydroaviation, G S Panatov and G P Kobyzev (Russia).
Overview of Planing Craft Developments, Daviel Savitzky (USA).
Structural Developments in High-Speed Offshore Powerboats, Ronnal P Reichard (USA).
The Development of Composites for Fast Rescue Craft, F D Hudson (UK).
Optimized Designs for Stepped Planing Monohulls and Catamarans, Eugene P Clement and Joseph G Koelbel, Jr. (USA).
Sea Trials & Model-Ship Correlation Analysis of the High-Speed Gas Turbine Vessel "DESTRIERO", D L Blount (USA), L Grossi and G Lauro (Italy).
Amphibious Warfare Vehicles - Challenges, Development and Progress, Michael A Gallagher (USA).
Side-by-Side Testing of Hard Chine and Round Bilge Semi-planing Models in Waves, John J Zseleczky, Bruce C Nehrling and Roger H Compton (USA).
The Efficient Use of Simulation in Planing Hull Motion Analysis, Armin W Troesch & John D Hicks, USCG (USA).
Model Tests and Numerical Drag Prediction for a Water-jet Powered Planing Hull with a Full Beam Stern Extension, Michael T Musatow and Gregory Lee (USA).
Underway Inclining Experiments Performed on a Planing Hull Model, Roger H Compton, John J Zseleczky and William S Abrams, USN (USA).
An Assessment of Advanced Naval Vehicles for the Rapid Route Surveillance MCM Role, J Goodwin, R G Heather, J Cook, P R James, N D T Smith (UK).
Transport Effectiveness in HPMV Design, Michael R Terry (USA).
The Integration of Operating Economics in the Early Design of High-Speed Passenger Vessels, Philippe Goubault and Brian Forstell (USA).
"When it Absolutely, Positively Has to Get to the Beach." - Technology Demonstrators that Meet the LOTS Challenge, Brian J David and Daniel L Wilkins (USA).
SWATH Ships in a Monohull World, Roy D Gaul (USA).
Progress of Some High-Speed Marine Vehicles: Analysis of Prospects, V B Latyshenko, S A Otlov and V V Pleshivtcev (Russia).
The Achievement of High Performance in Marine Vehicles over the Period of 1970-1990, Robert L Casanova & Robert Latorre (USA).
Well Deck Deployable Naval Combatants, Michael Bosworth, USN, Scott Black and John R Meyer (USA).
Matching Vehicle Characteristics to Seaway Environments, William H Buckley (USA).
Sea-keeping Evaluation of High Performance Marine Vehicles, Nere Skjomedal, Jan V Aarsnes and Sigurd Falch (Norway).
Advanced Marine Vehicle Structural Loads - Present State of the Art, Paul Kaplan (USA).
Non-linear Heave and Pitch Motions of Fast Ships in Irregular Head Seas, J A Keuning (Netherlands).
An Alarm and Monitoring System for High Performance Marine Vehicles, Timothy A Pannone and J Steven Goss (USA).
Applications of the "Air Drive" Ventilated Tunnel/Surface-Piercing Propeller Propulsion System, Gary W van Tassel (USA).
Ship Propulsion Systems with High-Speed Diesel Engines, Christian Gunther (Germany).
Dynamic Aspects of Marine Propulsion Systems with Diesel Engines, G Venturini (Italy).
Gas Turbine Control in High Performance Marine Vehicles, T B Lauriat (USA).

Papers presented at the Third Conference on High-Speed Marine Craft, 8-10 September 1992, Kristiansand, Norway, by the Norwegian Society of Chartered Engineers.
Alternative Concepts in Transportation Sea/Air/Road, Bjorn Foss, (Consultant, Norway).
New Concepts in Sea Transportation, Norwegian Shipping Company (Norway).
High-Speed Cargo Ships Market Trends, Types of Ships, Critical Technology Economy, Nere Skomedal (Kvaerner Mandal, Norway).
Classification Societies - are they up-to-date?, Douglas Faulkner (University of Glasgow, UK).
FOILCAT 2900 Design and performance, Egil Svennesby (Westamarin West A/S) and Knut Minsaas (Norwegian Technology Research Institute).
Rules and Regulation - IMO, Ivar Manum (Norwegian Maritime Directorate, Norway).
SeaCat Accident, Konrad M. Havig, (Norwegian Maritime Directorate, Norway).
Safety of Operation of HSMC, Terje Steen (SINTEF, Norway).
Operational Performance and Limitations, Per Werenskiold (Norwegian Technology Research Institute, Norway).
Human Performance Factor, Bjarne Dahl (Consultant, Norway).
Practical Operative Experience from Hong Kong, C A Jenman (Global Maritime London, UK).
How do I as a Passenger Experience a Passage?, Knut F Ramstad and Trond H Overland (Oslo Business School, Norway).
Operational Procedures and Training, Ole Fredriksen and Terje Solberg (Braathen Safe), Arild Nybakk (AS Bundefjorden DS).
Bridge Resource Management, Eric Wahren (SAS Flight Academy AB, Sweden).
Bridge Design for Improved Safety, Per Aanestad (Norwegian Defence Technology).
Operational Safety - Influence on Design, Frode Klepsvik (Det Norske Veritas, Norway).
Progress in Navigational Equipment, Lars Mathisen (Norwegian Technology Research Institute, Norway).
Reliability Failure Analysis for High-Speed Marine Craft and their Safety Equipment, Stephen Phillips (Seaspeed Technology Ltd, UK).

Papers presented at the International Marine Transit Association 17th Annual Conference, 26-29 October 1992, Hong Kong.
The Responsibility of a Marine Administration for Operational Safety under the Dynamically Supported Craft Code, A C Pyrke (Marine Department, Hong Kong).
Operation of Boeing Jetfoil, David Hill (Far East Hydrofoil Company Ltd, Hong Kong).
Discovery Bay Ferry Service, Jeremy C H Marriott (Hong Kong Resorts International Ltd , Hong Kong).
The Development and Current Use of Night Vision Equipment for High-Speed Passenger Craft in Hong Kong, P R Owen, (Marine Department, Hong Kong).
High Performance Propulsion Systems, Technical representative (MTU Motoren- und Turbinen-Union, Friedrichshafen GmbH, Germany).
Spanning the Golden Gate - The Bridge and the Ferry System, Gene Rexrode (Golden Gate Bridge, Highway & Transportation District, San Francisco, USA).
Textron C-7 Amphibious Transportation for the 90's, Frank Higgins (Textron Marine Systems, New Orleans, USA).
The Seaswift Series High-Speed SES Ferries of Royal Schelde, M J H Slegers (Vlissingen, Netherlands).

Papers presented at the High-Speed Surface Craft Conference, 9-11 March 1993.
Regulating high-speed and novel craft, A Blyth (Independent naval architect).
The semi-planing ship, a new concept for large high-speed ferries, J Lewthwaite (JCL High-Speed Marine Craft).
Why class?- classification society contributions to the structural design of multihull craft, A J Williams (Lloyds Register of Shipping).
Optimized gear drives for high-speed surface craft, H Sidler (MAAG Gear Co Ltd).
The bubbly water-jet - a promising high-speed marine propulsion concept, Professor A Gany (Technion Israel Institute of Technology).
Speed Z propulsion - advantages/full-scale experience, S O Halstensen (Ulstein Propeller AS).
Profit from pleasure, M Burgess (Quicksilver Connection).
Motions of high-speed vessels and their effect on passengers and crew, P A Weynberg and I M C Cambell (Wolfson Unit).
Regression analysis applied to model testing, J-H Jorde (Bergen College of Engineering).
Modern diesel engines for high-speed surface craft, G Haümann (MTU Friedrichshafen).
Fast ferry engines of choice - Caterpillar 3600 engines, R M Halleen, (Caterpillar).
Recent work on water-jet/hull interaction - K Alexander (CWF Hamilton).
The use of simulation in training for high-speed operation, R J Syms (Australian Maritime College).
Refurbishment of old hydrofoils for operation today, C Jenman and J Halligan (Global Maritime).
The rebirth of the amphibious hovercraft, G A Gifford, Griffon Hovercraft).
Intermediate technology catamarans, B Fehrenbach (F. Tech).
The speed competitive Swath fast ferry, T Kelley (Swath International).

Papers presented at the Symposium on High-Speed Marine Vehicles, 25-26 March 1993, at Naples, Italy.
Innovazioni, alte velocità, transporti marittimi, U Marchese.
Power prediction based on model tests for high-speed craft, G Jensen and V Bertram (Hamburg Ship Model Basin HSVA).
Computer-aided design techniques applied to a fast ferry, V Bertram (HSVA, Hamburg, Germany).
Full-scale manoeuvring trial results of two planing hulls, G Capurro (CETENA).
Study of service performances of surface effect ships, M Gronda (Studio Technico Navale Ansaldo, Genoa, Italy).
Advantages and Experiences with Load Profile-related and On-Condition Maintenance Concepts for High-Performance Diesel Engines, G Rechtsteiner.
Sistema do controllo digitale Rodriquez MEC1-FS, S Crupi.
A New Proposal of Performance Evaluation and Analysis for Flush-Inlet Water-jet Crafts, L Iannone and R Rocchi (INSEAN, Rome).

Structural Design Aspects of High-Speed Hulls, E Fasano and S Arena (Dipartimento di Ingegneria Navale, Naples, Italy).
A Case for the Viability of Fast Vehicle / Passenger Ferries, C Norman (Austal Ships, Western Australia).
On the Propulsion Plants of High-Speed Displacing Vessels, A Bisceglia and A Paciolla (University "Frederico II", Naples).
MDV 1200 Fincantieri - Analysis on the effects of ship motions on passenger comfort, S Saione and S Vaccarezza (Fincantieri CNI).
L'impresa del *Destrieo*, A Pietropaolo (Sperry Marine).
Technological Process for Big and Fast Ship Building, R Lembo (Cantieri di Baia).
Il nuovo 75 m della Kværner Fjellstrand: Con le auto a 35 nodi, P Johannesen.
Structural design and safety criteria for fast catamarans and Surface Effect Ships, A Pittaluga and G Casella (Registro Italiano Navale).
Flying the sea into the future, C G Biancardi (Instituto Universitario Navale, Naples).
Ship motion and passenger comfort of a high-speed SSC during service operation, H Yagi et al (Mitsui Engineering and Shipbuilding Co Ltd, Japan).
Classification of catamarans, A J Williams (Lloyd's Register of Shipping, London).
Technical economic evaluation of Diesel against gas turbine propulsion in passenger-carrying hydrofoil boats, E Gugliemino and R Sinatra (Università degli Studi di Catania).
The influence of Froude number calculated by displacement on the form of the Hydrodynamic comples of surface ships, M A Basin (Forma Ltd, St Petersburg, Russia).
Life Cycle Cost-Choosing Fast Ferry Engines, R M Hallen and D P Davis (Caterpillar Inc).
A back drived "sub-jet" as hydrofoil propeller, V Quaggiotti (University of Padua, Italy).
International Requirements for High-Speed Craft, G Pattofatto (Registro Italiano Navale).
Development of foil sections with delayed cavitation inception, M Ferrando et al (University of Genoa).
Analysis of partially cavitating profiles, M Caponetto (University of Genoa).
The next 1300 Engine family: a proposal for high-speed commercial transport, G Besio et al.
Deutz MWM marine engines for applications on high-speed vessels, A Gasparri.
Comparison and experimental validation of performance analysis procedure for high-speed propellers, E J Glover et al (Newcastle University, UK).
Sea-keeping: comparazione fra aliscafo, catamarano e monostab, C Buccini and M Sferrazza (Rodriquez Cantieri Navali SpA).
Structural optimization of a Swath design, M Chiaverini et al (CETENA SpA).
Hull interferance in wave resistance of catamarans, R Nabergoj and R Prever (Department of Naval Architecture, Trieste, Italy).
Efficient solution of the multiattribute design problem applied to fast passenger vessels, G Trincas et al (University of Zagreb, Croatia).

Papers presented at Cruise & Ferry 93 Conference, 11-13 May 1993, at Olympia 2, London.

Cruise Ferries v Channel Tunnel, B Langford (P&O European Ferries, UK).
Changes in traffic and operation strategies from new fast ferries entering the Scandinavian market, T Hagman and K Lumsden (Chalmers University of Technology, Gothenburg).
Developments of the Newbuilding and Secondhand Market for Fast Ferries, D Moe (Sea Service International Oslo).
Market Potential for Fast Ferries between Italy and Greece, O Vederhus and H Heijveld (Centre for International Shipping & Transport, University of Plymouth, UK).
Fast Ferry RORO Berths - Improving their Investment Profile by Providing a Range of Utilisation Options, D Byrne and S Hodgson (Transmarine Ltd, UK).
Ferry Rapido 92: a Monohull Solution for Trasmediterranea, H Sierra (E N Bazan, Spain).
Development of a Fast Monohull Ferry, P Viergutz (Blohm+Voss AG, Hamburg, Germany).
A New High-Speed SWATH, J Gollenbeck and J Holland (Schichau Seebeckwerft AG, Germany).
A Semi-Swath Catamaran Car Ferry, J V Jensen (Danyard, Denmark).
REAL Fast Car Ferries - Experience from 74 m Craft and Designs up to 115 m, P Hercus (Incat Designs, Sydney).
Can Superliners be fast and profitable?, K Levander (Kværner Masa-Yards, Finland).
Passenger Comfort and Safety (Interior Design and Craft Performance Related to New IMO 373 Code), P Werenskiold (Marintek, Norway).
Passenger and Furniture Restraints in the Collision Case. A New Look at the Deck Attachment, C Eden (Air Vehicles Ltd, UK).
The Problem of External Noise from Fast Ferries, L Thiele (Odegaard & Danneskiold-Samsoe ApS, Copenhagen).
Keeping Fast Ferries Quiet - New Developments in Propulsion Plant Silencing Systems, K Hall (Industrial Acoustics Company, UK).

Papers presented at the International Marine Transit Association 18th Annual Conference, 18-21 October 1993, San Francisco.

'Back to the Future'. Ferry Operations as part of a Regional Transportation Network, Rod McMillan (MTC Oakland, California).
The Oaklands Alameda Ferry: Competing with cars, buses and light rail mass transit, Roger Murphy (Blue and Gold Fleet, San Francisco).
Ferries as a Marketing Tool for a Land Development, Paul Bishop (Harbor Bay Express, Alameda, California).
Improving Finatial Results: Blending Commuter and Visitor/Attraction Services, Terry Koenig (Red and White Fleet, California).
High-Speed Ferries, (DnV, Norway).
Using Computer Technology to Enhance Passenger Comfort and Marketing, Merideth Tall (Clipper Navigation, Seattle).
Why Water Jets on Modern High-Speed Ferries, Bjorn Svensson (Kamewa AB, Sweden).

Papers presented at FAST '93, 13-16 December 1993, at Yokohama, Japan.

Comfort Inquiry and Motion Measurement During Commercial Passenger Service on the French SES *Agnes 200*, S Skorupka and P Perdon (Bassin d'Essais des Carènes de Paris, France).
Agnes 200: Structural Evaluation, Y-P Picart (DCN, France).
Agnes 200: Up-to-date Technical Information and Potential Use for Commercial and Military Applications, J-P Guezou (DCN, France).
The Second Stage of TSL-A Program, H Ozawa et al (Mitsui Engineering and Shipbuilding, Japan).
Integrated Structural Design and Strength Evaluation System for *TechnoSuperliner-A*, H Sueoka (Mitsubishi Heavy Industries, Japan).
Research on Hydrodynamic Performance of TSL-A, Y Kusaka et al (Mitsui Engineering and Shipbuilding, Japan).
The Norwegian High-Speed Marine Vehicle Research Programme, K O Holden (MARINTEK, Norway).
Design and Development of Hydrofoil Catamarans in Norway, K J Minsaas (MARINTEK, Norway).
The Future for High-Speed Light Craft, K M Wiklund (Det Norske Veritas, Norway).
A Study on the Structural Design of the Hydrofoil System for High-Speed Foil Catamaran Ships, K-S Min et al (Hyundai Heavy Industries, Korea).
A Study on the Prediction Method of Motion Characteristics for the High-Speed Catamaran Ship, K-S Min et al (Hyundai Heavy Industries, Korea).
Diesel Driven Fully Submerged Hydrofoil Catamaran: Mitsubishi Super-Shuttle 400, *Rainbow*, K Kihara et al (Mitsubishi Heavy Industries, Japan).
Model Tests and the Development of Control System for the Super-Shuttle 400 *Rainbow*, N Toki et al (Mitsubishi Heavy Industries, Japan).
Design and Manufacturing of the Foil Structure for Mitsubishi Super-Shuttle 400 *Rainbow*, H Sueoka et al (Mitsubishi Heavy Industries, Japan).
The Real-Time Simulation to Verify the Automatic Control System for a Submerged Hull and Foil Hybrid Super-High-Speed Liner, T Itoko (Kawasaki Heavy Industries, Japan).
A submerged Hull and Foil Hybrid Super-High-Speed Liner, R Ogiwara (Kawasaki Heavy Industries, Japan).
Structural Analysis of a Submerged Hull and Foil Hybrid Super-High-Speed Liner, I Neki (Ishikawajima-Harima Heavy Industries, Japan).
SUS-A: The State-of-the-Art of the German Research Programme for Fast Catamarans, A Kraus and A Naujeck (Howaldtswerke, Germany).
SUS-A: The Scope of the VWS Hard Chine Catamaran Series '89, B Müller-Graf (VWS, Germany).
SUS-A: The Effect of Section-Symmetry on Resistance, Performance and Sea-keeping Qualities of Fast Hard Chine Catamarans, B Müller-Graf (VWS, Germany).
SUS-B: First Results of the German Research Project for Swath Ships, A Nitz (EMIT, Germany).
SUS-B: A Computational Fluid Dynamics Method for SWATH Ships, V Bertram (University of Hamburg, Germany).
SUS-B: Numerical Simulation and Validation for SWATH Ships in Waves, P Blume and H Söding (HSVA, Germany).
Waveloads of a 30 m SSTH in Sea, A Ito et al (Ishikawajima-Harima Heavy Industries, Japan).
A Study on Manoeuvrability of the Super Slender Twin Hull, T Ishiguro (Ishikawajima-Harima Heavy Industries, Japan).
Development of a Foil-Assisted Catamaran *Superjet-30*, T Arii et al (Hitachi Zosen, Japan).
Development of a Motion Control System for a Foil-Assisted Catamaran *Superjet-30*, T Arii et al (Hitachi Zosen, Japan).
R&D of a Displacement-Type High-Speed Ship, N Takarada et al (Sumitomo Heavy Industries, Japan).
Sea-keeping Assessment of a Displacement Type Super High-speed ship in Directional Spectrum Waves, S Takezawa et al (Yokohama National University, Japan).
Experimental Study on Performance of V-CAT Hull Form by Sea Trial, O Yamamoto et al (NKK, Japan).
Design, Trial and Operation of Mitsui MightyCat 40, S Yamashita et al (Mitsui Engineering and Shipbuilding, Japan).
The Systematic Test of Wedge on Flat Plate Planing Surface, C S Chen et al (National Taiwan University, Taiwan, China).
Scale Effects on the Resistance Components of a High-Speed Semi-Displacement Craft, S Cordier and F X Dumez (Bassin d'Essais des Carènes, France).
Numerical Simulation of Free-Surface Flows around an Advancing Twin Hull Form, M-S Shin et al (KRISO, Korea).
Experimental and Numerical Investigation into Wave Exciting Surge Forces in Large Following Seas, J A Keuning et al (Deft University of Technology, Netherlands).
Design and Construction of a Seawater Survey Ship Built Using Aluminium Honeycomb Panels, Y Kaneko et al (Nagasaki Institute of Applied Science, Japan).
The Response of Various Ships Hull Plating Materials to Pressure Loads Caused by Slamming, R G Wraith et al (University of Melbourne, Australia).

Multiple Criteria Synthesis Technique Applied to the Reliability Based Structural Design of Hull Components of a Fast Swath Ship, P K Das et al (University of Glasgow, UK).
Structural design of Large, Fast Marine Vehicles Based on First Principals, O F Hughes et al (Virginia Poly. Institute, USA).
An Integrated Propulsion Lift-Control Design for Large High-Speed Hydrofoil Craft, P Kaplan (Hydromechanics Inc, USA).
On the application of Fuzzy Ride Control System to a Surface Effect Ship in Waves, K P Rhee et al (Seoul National University, Korea).
Attitude Control System for a High-Speed Catamaran with Hydrofoils in Waves, C-G Kang et al (KRISO, Korea).
Longitudinal Control of the SES based on Fuzzy Control Technique, H Yamato (University of Tokyo).
Study on Flow Characteristics and Resistance Components of Simple Planing Hull Forms, S Hirano and T Himeno (University of Osaka Prefecture, Japan).
A Consideration on Wave Loads Acting on High-Speed Monohulls in Irregular Waves by Non-linear Simulation Method, S K Chou et al (United Ship Design & Development Center, Taiwan, China).
Simulation of Running Attitude and Resistance of a High-Speed Craft Using a Database of Hydrodynamic Forces Obtained by Fully Captive Model Experiments, Y Ikeda (University of Osaka Prefecture, Japan).
Wave-Induced Motions and Loads on Fast Monohulls - Correlation of Theoretical Predictions with Model and Full-Scale Experiments, T Karppinen et al (VTT Ship Laboratory, Finland).
Structural Analyses of Composite Materials for Watercraft, T Kosugi and M Kashikawa (YAMAHA, Japan).
Loads and Responses of Steel and GRP Naval Ships in Random Seas, W G Price and P Temarel (University of Southampton, UK).
Residual Strength of Sandwich Structured - a Finite Element Study, M Heder (Chalmers University of Technology, Sweden).
Improvement with Hydrodynamic Characteristics of Catamaran with Hydrofoil, B-S Kim et al (DSHM, Korea).
Heave and Pitch Motions of a Catamaran Advancing in Waves, M Kashiwagi (Kyushu University, Japan).
Prediction of Relative Motion of a High-Speed Catamaran in Oblique Seas, M Ohkusu and G-C Wen (Kyushu University, Japan).
A Comparison of an Extended Strip Theory with a Three-Dimensional Theory for Computation of Response and Loads, R Tønnesen et al (Det Norske Veritas, Norway).
Hydroelastic Modelling of Slamming against Wetdeck of a Catamaran, J Kvålsvold and O M Faltinsen (Norwegian Institute of Technology, Norway).
Hydroelastic Analysis of Ship Hulls at High Forward Speed, M K Wu et al (Norwegian Institute of Technology, Norway).
A Simplified and Design-Orientated Method for Impacted Plated Structure Analyses, S-R Cho et al (University of Ulsan, Korea).
Slamming Impact Loads and Hull-Girder Response of a Large High-Speed Craft in Waves, H Takemoto et al (Ship Research Institute, Japan).
Completely Submerged Propellers for High-Speed Craft, E Bjärne (SSPA, Sweden).
Theoretical Analysis of Contra Rotating Propeller Systems and Experimental Validation, H Streckwall (HSVA, Germany).
A Contribution on the Performance of Partially Submerged Propellers, N Olofsson (Kamewa, Sweden).
Performance of a Supercavitating Propeller with Lip-Cup, H Kato et al (University of Tokyo, Japan).
Hydrofoil Research: Model Tests and Computations, F van Waltree and K Yamaguchi (MARIN, Netherlands).
Turning Motion and Directional Stability of Surface-Piercing Hydrofoil Craft, M Hamamoto et al (Osaka University, Japan).
Reduction of Hull Resistance with Hydrofoils, R Tasaki and R Sato (Ship and Ocean Foundation, Japan).
Validation of Hydrofoil Design Programme HYF3, R Latorre and D Bourg (University of New Orleans, USA).
On the Pressure Distribution of a Water-Jet Intake Duct in Self-Propulsion Conditions, Y Okamoto et al (NKK, Japan).
Hull-Water-jet Interaction Mechanisms: Theory and Validation, H G Coop and A J Bowen (University of Canterbury, New Zealand).
Surface-Piercing Propellers - Propeller/Hull Interaction, J C Rose et al (Rolla SP Propellers, USA).
Methods for Regulatory and Design Assessment of Planing Craft Dynamic Stability, P Werenskiold (MARINTEK, Norway).
Exhaust Emission Measurements on the High-Speed craft *M/S Salten*, B Meek-Hansen and O Bergh (MARINTEK, Norway).
Development of the ABS Guide for Building and Classing High-Speed Craft, C Morlan (ABS, USA).
Towards the Adoption of an IMO High-Speed Craft Code, F Plaza and K Sekimizu (IMO, UK).
A Study of Performance Predictions for High-Speed Slender Ship with Twin Wing Hulls, L Zhou et al (Hiroshima University, Japan).
Motion Responses of Air Cushion Catamaran in Regular Waves, Y Xie et al (Marine Design and Research Inst. of China).
A Study on the Hydrodynamic Aspects of Hybrid Hydrofoil Catamaran, K Shimizu et al (Mitsui Engineering and Shipbuilding, Japan).
A Numerical Solution of Three-Dimensional Gliding Plates, M Bessho and S Sakuma (Nihon University, Japan).
A Theoretical Model for the Powering Characteristics of Water-jet-Hull Systems, T van Terwisga (MARIN, Netherlands).
A Non-linear Simulation Method for Vertical Motions of Surface Effect Ships, H Ohtsubo et al (University of Tokyo, Japan).
Numerical Computations of the Non-linear Steady Waves Generated by a Two-Dimensional Hydrofoil, K J Bai (Seoul National University (Korea).
The TF40 Marine Gas Turbine, Some Recent High-Speed Applications, T B Lauriat (Textron Lycoming, USA).
Marine Propulsion with Industrial Derivative Gas Turbines, C M Waldheim (Solar Turbines Inc, USA).
Diesel Engine Behaviour Subject to Transient Loading in High-Speed Vessels, P O Moksnes and H Engja (Norwegian Institute of Technology, Norway).
Fast Vessel Engines-Environmentally Superior Power for Highly Reliable Transportation, R M Halleen et al (Caterpillar, USA).
Resistance and Motion Properties of Air Cushion Assisted Catamarans, H Miyata et al (University of Tokyo, Japan).
Sea-keeping and Comfort of Large SES, S Steen et al (MARINTEK, Japan).
Sea-keeping of an SES Experimental Craft. A Comparison between Computation and Measurements, N G Skomedal and S Falch (Kværner Mandal, Norway).
Sea-keeping Behaviour of an SES in Different Wave Directions, G K Kapsenberg (MARIN, Netherlands).
Operational and Cost Analysis of Fincantieri's Fast Ferries, G Arena and L De Martini (Fincantieri, Italy).
A Study of Transport Economy and Market Research for High-Speed Marine Passenger Vehicles, S Akagi (Osaka University, Japan).
Fast Sea Transportation System in the Aspect of Logistics, T E W Hagman and K R Lumsden (Chalmers University of Technology, Sweden).
Fast Sea Transportation - The Effect of Present and Future Technical Developments on Operating Economies, N I Gee and E Dudson (Nigel Gee and Associates, UK).
Global Strength Analysis of Wave-Piercing Catamarans, M Yamamoto et al (Kawasaki Heavy Industries, Japan).
Introducing Eurofast, G Arena and V Farinetti (Fincantieri, Italy).
Lift Fans Stability for SES, K C Witt (Witt & Sohn, Germany).
Bottom Plating Strength of High-Speed Fishing Craft, N Umeda et al (National Research Institute of Fisheries Engineering, Japan).
Fundamental Study on Optimum Position of Outriggers of Trimaran from View Point of Wave Making Resistance, K Suzuki and M Ikehata (Yokohama National University, Japan).
The Influence of Demihull Separation and River Banks on the Resistance of a Catamaran, L J Doctors and M R Renilson, AMECRC, Australia).
Experimental Investigations on Resistance and Sea-keeping Qualities of High-Speed Catamarans, S Matsui et al (West Japan Fluid Engineering Laboratory).
High-Speed Semi-Submersible Vehicle with Wing - Hydrodynamic Characteristics and Free-Running Experiments, K Mori et al (Hiroshima University, Japan).
Fast Ferry Mestral, J A Moret et al (E N Bazan, Spain).
Fast Slender Monohull Vessels for Cargo Transport, K Levander (Kværner Masa-Yards, Finland).
Dynamic Performance of Jet Skating Ship, S Naito et al (Osaka University).
Hydrodynamic Analysis and Design of a SWATH Multipurpose Research Vessel, A Papanikolaou et al (National Technical University of Athens, Greece).
Experimental Investigations on SWATH Models, V A Subramanian and C P Vendhan (Indian Institute of Technology, India).
One Fast Semi-Submersible Catamaran Vessel to Support Offshore Platforms, T Tachibana and O Caltabeloti (San Paulo State Institute of Technology (Brazil).
Assessment of High-Speed Navigation in a Congested Area by Traffic Simulation, A Nagasawa et al (Marine Safety Academy, Japan).
Safety Assessment of Advanced Marine Transportation System including High-Speed Vessels with Safety Margin as an Index, M Numano et al (Ship Research Institute, Japan).
Experimental Study of Fire Protection of a WPC Car Ferry, M Yamamoto et al (Kawasaki Heavy Industries, Japan).
Operational Procedures and Standards for the Operating Compartment, T Solberg et al (Braathen, SAFE, Norway).
High-Speed Monohulls in Extreme Sea Conditions: A Study of Operational Limits, J Lundgren (SSPA, Sweden).
Experience from Operation of Large Water-Jet Units, R Svensson (Kamewa, Sweden).
Flyable Hydrofoil Catamaran - A New Seaplane Concept, K Akashi (ShinMaywa Industries, Japan).
Motions of a Small Racing Boat Running in Steady Wind and Encountering Waves, M Nakato and M-K Ha (Hiroshima University, Japan).
On the Manoeuvring Simulation and the Steering Tests of an ACV Model, R Murao and H Kasai (Aoyama-Galuin University, Japan).
New IMO High-Speed Craft Code and the Problems of Ekranoplanes Certification, A I Bogdanov and D N Synitsin (Central Marine Res & Des Institute, Russia).
Optimization Tools for Ship resistance and Sea-keeping Problems, J J Maisonneuve (SIREHNA, France).
Performance and Behaviour of the Large Slender Monohull, E Jullunstrø et al (MARINTEK, Norway).
Optimization of Design Parameters of Water-Jet Propulsion System, K Matsumoto et al (Toshiba Corporation, Japan).
Water-Jet Propulsion Unit for High-Speed Hydrofoil Catamarans, T Kawakami (Mitsubishi Heavy Industries, Japan).
Some Notes on SES Hull Structural Design According to Classification Rules, T Jastrzebski and Z Sekulski (Technical University of Szczecin, Poland).
Integrated FEM Computer Program for Dynamic Analysis of Hovercraft Structure and its Machinery and Propulsion System, G X Yu et al (Shanghai Jiao Tong University, China).

Parametric Design Trade-Off Study and Preliminary Design of an SES Passenger Car Ferry, Y R Joo et al (Samsung Heavy Industries, Korea).
Structural Analysis of SEC's SES, J F Garside et al (ABS, USA).
WIGSIM-Wing-In-Ground-Effect Vehicle Flight Simulator, N Kornev (St Petersburg Marine Technical University, Russia).
Note on Prediction Aerodynamic Lift/Drag Ratio of WIG at Cruise, S Ando (Tokushima Bunri University, Japan).
A Concept of Wing-In-Surface-Effect Ship (WISES), T Fuwa et al (Ship Research Institute, Japan).
Design Philosophy and Design Procedures for Large High-Speed Craft, T E Svensen and S Valsgård (Det Norske Veritas, Norway).
Electric Manoeuvring and Drive Systems for Advanced Craft, R A Gellatly and D L Blount (EML Research, USA).
Propulsion Systems for Fast Ferries, G Haussmann (MTU, Germany).
Prospects for Hard Chine Monohull Vessels, D L Blount (Donald L Blount and Associates, USA).
State-of-the-Art and Perspectives of Development of Ekranoplans in Russia, K V Rozhdestvensky and D N Synitsin (Marine Technical University, Russia).
Prospect of High-Speed Marine Vehicles in China in the 21st Century, L Yun (Marine Des and Res Institute of China).
Some Aspects of Efficient Structural Design of Future Fast Multi-Hull Ships, D Faulkner (University of Glasgow).

Papers presented at the 10th Fast Ferry International Conference, 22-24 February 1994, London
Experience from the first operational season of the Rodriquez Aquastrada, E Tripiciano (Terrenia Navigazione).
Condor - Innovation by experience, A R White (Condor).
Superfast sea transport, V Airaksinen (Finnyards).
Design of an SES high-speed passenger and car ferry and development of a new ride control system, J Reischauer (MTG Marinetechnik).
Design philosophy behind the deep vee monohull MDV 1200 Pegasus, V Farinetti et al (Fincantieri).
A quarter century of high-speed craft safety development - A Canadian perspective, R Wade (Canadian Coast Guard).
The IMO code of safety for high-speed craft, A Blyth.
Performance standards for large high-speed craft, J Holland and A Kraus (Schicau Seebeckwerft and HDW).
30 years of Copenhagen to Malmo service, L Carlin (Dapskibsselskabet Oresund).
Operating a profitable commuter service in New York, M Stanisci and G Dunzelman (TNT Hydrolines).
Trials and tribulations of a shipbuilder, R Clifford (Incat Australia).
A formidable fast vehicle ferry, C Norman, Austal Ships.
Port facilities for fast ferries, K Fear (Posford Duvivier).
When do gas turbines make sense for passenger vessels, T Lauriat (Textron Lycoming).
Economical marine gas turbines, D Dunlevy (Caterpillar Solar Turbines).
Meeting the exacting propulsion demands of commercial operator of fast ferries, O Sandoy (Kvaerner Energy).
Stretching high-speed ferries - technical and economic considerations, N Gee and A Marchant (N Gee and Associates and AMTEC).
Tricat - the development of a 45+ knot ferry, M McSorley (FBM Marine Ltd).
New hydrofoil-assisted catamarans, N de Waal (Teknicraft Design).
Crew training - High-speed passenger craft, P Owen (Hong Kong Marine Dept).
Risk factors in high-speed craft operations - A study on Hong Kong to Macau routes, S Singh (Hong Kong Polytechnic).
Likely developments in large high-speed ferries by the year 2000, J Lewthwaite et al, (IMAA).

Papers presented at INEC '94 Cost Effective Maritime Defence, 31 August - 2 September 1994, London.
On the design of a propulsion power plant of high speed vessels, Prof A Paciolla, (University of Naples, Italy).
High speed and seaworthy small-displacement craft for coastal fleet, E A Aframeev, (Krylov Shipbuilding and Research Institute, Russia).

Papers presented at Ausmarine '94, November 22-24 1994, Fremantle Australia.
Trading ships, Captain Bill Bolitho, (Australian Shipowners' Association).
Patrol boats - their design and a way of buying them, Superintendant Arnie Highfield, (Royal Hong Kong Police).
Developments in South East Asia in the next decade, Commodore P K Nettur (Rtd), (Royal Malaysian Navy).
Requirements for naval vessels until the turn of the century, Commodore Peter Purcell, (Royal Australian Navy).
Fishing boats, P Talley, (Talley fisheries Ltd and Amaltal Fisheries Ltd).
Developing a maritime culture in Australia, Commodore Sam Bateman (Rtd), (Royal Australian Navy).
The changing environment - a shipowners expectations of a shipyards approach to safety and environmental awareness, R Fletcher, (P&O Towage and Salvage Pty Ltd).
Owners requirements for pilot vessels, Captain Robert Hall (Fremantle Port Authority).
Development of specialised oil and gas support vessels in Australia, Mr. Kenny Macleod, (M & P Subocean).
Requirements of Japanese passenger ferry operators, Mr. Naoki Hashimoto, (Diamond Ferry Co. Limited).
Company profile of Advanced Multi-hull Design, Paul Miller, (Advanced Multi-hull Design).
Designing around the bottom line, Stuart Ballantyne, (ASDMAR).
AMECRC research activities & consulting services, Giles Thomas, (Australian Maritime Engineering CRC Ltd).
Always an Austal vessel, Chris Norman, (Austal ships).
New joining technologies for steel aluminium fibre reinforced marine structures, Mike Turner, (Co-operative Research Centre for Materials Welding and Joining).
New high speed safety code - legal implications, Ian Morison, (Sly and Weigall).
Some notes on 100 years of the use of aluminium in shipbuilding, Stuart Ridland, (Lloyds Register).
Future trends for fast water transportation of cargo, Iwane Takahara, (NEC Logistics Ltd, Japan).
The Solar Taurus Gas Turbine Package, Thornton Lauriat, (Solar Turbines).
The evolution of the Caterpillar 3500 family of high performance marine propulsion engines, Jack Laird, (Caterpillar).
A new high speed diesel engine for high speed craft propulsion, (GEC Alsthom).
Gas turbine experience in Hong Kong, Carroll Oates, (Textron Lycoming).
Future thrust - optimum propulsion solutions towards the Twenty First Century, Philip Rae, (CWF Hamilton & Co Ltd).
Twin disc transmission and propulsion systems, Mark Dougall, (Twin Disc Transmission and Propulsion Systems).
Marine gears for propulsion systems of high-speed craft, Graeme Miller, (ZF Australia).
The Veem Enngineering Group, Paul Kay, (Veem Engineering).
Centa flexible couplings and driveshafts, Borre Karlsrud, (Centa Transmissions).

Papers presented at the International Symposium on Waterjet Propulsion - Latest developments, 1-2 December 1994, London.
The evolution of the modern waterjet propulsion unit, S Roy, (Southampton Institute of Higher Education).
Waterjet testing in the SSPA towing tank, Dr G Dyne and P Lindell, (SSPA Maritime Consulting AB, Sweden).
Waterjet propulsion - experience from high powered installations, R Svensson, (Kamewa AB, Sweden).
Waterjet propulsion: a shipbuilders view; N Warren, N Simms, J Ketchmar, (FBM Marine Group).
The medium speed diesel and waterjet propulsion, R G Hunt, (GEC Alsthom Ruston Diesels Ltd).
The waterjet as an engine dynamometer, Dr K Alexander, (CWF Hamilton and Co Ltd, New Zealand).
Steering and reversing gear for very large waterjets, J Allison and Dr C Dai, (Band, Lavis & Associates Inc, USA).
Jet drive steering and reversing: a new approach, P Roos, (American Hydro Jet Corporation, USA).
Influence of waterjet forces on ship design, R Verbeek, (Lips Jet BV, Netherlands).
An operators requirements for waterjet installations & control systems in high speed ferries, A Way, (Marine and General Engineers Ltd, Guernsey).
Practical considerations on waterjets with flush intakes, Dr J English, (Maritime Technology).
Some important factors in waterjet development; J G Stricker, A J Becnel and J G Purnell, (Naval Surface Warfare Centre, USA).
The importance of high manoeuvrability for efficient operation, G Torneman, (MJP Waterjets, Sweden).

Papers presented at the 11th Fast Ferry International Conference, 21-23 February 1995, Hong Kong.
A management information system as an estimating tool, D Hill, (Far East Hydrofoil Company).
30 years' experience of maintaining high speed surface craft for the Hong Kong Macao route, C K ff Nobbs, (CTS-Parkview Shipyard).
Real and Imaginary problems with the new IMO HSC Code, C A Jenman, (Global Maritime).
Caterpillar 3600 engine - Life cycle costs open non-traditional markets, J G Stevenson and R M Halleen, (Caterpillar).
Night vision equipment and its use, P R Owen, (High speed craft consultant).
Analyzing and troubleshooting poor vessel performance: Techniques available to operators using contemporary performance prediction software, D M MacPherson, (Hydrocomp).
The first twenty one year's experience of Hovermarine craft operations in Hong Kong, P J Hill and D C S Ho, (Hovermarine International and The Hong Kong & Yaumati Ferry Company respectively).
The fast ferry service between Central Hong Kong and Discovery Bay, Lantau Island; J Marriot, (Discovery Bay Transportation Services).
Looking after the customer, A M Whyte, (Red Funnel Group).
Hayabusa - the world's largest high speed wavepiercing catamaran car ferry (Kawasaki Jet Piercer), Y Saito et al, (Kawasaki Heavy Industries).
Developing a cargo carrying high speed ro-ro monohull; M Garguet (Euroyards), J de No (Astlleros Españoles), D Klug (Bremer Vulkan), M Garguet (Chantiers de L'Atlantique), V Farinett (Fincantieri), L Kinneman (Howaldtswerke-Deutsche Werft).
Developing a composite hull for a large high speed catamaran, H Enlund, (Finnyards).
The development of advanced and cost effective HT Hovercraft in China, Z H Wang, (Hang Tong High Speed Ship Development).
FMEA and the human element, R G Wade, (Canadian Coast Guard).

An evaluation of a fast ferry operation after one year of operation, T E W Hagman, (Chalmers University of Technology).
Operational experience with multiple waterjet installations, P Rae, (C W F Hamilton).
A novel approach to the improvement of fast catamaran seaworthiness, A D Kruglov, (Advanced Transportation Technologies).
Gas Turbines in today's passenger vessels, D Dunlevy, (Solar Turbines).
MTU 396 experience in fast passenger vessels, MTU 1163 the choice for large passenger vehicle ferries; G Haussman, (Motoren-und Turbinen-Union Friedrichshafen)
The Hong Kong experience, F C Chan, (Hong Kong Marine Department).
The law of fast ferries; Paul Turner (Clifford Chance), and Timothy Kelley (Jones, Waldo, Holbrook & McDonough).

Papers presented at the International Conference on Seakeeping and Weather, 28 February and 1 March 1995, London.

Weather and warships; past, present and future, D K Brown.
Measurement of encountered waves and ship motions during full scale seakeeping trials; A Rantanen, J Holmberg and T Karppinen, (VTT Manufacturing Technology, Finland).
Seakeeping for design: development and application of an inverse analysis design methodology to multihull forms; Grant Hearn, Peter Wright and Bill Hills, (University of Newcastle, UK).
Head sea slamming tests on a fast surface ship hull form series; J Colwell, I Datta and R Rogers, (Institute for Marine Dynamics, Canada).
Analysis of non-linear vessel motions: experiments and predictions; J Boyd, K Klaka and G Thomas, (Australian Maritime Engineering CRC Ltd).
A note on the effect of non-linearity on the prediction of vertical motions of a small high speed craft, G J Macfarlane and M R Renilson, (Australian Maritime Engineering CRC Ltd).

Papers presented at the International Maritime Defence Conference, 28-31 March 1995, London.

Future ASW frigate concept study of a trimaran variant, Andrew B Summers and John Eddison, (US Department of Defense, UK Ministry of Defence).
The trimaran frigate - recent research and and potential for the next generation, Professor David Andrews and J H Hall, (University College London, Defence Research Agency).
SMYGE-YS 2000 - future projects. Swedish development of state-of-the-art surface combatants; Commander Magnus Bergman, Carl Fagergren, Urban Mathiasson, Anders Lönnö.
The design of the FF-21 multi mission frigate, John Paul Mabry and Leonid Afanasieff, (Newport News Shipbuilding, John J McMullen Associates Inc).
Novel propulsion systems for future surface warships; Christopher Elliot, E S Matthews, T&EE Pyestock, (Ministry of Defence).
Ship design implications of the ICR marine gas turbine, Gordon Price and Elizabeth R Watson, (Rolls-Royce Industrial and Marine Gas Turbines Ltd).
The Ingalls Corvette; Chester A Hard, Kermit B Pethtel Jr, James P Brooks, (Litton Ingalls Shipbuilding).
Proposal for a frigate innovative propulsion system, Captain Alfio Todde, (Italian Navy).
The OKSØY Class MCMV; Commander Johs Instefjord, Nere Skomedal and Thomas Kjaer, (Royal Norwegian Navy, Kvæner Mandal Shipyard).

Papers presented at the Cruise and Ferry Conference, 16-18 May 1995, London.

SuperFast Ferries - 500 miles in 20 hours, K-W Brraun, Schichau Seebeckwerft.
Impact of the new IMO Code, Frode Klepsvik, (DnV, Norway).
Stena HSS - the coming of age for marine evacuation systems, (ML Lifeguard, UK).
The importance of system reliability, E. Kroto, (Lyngso Marine, Norway).
Operational experience from Hayabusa, Hisao Manabe, (Kawasaki, Japan).
A Giant Mestral - the Alhambra will carry 1250 passengers and 246 cars, Honorio Sierra, (Bazan, Spain).
The world's fastest car ferry Juan Patricio - breaking the 50 knot barrier, P. Miller, (AMD, Australia).
Tricat in service, M. McSorley, (FBM Marine, UK).
The seakeeping performance of fast single and multihull passenger ferries, T. Karppinen et al, (VTT, Finland).
High speed propellers or waterjets?, H. Bouwman, (Lips BV, Netherlands).
Beyond 5 MW, D. Dunlevy, (Solar Turbines, USA).
Keeping fast ferries in service, G. Rechtsteiner, (MTU, Germany).

Papers presented at the International Symposium Warship '95 - Offshore Protection Vessels, 14-15 June 1995, London.

The new generation Aviso patrol vessel; V Martinot-Lagarde, M Maynard and J M Grenier, (Ministere de la defense, DCN Ingenierie, France).
The new Danish OPV's based on the standard flex concept, I B Rodholm RADM (Ret) RDN, (IBRO Consult, Denmark).
Europatrol 250 - protecting the maritime frontiers of the EC, B Morrison, (Vosper International Ltd, UK).
'Protector III' - a new fisheries protection vessel for Eastern Sea Fisheries Joint Committee; D M Cannell & J R Pratt, S C Amos, (D M Cannell Naval Architects, Eastern Sea Fisheries Joint Committee, UK).
HM Customs - recent new ship procurement, R Farrer, (HM Customs and excise, UK).
Propeller tip vortex cavitation noise (on OPV's), K Brannstrom, (Karlskronavarvet AB, Sweden).
Measured seakeeping on an Australian offshore patrol boat, K J Hope, (Australian Defence Force Academy).
ABS M-10: Third Generation Hovercraft, A F White & Lt-Col E Southby-Tailyour RM (Ret), (ABS Hovercraft, UK).
SWATH ships for offshore protection, R Holcomb and A Blyth, (Swath International Ltd, Blyth Bridges Marine Consultants Ltd, UK).
Design, build and trial of the 20 m Ultra Fast Patrol Boat, S S C Huang, (Lung Teh Shipbuilding Co Ltd, Republic of China).
Very Slender Vessels, A Thompson, (Paragon Mann Ltd, UK).

Papers presented at FAST '95, 25-27 September 1995 at Lübeck-Travemünde, Germany.

Factors influencing the Selection of a Hard Chine or Round-Bilge Hull for High Froude Numbers, D L Blount (Donald Blount and Associates Inc, USA).
The Influence of Aft Buttock Shape on High-Speed Hull Performance, S A Hellström (SSPA, Sweden) and D L Blount (Donald Blount and Associates Inc, USA).
Effect of Spray Rails on the Resistance of Planing Hulls, G J Grigoropoulos and T A Loukakis (National Technical University of Athens, Greece).
Performance Predictions and Parametric Studies for Small High-Speed Displacement and Semidisplacement Vessels with Shallow Draft, D Radojcic (University of Belgrade, Yugoslavia).
Hydrodynamics of Fast Catamarans, M A Basin et al (Forma Ltd, Russia).
Numerical Resistance Prediction based on the Results of the VWS Hard Chine Catamaran Hull Series '89, J M Zips (Versuchsanstalt für Wasserbau und Schiffbau).
Influence of the Distance between Demihulls on the Characteristics of a Big, High Speed Catamaran, K Patrakka et al (Finnyards Ltd, Finland).
The Interaction Effects on a Catamaran Travelling with Forward Speed in Waves, A P van 't Veer and F R T Siregar (Delft University of Technology, The Netherlands).
Some Considerations on the Structural Requirement for the Classification of High Speed Craft, Y F Cheng and W Turnbull (Lloyd's Register of Shipping, UK).
Introduction of Systematic and Probabilistic Safety Assessment Methods for the Classification of High Speed Craft, U Petersen and J P Securius (Germanischer Lloyd, Germany).
New Rules for High Speed Craft, H Pinon (EEIG Unitas, Belgium).
Structural Design Philosophies and Classification Requirements for High Speed Craft, M Fan and C Mazonakis (University of Strathclyde, UK).
Revised Speed-Dependent Powering Predictions for High-Speed Transom Stern Hull Forms, S C Fung (David Taylor Model Basin, USA) and L Leibman (Proteus Engineering, USA).
Seaworthiness of Aquastrada Class of Ships, D Boote et al (University of Genova, Italy).
Optimisation of the Seakeeping Behaviour of a Fast Monohull, J A Keuning and J Pinkster (Delft University of Technology, The Netherlands).
Resistance and Seakeeping Characteristics of Fast and Large Multihull Vessels, H Helasharju et al (VTT Manufacturing Technology, Finland).
Seakeeping for Design: Balancing the Vertical and Horizontal Motions of a Catamaran, G E Hearn (University of Newcastle upon Tyne, UK).
Numerical Study of Water Impact Loads on Catamarans with Asymmetric Hulls, M Arai et al (Yokohama National University, Japan).
Local Strength of Plating in High Speed Craft, D McGeorge et al (Det Norske Veritas Research AS, Norway).
Structural Load Predictions in the Design of High Speed Vehicles, H-S Chan and A Incecik (University of Glasgow, UK)
Design Pressure for the Wet-Deck Structure of Twin-Hull Ships, L Zhu and D Faulkner (University of Glasgow, UK).
CORSAIRE 11,000 - Optimization and Contractual Validation of the Seakeeping Performance of the New Fast Ferry Ship for SNCM, R Dussert-Vidalet et al (Société Nationale Corse Méditerranée, France).
Fast Displacement Ships - An Economical Option for High Speed Transportation, H Langenberg (Blohm & Voss AG, Germany).
Superslender Monohull with Outriggers, J Lindström et al (Kværner Masa-Yards Technology, Finland).
Optimisation of Hydrofoil-Supported Planing Catamarans, K-G Hoppe (University of Stellenbosch, Republic of South Africa).
Feasibility Study on a High-Speed Catamaran: Comparison with Aquastrada, G Trincas et al (University of Trieste).
Predicted Performance and Seakeeping of the Semi-Planing Ship, J C Lewthwaite (JCL Consultancy, UK) and H Oehimann (MTG Marinetechnik GmbH, Germany).
The Behaviour of Single-Skin FRP Plate Structures under Extreme Lateral Pressure Loading, R A Shenoi et al (University of Southampton, UK).
Strength Aspects of Sandwich Panels with Foam Core, A S Herrmann (DLR Braunschweig, Germany) and K Delius (JAFO Technologie Hamburg, Germany).
How to Efficiently Join FRP Structures to Metal Ships, M Hentinen and M Hildebrand (VTT Manufacturing Technology, Finland).
A Hydrodynamics-Based Simulator for Fast Ship Manoeuvrability Assessment and Training, P Kaplan et al (Hydromechanics Inc, USA).
The Effect of Ship's Speed on Collision Avoidance, H Imazu (Tokyo University of Mercantile Marine, Japan).
Calm Water Handling Qualities in High Speed Rescue Craft, I W Dand (BMT SeaTech Limited, UK) and R M Cripps (Royal National Lifeboat Institution, UK).
Motion Sickness Incidence Study on Rottnest Island High Speed Ferries, R C Smith and L L Koss (Australian Maritime Engineering CRC, Australia).
Wave-Piercing Catamaran Type High-Speed Car Ferry *Hayabusa*, N Kamoi et al (Kawasaki Heavy Industries Ltd, Japan).

Optimum Design of a High Speed Ferry-Passengers Catamaran Vessel taking into account Operational Criteria and Cost, P Grosjean et al (Université de Liege, Belgium).
Development of a 1200 DWT High-Speed Container Ship, Y R Joo et al (Samsung Heavy Industries Co. Ltd, Korea).
Hydroelastic Response of Ships with Forward Speed in Waves, T Vada (Det Norske Veritas Research AS, Norway).
Long Term Springing and Whipping Stresses in High Speed Vessels, P F Hansen et al (Technical University of Denmark, Denmark).
Hydroelastic Analysis of a Flexible Catamaran and Comparison with Experiments, O A Hermundstad et al (Norwegian Institute of Technology, Norway).
Structural Responses of Mitsubishi Super-Shuttle 400 *Rainbow* in Seaways, H Sueoka et al (Mitsubishi Heavy Industries Ltd, Japan).
The HSVA Systematic SWATH Model Series, P Schenzle (Hamburg Ship Model Basin, Germany).
Research on Semi-SWATH Hull Form, C Schack (Danyard A/S, Denmark).
Comparison of Seakeeping Performance of a Monohull and a SWATH Design for a new Naval Research Vessel, H Oehimann and R Pereira (MTG Marinetechnik GmbH, Germany).
Energy Efficient Propulsors for SWATH Ships, M Atlar et al (University of Newcastle upon Tyne, UK).
Virtual Prototyping of Advanced Marine Vehicles, O P Jons and R L Schaffer (Advanced Marine Enterprises Inc, USA).
Hybrid Hydrofoil Monohulls, V Bertram et al (University of Hamburg, Germany).
Free-Running Turning Tests of a New Displacement-Type High Speed Semi-Submersible Ship with Wings, K Mori et al (Hiroshima University, Japan).
Aerodynamic Design of Wing In Ground Effect Craft, T Kühmstedt and G Milbradt (TechnoTrans e.V., Germany).
Simulation Study on the Behaviour of Wing-In-Surface Effect Ships, T Fuwa et al (Ship Research Institute, Japan).
Nonlinear Aerodynamics of Ekranoplan in Strong Ground Effect, K V Rozhdestvensky (Marine Technical University, Russia).
Development of IMO Safety Requirements for a New High Speed Seagoing Transportation-WIG Craft - Present State, A I Bogdanov (Central Marine Research and Design Institute Ltd, Russia).
Swath International's Super 4000 Class - Its Design, Construction and Performance, R S Holcomb (Swath International Ltd, UK).
Design of a High-Speed 300 Passenger SWATH Ship, K-S Min and Y-W Lee (Hyundai Maritime Research Institute, Korea).
SMUCC - SWATH Multipurpose Container Carrier, A D Papanikolaou et al (National Technical University of Athens, Greece).
Experiments at Sea by Large Scale Models of Techno-Superliner, K Sugai et al (TRA of Techno-Superliner, Japan).
The Seagoing Test Ship to Verify the Technologies Developed for a Submerged Hull and Foil Hybrid Super-High Speed Liner, N Yamanaka et al (Kawasaki Heavy Industries Ltd, Japan).
Study on the Cavitation of the Hydrofoil for the Techno-Superliner-F, O Watanabe and Y Shirose (Ishikawajima-Harima Heavy Industries Co. Ltd, Japan).
MTU 595/1163 - The Power for Fast Ferries, G Haussmann and P Kneipp (Motoren-und Turbinen-Union Friedrichshafen GmbH, Germany).
Technically and Economically Optimized Fast Ships Propulsion Systems from 18,000 to 30,000 kW, C M Gallin et al (Gallin Marine Consultants, The Netherlands).
Gas Turbine Propulsion for Fast Vessels, B Schwanter (AlliedSignal Engines, Germany).
Test Techniques and Prediction Methods for Assessment of High-Speed Craft Dynamic Stability, P Werenskiold et al (MARINTEK, Norway).
Dynamic Stability Assessment of Wave-Piercing Catamarans, D Vassalos (University of Strathclyde, UK).
On the Influence of Fully Cavitating Propellers on Interaction Effects and Dynamic Stability of Fast Craft, K R Suhrbier (Consultant, UK).
Basic Performance of TSL-A70 in Sea Tests, H Ozawa et al (Mitsui Engineering & Shipbuilding Co. Ltd, Japan).
Structural Responses of TSL-A70 in Sea Tests, H Sueoka et al (Mitsubishi Heavy Industries Ltd, Japan).
On the Evaluation of Structural Safety of a Large High-Speed Vessel, H Takemoto et al (Ship Research Institute, Japan).
Gear Units for Fast Vessels, M Hirt and K-H Merk (RENK TACKE GmbH, Germany).
Analysis, Design and In-Service-Experience of a Membrane Coupling made of Advanced Composites, G Lutz (Geislinger & Co Schwingungstechnik GmbH, Austria).
Universal Joint Shafts, W Grabietz et al (J M Voith GmbH, Germany).
Seakeeping Performance of High Speed Displacement Craft, D A Hudson et al (University of Southampton, UK).
Theoretical Prediction of Seakeeping Qualities of High Speed Vessels, M Takaki et al (Hiroshima University, Japan).
A Panel Method applied to Hydrodynamic Analysis of Twin-Hull Ships, T E Schellin and H Rathje (Germanischer Lloyd, Germany).
Review on German SES Developments and the Government funded R&D Programme SUS C, J Wessel (Blohm & Voss AG, Germany).
Exciting Forces caused by Regular Waves acting on Cushion and Seals of an SES, P Blume (Hamburg Ship Model Basin, Germany).
ExMOD MOSES - Sea Trials with a Self-Propelled, Manned Experimental Model of an SES, H W Gröning (BWB Bundesamt für Wehrtechnik und Beschaffung, Germany) and J Reischauer (MTG Marinetecknik GmbH, Germany).
Full Scale Torque and Thrust Measurements on Board the SES *Corsair/Mekat*, K Jordan and M Schmiechen (Versuchsanstalt für Wasserbau und Schiffbau, Germany).
Basic Principles of Propulsor Efficiency Comparisons, T B Ibragimova et al (Krylov Shipbuilding Research Institute, Russia).
Alternative Propeller Concepts for High Speed Planing Hull Catamarans, B Müller-Graf (Versuchsanstalt für Wasserbau und Schiffbau, Germany).
Full-Scale Measurements on a Ventilated Propeller, M Keller (Sulzer Hydro GmbH, Germany).
A Contrarotating Propeller Design for a High Speed Patrol Boat with Pod Propulsion, B Y-H Chen and C L Tseng (David Taylor Model Basin, USA).
Numerical and Experimental Studies of Nonlinear Motions and Loads of a High-Speed Catamaran, R Zhao and J V Aarsnes (MARINTEK, Norway).
Time Domain Simulation of the Motion of a High Speed Twinhull with Control Planes in Waves, C-G Kang and I-Y Gong (Korea Research Institute of Ships and Ocean Engineering, Korea).
Development of a New Calculation Method for a Large Motion in Following Seas for the Foil-Assisted Catamaran *Superjet-30*, R Shigehiro (Kagoshima University, Japan) and T Arii (Hitachi Zosen Corp, Japan).
Theoretical Prediction of Seakeeping Performance and Comparison with Sea Trial Results for High-Speed Foil Catamaran Ship, D-J Yum et al (Hyundai Maritime Research Institute, Korea).
Model Tests for a Large Surface Effect Ship at Different Scale Ratios, G K Kapsenberg (MARIN, The Netherlands) and P Blume (Hamburg Ship Model Basin, Germany).
Large Surface Effect Ship (SES) Air Cushion Dynamics: An Innovative Methodology for Theoretical Modelling Validation, J-F Masset et al (IFREMER, France).
Large SES Calm Water and Head Sea Performance - A Comparison between Model Basin Test Results and Estimates using 'PERF' Software, J Richards et al (Hamburg Ship Model Basin, Germany).
Linear Calculation of Seakeeping Properties of SES, Validation with Tank Tests and Measurements of the Full-Scale Version, H-D Ehrenberg (Blohm & Voss, Germany).
Waterjet Propulsion for Fast Craft - Optimized Integration of Hull and Propulsor, J L Allison and P Goubault (Band, Lavis & Associates Inc, USA).
Manoeuvrability of Waterjet-Propulsed Passenger Ferries, S Voulon (Lips Jets BV, The Netherlands) and A F Wesselink (Lips BV, The Netherlands).
Noise from Waterjet Propulsion, R Aartojärvi (Kamewa AB, Sweden).
New Approaches to Improvement of Propulsive Performance and Seakeeping Qualities of High-Speed Vessels, A V Ponomarev et al (Krylov Shipbuilding Research Institute, Russia).
CFD Simulation of the Flow around Planing Craft and Tandem Hydrofoils, T Kawamura et al (University of Tokyo, Japan).
Transient Wave Packets - An Efficient Technique for Seakeeping Tests of Self-Propelled Models in Oblique Waves, G F Clauss and W L Kühnlein (Berlin University of Technolgy, Germany).
Further SES Technology Development at technical Research and Development Institute of Japan Defense Agency, T Murakami (Tokai University, Japan) and K Yamakita (TRDI JDA, Japan).
Feasibility Study on a Payload 500 and 1000 Ton Class Air-Cushion Catamaran, M-S Shin et al (Korea Research Institute of Ships & Ocean Engineering, Korea).
Recent Experience with Parallel Operating Lift Fans in SES, H Witt et al (Witt & Sohn & Co, Germany).
Controversial Issues in Waterjet-Hull Interaction, T van Terwisga (MARIN, The Netherlands) and K V Alexander (Hamilton Jet, New Zealand).
Experiences from Design and Testing of Waterjet Inlets for High Speed Craft, S Steen and K J Minsaas (Marintek, Norway).
A Numerical Method for Hydrodynamic Analysis of Waterjets, J A Szantyr and T Bugalski (Institute of Fluid-Flow Machinery, Poland).
Results of Model Tests with Fast Unconventional Ships in Shallow Water, W Grollius et al (Versuchsanstalt für Binnenschiffbau e.V Duisburg, Germany).
Optimal Design of High-Speed River Catamarans, K P Pal and L J Doctors (Australian Maritime Engineering CRC Ltd, Australia).
On the Wavemaking, Resistance and Squat of a Catamaran Moving at High Speed in a Shallow Water Channel, T Jiang et al (Gerhard-Mercator-Universität - GH Duisburg, Germany).
Nonlinear Effects of a Flexible Stern Seal Bag on Cobblestone Oscillations of a SES, T Ulstein and O Faltinsen (Norwegian Institute of Technology, Norway).
The Development of the Ride Control System of a Surface Effect Ship by the Fuzzy-Neural Theory, K P Rhee and H J Lee (Seoul National University, Korea).
A Ride Control System for Surface Effect Ships, based on the Variable Structure Control Theory, H Laabs (MTG Marinetechnik GmbH, Germany).
A Novel Flush Inlet Design Methodology for Waterjet Propulsion, C Dai et al (David Taylor Model Basin, USA).
The Application of Computational Fluid Dynamics to Practical Waterjet Propulsion System Design and Analysis, G J Seil (Australian Maritime Engineering CRC Ltd, Australia).
A Numerical Analysis of the Flow around the Waterjet Inlet, C K Yang et al (Seoul National University, Korea).

Papers presented at the International Symposium on High Speed Vessels For Transport and Defence, 23 and 24 November 1995, London.

High Speed Vessels for Transport and Defense - Database Design for High Speed Catamarans, R Latorre (University of New Orleans, USA) and J M A Vasconcellos (Federal University of Rio de Janeiro, Brazil).
Comfort Assessment of Large High-Speed Catamarans, J Kvålsvold et al (Det Norske Veritas Classification AS, Norway).
Seakeeping Assessment of Catamarans Through Numerical and Experimental

Methods, C Boccalatte (Italian Navy, Rome) and G Caprino et al (CETENA, Genoa).
Seakeeping for Design: Identification of Hydrodynamically Optimal Hull Forms for Large High Speed Catamarans, G E Hearn et al (University of Newcastle-upon-Tyne, UK).
Hydrodynamically Optimal Hull Forms for River Ferries, L J Doctors et al (University of New South Wales, Australia).
Preliminary Resistance Prediction Method for Fast Mono- and Multihull Vessels, K Hanhirova et al (Helsinki University of Technology, Finland).
Implementing the IMO High Speed Code, A G Blyth (Blyth Bridges Marine Consultants Ltd, UK).
Fast Ships and Regulatory Safety, W A Cleary Jr (Maritime Consultant, USA).
Aiming For Mach Numbers Beyond 0.5 On Water, D Stinton (Darrol Stinton Ltd, UK).
Gas Turbine Experience In Ferry Operations, B R Schwanter (AlliedSignal Aerospace Service Corp, Germany).
The CPS High Speed Propulsion Programme, J Selmer (CPS Drive, Norway) and D O Ellingsen (CPS Production, Norway).
Are High-Speed Cargo Ships Economically Viable?, A Rodgers (BAeSEMA Ltd, UK).
Current And Future Possibilities In The Design of Fast Ferries, N F Warren et al (FBM Marine Ltd, UK).
The Design, Testing And Operating Of Low-Wash, High-Speed Trimaran Passenger Ferries to Class VB, E W H Gifford OBE (Griffon Hovercraft Ltd, UK).
Considerations In The Design Of A Trimaran Frigate, D J Andrews and J-W Zhang, University College London, UK).
The Design, Supply, Use And Operational Development Of The Griffon Amphibious Hovercraft For The Swedish Coastguard, J H Gifford (Griffon Hovercraft Ltd, UK) and Captain Å Dagnevik (Swedish Coastguard, Sweden).
The Rapid Marine Transportation Group, S Phillips (Seaspeed Technology Ltd, UK).

Papers presented at the 12th Fast Ferry International Conference, 20-22 February 1996, Copenhagen.
How To Make A Successful Fast Ferry Line, P Jepperson (Cat-Link A/S).
Fast Ferries In The Netherlands?, D C Zoutendijk (Traffic Test).
Fast Ferry Operation From The Bridge View, T Hagman (Chalmers University of Technology) and T Ahlman (Sea Containers Sweden),
Fast ferry Operation And The Human Factor, E Wahren (SAS Flight Academy).
Implementing the ISM Code In Fast Ferries, K Jensen (DSØ).
Concept Of An Information Support System For Damage Control Of Fast Sea Ferries, A D Kruglov (Advanced Transportation Technologies).
Code Of Safety For High Speed Craft - Practical Implications, S Okkenhaug and M Sverkmo (Marintek).
LR's New Rules For Special Service Craft, Y F Cheng et al (Lloyd's Register).
FPC-23 Fast Passenger Catamaran For Adriatic Sea Operation, D Bandula (Brodarski Institute).
The Planning And Design Of Major Routes Car and Passenger Fast Catamaran Ferries for The British Columbia Ferry Corporation, R G Allan et al (Robert Allan).
A Technical And Economic Appraisal For Four Potential HSMV Routes In China, B Z Lu et al (China Shipbuilding Trading Company (Guangzhou).
Progress In The Development Of the SPS High Speed Passenger/Car Ferry, J C Lewthwaite (JCL High Speed Marine Craft Consultancy).
Development & Assessment Of The Semo-SES High Speed Passenger Vessel, Y N Park et al (Semo).
Loads In Waterjet Inlet Ducts, K Alexander (Hamilton Jet).
Steel Structures For High-Speed Watercraft, P F Patou and R H Kefferstein (Sollac).
Changing Aluminium Products In The Marine Market, G M Raynaud (Pechiney - France).
Lightweight Materials In Naval Architecture, M J Turner (Ciba Composites).
Effect Of New Insurance Clauses On Fast Ferry Operations, S Groves (Richard Hogg).
Fast Ferries And The Environment - A Challenge To Builders And Operators?, B Foss (Molde College).
Light Industrial Gas Turbines Offer Strong Benefits In Propulsion Of Fast Ferries, S Svensson (ABB Stal).

Papers presented at the International Conference on Lightweight Materials In Naval Architecture, 28 and 29 February 1996, Southampton, UK.
Material Selection: Comparative Procedures And The Significance Of Form, R Birmingham and B Jopling (University of Newcastle-upon-Tyne, UK).
Composite Construction: A Design Process Guide, G Harvey (SP Technologies Ltd, UK) and A Shimell (Futura Yacht (UK) Ltd).
Structural Design Process For Large HSLC Vessels, K O Skjølsvik (Det Norske Veritas Classification A/S, Norway).
A Review Of Deck Buckling Considerations For Large Lightweight Monohull Ferries, R Loscombe (Southampton Institute, UK).
Large Scale FRP Structure Tests, R S Dow (Defence Research Agency, Dunfermline, UK).
Let Aluminium Take The Strain, R Woodward (Aluminium Federation, UK).
Fabrication Of Large Aluminium Panels By Mechanised MIG Welding, W J Allday (Independent Consultant, UK).
Development in Welding Techniques For Aluminium Alloys, J D Russell et al (The Welding Institute, UK).
Adhesively Bonded Aluminium Superstructures, G Judd et al (Vosper Thornycroft (UK) Ltd).
A Review Of Lightweight Composite Structural Materials For Naval Architecture, M J Turner (Ciba Composites).
Insight Into New Inorganic Matrix Incombustible Composites For Offshore Fire And Thermal Protection Systems, A Hall and P J Hogg (Claymore Systems Ltd, UK).
Approval For Sprayed Insulation, D C Miller (American Sprayed Fibers Inc, USA).
Advantages of Composite Couplings For Marine Drives, L MacKellar (Turboflex Ltd, UK).

ADDITIONAL PAPERS PUBLISHED 1991-1996
The Rolls-Royce Spey Marine Gas Turbine, J Ferrie, The Institute of Marine Engineers, London, 20 February 1990.
Jetfoils on the Ostend-Dover Route: a Technical and Commercial Appraisal, Jacques J Charlier (Institute of Geography, Catholic University of Louvain, Belgium), MARIT POL MGMT, 1990, Vol 7, No 2, pages 123-132.
An Evaluation of the SWATH Vessel Frederick G Creed in the Canadian North Atlantic, J E Goodyear, D Nicholson (Canadian Hydrographic Service, Science Branch Department of Fisheries and Oceans, St John's, Newfoundland) D J Hussey, C D Roushorn (RDS Donelad Limited, Bedford, Nova Scotia) and A Hayes (Geo-Resources Inc, St John's, Newfoundland), Proceedings of US Hydrographic Conference '90, Norfolk, Virginia, 1-3 May 1990, The Hydrographic Society of America.
Hydrostatic Propulsion Systems or Main Drives Now in the Water, Hanno Speich (Mannesmann Rexroth), presented for the Shipbuilding Seminar at Mannesmann Rexroth GmbH in Lohr am Main, 29-30 May 1990.
An Investigation into the Stability and Survivability of Passenger Carrying Catamaran Craft, S A Roberts, J Cook and B Matthewson (Vosper Thornycroft UK Ltd and UK Department of Transport) 28 November 1990, Meeting of the Royal Institution of Naval Architects at Southampton, UK.
Producibility Benefits of the Swath Configuration, Richard L De Vries, (US Navy) Marine Technology, Vol 28, No 1, January 1991, pages 23-29.
An Engineering Approach to Predicting the Hydrodynamic Performance of Planing Craft Using Computer Techniques (W5 1990), D Radojcic (Royal Institution of Naval Architects).
Drag Reduction by Riblets for Marina Applications (W6 1990), Kwing-So Choi (Royal Institution of Naval Architects).
MEC1 Hydrofoil and Hydrostatic Transmission, presented to Hydraulic und Elektronik im Schiffbau und Offshore-Berich Conference, Stadhalle Lohr/Main, 29 April to 3 May 1990.
Power Transmission Systems for Advanced Ships the Hydrostatic Powershaft System, Hanno Speich, Mannesmann Rexroth GmbH, & Alessandro Cappiello, Hydromarine Srl, Marin Jubilee Meeting 11 to 15 May 1992, Wageningen, Netherlands.
Pitch-Heave Dynamics Models for an Air Cushion Vehicle, Teremce Arthur Graham, University of Toronto Institute for Aerospace Studies (UTIAS), 4925 Dufferin Street, Downsview, Ontario, Canada.
Snelle Schepen voor Passagiersvervoer - een Overzicht (Fast Ships for the Carriage of Passengers, an Overview), G Delhasse, (Scheepswerf Beliard Polyship, Ostend) presented to Belgian Naval Architects Association, 3 November 1992.
The Economics of Designing High-Speed Ferries, Max Martin (International Maritime Transportation Advisory Services Pty Ltd, Sydney, Australia) at Eighth International High-Speed Surface Craft Conference, London, 22 January, 1992.
Propulzija Vodenim Mlazom (Water Jet Propulsion), Tomo Agustinovic, Bureau Veritas, Rijeka, published in Brodogradnja, Zagreb, No 3-4, 1992.
The Influence of Variations in Thickness of Joined Hydrofoil Shell Plates on the Stressed State, I K Tarasov, published in Sudostroenie (Shipbuilding), Russia, October 1992.
Safety Study of High-Speed Marine Craft, Marintek, SINTEF Group, Trondheim, Norway, 1992.
Surface Effect Ship (SES) Developments Worldwide, D R Lavis and K B Spaulding, SNAME, March 1991.
The Design and Comparison of High Performance Marine Craft, A Rational Approach to Selection, D R Lavis and R S Sippel, Band, Lavis & Associates, Inc, MARIN Jubilee Conference, Wageningen, Netherlands, May 1992.
Scaling SES Motions, D R Lavis, Band, Lavis & Associates, Inc, 23rd American Towing Tank Conference, New Orleans, Louisiana, USA, June 1992.
Marine Water-jet Propulsion, J L Allison, Band, Lavis & Associates, Inc, presented at the Chesapeake Section of the Society of Naval Architects and Marine Engineers, 15 September, 1992.
A Methodology Designed to Help Ferry Operators Define the Best Vessel for a Route, P Goubault, Band, Lavis & Associates, Inc, Ferries '92, Boston, 1992.
Gas turbine or CODAG/CODOG propulsion for high-speed ferries, Thornton B Lauriat (Marine Gas Turbine Marketing, Textron Lycoming), given at Ferries '93, 28-30 March, Fort Lauderdale, USA.
FT8-55, A New High Performance 25 MW Mechanical Drive Aero Derivative Gas Turbine, Aldo Prario (Turbo Power & Marine Systems Inc) and Heinrich Voss (MAN Gutehoffnungshutte AG), presented at the Gas Turbine and Aeroengine Congress and Exposition, 11 to 14 June 1990, Brussels, Belgium.
The Advancing Technical Innovation In Water Transport, Robert L Trillo, Consultant, Aquapolis No 6 November/December 1992, Centro Internazionale Città d'Acqua, S Marco 4403/A, I-30124 Venice, Italy.
Design Aspects Of 162 Passenger Air Cushion Catamaran, Sun Yong Quan, MARIC, presented at Cities on Water and Transport Conference, Venice,

17-19 March 1993, Centro Internazionale Città d'Acqua, S Marco 4403/A, I-30124 Venice, Italy.
Riverbus - An Urban Transportation System for Rivers, Harbours and Lakes. M McSorley, FBM Marine Ltd, presented at Cities on Water and Transport Conference, Venice, 17-19 March 1993, Centro Internazionale Città d'Aqua, S Marco 4403/A, I-30124 Venice, Italy.
The Safety Challenge Of High-Speed Navigation—how should we meet it? Arild Tomter, Norsk Forsvarsteknologi A/S, Norway.
High-Speed Marine Vehicles, A National R&D Programme 1989 to 1992, MARINTEK, N-7002 Trondheim, Norway.
High-Speed Unconventional Craft, Miroslav Sambolek and Darko Bandula, Brodogradnja, Quarterly Journal of Naval Architecture and Shipbuilding Industry (No 1-2,1992), Brodarski Institute, Godina 40, 41000 Zagreb, Slavonia
The wash of boats on recreational waterways, G E Godd, RINA 1994.

REFERENCE PUBLICATIONS, BOOKS AND PERIODICALS

BIBLIOGRAPHIES AND GLOSSARIES

Glossary for High-Speed Surface Craft, The Society of Naval Architects and Marine Engineers, 1 World Trade Center, Suite 1369, New York, New York 10048, USA.

Bibliography on Hovercraft (ACV), Compiled by H G Russell, TIL Reports Centre, UK, September 1968, TIL/BIB/101.

ITTC Dictionary of Ship Hydrodynamics, Maritime Technology Monograph No 6, 1978. The Royal Institution of Naval Architects, London, August 1978.

Bibliography and Proposed Symbols on Hydrodynamic Technology as Related to Model Tests of High-Speed Marine Vehicles, SSPA, Public Research Report No 101, 1984, SSPA, PO Box 24001, S-400 22, Gothenburg, Sweden.

High-Speed Waterborne Passenger Operations and Craft: Bibliography, US Department of Transportation, Urban Mass Transportation Administration, Washington DC, USA, UMTA-IT-32-0001-84-2, August 1984.

GENERAL INTEREST BOOKS

A Quest for Speed at Sea, Christopher Dawson. Hutchinson & Company Ltd. ISBN 0 09 109720 7.

Hovercraft and Hydrofoils, Roy McLeavy. Blandford Press Ltd. ISBN 0 7137 07674, pp 215.

Hovercraft and Hydrofoils, Jane's Pocket Book 21, Roy McLeavy. Jane's Publishing Company.

The Interservice Hovercraft (Trials) Unit, B J Russell. Hover Publications, 1979. ISBN 0 9506 4700 4.

The Law of Hovercraft, L J Kovats. Lloyd's of London Press Ltd, 1989.

Amazon Task Force, Peter Dixon. Hodder and Stoughton, London, UK, 1981. ISBN 0 340 32713 8 and 0 340 34578 0 Pbk.

The Great Himalayan Passage, Adventure Extraordinary by Hovercraft, Michel Peissel. William Collins Sons & Company Ltd, London, UK, 1974. ISBN 0 00 211841 6.

Hydrofoils and Hovercraft, Bill Gunston. Aldous Books, London, UK, 1969. ISBN 490 00135 1 and 490 00136 X.

An Introduction to Hovercraft and Hoverports, Cross & O'Flaherty. Pitman Publishing/Juanita Kalerghi.

Light Hovercraft Handbook, (ed) Neil MacDonald. Hoverclub of Great Britain Ltd (available from 45 St Andrews Road, Lower Bemerton, Salisbury, Wiltshire), 1976.

Hover Craft, Angela Croome. 4th edition, 1984 Hodder and Stoughton Ltd. ISBN 0-340-33201-8, ISBN 0-340-33054-6 Pbk.

Twin Deliveries, J Fogagnolo. International Catamarans Pty Ltd, Hobart, Tasmania. Paperback, 1986.

Ships and Shipping of Tomorrow, Rolf Schonknecht, Jurgen Lusch, Manfred Schelzel, Hans Obenaus, Faculty of Maritime Transport Economics, Wilhelm-Pieck University, Rostock, Germany. MacGregor Publications Ltd, Hounslow, UK, pp 240, 1987.

Power Boat Speed, Racing and Record-Breaking: 1897 to the Present, Kevin Desmond. Conway Maritime Press Ltd, London, UK, 1988. ISBN 0 85177 427 X, pp 256.

Hurtigbåten (The Fast Craft), Bjørn Foss, Published by: Nordvest Forlag, Norway, 1989, pp 160. In colour. ISBN 82 90330 464.

The Law of Shipbuilding Contracts, Simon Curtis (Partner, Watson, Farley & Williams, London) Lloyds of London Press Ltd, Sheepen Place, Colchester, Essex C03 3LP, UK, pp330, 1991. ISBN 10 85044 334 3.

The Hoverspeed Story, Miles Cowsill & John Hendy, Ferry Publications, 12 Millields Close, Pentlepoir, Kilgetty, Pembrokeshire SA68 0SA, UK.

Worldwide High-Speed Ferries, Paul Hynds (Hoverspeed), Conway Maritime Press Ltd, 101 Fleet Street, London EC4Y IDE, UK, pp 160, 1992. ISBN 0 0 85177 587 X.

From Sea to Air - the Heritage of Sam Saunders, A E Tagg and R L Wheeler, Crossprint, Daish Way, Dodnor Industrial Estate, Newport, Isle of Wight, UK, pp 316, 1989. ISBN 0 9509739 3 9.

TECHNICAL BOOKS

High-Speed Small Craft by P du Cane. Temple Press Books Ltd, London, 3rd edition 1964, pp 470.

Jane's Surface Skimmers (annual 1967-1985) compiler and editor: Roy McLeavy, published by Jane's Publishing Company.

Jane's High-Speed Marine Craft (annual 1986-1995) compiler and editor: Stephen J Phillips, published by Jane's Information Group.

Hovercraft Design and Construction, Elsley & Devereaux. David & Charles, Newton Abbot, UK, 1968, pp 262.

Dynamics of Marine Vehicles, Rameswar Bhattacharyya (US Naval Academy, Annapolis, Maryland, USA). John Wiley & Sons, 1978, ISBN 0 471 07206 0, pp 498.

Air Cushion Craft Development (First Revision), P J Mantle (Mantle Engineering Company, Inc, Alexandria, Virginia, USA). David W Taylor, Naval Ship Research and Development Center DTNSRDC-80/012, January 1980, pp 593.

Transport Ships on Hydrofoils, Blumin, Massejef and Ivanof Isdatelstvo Transport, Basmannij Tupik, D 6a, Moskowsaja Tipografija Nr 33, Glawpoligrafproma, Moscow, CIS, 1964.

Marine Hovercraft Technology, Robert L Trillo, pp 245, 1971. ISBN 0 249 44036 9. Available from Robert L Trillo, Broadlands, Brockenhurst, Hampshire SO42 7SX.

Resistance and Propulsion of Ships, Svend Aage Harvald (The Technical University of Denmark). John Wiley and Sons, 1983, ISSN 0275 8741 and ISBN 0-471-06353-3, pp 353.

Industrial Fans-Aerodynamic Design, Papers presented at a seminar organised by the Fluid Machinery Committee of the Power Industries Division of the IMechE, held London, 9 April 1987. Published: MEP Ltd.

Global Wave Statistics, N Hogben (British Maritime Technology Ltd). Unwin Brothers Ltd, Woking, UK, 1987, pp 656, £295.

Fibre Reinforced Composites 1986, Institution of Mechanical Engineers publication 1986, ISBN 0 8529 8589 4/297, pp 262.

Encyclopaedia of Composite Materials and Components, Editor: M Grayson, 1983. pp 1100, available from: AIAA, order number 57-8, ISBN 0 471 87357 8.

Marine Gas Turbines, J B Woodward. Wiley-Interscience (1-95962-6), 1975, pp 390.

The Marine Encyclopaedia Dictionary (2nd Edition), E Sullivan, May 1988, ISBN 1 85044 180 4, pp 468.

Design of High-Speed Boats. Vol 1 Planing, P R Payne. Fishergate Inc, Annapolis, Maryland, USA, pp 244, 1988. ISBN 0 942 720 06 07.

Hovercraft Technology, Economics and Applications. Editor: J R Amyot, Elsevier Science Publishers BV, l989, ISBN 0-444-88152-2 & 0-444-41872-5, pp 770, DFl.395.00.

Mechanics of Marine Vehicles, B R Clayton and R E D Bishop, Gulf Publishing Company, Houston, USA (not available in Bangladesh, Europe, Ireland or the United Kingdom).

The Leading Star of Future Overwater Commuter Transport - WIG, Shigenori Ando, Professor of Aeronautical Engineering, Nagoya University, Japan (In Japanese).

Theory and Design of Hovercraft, Professor Yun Liang, Marine Design & Research Institute of China (MARIC), Shanghai, China, pp 344, ISBN 7-118-00745-5/U.62. National Defence Industry Press, China, June 1990 (in Chinese). Industry Press, China, June 1990.

PERIODICALS

Fast Ferry International, (10 issues annually) ISSN 0954 3988, High-Speed Surface Craft Ltd, 69 Kings Road, Kingston upon Thames, Surrey KT2 5JB, UK.

Hovercraft Bulletin, (monthly) The Hovercraft Society, 24 Jellicoe Avenue, Alverstoke, Gosport, Hampshire PO12 2PE, UK.

Light Hovercraft, (monthly) The Hoverclub of Great Britain Ltd, 45 St Andrews Road, Lower Bemerton, Salisbury, Wiltshire, UK.

Work Boat World, (monthly) ISSN 1037-3748, Baird Publications Ltd 1993, 4A Carmelite Street, London EC4Y OBN, UK and 10 Oxford Street, South Yarra 3141, Melbourne, Australia.

Ship and Boat International, (ten times a year) 10 Upper Belgrave Street, London SW1X 8BQ, UK.

Small Ships, (bi-monthly) ISSN 0262 480X, International Trade Publications Ltd, Queensway House, 2 Queensway, Redhill, Surrey RH1 1QS, UK.

Cruise Ferry Info, ISSN 1102-934X. Marine Trading AB, Brogantan 7, S-302 43, Halmstad, Sweden.

Speed at Sea, ISSN 1359-4222. Halldale Pulblishing and Media Ltd, 84 Alexandra Road, Farnborough, Hants GU14 6DD, UK.

Index of Organisations

Index of Craft Types

Index of Craft Names

O

P

Q

R

S

T